# nature

## The Living Record of Science

## 《自然》百年科学经典

英汉对照版　套装共十卷

# 第六卷

## 1973-1984

总顾问：李政道（Tsung-Dao Lee）

英方主编：Sir John Maddox
Sir Philip Campbell

中方主编：路甬祥

外语教学与研究出版社　·　麦克米伦教育　·　自然科研

**FOREIGN LANGUAGE TEACHING AND RESEARCH PRESS　·　MACMILLAN EDUCATION　·　NATURE RESEARCH**

北京 BEIJING

## 图书在版编目（CIP）数据

《自然》百年科学经典：套装共十卷. 第六卷：英汉对照／（英）约翰·马多克斯（John Maddox），（英）菲利普·坎贝尔（Philip Campbell），路甬祥主编. —— 北京：外语教学与研究出版社，2020.9
ISBN 978-7-5213-2021-3

Ⅰ. ①自… Ⅱ. ①约… ②菲… ③路… Ⅲ. ①自然科学－文集－英、汉 Ⅳ. ①N53

中国版本图书馆 CIP 数据核字（2020）第 154887 号

地图审图号：GS（2020）5244 号

出 版 人　徐建忠
项目统筹　章思英
项目负责　刘晓楠　黄小斌
责任编辑　王丽霞
责任校对　黄小斌
封面设计　高　蕾
版式设计　孙莉明
插图设计　麦克米伦提供原图扫描版
出版发行　外语教学与研究出版社
社　　址　北京市西三环北路 19 号（100089）
网　　址　http://www.fltrp.com
印　　刷　北京华联印刷有限公司
开　　本　787×1092　1/16
印　　张　76.5
版　　次　2021 年 1 月第 1 版　2021 年 1 月第 1 次印刷
书　　号　ISBN 978-7-5213-2021-3
定　　价　8000.00 元

购书咨询：（010）88819926　电子邮箱：club@fltrp.com
外研书店：https://waiyants.tmall.com
凡印刷、装订质量问题，请联系我社印制部
联系电话：（010）61207896　电子邮箱：zhijian@fltrp.com
凡侵权、盗版书籍线索，请联系我社法律事务部
举报电话：（010）88817519　电子邮箱：banquan@fltrp.com
物料号：320210001

记载人类文明
沟通世界文化
www.fltrp.com

# 《自然》百年科学经典（英汉对照版）

总 顾 问: 李政道（Tsung-Dao Lee）

英方主编：Sir John Maddox　　　　　　中方主编：路甬祥

Sir Philip Campbell

## 编审委员会

英方编委：　　　　　　中方编委（以姓氏笔画为序）：

Philip Ball　　　　　　许智宏

Vikram Savkar　　　　赵忠贤

David Swinbanks　　　滕吉文

### 本卷审稿专家（以姓氏笔画为序）

# 编译委员会

### 本卷翻译工作组稿人（以姓氏笔画为序）

| | | | | | | |
|---|---|---|---|---|---|---|
| 王晓蕾 | 王耀杨 | 刘 明 | 刘晓楠 | 关秀清 | 李 琦 | 何 铭 |
| 沈乃澂 | 郭红锋 | 蔡 迪 | 蔡则怡 | | | |

### 本卷翻译人员（以姓氏笔画为序）

| | | | | | | |
|---|---|---|---|---|---|---|
| 王耀杨 | 毛晨晖 | 邓铭瑞 | 田晓阳 | 冯翀 | 吕 静 | 刘 霞 |
| 刘振明 | 刘皓芳 | 齐红艳 | 阮玉辉 | 孙惠南 | 李 响 | 李 梅 |
| 李任伟 | 肖 莉 | 吴 彦 | 沈乃澂 | 张玉光 | 张效良 | 张锦彬 |
| 周志华 | 周旻辰 | 郑建全 | 荆玉祥 | 姜 薇 | 钱 磊 | 高如丽 |
| 董培智 | | | | | | |

### 本卷校对人员（以姓氏笔画为序）

| | | | | | | |
|---|---|---|---|---|---|---|
| 于 萌 | 于平蓉 | 马 荣 | 马晨晨 | 王 可 | 王 羽 | 王 敏 |
| 王帅帅 | 王向东 | 王志云 | 王丽霞 | 王杰琼 | 王珊珊 | 王晓敏 |
| 王海纳 | 王德孚 | 云 欢 | 毛俊捷 | 公 晗 | 史 骁 | 巩克瑞 |
| 吕秋莎 | 乔萌萌 | 任 奕 | 任峰铭 | 刘 伟 | 刘 佩 | 刘 婷 |
| 刘子怡 | 刘良子 | 刘若青 | 闫 妍 | 许长虹 | 许梅梅 | 孙 瑶 |
| 李 四 | 李 芳 | 李 娟 | 李 景 | 李 静 | 李盎然 | 邱彩玉 |
| 攸 乔 | 邹伯夏 | 宋 乔 | 张 炜 | 张 越 | 张世馥 | 张向东 |
| 张宜嘉 | 张瑞玉 | 张颖之 | 陈 云 | 陈思婧 | 陈露芸 | 范艳璇 |
| 周少贞 | 周玉凤 | 周晓明 | 郑娇娇 | 宗伟凯 | 赵广宇 | 侯彦婕 |
| 施家靖 | 郭晓博 | 黄 欢 | 黄 瑢 | 黄 璞 | 黄小斌 | 黄元耕 |
| 黄晓东 | 崔天明 | 第文龙 | 葛 越 | 焦晓林 | 曾芃斐 | 谢周丽 |
| 蔡军茹 | 熊华晖 | 潮兴娟 | 潘卫东 | | | |

Eric Leher（澳）　　　Joanna Pierce（爱尔兰）

# Contents
# 目录

# Volume VI

# (1973-1984)

# Monitoring Underground Explosions

D. Davies

## Editor's Note

**During the Cold War, the testing of nuclear weapons proceeded in parallel with international discussions about whether they might be banned. One of the obstacles to a ban was the problem of verifying a nation's adherence to it. The Soviet Union was particularly reluctant to agree to external inspections of its weapons facilities, so that verification would need to rely on a capacity for detecting tests from afar. Underground tests, still being conducted in the early 1970s, create seismic waves, but to use these for verification they would need to be distinguished from earthquakes. Here David Davies of the Massachusetts Institute of Technology reviews progress towards a sufficiently discriminating seismology, concluding that techniques were becoming adequate but still not infallible.**

---

Seismological means for detecting and identifying underground nuclear explosions have improved steadily during the past ten years. A technique exists for separating explosions from earthquakes. The problem now is lowering the threshold and understanding the occasional problematic event.

---

AN underground nuclear explosion converts about 1 percent of its energy into seismic waves and these carry information about the time, size, and location of the event. They may also indicate that the event is indeed an explosion and not an earthquake. This information is somewhat more difficult to extract, and research in many countries for the past few years has been intensively directed towards discrimination between natural and artificial events. There is no other known way of identifying underground explosions that can be used on a world-wide basis. In this article, I shall describe the progress that has been made recently in this science, which has such obvious implications for arms control. The conclusions that I reach should not, however, be construed as a measure of the prospect of a total test ban. Many ingredients go into the making of a treaty, and ability to police it is only one of them. Seismological capability is thus not sufficient, but it may be necessary, at least down to some level of explosive yield. What would constitute an adequate level is a matter of some discussion at present. The science reported here is the result of the research of many seismologists. In order to reduce the number of references to a manageable level, however, I have cited only a few large compilations of results in which the genealogy of the various ideas and instruments may be found.

# 监控地下爆炸

戴维斯

## 编者按

冷战期间，核武器试验在进行的同时，国际上对于是否应该禁止核试验的讨论也在继续。禁止核试验的障碍之一是如何证实一个国家是否遵守此禁令。苏联特别不情愿外界对其核武器设施进行监测，因此，证实是否进行核试验将需要依赖于从远处监测核试验的能力。地下核试验直到20世纪70年代早期还在进行，试验会产生地震波，但是利用这些地震波进行核实的话需要将其和天然地震区分开来。本文中，麻省理工学院的戴维·戴维斯综述了地震学识别的进展，并得出结论，该技术已经能够胜任监测需要，但还不是绝对可靠的。

在过去的十年里，监测和识别地下核爆炸的地震学方法取得了稳步发展。这门技术可以将爆炸和地震区分开来。目前的问题是要降低阈值和理解偶然性的有问题事件。

一次地下核爆炸所释放的能量中，有百分之一转化为地震波，而这些地震波中就携带着关于这一事件的时间、规模和地点等信息。它们也可以说明，这一事件确实是一次爆炸而不是地震。这种信息的提取还要更难一些，因而在过去的几年中，很多国家的研究都集中指向了对天然事件与人为事件的识别。还不知道有其他识别地下爆炸的方法能够应用于全世界范围。在本文中，我将描述这一学科在最近所取得的进展，这些进展对于武器控制具有如此明显的作用。但是，我所得到的结论并不能被解释为完全禁止核试验前景的一种度量。促进条约制定的因素有很多，监管能力只是其中之一。由此看来，地震学方法的作用并不足够强，但是，至少具体到某些爆炸当量水平时，它可能是必要的。如何制定出合适的水平标准目前还是一件有争议的事情。这里所报道的是很多地震学家的研究成果。不过，为了将参考文献数量减少到可控制的限度，我只引用了一些大型的研究结果汇编，其中汇集了各种研究思想和研究工具。

The reason for testing nuclear weapons underground is not, of course a matter of public discussion, but a paper by Neild and Ruina[1] probably provides a reasonably complete list of purposes. Between 1968 and 1971 there was an average of about twenty-five underground tests a year announced by the United States compared with about ten presumed tests a year for the Soviet Union, one test per year for China and about five a year for France—all but one of the Chinese tests and all of the French tests being atmospheric. Britain has not announced a test for seven years.

When the banning of nuclear tests first became an international issue in 1958, a conference on the technical problems in Geneva clearly indicated that the science of seismology would need substantial advances to reach a stage at which instrumental observations could indicate unambiguously that an explosion with a yield of a few kilotons (kton) had been detonated. Indeed the rather meagre data available during that conference and the subsequent negotiations (there had at that time only been two or three quite small underground tests) suggested that a first objective could reasonably be an international network of about 170 stations which could detect seismic signals down to a certain threshold but not necessarily identify their source. It was expected that most seismic events would clearly indicate their earthquake nature by their location and depth, their radiation pattern and the shape of their signal, but there would be a residue which would need further investigation. In the early days of international negotiations, inspections of the sites of a fraction of these suspicious events were discussed in detail—the number and nature of such inspections being particularly contentious topics. With time, the position of the Soviet Union on the inspection issue hardened to the assertion that inspections were unnecessary, and that purely national means of policing would be satisfactory. Thus the "Geneva network" was never built.

The two issues which were seen as central in 1958 are central today. Background seismic noise (from wind, traffic, ocean waves, and so on) placed a limitation on the detection of events; and a certain number of earthquakes did not immediately reveal themselves as such. The advances in seismology have been substantial since 1958, but increasing the signal-to-noise ratio (s.n.r.) and finding improved methods of separating earthquakes and explosions are still the principal fields of research. The rather narrow frequency bands involved in seismology have controlled techniques rigorously, and because the work is concentrated in situations of low s.n.r., the problem has been that of finding the frequency at which the s.n.r. is highest, and aiming improvement at that frequency, rather than trying to encompass the whole spectrum of the seismic signal. This "mission-oriented" approach to seismology, when combined with the intellectually stimulating problems that have arisen on the way, has exerted a vital role in the development of seismology since 1958.

在地下进行核武器试验的原因，显然不是一个公开讨论的问题，不过尼尔德和鲁伊纳的论文中基本上为此提供了合理的完整解释 [1]。在 1968 年至 1971 年间，美国宣称平均每年进行大约 25 次地下核试验，与之相比，苏联每年大约进行 10 次核试验，中国每年 1 次，而法国大约每年 5 次——不过中国所进行的除 1 次以外的所有试验和法国进行的所有试验为地上试验。英国已有 7 年没有宣布过核试验。

1958 年，禁止核试验首次成为国际问题，在日内瓦举行的关于技术问题的会议明确指出，地震学需要取得实质性的进展，使得仪器观测毫不含糊地指出具有几千吨（kton）当量水平的爆炸的发生。确实，那次会议和随后的商谈中可用数据甚少（当时只有两次或者三次规模很小的地下试验），因此，首要目标是建立包括大约 170 个台站的国际台网，该台网能够检测到一定阈值之上的地震信号，但是不必确定其来源。人们期望，绝大多数地震事件可以通过其位置、深度、辐射模式和信号形状明确地体现出天然地震的特征，但还剩余少数事件有待于进一步研究。在早期的国际磋商过程中，详细讨论了如何对一小部分可疑事件发生的地点进行检查——检查的数量和性质是争议较大的问题。同时，苏联对于检查问题的立场渐趋强硬，并最终断言检查是不必要的，而单纯的国家监管方式就能满足需要了。因此"日内瓦国际台网"从未曾建立起来。

1958 年时所关注的两个中心议题到今天仍然是焦点。地震背景噪声（来自风、交通工具、海浪等）限制了地震事件检测的进行；而且某些地震也不是马上就显现出天然地震的性质。自 1958 年以来，地震学已经取得了显著进展，不过提高信噪比（s.n.r.）和寻找区分地震与爆炸事件的改进方法仍然是主要研究领域。地震学中所涉及的极为狭窄的频率段严格地限制着这项技术，由于研究工作集中于低信噪比条件下，因此关键是找到具有最高信噪比的频率，集中在该频率下取得进展，而不是试图包揽震动信号的全部图谱。地震学中这种"任务导向式"的方法，再加上研究过程中产生的理性所激发出的问题，对于地震学自 1958 年以来取得的发展具有重要的作用。

It was clear from very early in the Geneva discussions (which lasted until 1962) that whatever international arrangement might finally develop, national interests required an improved seismic capability. The United States, Britain and Sweden, in particular, started to modernize their seismological capability for the explicit purpose of test-ban monitoring. Other countries, notably Canada and Japan, were also improving their seismic capability. The US programme "Vela Uniform" has been easily the largest, and so far more than $150 million has been spent on research and development. What has been bought?

## Recording of Seismic Signals

In the first few years basic research was heavily supported and a network of 100 seismic stations, the World-Wide Standard Seismographic Network (WWSSN), was established—no stations were, however, sited on the territory of the Soviet Union or her allies. The network provided a huge data base, uniformly recorded, of short period (around 1 s) and long period (around 20 s) seismic signals.

Certain "realities" soon emerged from this work. The decreasing prospects of an international network with access to the Soviet Union led to the dominance of teleseismic studies; seismic body waves (P and S waves) are well registered up to a few degrees from the source; indifferently and variably from there to about 25°; and then clearly and predictably out to 100°. Distances are measured in central angle degrees. Some examples of P waves are given in Fig. 1. This last, teleseismic, zone covers half the world and would be crucial if access were not permitted to particular countries. The zone of observation having been restricted, immediate limits can be placed on the detectability of explosions. A 5 kton explosion in hard rock, such as granite or salt, produces in the teleseismic zone a P wave of amplitude around 5 nm at a period of 1 s. Background noise at 1 s is about a third of this figure for the best observatories. Thus in the absence of techniques for noise rejection, a network would usually detect a 5 kton explosion in hard rock (an event cannot be said to have been detected until recorded with a signal-to-noise ratio of at least 1.5 at four widely spaced stations). The capability declines drastically below this yield. Further, explosions in softer rocks, notably tuff, a volcanic ash common in Nevada, produce a smaller signal by a factor of at least two than comparable explosions in hard rocks. Explosions in dry alluvium have even smaller seismic effects—1 kton in hard rock and 10 kton in alluvium are roughly equivalent. There is, however, a limit to the thickness of dry alluvium to be found anywhere on Earth, and as an explosion has to be adequately buried for safety's sake, it is unlikely that explosions of more than about 20 kton can be fired and contained in known deposits of alluvium.

在日内瓦研讨会议的早期（该会议持续到 1962 年）就已明确，无论国际约定最终将如何发展，国家利益需要的是提高地震学能力。尤其是美国、英国和瑞典，出于明确的禁止核试验的监控目的，开始提高其地震学能力以适应现代化需求。其他国家，尤其是加拿大和日本，也在提高其地震学能力。最为浩大的工程无疑是美国的"船帆座计划"，目前已经为其研究和发展花费了超过 1.5 亿美元。收获的是什么呢？

## 地震信号的记录

在最初的几年中，基础研究得到大力支持，由 100 个地震台站组成的台网，即世界标准地震台网（WWSSN），建立起来——不过，没有一个地震台站是位于苏联或其盟友的疆域中的。这个台网提供了庞大的数据库，统一地记录了短周期（约 1 s）和长周期（约 20 s）的地震信号。

一些"事实"迅速从研究工作中显现出来。对于苏联加入国际台网的可能性逐渐降低使得远震研究居于主导地位；在距离震源只有几度的范围内可以很好地记录地震体波（P 波和 S 波）；此后到大约 25° 的范围内，体波信号质量一般且变化大；此后在远达 100° 范围内体波都是清楚和可判定的。距离以球心角度数来测量。图 1 中给出了一些 P 波的实例。最终，远震区域可以覆盖半个世界，这在某些国家不允许进入时显得至关重要。观测区域是受限制的，这直接限制了对爆炸的检测能力。一次发生在硬质岩石（例如花岗岩或盐岩）中的 5 kton 当量水平的爆炸，在远震区域中产生一个 P 波，其振幅大约为 5 nm，周期为 1 s。在最佳观测中，1 s 周期的背景噪声约为该信号的三分之一。因此，在没有噪声剔除技术时，监测台网一般可以检测到硬质岩石中发生的 5 kton 当量水平的爆炸（直到有四个彼此间隔较大的地震台站记录到信噪比至少为 1.5 的信号才能说一次震动事件被检测到了）。低于此当量水平时，检测能力剧烈下降。此外，发生在较软岩石（尤其是凝灰岩，在内华达很常见的一种火山灰）中的爆炸产生的信号较弱，与硬质岩石中发生的同级别爆炸相比，信号相差至少两倍。发生于干燥冲积层中的爆炸产生更小的震动效应——硬质岩石中的 1 kton 爆炸与冲积层中的 10 kton 爆炸基本相当。不过，在地球上任何地方发现的冲积层都有厚度的限制，对于一次基于安全考虑而必须充分深埋的爆炸来说，在已知的冲积层中不大可能引爆和容纳一次超过 20 kton 当量水平的爆炸。

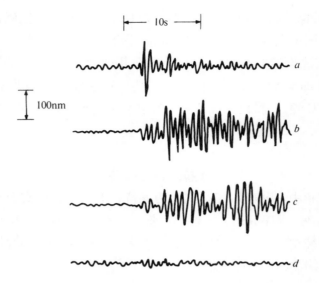

Fig.1. Short period teleseismic observations of P waves from events located in *a*, Eastern Kazakh, USSR; *b*, Alaska; *c*, Turkey and *d*, South Sinkiang Province, China. The top and bottom events are presumed underground explosions. All events have body wave magnitudes in the range 5.0 to 5.7. Note the great difficulty there would be in identifying the direction of first motion for these events.

At the same time that the WWSSN was being equipped with conventional instruments and photographic recording, several experiments with arrays were being conducted. The aim was to suppress noise, presumed incoherent, by the addition of many channels. Another advantage accrued in the recording of data on analogue and later digital tape. Although practically all decisions in seismology are taken on the basis of observation by eye, direct visual recording suffers obvious disadvantages of dynamic range. Further, there is a strong noise peak at a period of about 6 s arising from microseisms generated in the oceans and the rejection of these by WWSSN instruments, peaked at 1 s and 20 s, is usually not entirely satisfactory. As a result, film records, in which the magnification is controlled by the ease of viewing, are often dominated by 6 s microseisms and are thus not running at the best magnification for 1 or 20 s signals. The data processing possibilities of tape recording remove this obstacle.

The first arrays built in the United States had an aperture of 4 km. They were in many ways prototypes of possible arrays that the Geneva meetings had envisaged for an international network. Up to sixteen seismometers were spread out over this aperture, and the signals from all seismometers were added without phasing. Seismic signals from teleseismic distances arrive at steep angles—the signal sweeps across the ground with a horizontal phase velocity of at least 10 km s$^{-1}$, and up to 24 km s$^{-1}$ and at typical sites this corresponds to angles of incidence of less than 20°. Thus straight addition does not seriously degrade the 1 s component of a signal seen in the small aperture. It was found with these small arrays that the noise was coherent in this frequency band for distances typically greater than the 0.5 km spacing of instruments, so the gain in s.n.r. was somewhere between one (if the noise were totally coherent and travelling in a near

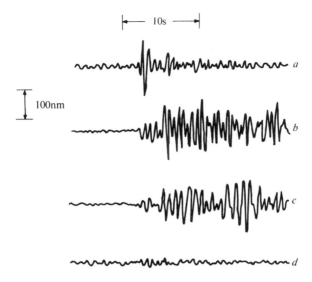

图 1. 短周期远震的 P 波观测结果，震动事件位置为：a，苏联东哈萨克；b，阿拉斯加；c，土耳其；d，中国新疆南部。顶部和底部的事件被推测为地下爆炸。所有上述事件的体波震级介于 5.0 至 5.7 之间。注意，这里最大的困难是识别事件中的初动方向。

    在 WWSSN 配备有常规仪器和照相记录装置的同时，还进行了若干台阵实验。其目的在于通过增加多通道来抑制假定不相关的噪声。另外一个优点是将数据记录在模拟磁带和后来的数字磁带上。尽管实际上地震学中的所有决定都是基于肉眼观测而做出的，但是直接的直观记录还是在动态范围内遭受到明显的不利影响。此外，在大约 6 s 周期出现一个源于海洋的微震所产生的强噪声峰值，而峰值周期在 1 s 和 20 s 的 WWSSN 仪器装置对于该噪声的限波，通常也不能完全让人满意。结果是，通过观察其放大率可调控的胶片记录，6 s 微震常常占据主导，而 1 s 和 20 s 信号则因此无法达到最佳放大。对磁带记录进行数据处理的可能则消除了这一障碍。

    建于美国的第一批台阵的孔径为 4 km。它在很多方面体现了日内瓦会议对于国际台网阵列的设想。在此孔径范围内布设了多达 16 台的地震仪，来自所有地震仪的信号不经过相位调整就叠加起来。远震信号到达时信号明显变化——信号以至少 $10 \text{ km} \cdot \text{s}^{-1}$ 直至 $24 \text{ km} \cdot \text{s}^{-1}$ 水平速度沿地表传播，在典型的场地对应的入射角小于 20°。因此，直接叠加不会严重减弱小孔径台阵观测到的 1 s 信号。通过这些小型台阵发现，特别是当仪器间距大于 0.5 km 时噪声在这一频率段是相干的，因此信噪比的增益将介于 1（如果噪声是完全相干的并且沿近垂直方向传播）和 $\sqrt{N}$（如果噪声

vertical direction) and $\sqrt{N}$ (if the noise were totally incoherent). Later arrays have used a seismometer spacing of around 2 km, at which distance local noise is substantially incoherent.

The next development was the medium aperture phased array implemented by the United Kingdom Atomic Energy Authority[2]. Up to twenty seismometers were laid out in two perpendicular lines. Arrays of this type are in operation in Canada, Brazil, Scotland, India and Australia. The aperture was large enough to require phasing of the signal after recording to steer the array in the appropriate direction, but small enough to ensure that the signal was still coherent. Signal-to-noise improvements approaching $\sqrt{N}$ (about 4.5) are obtainable.

The first large aperture seismic array (LASA in Montana) was completed by the United States in 1965, and a second array (NORSAR in Norway) has been in operation about two years. LASA has an aperture of 200 km and 350 short period seismometers; NORSAR is somewhat smaller. LASA is steered (by a computer) to be face-on to incoming seismic signals and the angle of approach is sufficiently well determined to locate the source with an accuracy of one or two hundred km. The real time digital operations of LASA and NORSAR each occupy entirely two medium sized computers in hunting for P waves. The gain for large arrays does not meet the $\sqrt{N}$ expectation, however, for over an aperture of 200 km crustal geological conditions can vary widely and this leads to a degrading of the coherence of the signal. An improvement in s.n.r. of a factor of ten is possible for LASA, however, and the array is capable of detecting and locating explosions in the teleseismic zone with yields down to about 2 kton in hard rock. Several thousand earthquakes occur each year with P waves of comparable or greater amplitude, and these form the population against which explosions have to be discriminated.

It became increasingly apparent in the mid 1960s that the registration of body waves was not sufficient to solve the discrimination problem; a broader spectrum of seismic data was necessary. The answer lay in the dominant signal on the long period seismic traces, the Rayleigh wave. This is a dispersed wave which has travelled over the Earth's surface and is well excited at 20 s periods—there are short period Rayleigh waves and long period P waves, but they are unimportant for discrimination. As for short period recording, noise is the limiting factor. The 6 s oceanic microseismic background, longer period fluctuations arising from atmospheric effects and the interference of Rayleigh wave trains from other earthquakes all contribute to the background. In the absence of an interfering event, most seismic stations have a background noise level at 20 s period of 50 to 100 nm; there is a great variability in noise level both from place to place and in time. For the reasons already given, tape recording is most desirable.

Rayleigh waves spread cylindrically, but also undergo other attenuation in the ground. The signal decays as distance ($\Delta$) to the power 1.6. This rapid decay makes it imperative that the seismic station be sited as near to the event as possible. Within a political requirement of non-intrusive monitoring we have to consider a value of $\Delta$ of 20° as the minimum

是完全不相干的）之间。后来的台阵使用的地震仪间距大约为 2 km，在这一距离，本地噪声是显著不相干的。

下一步发展是由英国原子能管理局装配的中等孔径的相控阵列[2]。多达 20 台地震仪放置于两条相互垂直的直线上。这种类型的台阵还安装在加拿大、巴西、苏格兰、印度和澳大利亚。孔径大到需要在记录信号后对其进行相位调制，以将台阵操控到合适的方向上，但又小到足以保证信号仍然是相干的。由此获得了接近于 $\sqrt{N}$（约为 4.5）的信噪比增益。

第一个大孔径地震台阵（蒙大拿的 LASA）是由美国于 1965 年完成的，第二个台阵（挪威的 NORSAR）也已工作了两年左右。LASA 的孔径达到 200 km，包含 350 个短周期地震仪；NORSAR 则要小一点。LASA 定向（由一台计算机来实现）地震信号的入射方向，并很好地确定入射角度，从而能够以 100 km 或 200 km 的精度定位信号源。LASA 和 NORSAR 的实时数字操作要各自占用整整两台中型计算机来搜寻 P 波。不过，大型台阵的增益不能达到 $\sqrt{N}$ 的预期，因为孔径超过 200 km 的地壳地质条件会出现很大的变化，这将导致信号相干性的减弱。不过，对于 LASA 而言信噪比增强 10 倍，并且该台阵能够在远震范围内对硬质岩石中至少 2 kton 当量水平的爆炸进行检测和定位。P 波振幅与此相当或大于此水平的地震，每年会发生几千次，它们构成了必须与爆炸相区分开的事件群。

到 20 世纪 60 年代中期，体波记录不足以解决识别的问题越来越明显；必须要有频谱更宽的地震资料。答案就是长周期地震道的优势信号，瑞利波。这是一种沿着地表传播的弥散波，在 20 s 周期处被充分激发——有短周期的瑞利波和有长周期的 P 波，不过它们对于识别问题无关紧要。对于短周期记录来说，噪声是限制因素。6 s 的海洋微震背景，由于大气效应所产生的长周期波动，以及其他地震所产生的瑞利波列的干涉，都会对背景有贡献。在没有干涉事件的情况下，大多数地震台站在20 s 周期的背景噪声水平为 50 nm 到 100 nm；噪声水平会随着地点和时间的不同而大幅度变动。由已给出的理由来看，磁带记录是最合适的。

瑞利波呈圆柱状传播，但在大地中也发生其他形式衰减。信号随距离（Δ）的衰减指数为 1.6。这种快速衰减就要求地震台站必须尽可能的接近事件发生地。在非侵犯性监控的政治要求范围内，我们只得考虑以 20° 的 Δ 值作为可用到的地震台

at which stations will be available. At 20°, the Rayleigh waves from a 10 kton explosion with 20 s period are somewhat less than 100 nm in amplitude, so individual stations at this distance have a relatively small probability of detecting surface waves. As with short period observations, arrays prove a valuable means of increasing the s.n.r. Instrument spacings have to be greater (typically 20 km) for noise to be incoherent. Small tripartite arrays are either under construction or recently completed in Sweden, Canada and India. LASA, NORSAR and ALPA (an exclusively long period array in Alaska) all have at least fifteen long period seismometers within them. Results from LASA indicate an improvement in s.n.r. of a factor of four—close to $\sqrt{N}$. In addition, knowledge of the nature of the dispersed waveform allows matched filter techniques to be applied, and these contribute up to another factor of two to the signal-to-noise ratio. Thus a twenty element long period array can yield an order of magnitude improvement in the s.n.r. against incoherent noise. In addition an array has a certain amount of directional discrimination (Rayleigh waves have a wavelength of 80 km at 20 s period) which makes it possible to study an event in the presence of an interfering signal, provided that the two are coming from directions differing by more than 30° and that the interfering signal is no more than a factor of ten larger than the signal being studied.

Recent developments in instrumentation have been successfully aimed at reducing the non-seismic noise in instruments by more effectively sealing and isolating them, and at broadening their response to cover a wide spectrum. There is also promise in the siting of instruments down boreholes where long period noise is frequently substantially lower.

## Seismic Magnitude

Both P waves and Rayleigh waves are used to define a magnitude for seismic events. The body wave magnitude ($m_b$) on the Richter scale is a measure of the excitation of P waves. The amplitude of the P wave signal on the record is converted to ground displacement ($A$) at a dominant period $T$, and then used in a formula

$$m_b = \log_{10}\frac{A}{T} + B(\Delta)$$

where $B(\Delta)$ is a term counteracting the variation of the signal with distance from the source. A ground displacement of 10 nm at 1 s period at a distance of 60° from a source indicates an event of magnitude 4.7, for example.

The surface wave magnitude is obtained by measuring on the Rayleigh wave the ground displacement $A$ at a period $T$ (usually near 20 s) and using a formula

$$M_s = \log_{10}\frac{A}{T} + 1.66 \log_{10}\Delta + 0.3$$

An event with an $M_s$ of 4.0 will have a ground displacement at 30° of 300 nm at 20 s period.

For earthquakes, there is an empirical and very scattered relationship between $M_s$ and $m_b$,

站的最小距离。在 20°时，周期为 20 s 的 10 kton 爆炸所产生的瑞利波振幅略小于 100 nm，因此在此距离单个地震台站检测到面波的可能性是很小的。就短周期观测而言，台阵证实为一种提高信噪比的有价值的方法。仪器间距必须较大（典型距离为 20 km）才能使噪声不相干。在瑞典、加拿大和印度，小的三重台阵有的正在兴建中，有的已在最近建成。LASA、NORSAR 和 ALPA（位于阿拉斯加的专用的长周期的台阵）都至少有 15 个长周期地震仪。LASA 得到的结果表明，信噪比增益系数增加了 4 倍——接近于 $\sqrt{N}$。此外，对于弥散波性质的了解使匹配滤波器技术得以应用，而这些使信噪比又增加了 2 倍。因此，一个由二十个地震仪组成的长周期台阵能使信噪比相对于不相干噪声的增强达一个数量级。除此之外，台阵还有一定的方向识别能力（瑞利波在 20 s 周期具有 80 km 的波长），这就使得研究干涉信号之中的事件成为可能，条件是两个信号来自于相差 30°以上的方向，并且干涉信号强度不超过所研究信号的十倍。

仪器制造领域最近取得了新的进展，如通过更为有效的密封和隔离技术来减少仪器中的非地震噪声，以及扩展仪器响应范围以覆盖广泛的宽频谱。另一种有前景的做法是将仪器置于往往可以明显降低长周期噪声的钻孔之中。

## 地 震 震 级

P 波和瑞利波都用于定义地震事件的震级。基于里氏标度的体波震级（$m_b$）是对 P 波激发程度的量度。将记录中的 P 波信号振幅转化为卓越周期 $T$ 时的地面位移（$A$），接着应用于下面的公式：

$$m_b = \log_{10} \frac{A}{T} + B(\Delta)$$

其中，$B(\Delta)$ 项用来补偿震中距离不同而导致的信号变化。例如，震中距离 60°处周期 1 s 内的地面位移为 10 nm 意味着震级为 4.7 的事件。

面波震级是通过测量周期为 $T$（通常约为 20 s）的瑞利波的地面位移 $A$，并应用下面的公式而得到的：

$$M_s = \log_{10} \frac{A}{T} + 1.66 \log_{10} \Delta + 0.3$$

$M_s$ 震级 4.0 的事件，在 30°距离和 20 s 周期处将有 300 nm 的地面位移。

对于地震来说，$M_s$ 与 $m_b$ 之间有经验性的、离散较大的关系，其最佳拟合

the best fit to which is

$$M_s = 1.59 m_b - 3.9$$

I shall discuss this relation further later.

It is possible to relate both $m_b$ and $M_s$ to the yield for explosions. Two kton in hard rock produces an event with an $m_b$ of 4.0, 20 kton an event with an $m_b$ of 5.0. For higher yields the equivalence of a factor of 10 in yield to a change of one unit in magnitude breaks down for several reasons. I have already noted that softer rocks produce smaller seismic signals; an $m_b$ of 4.0 is equivalent to 2 kton in granite, 3 or 4 kton in tuff and 20 kton in alluvium.

The surface wave magnitude $M_s$ can equally well be related to the yield, and is a more useful measure, for it seems to obey a relation (for hard rock) of the form

$$M_s = 1.3 \log_{10} Y + 1.5$$

over a range from at least 1 kton to 1 mton.

## Discrimination

In the early development of the subject, the concentration on the detection of events by means of P waves led to a hope that the study of P waves alone might show differences between explosions and earthquakes. It was soon found that such differences did exist, but not to the extent that all earthquakes could be separated from all explosions; it was only possible to quote probabilities. Diagnostic aids, as they have come to be called, are the location and depth of the event, the direction of first motion of the seismic trace and the complexity of the signal. Clearly if an event can be unequivocally identified as having occurred deeper than a few km it is not an explosion—likewise if it occurs under deep water. The quality of depth determination declines as the depth decreases and it is frequently impossible to assign depths to events shallower than 30 km. The first motion criterion uses the difference in radiation pattern between a totally compressive explosion and an earthquake for which the radiation is successively compressive and rarefactional in adjacent quadrants. There are numerous problems—the uneven distribution of stations around the globe and the high signal-to-noise ratio required to make polarity measurements both render the technique of little use for lower yields. "Complexity", a measure of the duration of the P wave signal, is a criterion which showed promise; signals that last more than a few seconds are likely to have come from earthquakes. Unfortunately there are many earthquakes which last for less than a second and these must be placed in the category of "suspicious events".

More recent work on the spectra of P waves has shown that even explosions of very small magnitude are significantly richer in high frequencies (2 to 3 Hz) than are earthquakes. This accords with generally accepted ideas of the nature of earthquake and

式为：

$$M_s = 1.59 m_b - 3.9$$

后面我将进一步讨论这一关系。

将 $M_s$ 和 $m_b$ 与爆炸当量联系起来是可能的。硬质岩石中的 2 kton 爆炸产生 $m_b$ 为 4.0 的地震事件，20 kton 爆炸则产生 $m_b$ 为 5.0 的地震事件。爆炸当量提高一个数量级对应于震级加一的关系因为几个理由而无法成立。我曾经提到过较软的岩石产生较小的地震信号；$m_b$ 为 4.0 的事件相当于花岗岩中的 2 kton 爆炸，凝灰岩中的 3 kton 或 4 kton 爆炸以及冲积层中的 20 kton 爆炸。

同样的，面波震级 $M_s$ 也可以与爆炸当量较好地联系起来，而且还是更为有用的一种量度，因为看起来至少在 1 kton 到 1 mton 范围内是遵循如下形式关系（对于硬质岩石而言）的：

$$M_s = 1.3 \log_{10} Y + 1.5$$

## 识　　别

在这一研究课题的早期发展历程中，对于通过 P 波检测事件的关注引起了一种希冀，即只凭对 P 波的研究就可以揭示出爆炸与地震之间的区别。人们很快发现这种区别确实是存在的，但还没到足以把所有的爆炸与所有的地震分离出来的程度；它只能提供可能的概率。我们所说的辅助性判断，是事件发生的方位和深度，地震道的初动方向，以及信号的复杂性。很明显，如果一个事件明确地确定为发生在几千米以下的位置，它就不是一次爆炸——如果发生于深水之下也是同理。深度测定的精度随着深度下降而降低，通常在低于 30 km 的地方就无法确定事件发生的深度了。初动准则利用爆炸与地震辐射图案的不同，前者辐射图案是完全压缩式的，后者则是压缩与膨胀相继出现在相邻象限中。有许多问题——地震台站在全球的分布不均以及极性测量所需要的高信噪比，这些都会使该技术对于低当量水平事件无计可施。"复杂性"是对 P 波信号持续性的量度，是一项有前景的判据；持续时间超过几秒钟的信号可能来自于地震。遗憾的是，有很多地震持续时间不到一秒钟，它们只能被归入"可疑事件"的类别中。

对 P 波频谱更新的研究指出，即使是震级很小的爆炸，其高频段（2 Hz 到 3 Hz）信号也比地震要丰富很多。这与人们普遍接受的地震和爆炸震源特征的观念

explosion sources. Regional variations present problems, however; it seems at present that the attenuation (and hence the frequency transmission characteristics) of the Upper Mantle varies sufficiently from place to place that genuine spectral differences between earthquakes and explosions are overprinted with the frequency absorption of the Upper Mantle in such a way that P waves from explosions can occasionally look like those from an earthquake.

The broadening of the spectrum that the joint study of Rayleigh and P waves brought with it provided the one indubitable "breakthrough" that the subject has seen. It had been realized for several years that explosions did not generate anything like the amount of Rayleigh waves that did earthquakes of comparable body wave magnitude. The WWSSN allowed these observations to be put on a more quantitative and global basis. It was noted that if the surface wave magnitude $M_s$ for each event was plotted against its body wave magnitude $m_b$, the natural and man-made events clustered round two well separated lines.

A typical example is shown in Fig.2. Clearly the earthquake population has a wider scatter than the explosion population, and this is unsurprising considering the diversity of earthquake types. Vagaries of propagation in the real Earth also contribute to the scatter. Nevertheless one point can be asserted—that the diagram has greatly increased our confidence in identifying events above a certain size. Of course the purist may reasonably object that a diagram such as Fig. 2 cannot offer certainty as it is only a modest sized population; nevertheless the diagram has been widely accepted.

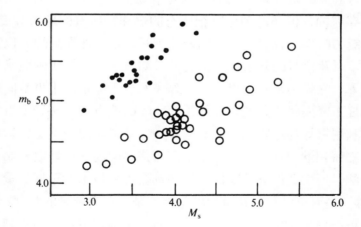

Fig. 2. An $M_s$ : $m_b$ diagram for Eurasia based on WWSSN recordings by Marshall and Basham. ○ , Earthquakes; ● , presumed explosions.

Earthquakes and explosions generate other seismic phases—shear or S waves and horizontally polarized surface waves called Love waves. In addition P waves have a long period component. All of these offer possibilities for discrimination, particularly because explosions in theory generate few S and Love waves. For large explosions and earthquakes,

是符合的。但是，区域性变化带来了问题；目前看来，上地幔衰减（也就是频率传输特性）随着地区不同而显著不同，地震和爆炸频谱的真实差异被上地幔的频率吸收所掩盖，以至于爆炸的 P 波有时候看起来像地震。

瑞利波与 P 波的联合研究产生的频谱拓展为该研究主题带来了一项毋庸置疑的"突破"。人们在几年前就已认识到，与地震相比，有相同体波震级的爆炸产生不了同样震级的瑞利波。WWSSN 使得这些观测有了一个更定量化的和全球化的基础。可以看到，如果对每一事件以表面波震级 $M_s$ 对应于体波震级 $m_b$ 作图，天然和人为事件将分别汇聚在两条明显分离的直线周围。

图 2 中给出了一个典型的实例。很明显，地震事件总体比爆炸事件总体更分散一些，考虑到地震类型的多样性，这并不令人惊奇。实际地球中复杂传播过程的不确定性也导致了这种分散。但是有一点可以确定——这幅图大大增加了我们识别超过一定规模的事件的信心。当然，纯粹主义者有理由反驳，类似图 2 这样的数据图并不能提供确定性，因为它只包含大小适中的样本集合；尽管如此，这幅图还是得到了广泛认可。

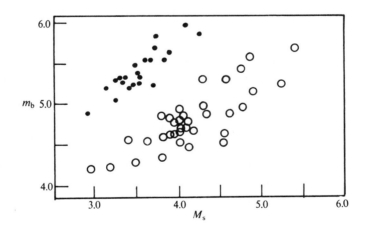

图 2. 马歇尔和巴沙姆基于 WWSSN 数据的亚欧大陆事件的 $M_s:m_b$ 图。○代表地震，●代表推测出的爆炸。

地震和爆炸还产生其他地震相——剪切波或称 S 波，以及被称为勒夫波的水平极化表面波。此外 P 波中还有一长周期成分。所有这些都为识别不同的事件提供了可能性，特别是由于在理论上爆炸是几乎不产生 S 波和勒夫波的。对于大规模爆炸

use of these waves works well, but it is found in general that the largest wave amplitude on the long period record is that of the Rayleigh wave.

## $M_s : m_b$ Discriminant

Fig. 2 is taken from a recent study[3] using WWSSN instruments only. Each point represents one event in Eurasia and it is necessary to have P wave detections at at least four widely separated stations before an event is listed. This places a lower limit on the body-wave magnitude for which events are reported. There are several reasons why this threshold should be rather blurred, but as a gross simplification one can say that the global network of seismometers (excluding arrays) will detect by P waves at four or more stations almost all events with an $m_b$ of 5.0 and greater and almost no events with $m_b$ less than 4.0.

Each point also represents a determination of surface wave magnitude, and it is customary to require at least four stations to have detected the surface wave before a value is accepted (this is a very crude way of allowing for the radiation pattern of earthquakes). An event with an $M_s$ of 4.0 is certain to be detected by its Rayleigh waves, but an event with an $M_s$ of 3.0 is unlikely to be detected. This is partially a statement about noise, but the locations of the receivers are also important as they need to be as close to the event as possible.

The thresholds of detection are such that an earthquake is likely to be seen both by its P and Rayleigh waves or by neither. This means that there are few earthquakes which are assigned an $m_b$ but cannot be placed on the diagram because $M_s$ is not measurable. On the other hand, there may be explosions which have, for instance, an $m_b$ of 4.5 and (by extrapolation) an $M_s$ of 2.5. If it is required that an event may be identified only if both parameters can be determined one can thus talk about a threshold for discrimination as the Rayleigh wave detection threshold. This threshold is statistical in nature, but may be defined in some such way as "If an event detected by P waves has an $M_s$ of 3.2 or greater there is a 90 percent chance that its surface waves will be detected at four or more stations and thus that it can be categorized as an explosion or earthquake". This somewhat portly statement is necessary because events are routinely detected by body waves but the crucial detection for discrimination purposes is of surface waves. An alternative version is "Explosions in hard rock of 20 kton or more can be identified as such; so can practically all earthquakes detected by the WWSSN".

It is obvious from Fig.2 that any attempt to lower the yield threshold should reasonably start from an attempt to improve the detection of the surface waves, for it is demonstrable that there are events in Russia with an $m_b$ of less than 5.0 which have no surface waves visible on present instruments but which may be presumed to be explosions. Obviously as a programme for improvement of surface wave capability developed it would be highly desirable to boost up body wave detection in order that almost all events with $m_b$ greater than 4.0 be reported. Such a strategy is discussed later.

和地震而言，利用这些波的效果很好，不过人们发现，一般来说，长周期记录中振幅最大的是瑞利波。

## $M_s : m_b$ 识别

图 2 来自于最近一次只利用 WWSSN 仪器的研究 [3]。每个点代表欧亚大陆上的一次事件，每一个被列出的事件必须要被至少四个相隔较远的地震台站检测到 P 波。这就为所报道的事件设置了一个体波震级的下限。有几个理由能说明为什么这一界限应该是模糊的，不过作为粗略的近似，可以说，全球地震仪台网（不包括台阵）可以通过四个或者更多地震台站的 P 波检测到几乎所有 $m_b$ 大于等于 5.0 的事件，而基本上检测不到 $m_b$ 小于等于 4.0 的事件。

每个点还代表了确定的面波震级，而且按照习惯，在接受一个数值之前需要至少有四个地震台站检测到面波（这是对地震辐射图案加以认可的一种十分粗略的方法）。$M_s$ 为 4.0 的事件肯定能因其瑞利波而被检测到，但是 $M_s$ 为 3.0 的事件就不大可能被检测到了。这在一定程度上是由于噪声的缘故，不过接收器的位置也很重要，因为它们需要尽可能靠近事件发生地。

检测阈值是指一次地震有可能同时被 P 波和瑞利波检测到，或者都未检测到。这意味着，几乎不会有这样的地震，即测得了 $m_b$ 但由于没有测得 $M_s$ 而无法在 $M_s : m_b$ 图上加以绘制。另一方面，有可能存在这样的爆炸，比如说，$m_b$ 4.5 和（通过外推法）$M_s$ 2.5 的爆炸。如果需要两个参数同时确定才能识别一次事件的话，就可以讨论以识别阈值作为瑞利波的检测阈值。这一阈值在本质上是统计的，但可以通过如下方式进行定义："如果 P 波检测到的事件的 $M_s$ 大于等于 3.2，其面波能被四个或者更多地震台站检测到的可能性有 90%，因此可以将之归为爆炸或地震中的一类。"这一稍嫌冗赘的陈述是必不可少的，因为事件的常规检测采用体波，但是关键的识别检测则用面波。另外一种描述是："硬质岩石中发生的大于等于 20 kton 当量水平的爆炸同样地可以识别；因此，在实践中，WWSSN 可以检测到几乎所有的地震事件。"

从图 2 中可以明显地看出，任何要降低当量阈值的尝试，都要合理的从尝试改进面波检测着手，理由是显而易见的，俄国有一些 $m_b$ 小于 5.0 的事件，目前的仪器无法看到它们的面波，但是可以假定它们是爆炸。显然，随着增强检测面波能力的进程的发展，体波检测能力的提高也被寄予厚望，从而能够检测到几乎所有 $m_b$ 大于 4.0 的事件。后面将讨论这一策略。

## Science of Discrimination

Fig. 2 clearly indicates a difference in excitation between 20 s Rayleigh waves and 1 s P waves for the two types of event. A natural question is how this difference arises, and the question is not purely academic, because in attempting to lower the threshold (that is to bring in points with lower $M_s$ and $m_b$) it is valuable to know exactly when the two populations merge. In Fig. 2 there is a clear separation, but least squares straight lines may not be the best representations of the relationships at lower magnitudes. Theoretical models for earthquakes and explosions should be extendable to any magnitude and thus should indicate whether capital investment to improve detection capability would be justified.

Unfortunately knowledge of the nature of both types of event is still shadowy. An earthquake is known to be a propagating rupture on a fault plane that leads to a finite offset across the fault; and an explosion as seen by seismometers is equivalent to the sudden application of an elastic stress on a notional surface of radius less than 1 km. It is also known in part how P waves and Rayleigh waves are generated from both types of source. This turns out not to be sufficient to answer the question of why the discriminant works. The question can be subdivided by recognizing that the discriminant may depend on the different partitioning of energy at source into body and surface waves; or differences in spectra at source that are reflected in differences in excitation at 1 and 20 s periods regardless of wave type; or some combination of these two.

I do not believe that we yet have a simple answer to this issue. This reflects the inability as yet to describe satisfactorily the processes at work at the focus of an earthquake. I think it is reasonable to say that it is not a depth dependence nor a size difference that controls discriminative capability. Beyond this it is difficult to go.

A more direct and at present more successful approach to the problem of the smaller magnitude events which are as yet beyond the global network's accessibility is to do pilot work in a region where there is the opportunity to get close in to events. Accordingly much research has been concentrated on observations of explosions at the Nevada test site and earthquakes in the western United States. Results have been reported by Evernden[4] and, even using standard definitions of $M_s$ and $m_b$, separation is good down to the lowest yields observed. When careful allowance is made for regional propagation effects separation can probably be improved.

These results show that, within the context of relatively unrestricted access to the area, explosions and earthquakes in the western United States can be discriminated to substantially lower levels than the global threshold of 20 kton in hard rock. There seems to be an order of magnitude of improvement possible without encountering insuperable problems of overlap. It is of the utmost importance that this be understood in context. Monitoring of the Soviet Union, for instance, would involve forgoing the nearby stations and attempting to make up for the loss by high grade instrumentation, arrays and digital

## 识 别 科 学

图 2 清晰地显示出对于两种类型事件，20 s 瑞利波与 1s P 波激发之间的差别。一个很自然的问题就是，这一差异是如何产生的，这不是纯理论性的问题，因为在努力降低检测阈值（也就是引入具有更小 $M_s$ 与 $m_b$ 值的点）的过程中，准确地知道两个样本总体在何时合并是非常有价值的。图 2 中是存在明显分隔的，但是在震级更小时，最小二乘拟合直线可能不是两者关系的最好表示法。关于地震和爆炸的理论模型应该可以适用于任何震级，并且可以说明，用于提高检测能力的资本投入是否是合理的。

遗憾的是，我们对于两种类型事件本质的了解仍然是模糊的。众所周知，地震是破裂沿断层面传播，导致了穿过断层的有限错位；而地震仪所观测到的爆炸则相当于在半径不到 1 km 的假想表面上突然施加了一个弹性应力。在某种程度上我们知道 P 波和瑞利波是如何从两种类型的震源产生的。这还不足以回答为什么可以识别这一问题。这个问题可以通过能量和震源谱加以细分，也就是说识别可能取决于震源的能量体波和面波的不同配分方式；或者取决于震源频谱的差异，这种差异体现在与波的类型无关的 1 s 和 20 s 周期激发的差异上；或者是上述两者的某种形式结合。

我认为我们对这一问题还没有找到一个简单的答案。这反映出迄今为止我们对于如何满意地描述震源发生的过程仍然无能为力。我有理由认为，掌控识别能力的既不是深度也不是尺寸的差异。除此之外就难讲了。

对于那些位于全球台网覆盖之外的较小震级事件这一难题来说，一种更为直接且目前更为成功的方法就是在能够有机会接近事件位置的区域进行试验工作。因此，很多研究集中在观测内华达试验区发生的爆炸以及美国西部的地震。艾文登[4] 报道了研究结果，即使是使用 $M_s$ 和 $m_b$ 的标准定义，在观测到的最低当量处，分离还是明显的。如果仔细地考虑区域传播效应的话，分离还能得到进一步改善。

这些结果表明，在对事件区域相对无限制的接近这一条件下，美国西部的爆炸和地震能够在比硬质岩石中 20 kton 这一全球阈值低得多的水平上加以识别。看起来，要是没有遇到无法克服的重叠问题的话，震级改善程度可能提高一个数量级。最要紧的是，这应该理解为是在一定条件下的。例如，对苏联的监测就要放弃在其附近建地震台站的想法，并努力以高级仪器、台阵和数字化过程来补偿损失。此外，也无法保证，地震和地震波在苏联的传播与在美国西部的传播有可比性（尽管有理

processing. Further, there is no guarantee that earthquakes and seismic wave propagation in the Soviet Union are comparable to those in the western United States (although there are grounds for optimism). Lowering the threshold of the monitoring network could, however, reasonably be expected to yield a lower discrimination threshold, and a large investment in such an improvement would be justifiable on scientific grounds.

## The Future

Several instrumental developments and deployments are under way at the moment. A small number of high quality, long period seismometers are now set up (in Spain, Israel, Thailand, Australia, Alaska and New Jersey). Others, suitable for deep boreholes where noise may be substantially reduced, are in production. Two large new long period arrays, in Alaska and Norway, and three three-element long period arrays in Canada, Sweden, and India, are now operating. The hope is that within two years there will be sufficient data from these instruments to assess a new level of discrimination. It seems reasonable to expect at least a diminution of a factor of two, to 10 kton in hard rock, on the basis of these investments. This is equivalent to saying that in monitoring the Soviet Union almost all events with an $M_s$ of 2.8 or greater will show detectable surface waves at four or more widely spaced stations. As a goal this is quite modest; the two large arrays plus the new stations in Thailand and Israel alone should accomplish this.

A considerably lower threshold seems, however, to be attainable. Extrapolations from the western United States suggest that it is not at all unreasonable to expect discrimination to be feasible at an $M_s$ of 2.0 (2 to 3 kton in hard rock). How would this be achieved? If a monitoring network is allowed the luxury of expanding, the country being monitored must be allowed the luxury of moving its test-site to the most remote spot possible. It would be possible for the Soviet Union to test at a distance of 30° from the nearest seismometers in a monitoring network, and, at this distance, surface waves from an explosion with an $M_s$ of 2.0 are less than 10 nm peak to peak. There are few stations with a noise level as little as a factor of ten higher than this; and a factor of ten might be the upper bound on what the largest possible array might contribute to the improvement of signal-to-noise ratios.

At this stage, economics may control the threshold more than seismology. For instance, Professor J. N. Brune of the University of California, San Diego, recently estimated that a thorough programme to upgrade seismic capabilities to such a high level would cost at least $200 million.

How might a major programme reasonably develop? The present operation of WWSSN is decidedly non-optimal, as the network was not designed for, nor is it dedicated to, discrimination. Resiting of some seismometers, particularly removal from centres of population, would yield reduced noise levels. Better protection from environmental changes, particularly pressure and temperature fluctuation, could not but be beneficial. The aim should be to record ground noise only, and it is worth a substantial amount of time and money to ensure that this is all that is coming out of the instruments. Placing

由持乐观态度）。但是有理由期待，降低检测台网的阈值会导致较低的识别阈值，从科学上讲，对于这一改进工作的大量投入是合理的。

## 前　景

若干仪器的研发和安装使用目前正在进行中。为数不多的高质量长周期地震仪目前正在装配中（位于西班牙、以色列、泰国、澳大利亚、阿拉斯加和新泽西州）。另外一些适用于深埋在可以明显减弱噪声的钻孔中的仪器，目前正在生产中。位于阿拉斯加和挪威的两个新的大型长周期台阵，以及位于加拿大、瑞典和印度的三个由三个地震仪组成的长周期台阵，目前正在运行中。希望在两年内，通过来自这些仪器的大量数据评定新的识别水平。看来有理由期待，基于这些仪器，阈值至少能减少一半，即硬质岩石中 10 kton 当量水平。这相当于说，在监测苏联时，几乎所有 $M_s$ 大于等于 2.8 的事件都会在四个或更多个彼此远离的地震台显示出可检测到的面波。这是一个很适度的目标；只凭两个大型台阵加上泰国和以色列的新建地震台站就可以实现这一目标。

不过，相当低的阈值也是可能达到的。对美国西部研究的外推指出，期待识别能力达到 $M_s$ 为 2.0（硬质岩石中 2～3 kton）是合理的。如何才能达到这一目标呢？如果监测台网可以充分扩展，那么被监测的国家就必须想尽办法将其试验场移动到尽可能远的位置。对于苏联来说，有可能在距离监测台网中最近的地震仪 30° 的位置进行试验，而在这一距离，$M_s$ 2.0 的爆炸所产生面波的峰峰值小于 10 nm。几乎没有一个地震台站的噪声水平能够低达该峰峰值的十倍，而十倍可能是最大台阵所能提供的信噪比增益上限了。

现阶段，经济对于阈值的限制可能超过了地震学。例如，最近加利福尼亚大学圣迭戈分校的布龙教授估计，将地震检测能力升级到这样高水平的整个计划将花费至少两亿美元。

如何才能使一个重要计划合理发展？ WWSSN 目前的运作明显还不够理想，因为监测台网既不是针对识别而设计，也没有致力于识别。对某些地震仪的重新选址，特别是远离人群活动中心，将降低噪声水平。进一步降低地震仪受环境变化的影响，特别是压强和温度的波动变化，不无裨益。其目标应该是只记录到大地噪声，为了确定仪器产生的全部噪声仅限于此，是值得花费大量时间和金钱的。将一些仪器置于钻孔中也必定会进一步减少噪声。相比于照相记录，数字记录因能采用前置滤波

some instruments down boreholes could certainly reduce noise further. Digital recording, in parallel with photographic recording, is highly desirable, preferably with prefiltering to eliminate 6 s microseisms.

At present the WWSSN produces data, but no one is required to analyse them. A small group of seismic analysts, having available both the superior data and also information from the large arrays and other seismic stations that cared to contribute, would greatly increase our number of body-wave detections of events and would develop knowledge about which stations were most useful both in body and surface wave observations. This knowledge would help decide what the next step should be.

It is likely that certain stations would be worth even further improvement. Spotting these sites involves more than just measuring the noise. Seismology is not a wholly predictable subject and, in some locations, signals are unusually high for little known reasons. This may work in favour of sites which would be rejected on the grounds of noise level alone. The improvement might take the form of development of arrays centred on good stations. The establishment of new stations in favourable locations would also make sense.

Beyond this stage it is not easy to speculate. Once one has started reinstrumenting the globe there is no limit to the ingenuity that could be employed. Political and economic realities, however, restrain the monitoring network from extending too far. The development sketched out might be accomplished within five years.

## Obstacles

The relative simplicity of Fig. 2 may give the impression that discrimination can be made into a list of instructions for seismic record readers. In most cases this is true, but there are nagging problems—some natural and some man-made.

In considering a population of events in a certain region it turns out that some events cannot be categorized on the basis of an $M_s : m_b$ discrimination because the surface waves from them are masked by surface waves from other unrelated earthquakes. These cannot be discriminated by the $M_s : m_b$ technique unless a way can be found to separate the two events. An array is highly desirable for this, and even then there are prospects of success only under the circumstances discussed earlier. If the masking event is very large (with an $m_b$ of 7.5 or greater) the global network is blotted out to such an extent that detection of even P waves from practically any event for an hour or more afterwards may be impossible because of the reverberations within the Earth. This opens up the possibility for evasion by firing explosion immediately after a large earthquake. It is difficult at present to see any seismic means of improving the prospect of detecting such evasions.

Another natural hazard is that of explosion-like earthquakes. If the time interval for which Fig. 2 had been compiled were expanded, earthquakes of quite high magnitude (an $m_b$ of 5.0 for instance) but which produce barely discernible surface waves would eventually be

最佳地消除 6 s 微震而倍受青睐。

目前 WWSSN 生成了数据，但还没有得到分析。一个地震分析小组，既能获得高质量数据，又能得到来自大型台阵和其他被关注其贡献的地震台站的信息，将极大地增加体波检测到的事件数量，并给出体波和面波观测都最有效用的地震台站。这些知识将有助于决定下一步该做什么。

可能某些地震台站还值得进一步改善。要找到这些位置，只靠测量噪声是不够的。地震学并不完全是一门可预测的学科，在某些地点，信号不知何故异乎寻常的高。这可能是由特定场地原因造成的，根据噪声水平就能排除这一理由。改进工作可以采取以好的地震台站为中心建立台阵的形式。在条件好的位置兴建新的地震台站也是有意义的。

再下一步就不容易推测了。一旦在地球上重新装备仪器，人的创造力将是无限的。不过，政治和经济现实限制着监测台网的扩张。前面所勾勒出的远景可能会在五年内实现。

## 障　　碍

图 2 的相对简单性给人造成的印象是，识别结果可以制成指示列表提供给地震记录的分析人员。在大多数情况下这是事实，但是还是有令人烦恼的问题——有些是天然地震，有些则是人为的。

在考察某一区域中的事件群时，某些事件是无法基于 $M_s : m_b$ 识别方法进行归类的，因为它们的面波被其他无关的地震面波所屏蔽。除非找到一种方法将两个事件分开，否则它们就不能用 $M_s : m_b$ 方法进行识别。这时就非常需要一个台阵，即使如此，也只有在更早时所讨论的情况下才有成功的可能。如果屏蔽事件很大（其 $m_b$ 大于等于 7.5），其在地球内部的混响甚至会使全球台网被遮盖一个小时以上，在此期间不可能检测到实际发生的任何事件的 P 波信号。这就为在一次大地震后立即进行爆炸的规避行为提供了可能性。目前还很难找到增强规避行为检测能力的地震学方法。

另外一个自然灾害就是类似爆炸的地震。如果将图 2 中所用资料的时间间隔展开，最终将发现震级较大（例如 $m_b$ 为 5.0）但面波几乎不能被察觉的地震。基于

found. These earthquakes, which come from very limited regions on the Earth's surface, would have to be classed as explosions according to the $M_s : m_b$ criterion. It is believed that they can be understood in terms of earthquakes in which the stress drop is abnormally high. Whether with improved instrumentation any earthquake-like features of these events will reveal themselves remains to be seen. It is not yet known whether, with improved body wave detection capability and hence larger populations of smaller events, more of these earthquakes would be encountered.

The chief man-made problem (apart from deliberate masking by earthquakes) is that of decoupling. The radiated seismic signal from an explosion fired in a sufficiently large hole can be at least a factor of 100 smaller than in the fully tamped case. Thus a 50 kton explosion could be moved below the bounds of detectability if fired in a deep hole of radius 80 m, and partial decoupling would occur if the radius were less than this. Although a removal enterprise of this magnitude might well excite attention if started after a treaty had been signed, there may at present be cavities in salt mines which could be used for partial decoupling. There seems no seismic way of detecting decoupled events, and entrants into a treaty would have to weigh the risks accordingly.

Although there are prospects of reducing the yield threshold to a figure of a few kton in hard rock, it must be borne in mind that a violator is unlikely to fire his explosions in granite. As a threshold of 2 kton in hard rock would be very difficult to achieve, this might be turned into a statement that all tests under 20 kton fired in alluvium would not be discriminable. This depressing situation is fortunately unlikely to be valid. The thickness of alluvium deposits limits the depth of the shot, but, on the other hand, the shot must be buried deep enough not to form a subsidence crater. These craters have formed more often than not after a test in alluvium, and there would be a clear risk of visual detection. Thus a violator would have to judge the risks of alluvium firing and might well conclude that a yield much smaller than 20 kton was all that could safely be tested.

## "Negative Evidence"

One may justifiably feel vaguely uneasy about the $M_s : m_b$ discrimination technique. It tends to enshrine a lot of science and technology in one diagram and it may be used misleadingly. For instance although the population of earthquakes in Fig. 2 is fairly representative, there can only be a limited number of explosions; most of these come from one test site and are thus not truly independent samples. Further, test sites could be moved around at will, and so the discriminant can only represent the past, not the future. These qualms can only be assuaged if the science of discrimination is seen to be well founded.

On the other hand, there may also be some uneasiness that the $M_s : m_b$ discriminant is not optimistic enough, and this is worth examining. When an event has both detectable P waves and detectable Rayleigh waves it can be placed on an $M_s : m_b$ diagram. If, however, P waves are detected but no Rayleigh waves are seen, it is unacceptable. For instance, an explosion in the Soviet Union with an $m_b$ of 4.5 will not generate detectable

$M_s : m_b$ 判据，这些来自地表非常有限的几个区域的地震只能归类为爆炸。我们相信，它们可以被理解为应力降异常高的地震。随着仪器的改进，无论这些事件具有什么类似地震的特征，都会暴露出来。目前尚不清楚，随着体波检测能力的提高和较小事件数量的随之增多，是否就会发现更多的此类地震。

主要的人为问题（除了故意地利用地震遮掩之外）是解耦。在一个足够大的洞中引发爆炸所辐射出的地震信号比完全夯实条件下的信号至少弱 100 倍。因此，如果在半径为 80 m 的深洞中引爆，一次 50 kton 爆炸就会低于检测界限，在半径小于 80 m 时将会发生部分解耦。显然签订协议后如此大兴土木可能会引起充分关注，目前盐矿中可能还存在可以用于解耦的洞穴。似乎还没有地震方法可以检测解耦事件，因此签署条约的成员国将不得不权衡所带来的风险。

尽管有希望将检测当量下限减少到硬质岩石中的几千吨的程度，我们必须意识到违约者不太可能会在花岗岩中引爆。由于硬质岩石中 2 kton 的阈值将是很难达到的，也就可以说，所有在冲击层中进行的低于 20 kton 的试验都将是无法识别的。很幸运，这种令人沮丧的情况可能不会出现。冲积层的沉积厚度限制了爆炸深度，但另一方面，爆炸必须在足够深度引发才能避免形成沉降坑。在冲积层实验之后往往形成弹坑，也就存在明显的被检测到的危险。因此违约者将不得不考虑在冲积层引爆的风险，并且可以充分肯定，安全试验的当量水平是远小于 20 kton。

## "反面证据"

对于 $M_s : m_b$ 识别技术感到隐约的不安是合理的。这项技术总是把大量科学技术置于一份图表之中，而且还可能被错误地应用。例如，尽管图 2 中所示的地震事件具有相当的代表性，其中只能包含有限的爆炸事件；其中大多数来自于一个试验场所，因此不是真正的独立样本。再说，试验场所是可以随意移动的，因此识别结果也只能代表过去而不是将来。只有当我们看到识别科学很好地建立起来时，才能减少疑虑。

另一方面，还可能存在着对于 $M_s : m_b$ 识别方法不够乐观而产生的一些不安，而这是值得核验的。如果一次事件同时具有可检测到的 P 波和瑞利波，它就能置于 $M_s : m_b$ 图中。但是，如果只检测到 P 波却没有看到瑞利波，就不能被接受。例如，苏联境内一次 $m_b$ 为 4.5 的爆炸就不会产生可检测到的瑞利波。能否根据其缺乏瑞利

Rayleigh waves. Could it be called an explosion on the basis of its lack of Rayleigh waves? Obviously this question depends on whether all earthquakes with an $m_b$ of 4.5 have detectable Rayleigh waves (we eliminate the masked event problem). The answer is that on present experience they do, with the exception of a limited number of events mentioned earlier. The spread of $M_s$ values for earthquakes with $m_b > 4.5$ is substantial, but it does not extend down to 3.2.

Up to the present so called "negative evidence" has always been looked on with some suspicion. The reason for this is probably that, although to a scientist the absence of a signal can be as important as its presence, to the politician with a different mode of thinking "negative evidence" sounds as unconvincing as would absence of fingerprints to establish not being present at the scene of a crime. It may well be that the $M_s : m_b$ diagram, for all its neatness, has placed an undue emphasis on the necessity for determining both $M_s$ and $m_b$.

The following would be a "negative evidence" type of discrimination statement. "When an event has been detected by P waves and assigned a body wave magnitude of 4.5 or greater it can be categorized as an earthquake if $M_s \geqslant (m_b - 1.3)$ and an explosion if $M_s < (m_b - 1.3)$ or if $M_s$ cannot be determined, but on the basis of noise observations must be less than $m_b - 1.3$". It would switch the threshold to a body wave magnitude of 4.5 or about 5 kton in hard rock, a figure that with the $M_s : m_b$ discriminant alone would take several years and much expenditure to achieve. Although this statement would let through as explosions those unusual earthquakes described previously, this would equally apply to the $M_s : m_b$ technique. For these events a pragmatic approach is necessary. A very detailed survey with a large population is necessary to establish the general validity of negative evidence. Such work is at present being pursued.

## The Broader Scene

I shall conclude with a description of recent activity beyond the laboratory. In 1968 the Stockholm International Peace Research Institute (SIPRI) convened a conference of seismologists from ten countries, east and west, at which technical progress since 1958 was reviewed. Subsequent SIPRI Progress Reports, the latest dated September 1971 (ref. 5), have kept the technical content up to date.

In the United States, numerous technical meetings have been held. Papers presented at the Woods Hole meeting in 1970 (ref. 4) have been widely used in this discussion. A recent meeting in Cambridge, Massachusetts, has allowed some of the projections to be strengthened and a growing appreciation of the problem events.

The Conference of the Committee on Disarmament of the United Nations (which has lived under several names) meets regularly at Geneva, and the issue of seismology and a test ban is frequently aired there. In 1970, at Canadian instigation, a register of seismic stations with guaranteed available data was compiled by the United Nations and

波而称之为爆炸？很明显，这个问题取决于是否所有 $m_b$ 为 4.5 的地震都有可检测到的瑞利波（我们排除了事件遮蔽的问题）。除了前面提到的数量有限事件之外，基于现有的经验，答案是确实如此。对于 $m_b>4.5$ 的地震有大量的 $M_s$ 数值展布，但是没有向下延伸到 3.2。

到目前为止，人们一直是带着怀疑的目光来看待所谓"反面证据"的。其理由很可能是，对科学家而言，一个信号的存在和缺乏同等重要，而在一个具有不同思维模式的政治家看来，"反面证据"听起来就像在犯罪现场缺少指纹一样不足以令人相信。很可能正是因为 $M_s:m_b$ 图的简洁性，而过分强调了确定 $M_s$ 和 $m_b$ 的必要性。

下面是关于"反面证据"类型的识别方法阐述。"当 P 波检测到一次事件并确定其体波震级大于等于 4.5 时，如果 $M_s\geq(m_b-1.3)$ 就将它归为地震，如果 $M_s<(m_b-1.3)$ 或者无法确定 $M_s$ 时就将它归为爆炸，不过前提是在噪声观测的基础上必须小于 $m_b-1.3$。"这将使阈值转变为体波震级 4.5 或者硬质岩石中的 5 kton，单独使用 $M_s:m_b$ 识别方法得到这一结果需要耗时数年且耗费巨资。尽管这一陈述将使前面所描述的那些异常地震事件被当作是爆炸，这也同样适用于 $M_s:m_b$ 技术。对于这些事件来说，一种实用方法是必要的。要建立反面证据的普适性，必须对大量样本进行详细调查。这样的工作目前正在进行中。

## 更广阔的前景

我将以一项最近在实验室以外进行的活动作为结束。1968 年，斯德哥尔摩国际和平研究所（SIPRI）召集了一次来自东西方十个国家的地震学家参与的会议，会上回顾了自 1958 年以来的技术进展。后来出版的 SIPRI 进展报告，最新一期为 1971 年 9 月（参考文献 5），记录了最新的技术内容。

在美国，召开了众多的技术会议。本文的讨论中大量引用了 1970 年伍兹霍尔会议上出现的论文（参考文献 4）。最近一次会议是在马萨诸塞州的剑桥，会议认为，一些预测能力得到了强化并加深了对于问题事件的认识。

联合国裁军委员会（曾几易其名）协商会议定期于日内瓦举行，期间会经常讨论地震学和禁止核试验的问题。1970 年，在加拿大的倡导下，联合国对承诺提供数据的地震台站进行了登记注册，随后，一项加拿大的调查考察了这一地震台网的理

subsequently a Canadian survey[6] examined the theoretical potential of this network. In the same year Britain submitted a proposal[7] to Geneva on a new network which would improve discriminative capability. In 1971 a United Nations technical meeting was held in Geneva against a background of increased international interest in a test ban.

It is clear that this subject will continue to remain alive before a more general public for the foreseeable future. During this time seismological advances are unlikely to be spectacular, but a continuing investment in seismology will undoubtedly produce a steady reduction of the threshold. Where this threshold ultimately comes to rest and whether a treaty will be signed will be determined by a multiplicity of factors, only one of which is seismology.

This work was sponsored by the Advanced Research Projects Agency of the Department of Defense.

Fig. 2 was kindly supplied by P. W. Basham and P. D. Marshall, and represents work done by them[3] at the Department of Energy, Mines and Resources, Ottawa, Canada.

(**241**, 19-24; 1973)

**David Davies**
Lincoln Laboratory, Massachusetts Institute of Technology, Lexington, Massachusetts 02173

---

References:

1. Neild, R., and Ruina, J. P., *Science*, **175**, 140 (1972).

2. *The Detection and Recognition of Underground Explosions* (United Kingdom Atomic Energy Authority, London, 1965).

3. Marshall, P. D., and Basham, P. W., *Geophys. J.*, **28**, 431 (1972).

4. *Proceedings of a Conference on Seismic Discrimination at Woods Hole, Massachusetts* (July 20-23, 1970).

5. *Seismic Methods for Monitoring Underground Explosions* (Progress Report, SIPRI, Stockholm, 1971).

6. Basham, P. W., and Whitham, K., *Seismological Detection and Identification of Underground Nuclear Explosions* (publication of the Earth Physics Branch, Ottawa, Canada, 1971).

7. Submission of the United Kingdom to the Geneva Conference on Disarmament, July 28, 1970 (CCD 296).

论潜力 [6]。同年，英国向日内瓦提交了一份建议，内容是关于一个能提高识别能力的新地震台网 [7]。在国际上对于禁止核试验问题日益关注的背景下，1971 年，在日内瓦召开了一次联合国技术会议。

很明显，在可预知的未来，对于广大公众而言，这将会是一个一直保持活跃的主题。在这段时期内，地震学不会有什么惊人的进展，但是对于地震学的持续投入无疑将导致检出阈值的稳步下降。阈值最终将落在何处，以及是否会签署条约，将取决于多方面的因素，地震学只是其中之一。

这一工作由美国国防部高级研究计划局发起。

图 2 为巴沙姆和马歇尔友情提供，其中凝聚了他们 [3] 在加拿大渥太华能源、矿产和资源部所付出的努力。

（王耀杨 翻译；吴庆举 审稿）

# DNA Replication Sites within Nuclei of Mammalian Cells

J. A. Huberman *et al.*

## Editor's Notes

**Nearly 20 years after the structure of DNA was published, molecular biologists were still struggling to understand how DNA, the genetic material, is replicated in living cells of higher organisms (eukaryotes). The interest of this article is that it shows how rudimentary were scientists' ideas of that process. Huberman *et al.* studied HeLa cells (a familiar strain of human cells derived from a cancer) during the process of mitosis (cell division). "S" phase is that during which a cell about to divide accumulates the material eventually needed to make two cells. They conclude that DNA is first synthesized near the nuclear membrane but that it later migrates to the whole nucleus.**

---

DNA replication can occur throughout the nucleus and is not restricted to the inner surface of the nuclear membrane.

---

THE involvement of a membrane site in DNA replication was first suggested by Jacob, Brenner and Cuzin[1] in their "replicon" model for replication of bacterial DNA, but the evidence accumulated since then is inconclusive. In prokaryotic cells, co-sedimentation of DNA replication points and cell membranes has been demonstrated[1-4], and the origin of replication and the membrane found to be associated[5]. A lipid-free replicating DNA-protein complex from *E. coli* has been isolated[6] and it has been reported that only the origin, but not the growing points, of the *E. coli* chromosome is attached to membrane[7].

In cell fractionation experiments with mammalian cells it was also found that replication points, detected by pulse-labelling with $^3$H-thymidine (TdR), are associated with the nuclear membrane (or some other large, light, hydrophobic cell structure)[8-11,13]. Association between replication points and the nuclear membrane has also been detected by electron microscope autoradiography of thin sections through pulse-labelled, unsynchronized HeLa cells. The label associated with the membrane apparently moved into the nuclear interior after a 1 h chase[13].

On the other hand, most electron microscope autoradiographic experiments suggest that replication can take place throughout the nucleus. For instance, Comings and Kakefuda[14] generally found grains located throughout the nucleus when unsynchronized human amnion cells were pulse-labelled for 5 min or more with $^3$H-TdR and then

# 哺乳动物细胞核内的DNA复制位点

休伯曼等

编者按

在 DNA 结构发表近 20 年后，分子生物学家们仍然在孜孜不倦地研究作为遗传物质的 DNA 在高等生物活细胞（真核细胞）中是如何复制的。这篇文章的意义在于，它显示了科学家们对于 DNA 的复制过程的认识仍然浅显。休伯曼等人研究了海拉（HeLa）细胞（一种源自人体癌细胞的细胞株）的有丝分裂过程。"S"期是指即将分裂的细胞积累分裂成两个细胞所需物质的阶段。他们总结认为 DNA 首先在核膜附近合成，然后迁移到整个细胞核。

---

DNA 复制发生在整个细胞核内，而不是局限于核膜的内表面。

---

雅各布、布伦纳和居赞 [1] 在关于细菌 DNA 复制的"复制子"模型中首次提出膜位点参与 DNA 的复制，但是其后这方面所积累的证据并不确凿。在原核细胞中，DNA 复制点和细胞膜的共沉淀已经得到证明 [1-4]，同时发现，此复制起点能与细胞膜结合 [5]。从大肠杆菌中分离得到了不含膜脂的复制的 DNA－蛋白复合体 [6]，且有报道称仅大肠杆菌染色体上的复制起点与细胞膜相连，生长点与其不相连 [7]。

通过 $^3$H－胸腺嘧啶核苷酸（TdR）脉冲标记的哺乳动物细胞的分级分离实验发现，复制点与细胞核核膜（或者其他一些大的、轻的、疏水的细胞结构）相结合 [8-11,13]。使用薄片电子显微放射自显影法检测脉冲标记非同步的 HeLa 细胞，同样发现了复制点与细胞核核膜相结合。追踪实验表明与核膜相连的标记 1 小时后明显转移到细胞核内部 [13]。

另一方面，大部分电子显微放射自显影实验表明，复制能在整个细胞核中发生。例如，科明斯和挂札 [14] 用 $^3$H-TdR 脉冲标记非同步的人羊膜细胞 5 分钟或者更长时间，然后将其切片进行放射自显影，研究结果发现颗粒遍布整个细胞核。然而，

sectioned and autoradiographed. When, however, cells that were supposedly synchronized at the beginning of S phase were pulse-labelled for 5 or 10 min, grains were found predominantly over the nuclear membrane. Comings and Kakefuda concluded that initiation of replication takes place on the nuclear membrane, whereas the replication occurs anywhere within the nucleus.

Somewhat different results were obtained by Blondel[15], using KB cells and pulse times of 2 min; Williams and Ockey[16], using Chinese hamster cells and pulse times of 10 min or longer; and Erlandson and de Harven[17], using HeLa cells and pulse times of 15 min. All three groups concluded, in agreement with Comings and Kakefuda[14], that during a large part of the S phase grains are produced over the entire nucleus, but they differed from them in finding a peripheral pattern of grains more frequently at the end of the S phase than at the beginning. A cell fractionation experiment by Kay *et al.*[18] also demonstrated association of late-replicating but not early-replicating DNA with the nuclear membrane.

## Higher Resolution Autoradiography

Regardless of the time in S phase at which replication occurs close to the nuclear membrane, one important implication of most of these electron microscope autoradiography experiments is that, in some parts of S phase, at least, replication occurs throughout the nucleus. How can this implication be reconciled with the experiments indicating that all replicating DNA is associated with the nuclear membrane? It is possible that a considerable amount of DNA is synthesized during a pulse as short as 2 min. Huberman and Riggs[19] have shown that the rate of DNA replication in Chinese hamster cells can be as much as 2.5 $\mu m$ $min^{-1}$, although most replication seems to occur at rates between 0.5 and 1.2 $\mu m$ $min^{-1}$. Thus as much as 5 $\mu m$ of DNA could be synthesized during a 2 min pulse. If this DNA were synthesized at the nuclear membrane and then stretched out, it could reach the centre of a nucleus of diameter 5-8 $\mu m$ and give rise to a false impression of the location of sites of DNA synthesis.

This effect could be ruled out by shorter pulses. We calculated that a pulse of 0.5 min would provide sufficient grains, after an exposure of several months, and the resolution (less than 1.25 $\mu m$ of DNA synthesized) necessary to distinguish between replication solely at the nuclear membrane and replication elsewhere in the nucleus.

In most experiments, we used Chinese hamster (CHO) cells, which can be easily synchronized. The cells were pulse-labelled for 0.5 min with $^3$H-TdR, then washed, fixed, embedded, sectioned and stained. The sections were placed on grids and autoradiographed by standard techniques[20]. After exposure times of several months, the emulsions were developed and the grids were examined by electron microscopy.

## Sites of Replication

Cells from an unsynchronized culture, shown in Fig. 1, illustrate the variety of distribution of grains over the nucleus. The cells in Fig. 1A and B are labelled throughout the nucleus

如果把同步化为 S 期初期的细胞脉冲标记 5 或 10 分钟，检测到的颗粒则主要分布在核膜上。科明斯和挂札由此推断，复制的起始发生在核膜上，而复制则发生在细胞核内的任何区域。

下面三个小组的研究得到的结果略有不同：布隆德尔 [15] 用脉冲处理 KB 细胞（一种口腔癌细胞）2 分钟，威廉姆斯和奥克伊 [16] 用脉冲处理中国仓鼠细胞 10 分钟或者更长时间，以及厄兰森和德阿尔旺 [17] 用脉冲处理 HeLa 细胞 15 分钟。与科明斯和挂札 [14] 的结论相一致的是，上述三个研究组都认为在 S 期的大部分时期，颗粒存在于整个细胞核中。但是与科明斯和挂札的结论不同的是，他们发现与 S 期初期相比这些颗粒在 S 期末期出现周边模式的频率更高。凯 [18] 等人的细胞分级分离实验同样阐明了 DNA 与核膜的结合主要是发生在复制的后期，而不是复制的初期。

## 高分辨放射自显影法

不考虑更接近细胞核核膜的复制时期到底出现在 S 期的哪个阶段，大部分电子显微放射自显影实验得到的一个重要的结论就是，至少在 S 期的某些阶段内，复制发生在整个细胞核内。这一结论是如何与那些表明正在复制的 DNA 与核膜相结合的实验保持一致的？在短短 2 分钟的脉冲时间内合成大量的 DNA 是可能的。尽管大部分 DNA 的复制速率在每分钟 0.5~1.2 μm，但是休伯曼和里格斯 [19] 的研究表明，中国仓鼠细胞的 DNA 复制速率可以达到每分钟 2.5 μm。因此在 2 分钟的时间内可以合成 5 μm 的 DNA。假设这些 DNA 是在细胞核核膜上合成，然后延伸出去，那么该 DNA 就可以到达直径为 5~8 μm 的细胞核的中心，从而造成了对 DNA 合成位点位置的错误判断。

上述这种影响可以通过缩短脉冲时间来排除。我们计算表明，在曝光几个月以后，0.5 分钟的脉冲时间能够提供足够的颗粒，其分辨能力（可分辨小于 1.25 μm 新合成的 DNA）可以将单独发生在细胞核核膜与发生在细胞核的其他区域的复制区分开来。

大部分实验中，我们使用中国仓鼠（CHO）细胞，因为这种细胞容易同步化。将这种细胞用 $^3$H-TdR 脉冲标记 0.5 分钟后，进行清洗、固定、包埋、切片以及染色。切片放在铜网上，按照标准技术进行放射自显影 [20]。曝光几个月后，显影冲洗，用电子显微镜观察铜网。

## 复 制 位 点

图 1 显示了非同步培养的细胞中颗粒在细胞核中的各种分布情况。图 1A 和图 1B 的细胞展示的是整个细胞核都被标记的情况（普遍模式），而图 1C 和图 1D 的

(general pattern), whereas the cells in Fig. 1C and D are labelled predominantly around the nuclear membrane (peripheral pattern). The grains in Fig. 1E are mostly clustered over regions of condensed chromatin, frequently near the membrane. Fig. 1F shows a cell with grains throughout the nucleus but with some concentration around the nuclear membrane.

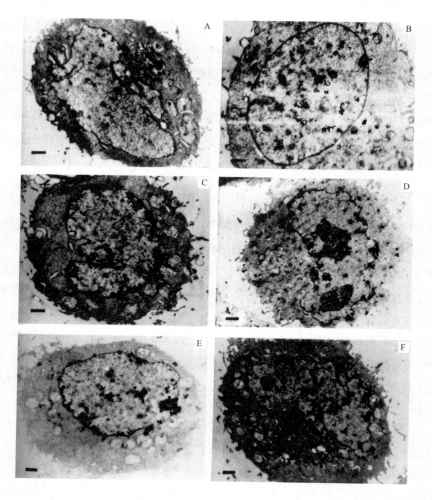

Fig. 1. Autoradiography of unsynchronized CHO cells exposed to $^3$H-TdR for 0.5 min. A and B, grains distributed over entire nucleus. C and D, grains distributed around nuclear membrane. E, clustered grain distribution. F, mixed grain distribution. CHO cells were grown on Petri plates in Joklik-modified MEM (Grand Island Biological Company) supplemented with 7% foetal calf serum and non-essential amino-acids. Pulse-labelling was performed by first adding 5-fluorouridine deoxyriboside (FUDR; Hoffmann-LaRoche) to a final concentration of 1.6 µg ml.$^{-1}$ to inhibit further biosynthesis of dTTP. After 1 min, $^3$H-TdR (51 Ci mmol$^{-1}$; New England Nuclear) was added to 17 µCi ml.$^{-1}$. After 30 s the plates were removed from 37°C, and the medium rapidly sucked off. The plates were then washed with ice-cold isotonic saline containing FUDR at 0.1 µg ml.$^{-1}$ (two changes). Cells were removed from the plates by trypsinization at room temperature in isotonic saline still containing FUDR. The cells were pelleted, then fixed with glutaraldehyde and OsO$_4$, dehydrated, embedded in epoxy resin[29] and cut into gold-purple sections. The sections were mounted on grids and autoradiographed by the technique of Caro and Van Tubergen[20] except that the acetic acid stop bath was replaced with distilled water. Exposure time was 3.5 months. The bar in each figure represents 1 µm.

细胞展示的是被标记区域主要出现在细胞核核膜周围的情况（周边模式）。图 1E 中颗粒主要集中在浓缩的染色质区域，通常靠近核膜。图 1F 中颗粒遍布细胞的整个细胞核，但是在核膜周围的密度相对较大。

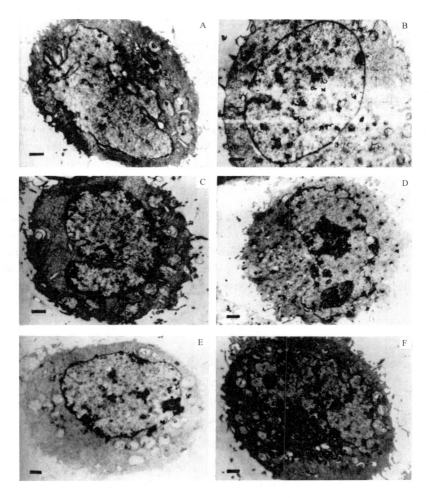

图 1. ³H-TdR 处理非同步 CHO 细胞 0.5 分钟后放射自显影图。图 A 和图 B 展示的是颗粒分布于整个细胞核的情况。图 C 和图 D 展示的是颗粒分布在细胞核核膜周围的情况。图 E 展示的是颗粒的聚集分布情况。图 F 展示的是颗粒的混合分布情况。用改良的乔克利克基础培养基（购自格兰德岛生物公司）在培养皿中培养 CHO 细胞，培养基中添加 7% 的胎牛血清和非必需氨基酸。脉冲标记操作按照以下步骤进行，首先添加 5- 氟尿嘧啶脱氧核苷（FUDR，购自霍夫曼 – 罗氏公司）至终浓度为 1.6 µg·ml⁻¹，以便进一步抑制脱氧胸苷三磷酸 dTTP 的生物合成。1 分钟后，加入 ³H-TdR（51 Ci·mmol⁻¹，购自新英格兰核公司），至终浓度 17 µCi·ml⁻¹。30 秒钟后，将培养皿从 37℃ 中移走，迅速吸掉培养基。然后用含有 0.1 µg·ml⁻¹ FUDR 的冰浴生理盐水冲洗培养板（换液 2 次）。室温下，在含有 FUDR 的生理盐水中进行胰蛋白酶消化，从培养皿中分解细胞。细胞离心后，用戊二醛和四氧化锇固定，脱水，环氧树脂[29]包埋，制成紫金色切片。除了用蒸馏水替代醋酸作为定影液，其他的按照卡罗和范·蒂贝根[20] 的方法将这些切片放在铜网上进行放射自显影。曝光 3.5 个月。图中标尺代表 1 µm。

Many grains are found in some cells more than 1.25 μm from the nuclear membrane (central grains), suggesting that replication is taking place at sites away from the membrane. To be certain of that conclusion, however, other possible explanations must be ruled out. The central grains cannot be due to background because few or no grains are found over the cytoplasm. They must be due to incorporation into DNA since no grains are found over G1 or G2 cells (see below), and the grains of isolated nuclei can be removed by DNAase. The central grains could also originate from DNA replication occurring on invaginations of the nuclear membrane either just above or just below the section plane. While this might explain some central grains, it certainly cannot explain most of them. Because the cells are sectioned with random orientations, we can get some idea of the frequency of invaginations which might bring nuclear membrane within 1.25 μm of the section plane from the frequency of invaginations in the nuclear periphery. Although some peripheral invaginations are evident in Fig. 1, they are not so frequent that most of the central area could be 1.25 μm or less from an invagination.

In some preliminary experiments we used HeLa cells, which have much more regular nuclei: central grains were also found over their nuclei (Fig. 2). Even serial sections up to 0.5 μm apart through a single cell all showed central grains. The change in pattern from general labelling in early S to peripheral labelling in late S suggests that general labelling is not an artefact of sectioning. Finally, the central grains cannot be accounted for by internal membranes within the nucleus. Such membranes have never been seen by other electron microscopists; apart from invaginations of the peripheral membrane we could see none in our sections.

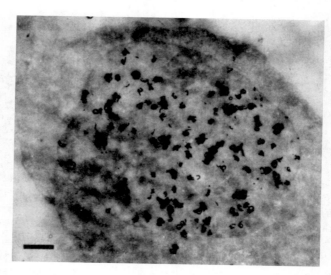

Fig. 2. Autoradiography of a HeLa cell exposed to $^3$H-TdR for 1.5 min. The cells were grown in suspension culture in Joklik-modified MEM (Grand Island Biological Company) supplemented with 5% horse serum. Pulse-labelling was done by adding $^3$H-TdR (20 Ci mmol$^{-1}$, New England Nuclear) to a concentration of 20 μCi ml$^{-1}$. Exactly 1.5 min after addition of $^3$H-TdR, the pulse was terminated by addition of an equal volume of ice-cold isotonic saline containing 1% glutaraldehyde. Subsequent processing was as in Fig. 1. Exposure time was 9.5 months. The bar represents 1 μm.

在一些细胞的研究中发现，许多颗粒距离核膜超过 1.25 μm（中间颗粒），这表明复制发生在远离核膜的位点上。但是为了确定这个结论，必须排除其他可能的解释。因为细胞质中几乎没有发现颗粒的存在，所以这些中间颗粒不可能是由于背景造成的。这些颗粒的形成一定是由于放射性标记分子成功结合到 DNA 分子上，因为在细胞的 G1 或者 G2 期也没有发现颗粒的存在（见下文），并且这些从细胞核中分离得到的颗粒可以被 DNA 酶除去。这些中间颗粒也可能是恰好高于或者低于切片平面的核膜内陷位置上 DNA 复制的结果。这或许可以解释一些中间颗粒的存在，但绝不能解释大部分中间颗粒的存在。因为这些细胞的切割方向是随机的，我们可以从细胞核外围内陷的频率获悉能让细胞核核膜在这 1.25 μm 范围内的内陷的几率。尽管图 1 中有一些明显的周边内陷，但是大部分中间区域与一个内陷之间的距离等于或小于 1.25 μm 的概率并不高。

我们使用 HeLa 细胞进行了部分的预实验，在这些实验中，HeLa 细胞具有形状更加规则的细胞核，并且在核周围都出现了中间颗粒（图 2）。甚至在单细胞 0.5 μm 厚的连续切片上都有中间颗粒的存在。从 S 期早期的普遍标记模式到 S 期后期的周边标记模式的变化说明普遍标记并不是由切割造成的假象。最后，细胞核内部的膜结构并不能解释中间颗粒的问题。其他电子显微镜观察者从未观察到这种膜，除了内陷的周边核膜，我们在切片中也没有观察到这种膜的存在。

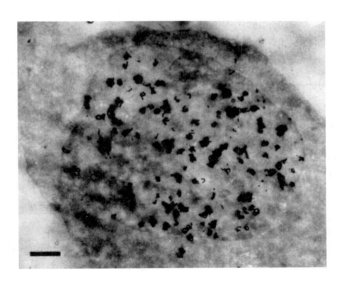

图 2. HeLa 细胞置于 ³H-TdR 1.5 分钟后的放射自显影图。用添加 5% 马血清的改良乔克利克基础培养基（购自格兰德岛生物公司）悬浮培养细胞。加入 ³H-TdR（20 Ci·mmol⁻¹，购自新英格兰核公司），至终浓度为 20 μCi·ml⁻¹，进行脉冲标记。1.5 分钟后，加入等体积冰浴的含 1% 戊二醛的生理盐水终止脉冲反应。随后的步骤同图 1。曝光 9.5 个月。图中标尺代表 1 μm。

To express quantitatively the proportion of cells showing peripheral labelling, we have modified the method of Williams and Ockey[16]. We defined central grains as those further than 1.25 μm from the nearest nuclear membrane, and peripheral grains to be those closer than 1.25 μm to the nuclear membrane. The "central activity" of a cell section was calculated as the ratio of the fraction of central grains : the fraction of nuclear area which was central. Nucleolar areas and grains were excluded because the nucleolus has less DNA than the rest of the nucleus. A histogram showing the frequency of various central activities for an unsynchronized cell population is shown in Fig. 3 (a central activity of 1.0 implies an equal concentration of grains over central and peripheral areas).

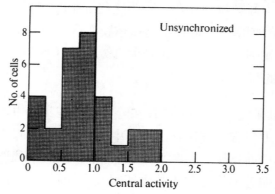

Fig. 3. Distribution of grains over unsynchronized CHO cells exposed to ³H-TdR for 0.5 min. Prints at about ×15,000 magnification were made of autoradiograms of individual randomly chosen cells similar to and including those in Fig. 1. A line was drawn within each nucleus which was at all points 1.25 μm away from the nearest nuclear membrane. This line divided the nucleus into a central area and a peripheral area. Grains were counted over each area, and the size of each area was measured. In these determinations, grains lying over the nucleolus, and nucleolar areas, were ignored because the nucleolus has so much less DNA than the rest of the nucleus. Grains lying outside the nucleus were also ignored. "Central activity" was calculated as the ratio of the fraction of grains which were central to the fraction of area which was central. Thirty nuclei were measured for the histogram.

Only 13% of the cells in Fig. 3 have central activities of less than 0.25, showing that DNA synthesis can go on at sites away from the nuclear membrane. The nuclear membrane is therefore not essential for DNA replication in Chinese hamster cells. But the fact that many cells do show a predominantly peripheral pattern remains to be explained.

## Peripheral Replication in Late S Phase

Since previous autoradiographic studies[14-17] had suggested that peripheral labelling occurs only at certain times during the S phase, we decided to try short pulse-labelling of cells synchronized to various times during the cell cycle. We chose "Colcemid" reversal[21] to synchronize the cells. Growing cells were treated with "Colcemid" for a few hours and the cells blocked in mitosis collected by selective trypsinization. These cells (90-100% mitotic) were allowed to continue growing in the absence of "Colcemid". Within 2 h, 98.5% of the cells completed division, and by 18 h after release from mitosis, more than 70% of the cells had divided again. We preferred this synchronization method to methods involving starvation of nucleotides[21], because cells recover excellently and normal DNA replication is not affected.

为了定量标定周边标记细胞的比例，我们对威廉姆斯和奥克伊[16]的方法进行了改进。我们将那些与最邻近的细胞核核膜相距大于 1.25 μm 的颗粒定义为中间颗粒，与核膜相距小于 1.25 μm 的颗粒定义为周边颗粒。一个细胞切片的"中间活性"是以中间颗粒的比例／中间核面积的比例来计算的。这需要排除核仁区域和该区域的颗粒，因为核仁的 DNA 含量比细胞核其他区域要少。图 3 显示了非同步细胞群中不同中间活性细胞的数量柱形图（中间活性 1.0 表示颗粒在中间区域和周边区域分布的密度相同）。

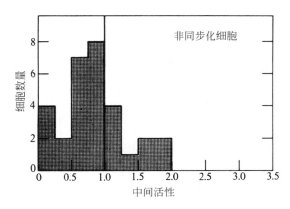

图 3. 非同步 CHO 细胞置于 ³H-TdR 0.5 分钟后颗粒的分布图。随机选择类似图 1 和图 1 中的单个细胞，将其进行放射自显影后以 15,000 倍放大并打印成图。将细胞核内所有与最近邻细胞核核膜相距 1.25 μm 的点用线连接起来。这条线将细胞核分成中间区域和周边区域。计算每个区域点的数量，并且测量区域面积的大小。在这种计算中，忽略靠近核仁和核仁区域的颗粒，因为核仁区的 DNA 含量比细胞核其他区域的少得多。位于细胞核外面的颗粒也忽略不计。"中间活性"是计算中间颗粒数量与中间区域面积的比值。该柱形图是对 30 个细胞核进行测定得到的结果。

图 3 中仅有 13% 的细胞中间活性小于 0.25，表明 DNA 合成可以在远离核膜的位点进行。因此在中国仓鼠细胞中，核膜并不是 DNA 复制必需的。但是许多细胞表现出的显著的周边模式仍然需要进一步的研究解释。

### S 期后期的周边复制

由于前面的放射自显影研究 [14-17] 表明周边标记仅发生在 S 期的特定时期，我们决定用短脉冲标记处于细胞周期不同时期的同步化细胞。我们采用"秋水仙酰胺"[21] 将细胞同步化。经秋水仙酰胺处理几个小时以后，生长细胞都停滞在有丝分裂期，然后用选择性胰蛋白酶消化收集这些细胞。这些细胞（90%~100% 处于有丝分裂期）在缺乏秋水仙酰胺的条件下可以继续生长。2 小时之内，98.5% 细胞会完成分裂，在完成有丝分裂 18 小时后，70% 以上的细胞会再次分裂。之所以采用这种方法进行同步化而不使用限制核苷酸供应的方法 [21]，是因为这样不会影响细胞的复苏和正常的 DNA 复制。

Table 1 and Fig. 4 show the distribution of grains within the nucleus as a function of time after release from mitosis. Peripheral labelling cannot be detected in the early stages of S but becomes predominant in later S.

Table 1. Extent of DNA Synthesis in Synchronized CHO Cells

| Hours after release from mitosis | 2 | 4 | 6 | 8 | 10 | 12 | 14 |
|---|---|---|---|---|---|---|---|
| Percentage of cells labelled* | 26 | 83 | 93 | 89 | 81 | 62 | 48 |
| Average number grains/cell section after 1 month exposure † | <1 | 6 | 16 | 16 | 24 | 17 | — |

* Cells were synchronized as in Fig. 4. At 2 h intervals after release from mitosis, $^3$H-TdR (20 Ci mmol$^{-1}$; New England Nuclear) was added to each plate (17 µCi ml.$^{-1}$ final concentration). After 10 min the cells were washed twice with cold isotonic saline, collected by trypsinization at room temperature, allowed to swell in hypotonic medium (2 mM MgCl$_2$, 1 mM EDTA, 10 mM KPO$_4$, $p$H 7.7) for 10 min, pelleted, fixed with methanol-acetic acid (3:1), spread onto subbed glass slides and allowed to dry. The slides were coated with autoradiographic stripping film ("Kodak AR-10") and exposed for 7 days. After development, the slides were stained with Giemsa stain, then mounted under "Permount". At least 312 cells were scanned to determine the percent of cells labelled at each time point.

† The total number of grains over each nuclear section was determined for the autoradiographs used in Fig. 4. These figures were divided by the exposure time in months. Extra data for 2 h and 8 h after release from mitosis are included here.

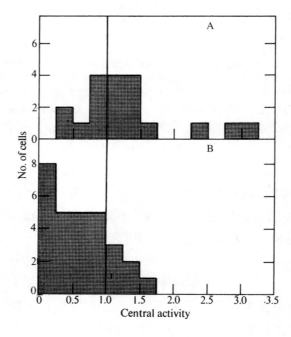

Fig. 4. Distributions of grains over synchronized CHO cells exposed to $^3$H-TdR for 0.5 min. A, Early S phase (4-6 h after release from mitosis). B, Late S phase (10-12 h after release from mitosis). CHO cells were synchronized by the "Colcemid" reversal method of Stubblefield. Pulse-labelling (performed at 2 h intervals after release from mitosis), preparation for electron microscopy, and autoradiography were performed as in Fig. 1. Exposure time was 2-4 months. Histograms were prepared as in Fig. 3. For A, eight nuclei pulse-labelled at 4 h and eleven nuclei labelled at 6 h after mitotic release were used. For B, thirteen nuclei labelled at 10 h and sixteen nuclei labelled at 12 h were used.

　表 1 和图 4 显示的是有丝分裂后细胞核内颗粒随时间变化的关系。虽然在 S 期早期观察不到周边标记，但在 S 期后期则是以周边标记为主。

表 1. 同步化的 CHO 细胞的 DNA 合成情况

| 有丝分裂后的时间 | 2 | 4 | 6 | 8 | 10 | 12 | 14 |
|---|---|---|---|---|---|---|---|
| 标记细胞的百分比 * | 26 | 83 | 93 | 89 | 81 | 62 | 48 |
| 曝光 1 个月后平均每个细胞切片的颗粒数量† | <1 | 6 | 16 | 16 | 24 | 17 | — |

\* 细胞的同步化与图 4 相同。有丝分裂后每间隔 2 小时，在每个培养皿中加入 $^3$H-TdR（20 Ci·mmol$^{-1}$，购自新英格兰核公司），至终浓度 17 μCi·ml$^{-1}$。10 分钟后，用冷生理盐水洗细胞两次，室温下用胰蛋白酶消化并收集细胞，在低渗溶液（2 mM MgCl$_2$，1 mM EDTA，10 mM KPO$_4$，pH 7.7）中溶胀 10 分钟，然后收集沉淀，用甲醇－乙酸溶液（3:1）固定，平铺在玻璃片上风干。用放射自显影乳胶片（"柯达 AR-10"）包裹这些玻片，并曝光 7 天。接着，用吉姆萨氏色素染料染色，然后用 "Permount" 中性树胶封埋。每一个时间点至少要观察 312 个细胞来确定被标记细胞的百分比。

† 对图 4 中用到的放射自显影图片进行了每个细胞核切片上的颗粒的总数的确定。这些图片按照曝光时间进行分类。有丝分裂后 2 小时和 8 小时的数据也包括在内。

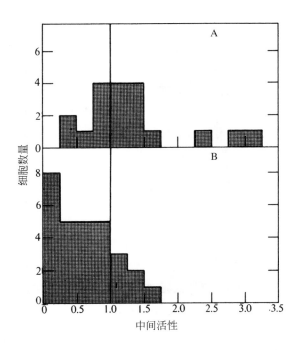

图 4. 置于 $^3$H-TdR 下 0.5 分钟后的同步化 CHO 细胞中颗粒的分布图。A，S 期早期（有丝分裂后 4~6 小时）。B，S 期后期（有丝分裂后 10~12 小时）。按照斯塔布菲尔德秋水仙酰胺逆转法将 CHO 细胞同步化。脉冲标记(有丝分裂后每隔 2 小时进行)，电镜切片的准备和放射自显影按照图 1 的操作。曝光 2~4 个月。按照图 3 的方法制作柱形图。A 图，有丝分裂后 4 小时统计了 8 个标记的细胞核，有丝分裂后 6 小时统计了 11 个标记的细胞核。B 图，有丝分裂后 10 小时统计了 13 个标记的细胞核，有丝分裂后 12 小时统计了 16 个标记的细胞核。

## Stable Location of DNA

If DNA is synthesized at the nuclear membrane (or other localized sites within the nucleus), then the DNA should move toward the membrane for replication and away from the membrane afterwards. The pattern of grains after a long pulse or pulse-chase should then be different from that after a simple short pulse. If, on the other hand, DNA replication can take place anywhere in the nucleus, then DNA movement is unnecessary and the grain pattern after pulse-chase labelling could be identical to that after simple pulse-labelling.

To test these possibilities, we first pulse-labelled synchronized cells for 0.5 min during the first half of the S phase (6 h after release from mitosis), and then chased with non-radioactive thymidine to late S phase (12 h after release from mitosis). Although the cells were examined in late S phase, they showed no higher proportion of peripheral labelling than expected for cells 6 h after release from mitosis (compare Figs. 4 and 5). In addition, unsynchronized cells pulse-labelled for 0.5 min show the same proportion of peripheral and general labelling as unsynchronized cells pulse-labelled for 10 min, or pulse-labelled for 0.5 min and then chased for 6.75 h(Fig. 5). In both of the chase experiments, the cells were more labelled after the chase than before, probably because incorporation of $^3$H-TdR continues from the cells' internal pools.

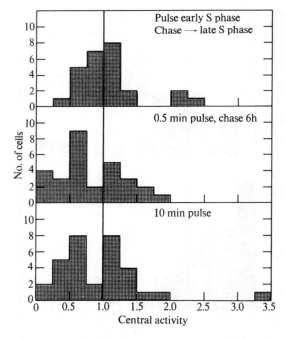

Fig. 5. Distribution of grains over CHO cells after pulse-chase or long pulse-labelling with $^3$H-TdR. A, Synchronized cells (see Fig. 4) were pulse-labelled 6 h after release from mitosis as in Fig. 1. Then 30 s after addition of label, the medium was sucked off and the plates were washed, then replaced with medium containing 2.5 µg ml.$^{-1}$ of TdR. After 6 h the cells were collected by trypsinization and prepared for electron microscope autoradiography as in Fig. 1. Exposure time was 1.5-4 months. B, Unsynchronized cells were pulse-labelled as in Fig. 1 and chased for 6.75 h as in A. Exposure time was 3.25 months. C, Unsynchronized cells were pulse-labelled as in Fig. 1 except that the $^3$H-TdR was left in contact with the cells for 10 min instead of 30 s. Exposure time was 1.5-6 months. In all cases, histograms were prepared as in Fig. 3. For A, twenty-four cells were used, whereas for B, twenty-nine cells were used, and for C, thirty-two cells were used.

## DNA 稳定的位置

如果 DNA 是在核膜处（或者在细胞核内其他的位置）合成的，那么 DNA 应该首先转移至核膜进行复制，然后再远离核膜。因而长脉冲或者脉冲追踪形成的颗粒模型应该与短脉冲处理所形成的颗粒模型不同。另一方面，如果 DNA 复制可以在细胞核的任意区域进行，那么 DNA 没有必要转移，而且脉冲追踪标记后的颗粒模型应该与简单脉冲标记的颗粒模型一致。

为了验证这些可能性，我们首先脉冲标记处于 S 期的前半期（有丝分裂完成后的 6 小时）的同步化细胞 0.5 分钟,然后用非放射性的胸腺核苷追踪至 S 期的后期（有丝分裂完成后的 12 小时）。尽管对这些细胞的检测是在 S 期后期进行的，但是这些细胞周边标记的比例未如预期,并不比处于 S 期前半期的细胞高（图4和图5对比）。此外，研究表明脉冲标记非同步化细胞 0.5 分钟与 10 分钟，或者先脉冲标记 0.5 分钟后再追踪 6.75 小时（图5），其周边标记和普遍标记的比例是相同的。两次追踪实验的结果都显示出有更多的细胞在示踪后被标记，这可能是从细胞内腔持续吸收结合 $^3$H-TdR 的结果。

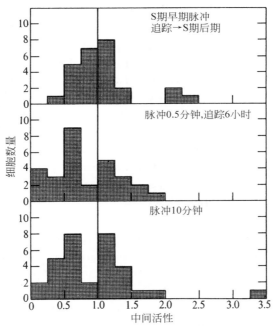

图 5. $^3$H-TdR 脉冲追踪或者长脉冲标记 CHO 细胞后的颗粒分布图。A，有丝分裂后 6 小时脉冲标记同步化的细胞（同步方法同图 4，标记方法同图 1）。标记 30 秒后，吸掉培养基，冲洗培养皿，然后加入含 2.5 μg·ml$^{-1}$ TdR 的培养基。6 小时后用胰蛋白酶消化收集细胞，按照图 1 的方法准备电子显微放射自显影。曝光时间为 1.5~4 个月。B，按照图 1 的方法脉冲标记非同步化的细胞，并且同图 A 一样追踪 6.75 小时。曝光时间为 3.25 个月。C，除了用 $^3$H-TdR 处理细胞的时间延长为 10 分钟，而非 30 秒外，其他操作同图 1。曝光时间为 1.5~6 个月。按照图 3 的方法制作柱形图 1。图 A,统计了 24 个细胞;图 B,统计了 29 个细胞;图 C，统计了 32 个细胞。

Thus DNA has a stable location in the nucleus. Because some of the unsynchronized cells must have divided during the chase, our results suggest that DNA bound closely to the membrane in one generation is also bound to the membrane in the succeeding generation.

Because we cannot detect any difference in labelling pattern between a 0.5 min pulse and a 10 min pulse, our results can be compared directly with those of previous investigators[15-17] who have used longer pulse times. Our results agree with most of the earlier results; a general-label pattern is obtained in early S phase and a peripheral one in late S phase[15-17], and chase experiments show that the nuclear position of DNA, once replicated, is stable[15,16].

The increased labelling during chase experiments, together with an apparently lower rate of synthesis in early S phase (Table 1), suggests an explanation for the autoradiographic results of O'Brien et al.[13]. In their pulse experiment, generally-labelled cells in early S phase may have been overlooked because they have few grains per nucleus (and a more disperse distribution at that); the increased labelling provided by the chase would have made the generally labelled cells sufficiently obvious to count.

## Initiation of Replication

Our results also partially disagree with those of Comings and Kakefuda[14]. They reported that cells synchronized to the beginning of S phase showed solely peripheral labelling. Williams and Ockey[16,22] suggested that Comings and Kakefuda's results might be due to cell damage during the lengthy nucleotide starvation (24 h in the presence of excess thymidine and then 14 h in the presence of amethopterin) used to synchronize their cells. Indeed, the cytoplasms of the synchronized cells in Comings and Kakefuda's experiments contain many large vacuoles (indicating serious cell damage), whereas their unsynchronized cells have normal cytoplasm. Why cell damage should result in a peripheral labelling pattern is not clear. The unexpected pattern may be related to the finding[12] that polyoma virus infection causes mouse satellite DNA, which is normally late replicating[23-25], to replicate before bulk DNA.

Because Comings and Kakefuda's[14] results must be discounted owing to cell damage, it seems that DNA synthesis can occur throughout the nucleus, and the nuclear membrane is not involved in initiation of replication. We have found, however, that in very early S phase (2 and 4 h after release from mitosis), the rate of replication per cell (measured as the average number of grains per nuclear section over labelled nuclei after a fixed exposure time) is much less than in later S phase (Table 1). This suggests that at the true beginning of S phase, the rate might be so low that we cannot detect labelling, let alone determine whether the pattern is peripheral or general.

## Euchromatin and Heterochromatin

Heterochromatin has been shown to be replicated later than euchromatin and is condensed during interphase[26,27]. Our sections and those of others[14-17], show a

因此，DNA 在细胞核内有稳定的定位。由于一些非同步化细胞在追踪过程中已经发生分裂，所以我们的结果还揭示了与核膜紧密结合的亲代 DNA 的子代 DNA 也是与核膜紧密结合的。

我们的检测结果显示，0.5 分钟和 10 分钟的脉冲标记模型没有任何差别，所以我们的实验结果可以直接与其他使用长脉冲时间的研究者的结果 [15-17] 进行比较。我们的结果与大多数早期发表的结果一致；普遍标记模型出现在 S 期早期，周边标记模型则出现在 S 期后期 [15-17]，追踪实验还表明，一旦复制开始，DNA 在细胞核的位置是稳定的 [15,16]。

在追踪实验中增加的标记，以及在 S 期早期明显较低的 DNA 合成速率（表 1），可以解释奥布赖恩等人的放射自显影实验结果 [13]。在他们的脉冲实验中，S 期早期标记的细胞通常会由于每个细胞核中颗粒过少（分布过散）而被忽略；而在追踪过程中增加的标记可以提供足够明显的标记的细胞便于统计。

## 复制的起始

我们的结果也与科明斯和挂札 [14] 的结果有些不同。他们的报道指出，同步至 S 期初期的细胞只表现周边标记。威廉姆斯和奥克伊 [16,22] 认为科明斯和挂札的结果可能是由于为了同步化，而将细胞处于长期缺乏核苷酸（用过量的胸腺核苷酸处理 24 小时，然后用氨甲蝶呤处理 14 小时）的状态，导致细胞损伤。事实上，科明斯和挂札的实验中所用的同步化细胞的细胞质含有许多大的空囊泡（这表明细胞严重损伤），而他们实验中的非同步化细胞的细胞质却正常。细胞损伤导致周边标记模式的原因尚不清楚。这或许与目前发现的由于多瘤病毒感染而导致的鼠卫星 DNA 复制早于主体 DNA 复制 [12] 的情况有些关联，通常情况下卫星 DNA 的复制会相对较晚 [23-25]。

由于出现细胞损伤，科明斯和挂札 [14] 结果的可信度大打折扣，他们的结果让人误以为 DNA 的合成发生在整个细胞核区域，且核膜没有参与复制的起始。然而我们的研究发现，在 S 期较早期（有丝分裂后 2、4 小时），每个细胞的平均复制速率（细胞核经过固定的曝光时间标记以后，每个核切片的平均颗粒数）要远低于 S 期后期（表 1）。这表明，在真正的 S 期初期，复制速率太低以至于检测不到标记，更无从确定是周边模式还是普遍模式。

## 常染色质和异染色质

已经证明异染色质的复制比常染色质晚，在分裂间期以浓缩的状态存在 [26-27]。我们以及其他研究者的切片观察 [14-17] 表明，浓缩的染色质主要与内核膜相连。因此

preponderance of condensed chromatin attached to the inner nuclear membrane. Thus our results are consistent with the notion[16] that euchromatin is replicated early in S phase and is distributed throughout the nucleus, whereas heterochromatin is replicated in late S phase and is condensed along the inner nuclear membrane and in other discrete areas.

## Reinterpretation of Cell Fractionation Experiments

Whereas many of the cell fractionation experiments on the intranuclear location of DNA synthesis[8-11,13] have been interpreted in favour of attachment of replication sites to the nuclear membrane, this is not the only possible interpretation. Equally valid is the possibility that, after cell lysis, special structural properties of the growing points (extensive single strandedness, for instance) might result in their binding more protein, membrane, or other material than bulk DNA. Alternatively, the growing points may actually be attached inside the cell to some material that causes their separation from bulk DNA during lysate fractionation.

As experiments with mammalian[8-11,13] and bacterial[2,3,5] cells used similar techniques and gave the same results, it is possible that the growing point in bacteria may also not be attached to the membrane.

We thank Elaine and Robert Lenk for advice and assistance. This research was supported by grants from the National Science Foundation and the US National Institutes of Health. The electron microscopy was carried out in the Electron Microscope Facility of the Biology Department at MIT.

*Note added in proof.* Fakan *et al.*[28] have recently obtained results similar to ours in both autoradiographic and cell fractionation experiments with mouse cells.

(**241**, 32-36; 1973)

**Joel A. Huberman, Alice Tsai and Robert A. Deich**
Departments of Biology, Massachusetts Institute of Technology, Cambridge, Massachusetts 02139

Received May 4; revised December 15, 1972.

---

References:

1. Jacob, F., Brenner, S., and Cuzin, F., *Cold Spring Harbor Symp. Quant. Biol.*, **28**, 329 (1963).

2. Ganesan, A. T., and Lederberg, J., *Biophys. Biochem. Res. Commun.*, **18**, 824 (1965).

3. Smith, D. W., and Hanawalt, P. C., *Biochim. Biophys. Acta*, **149**, 519 (1967).

4. Tremblay, G. Y., Daniels, M. J., and Schaechter, M., *J. Mol. Biol.*, **40**, 65 (1969).

5. Sueoka, N., and Quinn, W. G., *Cold Spring Harbor Symp. Quant. Biol.*, **33**, 695 (1968).

6. Fuchs, E., and Hanawalt, P. C., *J. Mol. Biol.*, **52**, 301 (1970).

7. Fielding, P., and Fox, C. F., *Biochem. Biophys. Res. Commun.*, **41**, 157 (1970).

8. Friedman, D. F., and Mueller, G. C., *Biochim. Biophys. Acta*, **174**, 253 (1969).

9. Mizuno, N. S., Stoops, C. D., and Sinha, A. A., *Nature New Biology*, **229**, 22 (1971).

10. Hanaoka, F., and Yamada, M., *Biochem. Biophys. Res. Commun.*, **42**, 647 (1971).

11. Pearson, G. D., and Hanawalt, P. C., *J. Mol. Biol.*, **62**, 65 (1971).

我们的结果与以下的想法 [16] 一致：常染色质的复制发生在 S 期早期而且分布在细胞核的整个区域，而异染色质的复制发生在 S 期后期，在内核模和其他分散的区域以浓缩的状态存在。

## 细胞分级分离实验的重新解释

尽管许多关于 DNA 在细胞核内合成位点的细胞分级分离实验 [8-11,13] 已经被诠释为倾向于支持复制位点与细胞核核膜相连的观点，但是这并不是唯一可能的解释。同样合理的一种可能性是，细胞裂解后，由于生长点的某种特殊结构属性（如大多是单链），可能导致其与体内其他大部分的 DNA 相比能够结合更多的蛋白、膜或者其他物质。当然，也可能生长点确实与细胞内的一些物质相连，造成生长点与体内主体 DNA 在细胞裂解分离过程中分离。

因为在哺乳动物细胞 [8-11,13] 和细菌细胞 [2,3,5] 上开展的实验研究使用了相似的实验技术，并得到相同的结果，所以在细菌体内生长点很有可能也不与膜相连。

特别感谢伊莱恩和罗伯特·伦克提供的建议和帮助。该项目受国家科学基金会和美国国立卫生研究院的资助。电子显微镜实验在麻省理工学院生物系电子显微镜实验室进行。

**附加说明**：最近福孔等人 [28] 用小鼠细胞进行自显影和细胞分级分离实验，结果与我们的结果类似。

（吕静 翻译；刘京国 审稿）

12. Smith, B. J., *J. Mol. Biol.*, **47**, 101 (1970).

13. O'Brien, R. L., Sanyal, A. B., and Stanton, R. H., *Exp. Cell Res.*, **70**, 106 (1972).

14. Comings, D. E., and Kakefuda, T., *J. Mol. Biol.*, **33**, 225 (1968).

15. Blondel, B., *Exp. Cell Res.*, **53**, 348 (1968).

16. Williams, C. A., and Ockey, C. H., *Exp. Cell Res.*, **63**, 365 (1970).

17. Erlandson, R. A., and de Harven, E., *J. Cell Sci.*, **8**, 353 (1971).

18. Kay, R. R., Haines, M. E., and Johnston, I. R., *FEBS Lett.*, **16**, 233 (1971).

19. Huberman, J. A., and Riggs, A. D., *J. Mol. Biol.*, **32**, 327 (1968).

20. Caro, L. G., and Van Tubergen, R. P., *J. Cell Biol.*, **15**, 173 (1962).

21. Stubblefield, E., in *Methods in Cell Physiology* (edit. by Prescott, D. M.), **3**, 25 (Academic Press, New York, 1968).

22. Ockey, C. H., *Exp. Cell Res.*, **70**, 203(1972).

23. Tobia, A. M., Schildkraut, C. L., and Maio, J. J., *Biochim. Biophys. Acta*, **246**, 258 (1971).

24. Bostock, C. J., and Prescott, D. M., *Exp. Cell Res.*, **64**, 267 (1971).

25. Flamm, W. G., Bernheim, N. J., and Brubaker, P. E., *Exp. Cell Res.*, **64**, 97(1971).

26. Lima-de-Faria, A., and Javorska, H., *Nature*, **217**, 138 (1968).

27. Brown, S. W., *Science*, **151**, 417 (1966).

28. Fakan, S., Turner, G. N., Pagano, J. S., and Hancock, R., *Proc. US Nat. Acad. Sci.*, **69**, 2300 (1972).

29. Lenk, R., and Penman, S., *J. Cell Biol.*, **49**, 541 (1971).

# Response of a General Circulation Model of the Atmosphere to Removal of the Arctic Ice-cap

R. L. Newson

## Editor's Note

This paper by R. L. Newson of the UK's Meteorological Office looks highly prescient today. For one thing, Newson shows how the advent of "very high speed computers" was transforming the ability to make predictions about global weather and longer-term patterns of climate change. To illustrate these possibilities, Newson considers how the climate of the Northern Hemisphere would be altered by complete melting of the Arctic sea-ice cap. This reduces reflection of the sun's rays, and provides a heat reservoir in polar waters. Significant temperature changes occur at least as far as mid-latitude Europe and North America. Newson presents this merely as a test case, but today the disappearance of the Arctic ice due to global warming is a distinct possibility.

OVER the past few years, numerical models have been developed for investigating the general circulation of the atmosphere and studying its long term behaviour. (See, for example, Smagorinsky et al.[1], Kasahara and Washington[2].) These models are firmly based on the equations of fluid motion and thermodynamics and simulate in mathematical terms the chief physical processes which are thought to be of importance in determining large scale atmospheric motions over long periods of time (a month or more). The advent of very high speed computers has made numerical experiments with these models reasonably easy.

One model has been described in detail by Corby et al.[3]. The mode of computation essentially consists of integration forward in time from an initial state for a considerable number of model days using physical parameters appropriate to a given season and obtaining the mean seasonal state by averaging the later computed states; in the experiments described here the model was integrated forward in time for 80 days under winter conditions and the mean seasonal state obtained as the average of the last 40 days.

It is possible to vary the model to determine its reaction to substantial changes in the assumed physical properties. In one of these variants the region of winter arctic ice, as defined by the mean climatological position, was replaced by open ocean maintained at freezing temperature; what had been a surface with a temperature determined by radiational balance became a surface of constant temperature. The results of computations with ice and with open ocean differ quite considerably. The most marked difference is, of course, the great warming of the lower layers of the troposphere over the arctic basin, where, in the ice-free arctic experiment, there was an oceanic reserve of heat to balance radiative losses; this was to be expected. It might also have been expected

# 大气环流模式对北极冰盖消融的响应

纽森

编者按

英国气象局纽森的这篇文章现在看来很有预见性。纽森展示了"超高速计算机"的出现能够改变人们对全球天气及气候变化的长期模式的预测能力。为了阐明这种可能性，纽森考虑了由于北极冰盖的完全融化而改变北半球气候的可能性。北极冰盖的融化减少了太阳辐射的反射，融化后所形成的极地水域变成了一个储热器。温度的显著变化至少会波及中纬度的欧洲和北美洲地区。虽然纽森只是作了一个试验，但如今，由于全球变暖引起北极冰盖消失是完全可能的。

过去几年，为研究大气环流及其长期特性发展建立了若干数值模式。（参见如斯马尔戈林斯基等 [1]、笠原和华盛顿 [2] 的文章。）这些模式均以流体运动方程和热动力学方程为基础，利用数学形式将那些被认为对长周期（一个月甚至更长）的大尺度大气运动具有重要作用的主要物理过程表达出来。超高速计算机的出现使这些模式中的数值计算变得相当容易。

科尔比等 [3] 对其中的一个模式作了详细描述。其计算模型的基本思路是：选用适合于指定季节下的物理参数，由初始状态向前（向未来）积分若干天，将这些天的结果取平均得到季节平均值。在本文所描述的试验中，该模式是在冬季条件下，积分 80 天，将最后 40 天的结果取平均作为该季节的平均值。

通过模式中的参数变化可以研究模式对某种假定的物理性质变化的反应。这些变化之一是，用保持冰点的开阔洋面取代平均气候态下的冬季北极冰川，这样就将由辐射平衡决定温度的表面作为恒温表面来处理。用冰川面和开阔洋面推算得出的结果相差很大，两者最明显的差别是：北极地区上空的对流层下部明显变暖，这应该是意料中的，因为在北极无冰条件下，海洋中储存的热量平衡了辐射损失。科学家预期中纬度地区大气层下部的温度似乎也可能升高。但实际上，在中纬度地区陆地上方的近地面层温度在下降；而洋面上方的温度变化很小，因为海面平均温度是

that in mid-latitudes temperatures in the lower atmosphere would be raised. In fact, there is a lowering of mid-latitude continental temperatures near to the surface but with little change over the sea where the mean sea surface temperature had been left unchanged. This result is illustrated in Fig. 1, which shows the temperature difference between the two computed seasonal means at the level in the model most representative of the surface. The changes are considerable. The mid-latitude cooling may be compared with the temperature anomaly of −5°C in the very severe January of 1963; a temperature anomaly of −2°C would indicate a very cold winter month.

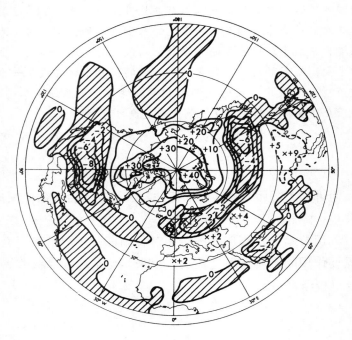

Fig.1. Temperature differences, in °C near the model surface, between the computation with an ice-free arctic and the computation with ice at the mean climatological position. Hatched areas indicate regions of cooling in the ice-free experiment.

Other results from these experiments show a distinct southward displacement and weakening of the prevailing mid-latitude westerlies when there was no polar ice-cap, and this is similar to the result obtained from another ice-free arctic general circulation experiment conducted with the Mintz-Arakawa model[4]. What seems to happen is that the general decrease of temperature gradient between equator and pole reduces the strength of westerly flow in mid-latitudes and, there, the circulations become more blocked. Consequently regions which at present benefit climatically from the westerlies might be cooler in an ice-free arctic regime.

I do not claim that these results necessarily indicate what might happen in the real atmosphere, because the model itself has several shortcomings, and one should not dwell on the results in particular areas because they are almost certainly not quantitatively

保持不变的。该结果见图 1，图中给出了两种计算条件下季节平均值的差异，所用的平均值为模式中最能代表地表温度的值。两者的差异非常明显。中纬度的降温幅度大概与 1963 年 1 月极端的 –5℃ 的异常相当，而 –2℃ 的温度异常就意味着一个极其寒冷的冬月。

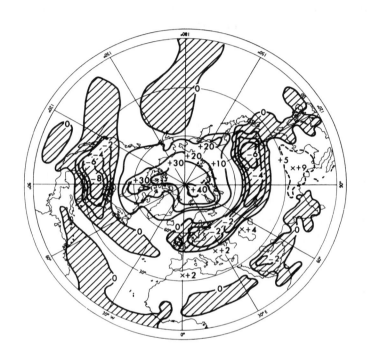

图 1. 在假定无冰和平均气候态下有北极冰川时，模拟计算出的近地表温度差异，单位为℃。阴影部分代表无冰实验中气候变冷的区域。

从上述试验得到的其他结果表明，如果没有北极冰盖，中纬度盛行西风带将大幅南移并减弱。这一点与利用明茨－荒川模式得到的北极无冰条件下大气环流试验结果相似[4]。看上去似乎是赤道与极地之间气温梯度的总体下降造成了中纬度地区西风带的强度减弱，因而大气环流被堵塞。所以，当北冰洋不再有冰川存在时，那些目前气候上受益于西风带的地区可能会变得更冷。

我并不是说上述结果必然表明发生在实际大气中的过程，因为模式本身存在许多不足之处，而且也不应该将这些结果用到某一特定地区，因为从定量上来看它们

correct. The sign of temperature changes in mid-latitudes is perhaps rather unexpected, and the results illustrate that qualitative arguments may be deceptive and unreliable in considering a physical system as complicated as the atmospheric circulation which includes so many non-linear interactions and feed-back mechanisms.

Considerable refinement and elaboration of numerical models will be required before their answers to questions of the kind raised in this letter can be accepted with any confidence. Nevertheless the potential superiority of the numerical approach for the investigation of problems of climatic modification is beyond doubt.

(241, 39-40; 1973)

**R. L. Newson**
Meteorological Office, Bracknell, Berkshire

Received October 23, 1972.

---

References:
1. Smagorinsky, J., Manabe, S., and Holloway, J.L., *Monthly Weather Review*, **93**, 727 (1965).
2. Kasahara, A., and Washington, W. M., *Monthly Weather Review*, **95**, 389 (1967).
3. Corby, G. A., Gilchrist, A., and Newson, R. L., *Quart. J. Roy. Met. Soc.*, **98**, 809 (1972).
4. Warshaw, M., and Rapp, R. R., *R-908-ARPA* (1972).

几乎都不正确。中纬度地区温度的变化更让我们意想不到；而且结果表明，定性的结论也是靠不住的，因为在一个像大气环流这样复杂的物理体系中，包含了太多非线性相互作用和反馈机制。

要对本文提出的问题给出可靠的答复，这些数值模式还需要更多的细化和改进。尽管如此，采用数值方法来研究气候变化问题的潜在优势是毋庸置疑的。

（齐红艳 翻译；王鹏云 审稿）

# Deep-sea Sediment Source Areas: Implications of Variable Rates of Movement between California and the Pacific Plate

J. R. Hein

## Editor's Note

The San Andreas Fault is the most conspicuous source of earthquakes in the US state of California. The fault is the boundary between the tectonic plate to the west which carries the floor of the Pacific Ocean and to the east which carries the continental United States. Here James Hein of the University of California at Santa Cruz presents an ingenious method of working out how the plates had moved relative to each other over the past 25 million years, using data gathered on expeditions of a deep-sea drilling ship supported by the US National Science Foundation. The relative displacement of the two plates is estimated at 5.5-7.0 centimetres per year.

RECENT work has indicated acceleration of motion on the San Andreas Fault[1], but previous studies have not delineated variable rates of motion with time between the Pacific and American plates. Offsets on the San Andreas and associated fault systems yield a mean rate of motion for a given period of time and deal with motion within the area of a wide plate boundary; therefore, these do not show total relative motion or variations in velocity between the two plates[2]. Magnetic anomalies can be used to measure the total relative motion and variations in velocity between the two plates. But magnetic anomalies at the mouth of the Gulf of California represent only the past few million years of movement which has been going on for at least 25 m.y. (ref. 3). Here I describe a method by which the amount and rates of motion between California and the Pacific plate with time can be determined.

The Delgada submarine fan lies off northern California, south of the Mendocino Fracture Zone, and is at least Oligocene in age[4]. The fan lies in a unique position on the eastern edge of the Pacific plate directly adjacent to the varied lithology of source areas on the American plate to the east. If the fan has passed source areas of distinctive lithologies on the American plate, then its stratigraphy may indicate the amount and rate of movement between the two plates. This area is particularly well located for such a study because there is no land mass (source area) between the fan and the margin of the Pacific plate and because the Mendocino Fracture Zone inhibits the introduction of sediment into the fan area from the north[4]. Therefore changes in sediment composition may indicate the position of the fan relative to these distinctive source area rocks on the American plate.

# 来自深海沉积物源区的启示：加利福尼亚板块与太平洋板块之间相对运动速率的变化

海因

## 编者按

圣安德烈亚斯断层是美国加利福尼亚州最显著的震源。该断层被认为是西部太平洋板块和东部北美板块之间的边界地带。本文中，加利福尼亚大学圣克鲁斯分校的詹姆斯·海因利用美国自然科学基金委员会资助下的深海钻探航次所搜集到的数据展示了一种独创性的方法，用于解释在过去的 2,500 万年中两个板块是如何相对运动的。据估算，两个板块间的相对位移为 5.5~7.0 厘米 / 年。

新近研究表明，圣安德烈亚斯断层的运动在加速[1]，然而之前的研究却并没有指出太平洋板块和美洲板块之间的运动速率是随时间而变化的。圣安德烈亚斯断层以及相关断裂体系的错移约束了某给定时段内的一个平均运动速率值，并且与广阔板块边界上区域内的运动有关。因此，它并不能表示两个板块之间的总相对运动量或速率变化[2]。磁异常可以用来测量两个板块之间的相对运动以及速率变化。但是，加利福尼亚湾湾口地区的磁异常只能代表过去几百万年中总的运动情况，而这种运动至少已持续了 2,500 万年（参考文献 3）。本文将介绍一种新的方法，可用于测定加利福尼亚板块和太平洋板块之间的运动量及运动速率随时间的变化情况。

德尔加达海底扇位于加利福尼亚北部，门多西诺断裂带南部，在地质年代上至少应该属于渐新世[4]。该海底扇处于太平洋板块东部边缘的一个比较特殊的位置上，向东直接与美洲板块上源区的各种岩性的岩石相邻。倘若海底扇穿过了美洲板块上特有的岩石源区，那么，其地层学上的特征可能可以指示两个板块之间的相对运动量和运动速率。这一源区的位置尤其适合此类研究，因为海底扇与太平洋板块边缘之间没有陆地（物源区）相隔，而且，门多西诺断裂带阻隔了沉积物从北部进入扇区[4]。因此，沉积物组成上的变化可能会指示海底扇相对于美洲大陆上的这些特有岩石源区的位置。

Semi-quantitative X-ray diffraction studies of the less than 2 µm fraction[5] from sites 32, 33 and 34, Leg V, of the DSDP, reveal significant changes in the percentages of the various clay minerals with time. The changes in percentages of kaolinite + chlorite/illite/montmorillonite occur at approximately 4 m.y., 5 m.y., 9 m.y. and 15 m.y. (Table 1).

Table 1. Computer Analysis of Maximum Variations in Percentages of Clay Minerals from Leg V, Sites 32, 33 and 34, DSDP

| Absolute age (m.y.) | Chlorite and /or kaolinite | Illite | Montmorillonite |
|---|---|---|---|
| 0 | | | |
| 2 | 48% | 42% | 7.5% |
| 4 | | | |
| 6 | | 30% | 26% |
| 8 | 32% | 52% | 16% |
| 10 | | | |
| 12 | | Clay minerals occur as a trace component of | |
| 14 | | the less than 2 µm fraction | |
| 16 | 14% | 42% | 46% |

Changes in the detrital coarse fraction mineralogy, amphibole and pyroxene assemblages and changes in degrees of stress and strain indicated by stretching and undulatory extinction show significant changes during these same time periods (manuscript in preparation).

The Delgada fan is assumed to be one basin of deposition and to have been built by turbidity current and hemipelagic deposition from continental source areas. A simple model of evolution of the fan can be constructed so that the changes in mineralogy and style of deformation of mineral grains are consistent with the changing source areas (Fig. 1). Important source areas in this model, schematically represented in Fig. 1, include: Northern Coast Ranges from Holocene to 4 m.y.; north-central Sierra Nevada from 4 m.y. to 5 m.y.; eastern Santa Cruz Mountains-northern Diablo Range from 5 m.y. to 9 m.y.; and southern Diablo Range-southern Sierra Nevada from 9 m.y. to 15 m.y. ago.

The greatest interpretative problem is: how far the fan travelled into a proposed source area before the influence of that source area dominated the fan sediment. The transition from one lithology to another in fan sediment is variable, spanning as little as 200,000 yr at the 4 m.y. change to as much as 1.5 m.y. at the 9 m.y. lithology change. Arbitrarily using the center point of these time intervals and the palaeogeographic lithologic boundaries allows a preferred interpretation of rates of motion with time between California and the Pacific plate (Fig. 2). In all cases distances to varying lithologies shown in Fig. 1 are measured from the head of Delgada Canyon.

利用 X 射线衍射，对深海钻探计划（DSDP）第五个航次的 32、33、34 站样品中小于 2 μm 的部分 [5] 进行了半定量分析，结果表明，各种黏土矿物的百分含量随时间变化明显。高岭石＋绿泥石、伊利石、蒙脱石的百分含量的变化分别出现在大约 400 万、500 万、900 万和 1,500 万年前（见表 1）。

表 1. 深海钻探计划（DSDP）第五航次的 32、33、34 站样品中黏土矿物百分含量最大变化值的计算机分析结果

| 绝对年龄（m.y.） | 绿泥石和（或）高岭石 | 伊利石 | 蒙脱石 |
|---|---|---|---|
| 0 | | | |
| 2 | 48% | 42% | 7.5% |
| 4 | | | |
| 6 | | 30% | 26% |
| 8 | 32% | 52% | 16% |
| 10 | | | |
| 12 | | 小于 2μm 的样品中黏土矿物是微量组分 | |
| 14 | | | |
| 16 | 14% | 42% | 46% |

碎屑状粗粒级矿物、角闪石和辉石组合中的变化以及拉伸和波状消光所指示的应力和应变的等级变化在相同的时期内显示出显著变化（完稿中）。

德尔加达海底扇被认为是一个沉积盆地，是由来自大陆源区的浊流和近海沉积物形成的。我们可以建立一个简单的海底扇演化模型，这样矿物颗粒的矿物学和变形方式的变化就与变化中的源区一致（图 1）。图 1 是该模型中重要源区的示意图，包括：从全新世到 400 万年前的海岸山岭北部，400 万到 500 万年前的内华达山脉中北部，500 万到 900 万年前的圣克鲁斯山东部和代阿布洛岭北部，900 万到 1,500 万年前的代阿布洛岭南部和内华达山脉南部。

解释过程中遇到的最大问题是：在某假定源区对海底扇沉积物的影响占主导地位以前，海底扇已经向该源区伸入了多远的距离？海底扇沉积物中由一种岩性向另一种岩性的转变是不固定的，岩性变化的时间跨度短至 400 万年前的 20 万年，长至 900 万年前的 150 万年。随机选用这些时间间隔的中心点以及岩相古地理边界，可以得到加利福尼亚板块和太平洋板块之间相对运动速率随时间变化的更好解释（图 2）。其中，对各种情况下图 1 所示的从德尔加达海底峡谷头部到不同岩石类型的距离都做了测算。

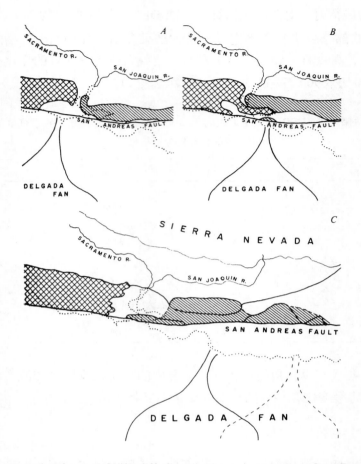

Fig. 1. Palaeogeography of central California[6-8]. Cross-lined represents northern Coast Ranges, lined the Diablo Range and eastern Santa Cruz Mountains, the dotted line is the present coast line. The Sierra Nevada Mountains would be outside the north margin of parts *A* and *B*. *A*, The fan at 4 m.y.; *B*, at 5.5 m.y.; *C*, at 9 m.y. (—) and 15 m.y. ago (- - -).

The rate of motion of 5.5 to 7.0 cm yr$^{-1}$ for the past 4 m.y. yielded by this method agrees with the rate calculated from marine magnetic anomalies[3] and adds validity to the choice of space-time boundaries. Reasonable variations in the placement of the palaeogeographic boundaries and possible errors in time boundaries would give ranges of rates of motion shown in Fig. 2. Even if the preferred interpretation is not correct, the data strongly suggest an increase in the rate of motion between California and the Pacific plate from about 16 m.y. to the present.

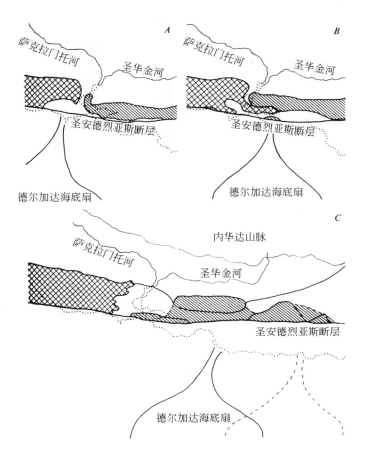

图 1. 加利福尼亚中部的古地理图 [6-8]。网格线充填部分表示海岸山岭北部，斜线充填部分表示代阿布洛岭和圣克鲁斯山东部，虚线代表现代的海岸线。内华达山脉应该位于图 A 和 B 中的北部边界以外。A 表示 400 万年前的沉积扇；B 为 550 万年前的情形；C 为 900 万年前（——）以及 1500 万年前（- - -）的情形。

    利用该方法得到的过去 400 万年的平均运动速率为 5.5~7.0 厘米 / 年，这与从海底磁异常计算出的速率 [3] 一致，而且使时空界线的选择变得更加合理。岩相古地理边界位置的合理变动以及时间界线上可能存在的误差，可给定图 2 中所示的相对运动速率的变化范围。即使所选取的解释不正确，这些数据仍能充分显示出：从 1,600 万年前到现在，加利福尼亚板块和太平洋板块之间的相对运动速率是增加的。

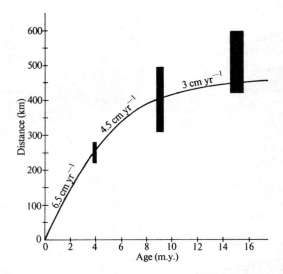

Fig. 2. Increasing rate of motion between California and the Pacific Plate. The ordinate is distance along the San Andreas Fault from the head of Delgada Canyon; the abscissa is absolute age of the fan sediment. The curve represents my preferred interpretation. Shaded areas are possible range of values: 5.5 to 7.0 cm yr[-1] from Holocene to 4 m.y., 3.4 to 5.5 cm yr[-1] from 4 to 9 m.y. and 2.8 to 4.0 cm yr[-1] from 9 to 15 m.y. ago.

I thank T. Atwater, D. Bukry, R. Coe, R. Garrison, G. Griggs, J. Sumner, and S. Wright (Leg V, DSDP) for help.

(**241**, 40-4l; 1973)

**James R. Hein**
Earth Sciences Board, University of California, Santa Cruz, California 95060

Received September 21, 1972.

---

References:

1. Dickinson, W. R., *et al.*, *Amer. Assoc. Petrol. Geol. Bull.*, **56/2**, 375 (1972).

2. Anderson, D.L., *Sci. Amer.*, **224/5**, 53 (1971).

3. Larsen, R. L., *et al.*, *Science*, **161**, 781 (1968).

4. McManus, D.A., *et al.*, *Initial Reports of the Deep Sea Drilling project*, **5** (1970).

5. Duncan, J.R., *et al.*, *J. Geol.*, **78**, 213 (1970).

6. Hackel, O., *Geology of Northern California, Bull.*, **190**, 217 (Calif. Div. of Mines, 1966).

7. Reed, R.D., *Geology of California* (Amer. Assoc. Petrol. Geol., 1933).

8. Howard, A. D., *Evolution of the Landscape of the San Francisco Bay Region* (Univ. Calif. Press, 1972).

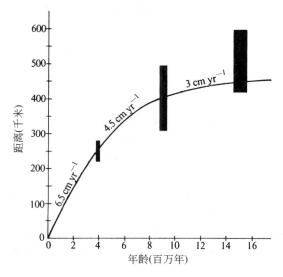

图 2. 加利福尼亚板块和太平洋板块之间的相对运动速率随时间递增的示意图。其中，纵坐标为从德尔加达海底峡谷头部沿圣安德烈亚斯断层一线的距离；横坐标为海底扇沉积物的绝对年龄；曲线表示我优先选取的解释。阴影部分表示速率值的大致范围：从全新世到 400 万年前为 5.5~7.0 厘米 / 年；400 万到 900 万年前为 3.4~5.5 厘米 / 年；900 万到 1,500 万年前为 2.8~4.0 厘米 / 年。

在这里，我要特别感谢阿特沃特、布克里、科、加里森、格里格斯、萨姆纳以及赖特（深海钻探计划第五航次）给予的帮助。

（齐红艳 李任伟 翻译；李三忠 审稿）

# *In vitro* Fertilization of Rat Eggs

H. Miyamoto and M. C. Chang

## Editor's Note

Chinese American scientist Min Chueh Chang is probably best known for his work developing the oral contraceptive, but here he builds on a wealth of animal *in vitro* fertilization (IVF) research demonstrating IVF of rat eggs. Successful IVF of mammalian eggs had been demonstrated in many other species, and Chang himself had previously achieved IVF in rabbits by implanting black rabbit embryos conceived in the laboratory into a white rabbit. Critically, Chang acknowledged the importance of post-ejaculatory sperm maturation or "capacitation", a phenomenon he had independently co-discovered with reproductive biologist Colin Russell Austin. Chang's research paved the way for IVF of human eggs, culminating in the birth of the world's first "test-tube baby", Louise Brown, in 1978.

AFTER the recognition of "capacitation of sperm" by Austin[1] and Chang[2], successful *in vitro* fertilization of mammalian eggs was achieved in many species[3-17]. Although fertilization of rat eggs *in vitro* has been attempted[1,18-20], incorporation of sperm into the vitellus was observed only after the dissolution of zona pellucida by chymotrypsin[19]. Here we report fertilization of intact rat eggs *in vitro* and the results obtained.

Mature female CD strain rats were kept in a constant temperature room (23-25°C) with artificial light (19.00-7.00 h darkness) and their vaginal smears inspected daily. As ovulation usually occurs at about 2.00 h on the pro-oestrous to oestrous night[21], the eggs were considered to be about 4 to 5 h and 7.5 to 8.5 h after ovulation when pro-oestrous rats were killed at 6.00 to 7.00 and 9.30 to 10.30 h respectively on the next day. Superovulation of mature rats was performed by i. p. injection of 30 IU of pregnant mare's serum (PMS) on the morning of oestrus and 30 IU of human chorionic gonadotrophin (HCG), 52 to 58 h later; the rats were killed 14 to 16 h after injection of HCG. Oviducts were placed under light paraffin oil, equilibrated with 5% $CO_2$ in air in the presence of a small volume of saline, in a watch glass kept at 37°C and the eggs in cumulus clot were released by dissecting the ampular portion of the oviducts. Sperm for insemination were prepared. The eggs were inseminated with sperm prepared as in Fig. 1.

After incubation for 8 to 12 h, the eggs were removed, mounted on a slide and examined. They were then fixed with neutral formalin and stained for the assessment of fertilization. The eggs which had sperm within their perivitelline space (supplementary sperm) were defined as "penetrated" eggs. When these eggs had either enlarged sperm head(s) or male pronucleus(ei) with fertilizing sperm tail(s) in or on the vitellus, they were considered as undergoing fertilization.

# 大鼠卵细胞的体外受精

宫本，张明觉

## 编者按

美籍华裔科学家张明觉最广为人知的工作是开发了口服避孕药，本文中他以大量的动物体外受精实验阐明了大鼠卵细胞的体外受精过程。在很多其他物种中，哺乳动物的卵细胞成功的体外受精已得到阐明。先前张明觉已经亲自完成了兔子的体外受精，他在实验室中将已受孕的黑兔的胚胎移植到一只白兔体内。关键问题是张明觉认识到射精后精子成熟或者称为"精子获能"的重要性，精子获能这种现象是他独立发现的，同时生殖生物学家科林·罗素·奥斯汀也独立发现了相同的现象。张明觉的研究为人类卵细胞的体外受精奠定了基础，最终在 1978 年诞生了世界上第一个"试管婴儿"路易丝·布朗。

奥斯汀[1] 和张明觉[2] 发现"精子获能"后，科学家已经在很多物种中实现了哺乳动物的体外受精[3-17]。尽管也有人尝试大鼠卵细胞的体外受精[1,18-20]，但只有在透明带被胰凝乳蛋白酶溶解后，才能观察到精子进入卵黄。我们在本文中报道了完整的大鼠卵细胞的体外受精及获得的结果。

成熟的 CD 系雌性大鼠饲养在具有人工照明（19:00~7:00 黑暗）且保持恒定室温（23~25℃）的恒温室中，并且每日进行阴道涂片检查。从发情前期过渡到发情期的夜晚，排卵通常发生在 2:00 左右[21]，因此发情前期的大鼠分别于次日 6:00~7:00 和 9:30~10:30 被处死时，卵细胞被视为处于排卵后大约 4~5 h 和 7.5~8.5 h。通过在发情期早上腹腔注射 30 国际单位的孕马血清（PMS）并在 52~58 h 后注射 30 国际单位的人绒毛膜促性腺激素（HCG），实现成熟大鼠超排卵；注射 HCG 14~16 h 后处死大鼠。在表面皿上盛放少量盐水并用轻质石蜡油覆盖，在含 5%$CO_2$ 的空气中于 37℃进行平衡，再将输卵管置于轻质石蜡油下，然后通过切开输卵管壶腹部释放卵丘细胞块内的卵子。准备好授精用的精子。以图 1 中的方式用准备好的精子对卵子授精。

培养 8~12 h 后，移出卵细胞，将其封装于一个载玻片并进行镜检。然后用中性福尔马林固定并染色，以评估受精状况。在卵周隙空间内存在精子（额外精子）的卵细胞被定义为"被穿透的"卵细胞。若在这些卵细胞的卵黄中或卵黄上，要么有膨大的精子头部，要么存在带有受精精子尾部的雄性原核，便可将其视为正在受精。

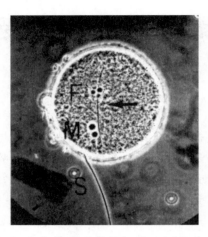

Fig. 1. A rat egg at pronuclear stage, fertilized *in vitro*, showing male pronucleus (M), female pronucleus (F), the fertilizing sperm tail (arrow) and a sperm attached to the zona pellucida (S). Photographed before fixation under a phase-contract microscope. Sperm for insemination were prepared either from the cauda epididymis or from the uterus of a female mated 0.5 to 1 h, or 10 to 11 h, previously. A drop of dense sperm mass was put into a watch glass and covered with 3 ml. of medium (modified Krebs-Ringer bicarbonate solution containing 114.2 mM NaCl, 4.78 mM KCl, 1.71 mM $CaCl_2 \cdot 2H_2O$, 1.19 mM $KH_2PO_4$, 1.19 mM $MgSO_4 \cdot 7H_2O$, 25.07 mM $NaHCO_3$, 0.55 mM sodium pyruvate, 21.58 mM sodium lactate and 5.55 mM glucose, to which 4 mg ml.$^{-1}$ of crystalline bovine serum albumin, 50 µg ml.$^{-1}$ of streptomycin sulphate and 75 µg ml.$^{-1}$ of penicillin G (potassium salt) were added). The *p*H value of the medium was adjusted to 7.4 to 7.5 by addition of 1 M NaOH and the final solution was filtered through a millipore filter to ensure asepsis. Blood of female rats was collected by heart puncture, allowed to clot and then centrifuged. Serum was sterilized by filtration through a millipore filter and stored under paraffin oil at 2 to 5°C for no longer than five days. The uterine fluid was collected from oestrous rats by means of a syringe needle. Insemination was performed by adding 0.4 ml. of the sperm suspension to the egg clot under the oil, after removing oviducts and débris. In some cases the egg clot was washed three times with the same medium to remove the oviducal fluid. After adding 0.1 or 0.2 ml. of heated rat serum (at 56°C for 40 min), the eggs and sperm were thoroughly mixed and incubated at 37°C in an atmosphere of 5% $CO_2$ in air. The final concentration of sperm in the suspension was 1,000 to 4,000 sperm mm.$^{-3}$.

Fig. 1 shows a rat egg fertilized *in vitro* at the pronuclear stage. Table 1 shows that the eggs recovered from naturally-ovulated rats have a better chance ($P<0.01$) of fertilization *in vitro* than those recovered from superovulated rats (highest penetration rates: 45% compared with 22%). The proportion of penetrated eggs was higher ($P<0.05$) following insemination with sperm recovered from the uterus 10 to 11 h (17-45%) than 0.5 to 1 h after mating (7%) for both the naturally-ovulated and superovulated eggs. The eggs recovered 4 to 5 h after ovulation appeared to have a better chance of penetration (24-45%) than those recovered 7.5 to 8.5 h after ovulation (1-5%). By washing the egg clot before insemination, the proportion of penetration was decreased for both the naturally-ovulated (24% compared with 45%) and superovulated eggs (9-11 compared with 17-22%, not statistically significant), indicating that some beneficial factor may have been removed by washing. Although there was no obvious difference when different proportions of rat serum were added in the medium, sperm penetration was not observed when whole rat serum was used in a few experiments. Sperm penetration, however, was not observed in 52 naturally-ovulated eggs and 229 superovulated eggs when epididymal sperm, which had been pre-incubated for 2 to 7 h in the medium containing rat serum and uterine

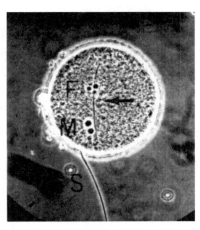

图 1. 一个在体外受精过程中处在原核阶段的大鼠卵细胞，图中显示雄性原核（M），雌性原核（F），受精精子的尾部（箭头）和一个附着在透明带上的精子（S）。样品固定前在相差显微镜下照相。用于授精的精子来源于附睾尾部或已经交配的 0.5~1 h 或 10~11 h 的雌性大鼠子宫。向表面皿上滴加一滴浓稠的精液，其上再覆盖 3 ml 培养基（该培养基是改良 Krebs-Ringer 碳酸氢钠溶液，含有 114.2 mM NaCl，4.78 mM KCl，1.71 mM CaCl$_2$ · 2H$_2$O，1.19 mM KH$_2$PO$_4$，1.19 mM MgSO$_4$ · 7H$_2$O，25.07 mM NaHCO$_3$，0.55 mM 丙酮酸钠，21.58 mM 乳酸钠和 5.55 mM 葡萄糖，并加入 4 mg·ml$^{-1}$ 结晶牛血清白蛋白，50 μg·ml$^{-1}$ 硫酸链霉素和 75 mg · ml$^{-1}$ 青霉素 G（钾盐）。用 1M NaOH 将培养基 pH 值调至 7.4~7.5 并将终溶液用微孔过滤器过滤以保证无菌。心脏穿刺收集雌性大鼠血液，凝固后离心分离。血清通过微孔过滤器过滤除菌后储存于石蜡油下，在 2~5℃ 保存不超过 5 天。用注射器针头从发情期雌性大鼠体内收集子宫液。去除输卵管及其碎片后，在石蜡油下，向卵细胞团块加入 0.4 ml 精子悬浮液进行授精。某些情况下，卵细胞团块用相同培养基清洗 3 次以除去输卵管液。加入 0.1 或 0.2 ml 温育处理（56℃，40 min）的大鼠血清后，卵细胞和精子充分混合，并在含 5% CO$_2$ 的空气环境中 37℃ 培养。悬浊液中精子的终浓度为每毫升 1,000~4,000 个精子。

　　图 1 显示了一个处于原核阶段的大鼠卵细胞体外受精的情况。表 1 显示从自然排卵的大鼠体内收集到的卵细胞比那些从超排卵大鼠体内收集到的卵细胞有更多机会（$P<0.01$）发生体外受精（最高穿透率为 45% 比 22%）。从子宫中分别收集大鼠交配后 0.5~1 h 和 10~11 h 的精子，对卵细胞授精并计算穿透率。无论自然排卵还是超排卵的卵细胞，用 10~11 h 精子授精的卵细胞穿透率（17%~45%）高于（$P<0.05$）用 0.5~1 h 精子授精的卵细胞穿透率 (7%)。排卵后 4~5 h 收集的卵细胞显示其被穿透的可能性（24%~45%）比排卵后 7.5~8.5 h 收集的卵细胞（1%~5%）要高。授精前清洗卵细胞团块，则正常排卵（45% 比 24%）和超排卵（17%~22% 比 9%~11%，无显著性差异）的卵细胞穿透率均下降，说明某些有益的因子可能被冲洗掉了。尽管不同比例的大鼠血清加入培养基后并未观察到明显差异，但在一些实验中，培养基内加入大鼠全血清后未观察到精子的穿透。然而，当使用在含大鼠血清和子宫液的培养基中预先培养了 2~7 h 的附睾精子时，在 52 个自然排卵的卵细胞和 229 个超

fluid, were used, they remained motile for longer than uterine-incubated sperm. This, and the higher proportion of eggs penetrated by sperm recovered from the uterus 10 to 11 h after mating demonstrated clearly that rat sperm do need capacitation in the female tract before they are capable of penetrating the egg. Hamster[6,8], mouse[15], guinea pig[17] and perhaps human[9,10] sperm can be capacitated *in vitro*, but we have shown the difficulty of capacitating rat sperm *in vitro*. Rat sperm is similar to rabbit sperm in this respect.

Table 1. *In vitro* Fertilization of Rat Eggs

| Mature female rats | Age of eggs (h after ovulation) | Sperm used | Medium used(medium: serum) | No. of females used | No. of eggs examined | No. of penetrated eggs (%) | No. of eggs undergoing fertilization (%) | No. of polyspermic eggs (%) |
|---|---|---|---|---|---|---|---|---|
| Naturally-ovulated | 4-5 | Uterine 0.5-1 h after mating | 4:1 | 5 | 54 | 4 (7) | 2 (4) | 0 |
| | 4-5 | Uterine 10-11 h after mating | 4:0 | 5 | 56 | 6 (11) | 4 (7) | 1 (25) |
| | | | 2:1 | 10 | 84 | 38 (45) | 22 (26) | 0 |
| | 4-5 | Uterine 10-11 h after mating | 4:1 | 5 | 55 | 25 (45) | 25 (45) | 9 (36) |
| | 4-5* | Uterine 10-11 h after mating | 2:1 | 5 | 54 | 13 (24) | 10 (19) | 1 (10) |
| | 7.5-8.5 | Uterine 10-11 h after mating | 2:1 | 6 | 78 | 1 (1) | 1 (1) | 0 |
| | 7.5-8.5 | Uterine 10-11 h after mating | 4:1 | 6 | 74 | 4 (5) | 3 (4) | 0 |
| | 4-5 | Epididymal † | With serum and uterine fluid | 5 | 52 | 0 | 0 | 0 |
| Super-ovulated | 1-3 | Uterine 0.5-1 h after mating | 4:1 | 12 | 280 | 19 (7) | 4 (1) | 0 |
| | 1-3 | Uterine 10-11 h after mating | 2:1 | 13 | 363 | 62 (17) | 30 (8) | 1 (3) |
| | 1-3 | Uterine 10-11 h after mating | 4:1 | 4 | 101 | 22 (22) | 13 (13) | 1 (8) |
| | 1-3* | Uterine 10-11 h after mating | 2:1 | 5 | 136 | 12 (9) | 8 (6) | 0 |
| | 1-3* | Uterine 10-11 h after mating | 4:1 | 4 | 133 | 14 (11) | 8 (6) | 0 |
| | 1-3 | Epididymal† | With serum and uterine fluid | 8 | 229 | 0 | 0 | 0 |

* Egg clot was washed three times before insemination.
† Epididymal sperm were incubated in the presence of uterine fluid for 2-7 h before insemination.

Of 126 eggs undergoing fertilization, 114 (90%) were monospermic and 12 (10%) were polyspermic; 12 had an enlarged sperm head and 114 had at least one male pronucleus. Fifty monospermic eggs and 12 polyspermic eggs had 1 to 26 supplementary sperm.

排卵的卵细胞中，均未观察到精子的穿透，它们比子宫培养的精子保持更长时间的活力。这种情况以及交配后 10~11 h 从子宫回收的精子，其穿透卵细胞的比例较高的事实明确说明大鼠精子在能够穿透卵细胞之前的确需要在雌性生殖道中获能。仓鼠[6,8]，小鼠[15]，豚鼠[17]，可能还包括人[9,10]的精子能够体外获能，但是我们已经看到了大鼠精子体外获能是很困难的。在这方面大鼠和兔的精子是类似的。

表 1. 大鼠卵细胞的体外受精

| 成熟雌性大鼠 | 卵细胞年龄（排卵后时间 (h)) | 所用的精子 | 所用的培养基（培养基：血清） | 所用的雌性动物数量 | 检验的卵细胞数量 | 穿透的卵细胞数量（%） | 经历受精的卵细胞数量（%） | 多精受精的卵细胞数量（%） |
|---|---|---|---|---|---|---|---|---|
| 自然排卵 | 4~5 | 交配后 0.5~1 h 的子宫中的精子 | 4:1 | 5 | 54 | 4 (7) | 2 (4) | 0 |
| | 4~5 | 交配后 10~11 h 的子宫中的精子 | 4:0 | 5 | 56 | 6 (11) | 4 (7) | 1 (25) |
| | | | 2:1 | 10 | 84 | 38 (45) | 22 (26) | 0 |
| | 4~5 | 交配后 10~11 h 的子宫中的精子 | 4:1 | 5 | 55 | 25 (45) | 25 (45) | 9 (36) |
| | 4~5* | 交配后 10~11 h 的子宫中的精子 | 2:1 | 5 | 54 | 13 (24) | 10 (19) | 1 (10) |
| | 7.5~8.5 | 交配后 10~11 h 的子宫中的精子 | 2:1 | 6 | 78 | 1 (1) | 1 (1) | 0 |
| | 7.5~8.5 | 交配后 10~11 h 的子宫中的精子 | 4:1 | 6 | 74 | 4 (5) | 3 (4) | 0 |
| | 4~5 | 附睾的精子† | 血清和子宫液 | 5 | 52 | 0 | 0 | 0 |
| 超排卵 | 1~3 | 交配后 0.5~1 h 的子宫中的精子 | 4:1 | 12 | 280 | 19 (7) | 4 (1) | 0 |
| | 1~3 | 交配后 10~11 h 的子宫中的精子 | 2:1 | 13 | 363 | 62 (17) | 30 (8) | 1 (3) |
| | 1~3 | 交配后 10~11 h 的子宫中的精子 | 4:1 | 4 | 101 | 22 (22) | 13 (13) | 1 (8) |
| | 1~3* | 交配后 10~11 h 的子宫中的精子 | 2:1 | 5 | 136 | 12 (9) | 8 (6) | 0 |
| | 1~3* | 交配后 10~11 h 的子宫中的精子 | 4:1 | 4 | 133 | 14 (11) | 8 (6) | 0 |
| | 1~3 | 附睾的精子† | 血清和子宫液 | 8 | 229 | 0 | 0 | 0 |

* 授精前清洗 3 次卵细胞团块。
† 授精前附睾精子在子宫液存在的情况下孵育 2~7 h。

在 126 个经历受精的卵细胞中，114 个（90%）是单精受精的，而 12 个（10%）是多精受精的；12 个有膨大的精子头部，而 114 个有至少一个雄性原核。50 个单精

Supplementary sperm (1 to 11) were also found in 88 unfertilized eggs, which indicates the occurrence of a vitelline block to sperm penetration as the eggs deteriorated *in vitro*. The incidence of polyspermy of rat eggs fertilized *in vivo* is about 1.2%[22]. The *in vitro* incidence of polyspermy is comparatively high as in the case of hamster[6] and mouse eggs[15]. Although fertilization of rat eggs *in vitro* was reported recently by Bregulla[20], the method used, the photographs published, and the high frequency of cleavage of unfertilized rat eggs *in vivo*[23], make his claim unconvincing.

This work was supported by grants from the US Public Health Service and the Ford Foundation. We thank Mrs Rose Bartke for assistance.

(**241**, 50-52; 1973)

**H. Miyamoto and M. C. Chang**
Worcester Foundation for Experimental Biology, 222 Maple Avenue, Shrewsbury, Massachusetts 01545

Received June 19; revised August 8, 1972.

References:

1. Austin, C. R., *Aust. J. Sci. Res., Series B, Biol. Sci.*, **4**, 581 (1951).

2. Chang, M. C., *Nature*, **168**, 697 (1951).

3. Thibault, C., Dauzier, L., and Wintenberger, S., C. *R. Soc. Biol.*, **148**, 789 (1954).

4. Chang, M. C., *Nature*, **184**, 466 (1959).

5. Brackett, B. G., and Williams, W. L., *Fertil. Steril.*, **19**, 144 (1968).

6. Yanagimachi, R., and Chang, M. C., *Nature*, **200**, 281 (1963).

7. Barros, C., and Austin, C. R., *J. Exp. Zool.*, **166**, 317 (1967).

8. Yanagimachi, R., *J. Reprod. Fertil.*, **18**, 275 (1969).

9. Edwards, R. G., Bavister, B. D., and Steptoe, P. C., *Nature*, **221**, 632 (1969).

10. Edwards, R. G., Steptoe, P. C., and Purdy, J. M., *Nature*, **227**, 1307 (1970).

11. Whittingham, D. G., *Nature*, **220**, 592 (1968).

12. Iwamatsu, T., and Chang, M. C., *Nature*, **224**, 919 (1969).

13. Cross, P. C., and Brinster, R. L., *Biol. Reprod.*, **3**, 298 (1970).

14. Mukherjee, A. B., and Cohn, M. M., *Nature*, **228**, 472 (1970).

15. Iwamatsu, T., and Chang, M. C., *J. Reprod. Fertil.*, **26**, 197 (1971).

16. Hamner, C. E., Jennings, L. L., and Sojka, N. J., *J. Reprod. Fertil.*, **23**, 477 (1970)

17. Yanagimachi, R., *Anat. Rec.*, **174**, 9 (1972).

18. Long, J. A., *Univ. Calif. Publ. Zool.*, **9**, 105 (1912).

19. Toyoda, Y., and Chang, M. C., *Nature*, **220**, 589 (1968).

20. Bregulla, K., *Arch. Gynäk.*, **207**, 568 (1969).

21. Everett, J. W., *Endocrinology*, **43**, 389 (1948).

22. Austin, C. R., and Braden, A. W. H., *Aust. J. Biol. Sci.*, **6**, 674 (1953).

23. Austin, C. R., *J. Endocrinol.*, **6**, 104 (1949).

受精卵细胞和 12 个多精受精卵细胞有 1~26 个额外精子。在 88 个未受精的卵细胞中也发现了额外精子（1~11 个），这提示由于卵细胞在体外变质，导致卵黄阻断精子的穿透。大鼠卵细胞体内受精时多精受精的发生率约为 1.2%[22]。而相比之下，仓鼠[6]和小鼠[15] 卵细胞体外多精受精发生率要高。尽管最近布雷古拉报道了大鼠卵细胞体外受精[20]，但其使用的方法、发表的照片以及体内未受精的大鼠卵细胞高频率的卵裂[23]，使得他的论断没有说服力。

本研究得到了美国公共卫生署和福特基金会的资助。我们感谢罗丝·巴特克女士的帮助。

（吴彦 翻译；曹文广 审稿）

# Earth-Moon Mass Ratio from Mariner 9 Radio Tracking Data

S. K. Wong and S. J. Reinbold

## Editor's Note

**The ratio of the mass of the Earth to that of the Moon is used to predict the evolution of the Moon's orbit into the future. The ratio can be determined without any assumptions using radio tracking data from spacecraft. Here S. K. Wong and S. J. Reinbold do just that, using data from the Mariner 9 mission to Mars. They find the mass ratio to be 81.3007, very close to the currently accepted value.**

THE navigation of the Mariner 9 spacecraft from Earth to Mars was performed using phase-coherent range and doppler tracking data recorded by the Jet Propulsion Laboratory (JPL) Deep Space Network. These data also determine the Earth-Moon mass ratio, which involves the following physics: as the Earth revolves about the centre of mass of the Earth-Moon system, a sinusoidal curve is impressed on the range and doppler tracking data with a frequency equal to the sidereal mean motion of the Moon. This signature is shown in Fig. 1, where a perturbation of 0.0003 was made in the mass ratio ($\mu^{-1}$ = mass of Earth over mass of Moon). This sinusoidal variation in the tracking data can be eliminated by finding a value for $\mu^{-1}$ that properly represents the amplitude of the barycentre motion of the Earth. The procedure is direct and for all practical purposes is completely uncoupled from other parameters used in reducing the tracking data.

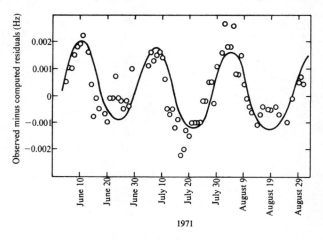

Fig. 1. The effect of Earth-Moon mass ratio on doppler residuals.

The mass ratio was determined from range and doppler data obtained over a period of

# 由水手9号射电跟踪数据得到的地月质量比

黄，赖因博尔德

编者按

地球质量与月球质量之比被用于预测月球轨道在未来的演化。不必进行任何假设，使用来自航天器的射电跟踪数据，我们就能够确定这个比值。本文中黄和赖因博尔德正是那样做的，他们使用的数据来自于被派往火星的水手9号。他们得到的质量比是81.3007，非常接近现在普遍接受的值。

从地球飞向火星的水手9号航天器使用由喷气推进实验室（JPL）深空探测网记录的相位相干测距和多普勒跟踪数据进行导航。这些数据也确定了地月质量比，这涉及以下物理事实：地球围绕地月系统的质心转动，使得测距和多普勒跟踪数据成为正弦曲线，频率与月球相对于恒星的平均运动相同。这个特征如图1所示，其中对质量比作了0.0003的扰动（$\mu^{-1}$为地球质量与月球质量之比）。通过找到恰当地反映地球质心运动幅度的$\mu^{-1}$，就可以在跟踪数据中去除此正弦变化。这是一种直接的方法，在实际应用中完全和处理跟踪数据用到的其他参量无关。

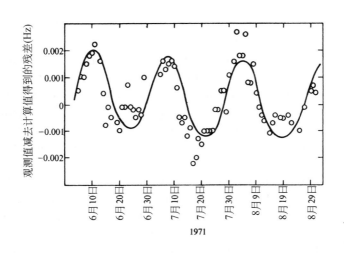

图 1. 地月质量比对多普勒残差的影响

地月质量比是基于15周的测距和多普勒数据（1971年6月5日到9月15日）

15 weeks (June 5 to September 15, 1971). The data coverage is shown in Table 1. We also show the statistics from the best determination. The data reduction was performed using the JPL Double Precision Orbit Determination Program[1], which uses a Cowell integrated trajectory and a batch least squares filter. In weighting the range data, we have taken extreme care to assure optimal data utilization without conflicting with the doppler data. The Mariner Mars 1969 results showed that such conflicts can cause significant perturbations in the estimated parameters.

Table 1. Tracking Data Statistics

| Tracking station | Data type* | Number Of points† | Data interval, 1971 (UTC) | Mean residual‡ | Root-mean-Square residual‡ |
|---|---|---|---|---|---|
| Goldstone-Echo, Calif. | Doppler | 1,069 | 6/5 08:37 to 9/14 04:59 | 0.000005 Hz | 0.00144 Hz |
| | Range-Mark 1A | 248 | 6/5 08:42 to 6/30 09:14 | −17.73 RU | 20.94 RU |
| | Range-Mu | 31 | 7/12 05:40 to 9/6 02:49 | −19.12 ns | 134.55 ns |
| Goldstone-Mars, Calif. | Doppler | 193 | 6/5 13:01 to 8/31 09:36 | 0.000002 Hz | 0.00132 Hz |
| | Range-Tau | 109 | 6/5 12:43 to 8/27 06:20 | −33.67 ns | 116.22 ns |
| Woomera, Australia | Doppler | 1,638 | 6/5 01:15 to 9/12 17:56 | −0.000012 Hz | 0.00139 Hz |
| | Range-Mark 1A | 594 | 6/5 01:09 to 7/13 17:40 | 5.28 RU | 19.21 RU |
| Johannesburg, South Africa | Doppler | 1,336 | 6/5 02:54 to 9/14 22:57 | −0.000117 Hz | 0.00140 Hz |
| | Range-Mark 1A | 776 | 6/5 03:00 to 7/18 04:31 | 4.38 RU | 20.60 RU |
| Cebreros, Spain | Doppler | 387 | 6/26 00:43 to 9/12 00:36 | 0.000023 Hz | 0.00188 Hz |
| | Range-Mark 1A | 27 | 7/5 02:40 to 7/15 02:50 | 1.97 RU | 21.04 RU |

* Mark 1A = near-Earth ranging system; Tau and Mu = ranging systems using different ground hardware.
† Sample rate for doppler and range was 20 min.
‡ 1 Hz = 65 mm/s; 1 RU (range unit) ≈ 1 m; 1 ns ≈ 0.15 m.

The Deep Space Network has three types of ranging systems: Mu, Tau, and Mark 1A. The Mu and Tau systems are capable of planetary distances, whereas the Mark 1A ranging system is limited to an effective one-way range of approximately $10^7$ km. In weighting the range data the following factors were taken into consideration. First, assuming no external errors, the Mu and Tau systems are accurate to about 20 m. This includes system noise and transponder and ground equipment calibration errors. The Mark 1A ranging system is accurate to about 30 m. Second, because the radio signals travel through the ionosphere of the Earth and the interplanetary space plasma, there is a change in the radio signal path length. The group wave path length is increased, while the phase wave path length is decreased, corrupting both range and doppler measurements made from the radio signal. The charged particles of the Earth's ionosphere could account for as much as a 15 m error in range; the charged particles in the interplanetary medium (space plasma) could account for as much as a 22 m error in range (J. F. Jordan et al., paper presented at AAS/AISS Astrodynamics Conference, August 1970). Third, another possible cause of range error is the Z component of station location. This component is parallel to the Earth's spin axis. The computed range value is sensitive to incorrect Z values when the probe declination becomes large in absolute value. An equation relating the two is[3]

而确定的。表1给出了数据范围，同时我们也列出了由最佳测定结果得到的统计数据。使用了喷气推进实验室双精度轨道测定程序处理数据[1]，该程序使用了考埃尔轨道积分和批处理最小二乘滤波器。在考虑测距数据的权重时，我们非常谨慎，以确保使用最优的数据，避免和多普勒数据出现不一致。1969年的火星水手号结果显示，这样的不一致性会导致估计参数出现较大误差。

表1. 跟踪数据的统计

| 跟踪站 | 数据类型 * | 数据点数 † | 数据间隔，1971 年（UTC） | 平均残差 ‡ | 均方根残差 ‡ |
|---|---|---|---|---|---|
| 戈尔德斯通－回波<br>加利福尼亚 | 多普勒 | 1,069 | 6/5 08:37 到 9/14 04:59 | 0.000005 Hz | 0.00144 Hz |
| | 测距－Mark 1A | 248 | 6/5 08:42 到 6/30 09:14 | −17.73 RU | 20.94 RU |
| | 测距－Mu | 31 | 7/12 05:40 到 9/6 02:49 | −19.12 ns | 134.55ns |
| 戈尔德斯通－火星<br>加利福尼亚 | 多普勒 | 193 | 6/5 13:01 到 8/31 09:36 | 0.000002 Hz | 0.00132 Hz |
| | 测距－Tau | 109 | 6/5 12:43 到 8/27 06:20 | −33.67 ns | 116.22ns |
| 伍默拉<br>澳大利亚 | 多普勒 | 1,638 | 6/5 01:15 到 9/12 17:56 | −0.000012 Hz | 0.00139 Hz |
| | 测距－Mark 1A | 594 | 6/5 01:09 到 7/13 17:40 | 5.28 RU | 19.21 RU |
| 约翰内斯堡<br>南非 | 多普勒 | 1,336 | 6/5 02:54 到 9/14 22:57 | −0.000117 Hz | 0.00140 Hz |
| | 测距－Mark 1A | 776 | 6/5 03:00 到 7/18 04:31 | 4.38 RU | 20.60 RU |
| 塞夫雷罗斯<br>西班牙 | 多普勒 | 387 | 6/26 00:43 到 9/12 00:36 | 0.000023 Hz | 0.00188Hz |
| | 测距－Mark 1A | 27 | 7/5 02:40 到 7/15 02:50 | 1.97 RU | 21.04RU |

*Mark 1A 为近地测距系统；Tau 和 Mu 表示使用不同地面硬件设备的测距系统。
† 测距和多普勒位移数据的采样间隔是 20 分钟。
‡ 1 Hz=65 mm/s；1 RU（测距单位）≈ 1 m; 1 ns ≈ 0.15 m。

深空探测网有三类测距系统：Mu、Tau 和 Mark 1A。Mu 和 Tau 系统可以测量行星距离，而 Mark 1A 系统的单程有效范围仅限于大约 $10^7$ km。使用这些测距数据的权重需要考虑以下因素：第一，假设不存在外部误差，Mu、Tau 系统精确度为大约 20 m，这包括系统噪声、转发器和地面设备的定标误差。Mark 1A 测距系统精确度为大约 30 m。第二，由于射电信号穿过了地球的电离层和行星际空间的等离子体，所以其光程也会发生变化。群光程增加，而相光程减小，这影响了由射电信号得到的测距和多普勒测量结果。地球电离层中的带电粒子会造成多达 15 m 的测距误差；行星际介质中的带电粒子（空间等离子体）会造成多达 22 m 的测距误差（乔丹等人在美国宇航学会、美国航空航天协会主办的航天动力学会议上发表的文章，1970 年8 月）。第三，造成测距误差的另一个可能的原因是站点位置中的 $Z$ 分量，这个分量和地球的自转轴平行。当探测器赤纬的绝对值较大时，计算得出的测距值对不正确的 $Z$ 值敏感，联系这两个量的方程为 [3]：

$$\Delta\rho = \Delta Z \sin \delta$$

Where $\rho$ is the range datum and $\delta$ is the geocentric declination of the spacecraft.

Because previous space mission data did not yield significant information on the $Z$ component of station locations, JPL analysts used the $Z$ values obtained by the Smithsonian Astrophysical Observatory (SAO) in 1969. The change in the $Z$ component was as much as 56 m. Assuming that the $Z$ values from SAO may be in error by 30 m and the maximum absolute value in geocentric declination for Mariner Mars 1971 is 29.15°, the above equation would yield a range error of 14.6 m. The doppler data are insensitive to this $Z$-component error. Even though the $Z$ component of a station location is not too well determined, the distances from the spin axis and the longitude are known to better than 3 and 5 m, respectively.

A number of solutions with different combinations of weights for each data type and different sets of estimated parameters were examined. The standard set of estimated parameters includes the probe position and velocity (6), solar pressure (3), attitude control leaks (3), station locations (15), and the Earth-Moon ratio (1). An *a priori* statistic of 0.0166 was applied to the mass ratio parameter. These solutions and their identifications are given as follows:

Case 1, Doppler only (doppler weight = 0.015 Hz) with standard estimated parameter set. Case 2, Range only (range weight = 100 m) with standard estimated parameter set. Case 3, Doppler and range (doppler weight = 0.015 Hz, range weight = 100 m) with standard estimated parameter set. Case 4, Doppler and range (doppler weight = 0.015 Hz, range weight = 100 m) with standard estimated parameter set plus Mars and Earth-Moon barycentre ephemeris parameters. Case 5, Doppler and range (doppler weight = 0.015 Hz, range weight = 50 m) with the estimated parameter set as in Case 4.

| Solutions | $\mu^{-1}$ |
|---|---|
| Case 1 | 81.30068 |
| Case 2 | 81.30067 |
| Case 3 | 81.30067 |
| Case 4 | 81.30067 |
| Case 5 | 81.30068 |

All solutions yielded nearly the same mass ratio. Cases 1 and 2 give remarkable agreement on a mass ratio between the two data types. With such good agreement, the relative weight of the two data types becomes less significant. Cases 3 and 4 show that the lunar ephemeris error is probably too small to have an effect on the mass ratio estimate. Possible error sources are the periodic variations in the interplanetary medium. W. G. Melbourne has shown (12th Plenary Meeting of the Committee on Space Research, Prague, 1969) that a 28 day sinusoidal variation of solar flux of 0.1% could produce an error of about 0.001 in the mass ratio, but that it is not likely. Also, the agreement of mass ratios computed from the data gathered from several interplanetary spacecraft does not indicate

$$\Delta\rho = \Delta Z \sin\delta$$

其中，$\rho$ 是测距值，$\delta$ 是航天器的赤纬。

由于之前的航天数据并未给出站点位置 $Z$ 分量的重要信息，所以喷气推进实验室的分析者使用了由史密森天体物理台（SAO）1969 年得出的 $Z$ 值。$Z$ 值的变化达到了 56 m。假设史密森天体物理台得到的 $Z$ 值存在 30 m 的误差，且 1971 年火星水手号赤纬的最大绝对值是 29.15°，则用上述方程可以得到一个 14.6 m 误差范围。多普勒数据对这个 $Z$ 分量误差不敏感。尽管站点位置的 $Z$ 分量没有得到充分确定，但其到自转轴的距离和经度可以分别在优于 3 m 和 5 m 的精确范围内确定。

在对每种数据类型取不同权重组合，并取不同的估计参数组后，可得到若干结果，本文对它们进行了检验。标准的估计参数组包括探测位置和速度（6）、太阳辐射压（3）、姿态控制的误差（3）、站点位置（15）和地月质量比（1）。将先验统计值 0.0166 作为质量比的初始参数。这些结果和相应的证认如下：

情况 1，基于标准估计参数组的多普勒位移（多普勒权重为 0.015 Hz）数据。情况 2，基于标准估计参数组的测距数据（测距权重为 100 m）。情况 3，基于标准估计参数组的多普勒位移和测距数据（多普勒权重为 0.015 Hz，测距权重为 100 m）。情况 4，基于标准估计参数组以及火星和地月质心的星历参数的多普勒位移和测距数据（多普勒权重为 0.015 Hz，测距权重为 100 m）。情况 5，基于和情况 4 相同的估计参数组的多普勒位移和测距数据（多普勒权重为 0.015 Hz，测距权重为 50 m）。

| 结果 | $\mu^{-1}$ |
|---|---|
| 情况 1 | 81.30068 |
| 情况 2 | 81.30067 |
| 情况 3 | 81.30067 |
| 情况 4 | 81.30067 |
| 情况 5 | 81.30068 |

所有的结果都得到了相近的质量比。情况 1、2 由两种类型的数据给出了相当一致的质量比。基于这么好的一致性，两组数据的相对权重就变得不太重要了。情况 3 和 4 表示月球星历表的误差对估算质量比结果的影响微不足道。误差的可能来源是行星际介质的周期性变化。墨尔本曾指出（空间研究委员会第 12 届全体会议，布拉格，1969 年）周期为 28 天的太阳流量正弦变化（幅度为太阳流量的 0.1%）会导致在质量比中出现 0.001 的误差，不过这好像不太可能。而且，由许多行星际航天

this sort of systematic error unless the phase of the flux variation is the same for each mission, which does not seem likely.

The results from the Mariner Mars 1971 data are given in Table 2 together with previous results obtained from Pioneers 8 and 9 and Mariners 2, 4, 5, 6 and 7. Values computed for Pioneers 8 and 9 and Mariner 2 were obtained from solutions using only doppler data. It is interesting to note that the Mariner 9 value and the mean of all spacecraft determined values of $\mu^{-1}$ are 81.3007. The deviations from the arithmetic mean of the Mariner and Pioneer values are tabulated in Table 1. Further, the mass ratio computed from the last five interplanetary spacecraft launched (Pioneers 8 and 9 and Mariners 6, 7 and 9) showed a spread of only 0.0004. The values for Pioneers 8 and 9 and Mariners 6, 7 and 9 are 81.3004, 81.3008, 81.3004, 81.3005 and 81.3007, respectively. This provides a good indication of the accuracy of $\mu^{-1}$. The decrease in the fluctuation of the mass ratio value can be attributed to the improvement of data quality owing to changes in Deep Space Network tracking systems and the change in computer software from single precision to double precision.

Table 2. Estimates of the Earth-Moon Mass Ratio, $\mu^{-1}$

| Spacecraft | $\mu^{-1}$ | $\mu^{-1} - \overline{\mu^{-1}}$ | Reference |
|---|---|---|---|
| Pioneer 8 | 81.3004±0.0001 | −0.0003 | 5 |
| Pioneer 9 | 81.3008±0.0001 | 0.0001 | 5 |
| Mariner 2 (Venus) | 81.3001±0.0013 | −0.0006 | 6 |
| Mariner 4 (Mars) | 81.3015±0.0017 | 0.0008 | 7 |
| Mariner 5 (Venus) | 81.3013±0.0002 | 0.0006 | 5 |
| Mariner 6 (Mars) | 81.3004±0.0002 | −0.0002 | 5 |
| Mariner 7 (Mars) | 81.3005±0.0002 | −0.0002 | 5 |
| Mariner 9 (Mars) | 81.3007±0.0001 | 0.0000 | |

$\overline{\mu^{-1}}$ = arithmetic mean.

We thank W. L. Sjogren for discussion and review of this article. This research was supported by NASA.

(**241**, 111-112; 1973)

S. K. Wong and S. J. Reinbold
Jet Propulsion Laboratory, Pasadena, California 91103

Received September 11, 1972.

References:
1. Moyer, T., *Technical Report 32-1527* (Jet Propulsion Laboratory, Pasadena, 1971).
2. Mottinger, N. A., *et al.*, *Technical Memorandum 33-469* (Jet Propulsion Laboratory, Pasadena, 1970).
3. Anderson, J. D., thesis, University of California at Los Angeles (1967).
4. Null, G. W., Gordon, H. J., and Tito, D. A., *Technical Report 32-1108* (Jet Propulsion Laboratory, Pasadena, 1967).

器得到的数据计算出的质量比也是一致的，这表明没有这种系统误差，除非辐射流变化的相位对于每次航行都相同，但这是不大可能的。

表 2 中给出了 1971 年火星水手号的数据以及以前由先驱者 8 号、9 号和水手 2 号、4 号、5 号、6 号和 7 号得到的结果。对于先驱者 8 号、9 号和水手 2 号的结果，计算时只用了多普勒数据。有趣的是，水手 9 号得到的数值和所有飞行器得到的 $\mu^{-1}$ 平均值都是 81.3007。水手号和先驱者号的结果与算术平均值的偏差列在了表 1 里。而且，由最后 5 次（先驱者 8 号、9 号和水手 6 号、7 号和 9 号）发射的行星际航天器的数据计算出的质量比差别都在 0.0004 的范围内。先驱者 8 号、9 号和水手 6 号、7 号和 9 号的结果分别是 81.3004、81.3008、81.3004、81.3005 和 81.3007。这很好地表明了 $\mu^{-1}$ 的精度。质量比变化的减小主要归因于数据质量的提高，这都源于深空探测网络跟踪系统的改进以及在计算机软件数据类型中单精度变为了双精度。

表 2. 地月质量比估算结果，$\mu^{-1}$

| 航天器 | $\mu^{-1}$ | $\mu^{-1} - \overline{\mu^{-1}}$ | 参考资料 |
|---|---|---|---|
| 先驱者 8 号 | $81.3004 \pm 0.0001$ | $-0.0003$ | 5 |
| 先驱者 9 号 | $81.3008 \pm 0.0001$ | $0.0001$ | 5 |
| 水手 2 号（金星） | $81.3001 \pm 0.0013$ | $-0.0006$ | 6 |
| 水手 4 号（火星） | $81.3015 \pm 0.0017$ | $0.0008$ | 7 |
| 水手 5 号（金星） | $81.3013 \pm 0.0002$ | $0.0006$ | 5 |
| 水手 6 号（火星） | $81.3004 \pm 0.0002$ | $-0.0002$ | 5 |
| 水手 7 号（火星） | $81.3005 \pm 0.0002$ | $-0.0002$ | 5 |
| 水手 9 号（火星） | $81.3007 \pm 0.0001$ | $0.0000$ | |

$\overline{\mu^{-1}}$ 是算数平均值。

我们感谢肖格伦的讨论和对此文的审阅。该研究得到了美国国家航空航天局（NASA）的支持。

（冯翀 翻译；沈志侠 审稿）

# Do Honey Bees Have a Language?

P. H. Wells and A. M. Wenner

## Editor's Note

In 1946, German ethologist Karl von Frisch proposed that honey bees communicate by means of an elaborate dance, a method used to guide foragers to food. Bee biologists Patrick H. Wells and Adrian M. Wenner greeted the theory with skepticism, and published data suggesting that bees find food by odour, not language. In 1973, the year von Frisch received a Nobel Prize for his work on insect communication, Wells and Wenner published counterarguments to their critics and additional data that they believed backed up their olfactory theory. Here they conclude that the "language hypothesis has little heuristic value and fails as a predictive tool". Today, further observations have convinced most biologists that von Frisch was in fact correct.

---

Von Frisch and later adherents of the theory that honey bees communicate by means of an elaborate dance are challenged by controlled experiments which show that their data can be explained in terms of olfactory cues.

---

WHENEVER new data and interpretations are presented which cannot be reconciled with established beliefs, it is proper and desirable that supporters of the traditional view should examine these data and interpretations with great care, and offer such objections as can be generated. In 1969, on the basis of studies of the recruitment of honey bee foragers to food sources, we compared the predictive powers of the classical "language" hypothesis of von Frisch[1] with those of a simple olfaction model for forager recruitment and concluded that olfaction provides the best interpretation of our data[2].

Investigators who believe that honey bees have a language have since challenged our conclusion[3-5], and two other recent articles[6-7], while not including a discussion of our results, cannot be reconciled with our interpretations. Our purpose here is to examine the principal objections to our interpretations and present additional data.

### Procedure and Results

From earlier experiments, we knew that scent fed into a hive on one day influences forager recruitment on the next. We established a hive and a line of three experimental sites, each 200 m from it, in a dry field. The sites were approximately 150 m apart and the prevailing light breeze never blew towards or from the hive. Instead, the wind moved from site 1 to site 3, with site 2 in the middle.

# 蜜蜂有语言吗？

1946 年，德国动物行为学家卡尔·冯·弗里施提出蜜蜂是通过一套精心设计的舞蹈语言来和同伴交流，引导觅食蜜蜂找到食物的。蜜蜂生物学家帕特里克·韦尔斯和阿德里安·温纳对该理论持怀疑态度，并发表数据提示蜜蜂是通过气味觅食的，而并非舞蹈语言。1973 年，冯·弗里施因其在昆虫通讯领域的工作而获得诺贝尔奖，韦尔斯和温纳发表了他们对批评者的反驳论点和一些他们认为可以支持嗅觉理论的更多数据。本文中他们得出这样的结论"语言假说没有启发价值，也不能成为一种预测工具"。今天，进一步研究使大多数生物学家相信实际上冯·弗里施是正确的。

---

冯·弗里施提出蜜蜂通过精心设计的舞蹈语言通讯的理论，他及其该理论的后继支持者受到来自对照实验的挑战，这些对照实验的数据能够用嗅觉信号来解释。

---

每当新的数据和解释与已建立的理论不一致时，传统观点的支持者应当特别仔细地检查这些数据和解释，并且提供能够提出的反对意见，这样才会令人满意。1969 年，在招引觅食蜂到食物源的研究的基础上，我们将冯·弗里施 [1] 经典的"语言"假说与那些简单的嗅觉模型在招引觅食蜂的预测能力方面进行了比较，得出的结论是，嗅觉为我们的数据提供了最好的解释 [2]。

认为蜜蜂有语言的研究者已经质疑过我们的结论了 [3-5]，在其他两篇最近的论文 [6,7] 中，虽然没有包含对我们结果的讨论，但也与我们的解释不一致。在此，我们的目的是检查对我们理论的主要反对意见，并补充更多数据。

## 步骤和结果

从早期研究中我们知道，前一天注入一个蜂巢的气味会影响第二天对觅食蜂的招引。我们在干燥的野外建一个蜂巢，并且在距它 200 米的地方设立了排成一行的三个实验站点。那些实验站点间距约 150 米，而且通常微风不会吹向蜂巢或从蜂巢吹来。相反，风从 1 号站点吹向 3 号站点，而 2 号站点在中间。

During experimental periods of three hours, we fed scented sucrose to ten marked regular foragers at each of sites 1 and 3. Recruited bees were captured and killed. On a following day we fed unscented sucrose at sites 1 and 3 and planted scented sucrose at site 2, which had not been visited by bees from our hive. In this situation, the language hypothesis predicts that recruited foragers would be captured at sites 1 and 3, both visited by successful foragers from the hive. If, however, recruited foragers locate food sources by olfaction, they should arrive at site 2 which was not visited by any bees from the hive.

In four repetitions of this experiment (on days 2, 7, 12 and 16) we captured a total of twenty-five new recruits at site 1, 224 at site 2, and eight at site 3. Thus, newly recruited foragers had located a site in the field not previously visited by them or their hivemates, and had failed to arrive at locations about which they should have been well informed (according to the language hypothesis).

When foragers are experienced at a food site, they are again recruited to it by odour cues rather than by language[8,9] and, when odour cues are rigorously excluded, recruitment of new foragers fails[2,10]. For example, on control days of our experiments reported in 1969 when no scented sucrose was made available (days 4, 9 and 14), arrival of recruits at our feeding stations was drastically curtailed[2]. As a further control, we allowed ten bees to fly to each of four unscented feeders for 3 h (July 25, 1968) for a total of 1,374 round trips. During this period only five recruits from a hive of 60,000 bees found the feeders[2].

Thus, both experienced and inexperienced foragers seem to require olfactory cues to locate a food source in the field. In the absence of compelling evidence to the contrary, it is conservative to suggest that olfaction alone is sufficient to account for recruitment of honey bees to a food source.

## Objections to Our Model

In spite of his polemic, Dawkins[3] does offer one substantive objection by arguing that bees are easily distracted from their "intended" (linguistically communicated) goals. In this view, the bees which arrive at site 2 have been distracted from sites 1 and 3, a possibility which deserves serious consideration. But in our experiment, site 2 was downwind from 1 and upwind from 3. Is it likely that recruited foragers could be simultaneously distracted upwind and downwind from their intended goals, or that any animal can be attracted to a downwind odour source? In any case, when all three sites were provided with unscented sucrose (days 9 and 14), recruits failed to arrive at sites about which they were supposedly linguistically informed[2]. We conclude that Dawkins's "distraction" model is not supported by the data.

Esch and Bastian[6] reported interesting new data but did not relate their findings to the literature on forager recruitment. In each of their experiments, a group of bees was trained to feed at a scent-marked site near the hive, and ten of the foragers were marked and confined temporarily in a cage. The feeder was next moved to a new location 200 m from the hive and the number of regular foragers reduced to one marked bee. The ten

在 3 个小时的实验中，我们在 1 号站点和 3 号站点用有香味的蔗糖各喂食 10 只标记后的普通觅食蜂。捕获新招引的蜜蜂并杀死。第二天，我们在 1 号站点和 3 号站点提供无香味的蔗糖，同时在 2 号站点提供有香味的蔗糖，其中 2 号站点还没有蜂巢里的蜜蜂来过。在这种情况下，按照语言假说预测将在 1 号站点和 3 号站点捕获新招引的觅食蜂，因为这两个站点均被来自蜂巢的觅食蜂光顾过。然而，如果蜜蜂觅食是靠嗅觉来定位食物源，它们应该去该蜂巢的蜜蜂从来没有光顾过的 2 号站点。

在 4 次重复实验（第 2、7、12、16 天）中，我们在 1 号站点共捕获 25 只新招引蜂，在 2 号站点共捕获 224 只，在 3 号站点共捕获 8 只。因此，新招引的觅食蜂在野外找到了一个它们及其同伴以前没有去过的站点，却没能到达那个它们本应该已经获知（根据语言假说）的地方。

当觅食蜂在一个食物站点有过经验后，它们会通过气味而不是语言被这个食物站再次吸引 [8,9]，当气味信号被完全排除后，食物站就不能再吸引新觅食蜂了 [2,10]。例如，在 1969 年我们做的对照实验中，当利用没有香味的蔗糖时（第 4、9 和 14 天），到达食物站的新招引蜂的数量大幅度减少了 [2]。作为进一步的对照，我们释放了 10 只蜜蜂飞向 4 个无气味的食物站(1968 年 7 月 25 日)，3 小时内共飞行了 1,374 个来回。在此期间，一个蜂巢 60,000 只蜜蜂中只有 5 只发现了食物 [2]。

由此看来，在野外，不管是有经验还是没有经验的觅食蜂似乎都需要用嗅觉信号来确定食物源的位置。由于缺少有力的反面证据，保守地来看，只靠嗅觉就足以解释蜜蜂如何寻找食物源。

## 对我们模型的反对意见

尽管道金斯 [3] 对我们的观点进行抨击，他的确提供了一个实际的反驳论据，即蜜蜂很容易受到干扰，而偏离"既定"（通过语言交流而确定的）目标站点。在这种观点下，到达 2 号站点的蜜蜂已经不能专心于 1 号站点和 3 号站点，这是一个值得认真考虑的可能原因。但是在我们的实验中，2 号站点在 1 号站点的顺风方向，3 号站点的逆风方向。是否可能是因为新招引的觅食蜂会受到干扰而同时沿着顺风与逆风方向偏离既定的目标站点，或者任何一种动物都会被处于顺风位置的气味源吸引。无论如何，当三个站点都提供没有香味的蔗糖时（第 9 和 14 天），蜜蜂没能到达原以为可根据语言交流而获知其位置信息的站点 [2]。由此我们得出结论，道金斯的"干扰"模型没有得到数据支持。

埃施和巴斯蒂安 [6] 报道了有趣的新数据，但却没有将他们的发现与招引觅食蜂的文献联系起来。在他们的每次实验中，训练一组蜜蜂使其在蜂巢附近具有气味标志的站点处觅食，其中 10 只觅食蜂被标记并暂时被关在笼子中。接着将食物站移动

marked former foragers were then released and observed, to discover whether they would be re-recruited to the scent-marked feeder at the new location, as they should be on the hypothesis of linguistic communication by dance attendance.

Fourteen of seventy experimental bees did attend dances and subsequently found the new feeder location. Nineteen additional marked bees attended dances and flew from the hive without arriving at the feeder. The remaining thirty-seven marked experimental bees had no contact with the dancer and did not fly to the new location of the feeder.

Ten of the fourteen successfully re-recruited bees required between one and nine exploratory flights with intermediate contacts with the dancer. Only four succeeded on the first flight, two of them within 1 min of flight time. Many of the nineteen unsuccessful dance attenders also made several flights from the hive; they attended between five and thirty-one dances (mean, 17.5) and made between one and nine exploratory flights (mean, 3.4), without finding the feeder.

For the fourteen successfully re-recruited bees the mean time in flight between first attending the dancer and locating the feeder was 8.5 min, compared with less than 0.5 min for experienced foragers[11]. Esch and Bastian did not report the durations of flights by unsuccessful dance attenders.

In spite of these negative results, Esch and Bastian consider that their data support the language hypothesis. Because four bees found the feeder on their first flights, it is inferred that, "since they could not have searched the entire experimental area in such a short time…", successful re-recruits must have had prior knowledge (obtained from the dance) of the feeder location.

By focusing attention on the performance of successful bees Esch and Bastian have failed to recognize that most of their data actually contradict the predictions of the language hypothesis. The population of experimental animals must be viewed as a whole. In reality, there was a total of 100 exploratory flights by marked bees after attending the dancer. If recruited bees simply flew out equally in all directions from the hive, like spokes in a wheel, 2% would be headed within 7° of the feeder location, a result which is consistent with the observations of Esch and Bastian.

More generally, the data obtained by Esch and Bastian do not bear out the claim by von Frisch[12]:"…the tail-wagging dance makes known the distance and the compass direction to the goal. … This description of the location enables the newcomers to fly rapidly and with certainty to the indicated flowers, even when these are kilometres away… an accomplishment on the part of the bees that is without parallel elsewhere in the entire animal kingdom". Nor do they eliminate the alternative possibility, that re-recruited foragers were flying about, using wind and odour, while seeking the scent to which they had been trained.

到离蜂巢 200 米的新位置，常规采食的觅食蜂的数量减少到 1 只。然后释放先前标记的 10 只蜜蜂并观察，以便揭示他们是否能重新被招引到新位置上的具有气味标记的食物站，当通过表演舞蹈实现语言通讯的假设成立时，它们应该能重新被招引。

70 只实验蜜蜂中有 14 只蜜蜂的确参与跳舞，接着找到了食物站的新位置。另外 19 只被标记的蜜蜂跳舞后从蜂巢离开但是没有到达食物站。剩下的 37 只被标记的实验蜜蜂没有与跳舞的蜜蜂接触，也没有飞往位于新位置的食物站。

14 只成功招引的蜜蜂中有 10 只蜜蜂需要依靠与舞蹈者之间的直接接触并进行 1 至 9 次的探索飞行。只有 4 只蜜蜂一次成功，其中的两只飞行不到一分钟的时间。19 只不成功的跳舞的蜜蜂大部分也离开蜂巢飞行了几次，它们参加了 5 到 31 次的跳舞（平均 17.5 次），进行了 1 至 9 次的探索飞行（平均 3.4 次），但是没有找到食物站。

对于 14 只成功招引的蜜蜂，从第一次跳舞到找到食物站的平均时间为 8.5 分钟，相比较而言，有经验的觅食蜂只需不到 0.5 分钟 [11]。埃施和巴斯蒂安没有报道尝试了跳舞却没有成功的蜜蜂的飞行时间。

尽管这些都是否定的结果，埃施和巴斯蒂安仍然认为他们的数据支持语言假说。因为 4 只蜜蜂在第一次飞出就找到食物站，也"因为它们不可能在如此短的时间内就找遍了整个实验区域……"，从而推测成功招引的蜜蜂一定是事先知道了食物站的位置（从舞蹈中获知）。

由于注意力集中在观察成功找到食物站的蜜蜂的行为上，埃施和巴斯蒂安并没有意识到他们大部分的数据实际上与先前的蜜蜂语言假说的预言相矛盾。实验动物群体应该被视为一个整体。实际上，被标记的蜜蜂参与跳舞后共进行了 100 次的探索飞行。如果从蜂箱中飞出的被招引蜜蜂是简单地以均等的机会飞向了各方向，如同车轮上的辐条，则 2% 的蜜蜂会飞向与食物站位置偏离 7° 的范围内，这个结果与埃施和巴斯蒂安的观察相一致。

从更普遍的意义上来说，埃施和巴斯蒂安获取的数据并不能支持冯·弗里施的论断 [12]："……尾部摇摆的舞蹈能够给出目标的距离和方向。……这种对于方位的描述能够使得新来的蜜蜂迅速而准确地找到被指示的花朵，即使这些花儿在数公里外……在整个动物王国里，蜜蜂的这一系列技能是独一无二的。"他们也不能排除下面这种可能性，即重新招引的觅食蜂可能利用风向和气味来寻找它们曾经受到训练的气味。

The article by Gould, Henerey and MacLeod[7] contains many data not available earlier, but some of their data do not fall in line with what one might expect from the dance language hypothesis. As in the study by Esch and Bastian, their experiments were "… designed to examine the behaviour of individual recruits as each attended a dance and subsequently arrived at a feeding station". In their series 1 experiment, marked bees were trained to two feeding stations 120 m distant from and in opposite directions from the hive, and many workers in the hive were given individual marks. During experiments, of 277 potential recruits observed to attend dances, 240 failed to arrive at any station, and only thirty-seven were subsequently captured at the feeding stations. Of these, a third arrived at a station in a direction opposite to and 240 m distant from that "indicated" in the dance manoeuvre. This result contradicts the prediction of the language hypothesis that all thirty-seven of the successful recruits should have arrived at the "correct" station.

These investigators also found that successful recruits spend a considerable amount of time in flight before reaching the food source. The direct line flight time between hive and a feeding station located at 120 m is less than 25 s[11], and recruited bees generally fly from the hive within a minute and a half after leaving a dancing bee (50% leave within 30 s)[13]. The data in Table 4 of Gould et al.[7] reveal that the twenty-five bees which did arrive at the "correct" station flew an average of more than thirty times longer than would be necessary to "fly rapidly and with certainty" to the food source. The twelve bees which ended up at the station in the opposite direction averaged only thirty-six times as long as necessary for a direct flight.

A greater number of marked bees arrived at the station regularly visited by the foragers which recruited them than to the one 240 m from it, and some successful bees found the food source quickly (two in less than a minute), so Gould et al. concluded that quantitative information was communicated by the dance. The authors thereby focus attention on successful performers as did Esch and Bastian.

In another experiment, these authors fed sucrose of high molarity at one station and very low molarity at the other. Most of the dancing in the hive was by foragers regularly visiting the high molarity food source; and during the experiments most of the recruits captured were at that location. This correlation is accepted by the authors as evidence of linguistic communication.

As Gould et al. carefully pointed out, the validity of their interpretations for both of the above experiments depends upon the assumption that perfect odour symmetry existed between the two stations. In experiments of this type even small asymmetries of location odour do influence recruitment[13]. Gould et al. located their stations in aromatic vegetation. They got uniformly high recruitment whether or not they added scent to the food, yet there is considerable evidence that recruitment is minimal to an unscented location[2,10]. The high recruitment they obtained indicates that the feeding locations had odours detectable by bees. The unanswerable question is: Did asymmetries of these odours exist between two feeding locations 240 m apart?

88

古尔德、黑纳雷和麦克劳德的论文 [7] 有很多早期无法获得的数据，而其中的一部分数据也不符合舞蹈语言交流假说的预测结果。埃施和巴斯蒂安的研究中，他们的实验"……设计的目的是观察单个参与舞蹈并据此到达既定食物站的被招引蜜蜂的行为"。在他们的系列 1 实验中，被标记蜜蜂能被训练到达距离蜂巢 120 米远在相反方向上的两个食物站点，同时给蜂巢中的许多工蜂做了个体标记。实验过程中，在观察到的 277 只参与舞蹈的潜在被招引蜜蜂中，240 只未能到达任何一个食物站点，只有 37 只随后在食物站点被捕获。在这些蜜蜂当中，1/3 到达的是在距离舞蹈动物指定目标相反方向 240 米远的区域。这个结果与语言假说的预测结果（所有 37 只成功招引的蜜蜂应该到达这个"正确"地点）相矛盾。

这些研究者也发现成功招引的新蜂在到达食物源之前花费了相当长时间飞行。蜂巢与食物地点之间 120 米的距离的直线飞行时间不超过 25 秒 [11]。招引的蜜蜂通常在接触舞蹈蜂后在一分半钟之内离开蜂巢（其中 50% 的蜜蜂在 30 秒之内离开）[13]。古尔德等人文章中表 4 的数据 [7] 显示 25 只蜜蜂到达"正确"食物站的时间比"快速而准确地飞行"至食物源的时间平均多花费了 30 倍以上。而 12 只到达相反方向食物站的蜜蜂，其平均飞行时间也仅是直线飞行所需时间的 36 倍。

被招引到先前觅食蜂经常到的食物站点的标记蜜蜂的数量，比被招引至距离该地点 240 米远的食物站点的蜜蜂数量更多，其中一些成功到达的蜜蜂能够迅速发现食物源（有 2 只在一分钟之内）。因此，古尔德等人推断蜜蜂通过舞蹈来传递交流定量信息。同埃施和巴斯蒂安一样，作者将关注点放在了成功的跳舞蜜蜂上面。

在另一实验中，研究者在一个地点为蜜蜂喂食了高摩尔浓度蔗糖，而在另一地点喂食低摩尔浓度蔗糖。蜂巢内大部分的舞蹈都是由经常光顾高摩尔浓度食物源的觅食蜂舞出的；实验期间，大部分新招引到的蜜蜂都是在该位置被捕获的。研究者认为这种相关性是语言交流的佐证。

正如古尔德等人所严肃指出的，上述两个实验解释的正确性建立在两地点之间气味均匀分布的假设基础上。因为这类实验中，站点之间即使少量的气味不对称都能影响对蜜蜂的招引 [13]。古尔德等人将地点设置在芳香植物中，无论是否给食物添加香味，他们都能捕捉到很多新的蜜蜂，而另一个有力的证据是，在无香味的地点，招引的蜜蜂数量极少 [2,10]。他们所获得的大量新招引蜂提示食物地点存在的气味能被蜜蜂觉察。但是不能解释的问题是：相距 240 米的两个食物地点之间气味是否存在不均匀性？

Mautz[5] also was concerned with the behaviour of individually marked workers which came in contact with a forager dancing in the hive. In his experiments, 32% of marked workers that attended dances found the feeder, and the amount of time the potential recruits attended the dancer was positively correlated with success at finding the food. In addition, the average flight time for successful recruits was more than ten times that expected of experienced foragers and the mean flight time of bees which flew out but failed to find the feeder was twice that of the successful recruits. Mautz noted that one bee found a goal at 400 m after following only five waggle cycles of the dance.

As with Gould *et al.*, and with Esch and Bastian, Mautz assumed that his feeder locations were not recognizable by bees as olfactorily distinctive and that only linguistic information could be communicated more effectively by increased duration of contact with the dancer. He does not discuss the possibility that a recruit which spends more time attending a dancing bee might, by so doing, gain a more accurate impression of the odour characteristics of a specific location. Again we see a supporter of the language hypothesis focusing attention on the successful recruits.

Of the several papers we review, Lindauer's[4] was the most deliberate and direct effort to obtain data contradictory to our findings. The first type of experiment undertaken by Lindauer resembled those of Gould *et al.*[7] in design, and yielded similar data. Forager bees were trained from a hive to two feeding sites, and were then fed high molarity sugar at one and low molarity sugar at the other. Virtually all dancing was by bees visiting the high molarity sugar site, and most successful recruits landed there. Lindauer assumed, as did Gould *et al.* and Mautz, a perfect symmetry (to bees) of environmental odours at his locations. From this he inferred that, "if the recruits followed only the odour signals given by the dancers... they should have appeared in equal numbers at (both) sites". In accordance with his assumption Lindauer attributed the asymmetry in recruit arrivals to linguistic communication. Thus, the untested assumption of station symmetry (to bees) is central to the reasoning of Lindauer as well as to the above authors.

In his second experiment, Lindauer put out three stations in a geometry similar to that used in our experiments[2] and trained bees to stations 1 and 3 but not to 2. Then, with scented sucrose at all three stations (a variation from our design), he collected recruits. Although the stations were deliberately asymmetrical (no foragers at station 2), approximately one-fourth of all captured recruits arrived at station 2. The language hypothesis predicts that the recruits should have travelled only to stations 1 and 3.

In order to reconcile these data with the language hypothesis Lindauer generated *ad hoc* the auxiliary hypothesis that potential recruits alternate their attentions between dancers visiting sites 1 and 3, and subsequently "integrate the directions communicated by both groups of foragers". Although the "integration" model satisfies Lindauer as an explanation of his data, it could not possibly predict the distribution of recruits in our earlier experiments[14,15] or, indeed, in the recent experiments of Gould *et al.*[7].

莫茨[5]同样关注那些有单独标记且在蜂巢中与舞蹈蜂接触的工蜂的行为。在他的实验中，32%参与舞蹈的被标记工蜂找到了食物站，潜在被招引的蜜蜂参与舞蹈的时间与成功找到食物成正相关。另外，成功招引到的蜜蜂的平均飞行时间是有经验的觅食蜂的预计时间的十倍多，而飞出去却不能找到食物站的蜜蜂的平均飞行时间是成功招引到的蜜蜂的两倍。莫茨注意到一只蜜蜂仅跟跳了5圈摇摆舞，就找到了400米外的食物。

与古尔德等人以及埃施和巴斯蒂安一样，莫茨假设食物站不能被蜜蜂嗅觉分辨识别，那么只有语言信息可以通过增加与舞蹈蜂接触的时间来实现更有效的交流。但他并没有讨论这样的可能性，即招引蜂通过花费更多的时间参与舞蹈，借此可能会获得对一个特定地点的气味特征更为精确的印象。我们再次看到了一个只片面关注成功招引蜂的语言假说的支持者。

在我们所研究的诸多文章中，林道尔的文章[4]是最为深思熟虑的，而且获得了与我们的发现直接相反的数据。林道尔所做的第一个实验在设计上类似于古尔德等人[7]的实验，也得出了相似的数据。蜂巢里的觅食蜂被训练在蜂巢与两个食物站点之间飞行，然后，一处站点喂食高摩尔浓度蔗糖，另一处站点喂食低摩尔浓度蔗糖。事实上，所有的舞蹈都由光顾过高摩尔浓度蔗糖站点的蜜蜂舞出，并且绝大多数招引成功的蜜蜂都降落在那儿。和古尔德等人以及莫茨一样，林道尔假设在他的站点周围环境气味的分布（对于蜜蜂而言）是完全均匀的。由此他推断"如果新招引的蜜蜂仅仅是追寻跳舞的蜜蜂所给的气味信号，那么它们出现在两个站点的数量应该相同"。为了与这一推论相符合，林道尔将招引到的蜜蜂到达的不均等归因于语言交流。因此，就如同以上几位作者一样，（对于蜜蜂而言）未经验证的环境气味均匀性假设对林道尔推理论证至关重要。

在第二个实验中，林道尔设置了3个在几何位置上与我们的实验[2]中所设置的相似的站点，并且训练蜜蜂到1号站点和3号站点而非2号站点。然后在3个站点都涂上有香味的蔗糖（与我们实验设计的不同之处），他收集了招引来的蜜蜂。尽管这些站点被故意设置得不对称（在2号站点没有觅食蜂），但被捕获的招引蜂中有将近1/4到达了2号站点。而蜜蜂语言假说预测招引到的蜜蜂应该只到达1号站点和3号站点。

为了用语言假说解释这些数据，林道尔提出特别的辅助性假设——潜在的招引蜂将它们的注意力在访问了1号站点和3号站点的舞蹈蜂之间转换，随后"综合两组觅食蜂交流的信息所指示的方向"。虽然这个"综合"模型满足了林道尔对于自己数据的解释，但是它不可能解释我们先前实验[14,15]中招引蜂的分布，事实上也解释不了在古尔德等人[7]最近的实验中招引蜂的分布。

Lindauer got good recruitment at his stations 1 and 3 when presenting unscented food at those locations. Interpreted in the light of our data[2,10] these results suggest that Lindauer's feeding sites were in some measure distinctive to bees. This may explain the asymmetry of recruitment he observed when foragers to station 1 were killed and bees visited only a single station. Unfortunately, the precise location and ecology of the sites for these experiments are not given in his paper (except that it was near Frankfurt), nor does he provide dates, wind speed and directions, number and sequence of observations contributing to the total data and other relevant information. These omissions make any interpretation difficult and speculative. Another portion of Lindauer's paper offers some philosophical and rhetorical objections to our paper, but we will consider these later.

Thus all the authors we have discussed[4-7] explicitly or implicitly assumed that the feeding stations they established in the field were in no way distinctive to bees and that the environment can be made symmetrical with respect to odours and other factors. They also assumed that, in order to find the food, a recruit must have prior quantitative information about its location. These assumptions lead the authors to interpret arrival of new workers at sites visited by dancing foragers as definitive evidence of linguistic communication. As pointed out earlier they have focused their attention on successful recruits. Experiments based on these assumptions invariably lead to affirmation of the consequence of the hypothesis (if bees have a language, recruits will reach the food. Some recruits find the food. Therefore, bees have a language). This reasoning is deductively invalid[19].

The experimental designs of these investigators suffer yet another serious disadvantage. It is not logically possible experimentally to establish the validity of the station symmetry assumption (failure to display asymmetry does not prove that none exists). It is quite practical, however, to seek positive evidence of station asymmetry in experiments of this design. One way would be to remove all directional information from dances performed by foragers regularly visiting food sites. If, in spite of this, recruits preferentially arrive at the feeder regularly visited by the foragers which recruited them, it could be concluded that they had done so without use of prior directional information, and that honey bees can exploit subtle environment asymmetries in the recruitment of new foragers to food sources.

We have incorporated the use of "directionless" dances in the design of the experiments reported below.

## Conditions and Observations

In the summer of 1970 we did experiments using a single frame observation hive and two feeding stations located 150m from it in approximately opposite directions (west and east of the hive, but slightly north of it). The hive and stations were located at the University of California, Santa Barbara. Both stations were located in dry fields, devoid of green vegetation. The West Station was nearer the sea and upwind; the East Station somewhat closer to the University buildings. Otherwise, the sites appeared to be symmetrical.

当林道尔在 1 号站点和 3 号站点提供没有香味的食物，他在这些站点仍然获得了良好的招引效果。用我们的数据 [2,10] 来解释，这些结果说明林道尔的喂食地点对于蜜蜂来说具有某种程度的特殊性。这可以解释当去 1 号站点的觅食蜂被杀死以及蜜蜂仅访问单独一个站点时所观察到的招引的不对称性。遗憾的是这些实验中准确的地点和这些地点的生态条件在他的文中都没有交代（除了交代地点挨近法兰克福），他也没有提供日期、风速、方向、对整体数据有用的观察数量和顺序以及其他有关信息。这些遗漏使得任何解释都很困难且具有投机性。林道尔文章的另一部分也对我们的论文在哲学上和修辞上提出了一些异议，我们将稍后考虑这些。

所有我们讨论的这些作者 [4-7] 都直接或者含蓄地假设他们在野外建立的这些喂食站点从任何方面对蜜蜂来说都是没有特别之处，并且认为在气味和其他因素方面的环境条件是可以被设置为均匀的。他们也假设，为了发现食物，一只新蜜蜂必须预先掌握足够多的相关地点的量化信息。这些假设导致作者把新的工蜂能够到达跳舞觅食蜂造访的地方解释为语言交流的确切证据。正如早先所指出的一样，他们把注意力放在了招引成功的新蜜蜂上面。因此基于这些假设的实验不可避免的导致了对语言假说的肯定（如果蜜蜂有语言，招引的蜜蜂就可以到达食物源从而发现食物，因此，蜜蜂有语言）。这种演绎推理是没有根据的 [19]。

这些研究者的实验设计还有一个严重的缺陷。建立站点对称性假设的有效性在实验逻辑上是不可能的（不能显示不对称性，并不能证明其不存在）。但是，在这个实验设计中寻找地点不对称性的确凿证据却很实用。有一种方式是从频繁访问食物点的觅食蜂所进行的舞蹈中去掉所有与方向相关的信息。尽管如此，如果招引蜂仍倾向于到达招引它们的觅食蜂经常造访的食物站，那么就可以得出结论在这个过程中它们没有使用已有的方向信息，并且蜜蜂可利用细微的环境不对称性来招引觅食蜂至食物源。

我们在下面的实验设计中已经包括了"没有方向性"舞蹈的使用。

## 条件和观察

在 1970 年的夏天我们利用一个单一架构的观察蜂巢和大致位于相反方向（蜂巢的东、西方向，但略微偏北）相距约 150 米的两个喂食站点做了一些实验。这个蜂巢和站点位于加州大学圣巴巴拉分校。两个喂食站点位于干旱且没有绿色植物的地方。西部的站点靠近海和逆风向。东部的站点稍微靠近大学的建筑。另外，两个站点位于对称的位置。

Ten marked foragers were trained to feed at each station; all successful recruits were either killed or marked as replacements for regular foragers which were then killed. Observations were made at the hive and stations during 3-h periods (08:30-11:30), August 21 to September 4, 1970, and food was provided only during those periods. A westerly breeze prevailed during this period (up to 5 mile h$^{-1}$ on most days) and the usual temperature was 65°-75°F.

A principal objective of the experiments was to examine relationships among food molarity, forager behaviour, and recruitment. Therefore, scent added to the food was held constant. All solutions used were scented with lavender oil (32 µl.l.$^{-1}$). Sucrose solutions of 0.8 M, 1.3 M, 1.8 M and 2.3 M were used. On any given day a solution of lower molarity was offered at one station and one of higher molarity at the other. Rotation of molarities between the stations controlled for possible inherent differences in location attractiveness, and on each day the stations acted as controls against each other. The experiments were run blind: the observers were not informed of molarities of sucrose provided at the feeding stations on any given day.

The hive had glass sides and was equipped with a clear plastic atrial chamber inside a diffusely lighted observation room. Hive conditions (well populated, and with little natural forage) ensured that our marked foragers danced in the atrial chamber, rather than on the comb. These dances were on a horizontal surface, and contained no discernible directional information. The straight (waggle) portions of the dance were apparently randomly oriented and highly variable within each dance episode.

Altogether, a total of 1,793 dances by our marked bees and 136 dances by unmarked bees foraging on natural sources were observed during eleven days (33 h) of experimentation. Thus, during our study periods, 93% of all dancing in the hives was by our marked foragers.

Although we were largely successful in eliminating oriented dances from our hive, occasionally a marked forager did enter and perform a dance episode on the vertical surface of the comb. These occurrences will be of great interest to proponents of the language hypothesis, so we will present data on oriented dances before proceeding to other aspects of the study.

There was a total of only 50 apparently oriented dances recorded during 33 h of experimentation; 1.5 such dances h$^{-1}$, on the average, or approximately 2.8% of all dance episodes recorded for our marked foragers. These occurred equally (24 to 26) for the two stations and did not correlate with recruitment (Table 1).

每一个站点都训练10只标记的觅食蜂在该处觅食。所有成功招引的蜜蜂都被杀死，或者作为被杀死的常规觅食蜂的替代品被标记起来。1970年8月21日到9月4日期间，从8∶30到11∶30这三个小时内我们对蜂巢和喂食站点进行了观察，并且只有在这段时间才有食物供应。这段时间西风盛行（多数日子风速小于5英里/小时），日常气温为65~75 ℉。

这些实验的一个主要目的就是在于探寻：食物摩尔浓度、觅食蜂的行为以及招引新成员这三者之间的联系。因此，添加在食物中的气味是恒定的。所有使用的溶液都加入了有香味的薰衣草油（浓度是32 μl·l⁻¹）。实验中还用到了浓度分别是0.8M、1.3M、1.8M和2.3M的蔗糖溶液。在同一天里，一个站点使用低浓度的蔗糖溶液，另一个站点则使用高浓度的溶液。在不同站点里轮换使用不同浓度溶液，以控制在站点吸引力方面的内在差异，每天这些站点互相作为对照。实验是以单盲设计：观察者并不知道每天在食物站点提供的蔗糖溶液的浓度。

蜂巢具有玻璃外壳，在散射光照射的观察室中间配置了一个透明的塑料小房间。蜂巢的条件（适宜的种群数量，几乎没有自然食物源）确保了标记过的觅食蜂在小房间里跳舞，而不是在巢脾上。它们所跳的舞蹈是在同一个水平面上的，其中没有任何可识别的方向信息，舞蹈中直线（摇摆）的那部分很显然是随机导向的，而且在每一个舞蹈节拍内的导向都是高度变化着的。

总之，在实验观察的11天中（33小时）总共有1,793次舞蹈是由标记过的蜜蜂跳的，136次舞蹈是没标记过的以自然食物源为食的觅食蜂跳的，因此在我们研究期间蜂巢中93%的舞蹈是由我们标记过的觅食蜂所舞出的。

尽管我们在消除蜂巢中的导向性舞蹈方面取得了巨大的成功，但是我们偶然发现一只被标记了的觅食蜂进入蜂巢并且在垂直于巢脾的平面跳舞，这种现象将会使支持语言假说的人产生极大的兴趣，所以我们将在继续其他方面研究之前展示有关导向性舞蹈的研究数据。

在33个小时的实验中，总共只记录有50次明显的导向性舞蹈。平均大概每小时1.5次这种舞蹈，约为我们记录到的标记的觅食蜂所有舞蹈节拍总数的2.8%。这种舞蹈在两个站点的发生几率均等（24比26），且与招引蜂的数量不相关（表1）。

Table 1. Dances by Unmarked Bees, Oriented Dances, Disoriented Dances, and Recruitment

| | First hour | Second hour | Third hour | Total |
|---|---|---|---|---|
| Dances by unmarked bees | 77 | 38 | 21 | 136 |
| Oriented dances by marked bees | 23 | 9 | 18 | 50 |
| Disoriented dances by marked bees | 337 | 675 | 731 | 1,743 |
| Successful recruits | 64 | 115 | 143 | 322 |

Data are partitioned according to time of occurrence in our experiments. Total data for 33 h of observation are presented.

These oriented dances were not distributed evenly throughout the experimental period, but occurred sporadically. For example, 40% of them occurred on one day, August 30, 1970. Occurrence of a block of oriented dances on a given day did not appear to influence recruitment. A comparison of data for August 30, 1970 (which had the greatest number of on-comb dances during the eleven days of experimentation) with the following (more typical) day is illustrative, and is presented as Table 2.

Table 2. Comparison of Visitation by Marked Foragers, Oriented and Disoriented Dances by Marked Foragers, and Successful Recruitment of New Bees for August 30, 1970 (with many Oriented Dances) and August 31, 1970 (with few)

| | Trips by marked foragers | | Oriented dances | | Disoriented dances | | Successful recruits | |
|---|---|---|---|---|---|---|---|---|
| | 1.3 M | 1.8 M | 1.3 M | 1.8 M | 1.3 M | 1.8 M | 1.3 M | 1.8 M |
| August 30, 1970 | 319 | 267 | 9 | 19 | 76 | 110 | 20 | 65 |
| August 31, 1970 | 304 | 312 | 1 | 2 | 59 | 143 | 19 | 67 |
| Total | 623 | 579 | 10 | 21 | 135 | 253 | 39 | 132 |

Table 1 also shows that dancing by unmarked bees foraging on natural food sources declined as the experiment progressed. This is consistent with our findings that insertion of a new food source in the hive-environment system may change the behaviour of bees regularly foraging on an established one[10]. Presumably this alteration is mediated through a change in the available recruit pool.

From our data on oriented dances (Tables 1 and 2) it is not possible to infer that these dances are responsible for the observed recruitment of new foragers to those feeders we had established in the field. There is, however, a positive correlation between the number of disoriented dances (or total dances) and recruitment of new foragers (Table 3).

表 1. 未被标记的蜜蜂的舞蹈，导向性舞蹈，非导向性舞蹈，招引蜂

|  | 第一小时 | 第二小时 | 第三小时 | 合计 |
|---|---|---|---|---|
| 未标记蜜蜂的舞蹈 | 77 | 38 | 21 | 136 |
| 标记过的蜜蜂的导向性舞蹈 | 23 | 9 | 18 | 50 |
| 标记过的蜜蜂非导向性舞蹈 | 337 | 675 | 731 | 1,743 |
| 成功的招引蜂 | 64 | 115 | 143 | 322 |

根据实验中的发生时间，将数据分组。列出了 33 个小时中观测到的所有数据。

这些导向性舞蹈并没有均匀地分布于整个实验周期中，而是偶发性的。例如它们当中 40% 是在 1970 年 8 月 30 日这一天发生的。这种导向性舞蹈集中发生在某一天并不影响蜜蜂的招引。1970 年 8 月 30 日（这一天在巢脾上进行的舞蹈的数量是这十一天的研究中最多的一次）的数据和接下来（更典型的）一天的数据的对比更具代表性，列于表 2。

表 2. 1970 年 8 月 30 日（发生多次导向性舞蹈）和 1970 年 8 月 31 日（发生少量导向性舞蹈）标记觅食蜂的导向性和非导向性舞蹈及新蜜蜂成功招引的情况的比较

|  | 标记过的觅食蜂的飞行次数 | | 导向性舞蹈数量 | | 非导向性舞蹈数量 | | 成功招引的蜜蜂数量 | |
|---|---|---|---|---|---|---|---|---|
|  | 1.3 M | 1.8 M | 1.3 M | 1.8 M | 1.3 M | 1.8 M | 1.3 M | 1.8 M |
| 1970 年 8 月 30 日 | 319 | 267 | 9 | 19 | 76 | 110 | 20 | 65 |
| 1970 年 8 月 31 日 | 304 | 312 | 1 | 2 | 59 | 143 | 19 | 67 |
| 合计 | 623 | 579 | 10 | 21 | 135 | 253 | 39 | 132 |

表 1 也显示，随着实验的进展没有被标记的以自然资源为食的蜜蜂的舞蹈数量在减少，这和我们的发现是一致的，即我们在蜂巢周围的环境中放入一个新的食物源可能会改变蜜蜂在已建立的食物站点进行常规采食的行为 [10]，推测这种变化可能是通过改变有效食物源来介导的。

从蜜蜂导向性舞蹈的数据（表 1 和表 2）不可能推出以下结论：所观察到的我们在野外建立的食物站能够招引到新觅食蜂的现象应该归因于这种舞蹈。然而非导向性的舞蹈（或者总的舞蹈）的数量与新招引的觅食蜂的数量呈正相关（表 3）。

Table 3. Mean Number of Trips by Marked Foragers; of Disoriented Dances by those Foragers; and of Successful Recruits per 3 h Observation Period for 0.8 M, 1.3 M, 1.8 M and 2.3 M Lavender Scented Sucrose Solutions

| Molarity | Forager trips | Disoriented dances | Successful recruits |
|----------|---------------|--------------------|---------------------|
| 0.8 | 308 | 26 | 5 |
| 1.3 | 320 | 86 | 19 |
| 1.8 | 293 | 117 | 42 |
| 2.3 | 231 | 107 | 17 |

Not less than four or more than seven observation periods at each molarity.

The experimental design is not rigorous enough to define the asymmetry in environmental cues used by recruits while searching for and locating a particular feeder in the field, but quantitative directional information does not appear to be a part of that system.

While doing this set of experiments, we also gathered information on Nasanov gland exposures at the food source by bees foraging on various molarities of sucrose. Our previous studies indicate that Nasanov gland exposure by regular foragers fails to attract undisturbed bees but apparently does provide a point of reference for disoriented members of the colony. Gland exposure is apparently a function of the interest potential recruits may have in a food source, rather than food quality *per se*[2,10]. Nasanov gland exposure by foragers visiting established food sources in the field was depressed at the lowest molarity we used (Table 4), a fact which indicates that few recruits were in the field searching for that source.

Table 4. Relationships Among Molarity of Sucrose Solutions Provided, Forager Visitations, and Nasanov Gland Exposures by Marked Foragers

| Molarity | Forager trips | Nasanov gland exposures |
|----------|---------------|-------------------------|
| 0.8 | 308 | 24 |
| 1.3 | 320 | 77 |
| 1.8 | 293 | 85 |
| 2.3 | 231 | 71 |

Means for 3 h observation periods are given ($7 \geq$ periods/molarity $\geq 4$).

## Further Considerations

We have done several experiments which were designed to determine whether honey bees use linguistic communication under defined conditions[2,8,9,14-16]. Results indicated that the language hypothesis has little heuristic value and fails as a predictive tool. The results further suggest that if one wished bees to pollinate a particular crop, it should be useful to

表 3. 标记觅食蜂的平均飞行次数；其非导向性的舞蹈的平均次数；每 3 小时观测周期内蜜蜂
被 0.8 M、1.3 M、1.8 M 和 2.3 M 有薰衣草香味的蔗糖成功招引所需平均飞行次数

| 摩尔浓度 | 觅食蜂飞行次数 | 非导向性舞蹈数量 | 成功招引的蜜蜂数量 |
|---|---|---|---|
| 0.8 | 308 | 26 | 5 |
| 1.3 | 320 | 86 | 19 |
| 1.8 | 293 | 117 | 42 |
| 2.3 | 231 | 107 | 17 |

每个摩尔浓度观察期不少于 4 个且不多于 7 个。

这个实验设计对招引蜂在野外寻找和定位特定食物源时所用的环境不对称信号的定义不够严密，但是定量的导向性信息看起来并不是该实验系统的一部分。

当做这一系列的实验时，我们还收集了蜜蜂在不同摩尔浓度的蔗糖上觅食时分泌在食物源上的奈氏腺体分泌物的信息。我们之前的研究提示常规采食的觅食蜂分泌的奈氏腺分泌物并不能吸引未受干扰的蜜蜂，但很明显能给迷失方向的蜂群提供一些参照。觅食蜂腺体分泌物的气味显然是促进潜在招引蜂对食物源，而不是食物本身质量的兴趣 [2,10]。觅食蜂造访野外已建立的食物源时奈氏腺分泌物在最低浓度食物站是非常少的（表 4），这个事实说明几乎没有招引蜂在野外寻找到该食物源。

表 4. 蔗糖溶液摩尔浓度、蜜蜂造访次数和标记觅食蜂奈氏腺分泌物之间的关系

| 摩尔浓度 | 觅食蜂的飞行次数 | 奈氏腺分泌物 |
|---|---|---|
| 0.8 | 308 | 24 |
| 1.3 | 320 | 77 |
| 1.8 | 293 | 85 |
| 2.3 | 231 | 71 |

给出了 3 小时观察期内的平均值（7 ≥ 观察期个数 / 摩尔浓度 ≥ 4）。

## 进一步的思考

我们已经设计了多次实验来确定蜜蜂在限定的条件下是否使用语言进行交流 [2,8,9,14-16]。结果表明语言假说没有一点启发价值并且也不能作为预测性工具。结果

regulate the odour carried into the hive by foragers, rather than the angle of dance on the comb.

More generally, we feel that honey bee foraging ecology is regulated by a complex system of hive, environmental and behavioural variables. With sufficient knowledge, it should be possible to manipulate the system and predict the consequences for the foraging ecology of a honey bee colony. We then might say that we understand colony function in terms which are neither teleological nor anthropomorphic; and we would be in a position to attack pragmatically problems of a comparative or practical nature. Accordingly, we have examined interrelationships among Nasanov gland exposure, visits of marked foragers to a food site, dancing in the hive, and recruitment of new foragers, and correlated these with the amount of odour in sucrose solutions provided in the field. In these experiments we have had some success in manipulating the system[10], as have Waller[17] and Friesen[18].

Waller showed that association of odours with food in the field, but not odours alone, could increase bee populations in experimental plots[17]. Friesen examined interrelationships among wind speed and direction, forager flight paths, odour levels and locations, forager visitation and recruitment of new foragers to sites in the field. He concluded that, after recruits leave the hive, their success and distribution depend upon an interaction of field variables affecting the distribution of odours[18]. Thus, evidence from several sources indicates that odour is of great importance in the system of variables which regulate honey bee foraging ecology.

Our comparison of the predictive values of the olfaction and language hypotheses of honey bee forager recruitment was an attempt to determine just how important odour is in this system[2]. To our surprise, our results and interpretations generated a controversy which deeply polarizes interested biologists. Along this line we must stress that the controversy does not emerge from a difference of opinion about the acceptability of various parts of a body of evidence.

The ingenious step and fan experiments of von Frisch have been repeated many times, and our own published data clearly show that when his procedures are closely followed, without insertion of additional controls, distributions of successful recruits may be expected to resemble those obtained by him[14,15]. Similarly, when Lindauer used an experimental geometry modelled after ours, he obtained data consistent with ours[4]; and the data presented in Table 3 of this paper resemble those obtained by Gould et al. and by Lindauer when they used similar experimental designs[4,7]. Neither the repeatability of experiments on honey bee behaviour nor the care and accuracy with which workers in this field gather and report data appears to be in question.

Proponents of the language hypothesis argue that the many repetitions of the von Frisch experiments make it highly probable that his interpretation is correct. One must realize, however, that the amount of additional confirmation affected by each new favorable repetition of an experiment becomes smaller as the number of previous repetitions

进一步说明如果人们希望蜜蜂为一种特定作物授粉，那么调控觅食蜂携带到蜂巢的气味应该是有用的，而不是调控在巢脾上跳舞的角度。

大体上说，我们认为，蜜蜂觅食生态是由蜂巢、环境和行为上的变量组成的复杂系统所调控的。有了足够的了解后，就有可能操控这个系统，并预测一个蜂群觅食生态的结果。然后我们可以说，我们明确地理解了蜂群功能，它既没有目的性也不是拟人的，我们将处于务实地解决可比性或实用性方面的问题的位置。因此我们检测了奈氏腺体分泌、标记觅食蜂对食物站的造访、在蜂巢中跳舞以及招引到的新觅食蜂之间的相互关系，并将这些与在野外所提供的蔗糖溶液中芳香物质的含量联系起来。在这些实验中，我们在操控这个系统方面取得了一些成功[10]，正如沃勒[17]和弗里森[18]取得的成功一样。

沃勒指出，野外食物与气味的结合（并不是单独的气味）能够增加实验点蜜蜂的数量[17]。弗里森检测了风速和风向、觅食蜂的飞行路径、气味水平和位置、觅食蜂的造访次数和野外站点新觅食蜂的招引之间的相互关系。他得出的结论是，招引蜂离开蜂巢后，它们的成功招引和分布取决于影响气味分布的各野外变量之间的相互作用[18]。因而，各种来源的证据表明气味在调节蜜蜂觅食生态的变量系统中起着很重要的作用。

嗅觉理论和语言假说在觅食蜂招引的预测价值上的比较是一种用于确定气味在系统中重要性程度的尝试[2]。令我们惊奇的是：我们的研究结果和解释引起了相关生物学家高度两极化的争论。在这方面我们必须强调这种争论的出现并不是源于针对同一证据主体不同方面的可接受性的观点差异。

冯·弗里施的这种独创性的步骤和有趣的实验已经被重复了许多次，我们自己发表的数据也清楚地表明：在没有加入额外对照实验的情况下，严格按照冯·弗里希的步骤操作，成功招引到的蜜蜂的分布与他得到的分布数据类似[14,15]。同样，林道尔用我们的几何实验模型模拟，他得到的数据和我们的一致[4]，本文表3所示数据与古尔德等人以及林道尔在用相似实验设计时所获得的数据类似[4,7]。实验中蜜蜂行为上的重复性和该领域工作人员在收集和报道数据时的注意力和精确性似乎都没有问题。

语言假说的支持者辩称：冯·弗里施实验的众多重复使得他的解释极有可能是正确的。然而人们必须认识到，随着重复实验数量的增加，每一个新的圆满重复实

grows[19]. Thus, even under the most favourable conditions, sheer number of repetitions is never sufficient to render a hypothesis immune to challenge. Furthermore, in the case of the bee language hypothesis, the existence of a considerable body of unfavourable evidence greatly diminishes the weight of even a large body of confirming data[20].

Any hypothesis which is generated as an explanation of certain observed events will, of course, imply their occurrence. The events to be explained will then be taken as supporting evidence for it. If the hypothesis is valid it also may lead to *a priori* predictions of facts and events in conditions different from those leading to its formulation.

It is exactly here that we have difficulty with the language hypothesis of honey bee orientation. Each time we have inserted previously omitted controls or altered the experimental design to create new test implications, the distribution of successful recruits to feeders located in the field is no longer that predicted by the language hypothesis. Similarly, much of the evidence recently obtained by Esch and Bastian, by Mautz, by Gould *et al.* and by Lindauer is contrary to the predictions of that hypothesis[4-7].

The difficulties we had in reconciling our data[14-16] with the language hypothesis led us to propose the alternative olfaction model[21,22]. The olfaction hypothesis allowed a satisfactory explanation of the distribution of successful recruits in those experiments which incorporated new controls[14-16] and could encompass the large body of existing data on honey bee forager recruitment. Furthermore, it had the advantage of simplicity.

Thus, in 1967 we had two hypotheses, olfaction and language, each generated *a posteriori* to explain an existing body of evidence. The language hypothesis had been well articulated by von Frisch twenty years earlier[1], but it had been expanded and modified through the years in an attempt to explain newer results. Olfaction, while new in the sense that it challenged the then currently accepted hypothesis and two decades of thought habits, was essentially a return to the position held by von Frisch and others in the earlier years of this century.

Lindauer not only presented new data but challenged our interpretation on philosophical grounds when he invoked Aristotelian (Darwinian) teleology as an argument in favour of language. He argued that in nature "each morphological structure and behavioural act is associated with a special function. On this basis alone, it would seem unlikely that information contained in the waggle dance of a honey bee is not transmitted to her nest mates"[4]. We have answered his challenge in part by discussing the relevant data in terms of philosophy of science which we consider to be more powerful[19,20].

An inherent weakness of Lindauer's teleological argument can be illustrated by giving one interesting example from another field of biology. Methyl eugenol is extremely attractive to male oriental fruit flies. In one test in Hawaii 1,300 male *Dacus dorsalis* were attracted a half-mile upwind to a muslin screen that had been treated with it. Methyl eugenol is not produced by the female fruit flies nor does it attract them. It is not a component of the

验所带来的肯定性却在减弱 [19]。因此，即使在最佳的条件下，重复实验的绝对数量也决不足以让一个假说免于挑战。而且，在蜜蜂语言假说的案例中，相当数量的不利证据的存在使大部分已经确认数据的重要性大打折扣 [20]。

任何一个源自于解释特定观察事件的假说都一定会暗示这些事件的发生。这些应该被解释的事件随后被作为假说的支持证据。如果假说是成立的，则可根据假说推导出对事实和现象的先验预测，即使这些事件发生的条件与假说成立的条件不同。

在这里我们很清楚在蜜蜂导向性的语言假说中存在很多问题。每次我们都会加入以前漏掉的对照实验或者改变实验设计来建立新的实验，但是被野外食物源成功招引到的蜜蜂的分布不再能够通过语言假说来预测。同样地，最近埃施和巴斯蒂安、莫茨、古尔德等人和林道尔获得的一些证据也与假说所预测的相矛盾 [4-7]。

在将我们的数据 [14-16] 与语言假说协调一致时遇到的困难使得我们提出另外的嗅觉模型 [21,22]。 嗅觉假说可以很好地解释那些包含了新对照的实验中成功招引到的蜜蜂的分布 [14-16]，而且可以涵盖觅食蜂招引研究中的大部分现有数据。另外，该假说还具有简单的优点。

因此，在 1967 年我们有两个假说，嗅觉假说和语言假说，二者都能对现有的部分证据进行解释。语言假说已经在二十年前被冯·弗里施所阐明 [1]，但在近几年人们尝试去解释新结果的过程中，它被不断拓展和完善。嗅觉假说是一种新的假说，对已被接受的观点和 20 年来的思维习惯提出挑战，本质上也回到了 20 世纪初冯·弗里施等人与更早之前的观点抗争时所处的位置。

当林道尔引用亚里士多德（达尔文）的目的论作为支持语言假说的论据时，他不仅提出了新的数据，而且从哲学基础上挑战了我们的解释。他认为在自然界中"每种形态结构和行为都是与一种特殊功能相关联的。单单以此为基础，蜜蜂摇摆舞中所含的信息没有传递给它的同伴的现象似乎不可能发生"[4]。我们已经以更有说服力的科学哲学形式，通过对其相关数据的讨论来部分地回答他的质疑 [19,20]。

用一个来自生物学其他领域的有趣的例子可以阐明林道尔目的论的一个先天缺点。甲基丁香酚对雄性东方果蝇极具吸引力。在一个实验中，夏威夷的 1,300 只雄性东方果蝇被甲基丁香酚处理过的薄纱屏幕吸引，迎风飞了半英里。甲基丁香酚不由雌性果蝇产生，也不吸引雌性果蝇。它不是该果蝇自然食物中的组成部分，而且

natural food of this fly and probably has no nutritional value. Yet male oriental fruit flies are irresistibly attracted to it and "apparently cannot stop feeding when they have free access to it, and they kill themselves with over indulgence"[23]. Their behaviour under these circumstances certainly cannot be construed as adaptive.

Admittedly, this is an extreme example of non-adaptive behaviour, but it does reveal a weakness in the teleology argument. The mere presence of a characteristic behavioural pattern in an animal cannot be construed as purposeful, adaptive or "associated with a special function".

Lindauer[4] also challenged us on grounds that we have not individually discussed three specific situations investigated earlier by von Frisch and his colleagues. First, at distances quite close to the hive, recruited foragers may be captured at scented dishes other than the one visited by the foragers which recruit them, while at distances of 100 m and beyond "the recruited workers all fly in the direction of the feeding plate". That the latter part of this quoted statement does not hold is well documented by the data of Gould et al.[7] as well as by ours[2,14,15], and even by Lindauer's own data[4] unless one is willing to accept his "integration" model. As for the first part of the statement, when the feeding dishes are close to the hive, we agree with von Frisch and Lindauer; the bees seem to be using odour.

A second situation involves disoriented dances performed by foragers on a horizontal surface. In an experiment using a tilted hive, von Frisch got approximately equal recruitment in four directions while regular foragers were fed in only one direction. Later that day, with the hive put upright again, he got preferential recruitment in the direction of the feeder visited by foragers[12]. We prefer a design in which two or more stations visited by bees simultaneously serve as controls against each other, and we set up our experiment accordingly. Our data on the effectiveness of disoriented dances (Table 3) seem to be in disagreement with those of von Frisch. During our 11 days of observation, new recruits preferentially arrived at the sites visited by dancing foragers even though there was no directional component in the dances.

The third situation involves the detour of foragers around an obstacle to a feeder on the other side of it. In one experiment performed by von Frisch, marked foragers were trained to fly around a rocky ridge to a scented feeder. Scent plates were placed on top of the ridge and 50 m laterally to the direct line between hive and feeder. During a 90 min period, three new recruits were captured at the lateral stations, eight on top of the ridge and twenty-three at the feeder. Because the new recruits apparently failed to follow the flight path used by the foragers which recruit them, von Frisch feels that they were linguistically informed of the feeder location[12].

We must argue that the flight paths and duration of searching by the twenty-three successful recruits are not known, and that a failure of bees to use the detour (if indeed they did not use it) does not differentially support either language or olfaction. Since neither hypothesis predicts that recruits will follow the same path as the marked foragers,

可能没有营养价值。然而，雄性东方果蝇却无法抵抗地被它所吸引并且"当它们可以自由接近该物质时，它们显然控制不住贪吃的欲望，以致死于这种过度的嗜好"[23]。在这种情况下，它们的行为当然不能被视为适应性。

不可否认，这是一个极端的非适应性行为的例子，但它确实揭示了目的论的一个缺点。动物单纯的特异行为模式不能被解释为是有目的性的，适应性的或是"与某种特殊功能相关的"。

林道尔[4]还质疑我们，没有对较早前由冯·弗里施和他的同事们所做研究中的三个具体情况进行单独讨论。首先，在食物站相当接近蜂巢时，招引的觅食蜂可能会在有香味的食物站捕获，而不是那些招引它们的觅食蜂所造访的食物站。而在食物站距离蜂巢 100 米或更远的情况下"所有的觅食蜂都向食物源的方向飞去"。后半部分所引述的观点并不成立，这已经被古尔德等人 [7] 和我们 [2,14,15] 的数据，甚至林道尔自己的数据 [4] 很好地证明了，除非有人愿意接受他的"综合"模型。至于第一部分，我们同意冯·弗里施和林道尔的观点：当食物站离蜂巢很近时，蜜蜂似乎是用气味去寻找食物。

第二种情况是觅食蜂在水平面上表演的非导向性舞蹈。在一个采用倾斜蜂巢的实验中，冯·弗里施仅从一个固定方向喂食常规采食的觅食蜂，但他在四个方向招引到的蜜蜂数量大致相等。当天晚些时候，重新将蜂巢放正，他发现被觅食蜂造访过的食物源方向更具招引的优势 [12]。我们更倾向于另外一个实验设计，实验中蜜蜂可以造访两个或更多的站点，同时它们相互之间可以作为对照，我们据此设置了实验。我们发现，我们关于非导向性舞蹈有效性的实验数据（见表 3）与冯·弗里施的数据不符。在我们 11 天的观察中，新的招引蜂会优先抵达跳舞的觅食蜂造访过的站点，即使该舞蹈中没有导向性的元素。

第三种情况是蜜蜂绕过障碍找到位于另一边的食物站。冯·弗里施在一个实验中，训练被标记的觅食蜂绕过岩石山脉去寻找有香味的食物站。有香味的食物盘被放置在山顶，且与蜂巢和食物站之间连线横向相距 50 米。在 90 分钟的观察期中，3 只新招引蜂在旁侧站点被捕获，8 只在山顶被捕获，23 只到达了准确的食物站点。基于新招引蜂显然不能按照之前招引它们的觅食蜂的飞行的路线飞行，冯·弗里施认为，蜜蜂通过语言来交流食物站的位置 [12]。

我们要说明的是，23 只成功到达的招引蜂的飞行路线和搜寻时间还不清楚，蜜蜂绕道而行的失败（如果事实上它们并没有绕道）在支持语言假说或嗅觉假说方面没有任何差异。因为两个假说都无法预测新招引蜂将遵循标记觅食蜂相同的路径，

the experiment is not crucial and the results do not support or refute either hypothesis.

We believe that experimentation does not "prove" or "disprove" hypotheses, but rather affects their credibility. If the credibility of a hypothesis at any given time is determined by the total body of relevant information available, then the language hypothesis of forager recruitment was very credible in 1946 when von Frisch proposed it. It is less so now, for the body of relevant information is quite different and includes much unfavourable evidence. In fact, it is so much less credible that we no longer can believe that honey bees communicate linguistically.

Do honey bees have a language? That is a question which may never be answered with certainty. It may be more useful to examine assumptions critically, state hypotheses and their consequences with precision, review the evidence objectively, and ask: can we now believe that honey bees have a language? Thus, it appears that the honey bee forager recruitment controversy is not about the nature of evidence but rather about the nature of hypotheses[25]. It is not what investigators observe (the data) but what they believe (infer) that is at the heart of the controversy.

We thank Nelson Dee and Stephanie Niebuhr for technical assistance. The research was supported by the US National Science Foundation. An analysis of earlier events and attitudes leading up to the bee language controversy is available elsewhere[24].

(**241**, 171-175; 1973)

Patrick H. Wells and Adrian M. Wenner
Department of Biology, Occidental College, Los Angeles, California 90041, and Department of Biological Sciences, University of California, Santa Barbara, California 93106

---

References:

1. Von Frisch, K., *Osterr. Zool. Z.*, **1**, 1 (1946); translation, *Bull. Anim. Behav.*, **5**, 1 (1947).

2. Wenner, A., Wells, P., and Johnson, D., *Science*, **164**, 84 (1969).

3. Dawkins, R., *Science*, **165**, 751 (1969).

4. Lindauer, M., *Amer. Nat.*, **105**, 89 (1971).

5. Mautz, D., *Z. Vergl. Physiol.*, **72**, 197 (1971).

6. Esch, H., and Bastian, J. A., *Z. Vergl. Physiol.*, **68**, 175 (1970).

7. Gould, J. L., Henerey, M., and MacLeod, M. C., *Science*, **169**, 544 (1970).

8. Johnson, D. L., and Wenner, A. M., *Anim. Behav.*, **14**, 261 (1966).

9. Johnson, D. L., *Anim. Behav.*, **15**, 487 (1967).

10. Wells, P. H., and Wenner, A. M., *Physiol. Zool.*, **44**, 191 (1971).

11. Wenner, A. M., *J. Apic. Res.*, **2**, 25 (1963).

12. Von Frisch, K., *Tanzsprache und Orientierung der Bienen* (Springer-Verlag, Berlin, 1965); translation, *The Dance Language and Orientation of Bees* (Harvard University Press, Cambridge, 1967).

13. Johnson, D. L., and Wenner, A. M., *J. Apic. Res.*, **9**, 13 (1970).

14. Johnson, D. L., *Science*, **155**, 844 (1967).

15. Wenner, A. M., *Science*, **155**, 847 (1967).

16. Wenner, A. M., Wells, P. H., and Rohlf, F. J., *Physiol. Zool.*, **40**, 317 (1967).

所以该实验并不是关键性的而且其结果不支持或驳斥任何假说。

我们认为上述实验并不能"证明"或"反驳"这些假说,但是却会影响它们的可信度。如果一个假说的可信度在任何特定时间都是由所能得到的有关信息的总体决定的,那么早在1946年冯·弗里施提出觅食蜂招引的语言假说时,它就是非常可信的。但现在可信度降低了,因为相关信息的总体情况已经颇为不同,并包括许多不利的证据。事实上,语言假说的可信度太低了,我们不能够再相信蜜蜂是通过语言沟通的。

蜜蜂有语言吗?这个问题可能永远也无法得到确定的回答。批判性地检验假设,精确地陈述假说及其结果,客观审查证据,并自问:我们现在可以认为蜜蜂有语言吗?这样做也许更有用。由此看来,关于觅食蜂招引的争议,并不在于证据本身,而在于假说本身 [25]。不是研究者观察到了什么(数据),而是他们相信什么(推论),这才是争议的核心。

我们感谢纳尔逊·迪伊和斯蒂芬妮·尼布尔提供技术支持。这项研究得到了美国国家科学基金会的资助。对引起蜜蜂语言争议的早期事件和看法在其他文献 [24] 中也有分析。

(董培智 翻译;张健旭 审稿)

17. Waller, G. D., *J. Apic. Res.*, **9**, 9 (1970).

18. Friesen, L., *Biol. Bull.* (in the press).

19. Hempel, C. G., *Philosophy of Natural Science* (Prentice-Hall, Englewood Cliffs, 1966).

20. Popper, K., in *British Philosophy in Mid-Century* (edit. by Mace, C. A.) (Macmillan, New York, 1957).

21. Wenner, A. M., and Johnson, D. L., *Science*, **158**, 1076 (1967).

22. Wenner, A., and Wells, P., *XXI Int. Apic. Congr. Summ.*, **88** (1967).

23. Steiner, L. F., *J. Econ. Ent.*, **45**, 241 (1952).

24. Wenner, A. M., *The Bee Language Controversy* (Educational Programs Improvement Corporation, Boulder, 1971).

25. Altmann, S. A., *Nature*, **240**, 361 (1972).

# The Search for Signals from Extraterrestrial Civilizations

J. C. G. Walker

## Editor's Note

James Walker, an expert on the evolution of the terrestrial environment, here turns his gaze beyond the Earth's atmosphere to consider the feasibility of detecting radio signals from extraterrestrial civilizations. This notion had been pursued experimentally since 1960, when astronomer Frank Drake performed a radio-telescope search. Drake devised an equation for estimating the probability of intelligent civilizations on other worlds. Walker combines a related estimate for the number of habitable planets with the detection capabilities of telescopes to deduce how long observations might need to proceed before an "intelligent" signal is found. The result is dispiriting: even with an optimistic estimate of how many inhabitable planets produce technologically advanced civilizations, it could take over a thousand years to spot them.

---

Although the technology exists for exchanging radio messages with extraterrestrial civilizations, a successful search for such civilizations among the many stars that might support them could take more than a thousand years, even if most habitable planets are occupied by communicative civilizations.

---

THAT the technology exists for sending and receiving radio messages over interstellar distances is not in doubt[1-5] so that, if there are similar technological civilizations based on stars not too distant from the Sun, we can, in principle, communicate with them. A problem, however, is to determine which star out of a large number of candidates is the home of a potentially communicative civilization[6-8]. The subject of this paper is the search problem of interstellar communication.

## Occurrence of Habitable Planets

Even the most optimistic estimates of the frequency of occurrence of potentially communicative civilizations suggest that a large number of stars will have to be searched before a civilization is encountered. If we let $P_c$ be the probability that a given star has a communicative civilization, we may write

$$P_c = f P_{HP} \qquad (1)$$

Where $P_{HP}$ is the probability that the star has a habitable planet in orbit around it, and $f$ is the fraction of habitable planets with communicative civilizations. This fraction involves

110

# 地外文明信号搜寻

沃克

编者按

本文中，一位地球环境演化方面的专家詹姆斯·沃克，将他的目光转向了地球大气之外，思考探测来自地外文明射电信号的可能性。这一理念自 1960 年开始实验性实施，当时天文学家弗兰克·德雷克用射电望远镜进行了一次搜寻。德雷克提出了一个估计其他星球中智慧文明出现概率的方程。沃克将对宜居行星数量的相关估计与望远镜的探测能力相结合，从而推导出需要多长时间的观测才能找到一个"智慧的"信号。结果令人沮丧：即使对宜居行星产生技术发达的文明的概率进行一个最乐观的估计，找到它们也可能需要超过一千年的时间。

---

尽管和地外文明交换射电信息的技术已经实现，但即使有通信能力的文明占据着大多数宜居行星，对能支持这样的文明的恒星的成功搜寻也可能将花费超过一千年。

---

毫无疑问，在星际距离上发送和接收射电信息的技术已经实现了 [1-5]。因此，如果太阳附近的其他恒星存在拥有类似技术的文明，原则上我们就可以与他们通信。然而，存在一个问题，就是如何在众多的候选体中确定哪颗恒星是这样的家园，即具有潜在的有通信能力的文明 [6-8]。本文的主题就是关于星际通信的搜寻问题。

## 宜居行星的发现

即使对潜在有通信能力的文明出现的概率做最乐观的估计，也必须搜寻大量的恒星才能找到一个地外文明。如果我们设 $P_c$ 为一个给定恒星拥有通信能力的文明的概率，我们可以写出：

$$P_c = f P_{HP} \tag{1}$$

其中 $P_{HP}$ 是围绕这颗恒星的轨道上有一颗宜居行星的概率，而 $f$ 是此行星上存在有通

the probability that a communicative civilization will evolve on a habitable planet as well as the average lifetime of communicative civilizations[6,9-11].

It may be impossible to determine the value of $f$ by other than empirical means, but $P_{HP}$ is a quantity that can, in principle, be estimated from a knowledge of cosmogony and planetology. Dole[12], for example, has made a detailed estimate of the probabilities that planets on which Man could exist are in orbit about stars of different spectral classes. His considerations lead him to conclude that $P_{HP}$ achieves a maximum value of 5.5% for stars of classes G0 to G4, and that 3.7% of stars in classes F2 to K1 have habitable planets; $P_{HP}$ is zero for stars outside this range. Dole's estimates involve many assumptions, and improved values of $P_{HP}$ will undoubtedly become available in time, but his values are adequate for present purposes. They show, first, that several tens of stars must be searched, even if $f$ is of order unity and, second, that we can estimate $P_{HP}$ for different stars and therefore can use this information to guide our search.

## Strategy for the Search

One approach to the search problem is to assume that the other civilization will do most of the work, which implies that the search is limited to "supercivilizations" able to transmit detectable signals in all directions all the time[5,13]. We could not do such a thing[14], for the power requirement of an isotropic call signal detectable at a range of 100 light year is approximately equal to the world's present total power consumption[2,15]. We can signal over interstellar distances only by using a large radio telescope to concentrate the radiated energy into a narrow beam. It would be possible to use a number of transmitters to send continuous signals to an equal number of target stars, but for such a strategy to have a reasonable chance of success, the number of transmitters would have to exceed

$$P_c^{-1} = (f P_{HP})^{-1}$$

This number is larger than 18, using Dole's values of $P_{HP}$, and it may be very much larger, since $f$ may be small.

Even if there were several interstellar transmitters—and there are not—a strategy of continuous transmission to a select group of stars would not, however, be optimal. So as $f$ is unknown, the probability of success for the transmitting civilization is proportional to the number of stars called regularly. In order to call the largest possible number of stars for a given level of effort, transmitter time must be shared among different target stars. How often, then, should a signal be sent to a given star?

Von Hoerner[6] has analysed this problem in general terms, pointing out that it is necessary to develop an optimal search strategy for both transmitter and receiver, and then to assume that the target civilization will perform the same analysis and arrive at the same conclusion. I present here a strategy for which the probability of success can be evaluated, at least as a function of $f$.

信能力的文明的比例。这个比例包含有通信能力的文明在宜居行星上能进化出来的概率以及有通信能力的文明的平均寿命 [6, 9-11]。

$f$ 值只能用经验性的方法来估计，但是原则上，$P_{HP}$ 却可以用天体演化学和行星学的知识来估算。例如，多尔 [12] 对不同光谱型的恒星周围存在人类能够生存的行星的概率进行了详细的估算。他得出结论：光谱型为 G0 到 G4 的恒星存在宜居行星的概率最大，$P_{HP}$ 达到 5.5%；而光谱型 F2 到 K1 的恒星有 3.7% 的可能存在宜居行星；在其他类型的恒星中，$P_{HP}$ 为 0。多尔的估计涉及很多假设，而且毫无疑问的是，随着时间发展 $P_{HP}$ 值会被改进，但他得出的值对于现在的目的来说已经足够了。首先，它们表明即使 $f$ 值为 1，我们也必须搜寻至少数十颗恒星；其次，我们可以估算出不同恒星的 $P_{HP}$，并用来指导我们的搜寻。

## 搜 寻 策 略

解决搜寻问题的一个方法是假设其他文明已经高度发展，这意味着搜寻仅限于"超级文明"，这些"超级文明"能够一直向各方向发射可探测的信号 [5,13]。我们做不到这样 [14]，因为发射一个各向同性的、在 100 光年的范围内可探测的呼叫信号的能量需求大约相当于现在世界总的能量消耗 [2,15]。我们只能通过使用一台大型射电望远镜将辐射能量集中到一个狭窄的波束中在星际距离发送信号。用若干发射机发送持续的信号给相同数量的目标恒星是可能的，但是要让这个策略有合理的成功机会，发射机的数量必须超过

$$P_c^{-1} = (f P_{HP})^{-1}$$

采用多尔的 $P_{HP}$ 值，这个数应该大于 18，因为 $f$ 可能会很小，所以这个数可能比 18 大得多。

即使有一些星际发射机——实际上没有——向挑选出的一组恒星持续发射信号的方法也不是最优策略。当 $f$ 未知，成功向其他文明发送信号的概率与定期向其发送信号的恒星的数量成正比。为了通过一定程度的努力向尽可能多的恒星发送信号，发射机时间必须被不同目标恒星共享。那么，给一个特定恒星发送信号的频率应该是多少呢？

冯·赫尔纳 [6] 大体上分析了这个问题，他指出，有必要针对发射机和接收机建立一个优化的搜寻策略，他假设目标文明也会进行同样的分析并得到相同的结论。这里我提出一个策略，以此可以估计成功的概率，至少可以表示为 $f$ 的一个函数。

An optimal search strategy should use all the information that we share with the target civilization. This includes the spectral classes of candidate stars and thus the values of $P_{HP}$; it includes the optimal spectral region in which to work, the region where unavoidable background noise is minimal[1-5] and the distances to the candidate stars.

This last quantity provides the only indication we have as to how often we should look at any given star. The natural repetition period[8] for a star at distance $R$ is

$$T = \frac{2R}{c} \tag{2}$$

where $c$ is the velocity of light. It is the time for a contact signal to travel to the star and for a reply to return. I shall assume that the transmitter sends a contact signal every $T$ years to every star within range having a non-zero $P_{HP}$. Excess transmitter capacity would be used to increase the range of the search rather than to provide more frequent contact signals.

Although there are a number of ideas about the wavelength to use for contact signals[1,5], a search in frequency cannot be eliminated entirely because extremely narrow bandwidths must be used for interstellar communication[2]. I shall not consider the frequency search explicitly, so for simplicity in the analysis I shall assign this task to the transmitter. Thus the contact signal to be sent out every $T$ years will sweep slowly over the optimal spectral region, and the receiver may confine its search to a single frequency.

## Probability of Success

With the transmitter strategy thus defined, it is possible to determine the optimal receiver strategy and evaluate the rate of success. From the point of view of the receiver, let us redefine $P_c$ to be the probability that a given star has a civilization that sends a contact signal to the receiving star every $T$ years at the wavelength on which the receiving civilization is listening. This redefinition introduces a corresponding change in the definition of the unknown fraction $f$, but no change in the known probability $P_{HP}$.

If, at the beginning of the search, the receiver devotes a period of time $\Delta\tau$ to listening to a given star, the probability that it will receive a call is

$$P_s = P_c \, \Delta\tau / T \tag{3}$$

The rate of success in the search is therefore $f P_{HP}/T \text{ yr}^{-1}$, where $P_{HP}/T$ depends on the spectral class and the distance of the target star and $f$ is the same for all stars. Because the repetition period $T$ increases linearly with distance to the target star, the success rate is highest for the closest stars. Using Dole's figures[17], we find a success rate for $\alpha$ Centauri of $1.3\times10^{-2} f \text{ yr}^{-1}$; for $\varepsilon$ Eridani and $\tau$ Ceti the success rates are both about $1.5\times10^{-3} f \text{ yr}^{-1}$. For a G0 star at 100 light year, however, the success rate is $2.7\times10^{-4} f \text{ yr}^{-1}$.

一个最佳的搜寻策略是应该使用我们和目标文明共享的所有信息。这包括候选恒星的光谱型以及相关的 $P_{HP}$ 值；也包括选取最佳的工作频段使得不可避免的背景噪声在此频段最小 [1-5]，还要考虑离候选恒星的距离。

最后这个计算结果将给出我们多久向指定恒星发射一次信息的唯一指标。对于一颗距离为 $R$ 的恒星来说，自然重复周期 [8] 为

$$T = \frac{2R}{c} \tag{2}$$

其中 $c$ 是光速，$T$ 是一个通信信号传送到该恒星后再返回所需的时间。我假设信号发生器每 $T$ 年向一非零 $P_{HP}$ 区域内的所有恒星发送信号。额外的信号发送能力将用来增加搜索范围而不是更频繁的提供通信信号。

尽管对通信信号波长的选择存在很多观点 [1,5]，但是频率搜索不能完全舍弃，因为星际通信必须要在极窄的波段 [2]。我将不仔细考虑频率搜索，为简化分析，我把这个任务交给发射机。因此，每 $T$ 年发送的通信信号将缓慢地扫过最优的频谱范围，同时接收机会把搜索限定在某一个单一频率上。

## 成功的概率

在这样定义的发射机策略下，就可能确定最优的接收机策略，同时也可以评估出成功的概率。从接收机的角度来讲，我们重新定义 $P_c$ 为给定恒星拥有一个文明的概率，此文明每 $T$ 年发送通信信号给可能的接收星，波长为接收信号的文明用于监听的波长。这种重新定义给未知参数 $f$ 的定义带来相应的变化，但是不改变已知的概率 $P_{HP}$。

如果在搜索开始时，接收机使用时间周期 $\Delta\tau$ 来接收给定恒星的信号，则它接收到一个呼叫的概率为

$$P_s = P_c \, \Delta\tau / T \tag{3}$$

因此，搜索成功的概率就是 $f P_{HP} / T \text{ yr}^{-1}$，这里 $P_{HP} / T$ 依赖于目标恒星的光谱型和距离，$f$ 对所有恒星都相同。因为重复周期 $T$ 随目标恒星的距离线性增加，所以对最近的恒星成功概率最高。使用多尔的图 [17]，我们发现对半人马座 $\alpha$（南门二）的成功概率为 $1.3 \times 10^{-2} f \text{ yr}^{-1}$；对波江座（天苑四）和鲸鱼座（天仓五）成功概率均为 $1.5 \times 10^{-3} f \text{ yr}^{-1}$。对一颗 100 光年处的 G0 型恒星，成功概率为 $2.7 \times 10^{-4} f \text{ yr}^{-1}$。

But the receiver should not devote all its time to the closest star. This star may not be the home of a communicative civilization. After the receiver has devoted a large number $n$ of randomly spaced listening periods $\Delta\tau$ to a given star, the probability that the receiver will have failed to receive a call, assuming that there is a transmitter associated with that star, is $\exp(-n\Delta\tau/T)$. The probability of success on the next look at the star is therefore

$$P_s(\tau) = f\,P_{HP}(\Delta\tau/T)\,\exp(-\tau/T) \tag{4}$$

where $\tau = n\Delta\tau$.

The optimal receiver strategy is now clear. The success rate is maximized if each listening period $\Delta\tau$ is devoted to the star for which $(P_{HP}/T)\exp(-\tau/T)$ is greatest. As the search progresses, the number of stars included in the search increases steadily, for each star within range the value of $\tau$ increases, and the instantaneous success rate grows steadily smaller. Each try, however, adds the greatest possible amount to the cumulative probability of success. How much time, on average, must elapse before success is achieved?

Suppose that there are $N_i$ stars of spectral class $i$ per unit volume and let $P_{HP}(i)$ be the probability that each of these stars has a habitable planet. After a total time $t$ has been devoted to the search, following the strategy outlined above, the cumulative probability of success is

$$P_s = \frac{4}{3}\,\varepsilon f t \tag{5}$$

where $\varepsilon$ is the instantaneous success rate at time $t$ given by

$$\varepsilon = \left[\frac{\pi c^3}{32t}\sum_i N_i P_{HP}{}^4(i)\right]^{\frac{1}{4}} \tag{6}$$

From Dole's Table 18, $\sum_i N_i P_{HP}{}^4(i) = 1.24 \times 10^{-9}$ per cubic light year, so

$$\varepsilon = 3.3 \times 10^{-3}\,t^{-\frac{1}{4}}\,\mathrm{yr}^{-1} \tag{7}$$

and
$$P_s = 4.4 \times 10^{-3}\,f t^{\frac{3}{4}} \tag{8}$$

where $t$ is expressed in years.

On the average, contact will be achieved when $P_s = 1$ or after a search that has lasted

$$t_0 = 1{,}380 f^{-4/3}\,\mathrm{yr} \tag{9}$$

Values of $t_0$ corresponding to several assumed values of $f$ are shown in Table 1. Also shown is the average distance that separates communicative civilizations for these values of $f$.

但是接收机不应该把所有的时间都放在最近的恒星上。这颗恒星可能不是一个具有通信能力的文明的家园。在接收机投入了 $n$ 个随机分布的接收周期 $\Delta\tau$ 给一颗特定恒星后，假定那里有一台发射机，那么这台接收机还未能接收一个呼叫的概率是 $\exp(-n\Delta\tau/T)$。因此，下一次搜索该星时成功的概率就是：

$$P_s(\tau) = f\, P_{HP}\,(\Delta\tau/T)\, \exp\,(-\tau/T) \tag{4}$$

其中 $\tau = n\Delta\tau$。

现在，最佳的接收策略已经清楚了。当投入到这颗恒星的每个接收周期 $\Delta\tau$ 使得 $(P_{HP}/T)\exp(-\tau/T)$ 最大时，成功概率最大。随着搜索的进行，搜索中包含的恒星数量稳步增长，搜索范围内每颗星的 $\tau$ 的增长，瞬时成功概率稳步减小。然而，每次尝试都会为累积的成功概率增加一个最大可能的量。问题是平均需要多少时间，才会成功搜索到地外文明的信号？

假定单位体积有 $N_i$ 颗光谱型 $i$ 的恒星，令 $P_{HP}\,(i)$ 为每一颗恒星有宜居行星的概率。在投入总时间 $t$ 搜索后，按照上面提到的策略，累积的成功概率是

$$P_s = \frac{4}{3}\,\varepsilon f t \tag{5}$$

其中 $\varepsilon$ 是在时刻 $t$ 的瞬时成功率，由

$$\varepsilon = \left[\frac{\pi c^3}{32t}\sum_i N_i P_{HP}{}^4(i)\right]^{\frac{1}{4}} \tag{6}$$

给出。由多尔的表 18，$\sum_i N_i P_{HP}{}^4(i) = 1.24\times10^{-9}$ 每立方光年，因此

$$\varepsilon = 3.3\times10^{-3}\,t^{-\frac{1}{4}}\,\mathrm{yr}^{-1} \tag{7}$$

$$P_s = 4.4\times10^{-3}\,f t^{\frac{3}{4}} \tag{8}$$

其中 $t$ 的单位为年。

平均来说，当 $P_s = 1$ 或者一次搜索已经进行了

$$t_0 = 1,380\,f^{-4/3}\,\mathrm{yr} \tag{9}$$

后，我们就能够与地外文明建立联系。对应于一些假定的 $f$ 值的 $t_0$ 值列在表 1 中。另外也列出了对于这些 $f$ 值，有通信能力的文明间的平均距离。

Table 1. Search Strategies for Various Distributions of Civilizations

| Fraction of habitable planets occupied by communicative civilizations $f$ | Average separation of communicative civilizations (light year) | Duration of search $T_0$(yr) |
|---|---|---|
| 1 | 24 | $1.4 \times 10^3$ |
| $10^{-3}$ | 240 | $1.4 \times 10^7$ |
| $10^{-6}$ | 2,400 | $1.4 \times 10^{11}$ |

We see that even with optimistic assumptions concerning the frequency of occurrence of communicative civilizations, the time required for a successful search is long. Of course, $t_0$ is, strictly speaking, telescope time devoted to the search, not total elapsed time. The duration of the search is therefore inversely proportional to the number of receiving telescopes and could be shortened by a massive effort. Alternatively, it is possible that the transmitter strategy I have assumed is incorrect, and that more frequent calls would be optimal, say $m$ calls every $T$ years. In this case the duration of the search differs from the values in Table 1 by a factor of $1/m$, provided the receiving civilization knows the value of $m$.

The conclusion, therefore, is disappointing. If every habitable planet has a communicative civilization there might be 50 such civilizations within 100 light year of us[18]. We possess the technology to exchange messages with this multitude of other worlds, if only we can find them. Unless my assumed transmitter strategy is seriously in error, however, or unless habitable planets are substantially more abundant than Dole has concluded, the problem of finding the other worlds is overwhelming. These circumstances may limit us to a search for supercivilizations[16].

This research has been supported, in part, by a NASA grant.

(**241**, 379-381; 1973)

James C. G. Walker
Department of Geology and Geophysics, Yale University, New Haven, Connecticut 06520

Received January 5; revised September 11, 1972.

References:
1. Cocconi, G., and Morrison, P., *Nature*, **184**, 844 (1959).

2. Drake, F. D., *Sky and Telescope*, **19**, 140 (1959).

3. Webb, J. A., in *Institute for Radio Engineers Seventh National Communications Symposium Record: Communications- Bridge or Barrier*, **10** (1961).

4. Oliver, B. M., in *Interstellar Communication* (edit. by Cameron, A. G. W.), 294 (W. A. Benjamin, New York, 1963).

5. Shklovskii, I. S., and Sagan, C., *Intelligent Life in the Universe* (Holden-Day, San Francisco, 1966).

6. von Hoerner, S., *Science*, **134**, 1839 (1961).

7. Bracewell, R. N., *Nature*, **186**, 670 (1960).

8. Huang, S.-S., in *Interstellar Communication* (edit. by Cameron, A. G. W.), 201 (W. A. Benjamin, New York, 1963).

表 1. 对各种文明分布的搜索策略

| 有通信能力文明占据宜居行星的比例 $f$ | 有通信能力文明的平均间距（光年） | 搜寻持续的时间 $T_0$（年） |
|---|---|---|
| 1 | 24 | $1.4 \times 10^3$ |
| $10^{-3}$ | 240 | $1.4 \times 10^7$ |
| $10^{-6}$ | 2,400 | $1.4 \times 10^{11}$ |

我们看到，即使对可通信联系的文明出现的频率做最乐观的假设，成功的搜索所需的时间还是很长。当然，严格来说 $t_0$ 是天文望远镜投入到搜索的时间，而不是流逝的总时间。搜索持续的时间反比于接收天文望远镜的数量，因此可以通过增加大量望远镜来缩短。另一种可能是，我所假设的发射机策略是不正确的，更加频繁的呼唤可能是最佳的，比如说每 $T$ 年进行 $m$ 次呼叫。在这种情况下，假如接收文明知道 $m$ 的值，搜索的持续时间与表 1 中的值有一个 $1/m$ 因子的差别。

综上，结论有些令人失望，如果每个宜居的星球都有可通信联系的文明，那么在距离我们 100 光年内大约会有 50 个这样的文明[18]。我们掌握着同这众多的其他世界交换信息的技术，只要我们能找到他们。但是，除非我假设的发射机策略是严重错误的，或者宜居行星的数量比多尔推断的多，否则搜寻其他地外文明的困难几乎无法克服。这些情况可能会限制我们搜寻超级文明[16]。

本研究部分得到了美国国家航空航天局基金的支持。

（周旻辰 翻译；沈志侠 审稿）

9. Morrison, P., *Bull. Phil. Soc. Washington*, **16**, 58 (1962).

10. Pearman, J. P. T., in *Interstellar Communication* (edit. by Cameron, A. G. W.), 287 (W. A. Benjamin, New York, 1963).

11. Cameron, A. G. W., in *Interstellar Communication* (edit. by Cameron, A. G. W.), 309 (W. A. Benjamin, New York, 1963).

12. Dole, S. H., *Habitable Planets for Man*, second edition, Table 17 (American Elsevier, New York, 1970).

13. Kardashev, N. S., *Soviet Astronomy—A. J.*, **8**, 217 (1964).

14. Webb, J. A., in *Interstellar Communication* (edit. by Cameron, A. G. W.), 188 (W. A. Benjamin, New York, 1963).

15. Hubbert, M. K., in *Resources and Man* (Committee on Resources and Man of the National Academy of Sciences-National Research Council), 157 (W. H. Freeman, San Francisco, 1969).

16. *Extraterrestrial Civilizations* (edit. by Tovmasyan, G. M.) (translated by Israel Program for Scientific and Technical Translations, 1964).

17. Dole, *Habitable Planets for Man*, second edition, Table 22 (American Elsevier, New York, 1970).

18. Dole, *Habitable Planets for Man*, second edition, Table 19 (American Elsevier, New York, 1972).

# On the Origin of Deuterium

F. Hoyle and W. A. Fowler

## Editor's Note

Deuterium is hydrogen that contains a neutron in its nucleus. It is relatively abundant in the universe, most having been created in the first few minutes after the Big Bang. Here Fred Hoyle and William Fowler investigate several ways in which it could also be created in astrophysical situations. The shock waves associated with supernovae (exploding old stars), and cosmic rays hitting clouds of gas can both generate deuterium, but not enough to explain the observations. The arguments advanced here were an attempt to avoid invoking a Big Bang at all, which Hoyle spent the later years of his life opposing. The Big Bang is, however, now the generally accepted explanation for the origin and properties of the Universe.

The origin of deuterium has always been a problem for theories of stellar nucleosynthesis. A general solution is proposed and shown to be applicable under several astrophysical circumstances in the light of new observations of the Galactic abundance of deuterium.

CESARSKY, Moffet and Pasachoff[1] have recently observed an absorption feature in the spectrum of radiation from the Galactic centre at 327.38837±0.00001 MHz. They interpret this as arising from the ground-state hyperfine transition in deuterium near 91.6 cm which is analogous to the well-known 21 cm line of ordinary hydrogen. If they assume the feature observed to be due to noise they are able to set an upper limit

$$D/H < 5 \times 10^{-4}$$

while an analysis assuming the feature to be due to deuterium yields

$$3 \times 10^{-5} < D/H < 5 \times 10^{-4} \tag{1}$$

These results are to be compared with the terrestrial value of $1.5 \times 10^{-4}$ and to the upper limit for the proto-solar value of $3 \times 10^{-5}$ (refs. 2, 3).

Jefferts, Penzias and Wilson[4] report line emission from a cloud within the Orion Nebula at 144,828 MHz and attribute it to the $J = 2$ to $J = 1$ transition in DCN. In a separate investigation of the $J = 1$ to $J = 0$ transition at 72,414 MHz, the hyperfine components expected for DCN have also been found[5], setting the identification beyond reasonable doubt. The cloud in question probably has dimensions of the order of a light year and a mass of order $10^2 \, M_\odot$, considerably less than the Orion Nebula itself. The H II region of Orion, which is the part seen optically, has mass $\sim 10^3 \, M_\odot$, whereas a larger scale molecular cloud, detected in the 2.6 mm radiation of the CO molecule, has been

# 氘的起源

霍伊尔，福勒

## 编者按

氘是原子核内有一个中子的氢。它在宇宙中相对丰富，大部分是在宇宙大爆炸之后的几分钟内产生的。在本文中，弗雷德·霍伊尔和威廉·福勒研究了在天体物理条件下也可能形成氘的几种方式。虽然与超新星（老年恒星在演化末期的爆炸）有关的冲击波，以及宇宙射线撞击气体云都能产生氘，但这不足以解释观测结果。本文中提出的论点是从根本上避免援引宇宙大爆炸理论的一个尝试，霍伊尔在他的晚期生涯中一直反对这一理论。然而，宇宙大爆炸理论却是目前被人们普遍接受的对宇宙的起源和特性的解说。

---

氘的起源一直是恒星核合成理论中的一个问题。根据对银河系氘丰度的新观测，本文对氘起源问题提出了一个一般性的解答并表明这一解答在一些天体物理环境条件下具有可行性。

---

塞萨尔斯基、莫菲特和帕萨乔夫[1] 最近观测到在来自银河系中心的辐射光谱中的 $327.38837 \pm 0.00001$ MHz 处具有吸收特征。他们把这解释为来自 91.6 cm 附近的氘基态的超精细跃迁，类似于众所周知的普通氢的 21 cm 线。如果假设观测到的特征是由噪声导致的，那么他们可以设定一个上限

$$D/H < 5 \times 10^{-4}$$

而另有一种分析，假设这一现象是由氘产生的，则

$$3 \times 10^{-5} < D/H < 5 \times 10^{-4} \tag{1}$$

这些结果将与地球上的 $1.5 \times 10^{-4}$ 和原始太阳的上限值 $3 \times 10^{-5}$ 相比较（参考文献 2、3）。

杰弗茨、彭齐亚斯和威尔逊[4] 报道了来自猎户座星云内部的一个云团在 144,828 MHz 处的发射线，并把它归因于 DCN 中从 $J=2$ 到 $J=1$ 的跃迁。在 72,414 MHz 处 $J=1$ 到 $J=0$ 跃迁的独立研究中也发现了预期的 DCN 的超精细跃迁组分[5]，使得这一识别毫无异议。所涉及云团大小远小于猎户座星云本身，大小可能在 1 光年量级，质量处在 $10^2\,M_\odot$ 量级。猎户座的 H II 区是可见光区，质量约为 $10^3\,M_\odot$，然而据所罗门（个人交流）估计，在 CO 分子 2.6 mm 处辐射中探测到的较

estimated by Solomon (private communication) to have mass $\sim 10^5\ M_\odot$.

The emission from the $J = 1$ to $J = 0$ transition is approximately as strong as that in $^1H^{12}C^{15}N$ and $^1H^{13}C^{14}N$, so

$$D/H = 6\times 10^{-3} \tag{2}$$

a remarkably high value. The ratio determined in this way applies to D and H in combination with CN, not to D and H in atomic form. Thus the D/H ratio in the interstellar gas could still be comparable with the terrestrial value, or with the value of $3\times 10^{-5}$ referred to above.

The position concerning deuterium has therefore changed from doubt concerning its widespread existence in the Galaxy to one in which it is a reasonable inference that D/H of order $10^{-4}$ occurs on a large scale, and the problem of the origin of deuterium now seems more urgent than it did before. Together with R. V. Wagoner[6], we found some years ago that significant quantities of D could arise in a low density Friedmann universe. Defining a parameter $h$ from the relation (applicable after $e^{\pm}$-pair annihilation in the universe)

$$\rho_b = hT_9^3\ \text{g cm}^{-3} \tag{3}$$

where $\rho_b$ is the baryon mass density and $T_9$ is the radiation temperature measured in units of $10^9$ K, we found D/H comparable with the terrestrial ratio of $1.5\times 10^{-4}$ when $h \simeq 6\times 10^{-6}$. Setting $T_9 = 2.7\times 10^{-9}$ K for the present temperature leads to $\rho_b \simeq 10^{-31}$ g ml.$^{-1}$ for the present baryon density, which is in good agreement with estimates which have been made of the average density of matter in galaxies by Oort[7] and Shapiro[8].

It is an unexpected feature of such a primordial mode of synthesis that the well-known cosmological parameter $q_0$ turns out to be small, and close to zero[6], instead of the value 0.5 required to "close" the universe. Many cosmological investigations, the formation of galaxies for example, are much more awkward in hyperbolic models ($q_0 \simeq 0$) than they are for $q_0 \geqslant 0.5$. One might seek to evade the resulting difficulties by arguing that, unlike an idealized Friedmann model, the actual universe is inhomogeneous. It might be supposed that the initial state of the universe was very patchy, with $h$ falling below $10^{-5}$ in some places. On the other hand, the 2.7 K radiation background is exceedingly uniform, both locally and from one part of the sky to other distant parts of the sky. This uniformity, while not forbidding sufficiently fine scale inhomogeneities, would seem to us to constitute a warning against this line of argument.

It is also important in the new circumstances of the problem to reconsider possible astrophysical modes of origin for deuterium. Should it turn out that D/H is locally variable, astrophysical processes would be preferred to primordial synthesis, but if the D/H ratio is found to be universal then primordial synthesis would be preferred.

大尺度的分子云的质量约为 $10^5 M_\odot$。

由 $J=1$ 到 $J=0$ 跃迁产生的辐射强度大约与 $^1H^{12}C^{15}N$ 和 $^1H^{13}C^{14}N$ 中的辐射强度相当，因此

$$D/H = 6 \times 10^{-3} \tag{2}$$

这是一个相当高的值。用这种方法确定的比值适用于与 CN 结合的 D 和 H，而对原子形式的 D 和 H 不适用。因此星际气体中的 D/H 比仍然有可能和地球上的值相当，或与上面提到的值 $3 \times 10^{-5}$ 相当。

于是对于氘的认识从怀疑其在银河系中的普遍存在性变为了下面这一合理的推断，即在大尺度上 D/H 处在 $10^{-4}$ 的量级。而现在看起来有关氘起源的问题较之从前也更为紧迫了。几年前，我们和瓦戈纳一道发现在低密度的弗里德曼宇宙中存在大量的 $D^{[6]}$。从关系式（在宇宙中的正负电子对湮灭后适用）

$$\rho_b = hT_9^3 \text{ g} \cdot \text{cm}^{-3} \tag{3}$$

中定义参数 $h$，其中 $\rho_b$ 是重子质量密度，而 $T_9$ 是以 $10^9$ K 为计量单位的辐射温度。我们发现在 $h = 6 \times 10^{-6}$ 时，D/H 和地球上 $1.5 \times 10^{-4}$ 的值相当。设定当前温度为 $T_9 = 2.7 \times 10^{-9}$ K，可以得到现在的重子密度为 $\rho_b \simeq 10^{-31}$ gml$^{-1}$，这和奥尔特 [7] 以及夏皮罗 [8] 估计的星系中物质的平均密度具有很好的一致性。

为人熟知的宇宙学参数 $q_0$ 最终被证明很小并且接近于零 [6]，而不是"封闭"宇宙需要的 0.5，这是原初核合成模式所没有预料到的。许多宇宙学研究，如星系形成，在双曲模型中（$q_0 \simeq 0$）要比 $q_0 \geqslant 0.5$ 难处理得多。有人提出，与理想的弗里德曼模型不同，真实的宇宙是非均匀的，以此来规避由于该参数小导致的困局。可以假设宇宙的初始状态是非常不均匀的，在某些地方 $h$ 小于 $10^{-5}$。另一方面，无论在局部天区还是从天空的一个区域到遥远的其他区域，2.7 K 的背景辐射值都非常均匀。这种均匀性，虽然没有完全排除很小尺度上不均匀性的存在，但似乎预示着并不支持这一论点。

在新的困局下，重新考虑氘起源的可能的天体物理模式也是重要的。如果证明局部 D/H 具有变化，那么天体物理过程比原初核合成更为合理，但如果 D/H 比值具有均一性，则原初合成模式较合理。

Investigations going back to the middle nineteen fifties have repeatedly shown that D is best produced astrophysically under non-thermodynamic conditions. We imagine α particles projected at high speed into an ionized gas composed mainly of hydrogen. If the gas temperature has some moderate value, say $10^5$ K for definiteness, nuclear reactions leading to D production can occur. D can be knocked out of an α particle by a spallation reaction, and neutrons knocked out of the $^4$He can subsequently be captured by protons of the ambient gas. For example, α particles entering gas at speed $c/3$ have a kinetic energy relative to the gas of ~200 MeV, which is 50 MeV per nucleon, and at such a bombarding energy the total cross section for all the reactions leading to D production is about $5 \times 10^{-26}$ cm$^2$, that is, 50 mb according to Audouze et al.[9]. Although the stopping cross section due to Coulomb scattering is greater than this, it is clear that a significant fraction of the α particles will produce a D nucleus. Because the D is thus formed within a comparatively low temperature gas it is not subject to subsequent breakup, except in rare cases where it happens to be hit by a further incoming α particle.

There are many ways in which this general idea can be used; for example, it can be applied to cosmic rays entering a cloud of gas. The production of D (and $^3$He) through the spallation of $^4$He was discussed a decade ago[10] in connexion with magnetic flares in the solar surface. The nuclear physics involved is largely independent of the acceleration mechanism. But processes involving cosmic rays are not capable of explaining large D concentrations of the kind that have now been reported. Cosmic rays are too wasteful of their energy in this respect. D production reaches the geometrical cross section and thus occurs most efficiently when the energy per nucleon is about 30 MeV. Energies as high as several GeV, which is where the main reservoir of cosmic ray energy lies, are not required. For greatest efficiency we must look therefore to processes involving speeds ~ $c/3$.

Such speeds have indeed been found for shock waves generated by stellar explosions[11]. The shock wave starts in the region of the explosion at a speed not much different from the speed of sound, which is always much less than $c$. As it travels outwards into the lower density regions of the envelope, however, the wave speeds up. It is therefore in the outer envelope that speeds of the required order have been reported in previous investigations.

The shock wave condition we have in mind can be applied much more generally than to a supernova. The basic requirement is for a supply of radiant energy (or of relativistic particles) to emerge from some local source into a diffuse outer envelope of gas containing $^4$He. The larger the energy supply the better. For a supernova we expect ~$10^{50}$ erg to be available, which is much less than a case reported recently by Appenzeller and Fricke[12-14]. Their work is concerned with objects having masses between $10^5$ and $10^6$ $M_\odot$ —that is, masses of the order of the whole Orion Nebula. Under suitable conditions nuclear energy generation in a time scale of a few thousand seconds, yielding ~$10^{56}$ erg, can lead to expansion and disruption of the whole object. Because most of the energy is taken up in the radiation field, it is possible that a bubble of radiation, say with total energy ~$10^{55}$ erg, may work its way to the outer part of the object and may propagate thence into a surrounding diffuse cloud. Outbursts involving relativistic particles, also with energies of

自 20 世纪 50 年代中期开始的研究已经不断地表明，在天体物理中 D 在非热力学条件下最容易产生。我们想象 α 粒子以高速射入一团主要由氢组成的电离气体中。如果气体具有某一适中温度，比如确切的 $10^5$ K，导致 D 形成的核反应就可以发生。D 可以通过散裂反应从一个 α 粒子中被击出，从 $^4$He 中击出的中子随后可以被周围气体中的质子俘获。例如，以 $c/3$ 的速度进入气体的 α 粒子相对气体的动能约为 200 MeV，也就是每个核子 50 MeV。根据奥杜兹等人的研究，在这样的轰击能量下，所有生成 D 反应的总截面大约是 $5 \times 10^{-26}$ cm$^2$，也就是 50 mb[9]。尽管库仑散射造成的阻止截面大于这一值，但显然，绝大部分的 α 粒子都将会产生 D 核。因为 D 是在相对低温的气体中形成的，除了一些很少见的情形（如：它刚好被另一个入射 α 粒子撞击），其不易继续分裂。

该一般性的想法在许多方面都可应用，例如，可应用于宇宙线进入一团气体云的情景。十年前，通过 $^4$He 散裂产生的 D（和 $^3$He）被认为与太阳表面的磁耀斑有关[10]。所涉及的核物理过程很大程度上独立于加速机制。但是与宇宙线有关的核物理过程不能解释目前已经报道的如此大丰度的 D。在这个方面，宇宙线太浪费能量了。D 的产量达到了几何截面，因此在每个核子能量大约为 30 MeV 时，产氘效率最高。这里并不需要高达几 GeV 的能量，也就是宇宙线能量的主要范围。为了达到最高的效率，我们必须考虑与速度约 $c/3$ 有关的过程。

事实上，这样的速度已经在恒星爆发产生的冲击波中被发现了[11]。冲击波在爆发区域以和声速差不多的速度开始，这一速度总是比 $c$ 小很多。但是，当它向外传播进入低密度包层时，冲击波开始加速。因此，之前的研究中所报道的所需速度是在外包层中的速度。

我们已知的产生冲击的条件不仅在超新星中存在，在其他更普遍的情况下也存在。基本的要求是辐射能量的供应（或者相对论性粒子的供应），其形成于局域源进入弥散的含有 $^4$He 的气体外包层过程中。能量供应越大越好。对于超新星，我们预计获得的能量约为 $10^{50}$ erg，这比最近阿彭策勒和弗里克报告[12-14]的情形小很多。他们的工作涉及的天体质量在 $10^5$ $M_\odot$ 到 $10^6$ $M_\odot$ 之间，也就是整个猎户座星云质量所处的量级。在适宜条件下，数千秒内产生的核能约为 $10^{56}$ erg，这一能量可以导致整个天体的膨胀和破裂爆炸。由于大部分能量被辐射场吸收，一个总能量约为 $10^{55}$ erg 的辐射泡有可能成功地到达天体外部，并因此传播到周围弥漫的云中。出现在射电星系中的相对论性粒子爆发，也具有约 $10^{55} \sim 10^{56}$ erg 能量。事实上，来自于射电源

$\sim10^{55}$–$10^{56}$ erg, occur in radio galaxies. Indeed, outbursts from radio sources involving energies up to $\sim10^{60}$ erg have been considered.

The energy in question, whether radiant or in the form of relativistic particles, would escape from the source at speed $c$ if it were not for the material of the surrounding envelope. But as the envelope becomes more tenuous the radiation is able to push material ahead of it at speeds which approach more and more to $c$. In such circumstances the material of the envelope is accelerated forward impulsively at a shock front, and nuclei present in it are subject to spallation if the shock becomes violent enough. Deuterium is then formed, either by direct spallation of $^4$He or from neutrons coming from $^4$He, the neutrons being captured subsequently by protons downstream of the shock.

The properties of shock waves are usually investigated through the equations of continuum mechanics. The complex physical processes taking place at the shock front are idealized by a discontinuity, much as an impulse to a body is idealized in classical mechanics. We define $v_i$, $v_s$ as velocity components normal to the shock, with subscripts i, s referring to conditions upstream and downstream of the front respectively. For simplicity, taking hydromagnetic effects to be small, and taking a frame of reference in which the front is stationary, we have the following conservation relations across the front:

$$\rho_i v_i = \rho_s v_s$$
$$p_i + \rho_i v_i^2 = p_s + \rho_s v_s^2 \tag{4}$$
$$u_i + \frac{p_i}{\rho_i} + \frac{1}{2}v_i^2 = u_s + \frac{p_s}{\rho_s} + \frac{1}{2}v_s^2$$

where $p$ is the pressure and $u$ is the internal energy per unit mass. Terms in $p_i$, $u_i$ are small in our case. Omitting them, we can satisfy equations (4) with

$$\rho_s = \rho_i \frac{\gamma+1}{\gamma-1}, \quad v_s = v_i \frac{\gamma-1}{\gamma+1}, \quad p_s = \frac{2\rho_i v_i^2}{\gamma+1} \tag{5}$$

where

$$(\gamma-1)\,\rho_s u_s = p_s \tag{6}$$

$\gamma$ is the ratio of specific heats downstream of the shock, and is close to 4/3 in a radiation dominated problem. Putting $\gamma = 4/3$ in equation (5) we get

$$\rho_s = 7\rho_i, \quad v_s = v_i/7, \quad p_s \simeq \frac{1}{3}aT_s^4 = \frac{6}{7}\rho_i v_i^2 \tag{7}$$

The third of these equations can be regarded as determining $v_i$ when $T_s$ and $\rho_i$ are given. The value to be used for $T_s$ depends on the energy supply, while $\rho_i$ is the density of the envelope upstream of the shock. From here on, we shall be concerned with situations in which $T_s$ is high enough in relation to $\rho_i$ for the resulting value of $v_i$ to be of order $c/3$.

Material flowing through the front experiences a change of velocity $v_i - v_s = 6v_i/7$, which for $v_i = c/3$ is $2c/7$. If we now think of the material in terms of individual particles, instead of from the point of view of continuum mechanics, the particles experience a change

的能量高达约 $10^{60}$ erg 的爆发也已经被考虑过。

如果没有周围包层的物质，无论是以辐射还是以相对论性粒子形式存在的能量都将以 $c$ 的速度逃离源区。但是随着包层变得稀薄，辐射可以推动它前面的物质达到越来越接近 $c$ 的速度。在这样的情况下，包层的物质在冲击波波前被有力地向前推动加速，如果冲击变得足够强烈，其中的原子核就易发生散裂。因此，氘要么由 $^4$He 的直接散裂产生，要么由来自 $^4$He 的中子被冲击波下游的质子俘获形成。

冲击波的性质通常用连续介质力学方程进行研究。在冲击波波前发生的复杂物理过程通过一个理想的不连续点来简化，正像在经典力学中对作用于一个物体的冲力的理想化一样。我们定义 $v_i$、$v_s$ 为与冲击波正交的速度分量，下标 i、s 分别表示波前的上游和下游。为简单起见，假设磁流体动力学效应很小，采用波前为静止的参考系，我们得到以下跨越波前的守恒关系式：

$$\rho_i v_i = \rho_s v_s$$
$$p_i + \rho_i v_i^2 = p_s + \rho_s v_s^2 \tag{4}$$
$$u_i + \frac{p_i}{\rho_i} + \frac{1}{2} v_i^2 = u_s + \frac{p_s}{\rho_s} + \frac{1}{2} v_s^2$$

其中 $p$ 是压强，$u$ 是单位质量内能。对我们的情景而言，$p_i$、$u_i$ 项值很小。忽略这些项，下列关系可以满足方程（4）

$$\rho_s = \rho_i \frac{\gamma+1}{\gamma-1}, \quad v_s = v_i \frac{\gamma-1}{\gamma+1}, \quad p_s = \frac{2\rho_i v_i^2}{\gamma+1} \tag{5}$$

其中

$$(\gamma-1)\rho_s u_s = p_s \tag{6}$$

$\gamma$ 是冲击波下游的比热比，在辐射主导的问题里接近于 4/3。在方程（5）中令 $\gamma = 4/3$，我们得到

$$\rho_s = 7\rho_i, \quad v_s = v_i/7, \quad p_s = \frac{1}{3} a T_s^4 = \frac{6}{7} \rho_i v_i^2 \tag{7}$$

其中第三个方程可以看作在给定 $T_s$ 和 $\rho_i$ 的时候计算确定 $v_i$。$T_s$ 的取值依赖于能量供应，而 $\rho_i$ 是冲击波上游包层的密度。从这里开始，我们将考虑与 $\rho_i$ 相联系的 $T_s$ 值足够导致 $v_i$ 值达到 $c/3$ 量级的情形。

流过波前的物质经历了一个 $v_i - v_s = 6v_i/7$ 的速度变化，在 $v_i = c/3$ 时变化值等于 $2c/7$。如果我们现在把物质想象为一些单独的粒子，而不是从连续介质力学的观点

in velocity of $2c/7$ as they pass from being upstream to being downstream of the shock. We have to think of the front as possessing a finite depth and of particles from upstream experiencing collisions as they pass through a finite shock zone. As a velocity of $2c/7$ is equivalent to a bombarding energy of $\sim 40$ MeV per nucleon we have a situation similar to that discussed above for $\alpha$ particles projected into a stationary gas. Thus $^4$He present in material upstream of the shock will be subject to fragmentation as it passes through the front.

The present situation is actually more favourable to fragmentation than the case of $\alpha$ particles projected into an ambient gas, because all particles in the shock zone have come from upstream and have therefore experienced collisions. About half of the bombarding energy will be transferred to electrons, but otherwise the bombarding energy will be retained as random motions of protons and $\alpha$ particles within the shock zone, and the $\alpha$ particles will therefore be subject to breakup over the whole of the time they are within the shock zone.

Material may be considered to have flowed downstream of the shock when electrons have had sufficient time to radiate the kinetic energy they have acquired from the heavy particles. Radiation through bremsstrahlung occurs with cross section

$$\sigma_{\text{brems}} \simeq 4 \frac{e^2}{\hbar c} \left( \frac{e^2}{mc^2} \right)^2 \ln(2E) \tag{8}$$

where $E$ is the electron energy in units of the rest mass. In our case the electron energies are $\sim 20$ MeV, and the logarithmic term in equation (8) is about 4, so the cross section is $\sim 10$ mb. This is about five times less than the spallation cross section. On the other hand, an electron of energy 20 MeV has a velocity about five times greater than a proton of the same energy. Hence

$$<\sigma v>_{\text{Bremsstrahlung}} \simeq <\sigma v>_{\text{Spallation}} \tag{9}$$

from which it follows that an appreciable fraction of the $\alpha$ particles must be fragmented by the time they pass downstream of the shock.

At this stage we have to distinguish two cases according to whether the gas density is high enough for neutrons from spallation to be captured by protons, or not. The former case is more efficient in its deuterium production by an order of magnitude. Considering this case, and taking the material of the initial cloud to have the usual helium concentration of $\sim 0.25$ by mass, and using say 40% for the fraction of the helium experiencing complete spallation, we arrive at a D concentration downstream of the shock of 0.1. Thus the mass density of D downstream of the shock is $0.1\ \rho_s$. Using (7), and setting $v_i = c/3$, we have

$$\rho(D) = 0.1\ \rho_s = \frac{7}{10}\ \rho_i = \frac{7}{10} \times \frac{7}{18}\ \frac{aT_s^4}{v_i^2}$$

$$= \frac{49}{20}\ \frac{aT_s^4}{c^2} = 2.7 \times 10^{-21}\ aT_s^4 \tag{10}$$

or $\qquad\qquad aT_s^4 / \rho(D) = 3.7 \times 10^{20}$ erg g$^{-1}$

来看，这些粒子在从冲击波的上游到下游的过程中，其速度变化了 2c/7。我们必须认为波前具有有限深度，并且来自上游的粒子在通过有限冲击区时经历了碰撞。由于 2c/7 的速度等效于每个核子约 40 MeV 的轰击能量，我们得到了与上面讨论过的 α 粒子射入静止气体类似的情景。因此，冲击波上游物质中的 ⁴He 在通过波前的时候会碎裂。

事实上，由于冲击区中的所有粒子都来自上游并经历了碰撞，当前情形比 α 粒子射入周围气体的情形更有利于碎裂。虽然大约一半的轰击能量将被转移给电子，但除此之外的轰击能量将以冲击区内无规则运动的质子和 α 粒子形式存在，这些 α 粒子在冲击区内的整个时间段内都易发生分裂。

当电子有足够的时间将它们从重粒子处得到的动能辐射出去时，物质就可以被认为已经流到了激波的下游。发生韧致辐射的辐射截面为

$$\sigma_{韧致辐射} \simeq 4\frac{e^2}{\hbar c}\left(\frac{e^2}{mc^2}\right)^2 \ln(2E) \tag{8}$$

其中 $E$ 是以静止质量为单位的电子能。在我们这个情形下，电子能量约为 20 MeV，方程（8）中对数项的值大约是 4，因此截面约为 10 mb。这大约是散裂截面的 1/5。另一方面，一个能量为 20 MeV 的电子的速度大约是具有同样能量的质子速度的 5 倍。因此

$$\langle\sigma v\rangle_{韧致辐射} \simeq \langle\sigma v\rangle_{散裂} \tag{9}$$

由此断定很大一部分 α 粒子在通过冲击区下游时必然会碎裂。

在这里，我们必须根据气体密度是否足够高到使得散裂产生的中子能被质子俘获两种情形来区分。前者氘的产生效率比后者高一个量级。鉴于此种情况，通常取初始云块物质中氦的质量丰度通常约为 0.25，假设其中的 40% 完全散裂，我们在冲击区下游得到的 D 的丰度是 0.1。因此冲击区下游 D 的质量密度是 0.1 $\rho_s$。根据方程（7），令 $v_i = c/3$，我们得到

$$\rho(D)=0.1\ \rho_s = \frac{7}{10}\ \rho_i = \frac{7}{10}\times\frac{7}{18}\frac{aT_s^4}{v_i^2}$$

$$=\frac{49}{20}\frac{aT_s^4}{c^2} = 2.7\times 10^{-21}\ aT_s^4 \tag{10}$$

或者 $\qquad aT_s^4/\rho(D) = 3.7\times 10^{20}\ \text{erg}\cdot\text{g}^{-1}$

This is a relation between energy supply and deuterium production. The energy "cost" in the radiation field to produce one gram of deuterium is seen to be $\sim 3.7 \times 10^{20}$ erg. So to produce an average D/H ratio equal to the proto-solar value of $\sim 3 \times 10^{-5}$ throughout a mass $M$ requires $\sim 10^{16} M$ erg, from which we see that to obtain D/H $\sim 3 \times 10^{-5}$ throughout the Galaxy requires $\sim 3 \times 10^{60}$ erg. Because this value is within the range that can be contemplated it seems possible for the present process to give a galactic deuterium concentration comparable to the initial solar system value.

The present considerations require neutrons from the spallation of $^4$He to be captured by protons. For this condition to be satisfied $\rho_i$ must not be much less than $\sim 10^{-8}$ g cm$^{-3}$. Otherwise the efficiency of D production is reduced by an order of magnitude, and the energy requirement is increased correspondingly. In the rest of this article we shall take $\rho_i = 10^{-7}$ g cm$^{-3}$ for definiteness, and will consider the rates which are then operative for various processes.

The first question to be asked is: what will be the order of the depth of the shock zone? Taking $\sim 3 \times 10^{-7}$ g cm$^{-3}$ as the average density within the shock zone, and noting that $<\sigma v>_{\text{Bremsstrahlung}} \simeq 3 \times 10^{-16}$, we see that the electrons lose their energy in a time $\sim 2 \times 10^{-2}$ s. In this time material flowing at a mean speed of say $\sim v_i/2 = c/6$ travels a distance $\sim 10^8$ cm. This gives the order of the depth of the zone.

To prevent radiation downstream of the shock from simply streaming through the front it is necessary that the optical depth of material within the shock zone shall be greater than unity. For the numerical values considered in the previous paragraph there are about 30 g of material per unit area of the front. This is sufficient to dam back the radiation through Thomson scattering by the electrons. Before the radiation can penetrate the shock zone new material is then added from upstream. This circumstance does not depend on the particular numerical values used here. It depends essentially on the Thomson scattering for radiation being much larger than the bremsstrahlung cross section, $\sim 10^{-24}$ cm$^2$ compared with $\sim 10^{-26}$ cm$^2$.

Once bremsstrahlung transfers energy from the electrons to the radiation field other processes become involved, particularly Compton scattering. Because most of the bremsstrahlung energy from 20 MeV electrons consists of $\gamma$ rays above 1 MeV, Compton scattering has a complex behaviour, certain scattering angles augmenting the radiation field, others transferring energy back to the electrons. A refined calculation would be necessary in order to consider such effects in detail. Here we shall simply take relation (9) to represent the order of magnitude of the relation of radiation losses to spallation. The conclusion from (9) is that an appreciable fraction of $\alpha$ particles are fragmented by the time they pass downstream of the shock.

Deuterium produced within the shock zone will itself be subject to spallation, as will be $^3$He and T. Consequently we shall not regard D production as being due to the immediate spallation of $^4$He, but as arising from neutrons released in the breakup of $^4$He. The lifetime

这是能量供应和氘产量之间的关系式。在辐射场中，产生 1 g 氘需要"消耗"的能量约为 $3.7 \times 10^{20}$ erg。因此，在一个质量为 $M$ 的天体中，为了使 D/H 达到原初太阳（约 $3 \times 10^{-5}$）的平均值，需要约 $10^{16} M$ erg 的能量，由此我们发现，在整个银河系中，D/H 达到约 $3 \times 10^{-5}$ 所需能量约为 $3 \times 10^{60}$ erg。由于这个值在合理的范围内，看起来有可能通过这个过程产生和原初太阳系相当的星系的氘丰度。

目前的考虑要求 $^4$He 散裂产生的中子被质子俘获，为满足这个条件，$\rho_i$ 必然不能比约 $10^{-8}$ g·cm$^{-3}$ 小很多。否则 D 产生的效率会减小一个量级，同时能量需求会相应增加。为了明确，在本文余下的部分我们将取 $\rho_i = 10^{-7}$ g·cm$^{-3}$，并将考虑应用于各种过程的速率。

首要回答的问题是：冲击区的厚度在什么量级？取约 $3 \times 10^{-7}$ g·cm$^{-3}$ 作为冲击区内的平均密度，并注意到 $<\sigma v>_{\text{韧致辐射}} \simeq 3 \times 10^{-16}$。我们发现电子在约 $2 \times 10^{-2}$ s 的时间内损失掉它们的能量。在这个时间内，流动物质的平均速度约为 $v_i/2 = c/6$，移动了约 $10^8$ cm 的距离。这给出了冲击区厚度的量级。

为防止冲击波下游的辐射简单地流过波前，冲击区域内物质的光深必须大于1。对上一段中考虑的数值，单位面积的波前有大约 30 g 物质。这足以挡住由电子产生的汤姆逊散射的辐射。在辐射能够穿透冲击区之前，就有新的物质从上游补充进来。这种情况不依赖于这里用到的具体数值。对辐射来说，由于汤姆逊散射的截面远大于韧致辐射的截面（约 $10^{-24}$ cm$^2$ 对约 $10^{-26}$ cm$^2$），光深在本质上由汤姆逊散射决定。

一旦韧致辐射把能量从电子传输到辐射场，其他过程就参与进来，特别是康普顿散射。由于 20 MeV 电子的韧致辐射大部分由能量高于 1 MeV 的 γ 射线组成，康普顿散射具有复杂的行为特征，某些散射角使辐射场扩张，其他散射角把能量返回给电子。为了详细地考虑这些效应，精确计算是必要的。这里我们将简单采用方程（9）表示与散裂有关的辐射损失程度。自关系式（9）得到的结论是，相当可观的一部分 α 粒子在通过冲击波下游时分裂了。

正如 $^3$He 和 T 那样，在冲击波区域产生的氘自身也易发生散裂。因此，我们将不把 D 产生归因于 $^4$He 的直接散裂，而是由 $^4$He 分裂释放的中子生成。中子弱衰变

of the neutrons against weak decay ($\sim 10^3$ s) is very long compared to the time spent ($\sim 10^{-2}$ s) in the shock zone. So the neutrons move downstream to regions where thermodynamic conditions can be considered to be established. Putting $\rho_i = 10^{-7}$ g cm$^{-3}$, $v_i = c/3$ in (7) gives $T_s \simeq 7.6 \times 10^6$ K, which is far too low for deuterium formed by n+p $\rightarrow$ D+$\gamma$ to be subject to spallation or to photodisintegration. The $<\sigma v>$ value for this reaction is $7 \times 10^{-20}$ cm$^3$ s$^{-1}$, so for a hydrogen density $\simeq 7 \times 10^{-7}$ g cm$^{-3}$ downstream of the shock it takes some 30 s for the neutrons to be captured by protons. Because this is much less than the neutron half-life, although amply long enough for the neutrons to flow downstream well clear of the shock, we conclude that essentially all neutrons go to form D.

To recapitulate to this point: Normal thermonuclear processes generate $^4$He from hydrogen with very little production of deuterium. But if $^4$He can be shaken loose into its constituent neutrons and protons in abnormal situations, such as those in the front of a high speed shock wave, conditions become favourable to D production provided the gas density is not so small that the neutrons decay before they are captured by protons. Conditions are then also favourable in that the temperature $T \simeq 7.6 \times 10^6$ K behind the front leads to a lifetime for D(p, $\gamma$) $^3$He of $\sim 10^{10}$ s, which is much longer than the time required for a local exploding object to disperse. The D/H ratio can be locally higher than the terrestrial value by as much as $10^2$, but after averaging with other exterior material the D/H value will be lowered. If the estimate of $3 \times 10^{-5}$ for the proto-solar value is typical of the interstellar medium as a whole, then the process described here could be the origin of all the deuterium in the Galaxy. Accompanying the production of D in the shock front will be that of a smaller amount of $^3$He, perhaps enough to yield the proto-solar values ($\sim 10^{-5}$) taken by Black[3] as typical. Further, because the explosion which produces the shock wave may well be due to nuclear energy generation converting a substantial fraction of hydrogen into helium, this process may also be the source of galactic $^4$He. This brings us back (see pp. 23, 24 of ref. 6) full circle to the fact that conversion of hydrogen into helium in one part in four by mass yields the full energy of the background microwave radiation at 2.7 K and once again forces us to ask if there could have been a mechanism which provided the necessary thermalization. So far we have found no plausible affirmative answer to this question, but the coincidence of the numbers remains puzzling.

We thank Dr Klaus Fricke for discussions on the production of shock waves in the implosion–explosion of massive objects, and the authors of refs. 1, 4 and 5 for informing us of their work in advance of publication. This work was supported in part by the National Science Foundation.

(**241**, 384-386; 1973)

Fred Hoyle & William A. Fowler
California Institute of Technology, Pasadena, California

Received December 12, 1972.

寿命（约 $10^3$ s）与其在冲击波区内的停留时间（约 $10^{-2}$ s）相比要长得多。所以中子向下游运动到可以被认为已形成热力学条件的区域。在（7）中令 $\rho_i = 10^{-7}$ g·cm$^{-3}$，$v_i = c/3$ 得到 $T_s \simeq 7.6 \times 10^6$ K，这一值远低于由 n+p → D+$\gamma$ 产生氘的温度，以至于不易发生散裂或光致分裂。这个反应的 $\langle \sigma v \rangle$ 值为 $7 \times 10^{-20}$ cm$^3$·s$^{-1}$，所以对于氢密度约为 $7 \times 10^{-7}$ g·cm$^{-3}$ 的冲击区下游，质子需要大约 30 s 的时间将中子俘获。虽然这一时间足够让中子流到下游摆脱冲击，但由于其远小于中子的半衰期，我们认为在本质上所有中子都形成了 D。

总结起来说：由氢产生 $^4$He 的一般热核过程几乎不生成氘。但是，如果在异常情况下，如在一个高速冲击波的前沿，$^4$He 能够被震动分解为组成它的中子和质子，在这种情况下，只要气体密度不小到中子在被俘获前就完全衰变，将会有利于 D 产生。随后的条件同样有利于 D 的形成，这是由于波前后面的温度为 $T \simeq 7.6 \times 10^6$ K，导致 D (p, $\gamma$) $^3$He 的寿命约 $10^{10}$ s，这比一个局域爆炸天体消散所需时间长得多。局部的 D/H 比可以比地球上的值高 $10^2$，但是和其他外部物质平均后，D/H 值会降低。如果总体上原初太阳的估计值 $3 \times 10^{-5}$ 是星际介质的特征值，那么这里描述的过程可能是银河系中所有氘的来源。伴随冲击波前锋中 D 的产生，将有少量的 $^3$He 形成，这可能足以产生原初太阳中的值（约 $10^{-5}$），也就是布莱克[3]认为的特征值。另外，因为产生冲击波的爆炸有可能正是由于将很大一部分氢转化为氦产生的核能导致的，所以这个过程可能也是星系中 $^4$He 的源头。这让我们回到（见参考文献 6 的 23、24 页）这样的事实，将氢转化为 1/4 质量的氦产生 2.7 K 的全部微波背景辐射的能量，并且再一次迫使我们提出问题：是否可能已经存在提供必要热化的机制。到目前为止，对这个问题，我们没有发现可信的确切答案，但是数字的巧合仍令人费解。

我们感谢克劳斯·弗里克博士对大质量天体在聚爆——裂爆中产生冲击波的讨论，也感谢参考文献 1、4 和 5 的作者们告知我们他们尚未发表的工作。这项工作部分得到了美国国家科学基金会的支持。

（钱磊 翻译；许冰 审稿）

References:

1. Cesarsky, D. A., Moffet, A. T., and Pasachoff, J. M., *Astrophys. J. Lett.* (in the press).

2. Reeves, H., Audouze, J., Fowler, W. A., and Schramm, D. N., *Astrophys. J.* (in the press).

3. Black, D. C., *Geochim. Cosmochim. Acta,* **36**, 347 (1972).

4. Jefferts, K. B., Penzias, A. A., and Wilson, R. W., *Astrophys. J. Lett.* (in the press).

5. Wilson, R. W., Penzias, A. A., Jefferts, K. B., and Solomon, P. M., *Astrophys. J. Lett.* (in the press).

6. Wagoner, R. V., Fowler, W. A., and Hoyle, F., *Astrophys. J.*, **148**, 3 (1967).

7. Oort, J. H., Solvay Conference on *Structure and Evolution of the Universe,* 163 (R. Stoops, Brussels, 1958).

8. Shapiro, S. L., *Astron. J.*, **76**, 291 (1971).

9. Audouze, J., Epherre, M., and Reeves, H., *High Energy Nuclear Reactions in Astrophysics,* chap. 9 (Benjamin, New York, 1967).

10. Fowler, W. A., Greenstein, J. L., and Hoyle, F., *Geophys. J. Roy. Astron. Soc.*, **6**, 148 (1962).

11. Colgate, S. A., and White, R. H., *Astrophys. J.*, **143**, 626 (1966).

12. Appenzeller, I., and Fricke, K., *Astron. Astrophys.*, **12**, 488 (1971).

13. Appenzeller, I., and Fricke, K., *Astron. Astrophys.*, **18**, 10 (1972).

14. Appenzeller, I., and Fricke, K., *Astron. Astrophys.*, **21**, 285 (1972).

# Afar Mantle Plume: Rare Earth Evidence

J–G. Schilling

## Editor's Note

**Iceland has an unusual geophysical setting, being located over two distinct sources of volcanic activity: a mid-ocean ridge, where hot material wells up from between two diverging tectonic plates, and a hotspot or mantle plume, where a column of magma rises from deep in the mantle. This paper by Jean-Guy Schilling was one of the first to provide confirmation of this picture. Since the two volcanic sources overlap at Iceland, they are hard to distinguish. But Schilling identifies a geochemical signature in the island's basaltic (volcanic) rock that is distinct from that of mid-ocean ridge material and probably comes from a more "primordial" mantle plume. This helped to secure the very notion of deep-seated mantle plumes.**

---

Rare earth pattern zonation about the Afar Triangle, in tholeiitic basalts erupting along the Red Sea Trough and the Gulf of Aden, suggests the presence of a primordial mantle plume rising beneath the Afar and overflowing in a star-like fashion into the soft asthenosphere.

---

THE origin of the Afar Triangle, the locus or near locus of the triple junction formed by the Red Sea–Gulf of Aden and East African Rift, has been debated in detail recently[1,2]. It is particularly important to determine whether the Afar Triangle has controlled the evolution of the three lines of plate divergence or *vice versa*, or what are the real relationships between these three different tectonic segments and the Afar Triangle.

The first analyses in terms of oceanic plate tectonics were made by fitting the Red Sea conjugated coastlines. McKenzie *et al.* suggested[3] that the Afar Depression has been largely created from mantle materials during the separation of Arabia from Africa and, in support, referred to a preliminary report on a magnetic survey of the Afar Triangle[4]. In its latest form, this survey[5] reveals magnetic anomalies of three kinds: first, westward extension of the Gulf of Aden oceanic magnetic anomalies into the southern Afar; second, small amplitude and wavelength anomalies of continental sialic origin; and third, northwest–southeast anomaly trends fanning towards the south, north of about 12°. This suggests complex tectonic trends and geology of both continental and oceanic kind. Considering in greater detail the geology and tectonics of the Afar, Mohr[6,7] objected in part to McKenzie's conclusions[3] and offered a refined model emphasizing the importance that the Danakil and Aisha Horsts may have played as continental remanent blocks. Independently Gass[8] proposed a three stage lithothermal model describing the embryonic development of a hot plume rising beneath the Afar. More recently and without further justification, Morgan[9-11] listed the Afar to be one of the 20 hot plumes which he believes

# 阿法尔地幔柱：稀土元素证据

席林

## 编者按

冰岛具有异常的地球物理背景，它处于两种不同的火山源之上：一个是洋中脊，即热物质从两个离散的构造板块之间上涌的部位；另一个是热点或地幔柱，即从地幔深处呈柱状上升的岩浆流。让－居伊·席林的这篇文章是最早证实上述情景的文章之一。由于两个火山源在冰岛地区有重叠，因此很难进行区别。但是席林指出洋岛玄武岩（火山岩）具有不同于洋中脊物质的地球化学标记，它可能来自于一个更"原生"的地幔柱。这有助于确定深层地幔柱的准确概念。

在阿法尔三角，沿红海海槽和亚丁湾喷出的拉斑玄武岩中稀土元素配分模式的分带性表明，阿法尔地区下部存在上涌的原生地幔柱，并呈星状溢流进入软流圈。

近年来，关于阿法尔三角，即红海、亚丁湾和东非大裂谷构成的三联点所在地或所在地附近区域的成因曾有过详细的讨论[1,2]。该问题对于确定到底是阿法尔三角控制着三条板块离散线的演化还是三条板块离散线的演化影响着阿法尔三角，或者三个不同的构造单元与阿法尔三角之间有何关系尤为重要。

最早的分析是以海洋板块构造理论为依据，利用拟合红海的共轭海岸线的方法提出的。麦肯齐等人认为[3]，阿法尔凹陷主要是在阿拉伯半岛从非洲大陆上分离出去时由地幔物质上涌形成的，为证明这一点，他还提到了一份关于阿法尔三角磁场调查的初步报告[4]。从其最新的结论来看，该项调查[5]揭示出了三类磁异常现象：一、亚丁湾海洋磁异常向西扩展进入阿法尔南部地区；二、硅铝质陆壳来源的、波长和振幅均较小的磁异常；三、在北纬12°以北区域的磁异常具有从北西向南东扇形展开的分布特征。这说明该区复杂的构造走向和地质状况，兼具陆壳和洋壳的双重特征。莫尔[6,7]对阿法尔地区的地质和构造作了更详细的研究后，不完全赞同麦肯齐的结论[3]，并给出了一个修正的模型，该模型强调了达纳基勒和艾沙地垒作为大陆残余块体所发挥的重要作用。加斯[8]则独立地提出了一个三阶段岩热模型，描述了阿法尔地区下部涌升热柱的初级发展。最近，在没有进一步证据的情况下，摩根[9-11]

may drive the lithospheric plates in a global way by viscous drag on their base.

I now present rare earth geochemical evidence which gives strong support to the existence of a hot mantle plume rising beneath the Afar Triangle.

## Afar—Iceland Mantle Plume Analogue: Rare Earth Evidence

I reinterpret rare earth abundance data from submarine tholeiitic basalts erupted along the Red Sea Trough, the Gulf of Aden, and tholeiites from Jebel-Teir Island, reported earlier, by first drawing analogy with similar but more extensive evidence obtained from the Iceland–Reykjanes Ridge-Plume System.

La, $K_2O$, $TiO_2$, $P_2O_5$, radiogenic lead and perhaps strontium in tholeiitic basalts, as well as pyroxene phenocryst abundance relative to plagioclase, are now known to decrease regularly with distance from Iceland along the Reykjanes Ridge[14-18]. Over Iceland and south of 61° N along the Reykjanes Ridge, the abundances of these elements stay relatively constant but the level is different for both regions. The transition between the two end-member types of tholeiites, distinct chiefly in large lithophile element contents and radiogenic isotopes, occurs over some 400 km. It bridges island tholeiitic basalt type (for example, Iceland, Hawaii, Galapagos, Réunion, Jebel-Teir) to submarine tholeiite type erupting along most mid-ocean ridges away from any hotspot interference, respectively[13].

The progressive depletion of large ionic lithophile trace elements is a regular function of the ionic radius, particularly for the rare earth series. The smallest ions from Gd-Lu remain relatively constant in abundance and the light rare earths show a more pronounced variation along the Reykjanes Ridge Axis. Lanthanum, the largest rare earth ion, shows the greatest variation, and Sm an intermediate one. The La/Sm concentration ratio or related functions, such as the ratio of enrichment factors relative to chondrites, illustrate this point (Fig. 1). The $[La/Sm]_{E.F.}$ decreases markedly away from Iceland (possibly in a stepwise fashion). This ratio is a good indicator of fractionation of the light rare earth and can, with the heavy rare earths, set rigorous limits on the genesis of these basalts[13].

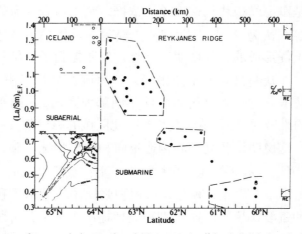

Fig. 1. La/Sm enrichment factors relative to chondritic meteorites[13] in tholeiitic basalts erupted along the post-glacial Reykjanes Ridge Axis and its extension over Iceland (see map insert).

140

又将阿法尔列为以岩石圈板块底部的黏滞曳力驱动全球板块运动的 20 个热柱之一。

本文将为阿法尔三角下部存在上涌热地幔柱这一理论提供稀土元素地球化学方面的有力证据。

## 阿法尔地幔柱与冰岛地幔柱的相似之处：稀土元素证据

首先通过与从冰岛—雷恰内斯的海岭-地幔柱体系中得到的类似但更全面的证据进行类比，我重新解译了沿红海海槽、亚丁湾喷发出的海底拉斑玄武岩以及之前报道的热贝尔-泰尔岛上的拉斑玄武岩中稀土元素丰度的数据。

目前已知，拉斑玄武岩中的 La（镧）、$K_2O$（氧化钾）、$TiO_2$（二氧化钛）、$P_2O_5$（五氧化二磷）、放射成因的 Pb（铅）和 Sr（锶），以及辉石斑晶相对于斜长石的丰度，随着沿雷恰内斯海岭到冰岛距离的增加而有规律地降低 [14-18]。在冰岛和 61°N 以南的雷恰内斯海岭沿线，上述元素的丰度保持相对恒定，但两地的丰度值水平不同。在两种端元拉斑玄武岩之间为过渡类型，它们的差别主要在于大离子亲石元素含量和放射性同位素上，整个过渡带延伸超过 400 km，分别连接着洋岛拉斑玄武岩（例如，冰岛、夏威夷岛、加拉帕戈斯岛、留尼汪岛以及热贝尔-泰尔岛）和沿大多数没有热点影响的海底玄武岩 [13]。

大离子亲石微量元素含量的逐渐亏损是离子半径的正则函数，对于稀土元素系列尤其如此。沿雷恰内斯海岭轴线，离子半径最小的 Gd—Lu（钆—镥）等稀土元素丰度相对恒定，而轻稀土元素则变化较显著。La 是离子半径最大的稀土元素，其含量变化最大，而 Sm（钐）则介于中间。La/Sm 的浓度比或相关函数，如相对于球粒陨石的富集因子之比等，就阐明了这一点（图 1）。随着到冰岛距离的增加，$[La/Sm]_{E.F.}$ 显著降低（可能呈阶梯式）。该比值是衡量轻稀土元素分异的良好指标，可以结合重稀土元素对此类玄武岩的成因给出严格的界限 [13]。

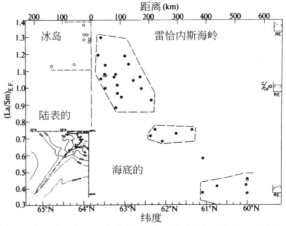

图 1. 沿冰后期雷恰内斯海岭轴线及其到冰岛上的延伸一线（见插图）喷发出的拉斑玄武岩中，相对于球粒陨石的 La/Sm 富集因子 [13]。

A $[La/Sm]_{E.F.}>1$ generally indicates light rare earth enriched fractionation patterns, such as for alkali basalts or island tholeiites (in the model I present here, tholeiites derived from primordial hot mantle plume [PHMP] including island tholeiites and related tholeiitic plateau basalts).

$[La/Sm]_{E.F.}<1$ generally indicates light rare earth depleted submarine mid-ocean ridge tholeiites (in my model, mid-ocean ridge tholeiites derived from the depleted low velocity layer far away from any hotspot interference [DLVL]).

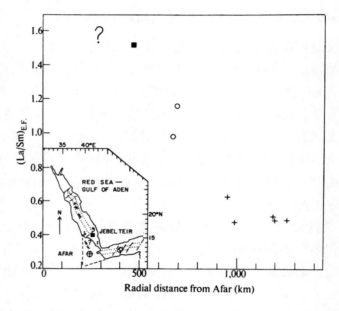

Fig. 2. La/Sm enrichment factors relative to chondritic meteorites[13] in tholeiitic basalts erupted along the Red Sea Trough and the Gulf of Aden, plotted as a function of radial distance from the centre of the Afar Triangle, irrespective of direction (see map insert).

Finally $[La/Sm]_{E.F.}\sim1$ refers to submarine mid-ocean ridge tholeiites generally occurring near Morgan's proposed hot mantle plumes or triple junctions, and which could not be explained at the time[13] (in my model these hybrid tholeiites are produced by mixing [PHMP] and [DLVL] derived tholeiites).

These results are not unique to the Reykjanes Ridge Iceland region. Similarly to Fig. 1, reconsideration of rare earth data for the Afar region[12,13] indicates that the $[La/Sm]_{E.F.}$ also decreases progressively with radial distance away from the proposed Afar hotspot centre[12,13] (Fig. 2). The rare earth patterns change from light RE enriched near the Afar hotspot (Jebel-Teir Island Volcano) to relatively flat RE patterns unfractionated but enriched relative chondrite abundances at intermediate radial distance (Gulf of Aden Ridge Axis), and finally to progressively more light RE depleted patterns along the Red Sea Trough further away from the Afar. All these basalts are tholeiitic in composition, again judging from the CIPW norm and Yoder and Tilley's classification[19-22].

一般来说，当 $[La/Sm]_{E.F.}>1$ 时，通常指示轻稀土元素富集型配分特征，主要见于碱性玄武岩、洋岛拉斑玄武岩等（按照本文提出的模型，拉斑玄武岩来自原生热地幔柱 (PHMP)，包括洋岛拉斑玄武岩和相关的高原拉斑玄武岩）。

当 $[La/Sm]_{E.F.}<1$，通常指示轻稀土元素亏损的海底洋中脊拉斑玄武岩（按照我的模型，洋中脊拉斑玄武岩来源于不受热点影响的亏损低速层 (DLVL)）。

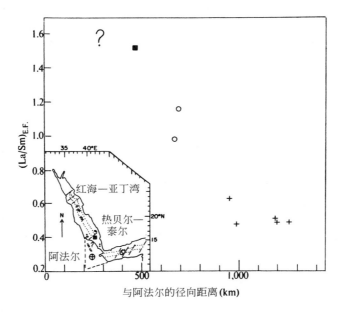

图 2. 沿红海海槽和亚丁湾喷出的拉斑玄武岩中相对于球粒陨石 [13] 的 La/Sm 富集因子，与到阿法尔三角中心的（不计方向，见插图）径向距离的相关关系。

最后 $[La/Sm]_{E.F.}\sim1$，指示的是海底洋中脊拉斑玄武岩。一般见于摩根提出的热地幔柱或三联点附近，这一点当时还无法解释 [13]（按照我的模型，这种混合型拉斑玄武岩是由来源于 PHMP 和 DLVL 来源的拉斑玄武岩浆混合形成）。

上述结果并不仅限于雷恰内斯海岭和冰岛地区。与图 1 相似，对阿法尔地区的稀土元素数据重新分析 [12,13] 表明，随着到假设的阿法尔热点中心的径向距离的增大，$[La/Sm]_{E.F.}$ 也逐渐降低 [12,13]（图 2）。在阿法尔热点附近（热贝尔-泰尔岛火山）稀土配分模式为轻稀土富集型，在中等的径向距离位置（亚丁湾脊轴），稀土分配模式变为未分异的相对平坦型，而球粒陨石相对富集，最后在远离阿法尔的红海海槽沿线则逐渐变为轻稀土元素亏损型。根据 CIPW 标准矿物及约德和蒂利的分类法 [19-22]，在成分上它们都属于拉斑玄武岩。

Thus a similar phenomenon seems to occur away from the Afar hotspot as in the case of the Iceland hotspot. The rate of progressive light RE depletion is smaller for the Afar. No data are available in tholeiitic basalt erupted from fissures along the Danakil Depression[23], but these would be very interesting, because the results should serve as a test of the hot mantle plume mixing model I recently proposed[14-15], and which is now applied to the Afar.

## Hot Mantle Plume Mixing Model

The model requires two mantle sources distinct in large ionic lithophile trace elements and in radiogenic lead and strontium contents. Tholeiitic basalts are derived by partial melting at shallow depth from either of these two sources, interact and mix in various proportions along the zones of plate divergence, such as the Red Sea Trough and the Gulf of Aden (or Reykjanes Ridge).

The first mantle source, primordial hot mantle plume [PHMP], upwells vertically and forcefully beneath the centre of the Afar Triangle (Iceland), and overflows into the surrounding upper asthenosphere either radially or preferentially along directions of lithosphere weakness, such as the Danakil Depression–Red Sea Trough, the Gulf of Aden, and perhaps the Ethiopian Rift (Reykjanes and Kolbeinsey Ridges). The PHMP is relatively richer in large ionic lithophile elements, and produces tholeiitic basalts with $[La/Sm]_{E.F.}>1$. Further, the PHMP material has remained before rising long enough as a closed system deep in the mantle (greater than 250 km) to build up its radiogenic isotopes[24-26]. During its rise and decompression at shallow depth it will produce with sufficient extent of partial melting[13], island tholeiite type basalt, such as for Iceland[27], Hawaii[28], Galapagos[29] and Réunion[30], and by prediction tholeiites erupted over the Afar along the Danakil Depression[23]. Such tholeiitic basalts are here called PHMP-tholeiites.

The second mantle source (DLVL), of more global extent, is the low velocity layer. This layer is characteristically depleted in large ionic lithophile elements (K, Rb, Cs, Ba, U, Th, light rare earths, and so on)[13,31], and low in radiogenic Pb and Sr (refs. 32, 33). Usually, away from any hot plume interference, the DLVL feeds, passively and in response to plate divergence, mid-ocean ridge spreading with accreting lithospheric and crustal materials such as refractory solids, solid and melt mush, and melt. Most mid-ocean ridge basalts, depleted in the above elements with $[La/Sm]_{E.F.}<1$, and also low in radiogenic Pb and Sr, are derived from the DLVL source. This is the case for tholeiites erupted along the Red Sea Trough, north of 22° N (south of 61° N on the Reykjanes Ridge).

Near hotspots, between these two extremes there is a zone of transition, where interaction and mixing of the two principal tholeiitic melt types will occur (and perhaps of the two mantle sources as well). This is the case for submarine ridge basalts analysed from the Gulf of Aden (comparable to the Reykjanes Ridge around 63° N), and characterized by hybrid rare earth patterns intermediate between the two extreme component melt types. Thus flat rare earth patterns with $[La/Sm]_{E.F.}\sim1$ roughly represents an equal mixture, whereas in Jebel-Teir the PHMP-tholeiite is likely to dominate.

144

因此在远离阿法尔热点的地区，也出现了与冰岛热点类似的现象。只是在阿法尔地区轻稀土元素的亏损速率相对较小。虽然沿达纳基勒凹陷[23]的裂缝喷出的拉斑玄武岩还没有可用数据，但这些数据将会非常有趣，因为得出的结果可以用来检验我最近提出[14,15]并且现在应用于阿法尔地区的热地幔柱混合模型。

## 热地幔柱混合模型

该模型要求存在两个地幔源，两者在大离子亲石微量元素以及放射性铅、锶的含量上不同。来自上述两个地幔源的物质，在较浅深度部分熔融生成了拉斑玄武岩，沿着板块离散区域上，如红海海槽和亚丁湾（或雷恰内斯海岭），这些幔源物质相互作用并以不同比例发生混合。

第一个地幔源，原生热地幔柱（PHMP）在阿法尔三角（冰岛）中心之下强烈垂直上涌，呈放射状溢流或优先沿岩石圈薄弱带流出，进入周围的浅部软流圈。举例来说，岩石圈薄弱带有：达纳基勒凹陷—红海海槽、亚丁湾，也许还有埃塞俄比亚裂谷（包括雷恰内斯和科尔本塞海岭）。PHMP 具有相对丰富的大离子亲石元素，所形成的拉斑玄武岩的 $[La/Sm]_{E.F.} > 1$。此外，在上升之前，PHMP 物质一直在地幔深处（深度大于 250 km）保持长时间封闭状态，故其放射性同位素累积量较高[24-26]。在上升过程中随着压力不断减小，到达较浅深度时，就发生程度足够大的部分熔融[13]，形成洋岛拉斑玄武岩，如冰岛[27]、夏威夷岛[28]、加拉帕戈斯岛[29]和留尼汪岛[30]等岛屿上的拉斑玄武岩。另外，据预测沿达纳基勒凹陷在阿法尔上部喷出的拉斑玄武岩也属此类[23]。本文中我们将这类拉斑玄武岩称为 PHMP 型拉斑玄武岩。

第二个地幔源即低速层（DLVL），更具有全球性。该层的典型特征是亏损大离子亲石元素（K（钾）、Rb（铷）、Cs（铯）、Ba（钡）、U（铀）、Th（钍）、轻稀土元素等）[13,31]以及放射性铅和锶含量较低（参考文献32、33）。通常，在远离热柱干扰的区域，由于板块离散，DLVL 被动地充填到扩张洋中脊，与此同时岩石圈和地壳物质例如难熔固体、固体和熔体混杂物以及熔融物质在此加积。大多洋中脊玄武岩亏损上述元素，即 $[La/Sm]_{E.F.} < 1$，且放射性铅和锶的含量也较低，它们来源于 DLVL。22°N 以北沿红海海槽喷出的拉斑玄武岩即是此种类型（61°N 以南的雷恰内斯海岭亦同）。

在热点附近，这两种端元之间存在着过渡带，两种主要的拉斑玄武岩融合类型将发生相互作用并混合（也许是两个地幔源的相互作用和混合）。亚丁湾地区（可类比于 63°N 附近的雷恰内斯海岭）的海底洋脊玄武岩当属此类，该类玄武岩的特征是其混合稀土配分模式介于两种端元组分配合类型之间。故稀土配分模式平缓，$[La/Sm]_{E.F.} \sim 1$，说明其基本上为等量混合，而在热贝尔-泰尔岛则可能以 PHMP 型拉斑玄武岩占主导。

So far the concept corresponds to Morgan's original paper on hot plumes[9], but differs over some minor points on which I have accumulated evidence and which can be easily tested. The model is also very similar to Gass's elegant model[8], but with some distinctions made on mantle source compositions. On the other hand, the model is quite distinct from Gass's recent convective model[34].

In considering the evidence for the Iceland–Reykjanes system in detail[14-15], I have proposed two mechanisms for the mixing of the two primary lava types to occur, both probably operating simultaneously. One mechanism calls for elongated magma chambers beneath the zones of rifting, and the other requires horizontal dike propagation over long distances as proposed and demonstrated for the Kilauea Rift Zone[35,36].

## Flow Patterns about the Afar Mantle Plume Centre: Rare Earth Evidence

The mixing proportions along transitional zones depend on the PHMP flow pattern and intensity about the plume into the surrounding LVL. The overflow differs for each plume as well as with time (ref. 37; and J-G. S., in preparation). It depends on local conditions such as vertical PHMP flux, local geometry of the spreading axis and other tectonic elements, related lithosphere spreading rate(s) and prevailing stress field and thermal field. Further, within the upper 200-300 km depth both mantle sources are composed of partially molten rocks to variable degrees; and Deffeyes's recent hot plume model[38] does not apply directly. I believe we are dealing with flow of porous media one into another, percolation of melts and penetrated convection. Such systems have been called lithothermal systems[39], and the concept has also been used for the Afar[8].

In the case of Iceland, the PHMP overflow about Iceland seems to be chiefly bi-directional, southward along the Reykjanes Ridge and northward along the Kolbeinsey Ridge[14,15]. This is in contrast to Morgan's proposed uniform radial asthenospheric flows about hot plumes[9-11]. Rather, I prefer more directional and perhaps more complex asthenospheric overflows about plumes as also considered by Vogt[37]. The choice is based on morphological, hydrodynamic, rheological and thermal grounds[14,15]. Such channelling of the overflow about the plume is controlled by existing zones of lithosphere weakness, especially spreading centres (actually lines). Once a steady state is approached or reached, zones of plate divergence in the upper asthenosphere should be characteristically hotter and mass deficient because of diapiric and magmatic injection, and therefore should favour mantle flows. Further, the overflow can be affected by damming effects caused by remanent continental blocks with colder roots such as the Danakil and Aisha Horsts and African blocks or fracture zones (Greenland, for the more complex flows along the Kolbeinsey Ridge relative to the Reykjanes Ridge). On this basis I suggest a three directional star-like flow for the PHMP about the Afar hotspot (see Fig. 3). The branching flows are along the Danakil Depression and Red Sea Trough, toward and along the Gulf of Aden, and also (but less vigorously) beneath the Ethiopian Rift. The spreading rate is very small and the thermal gradients less pronounced along this latter direction. The chemical gradients (Figs. 1 and 2) suggest a direct relationship between the $[La/Sm]_{E.F.}$ and radial distance irrespective of direction. This does not prove the flow to be

到目前为止，该设想与摩根关于热柱的最初论述 [9] 均相符，但在一些细节上有所不同，关于这些细节我已经积累了大量证据，而且很容易得到验证。本模型与加斯的精致模型 [8] 也很相似，只是对地幔源的成分的看法有所不同。另外，本模型与加斯最近提出的对流模型 [34] 大不相同。

通过详细研究关于冰岛—雷恰内斯体系的这些证据 [14-15]，我认为两种初始熔岩类型的混合可能存在两种机制，而且这两种机制很可能同时发挥作用。一种机制要求裂谷带下方的岩浆房被拉长；另一种则要求水平岩墙远距离的扩展，正如基于基拉韦石裂谷带所提出并已得到证明的那样 [35,36]。

### 阿法尔地幔柱中心的流动模式：稀土元素证据

过渡带沿线的混合比例取决于 PHMP 的流动模式以及热柱进入周围 LVL 的强度。热柱的溢流模式各不相同，且随时间不断变化（参考文献 37；让－居伊·席林，完稿中）。它取决于区域环境，如 PHMP 垂直通量、扩张脊的局部地形以及其他构造因素、相关岩石圈扩张速率与主应力场和热场等等。另外，在上部的 200~300 km 深处，两种幔源在不同程度上均由部分熔融的岩石组成。我们并未直接采用德费耶新近提出的热柱模型 [38]。我认为，这里的涌流是相互渗透的多孔介质流，即表现为熔体渗透和渗透对流。此类体系被称为岩热体系 [39]，且该概念已被引入对阿法尔地区的研究中 [8]。

在冰岛，PHMP 溢流似乎主要是沿两个方向的，即沿雷恰内斯海岭向南和沿科尔本塞洋脊向北 [14,15]。这与摩根提出的热柱呈均匀放射状在软流圈内流动 [9-11] 的观点不同。当然，我倾向于认为热柱的软流圈溢流更可能是定向的，且可能更复杂，沃格特 [37] 也这样认为。这是根据地形、流体力学特征、流变特征以及热特征等 [14,15] 作出的选择。热柱溢流的这种通道效应主要受先存的岩石圈薄弱带，尤其是扩张中心（实际上呈线状）的影响。一旦接近或达到稳定状态，由于底辟构造和岩浆的注入，浅部软流圈的板块离散带将呈现出温度升高和质量减小的特征，因此更有利于地幔流的形成。此外，溢流还可能受堰塞效应的影响。堰塞效应是由具有较低温度山根的残余陆块造成的，例如，达纳基勒和艾沙地垒以及非洲地块或各断裂带（格陵兰岛，因为科尔本塞洋脊沿线的地幔流相对于雷恰内斯海岭沿线的更复杂）。据此我认为，阿法尔热点的 PHMP 应为三向星状流（见图 3）。这些支流分别沿达纳基勒凹陷—红海海槽方向，朝向并沿着亚丁湾方向，以及在埃塞俄比亚裂谷下方（但不是很强）流动。沿第三种流向的扩张速率很小，且热梯度也不明显。化学梯度图（图 1 和图 2）显示，[La/Sm]$_{E.F.}$ 与径向距离（不计方向）直接相关。但这并不能证明流向是呈均匀放射状的，而是主要受流变约束影响并具有方向性。结合所提出的

uniformly radial but rather the rheological constraints prevail and the flow is directional. But the data of Fig. 2 do require, in conjunction with the mixing model proposed[14], that the flow intensity be about the same along the two principal directions of flow (Fig. 3), and vary chiefly as a function of distance from the hot plume centre. I conclude that the PHMP flow about the Afar is not vigorous enough to feed along the entire length of plate divergence the Danakil Depression–Red Sea Axial Trough and Gulf of Aden (no data are available as yet along the Ethiopian Rift). Where PHMP deficiency occurs, accreting material rising at ridge axis is complemented by the DLVL source. This mantle source typically feeds mid-oceanic ridge segments far away from any hot plume interference.

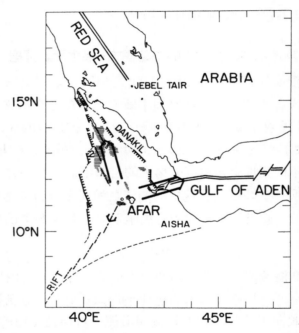

Fig. 3. Afar Triangle showing the three main zones of crustal attenuation also corresponding to preferred mantle plume flow direction about its centre in the upper asthenosphere. Length of arrows roughly proportional to intensity of flow. Estimate of the plume diameter cannot be made for lack of data on the Danakil Depression (see ref. 15 for Iceland). Hatched area 1 refers to Erta Ale Volcanic Range, and 2 to Alayta Volcanic Range[23].

Along transitional segments of spreading ridges or diverging lithospheric blocks, both mantle sources will rise as diapirs, decompress and partially melt. The primary melts mix by coalescence, as well as in elongated magma chambers accumulating at the base of the crust beneath ridge crests or troughs. These magma chambers are ready to feed intermittently volcanic eruptions above[40]. Such shallow depth volcanism will give rise to tholeiitic volcanism of a transitional type isotopically and in terms of trace element composition, provided the plate divergence is sufficiently rapid to set up an oceanic dynamical and thermal regime of rapid diapiric injections[13]. This, of course, corresponds to Gass's[8] third stage of volcanism with the distinction, however, that near the Afar such volcanism takes source from the PHMP material and not from the DLVL, just as beneath Iceland and for other hot plumes[14].

混合模型[14]来看,图2中所示数据确实要求沿两个主方向（图3）地幔流的强度相同,且主要随到热柱中心距离的变化而变化。据此我认为：阿尔法热点的PHMP流不很强,不足以补给板块离散区的所有区域,如达纳基勒凹陷、红海轴海槽和亚丁湾（目前还没有埃塞俄比亚裂谷的相关数据）。当PHMP流不足时,脊轴涌升出的增生物质就由DLVL源物质补充。这种地幔源通常成为不受热点影响的洋中脊的供应源。

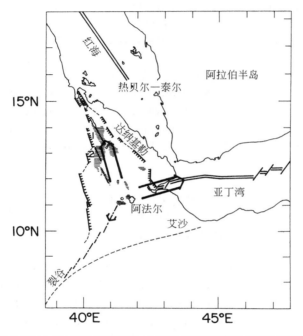

图3. 阿法尔三角显示了三个主要的地壳减薄带,同时对应着在浅部软流圈内以阿法尔三角为中心的地幔流的择优流向。箭头的长度大致与流动强度成正比。由于缺少达纳基勒凹陷的相关数据,因此无法估算热柱直径（参见文献15关于冰岛地区的相关论述）。阴影部分1代表埃尔塔阿勒火山群,2代表阿莱塔火山群[23]。

　　沿着扩张脊或离散岩石圈板块块体的过渡段,两个地幔源都将以底辟形式隆升,发生减压然后部分熔融。原始熔体通过聚结作用相互混合,并在脊峰或脊槽下面地壳底部的狭长岩浆房里不断累积。这些岩浆房随时可为上覆的间歇性的火山喷发提供物质来源[40]。倘若板块离散速度足够快,可形成快速底辟的热动力学环境,那么这样的浅源火山作用将引起在同位素和微量元素组成为过渡类型的拉斑玄武岩岩浆作用[13]。当然,这恰好对应着加斯[8]模型中火山作用的第三个阶段,不同之处在于,在阿法尔附近,这种火山作用以PHMP物质为来源,而非像冰岛下方和其他一些热柱[14]那样来源于DLVL。

## Flow Patterns about the Afar Mantle Plume Centre: Geophysical Evidence

Geophysically, the proposed direction of the PHMP flow about the Afar hot plume should correspond to zones of crustal attenuations and oceanization, to a degree depending on the intensity of the flow and local spreading conditions. Further, the general area where the plume rises should be underlain by anomalous mantle to some considerable depth just as beneath Iceland[41]. Makris *et al.*[42] interpret gravity field survey over the Afar to suggest just that. According to their model, the Afar region is underlaid by 3.25 g cm[-3] material, and along the Danakil Depression the crust is very strongly attenuated and partly oceanized; along the Wonji Fault Belt toward the Ethiopian Rift, the crust is slightly attenuated and most probably continental. This evidence is in excellent agreement with the prediction based on rare earth consideration. Unfortunately no gravity data are available from the hot plume centre toward the Gulf of Aden, but the available seismic data are also consistent with the rare earth inferences. Seismic profiles in the area[43] suggest that the part of the Gulf of Aden characterized by anomalously low mantle velocity extends toward the west. Near the Gulf of Tadjura the shallowing of the sea seems to be accompanied by a thickening of the crust and velocity-depth sections very similar to that derived by Palmason for Iceland[44]. Thus the Afar–Gulf of Aden plume-ridge system is analogous to the Iceland–Reykjanes system seismically[44-45] as well as chemically.

Other geophysical and tectonic data also focus toward a tri-directional shallow asthenosphere flow pattern. These are the direction and types of magnetic anomaly lineaments[4,5] and the so-called megastructures[46].

How can the plume centre be located? The centre of reference from which radial distances were measured on Fig. 2 was taken arbitrarily at 11°15′N, 41°25′E, northwest of Lake Abbe, approximately at the centre of the Afar Triangle. This choice was made at the triple junction of the west–southwest Gulf of Aden trend, the south–southeast extension of the Danakil Depression (characterized by the Erta Ale and Alayta Ranges disposed en-echelon fissures of tholeiitic basalt outpouring)[23], and finally the approximate extension of the Ethiopian African Rift along the Wonji Fault Belt (Fig. 3). I do not wish to imply that this point necessarily represents the centre of the hot plume. The exact position of these coordinates is not critical to the argument presented here. The plume centre could easily be displaced by some 100 km, without altering the conclusions reached from Fig. 3. Later, I found that this point coincides with the shaded area of Fig. 3 of Barberi *et al.*[23], characterized by centres of thermal activity, and where evidence for earlier submarine volcanism exists[47-48]. It also corresponds to the area where the Wonji Fault Belt seems to die out and lose its identity[47], and where direction of faulting and magnetic anomaly direction change from north–northwest to nearly west[4,5]. Finally, it corresponds to Mohr's proposed quaternary triple junction near Lake Abbe (11°N, 41°30′E, ref. 49). It seems, then, that the synthesis of entirely independent structural, tectonic, magnetic and geochemical data all focus toward the presence of the hot plume centre in this area.

## 阿法尔地幔柱中心的流动模式：地球物理证据

从地球物理学角度来看，前面提到的阿法尔热柱的 PHMP 流动方向应该对应着地壳的减薄带和洋化带，其程度则取决于地幔流的强度以及区域扩张环境。另外，通常在热柱涌升的区域，其下部的某一深处应该存在异常地幔，正如在冰岛下部一样 [41]。马克里斯等人 [42] 关于阿法尔地区重力场调查结果的解释恰好证明了这一点。根据他们的模型，阿法尔地区下方物质的密度为 $3.25\,g\cdot cm^{-3}$，沿达纳基勒凹陷，地壳的减薄非常明显且还有部分被洋化；而沿翁吉断裂带向埃塞俄比亚裂谷方向，地壳的减薄作用则较弱，而且绝大部分为陆壳。这些特征与根据稀土元素作出的预测非常一致。可惜的是，没有从热柱中心到亚丁湾一线上的重力资料，但已有的地震数据也与根据稀土元素得出的推断一致。该区的地震剖面 [43] 显示，亚丁湾地区地幔中存在向西延伸的异常低速带。在塔朱拉湾附近，海水不断变浅的同时似乎还伴随着地壳的加厚，速度－深度剖面与由保尔马松模型推导出的冰岛地区的非常相似 [44]。因此，无论是从地震特征 [44-45] 还是化学组成上来看，阿法尔—亚丁湾热柱－洋脊体系都可类比于冰岛—雷恰内斯体系。

其他地球物理和构造资料也显示，该处为三向浅层软流圈流动模式，而这正是磁异常线性构造 [4,5] 及所谓大型构造的方向和类型 [46]。

那么如何确定热柱中心的位置呢？图 2 中用于测定径向距离的参考中心（$11°15'N$，$41°25'E$），是人为选定的，在阿贝湖西北部，大致处于阿法尔三角的中心位置。这个位置是三个走向的三联点，即亚丁湾的西—南西走向，达纳基勒凹陷（以埃尔塔阿勒火山和阿莱塔山脉的拉斑玄武岩喷出形成雁列裂缝为特征）的南—南东走向 [23] 以及埃塞俄比亚非州大裂谷沿翁吉断裂带（图3）的大致延伸方向。当然，我并不是说该点一定就是热柱的中心。坐标的确切位置对于本文的论证并不是特别重要。热柱中心发生 100 km 左右的位移是很容易的，但不会改变根据图3所得出的结论。随后我又发现，该点的位置与巴尔贝里等 [23] 的论文中图3的阴影部分一致，而该阴影部分代表的是热活动中心，且有证据证明该处曾有海底火山存在 [47,48]。同时它还是翁吉断裂带尖灭而难以辨认的地方 [47]，也是断层活动和磁异常方向由北—北西转为正西的位置所在 [4,5]。最后，它与莫尔提出的位于阿贝湖（$11°N$，$41°30'E$，参考文献 49）附近的四元三联点也相对应。由此看来，综合各个独立获得的结构、构造、磁场以及地球化学等方面数据，均显示该区有热柱中心存在。

## PHMP and DLVL Mantle Source Characterization

Not only chemical but also mineralogical parameters seem to be correlative with distance from hot plume centres along mid-ocean ridges. The unusual presence of clinopyroxene phenocrysts in the Gulf of Aden pillow basalts[21] in contrast to mid-ocean ridge basalts which are usually rich in plagioclase phenocrysts, and the remarkable and regular increase of pyroxene phenocryst abundance over plagioclase toward Iceland along the Reykjanes Ridge[18], are examples. A petrographic inspection of pillow basalts erupted along the Mid-Atlantic Ridge over the Azores Platform, another proposed hotspot[9-11], also contains an unusual abundance of clinopyroxenes relative to plagioclase and olivine (unpublished). All these basalts are tholeiitic and have light rare earth enriched patterns similar to basalts derived from the Iceland and Afar hot mantle plumes. The presence of clinopyroxene in submarine ridge basalt erupting near hotspots thus seems to reflect the unusual PHMP mantle composition and thermodynamic melting conditions prevailing, which both need to be investigated further.

It is important to carry out geochemical, petrological and geophysical characterization of both the PHMP and the DLVL mantles. The trace element and isotopic composition of the DLVL have been indirectly but extensively inferred from the so-called low-$K_2O$ mid-ocean ridge tholeiites[13,32,33,50,51] erupting sufficiently far away from any hotspot. In addition Sr and Pb isotopic ratios[25,33] suggest that the DLVL must have undergone such a depletion at some considerably earlier time in the Earth's history, presumably by previous episodes of melting and magma extraction such as of alkali basalts[53], and/or during continental growth[54], and differentiation of the upper few hundred kilometers of the Earth's mantle during geological time[14].

The PHMP source is less well defined and may vary from one hot plume to another. The PHMPs rising beneath the Afar, Iceland, Hawaii, the Galapagos and Réunion hotspots seem undepleted in large ionic lithophile elements, and derived from deeper than the DLVL (refs. 14, 15). It is, of course, too early to speculate whether the plumes composed of relatively more primordial mantle originate from a single deep earth layer of worldwide extent (homogeneous or inhomogeneous), or whether each plume is generated from deep but localized pockets of gravitationally unstable mantle.

What seems more certain[13,24,25] is that such hot mantle plume source(s) have remained deep in the Earth as closed systems long enough to build up their radiogenic isotopes and heat content, before rising as plumes and transporting relatively more primordial material to the Earth's upper zones[14]. Although Vogt[55] has recently called for global synchronism of mantle plume activity, until this suggestion is further substantiated I believe the balance of evidence suggests that the time of plume upwelling differs from one ocean to another, and from one hot plume to another, and that the intensity of activity is variable with time (J-G. S. and Noe-Nygaard, unpublished). This further complicates direct isotopic comparisons and inferences on the depth location of plume sources.

## PHMP 与 DLVL 地幔源的特征描述

除化学数据外，矿物学参数似乎也与从热柱中心沿洋中脊向外延伸的距离相关。例如，亚丁湾枕状玄武岩[21]中单斜辉石斑晶的异常存在，与洋中脊玄武岩形成鲜明对比，因为洋中脊玄武岩中通常富含斜长石斑晶；例如，沿雷恰内斯海岭向冰岛方向，辉石斑晶的含量相对于斜长石呈明显而有规律的增加[18]。沿亚速尔地台（另一个可能的热点[9-11]）上的大西洋洋中脊喷发的枕状玄武岩岩相调查表明，其单斜辉石相对于斜长石和橄榄石的含量也异常丰富（尚未发表）。上述玄武岩均为拉斑玄武岩，其轻稀土元素富集类型与来自冰岛和阿法尔热柱的玄武岩相似。因此，热点附近喷出的海底洋中脊玄武岩中单斜辉石的存在，可能反映了 PHMP 地幔组成的特殊性以及主要热动力熔融条件的差异，具体情况还有待于进一步研究。

PHMP 和 DLVL 型地幔的地球化学、岩石学以及地球物理学特征的确定亦非常重要。DLVL 的微量元素及同位素组成是根据对距离任何热点足够远处喷出的所谓低氧化钾（$K_2O$）洋中脊拉斑玄武岩的大量研究间接推断出的[13,32,33,50,51]。另外，Sr 和 Pb 的同位素比值研究[25,33]显示，在地质历史早期 DLVL 必定就已经历了亏损。这一亏损过程可能与多阶段的熔融和岩浆分离作用如碱性玄武岩的形成[53]、大陆的增长作用[54]以及地质历史时期上地幔几百公里的分异[14]等有关。

对 PHMP 源还不是很明确，而且不同热柱之间也可能互不相同。在阿法尔、冰岛、夏威夷、加拉帕戈斯和留尼汪热点下部，涌升出的 PHMP 中大离子亲石元素似乎并未亏损，并且它产生的深度也大于 DLVL（参考文献 14、15）。当然，目前还不能推测到底是所有热柱均由来自同一个全球规模的单一深地层（均一或不均一）中相对较原始的地幔物质组成，还是各热柱分别由来自当地深处的重力不稳定的局部地幔物质组成。

不管怎样，比较确定的一点是[13,24,25]，此类热地幔柱源作为封闭体系一定在地球深处停留了足够长的时间，积累了大量放射性同位素和热量，尔后才以热柱形式上升，将相对较原始的物质带到了地球上部圈层[14]。虽然最近沃格特[55]又提出地幔柱活动在全球是同步进行的，但在该观点得到进一步证实以前，我仍相信各方面证据的综合结果，即不同大洋之间，不同热柱之间，其涌升时间是不同的；而且热柱的活动强度也随时间不断变化（让－居伊·席林和诺埃－尼高，尚未发表）。这使得不同热柱源之间同位素的直接比较及其所处深度的推断变得更加复杂。

I thank Mrs M. Osti and M. Zajac for help with typing and drawings. This work has been supported by the US Office of Naval Research and the National Science Foundation.

(*Nature Physical Science*, **242**, 2-5; 1973)

**J-G. Schilling**
Graduate School of Oceanography, University of Rhode Island, Kingston, RI 02881

Received January 23, 1973.

---

References:

1. Falcon, N. L., Gass, I. G., Girdler, R.W., and Laughton, A. S., *Phil. Trans. Roy. Soc.*, **267**,1 (1970).

2. Girdler, R. W. (ed.), *Tectonophysics Special Issue*, **15**, 1 (1972).

3. McKenzie, D. P., Davies, D., and Molnar, P., *Nature*, **226**, 243 (1970).

4. Girdler, R. W., *Phil. Trans. Roy. Soc.*, **267**, 359 (1970).

5. Girdler, R. W., and Hall, S. A., *Tectonophysics*, **15**, 53 (1972).

6. Mohr, P. A., *Nature*, **228**, 547 (1970).

7. Mohr, P. A., *J. Geophys. Res.*, **75**, 7340 (1970).

8. Gass, I. G., *Phil. Trans. Roy. Soc.*, **267**, 369 (1970).

9. Morgan, W. J., *Nature*, **230**, 42 (1971).

10. Morgan, W. J., *Bull. Amer. Assoc. Petrol. Geol.*, **56**, 203 (1972).

11. Morgan, W. J., *Mem. Geol. Soc. Amer.* (in the press).

12. Schilling, J-G., *Science*, **165**, 1357 (1969).

13. Schilling, J-G., *Phil. Trans. Roy. Soc.*, A, **268**, 663 (1971).

14. Schilling, J-G., *Nature* (in the press).

15. Schilling, J-G., *J. Geophys. Res.* (in the press).

16. Sun, S. S., Tatsumoto, M., and Schilling, J-G., *Earth Planet. Sci. Lett.* (in the press).

17. Hart, S. R., Powell, J. L., and Schilling, J-G., *Earth Planet. Sci. Lett.* (in the press).

18. Moore, J. G., and Schilling, J-G., *Contr. Min. Petrol.* (in the press).

19. Yoder, H. S., and Tilley, C.E., *J. Petrol.*, **3**, 343 (1962).

20. Chase, R. L., in *Hot Brines and Recent Heavy Metal Deposits in the Red Sea* (edit. by Degens, E. T., and Ross, D.A.), 122 (Springer-Verlag, New York, 1969).

21. Cann, J. R., *Deep-Sea Res.*, **17**, 477 (1970).

22. Gass, I. G., Makick, D. I. J., and Cox, K. G., *Geol. Soc. Lond. J.* (in the press).

23. Barberi, F., Borsi, S., Ferrara, G., Marinelli, G., and Varet, J., *Phil. Trans. Roy. Soc.*, **267**, 293 (1970).

24. Tatsumoto, M., *J. Geophys. Res.*, **71**, 1721 (1966).

25. Peterman, Z. E., and Hedge, C. E., *Geol. Soc. Amer. Bull.*, **82**, 493 (1971).

26. Welke, H., Moorbath, S., Cumming, G. L., and Sigurdsson, H., *Earth Planet. Sci. Lett.*, **4**, 221 (1968).

27. Jakobsson, S. P., *Lithos*, **5**, 365 (1972).

28. Schilling, J-G., and Winchester, J. W., *Contr. Min. Petrol.*, **23**, 27 (1969).

29. McBirney, A. R., and Williams, H., *Geol. Soc. Mem.*, **118** (1969).

30. Upton, B. G., and Wadsworth, W. J., *Phil. Trans. Roy. Soc.*, A, **271**, 105 (1972).

31. Kay, R., Hubbard, N. J., and Gast, P. W., *J. Geophys. Res.*, **75**, 1585 (1970).

32. Gast, P. W., *Phys. Earth Planet. Int.*, **3**, 246 (1970).

33. Tatsumoto, M., *Science*, **153**, 1094 (1966).

34. Gass, I. G., *Phil. Trans. Roy. Soc.*, A, **271**, 131 (1972).

35. Fiske, R. S., and Jackson, E. D., *Proc. Roy. Soc.*, **329**, 299 (1972).

36. Wright, T. L., and Fiske, R. S., *J. Petrol.*, **12**, 65 (1971).

37. Vogt, P. R., *Earth Planet. Sci. Lett.*, **13**, 153 (1971).

38. Deffeyes, K. S., *Nature*, **240**, 539 (1972).

39. Elder, J. W., *Liverpool Geol. Soc. Spec. Issue*, **2**, 245 (1970).

感谢奥斯蒂和扎亚克在文字录入和绘图方面给予的帮助。本研究得到了美国海军研究办公室和美国国家科学基金会的资助。

（齐红艳 翻译；徐义刚 审稿）

40. Cann, J. R., *Nature*, **226**, 928 (1970).

41. Bott, M. H. P., *Geophys. J. Roy. Astron. Soc.*, **9**, 275 (1965).

42. Makris, J., Menzel, H., and Zimmermann, J., *Tectonophysics*, **15**, 31 (1972).

43. LePine, J. C., Ruegg, J. C., and Steinmetz, L., *Tectonophysics*, **15**, 60 (1972).

44. Palmason, G., *Visindafelag Islendinga*, **40** (Reykjavik, 1971).

45. Talwani, M., Windisch, C. C., and Langseth, G., *J. Geophys. Res.*, **76**, 473 (1971).

46. Tazieff, H., Varet, J., Barberi, F., and Giglia, G., *Nature*, **235**, 144 (1972).

47. Bonatti, E., and Tazieff, H., *Science*, **168**, 1087 (1970).

48. Tazieff, H., *Geol. Rundschau* (in the press).

49. Mohr, P. A., *Tectonophysics*, **15**, 3 (1972).

50. Engel, A. E., Engel, C. G., and Havens, R. G., *Bull. Geol. Soc. Amer.*, **76**, 719 (1965).

51. Frey, F. A., Haskin, M. A., Poetz, J. A., and Haskin, L. A., *J. Geophys. Res.*, **73**, 6085 (1968).

52. Hart, S. R., and Brooks, C., *Carnegie Inst. Wash., Year Book*, **68**, 426 (1970).

53. Gast, P. W., *Geochim. Cosmochim. Acta*, **32**, 1057 (1968).

54. Philpotts, J. A., and Schnetzler, C. C., *Can. Mineralogist*, **10**, 375 (1970).

55. Vogt, P. R., *Nature*, **240**, 338 (1972).

# T and B Lymphocytes and Immune Responses

M. C. Raff

## Editor's note

In this paper, Canadian-born cell biologist Martin C. Raff sums up what was then known about T and B lymphocytes. The two white blood cell types are found in peripheral lymphoid organs where they look identical, and Raff had previously identified a T cell marker, an achievement that won him immediate international recognition. T and B cells have different origins, properties and immunological functions which modulate each other's activities. Their discovery, Raff says, marks a new era in immunology in which powerful research tools and accessible models are likely to light on biological issues as well as disease.

---

The recognition of two distinct classes of lymphocytes has been a turning point in immunology. Immunological models and tools may help to provide the answers to many biological problems.

---

IMMUNOLOGY has become an exciting science of its own. Nonetheless, what is being learned about lymphocytes and the immune responses that they mediate has important implications for medicine and other branches of biology. Unfortunately, the private language of immunology has made it difficult for non-immunologists to join in the excitement. This article attempts to review what is known in general terms about the cellular basis of immunity. (For a more detailed review of lymphocytes and their roles in immune responses, see ref. 1.)

Immunology is concerned with the specific responses an animal makes when foreign materials (antigens or immunogens) are introduced into its body. Such immune responses are made by all vertebrates and consist of the production of specific immunoglobulin protein molecules (antibodies) and/or specifically reactive cells, both of which can circulate in the blood and react specifically with antigen. As a result of this reaction, the foreign material may be inactivated (for example, bacterial toxins), killed (for example, infecting organisms or transplanted cells) and/or phagocytosed by cells of the reticuloendothelial system. On the other hand, in some cases, such immune responses may have deleterious effects on the host, such as in hypersensitivity reactions (hayfever and drug allergy, for example), where antigen reacting with antibody fixed to basophils and mast cells causes the release of histamine and other pharmacological mediators of inflammation. In general, immune responses which can be transferred to another animal by means of serum from a sensitized donor (containing antibody) are termed humoral immune (or antibody)

# T淋巴细胞、B淋巴细胞与免疫应答

拉夫

编者按

在这篇文章中，出生于加拿大的细胞生物学家马丁·拉夫就 T 淋巴细胞和 B 淋巴细胞已有的知识进行了总结。在外周淋巴器官中发现了两种不同类型的白细胞，这两类白细胞在外周淋巴器官中看起来是一样的。拉夫在之前的研究中就已经鉴定了一种 T 细胞标志物，并因此立即获得国际认可。T 细胞和 B 细胞具有不同的起源、特性和免疫功能，两者在功能上是相互调控的。拉夫说他们的这一发现标志着免疫学的新时代。在这个新时代中，强大的研究工具和可利用的研究模型很有可能为生物学问题和疾病的研究带来曙光。

---

认识到两类截然不同的淋巴细胞是免疫学研究中一个转折点。免疫学模型和工具将有助于解答多种生物学问题。

---

虽然免疫学已经发展成了一门独立的振奋人心的学科，但是关于淋巴细胞及其所介导的免疫应答的研究对医学和生物学其他分支学科也具有重要的影响。然而遗憾的是，免疫学独有的语言体系使得非免疫学家很难参与到这个振奋人心的领域中。因此，我们撰写了这篇综述文章，力图对已知的免疫学的细胞学基础进行概括性阐述。（关于淋巴细胞和它们在免疫应答中的作用，更详细的综述见参考文献 1。）

免疫学是一门研究动物对进入其体内的外源性物质（抗原或免疫原）所产生的特异性反应的科学。所有的脊椎动物都可以产生这种免疫应答。这个过程包括特异性免疫球蛋白分子（抗体）和（或）具有特异性反应活性的细胞的产生。它们都可以在血液中循环，并与抗原特异地结合。这种反应会使外源性物质失活（如细菌毒素）、被杀死（如受感染的器官或移植的细胞）和（或）被网状内皮系统中的细胞吞噬。另一方面，在某些情况下，这种免疫应答可能会对宿主自身产生有害的作用。例如在超敏反应中（比如花粉过敏和药物过敏），抗原与吸附在嗜碱性粒细胞和肥大细胞上的抗体发生反应，从而引起组织胺和其他药理炎症介质的释放。一般来讲，那些可以通过将致敏供体（携带抗体）的血清转移到另一个动物体而引起的免疫应答称为体液免疫（或抗体）反应，而那些不能通过血清只能通过致敏细胞才能转移的免

responses, whereas those that can be transferred by sensitized cells but not by serum are called cell-mediated immune responses.

While immunochemists were unravelling the structure of antibody in the 1950s and early 1960s, cellular immunologists were demonstrating that lymphocytes are the principal cells involved in immune reactions. The most convincing experiments were those showing that relatively pure populations of rat lymphocytes obtained from the chief lymphatic vessel, the thoracic duct, could transfer both cellular and humoral immunity to irradiated rats, which could not respond immunologically themselves as their lymphocytes had been killed by the radiation (reviewed in ref. 2). In addition, depleting animals of lymphocytes by prolonged drainage of the thoracic duct was found to impair their immune responsiveness[2]. Thus lymphocytes, whose origins and functions had been a mystery for so long, were established as "immunocompetent" cells.

It was soon realized that lymphocytes are not a homogeneous population. Several lines of evidence suggested that there are two distinct types of immunocompetent lymphocytes: one which requires the thymus gland for development and is responsible for cell-mediated immunity and another which develops independently of the thymus and mediates humoral antibody responses. The evidence came from studies in birds, rodents and man in the 1960s. In birds[3,4] and rodents[5] it was found that removing the thymus from an embryo or newborn markedly impaired the cell-mediated immune responses of the animals when they grew up, but had much less effect on humoral immunity. On the other hand, removal at hatching of the bursa of Fabricius[3,4], a cloacal lymphoid organ unique to birds, impaired the bird's ability to make antibody, but had little effect on cell-mediated immunity. Investigations of patients with immunological deficiency diseases also showed that humoral and cell-mediated immunity could be separately affected (reviewed in ref. 6): patients with Bruton-type congenital agammaglobulinaemia could not make antibody and were deficient in lymphoid cells producing antibody, but had normal cell-mediated immunity, whereas children with congenitally hypoplastic thymus glands (for example, Di George's syndrome) had markedly impaired cell-mediated immunity but could make relatively normal amounts of antibody in response to some antigens.

In the past few years the two-lymphocyte model of immunity has been firmly established (at least in birds and mammals), with two "central" lymphoid organs—the bursa, or its mammalian equivalent (still unidentified), and the thymus—producing lymphocytes independently of antigen, and seeding them out to the "peripheral" lymphoid organs (that is, lymph nodes, spleen and gut-associated lymphoid tissues) where they await contact with antigen which will induce them to differentiate into "effector" cells (see later). In the peripheral lymphoid tissues the lymphocytes derived from thymus are referred to as T cells, while those derived from the bursa in birds, or its equivalent in mammals, are called B cells[7].

疫应答则被称为细胞免疫反应。

二十世纪五十年代和六十年代早期，当免疫化学家们正在努力解析抗体结构的时候，细胞免疫学家们正致力于阐明淋巴细胞是参与免疫反应的主要细胞。最具说服力的实验是在大鼠中进行的：研究人员首先利用放射性射线照射杀死了受体大鼠的淋巴细胞从而使其自身无法进行免疫应答（见参考文献2），然后将从大鼠的主淋巴管—胸导管中分离出来的相对纯的淋巴细胞移植到受体大鼠体内，结果发现这样可以使受体大鼠同时获得细胞免疫和体液免疫。此外，研究人员还发现通过胸导管持续引流使动物体内的淋巴细胞耗尽会削弱免疫反应性 [2]。至此，长久以来起源和功能一直是个谜的淋巴细胞，终于被确认为"免疫活性"的细胞。

很快人们便认识到，淋巴细胞并不是一个同质的群体。许多证据表明存在两种截然不同的具有免疫活性的淋巴细胞：一种淋巴细胞需在胸腺中发育并与细胞免疫有关；另一种淋巴细胞的发育则与胸腺无关并且介导体液免疫应答。支持这一观点的证据来自于二十世纪六十年代在鸟类、啮齿动物以及人类中的研究：在鸟类 [3,4] 和啮齿动物 [5] 中，摘除胚胎或新生动物的胸腺，它们长大后细胞免疫应答会显著受损，而对体液免疫影响不大。另一方面，在孵化阶段摘除法氏囊 [3,4]（鸟类特有的泄殖腔淋巴器官）会削弱鸟类产生抗体的能力，而几乎不影响细胞免疫。对免疫缺陷病患者的研究也表明，体液免疫和细胞免疫分别受到不同因素的影响（见参考文献6）：由于缺乏产生抗体的淋巴细胞，患有布鲁顿型先天性丙种球蛋白缺乏症的病人不能产生抗体，但是细胞免疫正常；而先天性胸腺发育不全的儿童（如迪乔治综合征患者）则表现为细胞免疫功能显著受损，但对某些抗原产生免疫应答时可以产生相对正常量的抗体。

在过去的几年中，免疫的双淋巴细胞模型（至少在鸟类和哺乳动物中）已经确立。在这个模型中，有两个"中枢"淋巴器官——法氏囊或在哺乳动物中具有的同功能器官（目前尚不明确）和胸腺——产生不依赖于抗原的淋巴细胞，并将它们运送到"外周"淋巴器官（淋巴结、脾脏和肠道相关淋巴组织），淋巴细胞在那里等候与抗原接触从而诱导其进一步分化为"效应"细胞（见下文）。其中，在外周淋巴组织中胸腺来源的淋巴细胞被称为 T 细胞，而鸟类的法氏囊或哺乳动物相应器官来源的淋巴细胞被称为 B 细胞 [7]。

# Phylogeny

Until recently it was thought that specific immune responses were confined to vertebrates. There is now evidence, however, that some invertebrates, such as annelids and tunicates, can reject foreign tissues and that these primitive immunological responses can display specificity and possibly short-term memory[8] (that is, an increased and/or faster response on second exposure to the same antigens). These reactions are mediated by macrophage-like cells (coelomocytes) and possibly by soluble effector molecules having relatively little specificity[8]. As there is no evidence that invertebrates have lymphocytes or immunoglobulins, it seems likely that specific cellular immunity evolved before the appearance of these two principal mediators of vertebrate immunity.

All vertebrates have lymphocytes and probably thymus tissue (at least at some stage in their development) and are capable of producing antibody and cell-mediated immune responses[8]. Lower vertebrates (lampreys and hagfish, for example) have little organized lymphoid tissue and can produce only one class (IgM-like) of antibody. Rudimentary lymph node-like structures are first found in Amphibia which make two classes of antibody. Birds are the first vertebrates in which a clear dichotomy of the lymphoid system has been established, and are unique in having two discrete central lymphoid organs, thymus and bursa, producing T and B lymphocytes respectively. Mammals have abundant and highly organized lymphoid tissues, can elaborate a variety of different classes of antibody (such as IgG, IgM, IgA, IgE, IgD in man) and have distinct T and B lymphocyte populations, although the site of B cell development is still uncertain. It is not known whether vertebrates below birds have separate classes of T and B cells.

# Development of T Lymphocytes

In most animals, lymphocytes first appear in the foetal thymus. The thymus anlage is composed of epithelial cells and is derived from the third and fourth pharyngeal pouches. Although in the past it had been suggested that thymus lymphocytes (thymocytes) develop from thymus epithelial cells, experiments in chickens and mice have clearly established that haemopoietic stem cells from foetal yolk sac and liver migrate into the thymus anlage and there proliferate and differentiate into thymus lymphocytes, presumably under the inductive influence of the thymus epithelium[9]. In mice (gestation 20 days) the first stem cells, which seem to be large basophilic blast-like cells, arrive in the thymus around day 11, and the first small lymphocytes are seen by day 15 or 16 of embryonic life[9]. Using radioactive[10], chromosome[5,11] and surface antigenic[9] markers, it has been shown that lymphocytes migrate from thymus to peripheral lymphoid tissues to make up the T lymphocyte population. Although this begins just before birth in mice, most of the seeding occurs in the first week of life[9]. Therefore, if the thymus is removed in the first days of life the mouse will grow up with a marked deficiency of T cells and thus impaired cell-mediated immunity, whereas thymectomy done later in life has much less effect[5]. In adult animals, stem cells from bone marrow migrate to thymus, and thymus lymphocytes continue to seed to the periphery, but these processes take place at a much reduced rate by comparison with the foetus and newborn[5,11].

## 系 统 发 育

直到最近，人们都一直认为只有脊椎动物才具有特异性免疫反应。然而，现在有证据表明，诸如环节动物和被囊动物等无脊椎动物也可以排斥外源组织，并且这种原始的免疫应答也具有一定的特异性和短期的记忆效应 [8]（即在第二次接触到相同抗原时可以产生更强和（或）更快的免疫应答）。这些反应是由巨噬细胞样细胞（体腔细胞）介导的，也可能是由特异性相对较差的可溶性效应分子介导的 [8]。由于并没有证据表明无脊椎动物中具有淋巴细胞或免疫球蛋白，因此特异性细胞免疫很可能是在脊椎动物的两种主要免疫细胞出现之前形成的。

所有脊椎动物都有淋巴细胞，也可能有胸腺组织（至少在发育的某个阶段中），并且可以产生抗体、引发细胞免疫应答 [8]。低等脊椎动物（如七鳃鳗类和盲鳗类）几乎没有系统化的淋巴组织且只能产生一类抗体（IgM 样抗体）。初级淋巴结样结构是在两栖动物中首次发现的，这种结构可以产生两类抗体。第一种被发现具有明显两类淋巴系统的脊椎动物是鸟类；而且鸟类独一无二地具有两个独立的中枢淋巴器官——胸腺和法氏囊，二者可以分别产生 T 细胞和 B 细胞。尽管 B 细胞的发育位点尚未确定，但可以肯定的是哺乳动物具有大量的、高度系统化的淋巴组织，可以产生各种不同种类的抗体（例如人体可以产生 IgG、IgM、IgA、IgE、IgD 等），并且具有截然不同的 T 细胞和 B 细胞群。我们还不知道比鸟类低等的脊椎动物是否具有独立的 T 细胞和 B 细胞群。

### T 淋巴细胞的发育

在大多数动物中，淋巴细胞首先在胎儿胸腺中出现。胸腺原基由上皮细胞组成，来源于第三、第四咽囊。过去人们认为胸腺淋巴细胞（胸腺细胞）是由胸腺上皮细胞发育而来，但是鸡和小鼠的实验清楚表明，胎儿卵黄囊和肝脏中的造血干细胞会迁移到胸腺原基并在那里增殖、分化成胸腺淋巴细胞，这些过程大概是在胸腺上皮诱导作用下进行的 [9]。在小鼠（妊娠 20 天）中，在胚胎期第 11 天左右，可以观察到首批类似大嗜碱性母细胞的干细胞到达胸腺；而在胚胎期第 15 天或第 16 天的时候可以检测到首批小淋巴细胞 [9]。利用放射性示踪 [10]、染色体 [5,11] 和细胞表面抗原标志物 [9] 可以清楚地显示淋巴细胞从胸腺迁移到外周淋巴组织并分化为 T 淋巴细胞群。尽管这一过程在小鼠临出生前开始，但是大部分迁移过程发生在其出生后的第一周 [9]。因此，如果在小鼠出生的第一天便摘除其胸腺，那么其长大后则表现为明显的 T 细胞缺陷从而损伤细胞免疫；然而如果晚些时候进行胸腺切除，那么影响会小很多 [5]。在成年动物中，骨髓来源的干细胞会迁移到胸腺，胸腺淋巴细胞也会持续地向外周组织迁移。但是与胚胎和新生动物相比，成年动物的这一过程要缓慢得多 [5,11]。

Most thymus lymphocytes are immunologically incompetent (that is, they cannot respond to antigen) and differ in other ways from peripheral T cells, suggesting that there is another differentiation step from thymocyte to T lymphocyte. Recently it has been demonstrated that there is a small subpopulation (~2 to 5%) of thymus cells, located in the thymus medulla, which is immunologically competent and has most of the properties of peripheral T lymphocytes[9,12,13]. This suggests that the second differentiation step may occur within the thymus and that T cell development may be visualized as stem cell→thymocyte→ "mature" thymus lymphocyte→peripheral T lymphocyte (Fig. 1). This scheme is almost certainly an oversimplification, however, for there is some evidence that cells may leave the thymus at varying stages of maturation, or perhaps as distinct cell lines, giving rise to subpopulations of peripheral T cells with different properties and functions[13]. In addition, the role of putative thymus humoral factors or hormones (thymosin, for example) is still unclear, although there is evidence that they probably do not induce stem cells to differentiate to lymphocytes outside the thymus, but may influence peripheral T cells in some way[14].

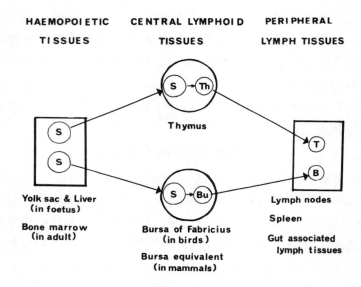

Fig. 1. Diagrammatic (and oversimplified—see text) representation of T and B lymphocyte development showing migration of stem cells (S) to thymus and bursa where they differentiate to thymus (Th) and bursal (Bu) lymphocytes, some of which migrate to the peripheral lymphoid tissues as T and B lymphocytes respectively.

## Development of B Lymphocytes

In birds, B cell development is dependent on the bursa of Fabricius which arises as a sac-like evagination of the dorsal wall of the cloaca on day 5. Chromosome marker studies have shown that stem cells (morphologically identical to those seen in the foetal thymus) begin to migrate from yolk sac to the bursa around days 12 to 13 and there differentiate to lymphocytes within 1 or 2 days[9]. By day 14, bursa lymphocytes with IgM on their

大多数胸腺淋巴细胞没有免疫活性（也就是说它们不能对抗原作出应答），并且在其他方面它们与外周T淋巴细胞也有所不同，这表明从胸腺细胞到T细胞存在另一个分化过程。最近有研究表明，在胸腺髓质中存在胸腺细胞小的亚群（约2%~5%），它们具有免疫活性并且具有外周T淋巴细胞的大部分特征[9,12,13]。这表明第二个分化步骤可能是在胸腺内完成的，可以把T细胞的发育看作如下过程：干细胞→胸腺细胞→"成熟"胸腺淋巴细胞→外周T淋巴细胞（见图1）。但是几乎可以肯定的是，上述模型只是一种过于简化的说明。因为有证据表明，细胞在成熟的各个阶段细胞都可能离开胸腺，或者作为不同的细胞系产生若干具有不同特性和功能的外周T细胞亚群[13]。另外，人们假定的胸腺体液因子或激素（例如胸腺素）的功能仍不清楚。尽管有证据表明在胸腺外它们很可能不能诱导干细胞分化为淋巴细胞，但它们可能以某种方式影响着外周T淋巴细胞[14]。

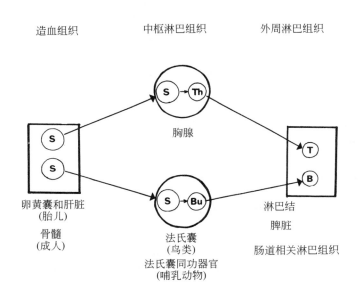

图 1. T淋巴细胞和B淋巴细胞的发育过程示意图（过于简化的——见正文）。干细胞（S）迁移到胸腺和法氏囊组织，并在那里分别分化成胸腺淋巴细胞（Th）和法氏囊淋巴细胞（Bu）。然后这些细胞的一部分迁移到外周淋巴组织中，分别成为T淋巴细胞和B淋巴细胞。

## B 淋巴细胞的发育

在鸟类中，B细胞的发育依赖于法氏囊。法氏囊是在胚胎发育第五天由泄殖腔背壁外翻所形成的一个囊状结构。染色体标记研究显示，在胚胎发育第12天到第13天时便有干细胞（与胎儿胸腺中检出的干细胞形态一致）从卵黄囊迁移到法氏囊中，并且在1~2天内在那里分化成淋巴细胞[9]。到第14天可以观察到表面有IgM的法氏囊

surface can be seen, and bursa lymphocytes bearing IgG are seen a few days later[15]. The migration of bursal lymphocytes to peripheral lymphoid tissues has been demonstrated by isotope labelling experiments. Embryonic bursectomy results in marked depletion of peripheral B lymphocytes and a marked impairment in antibody (that is, immunoglobulin) production[15]. Recently it has been found that injecting anti-μ antibody (that is, specific for the heavy chains of IgM) before hatching, combined with neonatal bursectomy, suppresses later production of IgG as well as IgM[15]. This suggests that even B cells that will eventually produce IgG initially express IgM on their surface, and is strong evidence for an IgM→IgG switch within individual B cells. Whether this switch is driven by antigen, as suggested by experiments in mice[16], or occurs independently of antigen stimulation, as suggested by experiments in chickens[15], is unsettled.

In mammals, it is still not clear where stem cells differentiate to B-type lymphocytes, although it is known not to be in the thymus. It has been suggested that gut-associated lymphoid tissues (like Peyer's patches, tonsils, appendix, and so on) may serve as "bursa-equivalent", but there is little evidence to support this. In rodents, at least, there is increasing evidence that lymphocytes are produced in large numbers in the haemopoietic tissues themselves[17] (that is, liver in embryos and bone marrow in adults) and it seems likely that these tissues not only supply the stem cells for both T and B cell populations but are also the sites where stem cells differentiate to B-type lymphocytes.

It is not clear at what stage stem cells are committed to becoming lymphocytes or to becoming T or B cells. The finding of multipotential haemopoietic stem cells (that is, cells capable of becoming any of the mature blood cell types, lymphoid or myeloid) in early mouse embryonic thymus[18] suggests that commitment may not occur until stem cells enter the microenvironment of the thymus or bursa (or bursa equivalent).

## Distinctive Properties of T and B Lymphocytes

As resting T and B lymphocytes are morphologically indistinguishable and are found together in all peripheral lymphoid tissue, it has been essential to find ways of distinguishing and separating them in order to study their individual properties. The demonstration of important surface differences between them has been particularly useful in this regard. Some of these surface differences can be recognized by antibody[19]. For example, the θ alloantigen (defined by alloantibody made in one strain of mouse against thymocytes of another strain) is present on mouse thymocytes and T cells, but absent from B lymphocytes, and this has proved to be a convenient surface marker for T cells in mice[19]. On the other hand, readily demonstrable surface immunoglobulin (Ig) (refs. 20, 21) and the heteroantigen, "mouse-specific B lymphocyte antigen" (MBLA) (ref. 19)—defined by hetero-antibody made in rabbits against mouse B cells—can serve as B cell markers. With antisera reacting specifically with the surface of one or other lymphocyte type, either cell population can be killed in the presence of complement, and thus eliminated from a cell suspension. Alternatively, one can use antibody on digestible solid-phase immunoabsorbents[22], or fluoresceinated antibody and fluorescence-activated electronic cell sorting[23], to purify either type of cell. In addition to surface antigenic differences

淋巴细胞，几天后可以观察到产生 IgG 的法氏囊淋巴细胞 [15]。同位素标记实验证明法氏囊淋巴细胞可以迁移到外周淋巴组织。在胚胎时期摘除法氏囊会导致外周 B 淋巴细胞的显著缺失和抗体（即免疫球蛋白）产量的显著减少 [15]。最近人们发现，向孵化前的胚胎注射抗 μ 抗体（特异靶向 IgM 重链）加上在胚胎孵化后摘除其法氏囊，抑制 IgM 的同时，也会抑制随后 IgG 的产生 [15]。这表明即使是那些最终产生 IgG 的 B 细胞，最初在其表面也会表达 IgM；同时强有力地证明，单个的 B 细胞中存在 IgM 到 IgG 的转换。但是这种转换是由抗原驱动（如小鼠实验结果显示 [16]），还是与抗原刺激无关（如鸡实验结果显示 [15]），目前尚不清楚。

在哺乳动物中，人们尚不清楚干细胞是在哪里分化成 B 淋巴细胞的，只知道肯定不是在胸腺中。有人认为哺乳动物的肠道相关淋巴组织（如派伊尔节、扁桃腺、阑尾等）可能充当"法氏囊同功结构"，不过尚缺乏证据证明这一点。但是至少在啮齿类动物中，越来越多的证据表明大量的淋巴细胞是在造血组织中（如胚胎的肝脏、成年动物的骨髓）产生的 [17]；并且似乎这些组织不仅为 T 细胞群和 B 细胞群提供干细胞，而且也是干细胞分化为 B 淋巴细胞的场所。

目前还不清楚哪个阶段的干细胞会分化为淋巴细胞或成为 T 细胞、B 细胞。研究人员在早期小鼠胚胎胸腺中观察到了多能造血干细胞（即可以分化为任何一种成熟血细胞、淋巴细胞或骨髓细胞的细胞）[18]，这表明干细胞直到进入胸腺或法氏囊（或法氏囊同功结构）微环境以前都不能完成分化。

## T 淋巴细胞和 B 淋巴细胞的不同性质

由于处于静息状态的 T 细胞和 B 细胞在形态上无法区分，并且都分布于外周淋巴组织中，因此寻找区别、分离它们的方法对研究其各自的特性来说极其重要。就这一点来说，揭示它们之间重要的表面差异尤为有效。有些表面差异可以通过抗体识别出来 [19]。例如 θ 同种异型抗原（由同种抗体识别，用一个种系的小鼠胸腺细胞免疫另一个种系的小鼠得到该抗体）存在于小鼠胸腺细胞和 T 细胞，而不存在于 B 淋巴细胞，因此其被证实为小鼠 T 细胞合适的表面标志物 [19]。另一方面，已确实证明的细胞表面免疫球蛋白（Ig）（参考文献 20、21）和"小鼠特异性 B 淋巴细胞抗原"（MBLA）（参考文献 19）可以作为 B 细胞的标志物，MBLA 是通过兔抗鼠 B 细胞产生的异种抗体识别的异种抗原。在补体存在下，抗血清能与一种或其他类型淋巴细胞表面发生特异反应，杀死相应细胞群，从而将它们从细胞悬液中清除。利用耦联到可消化的固相免疫吸附剂上的抗体 [22]，或荧光标记的抗体，通过荧光激发的电子细胞分选技术 [23]，就可纯化出任意一种细胞类型。除了上述 T 细胞与 B 细胞的

between T and B cells, the latter can bind antibody-antigen-complement complexes by means of surface complement receptors[24], and antibody-antigen complexes by means of receptors for the Fc part of complexed Ig[25]; resting T cells do not have these receptors. The functions of Fc and complement receptors on B cells are unknown, but it has been suggested that they may be important in antigen localization in the lymphoid tissues, in B cell activation by antigen and/or in putative killing by B cells of target cells coated with antibody.

Most T lymphocytes continuously recirculate between blood and lymph, passing out of the blood through specialized post-capillary venules in lymph nodes and Peyer's patches, passing through the substance of the lymphoid tissues and entering the efferent lymph; they then re-enter the bloodstream by way of the thoracic duct[2,5]. Although most B lymphocytes seem not to recirculate, some apparently do, but through different areas of the lymphoid tissues and with a slower transit time than T cells[26]. In the peripheral lymphoid tissues, T and B cells are found in more or less separate areas, the so-called thymus-dependent areas (periarteriolar sheath of spleen, paracortex of lymph nodes, and interfollicular areas of gastrointestinal lymphoid tissues) and thymus-independent areas (lymph follicles and peripheral regions of splenic white pulp, follicles and medulla of lymph nodes and follicles of gastrointestinal lymphoid tissues) respectively[27]. When radiolabelled T or B cells are injected into an animal, they migrate specifically to their respective areas[27]. Although both T and B lymphocyte populations are heterogeneous[1], T cells have a longer generation time[28] on average and are slightly larger[29], more dense[24], less adherent[24] (to various materials such as glass, plastic, nylon, and so on) and more negatively charged than B cells[30]. In addition, T lymphocytes are preferentially depleted by anti-lymphocyte serum[31] (which acts principally on recirculating cells), but in general are less sensitive to cytotoxic drugs (for example, cyclophosphamide[32]), corticosteroids[33] and irradiation[34]. T and B cells also differ in their *in vitro* responses to a variety of "mitogens", such as plant extracts (phytomitogens), bacterial products (like endotoxin) or antibodies to lymphocyte surface antigens, which stimulate a relatively large proportion of T and/or B lymphocytes to divide and differentiate into blast cells. Although pokeweed stimulates both T and B cell proliferation, concanavallin A (Con A), phytohaemag-glutinin (PHA) and lentil stimulate only T cells, and lipopolysaccharides (for example, E. *coli* endotoxin) and anti-Ig sera stimulate only B cells[35]. It is of interest that although soluble Con A and PHA selectively activate T cells, they bind equally well to B cells, and if covalently linked to solid-phase materials they stimulate B cell proliferation[35]. Mitogen stimulation of lymphocytes is being intensively studied as a possible model of lymphocyte activation by specific antigen. These studies have made it clear that there is more to lymphocyte activation than simple binding of ligand to surface receptors.

## Antigen Recognition and Specific Lymphocyte Receptors

The central dogma of immunology is the clonal selection hypothesis which suggests that at some time in ontogeny and independently of antigen, individual lymphocytes (or clones of lymphocytes) become committed to responding to one, or a relatively small number of antigens; they express this commitment through antigen-specific receptors on their surface.

表面抗原差异外，B 细胞还可以通过细胞表面的补体受体与抗体－抗原－补体复合物结合 [24]，或通过复杂的免疫球蛋白的 Fc 片段受体与抗原－抗体复合物结合 [25]；而静息状态的 T 细胞则不具有这些受体。虽然目前还不清楚 B 细胞上 Fc 片段和补体受体的功能，但有人认为它们可能在淋巴组织中抗原的定位、抗原激活 B 细胞和（或）一般认定的 B 细胞杀死抗体包被的靶细胞的过程中起重要作用。

大多数 T 淋巴细胞都会在血液和淋巴之间反复循环。T 细胞可以通过淋巴结和派伊尔节内特化的毛细血管后微静脉从血液中出来，穿过淋巴组织基质进入输出淋巴管；然后通过胸导管重新回到血液循环系统中 [2,5]。尽管大多数 B 淋巴细胞似乎并不参与上述循环过程，但其中有些 B 淋巴细胞确实会通过淋巴组织的不同部位，以比 T 细胞慢的运送速度进行再循环 [26]。在外周淋巴组织中，T 细胞和 B 细胞的分布区域基本上是相互分隔的，分别为所谓的胸腺依赖区（脾脏动脉周围鞘、淋巴结副皮质区、胃肠淋巴组织的滤泡间区）和非胸腺依赖区（淋巴滤泡和脾脏白髓的外周区域、淋巴结中的滤泡和髓质以及胃肠淋巴组织滤泡）[27]。将放射性标记的 T 细胞或 B 细胞注入动物体后，它们会特异地迁移到各自的区域 [27]。尽管 T 淋巴细胞群和 B 淋巴细胞群都是异质的 [1]，但是与 B 细胞相比，T 细胞的平均增代时间更长 [28]，并且体积略大 [29]，密度更高 [24]，粘附性更小 [24]（与玻璃、塑料、尼龙等各种材料的粘附性相比），带的负电荷也较多 [30]。此外，T 细胞更容易被抗淋巴细胞的血清清除 [31]（主要针对反复循环的细胞），但通常对细胞毒性药物（如环磷酰胺 [32]）、皮质类固醇 [33] 和辐射 [34] 的敏感性较低。另外它们在体外对于各种“有丝分裂原”的反应也是不同的，比如植物提取物（如植物有丝分裂原）、细菌代谢产物（如内毒素）或淋巴细胞表面抗原的抗体，其均可刺激很大一部分 T 和（或）B 淋巴细胞分裂、分化为母细胞。尽管美洲商陆可以同时刺激 T 细胞和 B 细胞增殖，但是伴刀豆球蛋白 A（Con A）、植物凝集素（PHA）和扁豆素只能刺激 T 细胞增殖，而脂多糖（如大肠杆菌内毒素）和抗免疫球蛋白血清则只能刺激 B 细胞增殖 [35]。有意思的是，尽管可溶的 Con A 和 PHA 只能选择性地激活 T 细胞，但它们同样可以很好地与 B 细胞结合；而一旦将它们共价耦联到固相支持物上，它们也可以刺激 B 细胞增殖 [35]。作为淋巴细胞被特异抗原活化的一种可能的模型，有丝分裂原刺激淋巴细胞活化被广泛研究。这些研究使得人们逐渐认识到淋巴细胞的激活不仅仅是配体与细胞表面受体结合那么简单。

## 抗原识别与特异性淋巴细胞受体

免疫学的中心法则是克隆选择学说。该学说提出在个体发生的一定时间内，单个淋巴细胞（或淋巴细胞克隆）通过细胞表面抗原特异性受体只对某一种或相对少数的几种抗原起反应，这一过程与抗原无关。于是，一旦抗原进入体内便会筛选出

Thus, when an antigen is introduced into the body it selects out those lymphocytes which already have receptors for the antigen on their surface; the interaction of antigen with receptors initiates the activation of the specific cells. There is now an impressive body of evidence supporting the clonal selection hypothesis for both T and B lymphocytes. Thus T and B cells have been shown to bind antigen to their surface[36] (although it has been more difficult to demonstrate T cells binding antigen than B cells) and in general only a small proportion of lymphocytes (~1 in $10^4$ to $10^5$ in unimmunized animals) bind any one antigen. Furthermore, if lymphocytes are exposed to a highly radioactive antigen, both T and B cell responses to that antigen can be selectively abolished, while responses to other antigens are unaffected[37]. Similarly, B cells capable of responding to a particular antigen specifically adhere to glass beads coated with the antigen and can thus be specifically removed from a cell suspension[38]. Although T cells tend not to adhere under these conditions[38] for reasons that are unclear, T cells responsive to cell surface alloantigens can be selectively removed in cell monolayers bearing the specific alloantigens[39].

In 1900, Ehrlich proposed that cells producing antitoxins (now known to be B cells) had antitoxin molecules as receptors on their surface. The more recent version of the receptor hypothesis suggests that B lymphocytes have antibody molecules (that is, Ig) as receptors for antigen, which, at least in their combining sites, are identical to the antibody which the cell or its progeny will eventually secrete. There is now good evidence for this view, in that B cells have been shown to have Ig molecules on their surface (~$10^4$ to $10^5$ a cell) (refs. 20, 40) and anti-Ig antibody inhibits their ability to bind or respond to antigens (reviewed in ref.1). There is also increasing evidence that the antigen-specificity of receptors and secreted antibody are the same for any one B lymphocyte clone[41,42]. The Ig class of the receptors and that of the ultimately secreted antibody may not, however, always be the same, for B cell precursors of some IgG secretory cells seem to have IgM receptors[15,16]. As different antibody classes (for example, IgG and IgM) seem to be able to share the same specificity (that is different Ig constant regions can be associated with identical Ig variable regions[43]) and IgM→IgG switch within a single clone need not imply a switch in specificity. In mice, at least, there is some evidence that most virgin B cells have IgM receptors (in its 7-8S monomeric form[44]) which may switch class after a primary exposure to antigen[16]. The more fundamental question of how antibody diversity is generated, that is how an animal develops the ability to synthesize such a large number of different Ig molecules (receptors and secreted antibodies) is still being debated. Germ-line theories, which suggest that one is born with a large number of variable region Ig genes, are competing with various somatic theories, which postulate that one is born with few variable region Ig genes and that some somatic process (for example, mutation or recombination) creates a large number.

The chemical nature of receptors on T cells is probably the most controversial issue in cellular immunology at present. The simplest and most logical view, that only antibody can recognize antigen and that all antigen-specific receptors must be Ig, has been challenged by the failure of many investigators to demonstrate Ig directly on the surface of T cells, or to inhibit various T cell responses with anti-Ig sera. Indeed, there is now growing support

表面已有相应受体的淋巴细胞；抗原与受体的相互作用可以激活这些特异性细胞。现在关于 T 淋巴细胞和 B 淋巴细胞的克隆选择学说都有了令人信服的证据。因此，人们发现 T 细胞和 B 细胞都可以结合抗原至其表面 [36]（尽管曾经证明 T 细胞结合抗原比证明 B 细胞结合抗原要困难得多），并且通常只有一小部分的淋巴细胞（在未免疫的动物中约为万分之一到十万分之一）能够与任何抗原结合。此外，如果用强放射性抗原作用于淋巴细胞，无论是 T 细胞反应还是 B 细胞反应都会被选择性摧毁，而针对其他抗原的免疫反应却不会受到影响 [37]。同样，如果把某种特定的抗原耦联到玻璃微珠上，那么可以与这种抗原反应的 B 细胞会特异性地黏附于玻璃微珠上，从而将它们从细胞悬液中特异地分离出来 [38]。尽管出于某种未知原因，在此条件下 T 细胞通常不能黏附 [38]，但用载有特异性同种抗原的单层细胞，可以选择性去除识别这种抗原的 T 细胞 [39]。

早在 1900 年，埃尔利希便提出那些可以产生抗毒素的细胞（现在知道是 B 细胞）在其表面有作为受体的抗毒素分子。这种受体学说的最新说法提出，B 淋巴细胞表面有作为抗原受体的抗体分子（即免疫球蛋白），这些受体与 B 细胞或其子细胞最终分泌的抗体至少在结合位点上是相同的。现在有很好的证据支持这一观点：B 细胞表面确实有免疫球蛋白分子（每个细胞大约 $10^4 \sim 10^5$ 个）（参考文献 20、40），并且这些抗 Ig 的抗体抑制它们与抗原结合或应答的能力（有关综述见参考文献 1）。此外，越来越多的证据表明，对于任何一个 B 淋巴细胞克隆来说，受体和分泌的抗体具有相同的抗原结合特异性 [41,42]。但是，受体与最终分泌的抗体在免疫球蛋白亚型方面可能不总是一样的，比如一些分泌 IgG 细胞的 B 细胞前体似乎有 IgM 受体 [15,16]。这些不同亚型的抗体（例如 IgG 与 IgM）可能具有相同的抗原识别特异性（也就是说不同的免疫球蛋白恒定区可以与同一可变区组合 [43]），而且单个克隆内 IgM 到 IgG 的转换并不意味着特异性的转变。至少在小鼠中有证据表明，大多数未经过抗原激活的 B 细胞表面都有 IgM 受体（以 7-8S 的单体形式存在 [44]），而在与抗原初次接触后，这些 B 细胞则会转换类型 [16]。关于抗体多样性是如何产生这一最根本的问题，也就是动物如何产生如此庞大的各种各样的免疫球蛋白分子（包括受体和分泌的抗体），目前仍存有争议。胚系学说认为动物生来就具有大量免疫球蛋白可变区基因；而体细胞突变理论认为动物生来只有很少的免疫球蛋白可变区基因，在随后的一些体细胞过程（例如突变或重组）中产生了大量可变区基因。

T 细胞表面受体的化学本质大概是当前细胞免疫学中最富争议性的问题。最简单也最合理的观点是：只有抗体可以识别抗原，而且所有抗原特异性受体必然是免疫球蛋白。但是由于许多研究人员都无法证明 T 细胞表面有免疫球蛋白的存在，或使用抗免疫球蛋白血清能抑制 T 细胞与抗原的作用，因此这一观点受到了质疑。事

for the idea that surface components other than classical immunoglobulin may play an important role in T cell recognition of and/or response to at least some antigens. The principal candidates for such T cell "receptors" are the products of the immune response (Ir) genes that are genetically linked to the chief histocompatibility loci[45]. These Ir genes influence T cell responses to a variety of antigens[46]. The exquisite specificity of T cell responses, which resembles very closely the specificity of antibody and B cell recognition[47], taken together with the various (but still controversial) demonstrations of Ig on T cells (reviewed in ref. 1), makes one reluctant, however, to give up the idea that T cells have Ig receptors. It is possible that T cells (and possibly B cells) have at least two "recognition" systems, one involving Ig and another mediated by Ir gene products, the general importance of each varying depending on the antigen, the response and/or the subclass of T cell. The putative non-Ig recognition system could be analogous to the primitive recognition of foreignness seen in invertebrates.

## Functions of T and B Cells

When an antigen combines with its corresponding receptors on a T or B lymphocyte, one of at least three things can happen to the lymphocyte: first, it may be stimulated to divide and differentiate to become an effector cell in some type of immune response (that is, it is induced to respond immunologically); second, it may become immunologically tolerant or paralysed, so that it will not be able to respond the next time antigen is given; it is not known if such cells are killed or simply inactivated in some way; third, it may be unaffected by the encounter. In addition, if the animal makes an immune response to the antigen, on subsequent exposure to the same antigen, it will usually give a faster, greater and sometimes qualitatively different response. This altered state of immune reactivity to a specific antigen is called immunological memory. It is likely that memory involves both clonal expansion (that is, division of virgin lymphocytes to give an increased number of cells able to respond on second exposure) and differentiation of virgin cells to memory cells[1], but it is unclear whether memory cells are simply retired effector cells, cells at an earlier stage of differentiation than effector cells, or are derived by differentiation along a separate memory pathway.

The "decision" of an individual lymphocyte on encounter with antigen—whether to "turn-on", "turn-off" or ignore—depends largely on the nature and concentration of the antigen, and upon complex interactions with other lymphocytes and with macrophages. Although most immunogens can stimulate both T and B cell responses, some, particularly those with repeating identical determinants and which are poorly catabolized—the so-called "thymus-independent antigens" (for example, pneumococcal polysaccharide, *E.coli* endotoxin, polyvinylpyrrolidone)—chiefly stimulate B cells (reviewed in ref.1), whereas others preferentially activate T cells[48]. In general, T cells respond to lower concentrations of antigen than do B cells, and although T cells may be paralysed at very low and very high concentrations of antigen (low and high zones of tolerance respectively) B cells seem to be paralysed only at high antigen concentrations[49]. The way in which the antigen-receptor interaction signals a lymphocyte is unknown, although it probably involves allosteric changes and/or redistribution (for example, aggregation into patches or

实上，越来越多的证据表明，至少在 T 细胞识别和（或）应答某些抗原中，除了传统的免疫球蛋白外，细胞表面组分也可能发挥重要作用。这些 T 细胞"受体"的优先候选分子很可能是免疫应答（Ir）基因编码的产物，Ir 基因在遗传上与主要组织相容性基因座相关联 [45]。这些 Ir 基因会影响 T 细胞对多种抗原的应答 [46]。T 细胞应答的精准特异性非常类似于抗体的特异性和 B 细胞识别的特异性 [47]；再加上种种（尽管存有争议）实证表明 T 细胞上有免疫球蛋白（有关综述见参考文献1），使得人们不愿放弃 T 细胞表面具有免疫球蛋白受体的观点。也许 T 细胞（可能也包括 B 细胞）表面至少具有两套"识别"系统，其中一套包含免疫球蛋白，另一套通过 Ir 基因编码的产物介导，对于不同的抗原、不同的免疫应答和（或）不同的 T 细胞亚型来说，这两套识别系统可能具有不同的重要性。此外，这种假定的非免疫球蛋白识别系统可能与无脊椎动物对外源性物质的简单识别类似。

## T 细胞和 B 细胞的功能

当抗原与 T 淋巴细胞或 B 淋巴细胞表面相应的受体结合时，淋巴细胞至少会发生下列三个事件中的一种：第一种是在某些免疫应答中，淋巴细胞在抗原刺激下会分裂并分化为效应细胞（即被诱导产生免疫应答）；第二种是这些淋巴细胞可能对这种抗原产生耐受或麻痹，以至于下次遇见该抗原时不能发生免疫应答，目前尚不清楚这些淋巴细胞是被杀死了还是仅仅在某种程度上失活了；第三种是淋巴细胞对于抗原的刺激不产生任何反应。此外，如果动物对某种抗原做出过免疫应答，那么当其再次接触此抗原时，通常会产生更快速、更强烈甚至有时会是性质改变了的免疫应答。这种针对同一特定抗原的免疫反应改变了的状态被称为免疫记忆。这种记忆可能既包括克隆扩增（即未经免疫的淋巴细胞通过分裂，使得再次接触同一抗原时，能产生应答的效应细胞数增加），也包括未经免疫的淋巴细胞分化为记忆细胞 [1]。但目前尚不清楚记忆细胞只是"退休"的效应细胞——比效应细胞处于更早的分化阶段，还是通过一个独立的记忆通路分化出来的细胞。

当淋巴细胞与抗原接触之后，这个淋巴细胞的"决定"是"激活"、"耐受"还是忽略主要取决于抗原的性质和浓度，还取决于它们与其他淋巴细胞和巨噬细胞的复杂的相互作用。尽管大多数的免疫原都可以激发 T 细胞和 B 细胞产生免疫应答，但是有些抗原，尤其是那些具有相同重复的抗原决定簇并且不容易在体内被代谢的抗原——所谓的"胸腺非依赖性抗原"（如肺炎球菌的荚膜多糖、大肠杆菌内毒素、聚乙烯吡咯烷酮）——首要激活 B 细胞（有关综述见参考文献1），其他抗原则优先激活 T 细胞 [48]。通常来讲，相比 B 细胞而言，T 细胞可以对更低浓度的抗原做出应答，而且尽管过高或过低浓度的抗原（分别为高、低耐受区间）都可以引发 T 细胞的耐受性，但是 B 细胞只会对高浓度的抗原产生耐受性 [49]。虽然人们并不清楚抗原和受体的相互作用是如何向淋巴细胞传递信号的，但是这个过程可能包含了膜上结合的受体的构

localization over one pole—cap formation[50]) of the membrane-bound receptors.

The most important differences between T and B cells concern their different functions in immune responses. When B cells are activated by antigen they divide and differentiate into blast cells with abundant endoplasmic reticulum, and some go on to become plasma cells. These cells remain in the lymphoid tissues for the most part and secrete large amounts of antibody which circulates in the blood. Individual antibody-secreting cells can be detected by a variety of techniques, the most common being the plaque-forming cell assay, in which anti-erythrocyte antibody released from single B cells lyses erythrocytes in their immediate environment in the presence of complement. Antibodies, in conjunction with various accessory cells (macrophages, mast cells and basophils, for example) and particular serum enzymes (complement components, for example), are responsible for a variety of hypersensitivity reactions and protective immunity against many pathogenic organisms. In addition, antibody serves to regulate the function of both T and B cells, inhibiting their responses by competing with lymphocyte receptors for the antigenic determinants, diverting antigen from the lymphoid tissues or by forming tolerogenic antibody-antigen complexes[51], and enhancing responses by localizing antigen to appropriate lymphoid tissues or perhaps forming immunogenic antibody-antigen complexes. It is also possible (but not established) that B cells themselves play a direct part in transporting antigen (perhaps as antigen-antibody ± complement complexes adhering to Fc or complement receptors on B cells) and/or in killing target cells with coated antibody[52].

When T cells are activated by antigen, they proliferate and differentiate to become blast cells, but they do not develop significant amounts of endoplasmic reticulum and do not become antibody-secreting cells. They do, however, secrete a variety of non-antigen-specific factors ("lymphokines") such as migration inhibition factors (MIF), chemotactic factors, cytotoxic factors and mitogenic factors, at least some of which presumably play a role in cell-mediated immune responses, for which T cells are primarily responsible[53]. The precise chemical nature of these factors, the relationship between them, their significance and mechanisms of action are, however, incompletely understood. Cell-mediated immune responses include delayed hypersensitivity, contact sensitivity, rejection of foreign tissues, graft *versus* host responses (where injected foreign T lymphocytes respond against the antigens of the recipient, often resulting in recipient death) and immunity to various microbes. In all of these responses, T cells enlist the help of macrophages (probably through the secretion of lymphokines). The latter are usually the predominant cells at the site of these reactions[54]. T cells can also be demonstrated to respond to antigen *in vitro* by dividing, secreting lymphokines, killing target cells, or supporting viral replication (reviewed in ref.1). Whether T cells themselves can directly kill target cells, or do so only by activating other cells (such as macrophages) is still controversial, although there is increasing evidence that they can become "killer cells" under some circumstances[55].

Although T cells do not themselves secrete antibody in the usual sense, it is now known that they play an important role in helping B cells to make antibody responses to most immunogens. Thus, in these responses T cells are referred to as "helper" cells, and B

象变化和（或）其在细胞表面的重新分布（例如聚集成斑或定位在一极聚集成帽状 [50]）。

T 细胞和 B 细胞最大的区别在于它们在免疫应答中的功能不同。当 B 细胞被抗原激活后，它会分裂并分化为含有丰富内质网的母细胞，且部分母细胞会继续分化为浆细胞。这些细胞大多存在于淋巴组织中，并分泌大量的抗体进入血液循环。有很多方法可以用来检测分泌抗体的细胞，其中最常见的是溶血空斑实验。该实验的原理是在补体存在的情况下，单个 B 细胞分泌的抗红细胞抗体可以使红细胞发生溶血，从而在每个 B 细胞周围形成一个空斑。抗体连同各种辅助细胞（如巨噬细胞、肥大细胞、嗜碱性粒细胞）以及特殊的血清酶（如补体成分）参与了一系列超敏反应以及抵抗多种病原体的保护性免疫。此外，抗体还可以调节 T 细胞和 B 细胞的功能，通过与淋巴细胞表面的受体竞争结合抗原决定簇、将抗原转移出淋巴组织或者通过形成耐受性抗原－抗体复合物 [51]，抗体可以抑制淋巴细胞的免疫应答；而通过将抗原定位于适当的淋巴组织或通过形成免疫性的抗体－抗原复合物，抗体可以增强淋巴细胞的免疫应答。B 细胞自身也可能（但不确定）直接参与抗原转运（可能通过黏附在 Fc 或 B 细胞补体受体上的抗原－抗体 ± 补体复合物来实现）和（或）杀死被抗体覆盖的靶细胞 [52]。

当 T 细胞被抗原激活后，它们会增殖、分化为母细胞，但不会产生发达的内质网也不会成为可以分泌抗体的细胞。然而，它们会分泌诸如迁移抑制因子（MIF）、趋化因子、细胞毒素、促有丝分裂因子等各种非抗原特异性因子（"淋巴因子"）。至少部分因子可能在 T 细胞起主要作用的细胞免疫应答中发挥作用 [53]。但是人们尚不完全了解这些因子的化学本质、它们之间的相互关系、它们的重要性和作用机制。细胞免疫应答包括迟发性超敏反应、接触过敏、对外来组织的排斥、移植物抗宿主反应（移植的外来 T 淋巴细胞对受体抗原的反应，经常会导致受体死亡）以及机体对各种微生物的免疫力。在所有这些免疫应答中，T 细胞要发挥功能都需要巨噬细胞（可能是通过分泌淋巴因子的方式）的参与，并且巨噬细胞通常在反应位点扮演主要的角色 [54]。在体外实验中，T 细胞也可以通过分裂、分泌淋巴因子、杀伤靶细胞或者维持病毒复制（有关综述见参考文献 1）等方式对抗原产生应答。尽管越来越多的证据表明，在某些环境下 T 细胞可以成为"杀手细胞" [55]，但是关于 T 细胞自身是否可以直接杀伤靶细胞还是必须通过激活其他细胞（如巨噬细胞）杀伤靶细胞目前尚有争论。

尽管 T 细胞本身一般不分泌抗体，但现在已经知道它们在帮助 B 细胞对免疫原作出应答方面发挥着重要的作用。因此，在这类免疫应答中，T 细胞被称为"辅助"

cells as "antibody-forming precursor" cells. The first direct evidence for such T-B cell cooperation was provided in 1966 by the observation that irradiated mice given both thymus cells and bone marrow cells made a far greater antibody response to sheep erythrocytes (SRBC) than recipients of either thymocytes or bone marrow cells alone[56]. Subsequently it was shown that all of the antibody-secreting cells (that is, those making anti-SRBC antibody) in this type of experiment came from the bone marrow inoculum[57]. Independent studies with chemically defined antigens showed that T-B cell cooperation in antibody responses involved T cells responding to one antigenic determinant on an immunogen and helping B cells to respond to different determinants on the same immunogen[58]. Although it is clear that cooperation is usually mediated by such an "antigen bridge" between T cell and B cell receptors, it is still uncertain whether the bridge is between T and B cells themselves, or between shed T cell receptors (perhaps taken up on the surface of macrophages) and B cells, and whether the bridge serves to "present" antigen to B cells in a particularly immunogenic form (concentrated and multivalent, for example) or to bring B cells close to T cells or a third party cell (such as macrophage) so that a nonspecific, short-range factor (for example, chemical mediator or membrane-membrane interaction) can operate between them (Fig. 2). Although it has been shown that T cells can secrete non-specific factors which can enhance B cell responses[59], their role in normal T-B cell cooperation is still uncertain. There is recent evidence that, in some *in vitro* responses at least, cooperation may involve the release by T cells of antigen-specific IgM-like factors (?receptors) complexed with antigen, which are subsequently taken up on macrophages[60].

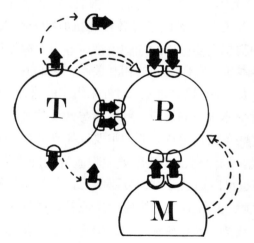

Fig. 2. Possible mechanisms of T-B cell collaboration in humoral antibody responses. The "antigen bridge" ( → ) between T and B cell receptors could serve to : (i) present antigen to B cells on the surface of T cells or as a matrix of released T cell receptors complexed with antigen, either free or on the surface of third party cells such as macrophages, or (ii) bring B cells together with T cells or a third party cell so that a short-range factor can operate between them.

细胞，而 B 细胞则被称为"抗体 – 形成前体"细胞。关于 T-B 细胞协作的首例直接证据是在 1966 年发现的。研究人员发现，向经放射照射的小鼠同时移植胸腺细胞和骨髓细胞，其产生抗绵羊红细胞（SRBC）抗体的能力比那些只移植胸腺细胞或骨髓细胞的小鼠产生抗体的能力强的多 [56]。后来人们发现，在这类实验中，所有抗体分泌细胞（也就是产生抗 SRBC 抗体的细胞）都来自于移植的骨髓细胞 [57]。用化学成分确定的抗原进行的独立研究显示，在抗体免疫应答中，T-B 细胞的协作包括 T 细胞对免疫原上的某一抗原决定簇进行识别，并且帮助 B 细胞对同一免疫原上不同抗原决定簇产生反应 [58]。尽管目前已经清楚这种协作通常是通过 T 细胞和 B 细胞受体之间的"抗原桥"来介导的，但人们尚不清楚这个桥是介于 T 细胞和 B 细胞之间还是介于脱落的 T 细胞受体（可能被巨噬细胞摄取后呈递在其表面）与 B 细胞之间。也不清楚这个桥的作用是以特定的免疫原形式（如浓缩或多价）向 B 细胞"呈递"抗原，还是把 B 细胞与 T 细胞或第三方细胞（如巨噬细胞）拉到一起，以便于非特异性的、小范围内起作用的因素（如化学媒介或细胞膜 – 细胞膜相互作用）在它们之间发挥作用（图 2）。尽管已经证明 T 细胞可以分泌一些能够加强 B 细胞免疫应答的非特异性因子 [59]，但是人们并不清楚这些因子在正常的 T-B 细胞协作中发挥着什么样的作用。最近有证据表明，至少在体外免疫应答中，T-B 细胞协作可能与 T 细胞分泌一种具有抗原特异性的 IgM 样因子（受体？）有关。这种因子可以与抗原结合形成复合物，然后会被巨噬细胞吞噬 [60]。

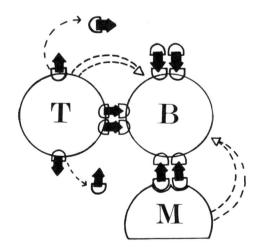

图 2. 体液免疫应答中 T-B 细胞协作的可能机理。T 细胞和 B 细胞受体之间的"抗原桥"（→），可能发挥如下作用：(i) 在 T 细胞表面将抗原呈递给 B 细胞；或者作为释放 T 细胞受体 - 抗原复合物的基体，这种复合物可以是游离的，也可以是位于第三方细胞如巨噬细胞表面的。(ii) 把 B 细胞和 T 细胞或第三方细胞拉到一起，从而使小范围内起作用的因素在它们之间发挥功能。

There are antigens ("thymus-independent antigens") which seem to be able to stimulate at least some B cell clones to secrete IgM antibody without the help of T cells (reviewed in ref. 1), suggesting that T-B cell collaboration is not always essential for antibody production. Nonetheless, the discovery that T cells cooperate with B cells in humoral immunity has been an important advance and has explained the previous paradox of impaired antibody responses in T cell deficient animals. There is recent indirect evidence that T cells can inhibit B cell activity as well as enhance it[61], and that they can enhance[62] and inhibit[63] the functioning of other T cells. It is not known if these interactions involve antigen bridging between the receptors of the interacting cells. Taken together with the enhancing and inhibiting effects of secreted antibody on both T and B cell functions, a picture is emerging of a highly complex and finely controlled immune system, with each type of cell and response modulating the others.

## Way Ahead

With the recognition that there are two distinct classes of lymphocytes with different origins, properties and immunological functions which modulate each other's activities, the door has opened to a new era of immunology. The resulting insight into the functioning of the immune system in health and disease has paved the way for rational attempts to manipulate selectively the different cell types and their various responses for the benefit of patients with infection, autoimmune disease, cancer, immune deficiency states, and organ grafts. And present day immunology provides a number of readily accessible models and powerful tools for studying a variety of biological problems, including differentiation, genetic control, cell interactions, and membrane receptor-ligand interactions.

I am grateful to M. F. Greaves, N. A. Mitchison and J. J. T. Owen for helpful discussion. The bibliography, which is incomplete, is meant only as an arbitrary way into the relevant literature.

(**242**, 19-23; 1973)

**Martin C. Raff**
Medical Research Council Neuroimmunology Project, Zoology Department, University College, Gower Street, London WC1

References:

1. Greaves, M. F., Owen, J. J. T., and Raff, M. C., *T and B Lymphocytes: Origins, Properties and Roles in Immune Responses* (Excerpta Medica, Amsterdam, in the press).

2. Gowans, J. L., and McGregor, D.D., *Prog. Allergy*, **9**,1 (1965).

3. Warner, N. L., Szenberg, A., and Burnet, F. M., *Austral. J. Exp. Biol. Med.*, **40**, 373 (1962).

4. Cooper, M. D., Peterson, R. D. A., South, M. A., and Good, R. A., *J. Exp. Med.*, **123**, 75 (1966).

5. Miller, J. F. A. P., and Osoba, D., *Physiol. Rev.*, **47**, 437 (1967).

6. Good, R. A., Biggars, W. D., and Park, B. H., in *Progress in Immunology* (edit. By Amos, B.), 699 (Academic Press, New York, 1971).

7. Roitt, I. M., Greaves, M. F., Torrigiani, G., Brostoff, J., and Playfair, J. H. L., *Lancet*, ii, 367 (1969).

8. Hildeman, W. H., and Clem, L. W., in *Progress in Immunology* (edit. By Amos, B.), 1305 (Academic Press, New York, 1971).

9. Owen, J. J. T., in *Ontogeny of Acquired Immunity, a Ciba Foundation Symposium*, 35 (Associated Science Publishers, Amsterdam, 1972).

在没有 T 细胞辅助的情况下，有一些抗原（"胸腺非依赖性抗原"）可以刺激部分 B 细胞分泌 IgM 抗体（有关综述见参考文献 1）。这表明 T-B 细胞的协作并不总是抗体产生所必需的。不过发现体液免疫中 T 细胞与 B 细胞的协作仍然是免疫学研究中的一个重大进展，它解释了之前提出的缺乏 T 细胞的动物为什么会出现抗体反应受损这一问题。最近还有间接证据表明 T 细胞不但可以抑制 B 细胞的应答，也可以增强 B 细胞的活性 [61]。同时，它们还可以增强 [62] 或抑制 [63] 其他 T 细胞的功能。人们并不清楚这些相互作用是否包括相互作用的细胞之间受体的抗原桥连接。总之，考虑所有这些分泌的抗体对 T 细胞和 B 细胞功能的增强或抑制作用，我们可以想象免疫系统是高度复杂且精密调控的，在这个系统中每种细胞和免疫应答都可以调控另一种。

展　望

随着我们的认识，免疫系统中存在着两种不同来源、不同性质、不同免疫功能的淋巴细胞，它们相互调控着彼此的活性，免疫学研究已进入一个新时代。在健康和疾病方面，对免疫系统功能的深入了解使我们有可能通过合理的实验，选择性地控制不同免疫细胞类型及其多样应答，以改善被传染病、自身免疫疾病、癌症、免疫缺陷疾病或器官移植所困扰的患者的生活。另外，现代免疫学也提供了许多可用于研究多种生物学问题（包括分化、遗传控制、细胞间相互作用以及细胞膜受体－配体间相互作用）的有效模型和强大工具。

非常感谢格里夫斯、米奇森和欧文宝贵的建议。此外，参考文献引用可能不全面，仅作为查阅相关文献的一个途径。

（张锦彬 翻译；秦志海 审稿）

10. Weissman, I., *J. Exp. Med.*, **126**, 291 (1967).

11. Davies, A. J. S., *Transplant. Rev.*, **1**, 43 (1969).

12. Blomgren, H., and Andersson, B., *Exp. Cell Res.*, **57**, 185 (1969).

13. Raff, M. C., and Cantor, H., in *Progress in Immunology* (edit. by Amos, B.), 83 (Academic Press, New York, 1971).

14. Stutman, O., Yunis, E. J., and Good, R. A., *J. Exp. Med.*, **130**, 809(1969).

15. Cooper, M. D., Lawton, A. R., and Kincade, P. W., in *Current Problems in Immunobiology* (edit. by Hanna, M. G.), **1**, 33 (Plenum Press, New York, 1972).

16. Pierce, C. W., Solliday, S. M., and Asofsky, R., *J. Exp. Med.*, **135**, 698 (1972).

17. Everett, N. B., and Caffrey, R. W., in *The Lymphocyte in Immunology and Haemopoiesis* (edit. by Yoffey, J. M.), 108 (Arnold, London, 1966).

18. Metcalf, D., and Moore, M. A. S., *Haemopoietic Cells* (North Holland, Amsterdam, 1971).

19. Raff, M. C., *Transplant. Rev.*, **6**, 52 (1971).

20. Raff, M. C., *Immunology*, **19**, 637 (1970).

21. Rabellino, E., Colon, S., Grey, H. M., and Unanue, E. R., *J. Exp. Med.*, **133**, 156 (1971).

22. Schlossman, S. F., and Hudson, L., *J. Immunol.*, **110**, 313 (1973).

23. Hulett, H. R., Bonner, W. A., Barret, J., and Herzenberg, L. A., *Science*, **166**, 747 (1969).

24. Bianco, C., Patrick, R., and Nussenzweig, V., *J. Exp. Med.*, **132**, 702 (1970).

25. Basten, A., Miller, J. F. A. P., Sprent, J., and Pye, J., *J. Exp. Med.*, **135**, 610 (1972).

26. Howard, J. C., *J. Exp. Med.*, **135**, 185 (1972).

27. Parrott, D. M. V., and de Sousa, M. A. B., *Clin. Exp. Immunol.*, **8**, 663 (1971).

28. Sprent, J., and Miller, J. F. A. P., *Eur. J. Immunol.*, **2**, 384 (1972).

29. Howard, J. C., Hunt, S. V., and Gowans, J. L., *J. Exp. Med.*, **135**, 200 (1972).

30. Wioland, M., Sabulovic, D., and Burg, C., *Nature New Biology*, **237**, 275 (1972).

31. Lance, E. M., *Clin. Exp. Med.*, **6**, 789 (1970).

32. Turk, J. L., and Poulter, L. W., *Clin. Exp. Med.*, **10**, 285 (1972).

33. Cohen, J. J., and Claman, H. N., *J. Exp. Med.*, **133**, 1026 (1971).

34. Cunningham, A. J., and Sercarz, E. E., *Eur. J. Immunol.*, **1**, 413 (1972).

35. Greaves, M. F., and Janossy, G., *Transplant. Rev.*, **11** (1972).

36. Roelants, G., *Nature New Biology*, **236**, 252 (1972).

37. Basten, A., Miller, J. F. A. P., Warner, N. L., and Pye, J., *Nature New Biology*, **231**, 104 (1971).

38. Wigzell, H., *Transplant. Rev.*, **5**, 76 (1970).

39. Brondz, B. D., *Transplant. Rev.*, **10**, 112 (1972).

40. Rabellino. E., Colon, S., Grey, H. M., and Unanue, E. R., *J. Exp. Med.*, **133**, 156 (1971).

41. Mäkelä. O., and Cross, A., *Prog. Allergy*, **14**, 154 (1970).

42. Cozenza, H., and Köhler, H., *Proc. US Nat. Acad. Sci.*, **69**, 2701 (1972).

43. Pink, R., Wang, A. -C., and Fudenberg, H. H., *Ann. Rev. Med.*, **22**, 145 (1971).

44. Vitetta, E. S., Baur, S., and S., Uhr, J. W., *J. Exp. Med.*, **134**, 242 (1971).

45. Shevach, E. M., Paul, W. E., and Green, I., *J. Exp. Med.*, **136**, 1207 (1972).

46. Benacerraf, B., and McDevitt, H. O., *Science*, **175**, 273 (1972).

47. Schlossman, S. F., *Transplant Rev.*, **10**, 97 (1972).

48. Alkan, S. S., Williams, F. B., Nitecki, D. E., and Goodman, J. W., *J. Exp. Med.*, **135**, 1228 (1972).

49. Mitchison, N. A., in *Cell Interactions and Receptor Antibodies in Immune Responses* (edit. by Mäkelä, O., Cross, A., and Kosunen, T.), 249 (Academic Press, New York, 1971).

50. Taylor, R. B., Duffus, W. P. H., Raff, M. C., and de Petris, S., *Nature New Biology*, **233**, 225 (1971).

51. Schwartz, R. S., in *Progress in Immunology* (edit. by Amos, B.), 1081 (Academic Press, New York, 1971).

52. MacLennan, I. C. M., *Transplant. Rev.*, **13**, 67 (1972).

53. *Mediators, of Cellular Immunity* (edit. by Lawrence, H. S., and Landy, M.) (Academic Press, New York, 1969).

54. Lubaroff, D. M., and Waksman, B. H., *J. Exp. Med.*, **128**, 1437 (1968).

55. Brunner, K. T., and Cerottini, J. -C., in *Progress in Immunology* (edit. by Amos, B.), 385 (Academic Press, New York, 1971).

56. Claman, H. N., Chaperon, E. A., and Triplett, R. F., *Proc. Soc. Exp. Biol.*, **122**, 1167 (1966).

57. Davies, A. J. S., Leuchars, E., Wallis, V., Marchant, R., and Elliot, E. V., *Transplantation*, **5**, 22 (1967).

58. Mitchison, N. A., Rajewsky, K., and Taylor, R. B., in *Developmental Aspects of Antibody Formation and Structure* (edit. by Sterzl, J., and Riha, I.), **2**, 547 (Academia, Prague, 1970).

59. Schimpl, A., and Wecker, E., *Nature New Biology*, **237**, 15 (1972).

60. Feldmann, M., *J. Exp. Med.*, **136**, 737 (1972).

61. Jacobson, E. D., Herzenberg, L. A., Riblet, R., and Hersenberg, L. A., *J. Exp. Med.*, **135**, 1163 (1972).

62. Cantor, H., and Asofsky, R., *J. Exp. Med.*, **135**, 764 (1972).

63. Gershon, R. K., Cohen, P., Hencin, R., and Liebhaber, S. A., *J. Immunol.*, **108**, 586 (1972).

# Cometary Collisions and Geological Periods

H. C. Urey

### Editor's Note

The idea that comet impacts on Earth could have caused mass extinctions in the geological past is usually attributed to geologist Walter Alvarez and his father Luis, who proposed in 1980 that such a catastrophic collision at the end of the Cretaceous period 65 million years ago killed the dinosaurs. But here Harold Urey (like Luis Alvarez a Nobel prize-winning nuclear physicist) anticipates much of that hypothesis, suggesting that comet impacts might terminate geological periods (including the Cretaceous) by altering global climate. The high temperatures created by the impact, says Urey, "would be most destructive to animals and plants". It is now generally accepted that the end of the Cretaceous was marked by a major cometary impact, probably in Mexico.

SOME fifteen years ago, I suggested that tektites were produced by collisions of comets with the Earth[1-3]. Many detailed investigations of these objects have added much to our knowledge, and these, together with the lunar investigations, have proved this hypothesis to be very probably correct. I have also suggested that the geological periods were terminated by such collisions, but this was published in the *Saturday Review of Literature*, and no scientist except me, so far as I know, reads that magazine. The energy of such collisions and their frequency was roughly estimated at that time, and the number of these collisions has been reviewed again by Durrani[4].

The energy of cometary collisions has been considered by several authors (see ref. 5), but to estimate this energy more quantitatively, I consider the energy of a Halley's comet type collision. Cometary orbits which extend to great distances have velocities at the Earth's distance from the Sun of 42.1 km s⁻¹; the Earth's velocity is 29.8 km s⁻¹. If the comet collides head on with the trailing surface of the Earth, the relative velocity is 12.3 km s⁻¹; if with the leading surface it is 71.9 km s⁻¹; and if with intermediate positions and directions the relative velocities are intermediate. Of course, the escape velocity of the Earth, 11.2 km s⁻¹, must be added, and is considerable for trailing type collisions. The two velocities, including this correction, are 16.6 and 72.8 km s⁻¹. The higher velocity corresponds to nineteen times the minimum energy. The higher energy collisions are more probable because comets generally cross the orbit of the Earth. The ones in the larger orbits, at least, move markedly toward and away from the Sun, so the Earth sweeps across their orbits. In the present calculations, I use an effective velocity of collision with the Earth of 45 km s⁻¹ though greater or lesser collision velocities are possible.

# 彗星碰撞与地质年代

尤里

## 编者按

在过去的地质时期中，由于彗星撞击地球导致了大规模的物种灭绝，这一观点主要是来自于地质学家沃尔特·阿尔瓦雷斯及其父亲路易斯·阿尔瓦雷斯。他们于 1980 年提出，6500 万年前白垩纪末的一次彗星撞击最终导致恐龙灭绝。但是，哈罗德·尤里（一位与路易斯·阿尔瓦雷斯一样得过诺贝尔奖的核物理学家）在本文中率先提出了下述假说，即彗星撞击地球使全球气候变化从而终结了一个个地质年代，其中就包括了白垩纪。尤里认为，碰撞所导致的高温"对于动植物来说应该最具毁灭性"。现在人们已普遍认为，白垩纪终结于一次剧烈的彗星撞击，撞击点可能就位于墨西哥。

大约在 15 年前，我曾提出，玻陨石由彗星与地球碰撞形成[1-3]。许多对这些物质的详细研究已经大大加深了我们的认识，而这些研究结合对月球的调查，已经证明该假说很可能成立。我还曾提出，正是这类碰撞导致了一个个地质时期的终结。然而，这一观点发表在了《星期六文学评论》上，而且据我所知，我可能是迄今为止唯一阅读过这本杂志的科学家。我当时已经对此类碰撞所产生的能量和它们发生的频率作过粗略的估计，并且杜拉尼[4]也曾对碰撞次数进行了回顾。

多位研究人员已经探讨过彗星碰撞所产生的能量（见参考文献 5），不过为了更精确地定量估计该能量，我研究了哈雷彗星型碰撞所产生的能量。彗星轨道的延伸距离非常远，当其与太阳的距离接近于地球到太阳的距离时，速度为 42.1 km·s$^{-1}$，而地球的速度为 29.8 km·s$^{-1}$。如果彗星从地球的后面与地球相撞，其相对速度为 12.3 km·s$^{-1}$；如果与地球迎面相撞，那么其相对速度将为 71.9 km·s$^{-1}$；如果相撞的位置和方向处于上述两种情况之间，那么其相对速度也在上述两个速度的区间内。当然，必须考虑上地球的逃逸速度，即 11.2 km·s$^{-1}$，对于从后面碰撞的情况来说，这个值是相当大的。经过校正后的两个速度分别为 16.6 km·s$^{-1}$ 和 72.8 km·s$^{-1}$。高速碰撞产生的能量相当于最低能量的 19 倍。由于彗星轨道大多与地球轨道相交，所以发生高能碰撞的可能性更大。至少轨道较大的那些彗星，面向太阳或背离太阳的运动都非常明显，因此，地球会穿越其轨道。在本计算中，我采用的与地球碰撞的有效速度为 45 km·s$^{-1}$，不过，较大或较小速度的碰撞也都有可能发生。

The masses of comets are largely unknown, but Russell *et al.*[5] and Whipple[6] give reasonable arguments indicating that Halley's comet may have a mass of $2 \times 10^{-9}$ M⊕ ($\sim 10^{18}$) g, and Russell *et al.* suggest that the comet of 1729 may have a mass of $6 \times 10^{21}$ g. For calculations, I shall use $10^{18}$ g.

Table 1 gives some estimates based on these assumptions for the effect of a cometary collision with the Earth. The energy, $10^{31}$ erg, is double the minimum energy required to remove the atmosphere and permit the tektites to be transported to great distances as estimated by Lin[7]. Of course, the energy was not dissipated in only vaporizing water or heating the atmosphere, or heating the ocean and so on, but the data indicate that a very great variation in climatic conditions covering the entire Earth should occur and very violent physical effects should occur over a substantial fraction of the Earth's surface. For example, the great seismic effects might initiate extensive lava flows. The scattering of melted bits of highly siliceous rocks should be only a very small and insignificant part of the physical effects. I suggest that the termination of a geological period would result and a new one would begin.

Table 1. Energetic Effects a Cometary Collison with Earth Could Produce

| | |
|---|---|
| Energy to the Earth from Sun in 1 yr | $3.48 \times 10^{31}$ erg |
| Earthquake of ninth magnitude | $2 \times 10^{25}$ erg |
| Energy of comet of $10^{18}$ g and velocity 45 km s$^{-1}$ | $10^{31}$ erg |
| Fraction of yearly solar energy | 0.29 |
| Energy required to remove atmosphere and scatter australites[7] | $4.4 \times 10^{30}$ |
| If all energy absorbed by | |
| (1) atmosphere, elevation of temperature | 190°C |
| or (2) ocean water, elevation of temperature | 0.175°C |
| or (3) 100 m of ocean water, elevation of temperature | 5°C |
| or (4) water volatilized at 100°C | $4 \times 10^{20}$ g |
| Edge of cube to contain this water | 74 km |
| Area of ocean 3 km deep to contain water | $1.33 \times 10^{5}$ km$^2$ |
| or (5) mass which could be thrown in circle about Earth | $3.24 \times 10^{19}$ g |
| or (6) earthquakes of ninth magnitude | $5 \times 10^{5}$ |

The scattering of ocean water over land areas would destroy land plants and animals, though probably such water would not fall uniformly and some would not be killed by this method. The earthquake effect would be great in the immediate neighbourhood of the collision site, and would be noticeable over the entire Earth. The smog effect due to the ammonia and other compounds of the comet would probably be minor. Because the total energy is equivalent to 0.29 of the energy from the Sun for one year, which would raise the temperature of the atmosphere to 190°C if all heat went into the atmosphere, it seems

大部分彗星的质量尚不清楚。不过，罗素等人[5]以及惠普尔[6]曾做了一些合理的推断，认为哈雷彗星的质量约为 $2 \times 10^{-9} M\oplus$（编者注：$M\oplus$代表地球质量）约 $10^{18}$ g。罗素等人还推断彗星 1729 的质量约为 $6 \times 10^{21}$ g。在本次计算过程中，我将采用 $10^{18}$ g。

根据上述假定，表 1 给出了彗星与地球相撞产生的一些能量效应的估算值。根据林绍基[7]的推算，$10^{31}$ erg 的能量是能够推移大气并使玻陨石长距离搬运所需最低能量的两倍。当然，这些能量不仅仅消耗在蒸发水、加热大气或海洋等方面。相关数据还表明，包围整个地球的气候条件可能会有很大变化，并且会在地球表面相当多的地区产生剧烈的物理效应。例如：大的地震活动可能会引起广泛的熔岩流。四处飞溅的高硅质岩石的小熔融体在这些物理效应中应该仅占很小一部分，微不足道。我认为这将导致一个地质时期的结束和一个新时期的开始。

表 1. 彗星与地球相撞可能产生的能量效应

| | |
|---|---|
| 每年太阳照射到地球上的能量 | $3.48 \times 10^{31}$ erg |
| 九级地震释放的能量 | $2 \times 10^{25}$ erg |
| 质量为 $10^{18}$ g，速度为 45 km·s$^{-1}$ 的彗星碰撞所产生的能量 | $10^{31}$ erg |
| 占每年太阳散发能量的比例 | 0.29 |
| 推移大气并使玻陨石分散所需的能量[7] | $4.4 \times 10^{30}$ |
| 假设碰撞产生的能量被以下过程吸收： | |
| （1）如果全被大气吸收，可以使大气温度升高 | 190℃ |
| （2）如果全被海水吸收，可以使海水温度升高 | 0.175℃ |
| （3）如果全被100 m深的海水吸收，可以使温度升高 | 5℃ |
| （4）将水加热到100℃并蒸发掉的量 | $4 \times 10^{20}$ g |
| 将这些水注入立方体中，立方体的边长 | 74 km |
| 将这些水注入3 km深的大洋，大洋的面积 | $1.33 \times 10^{5}$ km$^2$ |
| （5）可以抛出并使其绕地球旋转的物体质量 | $3.24 \times 10^{19}$ g |
| （6）九级地震的次数 | $5 \times 10^{5}$ |

海水向陆地泛滥会摧毁陆地动植物，然而，由于海水泛滥并不均匀，有些生物可能不会因此而灭绝。碰撞点附近的地震效应该会非常剧烈，全球都会有震感。由彗星上的氨和其他化合物引起的雾效应可能会比较小。由于碰撞的总能量相当于一年中地球得到的来自太阳能量的 0.29 倍，所以如果所有的热量都被大气吸收，大气温度可升高到 190℃，因此温度看起来将会出现明显的上升。短期高温对于动植物

that a considerable rise in temperature would occur. High temperatures for brief periods would be most destructive to animals and plants, and moderate rises in temperature with high humidity would destroy many living things. It seems that sea animals and plants would fare best if located at some distance where shock would not be important. But would this be true of the air-breathing marine dinosaurs? High humidity and air taken into cool bodies would produce considerable condensation of water in their bodies. Of course, other land based reptiles, such as alligators, as well as the primitive mammals and birds, survived from the Cretaceous into the Palaeocene. Such survival could be due to "good luck"—not all areas were equally affected and some animals and plants took the adverse conditions better than others. But it does seem possible and even probable that a comet collision with the Earth destroyed the dinosaurs and initiated the Tertiary division of geologic time.

Were the ages of Tertiary times determined by the fall of comets which produced the tektite fields? Table 2 lists the ages of these recent geologic periods and the ages of tektites. Rough agreement exists. Errors are probably present in both the geological estimates and the physical measurements of the tektite ages which are my averages of recent measurements. Probable errors in the Moldavites, Libyan Desert Glass and the Bediasites are about 2 m.y. The agreement is satisfactory. I wonder if tektites might not be found at some other boundaries between the Eocene, Palaeocene and Cretaceous periods? Lin[7] required nearly as great an energy as calculated here in order to account for the Indochina and Australian tektites, and this produced only a minor discontinuity in geologic strata, so it seems probable that the energy required for the termination of the Cretaceous was much greater than that estimated here.

Table 2. Ages of Geologic Periods and of Tektites

| Geologic period | Ages[8] (m.y.) | Ages[9] (m.y.) | Tektites |
|---|---|---|---|
| Pleistocene | 1 | 0.71±0.10 1.2±0.2 | Australites Ivory Coast |
| Pliocene | | | |
| Miocene | 13 | 14.7±0.7 | Moldavites |
| Oligocene | 25 | 28.6±2 | Libyan Desert Glass |
| Eocene | 36 | 34.7±2 | Bediasites |
| Palaeocene | 58 | ? | ? |
| Cretaceous | 63 | ? | ? |

It seems likely that interesting studies could be made by biologists and palaeontologists in regard to the selection of survivors of such catastrophes. It will most probably be millions of years before the next collision occurs, but survivors of such an event would now most probably need to be able to survive the intense radioactivity from nuclear power plants which will be scattered over the entire Earth's surface. As I stated previously, "If the

来说是极具灾难性的，并且在高湿度条件下，适当的温度上升就会导致大量生物死亡。对于海洋动植物来说，倘若处于离碰撞点较远、震动不强烈的地方，它们似乎就不会受到很大影响。但是对于呼吸空气的海洋恐龙来说，情况会是这样吗？由于体内温度较低，吸入的高湿度空气会在它们体内冷凝产生大量的水。当然，其他一些陆栖爬行动物，例如短吻鳄以及一些原始的哺乳动物和鸟类则从白垩纪幸存下来，并一直延续到古新世。它们的幸存可能由于"好运"，因为并不是所有地区都受到同样的影响，而且一些动植物比其他动植物更能适应不利的条件。彗星与地球的碰撞造成了恐龙的灭绝，并且使地质时期进入到第三纪，这一看法似乎不仅合理，而且具有很大的可能性成立。

第三纪各个地质时期年龄是否也取决于形成玻陨石的彗星陨落呢？表 2 列出了这几个近期地质时期的年龄以及玻陨石的年龄，两者基本一致。地质时期的估算和玻陨石年龄的物理测定可能都存在误差，我使用了最近测定结果的平均值。莫尔道玻陨石（绿玻陨石）、利比亚沙漠玻璃和贝迪阿玻陨石年龄的概率误差约为 200 万年。这种一致性还是令人满意的。我在想，在始新世、古新世和白垩纪的分界处是否有可能不会发现玻陨石？为了解释印度支那以及澳大利亚玻陨石的形成，林绍基 [7] 得出的能量几乎与本文计算的值相当，这仅造成了地层中一个较小的不整合面。由此可以看出，终结白垩纪所需的能量很可能比本文中的估算值要大得多。

表 2. 地质时期的年龄以及玻陨石的年龄

| 地质时期 | 年龄 [8]（百万年） | 年龄 [9]（百万年） | 玻陨石 |
|---|---|---|---|
| 更新世 | 1 | $0.71 \pm 0.10$<br>$1.2 \pm 0.2$ | 澳大利亚玻陨石<br>象牙海岸玻陨石 |
| 上新世 | 13 | $14.7 \pm 0.7$ | 莫尔道玻陨石 |
| 中新世 | 25 | $28.6 \pm 2$ | 利比亚沙漠玻璃 |
| 渐新世 | 36 | $34.7 \pm 2$ | 贝迪阿玻陨石 |
| 始新世 | 58 | ? | ? |
| 古新世 | 63 | ? | ? |
| 白垩纪 |  |  |  |

生物学家和古生物学家似乎可以做许多有趣的工作来研究何种生物可以从这类灾难中幸存下来。虽然离下一次碰撞的发生可能还有数百万年，但是经历过这些大灾难的幸存者如今却需要克服来自将要遍及全球的核电站的强辐射威胁。如我之前所说，对于玻陨石以及地质记录的间断，"倘若本文给出了它们的真正成因"，那么

present suggestion gives the true origin" of tektites and also of breaks in the geologic record, "all will agree that any demonstration of the process would cost far more than the scientific knowledge gained would justify."

I am indebted to Professor Shao-Chi Lin for some suggestions in regard to this paper.

(**242**, 32-33; 1973)

Harold C. Urey

Chemistry Department, University of California at San Diego, La Jolla, California 92037

Received December 1, 1972

References:

1. Urey, H. C., *Nature*, **179**, 556 (1957).

2. Urey, H. C., *Nature*, **197**, 228 (1963).

3. Urey, H. C., *Science*, **137**, 746 (1962).

4. Durrani, S. A., *Nature*, **235**, 383 (1972).

5. Russell, H. N., Dugan, R. S., and Stewart, J. Q., *Astronomy*, 446 (Ginn and Co., New York, 1945).

6. Whipple, F. L., in *Moon, Meteorites and Comets* (edit. by Middlehurst, B. M., and Kuiper, G. P.), chapter 19 (Chicago Univ. Press, 1963).

7. Lin, S. C., *J. Geophys. Res.*, **71**, 2427 (1966).

8. Laurence Kulp, J., *Science*, **133**, 1106 (1961).

9. Durrani, S. A., *Phys. Earth Planet. Int.*, **4**, 251 (1971).

10. Storzer, D., and Wagner, G. A., *Earth Planet. Sci. Lett.*, **10**, 435 (1971).

"所有人都会同意，我们目前所掌握的科学知识还远不足以证明对这一过程的论证。"

在此，特别感谢林绍基教授对本文提出的建议。

（齐红艳 翻译；孟庆任 审稿）

# On Estimating Functional Gene Number in Eukaryotes

S. J. O'Brien

## Editor's Note

Around 30 years before the Human Genome Project mapped the tens of thousands of protein-coding genes of the human genome, debate over the eukaryotic gene complement was rife. The total number of genes was thought to be far less than the amount of DNA in the haploid genome, leading some to suggest that over 90% of the eukaryotic genome was nonfunctional or "junk". Here geneticist Stephen J. O'Brien questions this assumption, arguing that the evidence for junk DNA is based on the response of the functioning genes to natural selection. Non-coding DNA is now thought to comprise most of the human genome, but the term "junk" is used with caution since functions have been ascribed to some so-called "junk" sequences.

MANY recent studies have been concerned with the construction of biological model systems to describe adequately regulation of gene action during development of eukaryotes[1-5]. The number of genes in mammals and *Drosophila* has been suggested to be 1 to 2 orders of magnitude less than the amount of available DNA per haploid genome could provide[2-7]. Although *Drosophila* and mammalian nuclei contain enough unique DNA to specify for respectively $10^5$ and $10^6$ genes of 1,000 nucleotide pairs[8,9], it has been argued that a much lower estimate of functional gene number is more reasonable[2-7]. Conversely, these conclusions indicate that more than 90% of the eukaryotic genome may be composed of nonfunctional or noninformational "junk" DNA. Here we demonstrate these estimations have not been fundamentally proven; rather they are based on simplifying assumptions of questionable validity, in some cases contradictory to experimental data.

The perceptive model proposed by Crick[5] provides that the structural genes for proteins are situated generally in the interbands observed in the giant salivary gland chromosomes of *Drosophila*. The chromosome bands, which contain all but a few % of the DNA, are the sites of regulatory elements and presumably large amounts of noninformational DNA. The model thus predicts approximately 5,000 structural genes in *Drosophila*, the approximate number of salivary gland bands which can be observed.

This model is strongly supported by the elegant work of Judd *et al.*[10] who examined 121 lethal and gross morphological point mutations that map in the *zeste* to *white* region of the tip of the X chromosomes in *D. melanogaster*. There are 16 salivary gland chromosome bands or chromomeres in this region corresponding to 16 complementation groups of the morphological or lethal point mutations. In addition a series of overlapping deficiencies

# 真核生物功能基因数的估计

奥布赖恩

## 编者按

在人类基因组计划定位了数万个人类基因组中的蛋白质编码基因之前，30 年间关于真核生物的基因数目存在很多争议。基因的总数被认为远少于单倍体基因组中 DNA 的数量，这导致一些人提出 90% 以上的真核生物基因组是没有功能的或者是"垃圾"。在本文中，遗传学家斯蒂芬·奥布赖恩质疑了这个假说，指出垃圾 DNA 实为功能基因对自然选择的反应的证据。现在认为非编码 DNA 占据了人类基因组的大部分，但是"垃圾"一词要谨慎使用，因为已经发现了一些所谓的"垃圾"序列的功能。

近来有许多研究都着眼于构建生物模型系统来充分描述真核生物发育过程中基因行为的调节 [1-5]。就一个单倍体基因组所能够容纳的 DNA 量来说，已发现哺乳动物和果蝇中的基因数目要比其少 1 到 2 个数量级 [2-7]。以 1,000 个核苷酸对构成一个基因来计算，尽管果蝇和哺乳动物细胞核含有足够的非重复 DNA 分别形成 $10^5$ 和 $10^6$ 个基因 [8,9]，但是看来对功能基因的数量更低的估计是更合理的 [2-7]。反过来说，这些结论则提示真核生物基因组超过 90% 的 DNA 可能由非功能性或者不编码信息的"垃圾"DNA 组成。本文中我们的结果显示这些估计都没有得到有力地证明，相反它们都是基于一些简化的假设所获得，而这些假设本身的正确性值得怀疑，其中有些甚至与实验数据相矛盾。

克里克 [5] 提出的模型指出，在果蝇巨大唾液腺染色体中，编码蛋白质的结构基因通常都位于观察到的染色体条带之间。调控元件和大量含有无编码信息的 DNA 序列位于染色体条带上，这些染色体条带包含了绝大多数 DNA。据此该模型预测果蝇大约有 5,000 个结构基因，这也是能够观察到的唾液腺染色体带的大致数量。

该模型得到了贾德等人的出色工作的有力支持 [10]。他们研究了黑腹果蝇位于 X 染色体末端 *zeste* 到 *white* 区域内的 121 个致死性和显著影响形态的点突变。该区域内一共有 16 个唾液腺染色体带或染色粒，与 16 个形态学改变或致死性点突变的互补群互为对应。此外一系列重叠的缺陷支持一个条带一个互补群的关系。外推至整

supports the 1 band : 1 complementation group relationship. Extrapolation over the entire genome gives approximately 5,000 complementation groups or genes to 5,000 chromosome bands. There are also estimates available on the total number of lethal loci in the *Drosophila* genome. By screening for large numbers of lethal chromosomes either in natural populations or following irradiation, it is possible to relate the frequency of allelism to the number of lethal loci by a simple Poisson distribution: and the number of lethals thus measured in *Drosophila* gives a result between 1,000-2,000[11,12].

The problem with extrapolation of the fine structure analysis and the lethal data to the functional gene number is our inability to answer the question: how many genes when mutated are capable of producing a lethal or gross morphological phenotype? The answer is not known specifically but the available data suggest that only a very small percentage of all gene products are critical enough to kill the organism if absent. In *Drosophila* over 30 genes have a known gene product[13], of which there are 14 at which "null" alleles eliminate the protein, its activity, or the RNA product entirely, and of these (Table 1) only the *bobbed* locus has lethal alleles[14]. Most alleles, however, at that locus, which is the structural gene for ribosomal RNA, are viable even at very low levels of rRNA. The other genes, which code for enzymes whose function *a priori* seemed essential for normal metabolism, are in no case lethal when homozygous for completely "null" alleles.

Table 1. Genes in *Drosophila melanogaster* with Known Gene Products and Recovered "Null" Alleles

| Locus | Product | Number of "null" alleles | Reference |
|-------|---------|--------------------------|-----------|
| Est-C | Esterase-C | 1 | 37 |
| Est-6 | Esterase-6 | 1 | 37 |
| Aph | Alkaline phosphatase | 1 | 38 |
| Acph-1 | Acid phosphatase | 15 | 39 |
| rosy | Xanthine dehydrogenase | 79 | 40 |
| Aldox | Aldehyde oxidase | 2 | 41 |
| Zw | Glucose-6-phosphate dehydrogenase | 5 | * |
| 6-Pgd | 6-Phosphogluconate dehydrogenase | 1 | * |
| Adh | Alcohol dehydrogenase | 14 | 42,43 |
| Idh | Isocitrate dehydrogenase | 2 | 44 |
| αGpdh-1 | α-Glycerophosphate dehydrogenase | 4 | 15 |
| bobbed | Ribosomal RNA | 25 | 45 |
| vermilion | Tryptophan pyrrolase | 10 | 17,46 |
| cinnebar | Kynurenine hydroxylase | 3 | 47 |

*W. J. Young, personal communication.

个基因组，大约 5,000 个这种互补群或者基因对应于 5,000 个染色体带。也有人估计了果蝇基因组中致死基因座的总数。通过筛查自然群体中或者经过辐射处理后的群体中的大量可致死染色体，就有可能通过简单的泊松分布将等位性的频率与致死基因座的数目联系起来，这样得到的果蝇中致死基因座的数目大约是 1,000~2,000 个 [11,12]。

在这种利用精细结构分析和致死性数据外推到功能基因数目过程中存在一个我们无法回答的问题：有多少基因突变后能够产生致死性的或者显著影响形态的表型？这无法明确地回答，但是已有数据提示所有基因产物中只有很少一部分重要到其缺失能够导致生物的死亡。在果蝇中，超过 30 个基因的基因产物是已知的 [13]，其中只有 14 个在具有"无效"等位基因时能够导致蛋白质及其活性或 RNA 产物的完全缺失，而这其中（表 1）只有 *bobbed* 基因座具有致死性的等位基因 [14]。然而，这个基因座是核糖体 RNA（rRNA）的结构基因，其大多数等位基因即使在所产生的 rRNA 浓度非常低时也能有活力。其他编码酶的基因即使它们对于正常代谢是必需的，在纯合的完全"无效的"等位基因中也没有一个是致死性的。

表 1. 具有确定基因产物和可恢复性"无效"等位基因的黑腹果蝇基因

| 位点 | 产物 | 无效等位基因数目 | 文献 |
|---|---|---|---|
| Est-C | 酯酶–C | 1 | 37 |
| Est-6 | 酯酶–6 | 1 | 37 |
| Aph | 碱性磷酸酶 | 1 | 38 |
| Acph-1 | 酸性磷酸酶 | 15 | 39 |
| rosy | 黄嘌呤脱氢酶 | 79 | 40 |
| Aldox | 醛氧化酶 | 2 | 41 |
| Zw | 葡萄糖–6–磷酸脱氢酶 | 5 | * |
| 6-Pgd | 6–磷酸葡萄糖酸脱氢酶 | 1 | * |
| Adh | 乙醇脱氢酶 | 14 | 42,43 |
| Idh | 异柠檬酸脱氢酶 | 2 | 44 |
| αGdph-1 | α–甘油磷酸脱氢酶 | 4 | 15 |
| bobbed | 核糖体 RNA | 25 | 45 |
| vermilion | 色氨酸吡咯酶 | 10 | 17,46 |
| cinnebar | 犬尿氨酸羟化酶 | 3 | 47 |

* 扬，个人交流。

Null alleles at the first eleven loci above were detected by the loss of histochemical stain development on an electrophoretic gel. The sensitivity of this assay detects at least 5% of normal enzyme levels. In several cases (*Acph-1, rosy, Adh, αGpdh-1*), analytical enzyme assays with a sensitivity near 0.1% of wild type enzyme levels also failed to detect trace activity in "null" homozygotes. In the two cases where cross reacting material (**CRM**) was measured (*Acph-1* and *ry*) it was also negligible.

Null alleles of at least two of the loci were induced in a crossing scheme that would have recovered lethal alleles (*αGpdh-1* and *Acph-1*). A lethal "null" allele would also be detected as an exceptional heterozygote with normal alleles of different eletrophoretic mobilities in those cases of "null" alleles discovered in natural or laboratory populations (*Est-C, Est-6, Aph, Aldox,* and *Idh*).

Five of the fourteen loci have alleles which produce visible recessive phenotypes; *ry, cn* and *v* affect eye colour, *bb* affects bristles, and *αGpdh-1* "null" mutations which, although they appear morphologically normal, lack ability to sustain flight. The fraction 5 of 14 should not, however, be taken as an estimation of the fraction of loci at which "null" alleles produce an observable phenotype. This number is probably an overestimate because 4 of the 5 loci in question (all except *αGpdh-1*) were discovered initially as morphological mutations and their gene product was deduced and identified from their visible phenotype.

The eye colour mutations affect enzymes involved in the biosynthesis of eye pigments, and the *bobbed* locus, which shows a syndrome of effects usually associated with protein synthesis, was identified as the gene for rRNA. The phenotype of the *αGpdh-1* "null" mutations might easily have been missed had not the importance of the enzyme in insect flight been known previously[15]. The 11 other loci were identified only as the genes for selected enzymes, and of these none exhibited lethality or any morphological phenotype when "null" alleles were found.

In two cases double "null" mutants of alkaline and acid phosphatase (R. S. MacIntyre, personal communication) and of *Zw* and *6-Pgd* (W. J. Young, personal communication) were constructed and proved viable, fertile, and morphologically normal. Also, in two of the five cases where there is an observable phenotype, *bb* and *αGpdh-1*, there occurs a modification of the phenotype in the afflicted stocks. In the case of *bb* the diminished rDNA cistrons become "magnified" to approach the wild type rRNA levels within a few generations[16]. Flies genetically deficient for α-glycerophosphate dehydrogenase lack the ability to sustain flight due to their disrupted α-glycerophosphate cycle[15], but after 25 generations this phenotype becomes modified and flies recover the ability to fly normally (S. O'Brien, unpublished data). Biological adaptive capacity for physiological compensation for lesions in the structural genes of important functions must be very extensive to protect the fly so efficiently from genetically sensitive loci even in the presumably critical functions.

One might argue that even the smallest cytologically observable mutations in most cases are recessive lethals[10,14,17]. Resolution of such cytology, however, demands that at least 1

上表中前 11 个基因座中的无效等位基因是通过凝胶电泳组织化学染色条带丢失检测出来的。这种方法的敏感性至少能够检测出正常酶水平 5% 的量。在一些例子中（*Acph-1*、*rosy*、*Adh*、α*Gdph-1*），灵敏度接近 0.1% 野生型酶水平的酶分析法也不能在"无效"纯合子中检测到痕量的酶活性。在通过交叉反应物质（CRM）检测的两个例子中（*Acph-1* 和 *ry*），测到的酶活性也是微乎其微。

在杂交实验中，无效等位基因中的至少两个基因座被诱导而恢复了致死性（α*Gdph-1* 和 *Acph-1*）。在自然或实验室群体中发现的"无效"等位基因中（*Est-C*、*Est-6*、*Aph*、*Aldox* 和 *Idh*），也能检测到一种致死性"无效"等位基因，这种等位基因与有着不同电泳迁移率的正常等位基因形成一个异常杂合子。

14 个基因座中有 5 个具有能够产生可见的隐性表型的等位基因，其中 *ry*，*cn* 和 *v* 影响眼睛的颜色，*bb* 影响刚毛，而 α*Gdph-1* "无效"突变使果蝇尽管在形态学上表现正常，但丧失了持续飞行的能力。但是 5/14 这个比例并不能作为产生可见表型的"无效"等位基因在基因座中所占比例的估算值。因为所研究的 5 个基因座中的 4 个（除了 α*Gdph-1*）最初就是作为形态学的突变而被发现的，其基因产物已经从它们的可见表型中推断和鉴定出来，所以这个数值很可能是被高估的。

眼睛颜色相关基因的突变会影响眼色素生物合成过程中的相关酶，而通常显示产生一系列蛋白质合成相关症状的 *bobbed* 基因座已被确定为 rRNA 基因。如果不是以前就清楚 α*Gdph-1* 产生的酶在昆虫飞行中的重要性 [15]，就很容易忽视 α*Gdph-1* 的"无效"突变的表现型。另外 11 个基因座都仅仅是被鉴定为特定酶的基因，并没有发现其"无效"等位基因具有致死性或者导致任何形态表型的改变。

有两个构建了双重"无效"突变体的例子，碱性和酸性磷酸酶突变体（麦金太尔，个人交流）以及 *Zw* 和 *6-Pgd* 突变体（扬，个人交流），它们均被证实能够生存、繁殖并且形态上正常。同时，在 5 个具有可见表型的例子中，*bb* 和 α*Gdph-1* 这两个突变的受累动物出现了表型修饰。在 *bb* 中，减少的 rDNA 顺反子被"放大"，以至在数代内达到野生型 rRNA 的水平 [16]。遗传上缺乏 α-甘油磷酸脱氢酶（α*Gdph-1*）的果蝇由于 α-甘油磷酸循环被破坏而丧失了持续飞行的能力 [15]，但是经过 25 代以后，这种表型发生了变化而且果蝇恢复了正常飞行的能力（奥布赖恩，未发表数据）。对具有重要功能的结构基因损伤进行生理补偿的生物学适应能力一定非常广泛，使得果蝇能相当有效地免受这些遗传敏感的基因座的影响，即使是那些功能被假定很关键的基因座。

有人可能说大多数情况下即便是最小的细胞学可见突变都是隐性致死的 [10,14,17]。

of the 5,000 chromomeres of *Drosophila* polytene chromosomes must be absent to detect a deletion. The precision of the technique then is at the level of $10^6$ nucleotides, the average amount per chromomere, enough DNA for 20 genes of average length. I suggest that there could be up to 20 functional genes in each region of which only one might be lethal in its mutant configuration.

A second widely used argument which suggests a minimum of informational DNA in the eukaryote genome (less than 10% of the available DNA) states that the mutational genetic load would be inordinate if mammals used all their DNA to carry and transmit biological information. Ohno[4] states that with a mutation rate of $10^{-5}$ in mammals containing enough DNA for $3 \times 10^6$ genes, if all this DNA were informative, each gamete would contain 30 new mutations, which would produce a genetic load sufficient to have exterminated mammals years ago. Evaluation of these mutational and substitutional load restrictions on functional gene number depends upon the unresolved question of the selective neutrality of gene substitutions, and will be treated from both perspectives.

If one accepts that the majority of gene substitutions and polymorphisms are selectively neutral, then the restrictions imposed by a genetic load on functional gene number become negligible. Neutral gene substitutions certainly cannot contribute to any accumulating substitutional or mutational load which depends upon selective disadvantage for its action. We must therefore estimate whether the number of functional genes are minimal, or rather that most gene substitutions are inconsequential with respect to natural selection. Proponents of selective neutrality feel that most substitutions are neutral, which removes any restrictions on large numbers of functional gene loci.

There have been serious objections raised concerning the role of selective neutrality[18,19]. One of the weakest tenets of this hypothesis is that it is based very heavily on the multiplicative aspect of fitness, which assumes that selection acts independently and in an additive fashion over all loci in a population. That this is not the case has been argued cogently by several authors[20-22]. The main point is that selection acts on the whole organism, not on the genotype at each polymorphic locus in each organism in a population[22]. If multiplicative fitness is an unrealistic assumption, then besides questioning selective neutrality as a major force, it also removes the restrictions imposed by the mutational and substitutional load on the number of functional genes.

There are a number of ways, suggested by myself and others, that a population can escape the rigours of multiplicative fitness, or more specifically, immediate selective consequence. These include diploidy[23], epistasis[20,21], synonymous base substitutions[7], frequency dependent selection[24], linkage disequilibrium[25], and alternative metabolic pathways (Table 1). All these factors, because they can effectively shield new mutations from the rigours of natural selection, even though the mutations may be deleterious in another genetic environment, counter the assumption of multiplicative fitness. If this assumption is removed, so also is the necessity of restrictive genome size in *Drosophila* and mammals.

但是要确定这种细胞学上的改变，所需要的分辨率是至少能检测到果蝇多线染色体中 5,000 个染色粒中的一个发生了缺失。这个技术精确度是在 $10^6$ 个核苷酸水平，差不多是一个染色粒的平均大小，即足以构成 20 个平均长度的基因的 DNA。我认为每个区域可有多达 20 个功能基因，在其突变谱中可能只有一个是致死性突变。

另一个被广泛采用的论点提出了真核生物基因组中信息 DNA 的最小量（小于可获得的 DNA 的 10%），并且认为如果哺乳动物用所有的 DNA 来携带和传递生物学信息的话，那么突变了的遗传负荷就会过度。大野 [4] 认为对含有足够组成 $3 \times 10^6$ 个基因的 DNA 的哺乳动物来说，如果突变率是 $10^{-5}$，而且所有的 DNA 都是携带信息的，那么每个配子会含有 30 个新的突变，这样的遗传负荷会使得哺乳动物在很多年前就灭绝了。评估这些突变和替换的负荷所限制的功能基因数目取决于基因替换的中性选择这个尚未解决的问题，而且需要从两方面进行考虑。

如果接受大部分基因替换和多态性都是中性选择的，那么遗传负荷对于功能基因数目的限制就变得微不足道了。中性的基因替换当然不会有助于替换负荷或突变负荷的累积，因为这些负荷的作用是由其选择劣势决定的。因此我们必须估计是否有个最少的功能基因数目，或者更确切地说，大部分基因替换不是自然选择的结果。中性选择的支持者们觉得大部分替换都是中性的，这就消除了突变对于大量功能基因座的任何限制。

对于中性选择的作用曾有很多严肃的反对意见 [18,19]。该假设最薄弱的一条是它很大程度上基于对适应的倍增性，即假设选择的作用是独立的并且以加和的方式在群体中所有的基因座发挥作用。数名作者已经中肯地指出事实并非如此 [20-22]。要点在于选择是作用于整个生物体，而不是群体中每个个体的每个多态位点的基因型 [22]。如果倍增性适应是一种不现实的假设，那么除了对于中性选择作为主要作用力的质疑，突变和替换负荷对于功能基因数目的限制也可不再考虑。

包括我本人在内，很多人认为一个种群有多种方法摆脱所谓倍增性适应，或者更确切地说是直接选择的结果。这些包括二倍性 [23]，上位显性 [20,21]，同义碱基替换 [7]，频率依赖的选择性 [24]，连锁不平衡 [25] 和替代代谢通路等（表 1）。由于这些因素可以有效地保护新的突变免于遭受严酷的自然选择，尽管突变在其他遗传环境中可能是有害的，这些因素也可以与倍增性适应的假设相抗衡。如果不考虑这个假设，那么果蝇和哺乳动物中也不必考虑对于基因组大小的限制。

Long sequences (150-300 nucleotides) of polyadenylic acid are generally attached to messenger RNA in eukaryote cells[26-28]. Although post-transcriptional addition of poly A to messenger RNA has been postulated[29-31], the presence of poly T of comparable length in the nuclear DNA suggests transcriptional addition also[32]. RNA-DNA hybridization kinetics show that up to 0.55% of mammalian nuclear DNA anneals with poly A, corresponding to 1.1% poly dA-dT sequences[32]. This suggests a minimum of $5 \times 10^4$ poly dA-dT sites. If each of these sequences is transcribed with an adjacent structural gene, the number of functional genes must be greater than $5 \times 10^4$ by the addition of post-transcriptionally added poly A messages, plus non-messenger RNA genes, plus all non-transcribed regulatory genes. This number may be considerable.

In the cellular slime mould, *Dictyostelium discoideum*, 28% of the nonrepetitive nuclear genome is represented in the cellular RNA during the 26 h developmental cycle[33]. If only one of the complementary strands of DNA of any gene is transcribed, the estimate represents 56% of the single copy DNA. Because the nonrepetitive genome size of *Dictyostelium* contains approximately $3 \times 10^7$ nucleotide pairs[34], there are at least 16,000 to 17,000 RNA transcripts of average gene size (1,000 nucleotides) present over the cell cycle. Similarly, 10% of the mouse single copy sequences are represented in the cellular RNA of brain tissue. This hybridization result implies that a minimum of 300,000 different sequences of 1,000 nucleotides each are present in the mouse brain alone[35]. Results of RNA-DNA annealing experiments with *Drosophila* larval RNA indicate that between 15-20% of the unique nuclear genome is represented in larval RNA (R. Logan, personal communication), which corresponds to 30,000-40,000 RNA gene transcripts of average length. As the mouse and *Drosophila* data include only certain tissues and developmental times respectively, they probably are underestimates of the total unique DNA transcribed by 10-30%, based upon the degree of differences in RNA sequences exhibited at various developmental stages in *Dictyostelium*.

Interpretation of DNA-RNA hybridization experiments as an estimation of functional genes could be argued to be invalid because a large proportion of cellular RNA is the rapidly degraded "heterogeneous nuclear RNA" which never leaves the nucleus for translation[26,28,36]. RNA does not have to be translated to have a function, indeed RNA has a number of functions other than translation. Three points support gene function of such RNA when considered together: first, the actual presence of the gene; second, the transcription of information, and third, the transcription of different non-repetitive sequences at different developmental times and in different tissues[33,35].

The major arguments supporting the contention that much of eukaryotic DNA is neither transcribed nor functional are based essentially on the response of the functioning genes to natural selection. The tremendous amounts of physiological and/or genetic compensatory mechanisms which defer the presumed deleterious effects of mutations make such arguments subject to re-evaluation. Furthermore, the molecular data with the poly A sites and RNA transcript estimates suggest greater amounts of gene action than have been presumed.

真核细胞中的信使 RNA 一般连有很长的（150~300 个核苷酸）多聚腺苷酸序列 [26-28]。尽管人们假设多聚腺苷酸添加到信使 RNA 末端发生在转录后 [29-31]，细胞核 DNA 中存在类似长度的多聚胸苷酸提示转录时添加也是可能的 [32]。RNA-DNA 杂交动力学显示高达 0.55% 的哺乳动物核 DNA 退火后结合多聚腺苷酸，对应于 1.1% 的多聚脱氧腺苷酸 – 脱氧胸苷酸序列 [32]。这提示至少有 $5 \times 10^4$ 个多聚脱氧腺苷酸 – 脱氧胸苷酸位点。如果这些序列的每一个都与邻近的结构基因一起转录，再加上转录后加入的多聚腺苷酸序列、非信使 RNA 基因以及所有的非转录性调节基因，那么功能基因数肯定会超过 $5 \times 10^4$。这个数目可能是相当可观的。

在细胞型黏菌盘基网柄菌阿米巴虫中，28% 的非重复性核基因组在 26 小时的发育周期中表达为细胞 RNA [33]。如果任何基因中只有互补 DNA 链中的一条被转录，那么此估计值代表 56% 的单拷贝 DNA。因为黏菌的非重复性基因组含有将近 $3 \times 10^7$ 个核苷酸对 [34]，所以在细胞周期中存在至少 16,000 到 17,000 个平均基因大小（1,000 个核苷酸）的 RNA 转录产物。与之类似，小鼠脑组织中 10% 的单拷贝序列表达为细胞 RNA。这个杂交结果提示单独在小鼠脑组织内部可能存在至少 300,000 个平均拥有 1,000 个核苷酸的不同序列 [35]。用果蝇幼虫 RNA 进行的 RNA-DNA 退火实验显示 15%~20% 的特异性核基因组都表达为幼虫 RNA（洛根，个人交流），相当于 30,000~40,000 个平均长度的 RNA 基因转录产物。由于小鼠和果蝇的数据仅仅分别包括了特定的组织和发育阶段，所以根据黏菌不同发育阶段 RNA 序列差异的程度，很可能将转录的特异 DNA 总量低估了 10%~30%。

将 DNA–RNA 杂交实验作为对功能基因数量的估计的解释可能会被认为不可靠，因为细胞 RNA 的大部分都是很快降解的"核不均一 RNA"，它们从不离开细胞核去进行蛋白质翻译 [26,28,36]。但是 RNA 并不是一定要翻译成蛋白质才具有功能，事实上 RNA 除了翻译之外还有很多功能。综合考虑有三点可以支持 RNA 的基因功能：第一，基因的实际存在；第二，信息的转录；第三，不同发育阶段和不同组织中不同的非重复序列的转录 [33,35]。

主流的观点认为大部分的真核 DNA 既不用于转录，也非功能性，支持这一论点的主要依据是功能基因对于自然选择的反应。大量延缓了突变可能产生的有害作用的生理和（或）遗传补偿机制使得我们需要重新评价这个论点。此外，针对多聚腺苷酸位点和 RNA 转录物估算的分子数据显示比预计数量更多的基因活动的存在。

Although it is impossible to measure exactly the number of functional genes in eukaryotes, the acceptance of evidence for these minimum amounts seems a little premature.

Supported by a postdoctoral award from the National Institute of General Medical Science.

I thank Drs. R. J. MacIntyre, W. Sofer, R. C. Getham, J. Bell, and M. Mitchell for criticism and discussion.

(**242**, 52-54; 1973)

S. J. O'Brien

Gerontology Research Center, National Institute of Child Health and Human Development, National Institutes of Health, Baltimore City Hospitals, Baltimore, Maryland 21224

Received August 28; revised December 11, 1972.

---

References:

1. Tomkins, G. M., Gelehrter, T. D., Granner, D., Martin, D., Samuels, H. H., and Thompson, E. B., *Science*, **166**, 1474 (1969).
2. Britten, R. J., and Davidson, E. H., *Science*, **165**, 349 (1969).
3. Ohno, S., *Nature*, **234**, 134 (1971).
4. Ohno, S., *Devel. Biol.*, **27**, 131 (1972).
5. Crick, F., *Nature*, **234**, 25 (1971).
6. Ohta, T., and Kimura, M., *Nature*, **233**, 118 (1971).
7. Muller, H. J., in *Heritage from Mendel* (edit. by Brink, R. A.), 419 (University of Wisconsin Press, Madison, 1967).
8. Laird, D. C., and McCarthy, B. J., *Genetics*, **63**, 865 (1969).
9. Britten, R. J., and Kohne, D. E., *Science*, **161**, 529 (1968).
10. Judd, B. H., Shen, M. W., and Kaufman, T. C., *Genetics*, **71**, 139 (1972).
11. Wallace, B., *Topics in Population Genetics*, 45 (W. W. Norton and Co., New York, 1968).
12. Herskowitz, I. H., *Amer. Nature.*, **84**, 225 (1950).
13. O'Brien, S. J., and MacIntyre, R. J., *Drosophila Information Service*, **46**, 89 (1971).
14. Lindsley, D., and Grell, E. H., *Genetics Variations of Drosophila melanogaster* (Carnegie Inst. Publ. No. 627, 1967).
15. O'Brien, S. J., and MacIntyre, R. J., *Genetics*, **71**, 127 (1972).
16. Ritossa, F., Malva, C., Boncinelli, E., Graziani, F., and Polito, L., *Proc. US Nat. Acad. Sci.*, **68**, 1580 (1971).
17. Lefevre, G., *Genetics*, **63**, 589 (1969).
18. Richmond, R., *Nature*, **225**, 1025 (1970).
19. Arnheim, N., and Taylor, C. E., *Nature*, **223**, 900 (1969).
20. Sved, J. A., *Amer. Nat.*, **102**, 283 (1968).
21. Smith, J. M., *Nature*, **219**, 1114 (1968).
22. Milkman, R. D., *Genetics*, **55**, 493 (1967).
23. Muller, H. J., *Amer. J. Hum. Genet.*, **2**, 111 (1950).
24. Kojima, K., and Tobari, Y., *Genetics*, **63**, 639 (1969).
25. O'Brien, S. J., and MacIntyre, R. J., *Nature*, **230**, 335 (1971).
26. Edmonds, M., Vaughan, M. H., and Nokatzato, H., *Proc. US Nat. Acad. Sci.*, **68**, 1336 (1971).
27. Lee, Y. S., Mendecki, J., and Brawerman, G., *Proc. US Nat. Acad. Sci.*, **68**, 1331 (1971).
28. Darnell, J. E., Wall, R., and Tushinski, R. J., *Proc. US Nat. Acad. Sci.*, **68**, 1321 (1971).
29. Edmonds, M., and Abrams, R., *J. Biol. Chem.*, **235**, 1142 (1960).
30. Niessing, J., and Sekeris, C. E., *FEBS Lett.*, **22**, 83 (1972).
31. Darnell, J. E., Philipson, L., Wall, R., and Adesnik, M., *Science*, **174**, 507 (1971).

尽管不可能精确测定真核生物功能基因的数量，但接受这些最小数量的证据似乎还有些为时过早。

本研究由国立综合医学研究所的博士后奖金资助。

感谢麦金太尔、索弗、盖塞姆、贝尔、米切尔博士的意见和讨论。

（毛晨晖 翻译；曾长青 审稿）

32. Shenkin, A., and Burdon, R. H., *FEBS Lett.*, **22**, 157 (1972).

33. Firtel, R. A., *J. Mol. Biol.*, **66**, 363 (1972).

34. Firtel, R. A., and Bonner, J., *J. Mol. Biol.*, **66**, 339 (1972).

35. Hahn, W. E., and Laird, C. D., *Science*, **173**, 158 (1971).

36. Soeiro, R., Vaughan, M. H., Warner, J. R., and Darnell, J. E., *J. Cell Biol.*, **39**, 112 (1968).

37. Johnson, F., Wallis, B., and Denniston, C., *Drosophila Information Service*, **41**, 159 (1966).

38. Johnson, F. M., *Drosophila Information Service*, **41**, 157 (1966).

39. Bell, J. B., MacIntyre, R. J., and Olivieri, A., *Biochem. Genet.*, **6**, 205 (1972).

40. Glassman, E., *Fed. Proc.*, **24** (Suppl. 14-15), 1243 (1965).

41. Dickinson, W. J., *Genetics*, **66**, 487 (1970).

42. Grell, E., *Ann. NY Acad. Sci.*, **151**, 441 (1968).

43. Sofer, W., and Hatkoff, M. A., *Genetics*, **72**, 545 (1972).

44. Tobari, Y., and Kojima, K., *Genetics*, **70**, 347 (1972).

45. Ritossa, F. M., Atwood, K. C., and Spiegelman, S., *Genetics*, **54**, 819 (1966).

46. Baglioni, C., *Nature*, **184**, 1084 (1959).

47. Ghosh, D., and Forrest, H. S., *Genetics*, **55**, 423 (1967).

# Descent of Lithosphere beneath New Hebrides, Tonga-Fiji and New Zealand: Evidence for Detached Slabs

M. Barazangi *et al.*

## Editor's Note

At subduction zones, one tectonic plate plunges down beneath another into the Earth's mantle. The descent of the lower plate can trigger deep earthquakes. Bryan Isacks of Cornell University, together with Peter Molnar, suggested that a "gap" in seismic activity below a subduction zone might indicate that part of the descending slab had broken off from the rest. Here Isacks and coworkers present evidence that this has happened in the subduction zone containing the New Hebrides islands in the southwest Pacific, and most probably in that of New Zealand. They also suggest that the New Zealand and Tonga-Fiji slab cannot penetrate below 700 km, owing to a "discontinuity" in the mantle that subsequently became a major focus of geophysical studies.

---

Study of seismic wave propagation in the mantle beneath the New Hebrides island arc shows that the remarkable gap in seismic activity between deep and intermediate depth earthquakes at the northern part of the arc corresponds to a gap in the lithospheric slab descending beneath the arc: the deep earthquakes mark a detached piece of lithosphere. Although observations for New Zealand deep earthquakes are ambiguous, other evidence suggests the detachment of lithosphere beneath New Zealand.

---

ONE of the outstanding features of the distribution of earthquakes in the upper mantle is the existence of gaps in seismic activity between depths of about 300 and 550 km. These gaps are prominent beneath South America, New Zealand, and the New Hebrides island arc. They are of great interest because of the implication that portions of lithosphere can break off from the descending plate and exist as isolated slabs within the mantle.

Here we present evidence from study of seismic wave attenuation for the detachment of lithospheric slabs in the upper mantle beneath the New Hebrides arc. Detachment is also indicated by travel time data and reconstructions of the past movements of plates in the region. We concentrate on the study of seismic attenuation because the effects are large and easy to observe and interpret[1-3].

Isacks and Molnar[4] suggest that the gaps in seismic activity as a function of depth can be explained by two models. In the first the stress inside a continuous slab varies from down-

# 新赫布里底群岛、汤加–斐济及新西兰地区岩石圈的下降：拆沉板片的证据

贝雷赞吉等

**编者按**

在俯冲带，一个板块俯冲到另一个板块之下进入地幔。下板块的下降会引发深源地震。康奈尔大学布赖恩·艾萨克斯和彼得·莫尔纳指出俯冲带下部的地震活动存在"空区"，这可能预示着下降的板片已经从其他部分断离。艾萨克斯和他的同事提供的证据表明在西南太平洋上，包括新赫布里底群岛的俯冲带存在这种情况，而且最有可能发生在新西兰。他们同时指出，由于地幔中的"不连续性"，新西兰和汤加－斐济板片不能俯冲至 700 公里以下。此后地幔中这种"不连续性"成为了地球物理研究的焦点。

---

通过研究地震波在新赫布里底岛弧下地幔中的传播，发现岛弧北部地震活动在深中源地震之间存在明显的空区，与岛弧下下降的岩石圈板片中的空区相对应：深源地震是岩石圈拆沉出来的小断块存在的标志。虽然对新西兰深源地震的观测结果不是很明确，但其他证据表明新西兰下部的岩石圈发生了拆沉。

---

上地幔中地震分布的一个最显著的特征就是 300~550 km 深度之间存在地震活动空区。在南美洲、新西兰以及新赫布里底岛弧下，这样的空区非常显著。它们受到了极大的关注，因为这意味着岩石圈的一部分可以脱离下降板片，以孤立板片的形式存在于地幔中。

本文将通过研究地震波的衰减来找出新赫布里底岛弧下的上地幔中岩石圈板片拆沉的证据。地震波走时数据以及对过去板块运动的重建也都显示，该区存在板片拆沉现象。我们关注地震波的衰减是因为其效应非常明显且易于观察和解释 [1-3]。

艾萨克斯和莫尔纳 [4] 提出，地震活动空区是深度的函数，具体可用两个模型来解释。第一个就是，连续板片内部的应力在中层深度上表现为下倾拉张而到更深处

dip extension at intermediate depths to down-dip compression at greater depths, and thus is near zero between these depths. In the second a piece of descending lithosphere breaks off, sinks into the upper mantle and leaves a gap between the piece and the plate to which it was attached. The character of seismic waves, especially shear waves, produced by deep earthquakes and recorded at stations along island arcs where large gaps in seismic activity exist provides evidence for determining which of these models is correct. Observation of attenuated, low frequency waves for the appropriate paths indicates a gap in the descending lithosphere. But if high frequency shear waves are observed, then the interpretation is ambiguous. The observations can be explained either by propagation along a continuous high $Q$ lithospheric slab or by propagation through the upper portion of a discontinuous slab that provides a low attenuation path through the asthenosphere. The second explanation implies that for 1-3 Hz shear waves attenuation is small below depths of about 300 km.

The New Hebrides island arc provides a unique opportunity to study the nature of the gap in seismic activity in the upper mantle. Seismograph stations are well distributed along the arc. The gap is well established between depths of about 300 and 600 km. The structure of the intermediate and deep seismic zones with the very steeply dipping intermediate zone and the approximately horizontal deep zone certainly suggests that the two zones may not be connected. Enough deep earthquakes have occurred since the stations were installed to provide a large sample of paths. Forty deep earthquakes in the 10 year period 1961-1970 were recorded at Noumea (NOU) and Port Vila (PVC) stations (Fig. 1). Lonorore (LNR) was established in 1968. NOU, PVC and LNR employ 1 Hz underdamped seismometers and 2 Hz overdamped galvanometers. The instruments have a relatively flat response for seismic wave frequencies between 0.5 Hz and 10 Hz and thus record very clearly the large variations of shear wave frequencies. Detailed description of the New Hebrides-New Caledonia seismic network is given by Dubois[5].

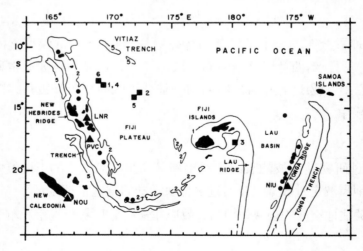

Fig. 1. Map showing the Tonga-Fiji-New Hebrides region of the southwest Pacific. ● , Historically active volcanoes; ▲ , seismic stations; ■ , locations of deep earthquakes used in Figs. 2 and 3. Water depths are in km.

则变为下倾挤压，所以上述深度之间的应力接近于零。第二个就是，下降的岩石圈有一部分断离，下沉至上地幔，使该碎片与其所属板块之间出现了空区。沿存在大型地震活动空区的岛弧设立的观测站所记录到的深源地震的地震波特征，特别是剪切波特征，就为确定上述哪个模型正确提供了依据。对特定路径上低频衰减波的观测结果表明，下降的岩石圈中存在一个空区。但倘若观测到的是高频剪切波，得出的解释就不明确了。这种观测结果可能是沿连续高 $Q$ 值岩石圈板片的传播引起的，也可能是沿不连续板片上部传播引起的，这样在软流圈中传播可使衰减作用降低。第二种解释就意味着，对于 1~3 Hz 的剪切波，它在大约 300 km 以下的深度上衰减较弱。


　　新赫布里底岛弧为我们研究上地幔地震活动空区的特征提供了极难得的机会。沿岛弧可以较好地布设地震台站。在大约 300~600 km 之间存在空区是确定无疑的。中深层地震带的构造表现为，中层的倾角非常陡峭，而深层地震带则近乎水平，这说明两个地震带可能不是相互连接的。观测站建立以来已发生了许多次深源地震，得到了许多路径样本。从 1961 年到 1970 年的 10 年间努美阿（NOU）和维拉港（PVC）观测站共记录了 40 次深源地震（图 1）。朗挪罗依（LNR）站建立于 1968 年。NOU、PVC 和 LNR 均采用 1 Hz 的欠阻尼地震计和 2 Hz 的超阻尼检流计。上述设备对频率介于 0.5 Hz 和 10 Hz 之间的地震波的响应相对较平缓，从而可以清晰地记录到剪切波频率发生的较大变化。杜波依斯 [5] 曾对新赫布里底–新喀里多尼亚的地震网作过详细描述。

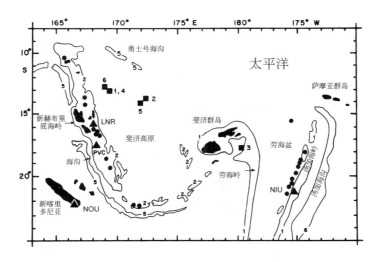

图 1. 西南太平洋汤加–斐济–新赫布里底地区示意图。●，历史上的活火山；▲，地震观测站；■，图 2 和图 3 中用到的深源地震的位置。水深单位为 km。

The inclined seismic zones of South America also have remarkable gaps in seismic activity between about 350 and 550 km. A detailed study of the records produced by almost all the South American deep earthquakes that occurred during the past 10 yr at stations along the western coast of South America is currently under way, and will be reported in a separate study.

## Lithospheric Gap in New Hebrides Arc

Fig. 1 shows the location of the stations in New Caledonia and New Hebrides used in this study. We have examined all the records produced at these stations by the New Hebrides deep earthquakes. The most striking observation is that predominantly low frequency (about 0.5 Hz) S waves are recorded at PVC and LNR from the deep earthquakes north of 15° S.

Fig. 2 shows a cross-section through the New Hebrides arc that intersects NOU, LNR and passes close to PVC. New Hebrides deep earthquakes located at the western part of the deep zone (very close to the downward projection of the intermediate depth zone) produce attenuated, low frequency S waves at PVC. The ray paths pass just beneath the dipping seismic zone. Frequencies greater than 1 Hz are absent and the amplitude of the S phase is generally less than that of P phase. As Oliver and Isacks[1] and Barazangi and Isacks[3] show, this can be explained by a transmission through an attenuating low $Q$ zone. In contrast, S waves recorded at NIU station on the Tonga island arc from Tongan deep earthquakes have predominant frequencies of 3-4 Hz and the amplitudes of S are generally larger than those of P.

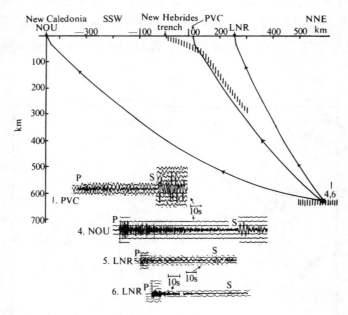

Fig. 2. Cross-section of the New Hebrides arc showing J-B ray paths to NOU, PVC and LNR stations and the corresponding records [E-W component at PVC, N-S component at NOU, and Z component at LNR] and the locations of seismic activity (vertical lines). Only low frequency S waves are recorded at the stations.

倾斜的南美洲地震带在 350~550 km 深度之间也存在明显的地震活动空区。沿南美洲西海岸的观测站记录了过去 10 年该区发生的几乎所有的深源地震，目前我们正在对其进行详细研究，具体将另文发表。

## 新赫布里底岛弧下的岩石圈空区

图 1 所示为本研究采用的新喀里多尼亚和新赫布里底的观测站位置。我们利用新赫布里底的深源地震对这些站位上记录到的所有数据进行了检验。最令人吃惊的一项观测结果是，PVC 和 LNR 站上均从 15°S 以北的深源地震记录到了低频（约 0.5 Hz）S 波占主导地位。

图 2 所示为穿过新赫布里底岛弧与 NOU、LNR 相交的一个横剖面，该剖面也通过 PVC 附近。新赫布里底深源地震位于深部地震带的西部（距中层深度带向下的投影很近），它在 PVC 站形成衰减的低频 S 波。地震波列的路径恰好穿过下倾地震带的下方。频率均不高于 1 Hz，且 S 相的振幅大都小于 P 相。如奥利弗与艾萨克斯 [1] 和贝雷赞吉与艾萨克斯 [3] 所示，这可以解释为地震波穿过衰减低 $Q$ 带的传播。相反，位于汤加岛弧的 NIU 站记录到的汤加深源地震 S 波的主要频率为 3~4 Hz，而且 S 相的振幅也比 P 相的大。

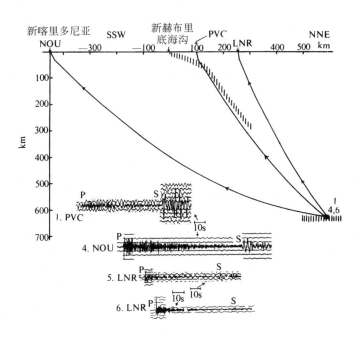

图 2. 新赫布里底岛弧的横剖面图。图中给出了地震波到 NOU、PVC 和 LNR 观测站的 J–B 传播路径及与之相对应的记录 [PVC 站的 E–W 分量、NOU 的 N–S 分量以及 LNR 上的 Z 分量]，同时还给出了地震活动发生的位置（竖线）。这些观测站仅记录到了低频 S 波。

Deep earthquakes also produce low frequency shear waves at LNR, a station close to the active volcanic line of the New Hebrides arc. This is in marked contrast to the observation of high frequency S waves from Tonga deep earthquakes at stations along the active volcanic line of the Tonga arc[6].

We interpret the observation of low frequency S waves at PVC and LNR to be mainly the result of attenuation along the path. The effect of the source can be excluded since New Hebrides deep earthquakes produce seismograms at Fiji stations that are similar to those produced by the Tonga deep earthquakes (the New Hebrides and Tonga deep earthquakes are approximately equidistant from the Fiji stations). The effect of the station can be excluded since intermediate earthquakes located along the New Hebrides arc produce, without exception, high frequency (about 3-4 Hz) S waves at PVC and LNR. This is so even where the path lengths are comparable or greater than those from the deep earthquakes. Further, the Tonga deep earthquakes produce seismograms at PVC and LNR that are strikingly similar to those produced at the Fiji stations. Thus, attenuation along the path is the main cause for the observed low frequency S waves at PVC and LNR.

The attenuation is chiefly below 300 km, judging by the abundant observations of high frequency shear waves from intermediate depth earthquakes to PVC and other New Hebrides stations. All observations taken together are best explained by the absence of lithospheric slab material between depths of about 300 and 600 km; the deep earthquakes of New Hebrides therefore represent a detached slab in the upper mantle. To our knowledge, this is the first direct evidence that the attenuating, asthenospheric layer is deeper than about 300 km in the upper mantle.

New Hebrides deep earthquakes always produce low frequency S waves at NOU (Fig. 2). This is most probably due to attenuation in the upper mantle (the asthenospheric layer), because the ray paths to NOU completely miss the dipping New Hebrides seismic zone.

New Hebrides deep earthquakes located at the eastern part of the deep zone produce attenuated, low frequency S waves at PVC and LNR. The ray paths, calculated for a laterally homogeneous mantle with a Jeffreys-Bullen (J-B) velocity structure, pass just above the inclined seismic zone (Fig. 3). S phases which similarly appear to pass above the Tonga inclined zone, however, have large amplitudes and high frequencies (we note that the time scale of NIU record is about twice that of PVC, as shown in Fig. 3). Even though the J-B ray path seems to miss the Tonga seismic zone, the high frequency S waves probably travel through the descending slab. Barazangi, Isacks and Oliver[7] describe other evidence that the slab descending beneath Tonga acts as a wave guide for high frequency shear waves and is therefore continuous. Thus by comparison the absence of these high frequency shear waves for the easternmost New Hebrides deep earthquakes can be taken as evidence for the detachment of lithosphere beneath the New Hebrides.

LNR 站位于新赫布里底岛弧活火山带附近，深源地震在该站亦产生低频 S 波。这与在沿汤加岛弧活火山带的观测站记录到的汤加深源地震高频 S 波明显相反 [6]。

我们认为，在 PVC 和 LNR 站上观测到的低频 S 波主要应该是沿传播路径衰减的结果。由于新赫布里底深源地震在斐济观测站形成的地震图与汤加深源地震图类似，因此可以排除震源的影响（新赫布里底和汤加深源地震到斐济站的距离基本相等）。而 PVC 和 LNR 站记录到的沿新赫布里底岛弧的中源地震都无一例外地生成高频（约 3~4 Hz）S 波，所以也可以排除观测站因素的影响。当路径长度与深源地震的相当或更大时亦是如此。此外，汤加深源地震在 PVC 和 LNR 站形成的地震图与斐济站上形成的惊人的一致。因此，沿传播路径的衰减应该是 PVC 和 LNR 站所观测到的低频 S 波的主要成因。

通过 PVC 站以及新赫布里底岛上其他观测站所记录的中源地震产生的高频剪切波的观测数据判断，衰减作用主要发生于 300 km 以下。综合所有观测结果，一个最好的解释就是，在 300~600 km 的深度上岩石圈板片物质缺失。因此，新赫布里底岛的深源地震说明，该地区上地幔中存在一个拆沉的小板片。据我们所知，这是首次发现直接证据，证明使地震波衰减的软流圈在上地幔中的位置位于 300 km 以下。

在 NOU 站上，新赫布里底岛深源地震总是形成低频 S 波（图 2）。这很可能是在上地幔中（软流圈）的衰减作用所致，因为到 NOU 站的传播路径完全处于下倾的新赫布里底地震带之外。

位于深部地震带东部的新赫布里底深源地震在 PVC 和 LNR 站均形成衰减的低频 S 波。而根据杰弗里斯－布伦（J–B）的速度结构计算，在横向均质地幔中，其传播路径恰好通过倾斜地震带的正上方（图 3）。然而，同样通过汤加倾斜带上方的 S 相，则具有高振幅、高频率的特征（我们注意到，NIU 记录的时间比例尺约是 PVC 的两倍，如图 3 所示）。尽管 J–B 传播路径似乎并未通过汤加地震带，高频 S 波很可能是穿过下降的板片传播的。贝雷赞吉、艾萨克斯和奥利弗 [7] 提出了其他证据，证明汤加地区下部下降的板片对高频剪切波具有波导的作用，因而其波谱也是连续的。因此，通过比较发现，新赫布里底岛最东端深源地震中高频剪切波的缺失，可以视为新赫布里底地区下部岩石圈拆沉的证据。

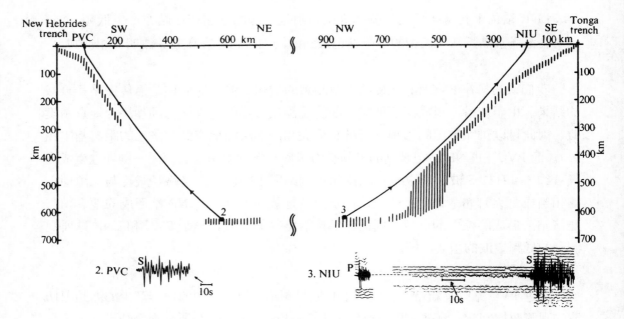

Fig. 3. Two cross-sections of Tonga and New Hebrides arcs showing ray paths to NIU and PVC stations and the corresponding records [E-W component at PVC, and Z component of P, and N-S component of S at NIU] and the locations of seismic activity in the upper mantle (vertical lines). Note the great difference in the signature of S waves at NIU and PVC in spite of the similarity in ray paths (time scale of NIU record is about twice that of PVC).

We will present a detailed study of the travel times of P waves of the New Hebrides deep earthquakes later. The travel time residuals of P waves of the New Hebrides deep earthquakes at PVC and LNR stations along the arc are close to normal (about 1 to 2 s earlier). This is in contrast to P residuals of about 4 to 5 s earlier from the Tongan deep earthquakes recorded at stations along the Tonga arc[8]. Thus the travel time data support those obtained from seismic wave attenuation and indicate that the deep earthquakes at the northeast of the arc represent a detached lithospheric slab.

During the past seven years three deep earthquakes occurred south of 15° S, south of the horizontal oblong-shaped zone, and are located along a line parallel to the southern part of the New Hebrides arc (Fig. 5). Records produced by these earthquakes at NOU in New Caledonia and at stations located in the northern part of the New Hebrides arc (to the north of about 16° S latitude, LNR and LUG) show attenuated, low frequency S waves. But records produced at PVC from the most recent event located at about 18° S and 173° E show large amplitude, high frequency S waves. This is the only one of the three shocks recorded at PVC with good quality records. This observation is quite clear, however, and may imply the continuity of the descending slab in the southern part of the New Hebrides arc. More data are required before a meaningful interpretation can be made for the southern deep earthquakes zone.

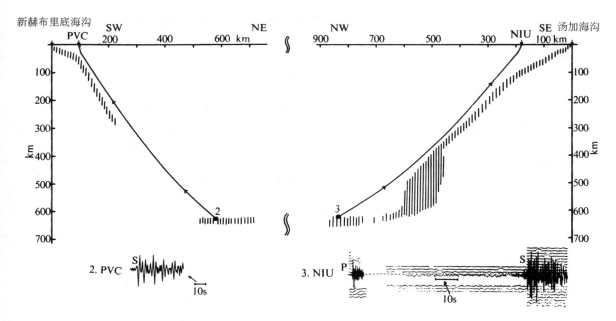

图 3. 汤加和新赫布里底岛弧的横剖面图。图中给出了到达 NIU 和 PVC 站的传播路径以及与之对应的记录 [PVC 站上的 E–W 分量、P 波的 Z 分量以及 NIU 站上 S 波的 N–S 分量]，另外还给出了上地幔中地震活动发生的位置（竖线）。注意，虽然 NIU 站和 PVC 站上的传播路径相同，但 S 波的特征差别却很大（NIU 站记录的时间比例尺是 PVC 站的两倍）。

下面我们将详细研究新赫布里底深源地震 P 波的走时。在新赫布里底岛弧沿线的 PVC 和 LNR 站上，新赫布里底深源地震的 P 波走时残差接近正常（约提早 1~2 s）。而汤加岛弧沿线的观测站上记录到的汤加深源地震的 P 波残差则为 4~5 s 左右 [8]，两者形成鲜明对比。所以，走时数据也支持了根据地震波衰减作用得到的结果，这说明，岛弧东北部的深源地震意味着存在一个从岩石圈拆沉下来的板片。

在过去 7 年中，15°S 以南，即水平长椭圆带的南部，共发生了 3 次深源地震，并且它们都发生在平行于新赫布里底岛弧南部的地带（图 5）。从新喀里多尼亚的 NOU 站和位于新赫布里底岛弧的北部各站（至北部约 16°S 处，LNR 和 LUG 站）得到的上述地震的记录均表现为衰减的低频 S 波。但在 PVC 站得到的最近一次发生在 18°S，173°E 附近的地震记录则表现为大振幅、高频率的 S 波。这是在 PVC 站记录到的三次地震中唯一一个质量较好的记录。不过该观测结果非常清晰，而且很可能意味着新赫布里底岛弧南部存在连续的下降板片。要对南部深源地震带作出实质性解释，还需要更多数据的支持。

## Detached Piece of Lithosphere beneath New Zealand?

In New Zealand earthquakes reach a depth of about 300 km in the North Island and about 200 km in the northernmost part of the South Island. In addition three earthquakes occurred at depths of about 600 km in 1953 and 1960 beneath the North Island[9]. Fig. 4 shows a cross-section of the New Zealand arc and examples of seismograms from the local New Zealand network. Deep earthquakes produce high frequency S waves at Wellington (WEL). Two quite different explanations can be made for this. One is that the slab beneath New Zealand is continuous and reaches depths of at least 600 km, and thereby provides a path for high frequency S waves. The second is that although the slab may have a gap beneath about 300 km, the portion above 300 km is sufficient to provide a "window" through the zone of high attenuation. This second explanation implies that the principal zone of attenuation is located above 300 km, and thus implies a significant difference between the New Zealand and New Hebrides regions with respect to attenuation below 300 km.

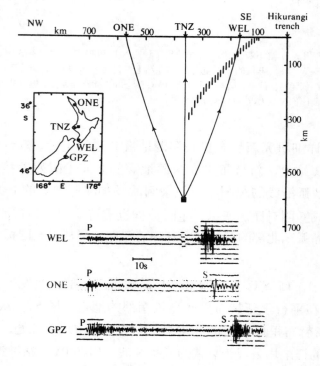

Fig. 4. Cross-section of the New Zealand arc showing ray paths to WEL, TNZ and ONE stations, horizontal records to WEL, ONE and GPZ stations, and the dipping seismic zone beneath the North Island (vertical lines). Insert map shows the locations of stations ( ● ) and the location of the deep earthquakes of New Zealand ( ■ ).

## 新西兰下部存在拆沉的岩石圈碎片？

在新西兰，北岛地区地震发生于约 300 km 深处，而在南岛的最北部大约为 200 km。另外，1953 年和 1960 年在北岛有三次地震发生在约 600 km 深处 [9]。图 4 所示为新西兰岛弧的横剖面图，同时还给出了由新西兰当地地震网获得的地震图示例。深源地震在惠灵顿站（WEL）形成高频 S 波。关于这一点可以有两种完全不同的解释。第一种，新西兰下部的板片是连续的而且至少可以到达 600 km 深处，由此为高频 S 波的传播提供了通道。第二种，虽然板片在大概 300 km 处有一段空白，但 300 km 之上的部分足以为地震波穿过高衰减区提供一个"窗口"。其中第二种解释暗含的意思就是，主要衰减带位于 300 km 以上，那么也就意味着，新西兰与新赫布里底地区差异很大，因为新赫布里底地区的衰减作用发生在 300 km 以下。

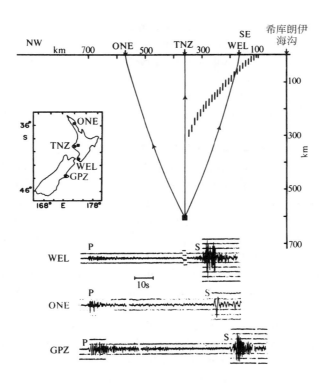

图 4. 新西兰岛弧横剖面图。图中给出了地震波到 WEL、TNZ 和 ONE 站的传播路径，以及到 WEL、ONE 和 GPZ 站的横向记录。另外图中还给出了北岛下部的倾斜地震带（竖线）。插图所示为站位位置（●）和新西兰深源地震发生的位置（■）。

The second alternative, that a detached lithosphere is present beneath the North Island of New Zealand, is supported by the variation of down-dip length of the inclined seismic zone as a function of latitude along the New Zealand—Kermadec—Tonga plate boundary. If New Zealand deep earthquakes are excluded, the down-dip length increases regularly northward as predicted by locations of the pole of relative motion between the Australian and Pacific plates[10,11]. The New Zealand deep shocks are thus distinctly anomalous in this respect and seem to mark a detached piece of plate.

New Zealand deep earthquakes produce low frequency, attenuated S waves at Tarata (TNZ) and Onerahi (ONE) which are located to the west of the line of active volcanoes in the North Island. Mooney[12] mapped a zone of anomalously high attenuation in the uppermost mantle also located west of the active volcanoes. Thus, the low frequency S waves at TNZ and ONE are probably the result of attenuation in the uppermost mantle to the west of the dipping seismic zone.

An interesting observation is that New Zealand deep shocks produce high frequency S waves at stations in the South Island. Fig. 4 shows an example recorded at Gebbies Pass (GPZ), a station located along the aseismic[13] east coast of the South Island. This observation suggests that beneath at least the northern part of the South Island no major zone of attenuation is present. The lithosphere marked by intermediate depth earthquakes beneath the North Island may thus extend beneath part of the South Island.

## Deep Earthquakes beneath Fiji

An unusual feature of the earthquake distribution in the Tonga-Fiji region is the occurrence of deep earthquakes west of the inclined seismic zone of the Tonga arc (Fig. 5). In the past 10 yr about 8 well located deep earthquakes occurred beneath the Fiji Islands. It is not clear whether these earthquakes represent a continuation of the descending Tonga slab, a slab(s) detached from the present descending slab, or a slab detached during an earlier episode of underthrusting. Evidence obtained from focal mechanisms by Isacks et al.[14] suggests that these earthquakes represent a contorted continuation of the northern edge of the descending Tonga slab. In any case these earthquakes and the New Hebrides deep earthquakes show a considerable horizontal extent away from the corresponding descending slabs. This suggests that the earthquakes mark lithospheric slabs that are unable to penetrate the 600-700 km discontinuity of the upper mantle, and hence the discontinuity may represent the lower limit of the asthenosphere. These slabs may pile up above the discontinuity until their assimilation in the mesospheric lower mantle.

第二种解释，即新西兰北岛下部存在拆沉的岩石圈，在新西兰—克马德克—汤加板块边界沿线，倾斜地震带的下倾长度是纬度的函数，它的变化就支持了上述观点。根据澳大利亚板块和太平洋板块的相对运动极点的位置推测，倘若将新西兰深源地震排除在外，向北下倾长度将呈规律递增[10,11]。从这方面来看，新西兰深源地震就显得极为反常，而且似乎是板块碎片存在的标志。

塔拉塔（TNZ）和奥内拉希（ONE）站位于北岛活火山带的西侧，这两站记录的新西兰深源地震均表现为低频衰减 S 波。穆尼[12] 所描绘的上地幔顶部异常强烈的衰减作用带也位于活火山带西侧。因此，TNZ 和 ONE 站记录到的低频 S 波很可能是地震波在上地幔顶部至倾斜地震带西侧衰减的结果。

有趣的是，在南岛的观测站上，新西兰深源地震形成的是高频 S 波。图 4 所示为在格比斯山口站（GPZ）记录到的一个实例，该站位于南岛上无地震发生的东海岸[13]。上述观测结果表明，至少在南岛的北部下方是不存在明显的衰减带的。那么北岛下部中源地震所标识的岩石圈可能一直延伸至南岛以下的大部分地区。

## 斐济下部的深源地震

汤加-斐济地区地震分布的一个独特特征就是汤加岛弧倾斜地震带西侧深源地震的发生（图 5）。在过去 10 年中，斐济群岛下部发生了约 8 次位置明确的深源地震。还不清楚这些地震是否意味着下降的汤加板片的一种延续，即从现今的下降板片上拆沉下来的一个小板片，或者说是在早期板块的俯冲过程中拆沉的一个小板片。艾萨克斯等[14] 从震源机制方面获得的证据表明，这些地震是下降汤加板片北部边缘一个扭曲延续体的标志。不管怎样，这些地震与新赫布里底深源地震共同证明，相关下降板片水平延伸出了相当远的距离。这说明，这些地震是无法穿过上地幔 600~700 km 深处不连续面的破碎岩石圈板片存在的标志，因此该不连续面可能就是软流圈的底界。这些板片一直堆积在不连续面上，直到它们在中层下地幔被同化。

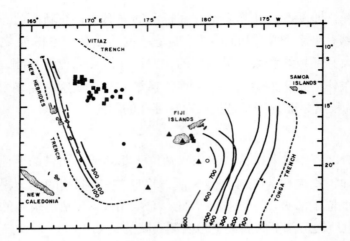

Fig. 5. Map showing contours of earthquake depths for Tonga and New Hebrides arcs, the deep seismic zone of New Hebrides, and well located deep earthquakes beneath the Fiji islands and the Fiji plateau. ▲, Events with depth range between 525 and 575 km; ●, events with 576 to 625 km depth; ■, events with 626 to 675 km depth. The open circle represents an event with a depth of 470 km.

## Overall Model

The New Hebrides and New Zealand deep earthquakes mark detached pieces of lithosphere in the upper mantle; considerable seismic wave attenuation probably exists below about 300 km of depth in the upper mantle beneath the northern part of the New Hebrides arc, which implies that the asthenosphere may extend deeper than 300 km in the mantle in this region; the spatial distribution of deep earthquakes between the New Hebrides and Tonga arcs suggests that slabs of lithosphere are unable to descend beneath about 700 km in the mantle.

We thank R. D. Adams for original seismograms, Walter Mitronovas for discussions, and Jim Gill and Dan Karig for preprints of their research. M. B. thanks Maurice Ewing for a research grant.

This work was supported by National Science Foundation grants.

(**242**, 98-101; 1973)

Muawia Barazangi*, Bryan L. Isacks*, Jack Oliver*, Jacques Dubois[†] and Georges Pascal[†]

*Department of Geological Sciences, Cornell University, Ithaca, New York 14850

[†]Office de la Recherche Scientifique et Technique, Outre-Mer, Noumea, New Caledonia, and Institut de Physique du Globe, Université de Paris, 6 Paris

Received October 24, 1972.

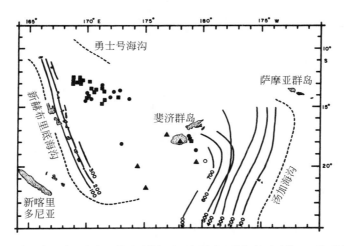

图 5. 图中所示汤加和新赫布里底岛弧的地震等深线，新赫布里底深部地震带、斐济群岛和斐济高原深源地震的准确位置。▲ 525~575 km 深处发生的地震；● 576~625 km 深处发生的地震；■ 626~675 km 深处发生的地震。空心圆圈代表 470 km 深处发生的地震。

## 总 体 模 型

新赫布里底和新西兰深源地震是上地幔中拆沉的岩石圈板片存在的标志；在新赫布里底岛弧北部地区下方 300 km 深处的上地幔中很可能存在地震波的显著衰减，这意味着该地区地幔的软流圈可能延伸至 300 km 以下；新赫布里底和汤加岛弧之间深源地震的空间分布表明，岩石圈板片不可能下降至地幔大约 700 km 的深处。

感谢亚当斯为我们提供的原始地震图，感谢沃尔特·米特罗诺瓦斯关于本文的讨论，感谢吉姆·吉尔和丹·凯里格提供了他们研究成果的预印本。作者感谢莫里斯·尤因提供的科研资助。

本研究得到了美国国家科学基金的资助。

（齐红艳 翻译；李三忠 审稿）

References:
1. Oliver, J., and Isacks, B., *J. Geophys. Res.*, 72, 4259 (1967).
2. Molnar, P., and Oliver, J., *J. Geophys. Res.*, 74, 2648 (1969).
3. Barazangi, M., and Isacks, B., *J. Geophys. Res.*, 76, 8493 (1971).
4. Isacks, B., and Molnar, P., *Rev. Geophys. and Space Phys.*, 9, 103 (1971).
5. Dubois, J., *J. Geophys. Res.*, 76, 7217 (1971).
6. Mitronovas, W., Isacks, B., and Seeber, L., *Bull. Seismol. Soc. Amer.*, 59, 1115 (1969).
7. Barazangi, M., Isacks, B., and Oliver, J., *J. Geophys. Res.*, 77, 952 (1972).
8. Mitronovas, W., and Isacks, B., *J. Geophys. Res.*, 76, 7154 (1971).
9. Adams, R., *N. Z. J. Geol. Geophys.*, 6, 209 (1963).
10. Le Pichon, X., *J. Geophys. Res.*, 73, 3661 (1968).
11. Chase, C., *Bull. Geol. Soc. Amer.*, 82, 3087 (1971).
12. Mooney, H., *J. Geophys. Res.*, 75, 285 (1970).
13. Hamilton, R., and Gale, A., *J. Geophys. Res.*, 73, 3859 (1968).
14. Isacks, B., Sykes, L., and Oliver, J., *Bull. Geol. Soc. Amer.*, 80, 1443 (1969).

# Fusion of Rat and Mouse Morulae and Formation of Chimaeric Blastocysts

G. H. Zeilmaker

## Editor's Note

Over ten years earlier, Polish embryologist Andrzej Tarkowski made chimaeric mice by fusing together eggs taken from different mouse strains. Here, Gerard H. Zeilmaker manages to fuse early mouse embryos with early rat embryos to produce chimaeric blastocysts—slightly more-developed embryonic structures containing a mix of mouse and rat cells. The study paved the way for production of viable intraspecies chimaeras, such as the goat-sheep mix or "geep", which has helped answer fundamental questions about development. The fusion of human DNA with bovine and rabbit eggs has since seen early-stage chimeras yield human stem cells without the need for human eggs, a major hurdle in stem cell research. These techniques for creating chimaeras could also help save endangered species.

THE induction of chimaerism by the aggregation of blastomeres of different mouse strains is one of the most remarkable recent contributions of experimental embryology[1,2].

Last year it was pointed out (Dr. A. McLaren, private communication) that the possibility to fuse morulae of different species had not been sufficiently explored[3]. I therefore undertook a series of experiments to investigate whether aggregation of rat and mouse morulae can be induced, using basically the same techniques as those for aggregation of mouse morulae[3,4].

Mouse morulae (C3Hf×Swiss, 8-16 cell stage) were flushed from the utero-tubal region with culture medium on day 2 of pregnancy at 21:00 h, day 0 of plug, 14 h of light, 10 h of darkness, the middle of the dark period at midnight. Rat morulae (R, Amsterdam Wistar, 8-16 cell stage) were isolated by flushing on day 3 at 21:30h. The isolated morulae were stored separately at 37°C under oil and 5% $CO_2$ in air in pyruvate containing culture medium[5].

# 大鼠与小鼠桑葚胚的融合
# 以及嵌合囊胚的形成

泽尔马克

## 编者按

十多年前，波兰胚胎学家安杰伊·塔尔科夫斯基通过融合不同种系的小鼠卵细胞，培育出了嵌合小鼠。在本文中，赫拉德·泽尔马克尝试将小鼠与大鼠的早期胚胎融合得到嵌合囊胚，也就是包含了小鼠细胞和大鼠细胞并且有了些许进一步发育的胚胎结构。这项研究为可育的种内嵌合体的产生，比如山羊和绵羊的杂交体即"山绵羊"，奠定了基础，这帮助人们回答了一些关于发育的基本问题。在人类DNA与牛、兔的卵细胞融合实验中观察到，在不需要人类卵细胞的条件下，早期嵌合体就能产生人类干细胞，这在干细胞研究中跨越了一个大的障碍。这些产生嵌合体的技术还有助于挽救濒临灭绝的物种。

通过将不同种系小鼠的囊胚细胞融合诱导产生嵌合体是近期实验胚胎学领域最卓越的成就之一 [1,2]。

去年，有人（麦克拉伦博士，私人交流）指出，将不同物种的桑葚胚融合在一起的可能性，这种可能性还没有得到充分的研究 [3]。因此我用与融合小鼠桑葚胚基本相同的技术 [3,4] 进行了一系列的实验，来研究能否诱导大鼠和小鼠桑葚胚的聚集。

在妊娠第2天的21:00，用培养液将小鼠桑葚胚（C3Hf×瑞士种，8细胞至16细胞阶段）从子宫－输卵管区域洗脱出来，未经历栓塞，见光14小时，置于暗处10小时，并使黑暗阶段的中期处于午夜。在妊娠第3天的21:30，洗脱出大鼠桑葚胚（R，阿姆斯特丹大鼠，8细胞至16细胞阶段）。分离出来的桑葚胚分别储存在37℃下油封的含丙酮酸的培养基中，培养空间空气中的$CO_2$含量保持在5%[5]。

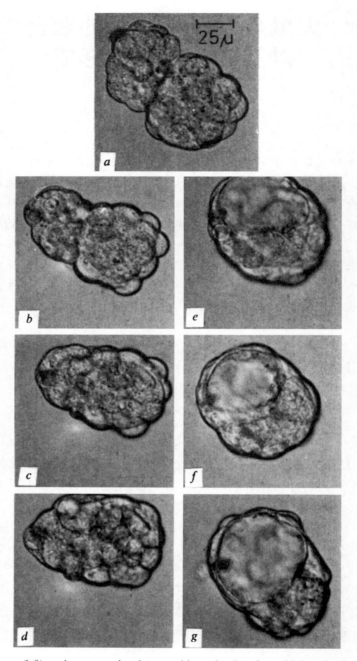

Fig. 1. *a*, Mouse (left) and rat morulae in apposition, shortly after withdrawal of egg holders. Developmental stages after 2 (*b*), 4 (*c*), 6 (*d*), 8 (*e*), 11 (*f*) and 12.5 h (*g*). In *d* the blastocoelic cavity is formed.

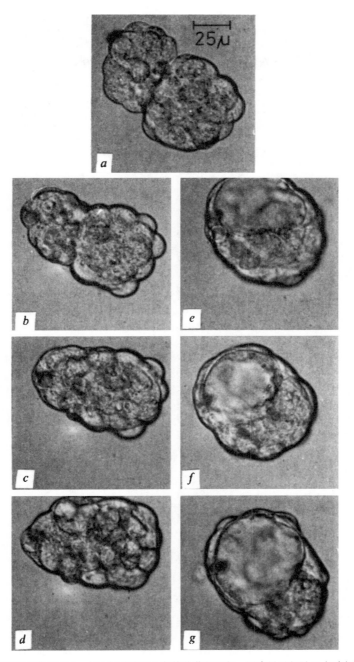

图 1. *a*，撤掉胚胎固定器后不久，小鼠（左侧）和大鼠的桑葚胚紧邻。图中显示经过 2 小时（*b*）、4 小时（*c*）、6 小时（*d*）、8 小时（*e*）、11 小时（*f*）和 12.5 小时（*g*）后的发育阶段。在 *d* 阶段，囊胚腔已经形成。

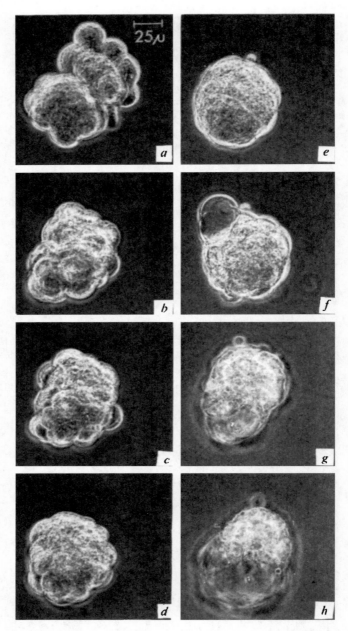

Fig. 2. Mouse (left) and rat (upper right) morulae in the process of fusion. Pictures taken after 30 min (*a*), 2 (*b*), 6 (*c*), 8 (*d*), 12.5 (*e*), 18.3 (*f*), 24 (*g*) and 34 h (*h*). Borderline between rat and mouse morulae still visible in (*e*). First cavity formed in (*f*), final cavity in (*g*).

The zona pellucida was dissolved by incubation of the eggs for 3 to 5 min in 0.5% pronase[6]. Final removal of the zona occurred in culture medium by forcing the eggs through a narrow pipette. In each experiment one mouse and one rat morulae were brought into contact in an oil drop culture at 37°C by means of 2 egg holders with a closed lumen[7] driven by a micromanipulator. During this apposition phase, which lasted

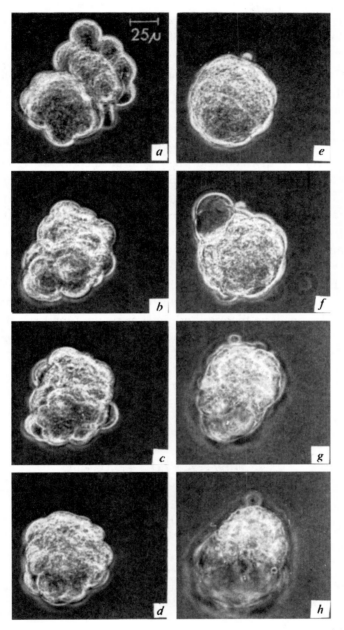

图 2. 融合过程中的小鼠（左侧）和大鼠（右上）桑葚胚。图片采自融合开始 30 分钟 (*a*)、2 小时 (*b*)、6 小时 (*c*)、8 小时 (*d*)、12.5 小时 (*e*)、18.3 小时 (*f*)、24 小时 (*g*) 和 34 小时 (*h*) 后。(*e*) 阶段仍可见到大小鼠桑葚胚的界线。第一空腔在 (*f*) 阶段形成，最终的空腔在 (*g*) 阶段形成。

将卵细胞在 0.5% 的链霉蛋白酶中温育 3 到 5 分钟即可溶解透明带 [6]。在培养基中，通过压迫卵细胞穿过狭窄的移液管从而最终去除透明带。在每个实验中，借助两个由显微操纵器驱动的含有封闭腔 [7] 的卵细胞固定器，一个小鼠的桑葚胚和一个大鼠的桑葚胚在 37℃ 下的油滴培养中彼此接触。在这个持续 20 到 30 分钟的接触阶

20 to 30 min, the Petri dish was not closed but a humid gas stream was directed over the oil surface in order to maintain $p$H and osmolarity of the medium.

After removal of the egg holders the development of the pair of morulae was followed continuously with a time-lapse movie camera connected to the inverted microscope. Photographs were taken every 30 s with flash light.

A total of sixteen identical experiments were carried out and, in twelve, successful aggregation had occurred in which both aggregate partners showed active proliferation as judged by the temporary bulging of dividing cells at the surface of the large morulae. Sometimes the individual morulae could be recognized for a long time after aggregation by a slight indentation. The way in which the blastocoelic cavity formed varied. In certain cases it appeared where the junction between the two morulae could be seen earlier (Fig. 1$b$-$d$), in others an abortive blastocoelic cavity formed in one of the partners (Fig. 2$f$), which disappeared later. In the same aggregate the lasting cavity formed in the other partner (Fig. 2$g$). In one experiment one of the aggregate partners formed a cavity before the cell mass had become round (Fig. 3$b$); this disappeared and a final one was formed after aggregation (Fig. 3$d$). The pictures and analysis of the time-lapse photographs show that both rat and mouse cells contribute to the formation of a large blastocyst.

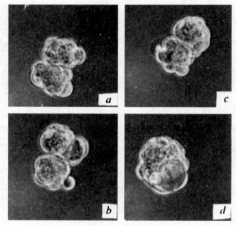

Fig. 3. Fusion of rat and mouse morulae after formation and disappearance of a cavity in the mouse morula. Pictures taken at approximately 30 min ($a$), 6.6 ($b$), 10 ($c$) and 19h ($d$).

A general feature of the chimaeric blastocysts was that the inner cell mass was comparatively large.

Preliminary observations have shown that the developmental stage of the rat eggs is critical for successful aggregation and the use of a micromanipulator was also very helpful.

A copy of the time-lapse movie is available for study.

(**242**, 115-116; 1973)

段，培养皿并不关闭，使潮湿气流直接吹向油表面以维持培养基的 pH 和渗透压。

移除卵细胞固定器以后，用连接在倒置显微镜上的间隔定时摄像机持续追踪这一对桑葚期胚胎的发育过程，每隔 30 秒打开闪光灯进行一次照相。

一共进行了 16 组相同的实验，其中有 12 组发生了成功的胚胎聚集性融合。根据在巨大的桑葚胚表面正在分裂的细胞的暂时性突起可以看出，融合双方都进行着活跃的增殖。有时通过细微的压痕可以鉴定出融合很长时间后的单个桑葚胚。囊胚腔形成的方式是多样化的。在某些情况中，它出现在能够在较早期看到的两个桑葚胚的连接位置（图 1b~d）；而在其他情况中，发育不完全的囊胚腔是在其中一个胚胎中形成的（图 2f），并在之后消失。在同一个融合胚胎中，最终的囊胚腔在另一个参与融合的胚胎内部形成（图 2g）。在一组实验中，参与融合的胚胎之一在细胞团变圆之前就形成了腔（图 3b），然后消失，最终的腔是在融合之后形成的（图 3d）。间隔定时拍摄的图片和分析显示大鼠和小鼠细胞均参与了巨大囊胚的形成。

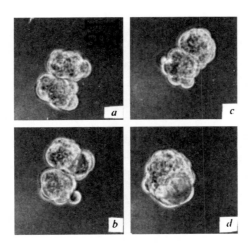

图 3. 在小鼠桑葚胚内形成腔并消失以后，大鼠和小鼠的桑葚胚发生融合。图片拍摄于融合开始大约 30 分钟（a）、6.6 小时（b）、10 小时（c）和 19 小时（d）。

嵌合囊胚的总体特征就是内细胞团相对较大。

初步的观察显示大鼠卵细胞的发育阶段对成功的融合至关重要，而且使用显微操作器非常有帮助。

我们可提供间隔定时拍摄所获得的录像拷贝用于研究。

（毛晨晖 翻译；梁前进 审稿）

229

**G. H. Zeilmaker**

Department of Endocrinology, Growth and Reproduction, Erasmus University, PO Box 1738, Rotterdam

Received September 29; revised October 20, 1972.

---

References:

1. Tarkowski, A., *Nature*, **190**, 857 (1961).

2. Mintz, B., *J. Exp. Zool.*, **157**, 273 (1964).

3. Mintz, B., in *Preimplantation Stages of Pregnancy*, CIBA Foundation Symposium (edit. by Wolstenholme, G. E. W., and O'Connor, M.), 207 (Churchill, London, 1965).

4. Tarkowski, A., in *Preimplantation Stages of Pregnancy*, CIBA Foundation Symposium (edit. by Wolstenholme, G. E. W., and O'Connor, M.), 183 (Churchill, London, 1965).

5. Biggers, J., Wittingham, D. G., and Donahue, R. P., *Proc. US Nat. Acad. Sci.*, **58**, 560 (1967).

6. Mintz, B., *Science*, **138**, 594 (1962).

7. Lin, T. P., *Science*, **151**, 333 (1966).

# Linkage Analysis in Man by Somatic Cell Genetics

F. H. Ruddle

## Editor's Note

**Today, linkage analysis, where the location of a gene is worked out relative to a known sequence, is a sophisticated affair involving high-throughput machinery and computers. But in the 1970s researchers had to resort to cell culture methods, mapping genes from somatic cell hybrids. Here geneticist Frank Ruddle describes the state of play. Hybrids combine different genomes within a single cell, and the discovery that chromosomes from parental genomes can be lost or segregated from the hybrid cell, enabled researchers to effectively isolate and identify chromosome fragments and assign genes to chromosomes. The technique correctly assigned many genes to their chromosomes, but was "unacceptably slow". Somatic cell recombination and gene transfer, Ruddle prophetically muses, could provide the way forwards.**

---

Techniques for the study of somatic cell genetics, and particularly those involving the expression of enzyme markers in hybrid cells, have already made possible a large number of gene-chromosome assignments. Genetic and family studies, as well as cellular studies on recombination and gene transfer, promise more and quicker results in the future.

---

SOMATIC cell hybridization, first demonstrated by Barski *et al.*[1], was an important early step in the formulation of somatic cell genetic systems, allowing as it does the combination of genetically different genomes within a single cell. In a series of investigations Ephrussi and his colleagues showed that hybrid combinations could be obtained between the cells of different species[2], and that chromosomes of one or both parental genomes could be lost or segregated from the hybrid cell[3]. Weiss and Green[4] first demonstrated the practical application of somatic fusion-segregation systems for the purpose of gene mapping in man (see below). Other investigators have contributed useful procedures which enhance the formation of hybrid cells and their enrichment. These developments now allow a completely new cell culture approach to gene mapping in man.

### Cultivation of Hybrid Cells

For the formation of hybrid cells the parental cells are mixed together and co-cultivated. Membrane fusion can be enhanced by treatment with inactivated Sendai virus[5,6] or with lysolecithin[7]. Fusion between two parental cells of different origins gives rise to a binucleate heterokaryon. Heterokaryons have a short life expectancy, and following their first mitosis, generally form mononucleated or hybrid daughter cells which contain chromosomes from both parental genomes. In many parental cell combinations, the hybrids have an infinite life expectancy and can be grown into large clonal cell populations. In man–

# 人类体细胞遗传学连锁分析

拉德尔

编者按

连锁分析是指分析确定某一基因相对于一段已知序列的位置，在今天，这是一项涉及高通量检测体系和计算机数据处理设备的复杂事务。但是在 20 世纪 70 年代，研究者们必须借助细胞培养方法，通过体细胞杂交来定位基因。在本文中遗传学家弗兰克·拉德尔描述了这项技术的研究进展。不同的基因组在一个细胞内形成杂交体以及亲本基因组染色体在杂交细胞中可能丢失或者发生分离的发现，都有助于研究者有效地分离、鉴定染色体片段，并将基因定位于染色体上。人们曾利用体细胞杂交技术将许多基因定位于染色体上，但其速度之慢让人难以接受。拉德尔预见性地思忖着，体细胞重组和基因转移或许能够为基因连锁分析提供更加便捷的途径。

---

体细胞遗传学的研究技术，尤其是涉及杂交细胞中酶标记表达的技术，已经使得对大量的基因 – 染色体匹配成为可能。遗传学和家族研究，以及基于重组和基因转移的细胞学研究，使我们有可能在未来更快更多地获得成果。

---

体细胞杂交是由巴尔斯基等人 [1] 率先证明的，其在构建体细胞遗传学系统的早期迈出了重要的一步，它使得在遗传学上不同的基因组可以在一个单独的细胞中进行组合。埃弗吕西和他的同事们经过一系列的研究发现不同物种的细胞之间可以进行杂交组合 [2]，并且来自一个或者两个亲代的染色体组可能会从杂交细胞中丢失或者分离 [3]。韦斯和格林 [4] 首次实现了体细胞融合 – 分离系统在人类基因作图中的实际应用（见下文）。其他研究者们也提出了一些有用的方法，可以增进杂交细胞的生成及其富集。现在，这些技术的发展使得我们可以得到一种全新的细胞培养方法来进行人类基因作图。

## 杂交细胞的培养

将亲代细胞混合并共同培养，用以形成杂交细胞。我们可以利用失活的仙台病毒 [5,6] 或者溶血卵磷脂 [7] 处理混合细胞，来促进细胞膜的融合。两种不同起源的亲代细胞融合后会产生一种双核的异核体。这些异核体的期望寿命很短，在接下来的第一次有丝分裂中会生成单核的或者含有来自两个亲代基因组的染色体的杂交子细胞。在许多亲代细胞的组合中，杂交细胞具有无限长的期望寿命，并可以生长成为一个巨大的克隆细胞群。在人类 – 小鼠和人类 – 中国仓鼠的杂交细胞中，会出现人

mouse and man–Chinese hamster hybrids there is a unilateral loss or segregation of human chromosomes. The segregation of human chromosomes is variable in extent in different clones, and in many instances clones can be obtained which maintain for many generations a partial human chromosome constitution. Thus, it is possible in effect to sample different numbers and combinations of human chromosomes in a series of man–rodent hybrids of independent origin. Each clone represents a partial human karyotype superimposed on an intact mouse or Chinese hamster genome. The experimental isolation of partial human chromosome complements forms the basis of somatic cell linkage analysis.

Enzyme complementation has been used to enrich for hybrids in mixed populations of parental cells. Littlefield has shown that drug resistance mutant cell lines can be useful in this regard[8]. Mutant cell lines can be selected which are deficient in the enzymes hypoxanthine-guanine phosphoribosyltransferase (HGPRT) and thymidine kinase (TK) by exposing cells to the antimetabolites thioguanine and BUdR respectively. HGPRT deficient cells cannot incorporate hypoxanthine, whereas TK deficient cells cannot metabolize thymidine. If *de novo* synthesis of purines and pyrimidines is blocked by the antimetabolite aminopterin, cells become dependent for survival on exogenous hypoxanthine and thymidine. HGPRT and TK deficient cells are thus conditional lethal mutants which are killed by aminopterin irrespective of the availability of hypoxanthine and thymidine. The fusion of HGPRT deficient with TK deficient parental cells yields hybrid cells whose enzyme deficiencies are complemented and which can grow in nonpermissive selection medium containing hypoxanthine, aminopterin, and thymidine (HAT medium). Kusano *et al.* have shown that adenine phosphoribosyltransferase (APRT) deficiency mutations can be used similarly for hybrid cell selection[9]. Conditional lethal mutants other than those based on drug resistance can also be used for hybrid selection. Puck *et al.* have used nutritional auxotrophs with good results[10,11], and it is likely that temperature sensitive mutations can be used in the same way[12]. Moreover, it is possible to make use of conditional mutant established rodent cell lines in combination with diploid human fibroblasts or leucocytes which have low growth potentials *in vitro*[12,13]. One can select against the rodent parent using nonpermissive medium and against the human diploid parent by virtue of its inherently poor growth characteristics.

Conditional lethal cell mutants in rodent cell populations are extremely useful for genetic analysis. In nonpermissive conditions only hybrids which retain the complementing human gene will survive. Thus, if one forms hybrids between HGPRT deficient rodent cells and wild type human cells (HGPRT+), and cultivates them in HAT medium, only those cells which retain the human HGPRT gene will survive. Generally, the intact human *X* chromosome which carries the HGPRT gene is retained in the complemented hybrid. It is possible to conceive of a series of rodent cell lines each of which carry different conditional lethal mutations which are complemented by genes on each of the human autosomes and sex chromosomes. Such a panel of rodent cell lines would be extremely useful in mapping studies because each would produce hybrids in which the segregation of a specific human chromosome would be fixed. Conditional lethal mutants

类染色体单方面缺失或者分离的现象。在不同的克隆中，人类染色体的分离存在着不同程度的变化，在许多情况下，获得的克隆细胞都保持一部分人类染色体组分，并延续多代。因此，在获得的一系列独立来源的人类－啮齿目动物杂交细胞中，很可能抽取到不同数量和组合的人类染色体。每个克隆体都表现出部分人类染色体的核型，这些核型叠加在小鼠或者中国仓鼠的完整的基因组中。因此对部分人类染色体组进行实验分离是进行体细胞基因连锁分析的基础。

酶互补技术已经应用于亲代混合细胞群中富集杂交细胞。利特菲尔德已经证明了耐药性突变细胞系在这方面很有用 [8]。我们可以分别通过抗代谢物硫鸟嘌呤和溴脱氧尿嘧啶核苷（BUdR）处理的方法筛选具有次黄嘌呤－鸟嘌呤磷酸核糖转移酶（HGPRT）和胸苷激酶（TK）缺陷的突变细胞系。HGPRT 缺陷的细胞不能利用次黄嘌呤，而 TK 缺陷的细胞不能代谢胸腺嘧啶。如果细胞体内嘌呤和嘧啶的从头合成被抗代谢物氨基蝶呤所抑制，那么细胞就只能依靠外源的次黄嘌呤和胸腺嘧啶来维持生存。因此，HGPRT 和 TK 缺陷的细胞是一种条件致死突变体，在没有外源的次黄嘌呤和胸腺嘧啶时，细胞将被氨基蝶呤杀死。将 HGPRT 缺陷的亲代细胞和 TK 缺陷的亲代细胞进行融合，产生的杂交后代的酶缺陷相互补偿，使其可以在非许可性选择培养基（含有次黄嘌呤、氨基蝶呤和胸腺嘧啶，即 HAT 培养基）中生长。草野等人证明了腺嘌呤磷酸核糖转移酶（APRT）的缺失突变可以应用在类似的杂交后代选择中 [9]。除了这些基于耐药性的突变体以外，其他条件致死突变体也可用于杂交后代的筛选。普克等人利用营养突变体获得了不错的结果 [10,11]，而温度敏感型突变也很有可能以相同的方式得到应用 [12]。而且，我们还可以利用这些条件突变体建立啮齿目动物细胞系，并将其与体外生长势较低的人类二倍体成纤维细胞或白细胞进行组合 [12,13]。人们可以利用非许可性培养基从啮齿目动物的亲代细胞筛选杂交后代，也可以利用人类二倍体细胞固有的缓慢生长特点筛选杂交后代。

啮齿目动物细胞群中的条件致死细胞突变体对遗传分析来讲是非常有用的。在非许可性选择条件下，只有那些保留了互补的人类基因的杂交后代才会存活下去。因此，如果用 HGPRT 缺失的啮齿目动物细胞与野生型人类细胞（HGPRT⁺）生成杂交后代，并在 HAT 培养基中进行培养，那么只有那些保留人类 HGPRT 基因的细胞才会存活。一般来说，带有 HGPRT 基因的完整人类 X 染色体会保留在补偿了这一缺陷基因的杂交后代中。我们可以建立一系列啮齿目动物细胞系：每个细胞带有不同的条件致死突变，这些突变体分别能被不同的人类常染色体和性染色体上的基因所补偿。这样的一组啮齿目动物细胞系在基因作图研究中将起到极大的作用，因为上述每一个细胞系都可以产生固定了某一条发生分离的人类染色体的杂交后代。表

of this type are tabulated in Table 1. It should be pointed out that the drug resistance complementation systems also lend themselves to counter selection. Cells which retain TK, APRT, and HGPRT activity are susceptible to the antimetabolites BUdR, fluoroadenine, and thioguanine, respectively[8-10]. Thus it is possible to use these agents in permissive medium to select against hybrid cells which have retained human chromosomes 17, 16 and $X$.

Table 1. Conditional Drug Resistance and Nutritional Auxotrophic Genetic Markers

| Rodent mutation | Rodent parent | Complementing human enzyme | Human linkage unit |
|---|---|---|---|
| HGPRT deficiency | Mouse | HGPRT$^+$ | X |
| TK deficiency | Mouse | TK$^+$ | 17 |
| APRT deficiency | Mouse | APRT$^+$ | 16 |
| Glycine A auxotroph | Chinese hamster | Serine hydroxymethylase | 12 |
| Adenine B auxotroph | Chinese hamster | Unknown | 4 or 5 |

## Rodent–Human Hybrids

In rodent–human hybrids, the human chromosomes are unilaterally segregated, both homologous human and rodent enzymes are expressed and can be identified, and human and mouse chromosomes can be discriminated and accurately identified on an individual basis. These hybrids are therefore particularly suitable for human gene linkage analysis.

The loss of human chromosomes from mouse–human and Chinese hamster–human hybrids is well documented, but the mechanism of loss is poorly understood. Preferential loss of human chromosomes in rodent $X$ human hybrids, irrespective of the origins of the parental cell populations, is the rule, and only one possible exception has been reported[15]. A mechanism of loss suggested by Handmaker (personal communication) is that human chromosomes cannot attach efficiently to the hybrid spindle apparatus and thus have higher incidence of loss. Another possibility, which is not necessarily incompatible with this, is a mechanism of segregation based on random non-disjunction of mouse and human chromosomes in combination with the preferential selection of hybrids which possess partial human karyotypes[16]. Nabholz et al.[17] have suggested that chromosomes are lost by two temporarily distinct processes. Early loss, possibly during the first several mitotic divisions after fusion, can result in the abrupt loss of a few or many human chromosomes. Late loss is characterized by slow progressive loss in some instances over many cell generations. Nabholz et al.[17] have also presented evidence that human chromosomes are segregated non-randomly into hybrid clones. Preliminary results in our laboratory, based on twenty-eight independent hybrid clones, indicate a very low frequency of retention of human chromosome 9 (7%) compared with the overall frequency of human chromosome retention (29%). It has been reported that hybrids with two rodent genomes (2s hybrids) retain more human chromosomes than 1s hybrids[15]. The relationship between rodent and human chromosome number is significant and should be resolved, because it is fundamental to the problem of chromosome segregation.

1 中列出了这种类型的条件致死突变体。但是应该指出的是，自身的抗药性互补系统也会产生抗基因选择的效应。那些保留 TK、APRT 和 HGPRT 活性的细胞分别易受抗代谢物 BUdR、氟腺嘌呤和硫鸟嘌呤的影响[8-10]。因此，我们可以利用这些突变体在许可性培养基中对那些保留人类的 17 号、16 号染色体和 X 染色体的杂交细胞进行选择。

表 1. 条件抗药性与营养缺陷型遗传标记

| 啮齿动物突变体 | 啮齿动物亲代 | 互补的人类酶 | 人类连锁遗传单元 |
|---|---|---|---|
| HGPRT 缺陷 | 小鼠 | HGPRT+ | X 染色体 |
| TK 缺陷 | 小鼠 | TK+ | 17 号染色体 |
| APRT 缺陷 | 小鼠 | APRT+ | 16 号染色体 |
| 甘氨酸 A 型营养缺陷 | 中国仓鼠 | 丝氨酸羟甲基酶 | 12 号染色体 |
| 腺嘌呤 B 型营养缺陷 | 中国仓鼠 | 未知 | 4 号或 5 号染色体 |

## 啮齿目动物 – 人类杂交细胞

在啮齿目动物 – 人类杂交细胞中，人类染色体发生单向分离；人类和啮齿目动物的同源酶表达并且被鉴定；在每个杂交后代上，我们可以清楚地区分并准确地鉴定人类和小鼠的染色体。因此，这些杂交细胞特别适用于人类基因连锁分析。

虽然在小鼠 – 人类和中国仓鼠 – 人类的细胞杂交中，人类染色体的缺失是有据可查的，但我们对缺失的机制还知之甚少。无论亲本细胞群的起源如何，在啮齿目动物 – 人类杂交细胞中，人类染色体更容易缺失是普遍的情况，研究者只报道了一个可能的例外[15]。汉德梅克提出了一种缺失机制（个人交流），即人类染色体不能有效地附着在杂交后代的纺锤体上，所以才会有较高的缺失发生率。另外一种并不与之相矛盾的可能性是一种分离机制，它基于小鼠和人类染色体的随机不分离以及含有部分人类细胞核型的杂交细胞的偏好性选择[16]。纳布霍尔茨等人[17]认为染色体的缺失是通过临时的两个不同的过程完成的。早期的缺失可能发生在细胞融合后的最先几次有丝分裂过程中，可引起几条或多条人类染色体的突然缺失。后来的缺失经确定是缓慢的逐步缺失，在某些情况下可持续多代细胞。纳布霍尔茨等人[17]也已给出证据表明，人类染色体是非随机地分离到杂交克隆中的。我们对 28 个独立的杂交克隆进行了实验，初步的结果显示相比于人类染色体保留的总频率（29%）来说，这些杂交克隆对人类 9 号染色体具有非常低的保留频率（7%）。据报道，拥有两个啮齿目基因组的杂交体 (2s 杂交体) 要比只有一个啮齿目基因组的杂交体 (1s 杂交体) 保留更多的人类染色体[15]。啮齿动物与人类染色体数目之间的关系很重要，并且应该得到解决，因为这是解析染色体分离机理所需要弄清的基本问题。

The amino-acid constitution of homologous enzymes between man and rodents generally differs to some degree as a result of evolutionary divergence, and it is generally possible to detect these differences by electrophoretic procedures. There is thus a very large potential catalogue of genetic markers in the rodent–human cell hybrid system, limited only by the development of adequate test procedures. A compilation of isozyme procedures has been reported by Ruddle and Nichols[18].

It is important for genetic testing that the enzyme markers be constitutive—that is, they must invariably be expressed if the corresponding structural gene is retained in the hybrid. Facultative markers are defined as those markers which are subject to modulation and which may not be expressed even if the corresponding cistron is present. It is very difficult to define phenotypes as being absolutely constitutive or facultative. Generally speaking, enzymes which are expressed in all cell types *in vivo* and which contribute to vital metabolic pathways are termed constitutive, whereas enzymes which are restricted to one or a few specialized cell types and which do not participate in vital metabolic activities at a cellular level are termed facultative. Good evidence exists for the modulation of certain facultative functions in hybrid combinations between parental cells of different epigenetic types[19]. This necessarily complicates the linkage analysis of such phenotypes. Phenotypes classified as constitutive may under certain conditions be modulated. For example, hybrid clones have been recovered by Ricciuti[20] which possess normal C-7 human chromosomes, but which do not express detectable levels of mannose-phosphate isomerase (MPI) activity. Linkage analysis in other cell hybrids shows a strong correlation between C-7 and MPI. I have concluded that MPI may represent a partially constitutive phenotype. Such phenotypes pose problems for linkage analysis, but they also provide useful material for studies on phenotype modulation.

## Cytological Identification of Chromosomes

It is now possible to identify all of the chromosomes of the Chinese hamster, laboratory mouse, and man by cytological procedures. Caspersson and co-workers[21] have shown that quinacrine binds differentially to specific regions of the human chromosomes, and that each chromosome possesses a unique banding pattern. Mouse chromosomes are similarly unique and the banding patterns have now been correlated with known murine linkage groups[22]. Giemsa banding procedures provide results comparable with those of quinacrine[23]. Pardue and Gall have introduced an *in situ* annealing technique which makes possible the localization of highly redundant DNA in mouse and human chromosomes[24]. Purified isotopically labelled redundant DNA is annealed to intact chromosomes which have been pretreated with DNA denaturation agents. The labelled redundant DNA is hybridized to complementary DNA in the chromosome, and its location revealed by autoradiography. Pardue and Gall have shown that the murine redundant DNA (satellite DNA) is restricted to the centromere regions and that denaturation followed by Giemsa staining reveals positively staining, constitutive heterochromatin regions in the chromosomes. Arrighi and Hsu[25] have adapted this method to the analysis of human chromosomes and subsequent studies have shown a correspondence between constitutive

由于进化趋异，人类和啮齿目动物间的同源酶的氨基酸组成在一定程度上普遍存在不同。通常情况下，我们可以通过电泳的方法来检测这些差异。因此，在啮齿目动物 – 人类细胞的杂交体系中存在着一大类具有潜力的遗传标记，这些遗传标记的发现取决于适当的检测方法的发展。拉德尔和尼科尔斯[18]已经报道了一种同工酶编译方法。

对于遗传学检测来说，很重要的是酶标记是组成型的，也就是说，如果相应的结构基因保留在杂交后代中，那么它们就会得以表达。功能型标记被定义为那些受调节的酶标记，这种酶即使在相应的顺反子存在下，也可能不表达。很难将表型定义为绝对的组成型或功能型。一般来讲，我们把那些可以在体内所有细胞类型中进行表达并且对重要代谢过程有贡献的酶称作组成型的，而那些受限于一个或几个特殊的细胞类型中并且在细胞水平上不参与重要代谢活动的酶被称为功能型的。有证据表明，不同的表观遗传类型的亲代细胞之间的杂交组合体具有某些兼性功能调节[19]。这必定会使得这类表型的连锁分析变得复杂化。那些属于组成型的表型在某种情况下可能也是受调节的。例如，里丘蒂筛选到的具有正常 C-7 人类染色体的杂交克隆[20]，但它并没有表达出达到可检测水平的甘露糖磷酸异构酶（MPI）活性。而在其他细胞杂交中进行的连锁分析表明，C-7 和 MPI 之间高度相关。我认为 MPI 也许代表一种部分组成性的表型。虽然这些表型给连锁分析带来了问题，但它们也为表型调节的研究提供了有价值的资料。

## 染色体的细胞学鉴定

现在我们可以通过细胞学的方法识别中国仓鼠、实验小鼠和人类的所有染色体。卡斯佩松和他的同事们[21]证明了喹吖因染料可区别性地结合到人类染色体的特定区域，并且每一条人类染色体都有一个独一无二的带型。小鼠的染色体也具有类似的独特性，其带型已经与目前已知的鼠类连锁群相联系[22]。吉姆萨显带方法得到的结果与喹吖因方法得到的类似[23]。帕杜和高尔发明了一种原位退火技术，这使得对小鼠和人类染色体中大量冗余 DNA 进行定位成为可能[24]。将提纯的用同位素标记的冗余 DNA 退火至完整的、已经用 DNA 变性剂进行了预处理的染色体。标记的冗余 DNA 就与染色体中的互补 DNA 进行杂交，其位置可用放射自显影技术显示出来。帕杜和高尔表明鼠类冗余 DNA（卫星 DNA）是被限制在着丝粒区域中的；在变性后的吉姆萨染色结果中出现阳性染料附着，在染色体上属于组成型异染色质区域。阿里吉和徐[25]采用这种方法分析了人类染色体，并在随后的研究中显示出组成型异染色质和冗余 DNA 之间的一致性关系[26]。人类和小鼠的卫星 DNA 是特异的，且无相互反应。因此，可以利用原位杂交技术来区分人类和小鼠的着丝粒区域，这在人类

heterochromatin and redundant DNA[26]. Human and mouse satellite DNA are specific and do not cross react. It is thus possible by hybridization *in situ* to distinguish human and mouse centromeric regions, which has proved useful in the detection of human–mouse chromosome translocations[27] (see below). Several laboratories have reported evidence indicating that the centromeric constitutive heterochromatin in man has different physical properties unique for several of the human chromosomes[28].

## Assigning Genes to Chromosomes

Linkage of enzyme phenotypes can be inferred from their concordant segregation. The human chromosomes maintain their integrity for the most part, seldom undergoing rearrangement or deletion, and the concordant segregation of markers thus provides evidence for their location on the same chromosome irrespective of map distance. It is therefore appropriate to employ the term "synteny" coined by Renwick to signify merely localization on the same chromosome. Synteny testing is performed by comparing the segregation pattern of all markers in all pairwise combinations. The synteny test is less biased if performed on clones of independent origin and the detection of valid syntenic relationships is enhanced by using clones derived from separate hybridization experiments, using different hybrid combinations. This generally entails computer analysis because of the number of clones and markers involved.

Individual genes or syntenic genes can be assigned to specific chromosomes by tabulating the human chromosomes in each of the clones and correlating them with the enzyme markers. The concordant presence or absence between a chromosome and a phenotype provides evidence for the assignment of the gene governing a particular phenotype to a specific chromosome. Twenty to thirty metaphases are analysed per clone by means of quinacrine banding, Giemsa banding, or constitutive heterochromatin staining techniques. Identification is enhanced if cells are first photographed by quinacrine fluorescence and then by constitutive heterochromatin staining procedures.

It is frequently possible to strengthen the assignment of a gene to a particular chromosome by correlating the frequency of a particular chromosome within a clone with the intensity of expression of an assigned phenotype(s). Discrepant clones of two classes can occur, however. In the first, presuming a valid assignment, the chromosome cannot be detected but the phenotype is present. We have demonstrated cryptic, rearranged chromosomes in a number of such instances which explain an apparently discordant chromosome/ gene relationship[29]. A second type of discrepant clone involves the presence of a specific chromosome, but the absence of its corresponding phenotype(s). Clones of this type are difficult to explain, but could involve subtle rearrangements in chromosome structure, gene mutation, modulation of gene expression, or technical failure in phenotype detection.

It is possible to assign genes to particular regions of chromosomes such as chromosome arms, or band regions as defined by particular staining reactions. This can be accomplished by making use of chromosome rearrangements such as translocations and deletions

240

– 小鼠染色体易位的检测上已经证明是有用的 [27]（见下文）。数个实验室已发表证据表明，人类着丝粒组成型异染色质具有异于人类某些染色体才具有的物理性质 [28]。

## 基因与染色体的匹配

酶表型的连锁关系可以从与它们对应的染色体分离中推断出来。人类染色体绝大部分都保持着它们的完整性，很少会发生重排或者缺失，因此在不考虑图谱距离的情况下，与酶标记一致的分离为它们定位在对应的染色体上提供了依据。所以，采用伦威克创造的术语"同线性"来表示仅在同一染色体上的定位，这是很合适的。同线性检测是通过对比所有配对组合中全部遗传标记的分离模式来进行的。如果在独立起源的克隆体上进行检测，则同线性检测的结果的偏差较小。采用独立杂交实验的源于不同杂交组合的克隆体，可以加强有效的同线性关系检测。通常这样的检测需要计算机来进行分析，因为所涉及的克隆体和遗传标记数量庞大。

我们可以对每个克隆体的人类染色体进行列表并将它们与酶标记相联系，以此将单个基因或者同线性基因定位到特定的染色体中。染色体和酶表型同时存在或者缺失为控制将某一特定表型的基因定位到特定染色体中提供了证据。通过喹吖因显带、吉姆萨显带或者组成型异染色质染色技术，我们对每个克隆体的 20~30 个有丝分裂中期的染色体组型进行了分析。如果先用喹吖因对细胞进行荧光成像，然后再使用组成型异染色质染色技术，识别效果会增强。

通过将一个克隆体中某一特定的染色体频率与指定表型的表达强度联系起来，往往可以强化该基因在特定染色体上的定位。然而，克隆体可以产生两种类型的差异克隆。第一种类型，假设基因分配有效，染色体不能检测到，但其表型存在。我们已经证明了在大量案例 [29] 中存在隐性的、重排的染色体，能够解释这种染色体与基因之间关系的不一致。第二种类型的差异克隆体是存在特定的染色体，但缺少其相应的表型。这种类型的克隆体很难解释，其可能涉及染色体结构的精细重排、基因突变、基因表达的调节，或者在表型检测上的技术缺陷。

将基因定位到染色体的特定区域中是可能实现的，例如染色体臂或者由特定的染色反应界定的带型区域。利用染色体重排，如在人类亲代细胞群中的染色体易位和缺失，或者发生在杂交细胞中的染色体自发重排，我们可以完成上述的基因定位。

in the human parental cell population or by making use of spontaneous chromosome rearrangements which are generated in the hybrids. Translocations of chromosomes to or between chromosomes $X$, 17, and 16 are useful because these chromosomes possess selectable loci. A number of translocations affecting the same chromosome but with different breakpoints can be used to restrict the localization of genes. For this purpose it will be particularly useful to characterize and store in central repositories all detected human translocations, to serve as a library of rearrangement products for future somatic cell gene mapping. Programs of human mutant cell banking are now being formulated in several countries. An example of regional linkage assignments based on translocations in parental cells is cited below for the $X$ chromosome.

It is also possible to make use of spontaneous, sporadic chromosome rearrangements which occur in hybrid cells to fix the location of genes within subregions of particular chromosome. Human chromosomes within hybrids may undergo rearrangement and even translocation to mouse chromosomes[29] and it has been possible to make use of such rearrangements to restrict the localization of the thymidine kinase gene to the long arm of human chromosome 17[29]. The translocation of human chromosome segments to the mouse chromosome set is significant from a genetic point of view because it may serve to restrict the further segregation of human genes involved in the translocation. It is conceivable that treatment of parental cells or hybrids with physical or chemical chromosome breaking agents could be used to induce chromosome rearrangements. Enrichment procedures could be devised to select particular classes of rearrangement products. Such systems could be used to increase the resolution of subregional chromosome gene assignments.

## Known Human Linkage Groups

A significant number of syntenic relationships and chromosome assignments has been established by somatic cell genetics. A survey of the current linkage information is presented below for each of the human chromosomes in turn. The results are also summarized in Table 2. For chromosome 1, Van Cong et al.[30] have reported a syntenic relationship between phosphoglucomutase-1 (PGM$_1$) and peptidase C (Pep C) using mouse–human hybrids. This synteny has been confirmed by Ruddle et al.[31]. Using Chinese hamster–human hybrids, Westerveld et al.[32] have reported a synteny between 6-phosphogluconate dehydrogenase (PGD) and Pep C. Taken together, these findings imply that PGD, Pep C, and PGM$_1$ are all syntenic. Pep C has been assigned to chromosome 1 using mouse–human cell hybrids[31]. This assignment has been confirmed by the assignment of PGD to chromosome 1 independently by Bootsma et al. (personal communication) and Hamerton et al.[34] using Chinese hamster–human hybrids. If the findings based on cell hybrids are combined with linkages known from human pedigree analysis, the following additional gene markers can be assigned to chromosome 1: zonular pulverulent cataract, Duffy blood group, auriculo-osteodysplasia, salivary amylase, pancreatic amylase, elliptocytosis and rhesus blood group. For complete literature citations see Ruddle et al.[31]

在 X、17 号和 16 号染色体或它们之间进行的染色体易位是非常有用的，因为这些染色体具有筛选标记的位点。可以采用一些作用于同一染色体但具有不同断裂位点的染色体易位来限定基因的位置关系。为此目的，将所有检测到的人类染色体易位进行表征分析并集中储存，这对将来建立体细胞基因作图中重排产物的基因库非常有用。目前有几个国家正在酝酿建设人类突变细胞库。下文中将会提到的一个例子是基于亲代细胞 X 染色体上的染色体易位的区域连锁基因定位的。

我们还能够利用发生在杂交细胞中自发的、零星的染色体重排将基因定位在某个特定染色体的亚区域内。杂交后代中的人类染色体可以发生重排甚至易位至小鼠的染色体中 [29]。我们已可以利用这样的重排技术将胸苷激酶基因定位到人类 17 号染色体的长臂上 [29]。从遗传学的观点上来看，人类染色体片段易位至小鼠的染色体组中具有重要的意义，因为它可以用于限制参与染色体易位的人类基因的进一步分离。可以想象的是，用物理的或者化学的染色体断裂剂处理亲代细胞或者杂交细胞可以诱导染色体重排。同时人们设计出富集流程来筛选特定种类的重排产物。这样的体系可以用来提高亚区域内染色体基因定位的分辨率。

## 已知的人类连锁群

大量的同线性关系和染色体重排已经通过体细胞遗传学建立起来。下面将依次对每条人类染色体目前的连锁资料进行调查。并将调查结果归纳于表 2 中。对于 1 号染色体，范康等人 [30] 对小鼠－人类杂交细胞进行研究，报道了葡糖磷酸变位酶－1（$PGM_1$）和肽酶 C（Pep C）之间的同线性关系。这样的同线性被拉德尔等人 [31] 所证实。韦斯特费尔德等人 [32] 利用中国仓鼠－人类杂交细胞得到了 6-磷酸葡萄糖酸脱氢酶（PGD）和 Pep C 之间的同线性关系。结合两个研究结果，提示 PGD、Pep C 和 $PGM_1$ 都是同线性关系。利用小鼠－人类杂交细胞，人们已经将 Pep C 基因定位到 1 号染色体中 [31]。这个定位已经分别被布茨马等人（个人交流）以及哈默顿等人 [34] 独立地利用中国仓鼠－人类杂交细胞将 6-磷酸葡萄糖脱氢酶（PGD）基因定位到 1 号染色体中所证实。如果将上述的基于杂交细胞的研究结果与从人类谱系分析中得到的已知连锁相结合，那么下列补充的基因标记就可以被定位到 1 号染色体中：带粉状白内障、达菲血型、耳骨发育异常、唾液淀粉酶、胰淀粉酶、椭圆形红细胞增多症和恒河猴血型。完整的引用文献请参见拉德尔等人的文章 [31]。

Table 2. Assignments of Genes to Chromosomes

| | |
|---|---|
| Chromosome 1 | PGM$_1$, 17190; PGD, 17220; Pep C, 17000 |
| Chromosome 2 | IDH, 14770; MOR, 15425 |
| Chromosome 3 | — |
| Chromosome 4–5 | Adenine B$^+$, 10265 |
| Chromosome 6 | MOD, 15420; IPO-B, 14745 |
| Chromosome 7 | MPI, 15455; PK$_3$, 17905 |
| Chromosome 8–9 | — |
| Chromosome 10 | GOT, 13825 |
| Chromosome 11 | LDH-A, 15000; Es-A$_4$, 13340; KA, 14875 |
| Chromosome 12 | LDH-B, 15010; Pep B, 16990; GlyA$^+$ (serinehydroxymethylase ?), 13845 |
| Chromosome 13 | — |
| Chromosome 14 | NP, 16405 |
| Chromosome 15 | |
| Chromosome 16 | APRT, 10260 |
| Chromosome 17 | TK, 18830 |
| Chromosome 18 | Pep A, 16980 |
| Chromosome 19 | GPI, 23575 |
| Chromosome 20 | ADA, 10270 |
| Chromosome 21 | IPO-A, 14744; AVP, 10745 |
| Chromosome 22 | — |
| Chromosome X | HGPRT, 30800; PGK, 31180; GPD, 30590; α-Gal, 30150 |
| Chromosome Y | — |

These genes were assigned or confirmed by cell hybrid analysis. Each trait is identified by McKusick's human gene catalogue number[59]. IPO-A and B used here agree with the original designation of Brewer[33].

Preliminary results in our laboratory (R. P. Creagan and F. H. R.) suggest that isocitrate dehydrogenase (IDH) and NADP-malate dehydrogenase (MOD) which have been shown to be syntenic[44] can be assigned to chromosome 2. No loci have been assigned to chromosome 3. For chromosomes 4 and 5, Kao and Puck[35] using Chinese hamster–human hybrids have demonstrated a positive association between hamster adenine B auxotrophy and a human B group chromosome when hybrids are propagated on minimal medium. The specific enzyme involved is unknown. Chen *et al.*[36] using mouse–human hybrids have shown that cytoplasmic malate dehydrogenase (MOD) is assignable to chromosome 6 and there is evidence to support a syntenic relationship between indolephenol oxidase, tetrameric form B (IPO-B) and MOD (J. A. Tischfield, R. P. Creagan and F. H. R., unpublished).

表 2. 基因在染色体中的定位情况

| 1 号染色体 | PGM$_1$, 17190；PGD, 17220；Pep C, 17000 |
|---|---|
| 2 号染色体 | IDH, 14770；MOR, 15425 |
| 3 号染色体 | — |
| 4~5 号染色体 | 腺嘌呤 B$^+$, 10265 |
| 6 号染色体 | MOD, 15420；IPO-B, 14745 |
| 7 号染色体 | MPI, 15455；PK$_3$, 17905 |
| 8~9 号染色体 | — |
| 10 号染色体 | GOT, 13825 |
| 11 号染色体 | LDH-A, 15000；Es-A$_4$, 13340；KA, 14875 |
| 12 号染色体 | LDH-B, 15010；Pep B, 16990；GlyA$^+$（丝氨酸羟甲基化酶？）, 13845 |
| 13 号染色体 | |
| 14 号染色体 | NP, 16405 |
| 15 号染色体 | |
| 16 号染色体 | APRT, 10260 |
| 17 号染色体 | TK, 18830 |
| 18 号染色体 | Pep A, 16980 |
| 19 号染色体 | GPI, 23575 |
| 20 号染色体 | ADA, 10270 |
| 21 号染色体 | IPO-A, 14744；AVP, 10745 |
| 22 号染色体 | — |
| X 染色体 | HGPRT, 30800；PGK, 31180；GPD, 30590；α-Gal, 30150 |
| Y 染色体 | — |

这些基因的定位或确认是通过细胞杂交分析完成的。每一个特征都与麦库西克的人类基因目录编号一致 [59]。这里提及的吲哚苯酚氧化酶 A 和 B（IPO-A 和 B）与布鲁尔 [33] 最初的命名一致。

我们实验室（克里根和拉德尔）初步的研究结果表明具有同线性关系 [44] 的异柠檬酸脱氢酶（IDH）和 NADP–苹果酸脱氢酶（MOD）基因都在 2 号染色体上。在 3 号染色体上没有可确定的位点。对于 4 号和 5 号染色体，高和普克 [35] 利用中国仓鼠 – 人类杂交细胞证明了杂交后代在基本培养基中进行繁殖时，仓鼠的腺嘌呤 B 营养缺陷型与人类的 B 族染色体之间呈现正相关。但是目前还不清楚具体参与的特异性酶。陈等人 [36] 利用小鼠 – 人类杂交细胞证明了胞质苹果酸脱氢酶（MOD）基因可以被定位到 6 号染色体中。也有证据表明四聚体型吲哚苯酚氧化酶 B（IPO-B）和 MOD 之间存在同线性的关系（蒂施菲尔德、克里根和拉德尔，未发表）。

McMorris *et al.*[37] using mouse $\times$ human hybrids have assigned mannose phosphate isomerase (MPI) to chromosome 7. Shows[38] has reported a syntenic relationship between MPI and the leucocytic form of pyruvate kinase₃ (PK₃).

There are no assignments to chromosomes 8 or 9. There is evidence from mouse–human hybrids for the assignment of the cytoplasmic form of glutamate oxaloacetate transaminase (GOT) to chromosome 10 (unpublished work of R. P. Creagan, J. A. Tischfield, F. A. McMorris, M. Hirschi, T. R. Chen and F. H. R.)

Boone *et al.*[29] using mouse–human hybrids have assigned lactate dehydrogenase A (LDH-A) to chromosome 11. Shows[39] using mouse–human hybrids has reported a syntenic association between LDH-A and human esterase A₄ (EsA₄). Van Someren *et al.*[40] have reported a syntenic association between glutamic-pyruvic transaminase (GPT-C) and LDH-A. The possibility exists, however, that their enzyme detection system is recording LDH-A activity. This may also apply to LDH-B and GPT-B (see below). Nabholz *et al.*[17] using mouse–human cells have reported a positive correlation between the segregation of LDH-A or B activity and sensitivity of hybrid cells to anti-human cytotoxic antisera. Puck *et al.*[41] have reported on the segregation of a possibly similar human antigen(s) in Chinese hamster–human hybrid cells, which they have found to be syntenic with LDH-A.

Ruddle and Chen[42] and Chen *et al.*[36] using mouse–human hybrids have demonstrated positive correlation between lactate dehydrogenase B (LDH-B) and chromosome 12. Hamerton *et al.*[34] have confirmed this assignment using Chinese hamster–human hybrids. In mouse–human hybrids a syntenic relationship has been demonstrated between LDH-B and peptidase-B (Pep-B)[14,43]. The Pep-B/LDH-B synteny has been confirmed by Shows[39,44], Van Cong *et al.*[30] and van Someren *et al.*, who have also reported a syntenic association between glutamic-pyruvic transaminase-B (GPT-B) and LDH-B[40]. Jones *et al.*[45] using Chinese hamster–human hybrids have reported a syntenic relationship between LDH-B and the complement to the Chinese hamster glycine auxotrophic mutant A. Serine hydroxymethylase has been implicated as the specific deficiency in glycine A auxotrophy.

No assignments have been made to chromosome 13. For chromosome 14, Ricciuti and Ruddle (ref. 46 and F. Ricciuti and F. H. R., unpublished) using a $14/X$ translocation in a human diploid fibroblastic cell strain (KOP) hybridized to a mouse cell line have demonstrated a segregation of nucleoside phosphorylase (NP) with the $X$ linked markers, HGPRT, GPD, and PGK. Somatic cell genetic[46] and family studies[47] have provided evidence for the autosomal linkage of NP. The studies of Ricciuti and Ruddle thereby support the assignment of NP to chromosome 14. Unreported experiments from our laboratory using a $14/22$ translocation also confirm the assignment of NP to 14. Hamerton *et al.*[34] have reported results based on Chinese hamster–mouse hybrids which are consistent with the above findings of Ricciuti and Ruddle. No assignments have been made to chromosome 15.

Tischfield and Ruddle (unpublished) using an adenine phosphoribosyltransferase (APRT)

麦克莫里斯等人 [37] 利用小鼠 – 人类杂交细胞将甘露糖磷酸异构酶（MPI）基因定位到 7 号染色体上。肖 [38] 报道了 MPI 和丙酮酸激酶 3（PK₃）的白细胞型之间存在同线性关系。

没有基因定位于 8 号或 9 号染色体上。来自小鼠 – 人类杂交细胞的证据显示与细胞质型相关的谷氨酸 – 草酰乙酸转氨酶（GOT）基因可被定位到 10 号染色体上（克里根、蒂施菲尔德、麦克莫里斯、赫胥、陈和拉德尔，未发表）。

布恩等人 [29] 利用小鼠 – 人类杂交细胞将乳酸脱氢酶 A（LDH-A）定位到 11 号染色体上。肖 [39] 利用小鼠 – 人类杂交细胞报道了 LDH-A 和人类酯酶 A4（EsA₄）之间的同线性关系。范索梅伦等人 [40] 报道了谷氨酸 – 丙酮酸转氨酶 C（GPT-C）和 LDH-A 之间的同线性关系。然而，他们的酶检测系统存在着同时记录 LDH-A 活性的可能。这样的方法也被应用到 LDH-B 和 GPT-B 中（见下文）。纳布霍尔茨等人 [17] 利用小鼠 – 人类细胞杂交后代报道了 LDH-A 或 B 活性性状分离与杂交细胞抗人类细胞毒性的抗血清敏感性之间的正相关性。普克等人 [41] 报道了在中国仓鼠 – 人类杂交细胞中可能类似于人类抗原的分离，并发现其与 LDH-A 具有同线性关系。

拉德尔和陈 [42] 以及陈等人 [36] 利用小鼠 – 人类杂交细胞证明了乳酸脱氢酶 B（LDH-B）和 12 号染色体之间的正相关性。哈默顿等人 [34] 利用中国仓鼠 – 人类杂交细胞证实了这样的基因定位关系。在小鼠 – 人类杂交细胞中，已经证明 LDH-B 和肽酶 B（Pep-B）之间具有同线性关系 [14,43]。肖 [39,44]、范康等人 [30] 和范索梅伦等人证实了 LDH-B 和 Pep-B 之间的同线性关系。范索梅伦等人还报道了谷氨酸 – 丙酮酸转氨酶 B（GPT-B）和 LDH-B 之间的同线性关系 [40]。琼斯等人 [45] 利用中国仓鼠 – 人类杂交细胞后代报道了 LDH-B 和中国仓鼠甘氨酸营养缺陷突变体 A 的补偿物之间的同线性关系。丝氨酸羟甲基化酶可能与甘氨酸 A 型营养缺陷中的某种缺陷有关。

13 号染色体中没有可确定的位点。对于 14 号染色体，里丘蒂和拉德尔（文献 46，以及里丘蒂和拉德尔未发表结果）利用人类二倍体成纤维细胞系（KOP）与小鼠细胞系杂交中的 14 号染色体和 X 染色体的易位（14/X 易位）证明了核苷磷酸化酶（NP）与 X 染色体上的连锁标记 HGPRT、葡萄糖–6–磷酸脱氢酶（GPD）和磷酸甘油酸激酶（PGK）的分离。体细胞遗传学 [46] 和家族研究 [47] 为 NP 与常染色体连锁提供了证据。因而，里丘蒂和拉德尔的研究结果支持了 NP 基因被定位到 14 号染色体的结论。我们实验室利用染色体 14/22 易位也证明了 NP 基因位于 14 号染色体（未发表）。哈默顿等人 [34] 利用中国仓鼠 – 人类杂交细胞报道的研究成果与上述里丘蒂和拉德尔的发现是一致的。15 号染色体上没有找到可确定的基因。

蒂施菲尔德和拉德尔（未发表）利用腺嘌呤磷酸核糖转移酶（APRT）缺陷的小

deficient mouse cell line hybridized to normal human diploid cells have obtained evidence for the assignment of APRT to chromosome 16. On evidence from family studies, Robson et al.[48] have assigned α-haptoglobin to chromosome 16. APRT activity variants have been reported in man, and it would be reasonable to identify kindreds in which α-haptoglobin and APRT variants are jointly expressed to test for linkage between these two markers.

For chromosome 17, Green[49] and Migeon and Miller[50] using mouse–human cell hybrids assigned thymidine kinase (TK) to an E group chromosome. This assignment was based on the earlier findings of Weiss and Green[4] and has since been verified by Boone and Ruddle[51]. Miller et al.[52], Ruddle and Chen[53], and Boone et al.[29] have now assigned TK specifically to chromosome 17. Boone et al.[29], making use of a spontaneously occurring 17 translocation to a mouse chromosome, have provided evidence for the assignment of TK to the long arm of chromosome 17. Kit et al.[54] and McDougall et al.[55] have demonstrated that adenovirus 12 infection induces host TK activity, and concurrently a secondary constriction in the proximal segment of the long arm of 17. These findings suggest that the TK gene may be located near the adeno-12 induced gap region.

Creagan et al. (unpublished) using mouse–human cell hybrids have provided evidence for the assignment of peptidase-A (Pep-A) to chromosome 18.

Glucosephosphate isomerase (GPI) has been assigned to chromosome 19 on the basis of evidence from mouse–human cell hybrids[37]. Hamerton et al.[34] have confirmed this assignment using Chinese hamster–human cell hybrids. Linkage studies in the mouse have revealed a loose linkage between GPI and $\beta$ haemoglobin: it will be of interest to test for a similar linkage relationship in human kindreds.

Boone et al.[29] using mouse–human hybrids reported a weak association between cytoplasmic isocitrate dehydrogenase (IDH), cytoplasmic maleate oxidoreductase (MOR) and chromosome 20. More extensive data from mouse–human hybrids have now shown that IDH and MOR cannot be assigned to 20 and using mouse–human hybrids we have obtained evidence of the assignment of tissue-specific adenosine deaminase (ADA) to chromosome 20 (J. A. Tischfield, R. P. Creagan and F. H. R., unpublished). ADA is asyntenic with both IDH and MOR. Family studies have demonstrated linkage between HL-A phosphoglucomutase 3, P blood group, and ADA[56].

On chromosome 21, Tan et al.[57], using somatic cell hybrids, have provided evidence for the syntenic association between indolephenoloxidase-A, dimeric (IPO-A) and a genetic factor (AVP) which controls an antiviral response specifically induced by human interferon. The genetic factor may regulate the interferon receptor and/or the antiviral protein. We have also shown that the interferon and AVP loci are asyntenic[57]. These results confirm earlier studies by Cassingena et al.[58] on their asyntenic association based on monkey–rat somatic cell hybrids. Tan et al.[57] have assigned AVP/IPO-A to chromosome 21. No assignments have yet been made to chromosome 22.

鼠细胞系与正常的人类二倍体细胞进行杂交，得到了将 APRT 基因定位到 16 号染色体的证据。在体细胞的家族研究所得到的证据基础上，罗布森等人 [48] 将 α– 珠蛋白定位到 16 号染色体上。人类 APRT 活性变体已有报道，通过 α– 珠蛋白和 APRT 变体的共表达现象来分析检测两个遗传标记间相互连锁的遗传关系是合理的。

对于 17 号染色体，格林 [49] 还有米金和米勒 [50] 利用小鼠 – 人类杂交细胞将胸腺嘧啶激酶（TK）基因定位到 E 组染色体中。这个基因定位关系基于韦斯和格林 [4] 的早期发现，并且已经被布恩和拉德尔 [51] 所证实。米勒等人 [52]、拉德尔和陈 [53] 以及布恩等人 [29] 现在已将 TK 基因特异性地定位到 17 号染色体上。利用 17 号染色体对小鼠染色体的自发易位，布恩等人 [29] 提出证据表明 TK 基因应该定位在 17 号染色体的长臂上。基特等人 [54] 和麦克杜格尔等人 [55] 已证明腺病毒 12 感染会诱导宿主的 TK 活性，同时在最接近 17 号染色体长臂的区域引起二级收缩。这些发现提示 TK 基因也许就位于腺–12 诱导的缺口区域附近。

克里根等人（未发表）利用小鼠 – 人类细胞的杂交后代提供了肽酶 A（Pep-A）基因可被定位到 18 号染色体上的证据。

来自小鼠 – 人类细胞杂交后代的证据表明葡萄糖磷酸异构酶（GPI）基因位于 19 号染色体上 [37]。哈默顿等人 [34] 后来利用中国仓鼠 – 人类细胞的杂交证实了这一基因定位关系。在小鼠身上进行的连锁分析提示葡萄糖磷酸异构酶（GPI）与 β– 血红蛋白之间松散的连锁关系：在人类近亲中检测类似的连锁关系将会非常有趣。

布恩等人 [29] 利用小鼠 – 人类细胞的杂交后代报道了细胞质异柠檬酸脱氢酶（IDH）、细胞质马来酸氧化还原酶（MOR）和 20 号染色体之间存在着弱关联。现在，来自小鼠 – 人类细胞杂交后代的更广泛的数据表明 IDH 和 MOR 基因是不能够被定位到 20 号染色体上的。我们利用小鼠 – 人类杂交细胞得到了组织特异性的腺苷脱氨酶（ADA）基因位于 20 号染色体上的证据（蒂施菲尔德、克里根和拉德尔，未发表）。ADA 与 IDH 和 MOR 之间均是非同线性的。体细胞家族的研究证明人类白细胞抗原葡糖磷酸变位酶 3、P 血型和 ADA 之间存在着连锁关系 [56]。

对于 21 号染色体，谭等人 [57] 利用体细胞杂交证明了二聚体型吲哚苯酚氧化酶 A、（IPO-A）和一种遗传因子（精氨酸加压素，AVP）之间存在同线性关系。这种遗传因子可在人类干扰素的诱导下控制抗病毒反应，可以调节干扰素受体和（或）抗病毒蛋白。我们还证明了干扰素和 AVP 位点之间是非同线性关系 [57]。这些结果证实了卡西季娜等人 [58] 早期在猴子 – 大鼠体细胞杂交上得到的干扰素和 AVP 之间非同线性关系的结论。谭等人 [57] 已经将 AVP / IPO-A 基因定位到 21 号染色体上。在 22 号染色体上还没有发现基因定位关系。

Glucose-6-phosphate dehydrogenase (GPD), hypoxanthine-guanine phosphoribosyltransferase (HGPRT), and phosphoglycerate kinase (PGK) have all been assigned to the $X$ chromosome by segregation analysis in families[59]. Nabholz et al.[17] using mouse–human hybrids confirmed the $X$ linkage of HGPRT. Meera Kahn et al.[60] have demonstrated the $X$ linkage of PGK by cell hybrid analysis. Ruddle et al.[61] using mouse–human hybrids confirmed the $X$ linkage of HGPRT, glucose-6-phosphate dehydrogenase (GPD), and Phosphoglycerate kinase (PGK). Grzeschik et al.[62] have recently provided evidence based on Chinese hamster–human hybrids for the assignment of α-galactosidase (α-Gal) to the $X$ chromosome. In an earlier report, Grzeschik et al.[63] analysed cell hybrids between human KOP cells which possess a $14/X$ translocation (KOP) and mouse and Syrian hamster cells. They observed an infrequent segregation of HGPRT and GPD from PGK, which led them to postulate the assignment of PGK to the long arm, and the possible assignment of HGPRT and GPD to the short arm, although assignment to the long arm was not altogether discounted. Ricciuti and Ruddle (ref. 46 and unpublished results) using the same KOP material hybridized to mouse cells have obtained data which indicate that all three markers are located on the $X$ long arm. This suggests that PGK is proximal to the centromere and distant from the other two markers. HGPRT and GPD seem to be close together and distal to the centromere with respect to PGK; preliminary evidence indicates that HGPRT is proximal to GPD. P. Gerald and co-workers (personal communication) have recently studied a human cell with a $19/X$ translocation hybridized to mouse cells. A translocation product composed of the 19 long arm, the proximal half of 19 short arm, and the distal half of the $X$ long arm was correlated with GPI, HGPRT, and GPD, but not PGK. This result is consistent with the human $X$ linkage map proposed by Ricciuti and Ruddle[46]. It also confirms the assignment of GPI to 19.

No assignments have been made to the Y chromosome.

## Possibilities for New Approaches

The development of a detailed human genetic map is certain to provide insight into the evolutionary origins of man and the primates. LDH-A and LDH-B are located on chromosomes 11 and 12 respectively. These chromosomes are similar in size, centromere position, and banding pattern, which is consistent with the occurrence of a primordial polyploid event in the early primate genome as discussed by Comings[64]. Somatic cell genetic analysis should be feasible for representative members of the order primates using rodent–primate hybrids. Linkage data from such hybrids should provide information on the relatedness of these forms, and yield estimates for rates of evolutionary divergence, especially when combined with comparative studies on the chromosome constitutions and amino-acid sequences of proteins in the representative specimens.

It is already obvious that somatic cell genetics has contributed and will in the future contribute important data to human genetics. Moreover, these developments enhance the significance and future role of family and population genetic studies. Already map

通过对体细胞杂交细胞系分离的分析发现，葡萄糖–6–磷酸脱氢酶（GPD）、次黄嘌呤–鸟嘌呤磷酸核糖转移酶（HGPRT）和磷酸甘油酸激酶（PGK）基因都可以被定位到 X 染色体上[59]。纳布霍尔茨等人[17]利用小鼠–人类细胞杂交证实了 X 染色体与 HGPRT 之间的连锁关系。米拉·卡恩等人[60]通过对细胞杂交的分析证明了 PGK 与 X 染色体的连锁关系。拉德尔等人[61]利用小鼠–人类细胞杂交证实了 X 染色体与 HGPRT、葡萄糖–6–磷酸脱氢酶（GPD）和磷酸甘油酸激酶（PGK）之间的连锁关系。最近，格尔策希克等人[62]利用中国仓鼠–人类细胞杂交提供了 α–半乳糖苷酶（α-Gal）定位到 X 染色体上的证据。在早期的报道中，格尔策希克等人[63]分析了人类 KOP 细胞（具有 14/X 的易位）与小鼠和叙利亚仓鼠细胞之间的细胞杂交。他们观察到 HGPRT 和 GPD 与 PGK 的低频分离，这使得他们推测出这样的结论：PGK 基因应该位于染色体长臂，而 HGPRT 和 GPD 基因则在短臂上（尽管其在长臂上的可能性并没有完全排除）。里丘蒂和拉德尔（文献 46 和未发表结果）利用同样的 KOP 细胞与小鼠细胞进行杂交得到的数据显示上述的三种酶标记都位于 X 染色体的长臂上。这提示 PGK 的位点接近着丝粒并远离其他两种酶标记。HGPRT 和 GPD 基因似乎挨得很近，且相对于 PGK 基因而言远离着丝粒；初步证据提示 HGPRT 基因的位置最接近 GPD 基因。近来，杰拉尔德和他的同事们（个人交流）对 19/X 易位的人类细胞与小鼠细胞的杂交进行了研究。杂交后得到的易位产物由 19 号染色体的长臂、19 号染色体短臂近端的一半和 X 染色体长臂远端的一半组成，该产物与 GPI、HGPRT 和 GPD 相关，而与 PGK 无关。该结果与里丘蒂和拉德尔[46]提出的人类 X 染色体连锁图谱是相一致的，还证实了 GPI 基因位于 19 号染色体上。

在 Y 染色体上没有发现基因定位关系。

## 新方法的契机

建立详细的人类基因图谱无疑使人们能够更加深入地了解人类与灵长类动物的进化起源。LDH-A 和 LDH-B 基因分别位于 11 号和 12 号染色体上。这两条染色体的大小、着丝粒的位置以及带型都是相似的。这与科明斯[64]讨论的在早期灵长类动物基因组中发生过原始多倍体的事实相一致。通过啮齿目–灵长类的细胞杂交，对具有代表性的灵长目动物进行体细胞遗传分析应是可行的。这些杂交后代的连锁数据可以提供有关这类关联性的信息，并且可以对进化趋异的速率进行评估，尤其是在结合了对代表性样本中染色体结构和氨基酸序列的比较研究以后。

很显然，体细胞遗传学已经并将继续为人类遗传学提供重要的数据。此外，体细胞遗传学的发展提高了家族和群体遗传研究的重要性和在今后的作用。通过体细胞遗传学中准确的信息，即某些基因对是同线性的，已经绘制的基因间图谱得到完

distances between genes have been refined or established by the certain knowledge from somatic cell genetics that certain gene pairs are syntenic. We should expect a fruitful interaction and collaboration between practitioners of somatic cell genetics and classical genetics. We must, however, keep clearly in mind that somatic genetic procedures as they now exist are still unacceptably slow and linkage estimates cannot yet be made. If we are soon to develop genetic maps of man comparable to those available for the lower eukaryotes, it will be necessary to develop new procedures. Possibilities for this are to be found in somatic cell recombination and gene transfer.

(**242**, 165-169; 1973)

**Frank H. Ruddle**

Kline Biology Tower, Yale University, New Haven, Connecticut 06520

References:

1. Barski, G., Sorieul, S., and Cornefert, F., *CR Acad. Sci.*, **251**, 1825 (1960).

2. Ephrussi, B., and Weiss, M. C., *Proc. US Nat. Acad. Sci.*, **53**, 1040 (1965).

3. Ephrussi, B., and Weiss, M. C., *Develop. Biol. Suppl. I.*, 136 (1967).

4. Weiss, M. C., and Green, H., *Proc. US Nat. Acad. Sci.*, **58**, 1104 (1967).

5. Harris, H., and Watkins, J. F., *Nature*, **205**, 640 (1965).

6. Okada, Y., and Murayama, F., *Exp. Cell Res.*, **52**, 34 (1968).

7. Lucy, J. A., *Nature*, **227**, 815 (1970).

8. Littlefield, J. W., *Science*, **145**, 709 (1964).

9. Kusano, T., Long, C., and Green, H., *Proc. US Nat. Acad. Sci.*, **68**, 82 (1971).

10. Puck, T. T., and Kao, F. A., *Proc. US Nat. Acad. Sci.*, **58**, 1227 (1967).

11. Kao, F. T., and Puck, T. T., *Nature*, **228**, 329 (1970).

12. Thompson, L. H., Mankovitz R., Baker, R. M., Tell, J. E., Seminovitch, L., and Whitmore, G. F., *Proc. US Nat. Acad. Sci.*, **66**, 377 (1970).

13. Davidson, R. L., and Ephrussi, B., *Nature*, **205**, 1170 (1965).

14. Santachiara, A. S., Nabholz, M., Miggiano, V., Darlington, A. J., and Bodmer, W., *Nature*, **227**, 248 (1970).

15. Jami, J., Grandchamp, S., and Ephrussi, B., *CR Acad. Sci.*, **272**, 323 (1971).

16. Ruddle, F. H., *Adv. Hum. Genet.*, **3**, 173 (1972).

17. Nabholz, M., Miggiano, V., and Bodmer, W., *Nature*, **223**, 358 (1969).

18. Ruddle, F. H., and Nichols, E., *In Vitro*, 7, 120 (1971).

19. Davidson, R. L., *In Vitro*, 6, 411 (1971).

20. Ricciuti, F., thesis, Yale Univ. (1972).

21. Caspersson, T., Zech, L., Johansson, C., and Modest, E., *Chromosoma*, **30**, 215 (1970).

22. Miller, O. J., Miller, D. A., Kouri, R. E., Alderdice, P. W., Dev, V. G., Grewal, M. S., and Hutton, J. J., *Proc. US Nat. Acad. Sci.*, **68**, 1530 (1971).

23. Sumner, A. T., Evans, H. J., and Buckland, R. A., *Nature New Biology*, **232**, 31 (1971).

24. Pardue, M. L., and Gall, J. G., *Science*, **168**, 1356 (1970).

25. Arrighi, F. E., and Hsu, T. C., *Cytogenetics*, **10**, 81 (1971).

26. Chen, T. R., and Ruddle, F. H., *Chromosoma*, **34**, 51 (1971).

27. Ruddle, F. H., *Symp. Intern. Soc. Cell Biol.*, 9, 233 (1970).

28. Bobrow, M., Madan, K., and Pearson, P. L., *Nature New Biology*, **238**, 122 (1972).

29. Boone, C. M., Chen, T. R., and Ruddle, F. H., *Proc. US Nat. Acad. Sci.*, **69**, 510 (1972).

30. Van Cong, N., Billerdon, C., Picard, J. Y., Feingold, J., and Frizal, J., *CR Acad. Sci.*, **272**, 485 (1971).

31. Ruddle, F. H., Ricciuti, F., McMorris, F. A., Tischfield, J., Creagan, R., Darlington, G., and Chen, T. R., *Science*, **176**, 1429 (1972).

32. Westerveld, A., and Meera Khan, P., *Nature*, **236**, 30 (1972).

33. Brewer, G. J., *Amer. J. Hum. Genet.*, **19**, 674 (1967).

34. Hamerton, J., *Cytogenetics* (in the press).

35. Kao, F. T., and Puck, T. T., *Proc. US Nat. Acad. Sci.*, **69**, 3273 (1972).

36. Chen, T. R., McMorris, F. A., Creagan, R., Ricciuti, F., Tischfield, J., and Ruddle, F. H., *Amer. J. Hum. Genet.* (in the press).

善或建立。我们可以期待从事体细胞遗传学和经典遗传学研究的科研人员进行富有成果的互动与协作。但是，我们必须牢记，现在的体外遗传学的研究速度仍然慢得令人难以接受，也不能进行连锁评估。如果我们要尽快作出人类的基因图谱，即类似于那些从低等真核生物上获得的，那么必须要制定新的研究方法。而对这种新的研究方法的发现将寄希望于对体细胞重组和基因转移的研究。

（刘振明 翻译；梁前进 审稿）

37. McMorris, F. A., Chen, T. R., Ricciuti, F., Tischfield, J., Creagan, R., and Ruddle, F. H., *Science* (in the press).

38. Shows, T. B., Abstr., *Amer. J. Hum. Genet.*, **24**, 13a (1972).

39. Shows, T. B., *Proc. US Nat Acad. Sci.*, **69**, 348 (1972).

40. van Someren, H., Meera Khan, P., Westerveld, A., and Bootsma, R., *Nature New Biology*, **240**, 221 (1972).

41. Puck, T. T., Wuthier, P., Jones, C., and Kao, F., *Proc. US Nat. Acad. Sci.*, **68**, 3102 (1971).

42. Ruddle, F. H., and Chen, T. R., in *Genetics and the Skin, Twenty-first Ann. Symp.: Biol. Skin* (1972).

43. Ruddle, F. H., Chapman, V. M., Chen, T. R., and Kleke, R. J., *Nature*, **227**, 251 (1970).

44. Shows, T., *Biochem. Genet.*, **7**, 193 (1972).

45. Jones, C., Wuthier, P., Kao, F., and Puck, T. T., *J. Cell Physiol.* (in the press).

46. Ruddle, F. H., in *The Use of Long Term Lymphocytes in the Study of Genetic Diseases* (edit. by Bergsma, D., Smith, G., and Bloom, A.) (National Foundation, in the press).

47. Edwards, Y. H., Hopkinson, D. A., and Harris, H., *Ann. Human Genetics*, **34**, 395 (1971).

48. Robson, E. B., Polani, P. E., Dart, S. J., Jacobs, P. A., and Renwick, J. H., *Nature*, **223**, 1163 (1969).

49. Green, H., in *Heterospecific Genome Interaction Wiston Inst. Lymp. Monograph*, No. **9**, 51 (1969).

50. Migeon, B. R., and Miller, O. S., *Science*, **162**, 1005 (1968).

51. Boone, C. M., and Ruddle, F. H., *Biochem. Genet.*, **3**, 119 (1969).

52. Miller, O. J., Alderdice, P. W., Miller, D. A., Breg, W. R., and Migeon, B. R., *Science,* **173**, 244 (1971).

53. Ruddle, F. H., and Chen, T. R., in *Perspectives in Cytogenetics* (edit. by Wright, S. W., and Crandall, B. F.) (Charles C. Thomas, Illinois, 1971).

54. Kit, S., Nakajima, K., and Dubbs, D. R., *J. Virol.*, **5**, 446 (1970).

55. McDougall, J. K., *J. Gen. Virol.*, **12**, 43 (1971).

56. Edwards, J. E., Allen, F. H., Glenn, K. P., Lamm, L. U., and Robson, E. B., *Histocompatibility Testing* (in the press).

57. Tan, Y. H., Tischfield, J., and Ruddle, F. H., *J. Exp. Med.* (in the press).

58. Cassingena, R., Chany, C., Vignal, M., Suarez, H., and Estrade, S., *Proc. US Nat. Acad. Sci.*, **68**, 580 (1971).

59. McKusick, V. A., *Mendelian Inheritance in Man*, third ed. (Johns Hopkins Press, Baltimore, 1971).

60. Meera Khan, P., Westerveld, A., Grzeschik, K. H., Deys, B. F., Garson, O. M., and Siniscalco, M., *Amer. J. Hum. Genet.*, **23**, 614 (1971).

61. Ruddle, F. H., Chapman, V. M., Ricciuti, F., Murnane, M., Klebe, R., and Meera Khan, P., *Nature*, **232**, 69 (1971).

62. Grzeschik, K. H., Romeo, G., Grzeschik, A. M., Banhof, S., Siniscalco, M., van Someren, H., Meera Khan, P., Westerveld, A., and Bootsma, R., *Nature* (in the press).

63. Grzeschik, K. H., Alderdice, P. W., Grzeschik, A., Opitz, J. M., Miller, O. J., and Siniscalco. M., *Proc. US Nat. Acad. Sci.*, **69**, 69 (1972).

64. Comings, D. E., *Nature*, **238**, 455 (1972).

# Non-equilibrium Isotopic Fractionation between Seawater and Planktonic Foraminiferal Tests

N. J. Shackleton *et al.*

## Editor's Note

**Harold Urey suggested in 1947 that, because the differential uptake of the two stable isotope of oxygen ($^{16}O$ and $^{18}O$) by marine microorganisms that form calcium carbonate exoskeletons depends on temperature, measuring this isotope ratio for these structures preserved in seafloor sediments could reveal the temperature of the seawater in which they formed, opening a window on past climate. Here Nicholas Shackleton at Cambridge and his coworkers cast doubt on whether this will work for foraminifera, because they don't form their exoskeletons under chemical equilibrium. Several subsequent reports cast doubt on the use of oxygen isotope measurements to gauge palaeotemperature. But in the early 1980s it was shown that, with proper calibration, these did not preclude the technique after all.**

---

Planktonic foraminiferal tests are not formed in isotopic equilibrium with seawater; the deviation is species dependent.

---

UREY[1] has suggested that the temperature dependence of the isotopic fractionation factor between the oxygen in water and the oxygen in calcium carbonate could be used as a geological thermometer. For estimating Earth surface temperatures, biologically deposited calcium carbonate is more widely available than inorganic precipitates. So it was necessary to discover whether or not organisms deposit carbonate under equilibrium conditions. Epstein *et al.*[2,3] investigated this using molluscs; although they found one case where a mollusc seemed to have deposited some carbonate in non-equilibrium conditions, they ascribed this to special circumstances. Apart from this one case, they inferred that the Mollusca deposit calcium carbonate in isotopic equilibrium with the surrounding water.

Until recently it has been assumed that this is also true of the Foraminifera. Support for this assumption comes from the seemingly reasonable temperature values which Emiliani[4,5] derived making this assumption. Indeed, whereas the first work on molluscs was performed with the intention of investigating the isotopic fractionation as a function of temperature, the first work on planktonic foraminifera[6] was an investigation of the depth (temperature) habitat of recent foraminifera, performed on the assumption that the isotopic fractionation factor was known. We now find that this was an unwarranted assumption, and that a substantial portion of the variation in isotopic composition between one species and another in foraminiferal death assemblages is due to different fractionation factors rather than to different life habitats.

256

# 海水与浮游有孔虫壳体间的非平衡
# 同位素分馏

沙克尔顿 等

编者按

由于形成碳酸盐壳体的海洋微生物对两种稳定同位素 $^{16}O$ 和 $^{18}O$ 的不同摄取量取决于温度，1947 年，哈罗德·尤里认为通过测量保存在海底沉积物中的碳酸盐壳体的同位素比例可以显示它们形成时海水的温度，这为研究过去的气候开启了一扇窗。在本文中，剑桥大学的尼古拉斯·沙克尔顿和他的同事们怀疑这一理论是否也适用于有孔虫，因为它们不是在化学平衡条件下形成其壳体的。随后的几项报道对使用氧同位素作为测试手段来判断古温度提出质疑。但是 20 世纪 80 年代早期就已经证明，经过适当校准，该技术还是有应用的可能。

浮游有孔虫壳体并非产生于与海水间的同位素平衡条件下；其偏差具有物种依赖性。

---

尤里 [1] 曾经指出，水和碳酸钙中氧同位素分馏系数的温度依赖性可以作为一种地质温度计。就估算地表温度而言，使用生物沉积的碳酸钙比使用无机沉积的碳酸钙更具有广泛的可行性。所以有必要弄清楚生物体能否在平衡条件下沉积碳酸盐。爱泼斯坦等人 [2,3] 用软体动物对此进行了研究，虽然他们发现了一例软体动物似乎在非平衡条件下沉积了某种碳酸盐，但是他们却将其归为特殊情况。排除这一特例，他们推断软体动物都与周围水体在同位素平衡条件下沉积碳酸钙。

直到最近，人们依然认为这个规律也适用于有孔虫。追其原因，是因为埃米利亚尼 [4,5] 所推导出来的貌似合理的温度值支持了该假设。事实上，最初对软体动物进行研究的目的是考察同位素分馏与温度变量之间的关系；而最初对浮游有孔虫的研究 [6] 是对现今有孔虫深度（温度）栖息习性的研究，该研究是在假设同位素分馏系数已知的前提下进行的。现在我们发现这样的假设是没有确切根据的，真正导致有孔虫死亡群体之间同位素组成差异的因素是不同种间同位素分馏系数的差别，而不是它们栖息环境的不同。

## Oxygen Isotope Analyses

Duplessy *et al.*[7] have previously reported differential isotopic fractionation among benthonic foraminiferal species, and van Donk[8] obtained evidence suggesting that the planktonic species may also deposit calcite out of equilibrium with water. But although a fossil population such as that studied by Duplessy *et al.* enables a comparison to be made between benthonic species, it cannot be used for planktonic species because they do not derive from the same temperature habitat. For this reason, it is only possible to compare the departure from isotopic equilibrium among planktonic species if they are collected in plankton tows within the isothermal layer of the ocean.

With the exception of a few samples analysed by van Donk all oxygen isotope analyses of planktonic foraminifera so far published have been performed using fossil or sub-fossil material. The reason is that it is in general difficult to collect large enough samples from plankton tows for conventional isotope analysis. In the present work we have been able to analyse samples as small as 0.04 mg carbonate, and so have been able to make use of a series of plankton tows made in the Indian Ocean by US Coastal and Geodetic Survey Ship Oceanographer in 1967. The stations from which we have used samples in this study are given below in Table 1. Some samples are shown in Fig. 1.

Fig. 1. Electron scanning micrographs of planktonic foraminifera from a 50 m horizontal tow (16°38′S, 113°03′E). *a*, *G. ruber* (×65); *b*, *G. sacculifera* (×65); *c*, *G. dutertri* (×120); *d*, *P. obliquiloculata* (×65).

## 氧同位素组成分析

早先，迪普莱西等人[7]就已经报道了底栖有孔虫不同种间具有不同的同位素分馏特性。而且范当柯[8]已有证据表明，浮游有孔虫同样可以与水在非平衡的条件下沉积方解石。不过，尽管对化石种群的研究（如迪普莱西等人的研究）使得底栖有孔虫不同种间的比较成为了可能，但是这并不适用于浮游有孔虫种间的比较研究，因为它们栖息环境的温度不同。正因为如此，研究人员只能对从海洋等温层中、用浮游生物网采集到的浮游有孔虫不同种间的同位素平衡偏差进行比较。

到目前为止，除了范当柯分析的一些样品外，所有已发表的针对浮游有孔虫氧同位素分析使用的材料均是化石或亚化石。这是因为在通常情况下，采用拖网的方法采集浮游有孔虫很难得到足够大的样本容量，因而不能满足常规同位素分析的要求。目前，我们已经能够对只有 0.04 mg 碳酸盐的小样本进行分析，并且用到美国海岸与陆地考察船"海洋学家"号在 1967 年制作的一系列印度洋拖网浮游样本。表 1 列出了本研究中样本的采集站位信息，图 1 显示了一些样本的相关信息。

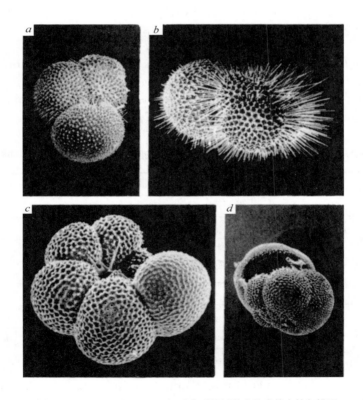

图 1. 50 m 水平拖网（南纬 16°38′，东经 113°03′）采集到的浮游有孔虫的电镜扫描图。*a*, *G. ruber* (×65)（红拟抱球虫）；*b*, *G. sacculifera* (×65)（袋拟抱球虫）；*c*, *G. dutertri* (×120)（拟抱球虫属的一种有孔虫）；*d*, *P. obliquiloculata* (×65)（斜室普林虫）。

259

Table 1. Sites of Sampling Stations 150 m Horizontal Tows

| BM number | Station number | Latitude | Longitude |
|---|---|---|---|
| 1968,0,433 | 3 | 08°11' N | 75°13' E |
| 1968,0,434 | 4 | 06°52' N | 77°43' E |
| 1968,0,435 | 5 | 05°55' N | 80°07' E |
| 1968,0,436 | 6 | 05°34' N | 83°38' E |
| 1968,0,437 | 7 | 05°26' N | 85°37' E |
| 1968,0,445 | 15 | 16°38' S | 113°03' E |

Where possible, the samples for isotope analysis were divided and two independent analyses made. This provides a check on the reproducibility of the analyses, which we considered desirable because plankton have not previously been analysed at the Cambridge laboratory. Samples were roasted *in vacuo* for 30 min at 450°C prior to analysis. Carbon dioxide for mass spectrometric analysis was released by the action of 100% orthophosphoric acid at 50°C. The oxygen isotopic composition of the gas was compared with that of an aliquot from a standard bulk gas sample, using the mass spectrometer described by Shackleton[9], and the results calibrated by analysing standard carbonates under the same conditions.

In this work Emiliani's belemnite standard B1 has been used as a calibration standard, assuming its $^{18}O$ content to be +0.1‰ with respect to the PDB standard. Analyses listed in Table 2 are referred to the PDB standard on this basis. PDB is a standard based on a belemnite from the Carolina Peedee Formation[10].

Table 2. Oxygen Isotopic Composition ($\delta$, ‰) of Foraminifera (Fig. 1) from Plankton Tows

| Station | G. ruber | G. sacc. | G. dutert. | Pull. obl. |
|---|---|---|---|---|
| 3 | −2.69 | −2.42 | −2.27 | −2.08 |
| 4 | −2.77 | −2.50 | −2.16 | −1.98 |
| 5 | −2.59 | −2.55 | −2.15 | −2.01 |
| 6 | −2.64 | −2.65 | −2.37 | −2.36 |
| 7 | −2.65 | −2.69 | −2.30 | −2.22 |
| 15 | −2.40 | −2.28 | −2.14 | −1.71 |

Fourteen of these figures are the mean of two independent analyses. The standard error of a single analysis may be estimated from the difference between pairs as ±0.11‰.

Not all the species in each plankton tow sample have the same isotopic composition. We have performed an analysis of variance to isolate between species, between station and residual variation.

表 1. 150 m 水平拖网采样站位位置

| 采样编号 | 工作站编号 | 纬度 | 经度 |
|---|---|---|---|
| 1968,0,433 | 3 | 北纬 08°11′ | 东经 75°13′ |
| 1968,0,434 | 4 | 北纬 06°52′ | 东经 77°43′ |
| 1968,0,435 | 5 | 北纬 05°55′ | 东经 80°07′ |
| 1968,0,436 | 6 | 北纬 05°34′ | 东经 83°38′ |
| 1968,0,437 | 7 | 北纬 05°26′ | 东经 85°37′ |
| 1968,0,445 | 15 | 南纬 16°38′ | 东经 113°03′ |

在同位素分析过程中，尽可能将样品分成两组并进行独立的平行分析。由于在此之前剑桥实验室没有对浮游生物进行过此类分析，因此这样做可以检验分析结果的可重复性，而且我们认为平行测试十分可取。在分析之前，首先将样品置于450℃高温下真空烘烤 30 min。随后，在 50℃ 条件下用 100% 正磷酸处理样品使其释放出二氧化碳以进行质谱分析。利用沙克尔顿[9]描述的质谱分析方法，将这些气体中的氧同位素组分与标准气体样品进行比较，并利用同等条件下的标准碳酸盐分析来校正结果。

这项研究中，研究人员将埃米利亚尼的拟箭石 B1 标准作为校正标准，并参照 PDB 标准假定氧同位素（$^{18}O$）的含量为 +0.1‰。表 2 列出的是参比 PDB 标准而得出的一系列分析结果。PDB 是以卡罗来纳州白垩纪皮狄组拟箭石化石为基础的碳同位素组成标准[10]。

表 2. 浮游拖网所得有孔虫（图 1）的氧同位素组成（δ，‰）

| 站位 | G. ruber | G. sacc. | G. dutert. | Pull. obl. |
|---|---|---|---|---|
| 3 | −2.69 | −2.42 | −2.27 | −2.08 |
| 4 | −2.77 | −2.50 | −2.16 | −1.98 |
| 5 | −2.59 | −2.55 | −2.15 | −2.01 |
| 6 | −2.64 | −2.65 | −2.37 | −2.36 |
| 7 | −2.65 | −2.69 | −2.30 | −2.22 |
| 15 | −2.40 | −2.28 | −2.14 | −1.71 |

上表中有 14 个数据是取自两组独立平行测验结果的平均值。根据两组数据估计出的单次分析的标准差大约是 ±0.11‰。

同一次拖网采样中，不同种间的氧同位素组成会有所不同，因此我们对不同种、不同站位的浮游生物进行了方差和残差分析。

Between species variation proves to be highly significant ($P<0.001$). The Students $T$ test was used to test variation between species (Table 3).

Table 3. Variation Between Species

| | |
|---|---|
| *G. ruber*×*G. dutert.* | $T=6.903$ DF 15 significant $P<0.001$ |
| *G. ruber*×*P. obliqui.* | $T=9.958$ DF 15 significant $P<0.001$ |
| *G. sacc.*×*G. dutert.* | $T=4.993$ DF 15 significant $P<0.001$ |
| *G. sacc.*×*P. obliqui.* | $T=8.048$ DF 15 significant $P<0.001$ |
| *P. obliqui.*×*G. dutert.* | $T=3.055$ DF 15 significant $P<0.01$ |

The residual variation is 0.1‰, which may be compared with the standard deviation of ±0.11‰ derived from the pairs of analyses. The apparent difference between *G. ruber* and *G. sacculifera* is only 0.11‰, too small to be estimated reliably in the present experiment.

## Implication for Depth-Habitat Studies

Emiliani[6], Lidz *et al.*[11] and Hecht and Savin[12] have used $^{18}O/^{16}O$ ratio determinations in foraminiferal tests as a method of investigating their life habitats. In the course of a study of a core in the Indian Ocean, Oba[13] did the same for one sample. It is clear from our study that this is not a valid approach; indeed, as regards the four species discussed here the between species differences found in plankton samples from 50 m horizontal tows are indistinguishable from the variations found by Oba in a sediment sample. This means that in all probability none of the variation measured by Oba can be ascribed to different depth habitat among the four species; they all derive from populations living in the isothermal layer.

In the Atlantic province, larger differences between the species have been measured[6,11,12]; it seems likely that in that case there is a contribution which may be safely ascribed to difference in depth habitat. At the same time we need to know much more about the differential fractionation effect before we can begin to use isotopic determinations in order to deduce life habitat.

Hecht and Savin[12] have gone further, and attempt to use isotopic determinations to discover whether morphological variation within a population of foraminifera is due to varying ecological stress; they deduce, for example, that specimens of *Globigerinoides ruber* with a diminutive final chamber are those which have lived in deeper (colder) water, by comparing their oxygen isotopic composition with that of normal individuals. Although this seems to be an ingenious test, we cannot exclude the possibility that whatever factor influences the shape of the final chamber also influences the departure from isotopic equilibrium in the test carbonate. This is by no means impossible, particularly because the suggestion made by Parker[14], that no-equilibrium isotopic composition could be causally related to the presence of symbiotic zooxanthellae, has never been excluded.

结果表明,不同种间具有显著差异性($P < 0.001$)。种间差异的 $T$ 检验结果见表 3。

表 3. 种间差异

| | |
|---|---|
| G. ruber × G. dutert. | $T$=6.903 DF 15 $P$<0.001 |
| G. ruber × P. obliqui. | $T$=9.958 DF 15 $P$<0.001 |
| G. sacc. × G. dutert. | $T$=4.993 DF 15 $P$<0.001 |
| G. sacc. × P. obliqui. | $T$=8.048 DF 15 $P$<0.001 |
| P. obliqui. × G. dutert. | $T$=3.055 DF 15 $P$<0.01 |

与成对分析的标准差 ±0.11‰ 相比,残差为 0.1‰。而 *G. ruber* 和 *G. sacculifera* 之间的表观变异仅为 0.11‰,以目前的实验水平,我们还不能对这么小的差异进行可靠的评估。

## 深海栖息研究的意义

埃米利亚尼 [6] 和利兹等人 [11] 以及赫克特和萨文 [12] 已经将测定 $^{18}O/^{16}O$ 比率作为研究有孔虫栖息习性的一种方法。在研究一个印度洋岩芯的课题当中,奥巴 [13] 对一个样品使用了同样的方法。显然,根据我们的研究,这不是一个有效的方法。事实上,我们通过 50 m 水平拖网采集到的四种浮游生物的种间差异与奥巴所测定的沉积样品中的种间差异几乎是一样的。这就意味着,在所有可能性中,奥巴所测得的差异不可能是由四个物种的栖息地不同造成的,这四个物种来源于同一等温层的种群。

在大西洋海域,科学家们发现了更大的种间差异 [6,11,12]。如此看来,这种差异很可能是由栖息地的深度不同所引起的。与此同时,我们需要更深入地了解分馏变异效应,以便利用上述同位素测定来推导浮游生物的栖息习性。

赫克特和萨文 [12] 已经进行了更为深入的研究,他们尝试用同位素测定来研究有孔虫种群的形态学变异是否是由于生态压力不同所引起的。例如,他们通过比较具有短小终室的 *Globigerinoides ruber* 样本的氧同位素组成与正常个体的氧同位素组成,推测出该样本曾生活在较深(冷)的水域中。尽管该检测看起来极富创造性,我们仍然不能排除其他影响终室的形状的因素也会影响待测碳酸盐中同位素平衡的可能性。这种可能性是绝对存在的,帕克的观点 [14] 尤其不容忽视,他指出上述一系列实验从未排除共生的虫黄藻对非平衡同位素组成的影响。

## Implications for Palaeotemperature Studies

Because isotope analysis was not envisaged when the samples were collected, we do not have information on the temperature and isotopic composition of the water in which the foraminifera were living. This means that we cannot estimate exactly the isotopic composition which would have been measured had the test carbonate been deposited in isotopic equilibrium; however, an approximate estimate may be made. Craig and Gordon[15] show that in the equatorial region the observed variation in surface isotopic composition with salinity is small, about 0.11‰ for 1‰ change in salinity. Using Defant's[16] plate V, we may assume that at stations 6, 7 and 15 the salinity was in the region of 34.5‰, and that the isotopic composition of the water was near zero on the PDB scale (+0.2‰ on the SMOW scale[15]). At stations 3, 4 and 5 the salinity is likely to have been a little higher and the isotopic composition about +0.1‰ on the PDB scale. As regards temperature, the mean August surface temperatures (Defant[16], Plate 3B) are about 27°C for stations 3, 4, 5, 6 and 7, and about 25°C for station 15. Using these estimates and the relation between temperature and isotopic composition given by Craig[17] yields the values in Table 4. Comparison with the measured isotopic composition for each species from Table 2 gives the extent of departure from isotopic equilibrium for each species. The estimates range from −0.50‰ for *G. ruber* to +0.06‰ for *P. obliquiloculata*.

Table 4. Estimated Deviation from Isotopic Equilibrium

| Station | Test | $\delta_{west.}$ | $\delta_{cest.}$ | Difference between $\delta_{meas}$ and $\delta_{est}$ | | | |
|---------|------|-------|-------|----------|----------|-----------|------------|
| | | | | *G. ruber* | *G. sacc.* | *G. dutert.* | *P. obliqui.* |
| 3 | 27° | +0.1‰ | −2.14‰ | −0.55 | −0.28 | −0.13 | +0.06 |
| 4 | 27° | +0.1‰ | −2.14‰ | −0.63 | −0.36 | −0.02 | +0.16 |
| 5 | 27° | +0.1‰ | −2.14‰ | −0.45 | −0.41 | −0.01 | +0.13 |
| 6 | 27° | 0.0‰ | −2.24‰ | −0.40 | −0.41 | −0.13 | −0.12 |
| 7 | 27° | 0.0‰ | −2.24‰ | −0.41 | −0.45 | −0.06 | +0.02 |
| 15 | 25° | 0.0‰ | −1.83‰ | −0.57 | −0.45 | −0.31 | +0.12 |
| | | | | −0.50‰ | −0.39‰ | −0.11‰ | +0.06‰ |

In column 4 of Table 4 the isotopic composition of carbonates deposited at the temperature given in column 2, and in water having the isotopic composition of column 3, is estimated on the basis of the equilibrium relationship of Craig[17]. The remaining columns are the differences between the measurements from Table 2 and the values in column 4, and thus represent deviations from isotopic equilibrium for the species concerned.

For this last species, the deviation is insignificant; it may well be that this species does in fact deposit its test in isotopic equilibrium with the surrounding water. If one could extract confidently from the sediment only those tests of *P. obliquiloculata* which lived

## 古温度研究的意义

由于采样时并未设置同位素分析实验，所以我们并没有有孔虫栖息水域的温度及同位素组成的信息。这就意味着，我们并不能精确地估算同位素组成，但可以估算出近似值，如果当时碳酸盐壳体是在同位素平衡条件下沉积的话，本来是可以测定该同位素组成的。不过，我们可以估算出近似值。克雷格和戈登[15]的研究表明，在赤道区域，表层同位素组成随盐度变化可观察到的变异是比较小的，1‰盐度变化只引起约0.11‰的同位素组成变异。利用德凡特[16]的图版V，可以估算出站位6、7和15的盐度区间是34.5‰；参照PDB标准，估算出水的同位素含量几乎为零（而参照SMOW则为+0.2‰[15]）。而站位3、4和5的盐度似乎略高一些，相应的PDB标准下测定的同位素组成为+0.1‰。关于温度方面，站位3、4、5、6和7的八月份平均表层水温（德凡特[16]，图版3B）都是27℃，而站位15的八月份平均表层水温则为25℃。利用这些估算值以及克雷格[17]给出的温度和同位素组成之间的关系得到了表4中的一系列数值。通过与表2中列出的各物种的同位素组成相比较，可以得出不同物种偏离同位素平衡的区间。估算值从 G. ruber 的 −0.50‰到 P. obliquiloculata 的 +0.06‰之间不等。

表 4. 据同位素平衡估计的偏差

| 站位 | 测量温度 | $\delta_w$est | $\delta_c$est | $\delta_{meas}$ 和 $\delta$est 之间的差异 | | | |
|---|---|---|---|---|---|---|---|
| | | | | G. ruber | G. sacc. | G. dutert. | P. obliqui. |
| 3 | 27° | +0.1‰ | −2.14‰ | −0.55 | −0.28 | −0.13 | +0.06 |
| 4 | 27° | +0.1‰ | −2.14‰ | −0.63 | −0.36 | −0.02 | +0.16 |
| 5 | 27° | +0.1‰ | −2.14‰ | −0.45 | −0.41 | −0.01 | +0.13 |
| 6 | 27° | 0.0‰ | −2.24‰ | −0.40 | −0.41 | −0.13 | −0.12 |
| 7 | 27° | 0.0‰ | −2.24‰ | −0.41 | −0.45 | −0.06 | +0.02 |
| 15 | 25° | 0.0‰ | −1.83‰ | −0.57 | −0.45 | −0.31 | +0.12 |
| | | | | −0.50‰ | −0.39‰ | −0.11‰ | +0.06‰ |

表4中，第4列显示了在第2列的温度下沉积的碳酸盐的同位素组成；而第3列显示的水的同位素组成是根据克雷格平衡关系估算所得[17]。其余各列则是表2的测量值与第4列数值之间的差异，因而代表了相关种间的同位素平衡偏差。

至于最后一个物种，与同位素平衡的偏差并不显著，可能由于该物种确实是在与周围水环境保持同位素平衡的状态下沉积矿物质的。如果人们能够很有把握地从沉积物中提取出生活在海洋等温层的 P. obliquiloculata 样品，那么该物种很有可能

in the isothermal layer of the ocean, this might well be an ideal species to use for palaeotemperature determination; it is possible that these could be recognized by the lack of the smooth external cortex which is a characteristic feature in tests from deeper water.

At the other end of the scale, G. ruber yields a value 0.5‰ lighter than it would if isotopic equilibrium prevailed. This is equivalent to an error of about 2.5°C.

Before these values are used to correct estimates of palaeotemperature, it is important to establish whether the "vital effect"[1] remains constant for each species. We have only measured the effect for foraminifera living at 50 m and in a restricted area of an ocean; it is of great interest to discover whether our results have general application.

It is in any case not possible to use the data to correct measurements made in other laboratories because at present results from different laboratories do not seem to be related to each other. For example, specimens of Globigerinoides sacculifera from the top of core P6304-8 gave −1.29‰ when analysed by Emiliani[6]; samples from the same level in the same core gave −1.69‰ when analysed by Lidz et al.[11] and the same species from nearby core V12-122 yielded −2.2‰ (ref. 18). When corrected for the isotopic composition of the Caribbean water (+0.92‰) these figures yield temperatures from near 27°C to near 32°C. At present these differences seem more serious than the fundamental problem posed by the present work.

We conclude that whether the isotopic composition of a foraminiferal test is analysed with a view to determining its present-day life habitat, or with a view to elucidating the mysteries of climatic change in the past, it is not possible to translate the value obtained into an equivalent temperature on the basis of thermodynamic principles alone. In some manner yet to be determined the organism deposits carbonate of isotopic composition differing slightly from the thermodynamically predicted value.

This work was supported by an NERC grant. We thank M. A. Hall for operation of the mass spectrometer, and the Oceanographic Sorting Center, Smithsonian Institution, for plankton aliquots.

(**242**, 177-179, 1973)

N. J. Shackleton*, J. D. H. Wiseman† and H. A. Buckley†
* Sub-Department of Quaternary Research, University of Cambridge;
†British Museum (Natural History), London

Received December 4, 1972.

---

References:
1. Urey, J. C., J. Chem. Soc., 562 (1947).
2. Epstein, S., Buchsbaum, R., Lowenstam, H. A., and Urey, H. C., Geol. Soc. Amer. Bull., **62**, 417 (1951).

成为古温度测定研究的理想物种。或许我们可以通过粗糙的外部皮质这一深水有孔虫的典型特征来对它们加以识别。

从标准的另一角度看，*G. ruber* 值比同位素平衡占主导时所得值低 0.5‰，这相当于 2.5℃ 的温度误差。

在将这些数值用于古温度估算校正之前，弄清楚所谓"生命效应"[1] 是否在每个物种中保持不变是很重要的。目前，我们只测定了生活在某个海洋下一处 50 m 水深的有限范围的有孔虫的生命效应；这对弄清楚我们的结果是否具有普遍适用性有重大意义。

在目前情况下，这些数据不能用于校正其他实验室的测量结果，因为不同实验室的测量结果之间似乎不具有相关性。例如，在对来自同一海底上层位置 P6304-8 的 *Globigerinoides sacculifera* 样品进行分析时，埃米利亚尼 [6] 的测验结果为 −1.29‰，利兹等人 [11] 对同一水平的样品分析结果则为 −1.69‰，在其附近区域 V12-122 取同种样品得到的测验结果是 −2.2‰ [18]。而据此校正 (+0.92‰) 加勒比海水同位素组成时，这些数据得到的海水温度范围则大约在 27℃ 到 32℃ 之间。由此看来，这些差异似乎比我们目前研究工作所引起的根本问题严重得多。

因此我们认为，无论有孔虫同位素组成的分析测验是用于确定其现今有孔虫的栖息习性，还是用于阐明过去气候变化的奥秘，我们都不能仅仅依据热力学原理将所得结果转换为相应的温度。关于生物体沉积碳酸盐同位素组成的测量值和热力学预测值相差甚微，从某种意义上来说，这一点仍有待确定。

该研究得到了英国自然环境研究理事会的资助。其间，霍尔帮我们做了质谱分析，史密森学会海洋观测分类中心为我们提供了浮游生物样品，在此深表感谢。

（高如丽 翻译；李三忠 审稿）

3. Epstein, S., Buchsbaum, R., Lowenstam, H. A., and Urey, H. C., *Geol. Soc. Amer. Bull.*, **64**, 1315 (1953).

4. Emiliani, C., *J. Geol.*, **63**, 538 (1955).

5. Emiliani, C., *J. Geol.*, **74**, 109 (1966).

6. Emiliani, C., *Amer. J. Sci.*, **252**, 149 (1954).

7. Duplessy, J. C., Lalou, C., and Vinot, A. C., *Science*, **168**, 250 (1970).

8. Van Donk, J., thesis, Columbia Univ. (1970).

9. Shackleton, N. J., *J. Sci. Instrum.*, **42**, 689 (1965).

10. Urey, H. C., Lowenstam, H. A., Epstein, S., and McKinney, C. R., *Bull. Geol. Soc. Amer.*, **62**, 399 (1951).

11. Lidz, B., Kehm, A., and Miller, H., *Nature*, **217**, 245 (1968).

12. Hecht, A. D., and Savin, S. M., *Science*, **170**, 69 (1970).

13. Oba, T., *Sci. Rep. Tohoku Univ., Second Ser. (Geology)*, **41**, 129 (1969).

14. Parker, F. L., *Rep. Swedish Deep-Sea Exped.*, **8**, 2, 219 (1958).

15. Craig, H., and Gordon, L. I., in *Stable Isotopes in Oceanographic Studies and Palaeotemperatures* (edit. by Tongiorgi, E.) (Pisa, 1965).

16. Defant, A., *Physical Oceanography* (Pergamon, Oxford, 1961).

17. Craig, H., in *Stable Isotopes in Oceanographic Studies and Palaeotemperatures* (edit. by Tongiorgi, E.) (Pisa, 1965).

18. Broecker, W. S., and Van Donk, J., *Rev. Geophys. Space Phys.*, **8**, 169 (1970).

# Image Formation by Induced Local Interactions: Examples Employing Nuclear Magnetic Resonance

P. C. Lauterbur

## Editor's Note

**Physicists in the 1940s learned to exploit the response of nuclear spins to applied magnetic fields to probe the structure of solids and liquids. A magnetic field splits the energies of spin states of a nucleus, and radio-frequency radiation can induce transitions between them. Because different nuclei absorb energy at different frequencies, and because the chemical environment also influences this frequency, the technique of nuclear magnetic resonance (NMR) can be used to probe the chemical structure of a sample. Here chemist Paul Lauterbur shows how to adapt this technique to produce detailed spatial images. The technique, known now as magnetic resonance imaging (MRI), is used ubiquitously in basic and applied science, especially medicine. In 2003 Lauterbur shared a Nobel Prize with Peter Mansfield, who developed methods for analysing MRI signals.**

AN image of an object may be defined as a graphical representation of the spatial distribution of one or more of its properties. Image formation usually requires that the object interact with a matter or radiation field characterized by a wavelength comparable to or smaller than the smallest features to be distinguished, so that the region of interaction may be restricted and a resolved image generated.

This limitation on the wavelength of the field may be removed, and a new class of image generated, by taking advantage of induced local interactions. In the presence of a second field that restricts the interaction of the object with the first field to a limited region, the resolution becomes independent of wavelength, and is instead a function of the ratio of the normal width of the interaction to the shift produced by a gradient in the second field. Because the interaction may be regarded as a coupling of the two fields by the object, I propose that image formation by this technique be known as zeugmatography, from the Greek ζευγμα, "that which is used for joining".

The nature of the technique may be clarified by describing two simple examples. Nuclear magnetic resonance (NMR) zeugmatography was performed with 60 MHz (5 m) radiation and a static magnetic field gradient corresponding, for proton resonance, to about 700 Hz $cm^{-1}$. The test object consisted of two 1 mm inside diameter thin-walled glass capillaries of $H_2O$ attached to the inside wall of a 4.2 mm inside diameter glass tube of $D_2O$. In the first experiment, both capillaries contained pure water. The proton resonance

# 诱导局域相互作用成像：
# 核磁共振应用实例

劳特布尔

## 编者按

20 世纪 40 年代，物理学家们掌握了利用核自旋对外加磁场的响应来探索固体和液体的结构的方法。磁场使核自旋态发生能级分裂，而射频辐射可使原子核发生能级跃迁。由于不同的核吸收不同频率的能量，并且化学环境也会影响到这个频率，因此核磁共振技术就可以用来探索样品的化学结构。本文中，化学家保罗·劳特布尔展示了如何利用这一技术获得清晰的空间影像。这一技术——现在被称为磁共振成像，已在基础和应用科学，尤其是在医学中都得到了广泛应用。2003 年，劳特布尔和彼得·曼斯菲尔德（后者发展了磁共振成像信号分析方法）共同获得了诺贝尔奖。

一个物体的像可以定义为它的一个或多个特征量的空间分布的图像化表示。成像通常需要该物体与某种物质或辐射场相互作用，且与之作用的物质或辐射场的波长应与期望分辨的物体特征量的最小尺寸相当或更小，从而可能限定相互作用的区域，并产生足够分辨率的图像。

利用诱导局域相互作用可以克服上述波长对成像分辨率的限制，并由此可发展出一类新成像方法：通过施加一个额外场可以将物体与辐射场的相互作用限制在一个有限区域。由此而获得的像的分辨率只是相互作用的标准宽度与由额外场梯度产生的变化量的比值相关的函数，而与波长无关，因为这个相互作用可以看作是两个场借助物体而产生耦合，故建议将基于此技术的成像命名为"zeugmatography"（常被翻译为"共轭成像法"，"结合成像法"或"组合层析成像法"），其来源于希腊语"ζευγμα"，是"结合"的意思。

下面举两个简单的例子来说明该技术的本质。核磁共振共轭成像（现在一般称为"核磁共振成像"或"磁共振成像"）实验采用 60 MHz（波长为 5m）的射频场和一个带梯度的静磁场，对质子共振而言，该静磁场的梯度场强为 700 Hz·$cm^{-1}$。实验样品是两根装有水（$H_2O$）的内径为 1 mm 的薄壁玻璃毛细管，它们被置于一根装有重水（$D_2O$）的内径为 4.2 mm 的玻璃管中。在第一个实验中，两根毛细管中均装

line width, in the absence of the transverse field gradient, was about 5 Hz. Assuming uniform signal strength across the region within the transmitter-receiver coil, the signal in the presence of a field gradient represents a one-dimensional projection of the $H_2O$ content of the object, integrated over planes perpendicular to the gradient direction, as a function of the gradient coordinate (Fig. 1). One method of constructing a two-dimensional projected image of the object, as represented by its $H_2O$ content, is to combine several projections, obtained by rotating the object about an axis perpendicular to the gradient direction (or, as in Fig. 1, rotating the gradient about the object), using one of the available methods for reconstruction of objects from their projections[1-5]. Fig. 2 was generated by an algorithm, similar to that of Gordon and Herman[4], applied to four projections, spaced as in Fig. 1, so as to construct a 20×20 image matrix. The representation shown was produced by shading within contours interpolated between the matrix points, and clearly reveals the locations and dimensions of the two columns of $H_2O$. In the second experiment, one capillary contained pure $H_2O$, and the other contained a 0.19 mM solution of $MnSO_4$ in $H_2O$. At low radio-frequency power (about 0.2 mgauss) the two capillaries gave nearly identical images in the zeugmatogram (Fig. 3a). At a higher power level (about 1.6 mgauss), the pure water sample gave much more saturated signals than the sample whose spin-lattice relaxation time $T_1$ had been shortened by the addition of the paramagnetic $Mn^{2+}$ ions, and its zeugmatographic image vanished at the contour level used in Fig. 3b. The sample region with long $T_1$ may be selectively emphasized (Fig. 3c) by constructing a difference zeugmatogram from those taken at different radio-frequency powers.

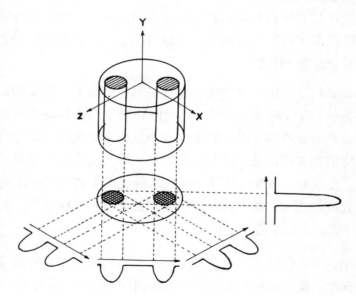

Fig. 1. Relationship between a three-dimensional object, its two-dimensional projection along the Y-axis, and four one-dimensional projections at 45° intervals in the XZ-plane. The arrows indicate the gradient directions.

的是纯水，在未施加横向梯度场时，质子共振线宽约为 5 Hz。假定发射—接收线圈区域内的信号强度均匀，在施加梯度场后获得的信号代表了实验样品中水含量分布沿梯度垂直方向的一维投影，它是与梯度坐标相关的函数（如图 1 所示）。绕垂直于梯度场方向的轴转动实验样品（或如图 1 所示，以样品为轴转动梯度场），获得实验样品的一系列一维投影。以此为基础，采用投影重建的方法 [1-5] 可构建出表示实验样品水含量分布的二维投影像。利用如图 1 所示的四个不同方向的一维投影并采用类似于戈登和赫尔曼的投影重建算法 [4]，可以构建出如图 2 所示的 20×20 的图像矩阵，此图像是由矩阵点间轮廓线插值的描影法来显示，它清楚地表征了这两组圆柱体水的位置和大小。在第二个实验中，一根毛细管内装的是纯水，另一根毛细管中装的是 0.19 mM 浓度的 $MnSO_4$ 水溶液。在低射频功率（功率约为 0.2 mGs）下，这两组毛细管水呈现出几乎相同的核磁共振像（如图 3a 所示）。但在高功率射频场（功率约为 1.6 mGs）作用下，纯水样品的信号被饱和，导致其在同标准等高线图显示的核磁共振像消失；而对于加入顺磁性 $Mn^{2+}$ 离子的水溶液样品，由于其自旋－晶格弛豫时间 $T_1$ 变短，故信号不容易饱和，其核磁共振像仍然出现，如图 3b 所示。比较不同射频功率作用下生成的核磁共振像的差分像，即可发现样品中 $T_1$ 时间长的区域得到选择性的突出显示（如图 3c 所示）。

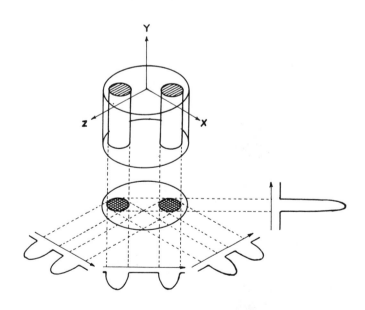

图 1. 核磁共振成像实验的三维示意图：其二维投影方向沿着 Y 轴，四个 45° 间隔的一维投影位于 XZ 平面内，箭头所示方向为梯度场方向。

Fig. 2. Proton nuclear magnetic resonance zeugmatogram of the object described in the text, using four relative orientations of object and gradients as diagrammed in Fig. 1.

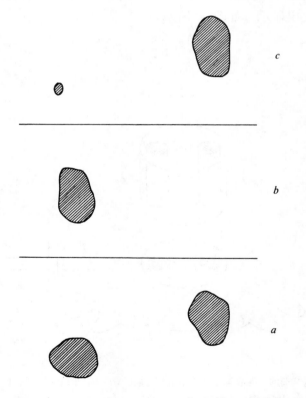

Fig. 3. Proton nuclear magnetic resonance zeugmatograms of an object containing regions with different relaxation times. *a*, Low power; *b*, high power; *c*, difference between *a* and *b*.

图 2. 样品的质子核磁共振像：利用如图 1 所示的四个不同方向的一维投影按文中所述的投影重建方法构建而成。

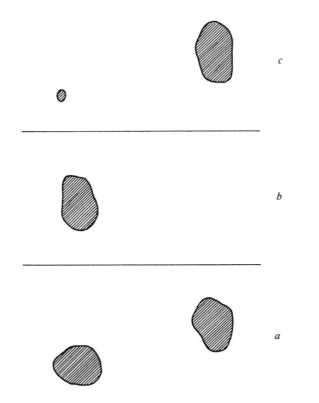

图 3. 样品中弛豫时间不同的区域的质子核磁共振像：a, 低强度射频；b, 高强度射频；c, 图 a 和图 b 的差分像。

Applications of this technique to the study of various inhomogeneous objects, not necessarily restricted in size to those commonly studied by magnetic resonance spectroscopy, may be anticipated. The experiments outlined above demonstrate the ability of the technique to generate pictures of the distributions of stable isotopes, such as H and D, within an object. In the second experiment, relative intensities in an image were made to depend upon relative nuclear relaxation times. The variations in water contents and proton relaxation times among biological tissues should permit the generation, with field gradients large compared to internal magnetic inhomogeneities, of useful zeugmatographic images from the rather sharp water resonances of organisms, selectively picturing the various soft structures and tissues. A possible application of considerable interest at this time would be to the *in vivo* study of malignant tumours, which have been shown to give proton nuclear magnetic resonance signals with much longer water spin-lattice relaxation times than those in the corresponding normal tissues[6].

The basic zeugmatographic principle may be employed in many different ways, using a scanning technique, as described above, or transient methods. Variations on the experiment, to be described later, permit the generation of two- or three-dimensional images displaying chemical compositions, diffusion coefficients and other properties of objects measurable by spectroscopic techniques. Although applications employing nuclear magnetic resonance in liquid or liquid-like systems are simple and attractive because of the ease with which field gradients large enough to shift the narrow resonances by many line widths may be generated, NMR zeugmatography of solids, electron spin resonance zeugmatography, and analogous experiments in other regions of the spectrum should also be possible. Zeugmatographic techniques should find many useful applications in studies of the internal structures, states, and compositions of microscopic objects.

(242, 190-191; 1973)

**P. C. Lauterbur**

Department of Chemistry, State University of New York at Stony Brook, Stony Brook, New York 11790

Received October 30, 1972; revised January 8, 1973.

---

References:

1. Bracewell, R. N., and Riddle, A. C., *Astrophys. J.*, **150**, 427 (1967).

2. Vainshtein, B. K., *Soviet Physics-Crystallography*, **15**, 781 (1971).

3. Ramachandran, G. N., and Lakshminarayan, A. V., *Proc. US Nat. Acad. Sci.*, **68**, 2236 (1971).

4. Gordon, R., and Herman, G. T., *Comm. Assoc. Comput. Mach.*, **14**, 759 (1971).

5. Klug, A., and Crowther, R. A., *Nature*, **238**, 435 (1972).

6. Weisman, I. D., Bennett, L. H., Maxwell, Sr., L. R., Woods, M. W., and Burk, D., *Science*, **178**, 1288 (1972).

核磁共振成像是不同于那些传统的核磁共振谱技术，不太受样品大小（以及均匀性）的限制，可以预期，此技术将会被应用于诸多非均匀样品的研究。上述实验证明，这项技术能够用于获得样品中稳定同位素（如 H 和 D）含量的分布图像。在第二个实验中，图像的相对强度取决于对应核的弛豫时间的长短。根据生物组织中水的含量和质子弛豫时间的不同，当外加的梯度场远大于生物组织的内部梯度场时，可以利用有机体中相对窄的水共振信号获得有用的核磁共振像，实现各种生物体软组织的选择性成像。当前，一个非常诱人的可能应用是恶性肿瘤的活体研究。因为恶性肿瘤组织中水的质子自旋 – 晶格弛豫时间比相应正常组织中的要长得多[6]。

基于上文提到的扫描技术或瞬态方法的共轭成像的基本原理有着诸多不同的潜在应用。将上述实验进行拓展延伸，能够产生显示样品的化学成分、扩散系数以及依靠谱学技术测量的其他特征量的二维或三维图像，这些在以后描述。核磁共振成像技术在液体和液体状的体系中的应用简单且引人注目，这是因为此时梯度场足够大且足以移动较窄的共振信号使其空间位置得以区分。而类似的固体核磁共振共轭成像、电子自旋共振共轭成像以及其他频谱学的共轭成像同样有实现的可能。可以预见，共轭成像技术未来将在微观物质的内部结构、状态和构成的研究中也会被广泛应用。

（王耀杨 翻译；刘朝阳 陈方 审稿）

# Isolation of the Islets of Langerhans for Transplantation

D. R. Thomas *et al.*

## Editor's Note

This paper describes a method for isolating rat islets of Langerhans as a potential transplant source for diabetes. Attempts to treat diabetes by transplanting a whole pancreas had met with limited success, and efforts to isolate the component insulin-producing islets of Langerhans were hampered by methodological problems and low viability. The revised method, by D. R. Thomas and colleagues at Sheffield in England, includes digestion, washing and separation steps and yielded large numbers of viable islets of Langerhans. Islet cell transplantation is currently being assessed as a potential treatment for type I diabetes mellitus, where the immune system destroys insulin-producing beta cells in the islets of Langerhans. Successful transplants have reduced or removed the need for insulin therapy.

PANCREATIC transplantation with the aim of treating diabetes mellitus has so far met with little success. Of 23 patients thus treated and reported to the Transplant Registry in 1971[1], 15 died within 3 months and the longest survived one year. One of the major problems has been to overcome pancreatic exocrine digestion, and pancreatic duct ligation ("Banting pancreas") before transplantation has been performed. It was shown by Dragstedt[2], however, that dogs treated in this way often became diabetic or showed a diabetic glucose tolerance test after several months, probably due to fibrosis and consequent ischaemia of the Islets. Transplantation of the whole gland with its vascular supply is a major undertaking and the problems of thrombosis, leakage and digestion, coupled with immunological rejection, have prevented success so far.

Attempts have been made to isolate the Islets of Langerhans from the pancreas in order to study glucose metabolism. A micro-dissection technique was described by Hellerstrom[3] but this was tedious and produced only small numbers of Islet clumps. Subsequently Moskalewski[4] described a method of collagenase digestion which was successful in the rabbit and improved the yield, and Lacy and Kostianovski[5] modified the method for the rat. There were still difficulties in harvesting the liberated Islets, however, even with methods of separation such as zonal centrifugation and density gradients, and there were also problems with viability of the cells.

We have developed a technique by which large numbers of Islets of Langerhans are prepared consistently from the rat pancreas for purposes of transplantation. Viability was confirmed by transplantation.

Initially, albino outbred rats and subsequently young adult inbred hooded rats (strain PVG/C) were used. Following killing by cervical dislocation, the ventral surface of the

# 用于移植的朗格汉斯岛（胰岛）的分离

托马斯 等

**编者按**

本文介绍了一种用于分离大鼠朗格汉斯岛（胰岛）的方法，以用作治疗糖尿病的潜在移植来源。通过移植整个胰腺治疗糖尿病的尝试收效甚微，而分离产生胰岛素的胰岛的尝试受到了方法学问题和低生存力的限制。由托马斯和他的同事在英国谢菲尔德所改良的方法，获得了大量可存活的胰岛，这种方法包含消化、洗涤和分离几个步骤。现在胰岛细胞移植正被评估是否可作为一种治疗 I 型糖尿病的潜在方法，在 I 型糖尿病中，免疫系统会破坏产生胰岛素的胰岛 β 细胞。成功的移植可以减少或消除对胰岛素治疗的依赖。

迄今为止，胰腺移植用于治疗糖尿病成效甚微。1971 年，经过这样治疗并在移植登记处登记备案的 23 例患者中 [1]，有 15 例在 3 个月内死亡，生存时间最长的患者也只有 1 年。一个主要的问题就是患者在移植前需要克服胰腺外分泌消化和胰管结扎（"班廷胰腺"）。但是，德拉格施泰特 [2] 发现，经过这样治疗的狗在数月后会患糖尿病或者表现出糖尿病糖耐量试验的结果，这很可能是由于胰岛的纤维化以及继发的贫血造成的。伴血液供应的全腺体移植是目前的主流，但是伴随免疫排斥发生的血栓、渗漏和消化等问题使得该方法到目前为止也没能取得成功。

人们试图从胰腺中分离出胰岛以研究葡萄糖代谢。赫勒斯特伦 [3] 描述了一种显微解剖技术，但是这种方法非常繁冗，而且只能得到少数的胰岛细胞团。此后，莫斯卡勒夫斯基 [4] 描述了一种胶原酶消化法，该法已经在兔子中取得成功，而且分离出的胰岛数量也得到提高，后来莱西和科斯蒂安诺夫斯基 [5] 在大鼠中对这个方法进行了改进。但是，即便使用了诸如区带离心和密度梯度离心的分离方法，仍然很难获得游离的胰岛，而且这些细胞的生存能力也是一个大问题。

我们建立了一种方法，并用此法从大鼠胰腺中稳定制备了大量用于移植的胰岛，并且通过移植确认了细胞的生存能力。

起初使用的是白化的远交系大鼠，后来使用年轻成年的头部有斑点的顶罩大鼠（PVG/C 系）的近交系。颈椎脱臼法处死大鼠后，刮除腹面毛发，用溶于酒精的氯

animal was shaved, prepared with chlorhexidine in spirit and the abdomen opened with a midline incision. Using a dissecting microscope, magnification × 10, a fine polyethylene catheter ("Intracath"—B. R. Bard, London) was introduced into the common bile duct and secured with a 2-0 linen thread ligature. The lower end of the duct was occluded with an artery forceps just before its entry into the duodenum. The pancreas was distended by injection of 10 ml. Hanks' solution containing bovine albumen (fraction V), 2 mg · ml.$^{-1}$. It was found that after some practice this procedure could be completed within 5 min of the death of the animal. The pancreas was removed, transferred to a glass Petri dish, cut into small pieces with scissors and any excess fat removed. It was then transferred to a tube to which a further 10 ml. of Hanks' solution was added. The pancreatic tissue sank to the bottom and any remaining fat floated on the surface and was readily aspirated and discarded. The prepared tissue was transferred to a small conical flask together with 2 ml. Hanks' solution containing glucose 0.6 mg ml.$^{-1}$ and collagenase type 1 (Sigma Chemicals, London). The stoppered flask was placed in a shaking water bath at 37°C for about 30 min. The exact time for separation was determined by frequent sampling and examination under the dissecting microscope.

The digested pancreas was transferred to a tube and diluted with further cold Hanks' solution containing glucose in the same concentration as before and gently centrifuged for 1 min. The supernatant was discarded and fresh medium added, and the resultant suspension filtered into a Petri dish with a blackened base for examination under the dissecting microscope at × 10 magnification.

Initially the view was obscured by fine fragments of acinar tissue, which were removed by gently agitating the Petri dish and allowing them to become suspended in the Hanks' solution, then aspirated and discarded, the Islets remaining on the bottom of the vessel. They could then be seen clearly (Fig. 1) by the aid of dark ground illumination as yellowish white domes and were picked out with a finely drawn Pasteur pipette. Fig. 2 shows the histological appearance of an isolated pancreatic Islet. Its architecture and cells appear normal.

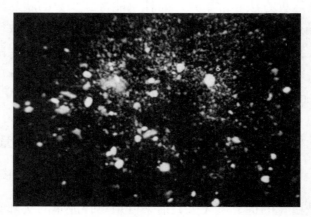

Fig. 1. Islet cell tissue seen after isolation from the pancreas using dark ground illumination. Dissecting microscope, ×5.

己定处理后选取正中线切口开腹。使用解剖显微镜放大 10 倍，将一条细小的聚乙烯导管（"Intracath"（译者注：一种留置针）—巴德，伦敦）插入胆总管，并用 2–0 的亚麻缝合线固定。在导管恰好进入十二指肠前，用动脉钳夹闭其下端。注射 10 ml 含有 2 mg · ml⁻¹ 牛血清蛋白（第五组分）的汉克氏液（译者注：一种用于细胞培养的平衡盐溶液）使胰腺膨胀。经过一些实践之后我们发现，这些步骤可以在动物死后 5 分钟之内完成。将胰腺摘除并转移到一个玻璃培养皿内，用剪刀将其剪碎并去除所有多余的脂肪。然后将其转移到一个试管内，并加入 10 ml 的汉克氏液。胰腺组织沉到管底，所有残存的脂肪都会漂浮在表面，将它们吸出并丢弃。将制备好的组织转移到一个小的锥形瓶内，该瓶内装有 2 ml 含 0.6 mg · ml⁻¹ 葡萄糖和 I 型胶原酶（西格玛化学公司，伦敦）的汉克氏液。把盖好的瓶子置于 37℃ 水浴摇床内约 30 分钟。分离过程的限速步骤是解剖显微镜下的频繁取样和检查。

将消化好的胰腺转移到一个试管内，用含有相同浓度葡萄糖的冷的汉克氏液稀释，温和离心 1 分钟。弃上清液并加入新鲜的培养液（汉克氏液），得到的悬浮液过滤到培养皿内；该培养皿的底为暗色，以便于在放大 10 倍的解剖显微镜下进行观察。

起初，许多细小的腺泡组织碎片使得视野很模糊；轻轻地摇动培养皿使其悬浮在汉克氏液中，然后将其吸出并丢弃，而胰岛则存留在容器底部。通过暗场照明能够清晰地看到它们呈黄白色的圆顶状（图 1），用尖端拉长的巴斯德吸管将其移出。图 2 显示了分离出来的胰岛的组织学形态。其结构和细胞表现正常。

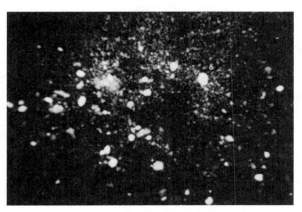

图 1. 通过暗场照明观察到的从胰腺中分离出来的胰岛细胞组织。解剖显微镜下放大 5 倍。

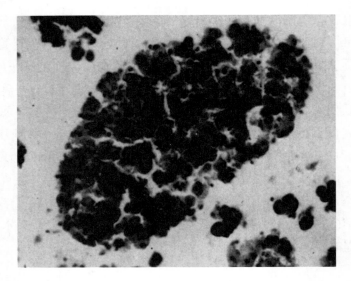

Fig. 2. Isolated pancreatic Islet. Normal architecture and appearance of cells. Haematoxylin and eosin, ×300.

Yields of up to 350 Islets per rat pancreas have been achieved using this method. To obtain larger quantities, rat pancreases have been processed in batches of four.

Viability of the isolated cells was confirmed by transplantation beneath the renal capsule and into the testis of isogeneic rats. The longest period of follow-up was one month, when viable looking Islet cells containing beta cell granules staining with aldehyde-fuchsin were seen. A similar method has been successfully applied in the rabbit.

The relationship of the Islets of Langerhans to diabetes mellitus was established in 1889 by Von Mering and Minkowski[6], and in 1892 Hedon[7] demonstrated that subcutaneous implantation of a small piece of pancreas could delay the appearance of diabetes in an animal that had undergone pancreatectomy. The concept of Islet cell grafting appears to be neglected in the extensive literature on pancreatic transplantation, although one early report suggests that transplanted Islets may modify alloxan diabetes in the rat[8].

We have now established a successful method of isolation of Islets of Langerhans in an animal strain in which inbred immunologically isogeneic lines are available, making possible transplantation studies uncomplicated by rejection problems. These cells can be grafted and survive for appreciable periods of time as shown by the viability studies. Histological and functional studies of Islet cell transplantation will be reported elsewhere.

We acknowledge a grant from the Endowment Fund of the United Sheffield Hospitals and from the Medical Research Council. We thank Dr. Laurence Henry for his help with the histology and Mr A. Tunstill and his staff for photography.

(**242**, 258-260; 1973)

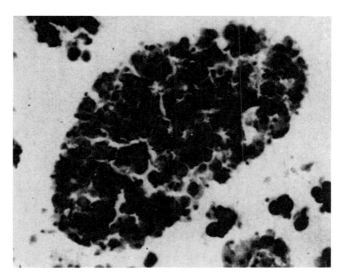

图 2. 分离出的胰岛。正常的结构和细胞外观。苏木精—伊红染色，放大 300 倍。

用这种方法能够在每个大鼠胰腺中得到多达 350 个胰岛。为了获得更多胰岛，大鼠胰腺以四个为一组一起处理。

将分离的胰岛细胞移植到同种大鼠的肾小囊内或者睾丸内以确认其生存能力。最长的随访期是 1 个月，此时可以观察到成活的胰岛细胞含有能被醛复红染色的 β 细胞颗粒。同样的方法在兔子中也获得了成功。

1889 年，冯·梅灵和明科夫斯基阐述了胰岛和糖尿病之间的关系 [6]。1892 年，埃东 [7] 证明了移植到皮下的一小块胰腺可以延缓进行胰腺切除术后的动物出现糖尿病症状。在大量有关胰腺移植的文献中，人们都忽略了胰岛细胞移植的想法，尽管有一篇早期报道提出移植的胰岛可能会减轻在大鼠中由四氧嘧啶诱导的糖尿病 [8]。

现在，我们已经在近交的免疫同系的动物品系中成功地建立了一种分离胰岛的方法，这使得移植研究摆脱排斥问题的困扰成为可能。正如在对胰岛细胞的生存力研究中所证实的，这些细胞能够被移植并能生存相当长的时间。胰岛细胞移植的组织学和功能方面的研究将另作报道。

我们感谢联合谢菲尔德医院的捐助基金和医学研究理事会的资金。我们感谢劳伦斯·亨利博士帮助进行组织学检查，感谢滕斯蒂尔先生及其职员在成像方面的帮助。

（毛晨晖 翻译；王敏康 审稿）

**D. R. Thomas, M. Fox and A. A. Grieve**
Royal Hospital, Sheffield

Received October 12, 1972. Requests for reprints to M. F.

References:

1. *Brit. Med. J.*, i, 326 (1972).

2. Dragstedt, L. R., *Ann. Surg.*, **118**, 576 (1943).

3. Hellerstrom, C., *Acta Endocr.*, **45**, 122 (1964).

4. Moskalewski, S., *Gen. and Comp. Endocrin.*, 5, 342 (1965).

5. Lacy, P. E., and Kostianovski, M., *Diabetes*, **16**, 35 (1967).

6. Von Mering, J., and Minkowski, O., in Major, R. M., *Classic Descriptions of Disease*, second ed., 246 (Charles C. Thomas, Springfield, Ill., 1939).

7. Hedon, E., *Compt. Rend. Soc. Biol.*, 44, 678 (1892).

8. Younoszai, R., Sorenson, R. L., and Lindall, jun., A. W., *Diabetes*, 19, Suppl 1, 406 (1970).

# Seismic Travel Time Evidence for Lateral Inhomogeneity in the Deep Mantle

B. R. Julian and M. K. Sengupta

## Editor's Note

The Earth's lower mantle is inaccessible for direct study. The best method for probing it is through the measurement of seismic waves, which travel at different speeds through materials of different density or composition. Although there were some earlier signs that the lower mantle is not uniform but somehow "lumpy", Bruce Julian and Mrinal Sengupta at the Massachusetts Institute of Technology here provide clear evidence from seismic travel times that the lowest part of the mantle is inhomogeneous on scales of around 1,000 km. They could not offer definitive reasons, but suggest that at least some of the irregularities might be caused by convection structures: specifically, by plumes of rising, hot material, which others had proposed earlier.

We present evidence from seismic travel time data of lateral variations in the properties of the lower mantle. The size of some anomalies is about 1,000 km.

EVIDENCE from seismic body wave and surface wave data has long indicated that the Earth's upper mantle (depth <700 km) is strongly laterally heterogeneous. Lateral variations of the compressional wave velocity as large as 10% have been reported for the upper 200 km, and the shear velocity probably varies even more. For depths greater than 700 km, however, the existence of lateral variations has been more difficult to establish, although such variations have been invoked by various workers[1,2] to explain the scatter of some seismological data. Greenfield and Sheppard[3], in a study of $dT/d\Delta$ measurements made at the Large Aperture Seismic Array in Montana, found a pronounced difference between data from events to the northwest and the southeast for epicentral distances greater than 60°, which could not be attributed to the structure beneath the array, and seems explicable only in terms of heterogeneities in the lower mantle. Davies and Sheppard[4] have presented a more extensive collection of data of this type in the form of an "array diagram", on which $dT/d\Delta$ and azimuth anomalies are represented as vectors in slowness space. Many anomalies are found which are too large to be effects of upper mantle heterogeneities in the source regions; on the other hand, the anomalies often vary rapidly with the direction of approach of the waves, implying that structure directly beneath the array is not responsible. Further evidence has come from a study of the diffraction of compressional waves by the Earth's core, in which Alexander and Phinney[5] found that the region of the core-mantle boundary beneath the Pacific Basin is distinctly different from the region beneath the North Atlantic and Africa.

# 深地幔横向非均匀性的地震波走时证据

朱利安，森古普塔

## 编者按

对地球的下地幔是无法进行直接研究的。探测下地幔的最好方法是测量地震波，因为在不同密度或不同组分的岩层中，地震波传播速度会有所不同。早前已有一些迹象表明下地幔不是均一的并且多少呈"块状分布"，本文中，麻省理工学院的布鲁斯·朱利安和姆里纳尔·森古普塔给出了确切的证据，他们从地震波走时的研究中发现，地幔最深处具有约 1,000 km 尺度范围的非均质体。他们没能给出确切的解释，但是他们提出，至少有部分非均质体可能是由对流结构所致：特别是受到了地幔柱上升、热物质的影响，这一点早前已有人提出。

---

我们提供了来自地震波走时的、能表明下地幔物质存在横向变化的证据，一些异常体的尺度约为 1,000 km。

---

地震体波和表面波的数据早已证明，地球上地幔（深度 < 700 km）的横向不均匀性是非常突出的。有报告显示，在地幔上部 200 km 以内纵波速度的横向变化可达 10%，而切变波速度的变幅可能更大。然而，在大于 700 km 的深处很难确定地震波的横向变化，不过还是有一些人 [1,2] 曾引用这种变化来解释某些地震数据的离散现象。在蒙大拿州的大孔径地震台阵测量 dT/dΔ 的研究中，格林菲尔德和谢泼德 [3] 从实验数据中发现，在西北和东南方向上震中距相差达 60°以上，这不能归因于台阵下方的构造，似乎只能用下地幔的不均匀性来解释。戴维斯和谢泼德 [4] 以"阵列图"的形式广泛收集了这类数据。在这幅图中，dT/dΔ 和方位角差异表示慢度空间矢量。图中显示出大量的异常，由于这些异常过大，因此不可能是震源区上地幔不均匀效应所致；另一方面，这些异常会随着地震波传播方向的改变而快速变化，表明这与台阵正下方的地质构造没有关系。而且对于由地核引起的压缩波衍射的研究进一步验证了上述观点，亚历山大和菲尼 [5] 发现，位于太平洋海盆下方的核幔边界区和位于北大西洋及非洲下方的核幔边界区迥然不同。

## Travel Time Anomalies

We have found evidence that significant lateral variations occur in the lowest few hundred km of the mantle, this region being much more heterogeneous than that which lies above it. The methods of this travel time study are described in detail elsewhere[6].

We restricted the study to data from deep focus earthquakes in an attempt to avoid systematic errors caused by near source velocity variations in the upper mantle, which are particularly severe in seismically active regions. About 3,300 arrival time data from 47 earthquakes with depths between 450 and 650 km were used, all events being located in the deepest parts of their respective seismic zones. For most of the 18 seismic regions involved, two or more events were available, and for each station a consistency check was made to eliminate data contaminated by gross errors. An iterative procedure, similar to the one described by Herrin *et al.*[7], was then used to determine the earthquake locations, the travel time curve for a 550 km focal depth, and a set of "station corrections" (each represented by a constant) to account for the effect of lateral variations in the upper mantle beneath the stations.

The travel time curve thus determined is shown in Fig. 1 (in terms of deviation from the standard Jeffreys-Bullen tables), together with the data means and their standard errors for 2° distance intervals. This curve is similar in shape to those found in other recent studies[7,8] except beyond 85°, where most other curves remain approximately parallel to the Jeffreys-Bullen curve, but ours becomes progressively earlier by about 0.9 s. Fig. 2 shows some of the data which have contributed to the determination of the travel time curve; the observed times show a striking dependence upon the location of the earthquakes. The difference between the curves in Fig. 1 results from differences in the geographic regions sampled. Possible causes of a regional dependence of this nature are velocity variations in the upper mantle in the source or receiver regions or in the lower mantle, and mislocation of the events (caused by uneven station distribution, and so on). Event mislocation and structure in the receiver regions can be ruled out because they would be expected to produce similar effects at all epicentral distances. Although the observed variations are most striking beyond 85°, we shall show that they are much smaller at distances less than 70°. It is conceivable that structure in the source regions could produce a distance dependent regional variation of this kind, if the velocity anomalies were systematically located relative to the earthquake hypocentres (as indeed they are beneath island arcs). In that case the variations would have to be localized in a very small region beneath the hypocentres, because a 10° distance interval maps into about a 5° difference in angle at the focus. Even if the anomalous regions are as deep as 1,000 km, the velocity change must occur over a horizontal distance of only 50 km or so. This possibility may be ruled out because all the earthquakes in each source region yield a similar pattern of travel time residuals, even though the epicentre locations in each region are typically distributed over >200 km. Velocity variations near the focus are further ruled out because early arrivals beyond 85° are not restricted to observations of deep earthquakes; they also occur, for example, in data from nuclear explosions in the Marshall Islands[9].

288

## 走 时 异 常

我们已经发现，在地幔最底层的数百公里内，地震波的走时发生明显的横向变化，这一区域与其上方区域相比具有更大的不均匀性。这种基于走时的研究方法在另一篇文章[6]中已作详述。

我们将研究范围限于深源地震，以避免上地幔中由近源速度变化引起的系统误差，而这种变化在地震活动区尤为强烈。我们选用了 47 次地震的 3,300 个到时数据，这些地震的震源深度在 450 km 至 650 km 之间，并且均位于各自所处地震带的最深处。所涉及的 18 个地震带中，大多都有两次或两次以上的地震数据是可用的。另外，为了消除含有过失误差的数据，每个台站的资料都进行了一致性检验。利用一种类似于赫林等人[7]所描述的迭代法，我们确定了地震位置、一条震源深度为 550 km 的地震波走时曲线和一组"台站校正量"（每个台站对应一个常数），每个常数代表走时在该台站下方上地幔的横向变化造成的影响。

由此得出的走时曲线如图 1 所示（以相对于标准的杰弗里斯 - 布伦走时表的偏差表示），图中也显示了间距为 2° 的数据的平均值及其标准误差。在 85° 以下，曲线的形状与近期其他研究发表的曲线[7,8]相似，大部分其他曲线仍然与杰弗里斯 - 布伦曲线近似平行，但我们的结果逐渐提前了约 0.9 s。图 2 显示了绘制走时曲线所使用的一些数据；观测到的走时大小很大程度上取决于地震发生的位置。图 1 中几条曲线的差异是由采样点的地理区域不同引起的。导致区域性差异的原因可能是源区或接收区上地幔地震波速度变化造成，或是由下地幔传播速度的变化引起，还可能是震源定位存在误差（由台站分布不均匀等原因造成）。震源定位的误差以及接收区的地质构造造成的影响可以排除，因为无论震中距大小，这两种因素所造成的影响是相似的。虽然在 85° 以上观测到的差异最为显著，但同时我们看到，在震中距小于 70° 时这种差异要小得多。如果传播速度的异常相对于震源呈系统性分布的话（在岛弧下方确实如此），那么可以推断，这种依赖于距离的区域差异是由震源区的地质构造引起的。如果是这样的话，距离的变化应该只局限在震源下方一个很小的区域，因为 10° 震中距间距可映射为震中处 5° 角度差。即使异常区深达 1,000 km，速度变化肯定也只会发生在 50 km 左右的水平距离上。这种可能性应该可以排除，因为每一震源区内所有的地震都产生相类似的走时残差，即便在同一地震区内其震中位置的分布范围超过 200 km 也不例外。震源附近传播速度的差异也被进一步排除，因为在 85° 以上较早到达的地震波并不仅仅能在深源地震中观测到。例如，在马绍尔群岛的核爆炸数据中就出现过这种情况[9]。

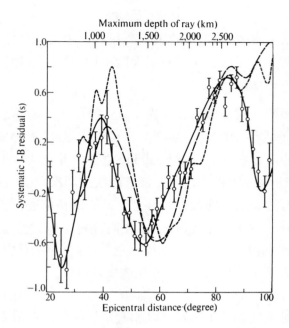

Fig. 1. P wave travel time curve (focal depth 550 km) determined in this study (———), expressed in terms of deviations from the Jeffreys-Bullen values. Data means and their standard errors are indicated for 2° distance intervals. Surface focus curves of Herrin *et al.*[7] (— —) and Lilwal and Douglas[8] (---) have been displaced vertically for ease of comparison.

## Deep Mantle Structure

It seems, then, that lateral variations of compressional velocity in the middle or lower mantle are required to explain the travel time anomalies. But because of the uneven distribution to seismological observatories and deep earthquakes, the sampling of the mantle provided by available data is uneven, and it is impossible to determine uniquely the complete three dimensional velocity structure of the mantle. What can be determined is the average travel time residual for each of a number of "bundles" of rays following nearly identical paths from a seismic region to a group of stations, and from this information we infer the most probable cause of the variations. Table 1 summarizes the travel time data for all paths for which 9 or more observations are available. For each path a Student's *t* test has been used to evaluate the hypothesis that the mean travel time (after station corrections have been applied) is the value given by the curve in Fig. 1 and that deviations from this curve can be attributed to random measuring errors. Those ray paths for which the hypothesis could be rejected at the 99.5% confidence level are indicated in Table 1. Fig. 3 shows histograms of the residual distribution for these anomalous paths. For observations at distances beyond 70°, 16 paths (out of 34 tested) showed significant variations from the average curve, whereas for smaller distances, only 3 anomalous paths (out of 22) were found. This strongly suggests that most of the scatter originates in the deep mantle (depth >2,000 km). The possibility of the variations occurring at a shallower depth cannot be absolutely disproved, but the velocity distribution in the

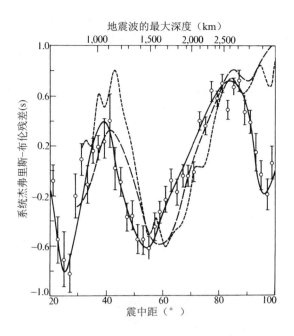

图 1. 本项研究在震源深度 550 km 条件下得出的 P 波走时曲线（——），以相对于杰弗里斯－布伦走时表的偏差表示。数据平均值及其标准误差以 2°的间距表示。为了便于对比，赫林等人 [7]（———）以及利尔沃和道格拉斯 [8] (---) 的浅源地震曲线也垂直呈现于图中。

## 深地幔结构

那么，似乎可以用纵波在中地幔或下地幔中传播速度的横向变化来解释走时的异常。但是，因为地震观测台站的分布不均匀且震源较深，所以现有数据提供的地幔采样也是不均匀的，因此也不可能确定地幔中完整的三维速度结构。对于每一组沿着近似相同的路径、从一个震区传播到一组接收台站的射线束，我们可以确定它的平均走时残差，根据残差信息我们可以推测造成这些差异最有可能的原因。表 1 总结了所有路径的走时数据，这些路径均有不少于 9 次的有效观测值。对每个路径应用学生 t 检验方法来检验下述假说：平均走时（经过台站校正以后）为图 1 中曲线给出的数值，并且相对这条曲线的偏差可以归因于随机测量误差。表 1 中对在 99.5% 的置信水平上背离上述假说的射线路径进行了标记。图 3 是这些异常路径的走时残差分布直方图。对于震中距超过 70° 的那些观测值，有 16 个路径（共检验了 34 个）显著偏离平均曲线；而对于震中距较小的那些观测，则只有 3 个异常路径（共检验了 22 个）。这有力地表明大部分散射产生于深地幔（深度 > 2,000 km）。在较浅处发生这种变化的可能性也不能绝对排除，但是如此一来，鉴于地震以及地震台站的分布情况，地球内部传播速度的分布就必须具有如下特点：观测到的底及非均质体底部的地震波恰巧未受到这些非均质体的影响（虽然 P 波在穿过最下方的 10%

291

Earth would have to be such that, given the distribution of earthquakes and seismic stations, all observed waves bottoming at the depth of the heterogeneities happen to be unaffected by them (even though P waves spend about 25% of their travel time traversing the lowest 10% of the ray path), while waves penetrating beneath the heterogeneities are affected. It seems unreasonable to assume such a conspiratorial behaviour on the part of the velocity variations when a much simpler hypothesis is available.

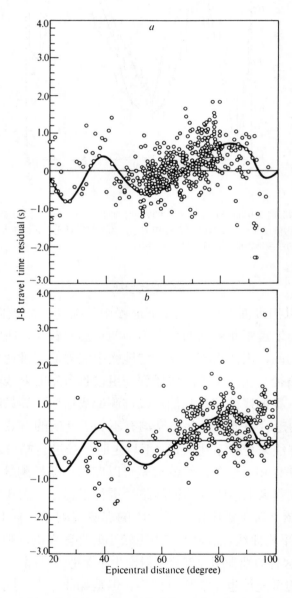

Fig. 2. Travel time data (with station corrections applied) for earthquakes in (*a*) the Sea of Okhotsk and (*b*) Argentina. The solid line is the curve derived from all data.

的路径上消耗了近 25% 的走时），而穿过非均质体下方的地震波却受到了影响。当一个更简单的假设存在时，在速度变化上作这样一个特性诡秘的假设似乎并不合理。

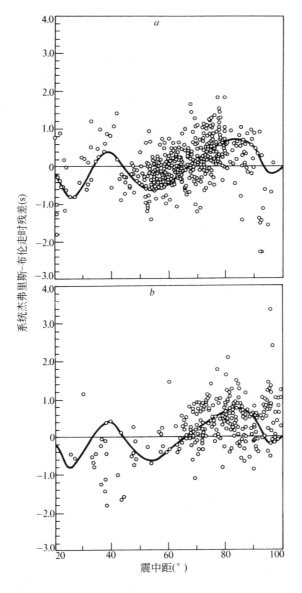

图 2. 鄂霍次克海（*a*）和阿根廷（*b*）区域的地震波走时数据（已经过台站校正）。实线是由全部数据的拟合得到的。

## Table 1. Travel Time Statistics for Mantle P Wave Paths

| Identification No. | $N$ | $\bar{x}$ | $s$ | $t$ | $t_{99.5}$ | Path |
|---|---|---|---|---|---|---|
| (a) $85° < \Delta < 100°$ | | | | | | |
| 1-1* | 17 | 0.46 | 0.43 | 4.41 | 3.25 | Japan—USA |
| 1-2 | 12 | −0.11 | 0.56 | −2.15 | 3.50 | Bonin and Marianas Arc—USA |
| 1-3* | 15 | −0.76 | 0.48 | −6.13 | 3.33 | Tonga Arc—Alaska |
| 1-4* | 90 | 0.23 | 0.50 | 4.37 | 2.89 | Tonga Arc—Western North America |
| 1-5* | 29 | −0.34 | 0.57 | −3.21 | 3.05 | Argentina—Western North America |
| 1-6* | 40 | 0.37 | 0.70 | 3.34 | 2.97 | South America—Northwestern Europe |
| 1-7* | 84 | 0.38 | 0.79 | 4.40 | 2.89 | South America—Southern Europe |
| 1-8 | 11 | 0.06 | 0.56 | 0.36 | 3.58 | South America—Southern Africa |
| 1-9* | 13 | −1.09 | 0.91 | −4.31 | 3.43 | Kuril Arc—Spain, Morocco and Algeria |
| 1-10 | 16 | −0.36 | 0.58 | −2.48 | 3.29 | Bonin Arc—Europe |
| 1-11 | 42 | −0.19 | 0.65 | −1.90 | 2.97 | Indonesia and Philippine Is.—Central and Northern Europe |
| 1-12 | 14 | 0.16 | 0.48 | 1.25 | 3.37 | Indonesia and Philippine Is.—Middle East and Balkans |
| 1-13 | 13 | 0.47 | 0.96 | 1.77 | 3.43 | Indonesia and Philippine Is.—Central ad Southern Africa |
| 1-14 | 10 | −0.12 | 0.56 | −0.68 | 3.69 | Tonga Arc—Siberia and China |
| 1-15 | 9 | −0.24 | 0.28 | −2.57 | 3.83 | Indonesia—Alaska |
| 1-16* | 56 | 0.34 | 0.61 | 4.17 | 2.92 | Solomon Is.—Western USA |
| 1-17 | 29 | 0.04 | 0.33 | 0.65 | 3.05 | New Hebrides—Western North America |
| (b) $70° < \Delta < 85°$ | | | | | | |
| 2-1 | 57 | −0.12 | 0.45 | −2.02 | 2.92 | Japan—USA |
| 2-2* | 12 | −0.51 | 0.36 | −4.90 | 3.45 | Japan—Southwestern USA |
| 2-3* | 34 | −0.38 | 0.37 | −5.99 | 3.01 | Bonin Arc—Western USA |
| 2-4* | 122 | 0.16 | 0.40 | 4.38 | 2.86 | Tonga Arc—Western North America |
| 2-5* | 27 | −0.27 | 0.39 | −3.60 | 3.07 | Kuril Arc—Eastern North America |
| 2-6* | 76 | −0.19 | 0.45 | −3.68 | 2.90 | Argentina and Bolivia—Central and Western USA |
| 2-7* | 30 | 0.25 | 0.44 | 3.11 | 3.04 | South America—Spain and Northern Africa |
| 2-8 | 20 | −0.09 | 0.45 | −0.89 | 3.17 | South America—Central and Southern Africa |
| 2-9* | 58 | 0.19 | 0.43 | 3.36 | 2.92 | Kuril Arc—Western Europe |
| 2-10* | 69 | −0.33 | 0.52 | −5.28 | 2.91 | Japan—Western Europe |
| 2-11 | 22 | 0.02 | 0.36 | 0.26 | 3.14 | New Hebrides—Western North America |
| 2-12 | 20 | −0.06 | 0.47 | −0.57 | 3.17 | Indonesia and Philippine Is.—Middle East |
| 2-13 | 30 | −0.09 | 0.52 | −0.95 | 3.04 | Bonin and Marianas Arcs—Scandinavia and Western Russia |
| 2-14 | 23 | 0.14 | 0.38 | 1.77 | 3.12 | Japan and Kuril Arc—Australia |
| 2-15 | 11 | −0.06 | 0.54 | −0.37 | 3.58 | Kuril Arc—Middle East |

## 表1. 地幔中 P 波沿各条路径走时的统计

| 识别编码 | $N$ | $\bar{x}$ | $s$ | $t$ | $t_{99.5}$ | 路　径 |
|---|---|---|---|---|---|---|
| (a) $85° < \Delta < 100°$ | | | | | | |
| 1-1* | 17 | 0.46 | 0.43 | 4.41 | 3.25 | 日本—美国 |
| 1-2 | 12 | −0.11 | 0.56 | −2.15 | 3.50 | 小笠原和马里亚纳岛弧—美国 |
| 1-3* | 15 | −0.76 | 0.48 | −6.13 | 3.33 | 汤加岛弧—阿拉斯加 |
| 1-4* | 90 | 0.23 | 0.50 | 4.37 | 2.89 | 汤加岛弧—北美洲西部 |
| 1-5* | 29 | −0.34 | 0.57 | −3.21 | 3.05 | 阿根廷—北美洲西部 |
| 1-6* | 40 | 0.37 | 0.70 | 3.34 | 2.97 | 南美洲—欧洲西北部 |
| 1-7* | 84 | 0.38 | 0.79 | 4.40 | 2.89 | 南美洲—欧洲南部 |
| 1-8 | 11 | 0.06 | 0.56 | 0.36 | 3.58 | 南美洲—非洲南部 |
| 1-9* | 13 | −1.09 | 0.91 | −4.31 | 3.43 | 千岛岛弧—西班牙，摩洛哥，阿尔及利亚 |
| 1-10 | 16 | −0.36 | 0.58 | −2.48 | 3.29 | 小笠原岛弧—欧洲 |
| 1-11 | 42 | −0.19 | 0.65 | −1.90 | 2.97 | 印度尼西亚和菲律宾群岛—欧洲中部及北部 |
| 1-12 | 14 | 0.16 | 0.48 | 1.25 | 3.37 | 印度尼西亚和菲律宾群岛—中东和巴尔干半岛 |
| 1-13 | 13 | 0.47 | 0.96 | 1.77 | 3.43 | 印度尼西亚和菲律宾群岛—非洲中部及南部 |
| 1-14 | 10 | −0.12 | 0.56 | −0.68 | 3.69 | 汤加岛弧—西伯利亚和中国 |
| 1-15 | 9 | −0.24 | 0.28 | −2.57 | 3.83 | 印度尼西亚—阿拉斯加 |
| 1-16* | 56 | 0.34 | 0.61 | 4.17 | 2.92 | 所罗门群岛—美国西部 |
| 1-17 | 29 | 0.04 | 0.33 | 0.65 | 3.05 | 新赫布里底群岛—北美洲西部 |
| (b) $70° < \Delta < 85°$ | | | | | | |
| 2-1 | 57 | −0.12 | 0.45 | −2.02 | 2.92 | 日本—美国 |
| 2-2* | 12 | −0.51 | 0.36 | −4.90 | 3.45 | 日本—美国西南部 |
| 2-3* | 34 | −0.38 | 0.37 | −5.99 | 3.01 | 小笠原岛弧—美国西部 |
| 2-4* | 122 | 0.16 | 0.40 | 4.38 | 2.86 | 汤加岛弧—北美洲西部 |
| 2-5* | 27 | −0.27 | 0.39 | −3.60 | 3.07 | 千岛岛弧—北美洲东部 |
| 2-6* | 76 | −0.19 | 0.45 | −3.68 | 2.90 | 阿根廷和玻利维亚—美国中部及西部 |
| 2-7* | 30 | 0.25 | 0.44 | 3.11 | 3.04 | 南美洲—西班牙和非洲北部 |
| 2-8 | 20 | −0.09 | 0.45 | −0.89 | 3.17 | 南美洲—非洲中部及南部 |
| 2-9* | 58 | 0.19 | 0.43 | 3.36 | 2.92 | 千岛岛弧—欧洲西部 |
| 2-10* | 69 | −0.33 | 0.52 | −5.28 | 2.91 | 日本—欧洲西部 |
| 2-11 | 22 | 0.02 | 0.36 | 0.26 | 3.14 | 新赫布里底群岛—北美洲西部 |
| 2-12 | 20 | −0.06 | 0.47 | −0.57 | 3.17 | 印度尼西亚和菲律宾群岛—中东 |
| 2-13 | 30 | −0.09 | 0.52 | −0.95 | 3.04 | 小笠原和马里亚纳岛弧—斯堪的纳维亚半岛和俄国西部 |
| 2-14 | 23 | 0.14 | 0.38 | 1.77 | 3.12 | 日本和千岛岛弧—澳大利亚 |
| 2-15 | 11 | −0.06 | 0.54 | −0.37 | 3.58 | 千岛岛弧—中东 |

*Continued*

| Identification No. | $N$ | $\bar{x}$ | $s$ | $t$ | $t_{99.5}$ | Path |
|---|---|---|---|---|---|---|
| 2-16 | 12 | −0.39 | 0.56 | −2.41 | 3.50 | Indonesia—Antarctica |
| 2-17 | 10 | −0.22 | 0.25 | −2.78 | 3.69 | Marianas Arc—Western USA |
| 2-18 | 12 | −0.22 | 0.69 | −1.10 | 3.50 | Japan—Middle East |
| *(c)* $55° < \Delta < 70°$ | | | | | | |
| 3-1* | 93 | 0.23 | 0.38 | 5.84 | 2.89 | Kuril Arc—Western USA |
| 3-2 | 45 | 0.12 | 0.40 | 2.01 | 2.96 | Northern South America—Western USA |
| 3-3 | 42 | 0.06 | 0.49 | 0.79 | 2.97 | Bolivia and Argentina—Central USA |
| 3-4 | 93 | −0.05 | 0.54 | −0.89 | 2.89 | Kuril Arc and Sea of Japan—Northern and Eastern Europe and Middle East |
| 3-5 | 30 | −0.09 | 0.41 | −1.20 | 3.03 | Indonesia and Philippine Is.—Southwestern Asia |
| 3-6 | 15 | 0.18 | 0.62 | 1.12 | 3.33 | Japan and Kuril Arc—Melanesia |
| 3-7 | 12 | −0.04 | 0.41 | −0.34 | 3.43 | Tonga Arc—Western Australia |
| 3-8 | 10 | −0.28 | 0.45 | −1.97 | 3.58 | Japan and Kuril Arc—Australia |
| 3-9 | 9 | −0.19 | 0.55 | −1.04 | 3.69 | New Hebrides—China and Siberia |
| 3-10 | 8 | 0.13 | 0.78 | 0.47 | 4.03 | Solomon Is.—Japan |
| 3-11 | 15 | 0.26 | 0.47 | 2.14 | 3.29 | Tonga Arc—Antarctica |
| 3-12 | 9 | 0.22 | 0.58 | 1.14 | 3.69 | Indonesia—New Zealand |
| 3-13 | 10 | 0.15 | 0.59 | 0.80 | 3.58 | Indonesia—Antarctica |
| *(d)* $40° < \Delta < 55°$ | | | | | | |
| 4-1* | 23 | 0.41 | 0.48 | 4.10 | 3.12 | Kuril Arc—Northwestern North America |
| 4-2 | 44 | −0.18 | 0.48 | −2.49 | 2.97 | Northern South America—USA |
| 4-3 | 15 | 0.35 | 0.41 | 3.31 | 3.33 | Kuril Arc—Northern Europe |
| 4-4 | 34 | 0.16 | 0.43 | 2.17 | 3.01 | Japan—Southwestern Asia |
| 4-5 | 17 | −0.25 | 0.51 | −2.02 | 3.22 | Indonesia—India and Pakistan |
| 4-6* | 17 | 0.82 | 0.56 | 6.03 | 3.25 | Japan—Alaska |
| 4-7 | 13 | −0.51 | 0.65 | −2.82 | 3.37 | Indonesia—Japan and Korea |
| 4-8 | 40 | 0.02 | 0.55 | 0.23 | 2.97 | Indonesia—Southeastern Australia and Tasmania |
| 4-9 | 20 | −0.06 | 0.58 | −0.46 | 3.15 | Solomon Is.—Japan, Korea, and Eastern China |

$N$=Number of observations.

$\bar{x}$=Mean travel time residual after station correction (s).

$s$=Standard deviation of residuals (s).

$$t=\frac{\bar{x}}{s/\sqrt{N}}$$

$t_{99.5}$=99.5% confidence limit for $|t|$ if true mean is zero.

* Indicates paths with mean significantly different from zero.

续表

| 识别编码 | $N$ | $\bar{x}$ | $s$ | $t$ | $t_{99.5}$ | 路 径 |
|---|---|---|---|---|---|---|
| 2-16 | 12 | −0.39 | 0.56 | −2.41 | 3.50 | 印度尼西亚—南极大陆 |
| 2-17 | 10 | −0.22 | 0.25 | −2.78 | 3.69 | 马里亚纳岛弧—美国西部 |
| 2-18 | 12 | −0.22 | 0.69 | −1.10 | 3.50 | 日本—中东 |
| (c) $55° < \Delta < 70°$ | | | | | | |
| 3-1* | 93 | 0.23 | 0.38 | 5.84 | 2.89 | 千岛岛弧—美国西部 |
| 3-2 | 45 | 0.12 | 0.40 | 2.01 | 2.96 | 南美洲北部—美国西部 |
| 3-3 | 42 | 0.06 | 0.49 | 0.79 | 2.97 | 玻利维亚和阿根廷—美国中部 |
| 3-4 | 93 | −0.05 | 0.54 | −0.89 | 2.89 | 千岛岛弧和日本海—北欧、东欧和中东 |
| 3-5 | 30 | −0.09 | 0.41 | −1.20 | 3.03 | 印度尼西亚和菲律宾群岛—西南亚 |
| 3-6 | 15 | 0.18 | 0.62 | 1.12 | 3.33 | 日本和千岛岛弧—美拉尼西亚群岛 |
| 3-7 | 12 | −0.04 | 0.41 | −0.34 | 3.43 | 汤加岛弧—澳大利亚西部 |
| 3-8 | 10 | −0.28 | 0.45 | −1.97 | 3.58 | 日本和千岛岛弧—澳大利亚 |
| 3-9 | 9 | −0.19 | 0.55 | −1.04 | 3.69 | 新赫布里底群岛—中国和西伯利亚 |
| 3-10 | 8 | 0.13 | 0.78 | 0.47 | 4.03 | 所罗门群岛—日本 |
| 3-11 | 15 | 0.26 | 0.47 | 2.14 | 3.29 | 汤加岛弧—南极大陆 |
| 3-12 | 9 | 0.22 | 0.58 | 1.14 | 3.69 | 印度尼西亚—新西兰 |
| 3-13 | 10 | 0.15 | 0.59 | 0.80 | 3.58 | 印度尼西亚—南极大陆 |
| (d) $40° < \Delta < 55°$ | | | | | | |
| 4-1* | 23 | 0.41 | 0.48 | 4.10 | 3.12 | 千岛岛弧—北美洲西北部 |
| 4-2 | 44 | −0.18 | 0.48 | −2.49 | 2.97 | 南美洲北部—美国 |
| 4-3 | 15 | 0.35 | 0.41 | 3.31 | 3.33 | 千岛岛弧—北欧 |
| 4-4 | 34 | 0.16 | 0.43 | 2.17 | 3.01 | 日本—西南亚 |
| 4-5 | 17 | −0.25 | 0.51 | −2.02 | 3.22 | 印度尼西亚—印度和巴基斯坦 |
| 4-6* | 17 | 0.82 | 0.56 | 6.03 | 3.25 | 日本—阿拉斯加 |
| 4-7 | 13 | −0.51 | 0.65 | −2.82 | 3.37 | 印度尼西亚—日本和朝鲜半岛 |
| 4-8 | 40 | 0.02 | 0.55 | 0.23 | 2.97 | 印度尼西亚—澳大利亚东南部和塔斯马尼亚 |
| 4-9 | 20 | −0.06 | 0.58 | −0.46 | 3.15 | 所罗门群岛—日本、朝鲜半岛和华东 |

$N=$ 观测次数

$\bar{x}=$ 经台站校正后的平均走时残差（s）

$s=$ 残差的标准差（s）

$$t = \frac{\bar{x}}{s/\sqrt{N}}$$

$t_{99.5}=$ 当真均值为零时，$|t|$ 的置信水平为 99.5%

* 指真均值明显不为零的传播路径。

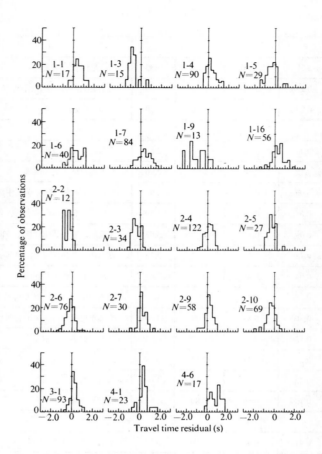

Fig. 3. Histograms of travel time residuals (relative to curve of Fig. 1 with station corrections applied) for different ray paths through the mantle. Identification numbers correspond to those in Table 1 and Fig. 4. *N* is the number of observations.

The actual details of the velocity distribution cannot, however, be determined precisely, because rays travel a great distance at approximately the same depth near their turning points. Fig. 4 shows the regions of the lower mantle sampled by the various ray bundles (defined arbitrarily as the central 30° of each path) and indicates which paths correspond to early and late arrivals. These are in most cases probably the regions where the actual velocity anomalies occur. Where regions overlap on the figure, they are generally consistent with each other (for example, regions 1-6 and 1-7, regions 2-2 and 2-3, and regions 4-1 and 4-6). This consistency is encouraging, in that it supports our argument that the travel time anomalies originate in the deep mantle and are not the result of some other type of systematic error. An apparent inconsistency exists between regions 1-3 and 1-16, but this is not surprising because of the uncertainty as to exactly where the travel time anomalies actually originate. The rays following path 1-3 also pass through regions 2-2 and 2-3 further to the north, and it is likely that the travel time anomaly actually originates there. Another interesting feature of Fig. 4 is a correlation between the anomalies in the two greatest distance ranges (for example, regions 1-7 and 2-7, regions 1-4 and 2-4, and regions

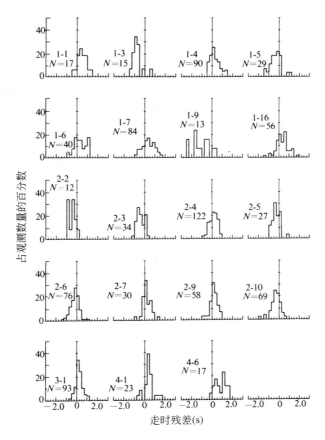

图 3. 地震波沿不同路径穿过地幔的走时残差直方图（残差是相对于图 1 的曲线，且经过台站校正）。识别编码与表 1 和图 4 上的编码对应。$N$ 是观测到的地震数量。

　　然而，速度分布的细节无法精准测定，因为经过回折点附近几乎相同深度的不同射线传播距离相差很大。图 4 显示了不同路径射线束（人为限制在每条路径中心的 30°）的下地幔采样区域，并指出哪些路径对应早到或晚到。这些区域往往都是真正可能出现速度异常的区域。图中一些区域重叠的地方，它们的数据也基本保持一致（例如区域 1-6 和 1-7、2-2 和 2-3、4-1 和 4-6）。这种一致性是令人鼓舞的，因为这支持了我们的观点，即走时的异常产生于深地幔，而不是由某种系统误差所引起的。在区域 1-3 和 1-16 之间存在着显著的不一致性，但是这并不奇怪，因为走时异常实际源于何处并不确定。沿着路径 1-3 传播的射线穿过了区域 2-2 和 2-3 后继续向北，很可能走时异常就产生于此。图 4 还有一个有趣的特征，即在两个距离间隔最大的异常之间存在相关性（例如区域 1-7 和 2-7、区域 1-4 和 2-4、以及区域 1-5 和 2-6），这表明深地幔的结构在垂直方向上至少在几百公里内具有一种空间"一

1-5 and 2-6), suggesting that the structure in the deep mantle has a spatial "coherence" of at least a few hundred km vertically.

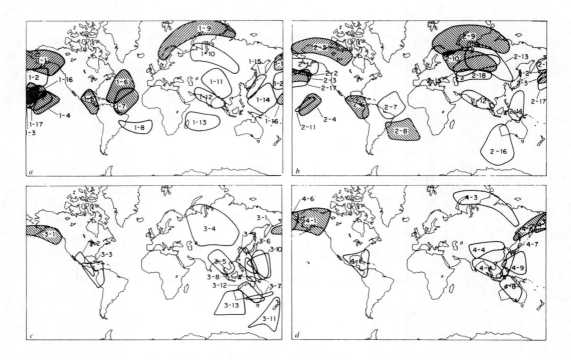

Fig. 4. Regions where paths of observed P waves bottom in the mantle. Cross-hatching indicates regions differing significantly from the mean determined from all data. Other regions tested are outlined. The identification numbers correspond to those in Table 1 and Fig. 3. ▨ Late; ▨, Early.

The mean travel times in Table 1 show a variation of about 1.5 s for rays bottoming below 2,600 km, and about 0.6 s for rays bottoming between 2,000 and 2,600 km. These numbers are somewhat uncertain, but it is likely that the true travel times vary by at least 1 s. The amount by which the actual velocity in the mantle varies depends on the size of the regions within which the variations occur. The data of Fig. 4 suggest that the size of some of the anomalies, at least, is about 1,000 km or less, in which case the velocity must vary by at least 1%. This is a lower bound both because we have probably overestimated the scale of the inhomogeneities and because we are measuring averages of the velocity in rather large regions and some cancellation of the effects of positive and negative velocity anomalies is likely. Combined interpretation of travel time and $dT/d\Delta$ measurements can probably improve the resolution of structural details.

Might the deep mantle variations be related in some way to the convection plumes hypothesized by Wilson[10] and Morgan[11] to exist in the deep mantle? To answer this the region of the Hawaiian Islands provides the best data, and here they indeed indicate a pronounced lateral variation, the velocities being high to the northwest of Hawaii (regions

致性"。

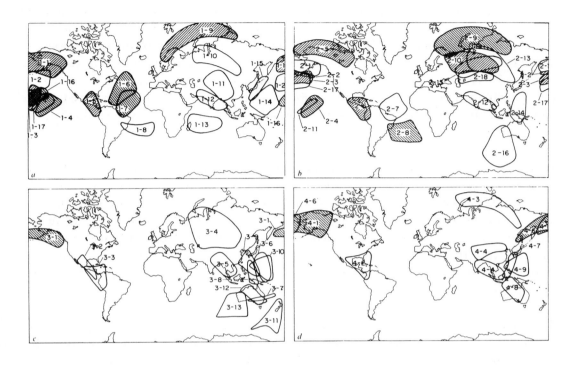

图 4. 探及地幔底界的 P 波传播路径分区图。斜线部分表示与全部数据的平均值显著不同的区域。检测的其他区域以轮廓线表示。图中的识别编码与表 1 和图 3 的编码对应。▨: 晚;▨: 早。

表 1 中的平均走时数据表明对于能底及 2,600 km 以下的射线而言,变化量约为 1.5 s,而对于能底及 2,000 至 2,600 km 之间的射线来说,变化量约为 0.6 s。虽然这些数据有些不确定,但是真实的走时很可能至少有 1 s 的变化量。地幔中实际传播速度的变化值取决于产生速度变化的区域的大小。图 4 中的数据显示,某些异常的尺度至少可达 1,000 km 或稍小,在这种情况下,传播速度至少要有 1% 的变化。这是一个下限,因为我们可能高估了非均质体的规模,也因为我们是在相当大的区域里测量速度平均值,很可能存在一些正负速度异常的相消效应。把有关走时的解译和 d$T$/d$\triangle$ 测量值结合起来有助于提高地幔结构细节的分辨率。

深地幔的变化是否可能与威尔逊 [10] 和摩根 [11] 的地幔柱对流假说存在某种意义上的关联?对于这个问题,夏威夷群岛地区提供了极好的数据,这些数据的确显示出极其明显的横向变化:夏威夷西北部(区域 2-2、2-3、可能还有 1-3)的传播速度

2-2, 2-3, and probably 1-3) and low in the vicinity of the islands (regions 1-4, 2-4, and 1-6). Interestingly, the $dT/d\Delta$ data presented by Davies and Sheppard[4] also indicate a horizontal velocity contrast of this sort in the vicinity of Hawaii. Unfortunately, no other proposed plumes are well sampled by our data. Region 1-13 includes the Mascarene Islands, but the data here are highly scattered, and no conclusion can be drawn. Regions 1-5 and 2-6, both with apparently high velocities, are located slightly to the northeast of the Galapagos Islands, so it is not clear what relation, if any, this velocity anomaly may bear to a possible plume. If travel time data for rays passing through more proposed plume regions can be obtained, they may provide valuable evidence relevant to the Wilson-Morgan hypothesis.

Except, perhaps, for the Hawaiian Islands, no geological or tectonic features show an obvious correlation with the inferred deep mantle velocity anomalies. At shallower depths, however, this is not the case; regions 3-1, 4-1, and 4-6, all seeming to have low velocities, lie beneath the Kurile and Aleutian Island arcs. The only other island arc adequately sampled at these depths lies beneath Middle America (region 4-2) and is associated with early arrivals (though they are not significant at the 99.5% confidence level). The data thus suggest that low velocities may be characteristic of island arcs at depths greater than 1,000 km.

The data considered here do not support any correlation between velocity variations below 2,000 km and global gravity anomalies or geoid heights. At shallower depths such a correlation does exist, but it is merely another manifestation of the low velocities beneath the Kurile and Aleutian Islands, because the concave sides of island arcs are generally the sites of prominent positive free air gravity anomalies.

It is not possible to make a direct comparison between these results and those of Alexander and Phinney[5]. The region of the North Atlantic found by them to be anomalous is further east than the corresponding region sampled by our data. Further, travel time measurements such as ours provide a measure of the average velocity in a region, whereas the behaviour of core diffracted waves depends on features such as the velocity gradient in the lower mantle. Further studies of variations in the "visibility" within the core shadow would be a useful complement to travel time and $dT/d\Delta$ studies of the lower mantle.

We thank Dr. David Davies and Dr. M. Nafi Toksöz for helpful suggestions. This work was sponsored by the Advanced Research Projects Agency of the Department of Defense.

(**242**, 443-447; 1973)

Bruce R. Julian and Mrinal K. Sengupta
Lincoln Laboratory, Massachusetts Institute of Technology, Lexington, Massachusetts 02173

Received January 2, 1973.

很高，而群岛附近（区域 1-4、2-4 和 1-6）的传播速度则很低。有趣的是，戴维斯和谢泼德 [4] 提供的 dT/dΔ 数据也表明在夏威夷群岛附近也存在这类水平方向上的速度差异。可惜我们没能对其他设想的地幔柱进行很好的取样。区域 1-13 包括马斯克林群岛，但是这里的数据高度分散，不能据此得出任何结论。均具有很高传播速度的区域 1-5 和 2-6 略微靠近加拉帕戈斯群岛的东北部，因此并不清楚这里的速度异常与可能存在的地幔柱之间具有怎样的关系（假设存在一定关系的话）。如果能够获得更多穿过地幔柱的区域的地震波走时数据，或许就可以为威尔逊和摩根的假说提供有价值的证据。

可能除夏威夷群岛外其他群岛的地质和构造特征没有表现出与推断的深地幔速度异常有明显的相关性。但是在较浅的深度，情况并非如此；位于千岛岛弧和阿留申岛弧下方的区域 3-1、4-1 和 4-6，似乎都有低速异常。在这个深度上，经过充分的采样后唯一例外的一个岛弧位于中美洲下方（区域 4-2），这里地震波到达得早些（虽然这些时间在 99.5% 的置信水平上不显著）。因此，这些数据表明在超过 1,000 km 的地下深处，较低的传播速度可能是岛弧的特征。

这里引述的数据并不能证明在 2,000 km 以下的传播速度变化与地球重力异常或大地水准面高程之间有任何相关性。在较浅的深度上这种相关性确实存在，但这仅仅是地震波在千岛群岛和阿留申群岛下方低速传播的另一种表现，因为岛弧凹面一侧通常是自由空气重力正异常显著的地方。

然而，这些结果与亚历山大和菲尼 [5] 的研究成果并不能进行直接比较。因为他们在北大西洋发现的异常区比我们采样的相应区域要偏东。另外，我们测量走时的方法提供了一个区域内平均传播速度的量度，而地核衍射波的情况却依赖于诸如下地幔的速度梯度等属性。对于地核盲区内传播速度的进一步研究将是下地幔走时和 dT/dΔ 的研究一个有益的补充。

感谢戴维·戴维斯博士和纳菲·托克瑟兹博士给我们提出的建设性意见。本项研究由国防部高级研究计划局资助完成。

（张效良 翻译；张忠杰 审稿）

References:

1. Toksöz, M. Nafi, Chinnery, M. A., and Anderson, D. L., *Geophys. J. Roy. Astron. Soc.*, **13**, 31(1967).

2. Hales, A. L., and Roberts, J. L., *Bull. Seismol. Soc. Amer.*, **60**, 1427(1970).

3. Greenfield, R. J., and Sheppard, R. M., *Bull. Seismol. Soc. Amer.*, **59**(1969).

4. Davies, D., and Sheppard, R. M., *Nature*, **239**, 318(1972).

5. Alexander, Shelton S., and Phinney, R. A., J. *Geophys. Res.*, 7, 5943(1966).

6. Sengupta, Mrinal K., thesis, MIT(1972).

7. Herrin, E., Tucker, W., Taggart, J., Gordon, D. W., and Lobdell, J. L., *Bull. Seismol. Soc. Amer.*, **58**, 1273(1968).

8. Lilwal, R. C., and Douglas, A., *Geophys. J. Roy. Astron. Soc.*, **19**, 165(1970).

9. Carder, D. S., Gordon, D. W., and Jordan, J. N., *Bull. Seismol. Soc. Amer.*, **56**, 815(1966).

10. Wilson, J. T., *Phil. Trans. Roy. Soc.*, A, **258**, 145(1965).

11. Morgan, W. J., *Nature*, **230**, 42(1971).

304

# Evidence for an Advanced Plio-Pleistocene Hominid from East Rudolf, Kenya

R. E. F. Leakey

## Editor's Note

**Richard Leakey followed his father Louis' vocation in palaeontology at first very reluctantly, but soon began to make remarkable discoveries of his own. This one, from the eastern shore of Lake Rudolf (now Lake Turkana), was indeed spectacular—a skull and other skeletal material attributed to the genus *Homo*. The face of "1470 man" (after its catalogue number, KNM-ER 1470), with its remarkably human shape and relatively high forehead, was especially emotive. The specimen was later assigned to a new taxon, *Homo rudolfensis*. Notable in this study is Leakey's assertion of the age of this specimen at more than 2.6 million years: this was later found, after much controversy, to be an overestimate of almost a million years.**

---

Four specimens collected last year from East Rudolf are provisionally attributed to the genus *Homo*. One, a cranium KNM-ER 1470, is probably 2.9 million years old.

---

**P**RELIMINARY descriptions are presented of four specimens collected from East Rudolf during 1972. Most of the collection recovered during this field season has been reported recently in *Nature*[1]; the specimens described here are sufficiently important to be considered separately and in more detail. The collections of fossil hominids recovered from East Rudolf during earlier field seasons and detailed descriptions of some of these specimens have been published previously[2-5].

The specimens described here are: (1) a cranium, KNM-ER 1470; (2) a right femur, KNM-ER 1472; (3) a proximal fragment of a second right femur, KNM-ER 1475; and (4) an associated left femur, distal and proximal fragments of a left tibia, and a distal left fibula, KNM-ER 1481. They were all recovered from area 131 (see Fig. 1) and from deposits below the KBS Tuff which has been securely dated at 2.6 m.y.[6].

Area 131 consists of approximately 30 km² of fluviatile and lacustrine sediments. The sediments are well exposed and show no evidence of significant tectonic disturbance; there is a slight westward dip of less than 3°. Several prominent marker horizons provide reference levels and have permitted physical correlation of stratigraphical units between area 131 and other areas in the East Rudolf locality.

# 来自肯尼亚鲁道夫湖以东的一个高级上新世– 更新世人科动物证据

利基

## 编者按

*理查德·利基最初并不情愿承接他父亲路易斯的职业，从事古生物学的研究，但是很快他就有了自己的重大发现。在鲁道夫湖（即现在的图尔卡纳湖）东畔发现了一件头骨和其他的骨骼材料，这些标本均可被归入人属，这是十分令人震惊的发现。其中，带有显著人类形态和较高前额的"1470 号人"（根据其标本号'KNM-ER 1470'命名）的面部尤为令人激动。这个标本后来被归类为一个新种：人属鲁道夫种（Homo rudolfensis）。本次研究中值得关注的一点是，利基原本断定这个标本的年代至少为 260 万年前，但是经过后来的许多争论，人们发现这个年代被高估了约 100 万年。*

去年在鲁道夫湖以东搜集到的四件标本暂时被归入人属。其中的一件颅骨 KNM-ER 1470 可能有 290 万年的历史。

---

本文是对 1972 年间在鲁道夫湖以东搜集到的四件标本的初步描述。本次野外作业期间搜集到的大部分标本最近已经在《自然》杂志上进行了报道 [1]；本文描述的标本特别重要，因此需要单独研究并进行更详细的介绍。以往在鲁道夫湖以东的野外考察中发掘到的人科动物化石标本及对其中部分标本的详细描述也已经发表 [2-5]。

本文描述的标本包括：（1）一件颅骨，KNM-ER 1470；（2）一件右侧股骨，KNM-ER 1472；（3）另一件右侧股骨的近端破片，KNM-ER 1475；以及（4）相关联的左侧股骨，左侧胫骨的远端和近端破片以及左侧腓骨的远端，KNM-ER 1481。这些标本都是从 131 区（见图 1）的被确定为有 260 万年历史的 KBS 凝灰岩以下的沉积物中发掘出来的 [6]。

131 区由大约 30 km² 的河流沉积物和湖沼沉积物组成。这些沉积物都充分暴露，并且没有证据显示发生过重大的地质构造扰动；只有一个向西倾斜的不足 3° 的小倾角。几个明显的标志性地层可作为参考地层，据此可以将鲁道夫湖以东地点的 131 区和其他几个区之间的地层单元进行岩性对比。

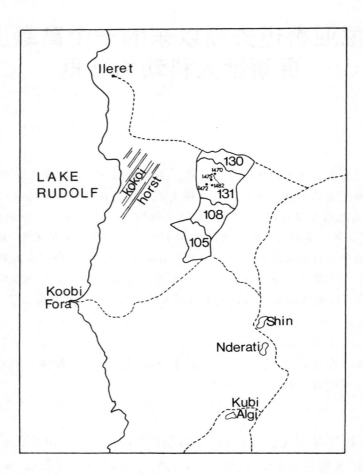

Fig. 1. Map showing sites of discovery of fossil hominids KNM-ER 1470, 1472, 1475 and 1481 in the East Rudolf locality. Succession shown in Fig. 2 was taken from the position indicated by the dotted line.

Several tuffs occur in the vicinity of area 131. The lowest of these is the Tulu-Bor Tuff which is not exposed in the area itself but does outcrop nearby in several stream beds. Above this horizon, in a composite section, there is some 60 m of sediment capped by the prominent KBS Tuff. This latter tuff has been mapped into areas 108 and 105 (also shown in Fig. 1) from where samples have been obtained for K/Ar dates. An account of the geology is given by Vondra and Bowen[7]. A section showing the vertical position of these four hominids in relation to the KBS Tuff is given in Fig. 2.

At present, analysis of samples collected for dating from the KBS Tuff in area 131 has proved inconclusive because of the apparent alteration of the sanidine felspars. This was not seen in the 105/108 samples from the same horizon which provided the date of 2.61 m.y. and there is no reason to suspect the validity of that date (personal communication from J. A. Miller).

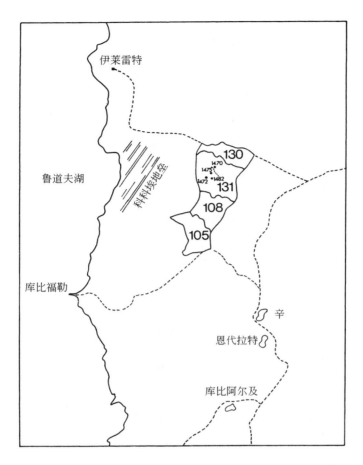

图 1. 此图显示了在鲁道夫湖以东遗址出土人科动物化石 KNM-ER 1470、1472、1475 和 1481 的地点位置。
图 2 显示的剖面序列取自本图中虚线所示的位置。

131 区周围存在好几层凝灰岩。其中处于最底层的是 Tulu-Bor 凝灰岩，它本身在该区域并没有暴露出来，仅在几处河床附近有露头。在这层之上，是一个复合剖面，其中有被 KBS 凝灰岩覆盖着的约 60 m 厚的沉积物。这些凝灰岩已经在 108 区和 105 区被定位（见图 1），K/Ar 年代测定的样品就是在这两个区采集的。冯德拉和鲍恩已经对该处的地质情况进行了说明 [7]。图 2 给出了垂直方向上这四个人科动物标本的位置与 KBS 凝灰岩关系的剖面示意图。

目前，由于透长石存在明显的变化，所以对从 131 区的 KBS 凝灰岩层采集到的样品进行的年代测定分析结果已不具有决定性。但这种现象并未在 105/108 区同一层位采集到的被确定为 261 万年前的样品中出现，因此，没有理由怀疑 261 万年这一年代的真实性（来自与米勒的个人交流）。

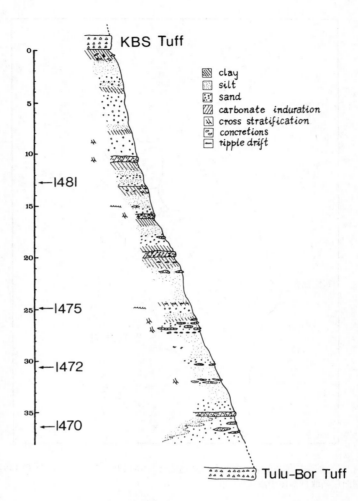

Fig. 2. Stratigraphical succession of the sediments in area 131 and the vertical relationships of the fossil hominids KNM-ER 1470, 1472, 1475 and 1481 to the KBS Tuff. Dotted line shown in Fig. 1 marks the position at which the section was taken.

Detailed palaeomagnetic investigation of the sedimentary units is being undertaken by Dr. A. Brock (University of Nairobi). Systematic sampling closely spaced in the section has identified both the Mammoth and Kaena events in area 105 between the Tulu-Bor and KBS Tuffs, a result which supports the 2.61 m.y. date on the latter. The mapping of several horizons has established a physical correlation between areas 105 and 131. During the 1973 season, the area 131 succession will be sampled in detail in an attempt to confirm this correlation. Available evidence points to a probable date of 2.9 m.y. for the cranium KNM-ER 1470, and between 2.6 and 2.9 m.y. for the other specimens reported here.

Collections of vertebrate fossils recovered from below the KBS Tuff in areas 105, 108 and 131 all show the same stage of evolutionary development and this evidence supports the

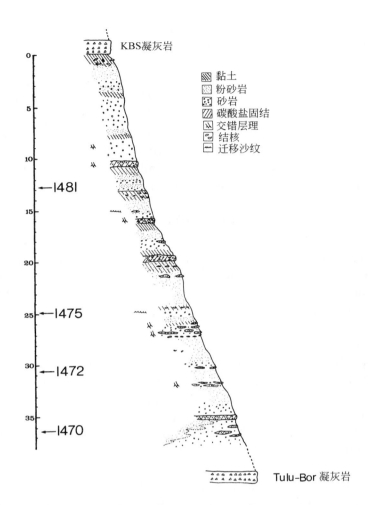

图 2. 此图显示了 131 区沉积物的地层序列以及人科动物化石 KNM-ER 1470、1472、1475 和 1481 与 KBS 凝灰岩在垂直方向上的关系。图 1 中虚线表示该剖面所选择的位置。

布罗克博士（内罗毕大学）正在对沉积物单元进行详细的古地磁学研究。在剖面处进行的小间隔的系统采样工作已经识别出了 105 区的 Tulu-Bor 和 KBS 凝灰岩层间与马莫斯事件和凯纳事件相对应的地层，该结果支持基于 KBS 凝灰岩得到的 261 万年的年代测定结果。对几处地层进行的绘图已经在 105 区和 131 区之间建立了岩性上的相关关系。在 1973 年的挖掘工作中，我们将对 131 区地层序列进行详细采样以期进一步确定这一关系。现有证据表明颅骨 KNM-ER 1470 的年代可能为 290 万年，而本文报道的其他标本的年代则介于 260 万年到 290 万年之间。

从 105、108 和 131 区的 KBS 凝灰岩之下的地层发掘出来的脊椎动物化石都显示出它们处于同样的演化阶段，这一证据支持鲁道夫湖以东沉积物的年代测定结果。

indicated age for this phase of deposition at East Rudolf. Maglio[8] has discussed the fossil assemblages following detailed studies of field collections from various horizons.

The cranium (KNM-ER 1470) and the postcranial remains (KNM-ER 1472, 1475 and 1481) were all recovered as a result of surface discovery. The unrolled condition of the specimens and the nature of the sites rules out the possibility of secondary deposition— there is no doubt in the minds of the geologists that the provenance is as reported. All the specimens are heavily mineralized and the adhering matrix is similar to the matrix seen on other fossils from the same sites. In due course, microscopic examination of thin sections of matrix taken from the site and on the fossils might add further evidence.

## Cranium KNM-ER 1470

Cranium KNM-ER 1470 was discovered by Mr. Bernard Ngeneo, a Kenyan, who noticed a large number of bone fragments washing down a steep slope on one side of a gully. Careful examination showed that these fragments included pieces of a hominid cranium. An area of approximately 20 m × 20 m was subsequently screened and more than 150 fragments were recovered.

The skull is not fully reconstructed. Many small fragments remain to be included and it may be some time before the task is completed. At present the cranial vault is almost complete and there are good joins between the pieces. The face is less complete and although there are good contacts joining the maxilla through the face to the calvaria, many pieces are still missing. The orientation of the face is somewhat uncertain because of distortion of the frontal base by several small, matrix filled cracks. The basicranium shows the most damage and is the least complete region.

The cranium (see Fig. 3) shows many features of interest. The supraorbital tori are weakly developed with no continuous supratoral sulcus. The postorbital waisting is moderate and there is no evidence of either marked temporal lines or a temporal keel. The vault is domed with steeply sloping sides and parietal eminences. The glenoid fossae and external auditory meati are positioned well forward by comparison with *Australopithecus*. The occipital area is incomplete but there is no indication of a nuchal crest or other powerful muscle attachments.

In view of the completeness of the calvaria, it has been possible to prepare in modelling clay an endocranial impression which has been used to obtain minimum estimates for the endocranial volume. Six measurements of the endocast by water displacement were made by Dr. A. Walker (University of Nairobi), and gave a mean value of 810 cm$^3$. Further work on this will be undertaken but it seems certain that a volume of greater than 800 cm$^3$ for KNM-ER 1470 can be expected.

马利奥[8]在对来自于各个不同地层的采集物进行详细研究后，对该化石群进行了讨论。

颅骨（KNM-ER 1470）和颅后骨骼（KNM-ER 1472、1475 和 1481）都是在地表采集的。标本的状况和发现标本的地点的性质排除了二次沉积的可能性——地质学家们都确认关于化石出产层位的报道属实。所有标本的石化程度都很高，附着于其上的围岩与同一遗址的其他化石中看到的围岩都很相似。对从该遗址和化石上取得的围岩进行薄切片显微镜检测已经列入研究计划之中，可能会进一步充实这方面的证据。

### 颅骨 KNM−ER 1470

颅骨 KNM-ER 1470 由肯尼亚的伯纳德·恩格奈奥先生发现，他注意到在一条冲沟一侧的陡坡上有大量骨骼破片被冲下来。经过仔细研究后发现这些破片包括了数块人科动物颅骨。随后对约 20 m × 20 m 的区域进行了筛查，又发现了 150 多块破片。

该头骨没能完全重建出来。还有许多小碎片没有找到，所以重建整个头骨的工作尚需时日才能完成。现在头骨穹隆几乎是完整的，各个碎片之间的连接情况很好。与之相比，面部则稍欠完整，尽管上颌骨从面颅到脑颅之间的部分有着很好的连接，但是还有许多骨片缺失。因为几处小的、填有填充物的裂缝造成额底有些变形，所以脸部的朝向尚未确定。颅底是受损最严重的区域，也是最不完整的部位。

颅骨（见图 3）显示出许多有趣的特征。眶上圆枕并不发达，也没有连续的圆枕上沟。眶后缩狭程度中等，没有显著的颞线或颞龙骨突。颅顶两侧的斜坡和顶骨结节突出组成了颅顶的圆拱。与南方古猿相比，颞骨关节窝和外耳道的位置更靠前。枕区不完整，但没有显示存在项嵴或其他有力的肌肉附着的迹象。

鉴于颅骨的完整性，可以使用黏土制作颅内模，以获得其颅容量的最小估计值。沃克博士（内罗毕大学）通过测量排水量得到了内腔模型的 6 项尺寸，给出了 810 cm³ 的颅容量平均值。对于这方面的进一步研究还会继续，但可以预料到的是，KNM-ER 1470 的颅容量似乎肯定大于 800 cm³。

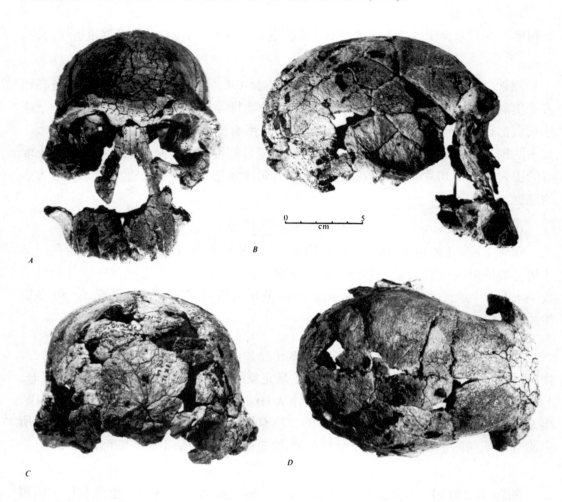

Fig. 3. Cranium KNM-ER 1470. *a*, Facial aspect; *b*, lateral aspect; *c*, posterior aspect; *d*, superior aspect.

The palate is shallow, broad and short with a nearly straight labial border that is reminiscent of the large *Australopithecus*. The great width in relationship to the length of the palate does contrast markedly, however, with known australopithecine material. The molars and premolar crowns are not preserved, but the remaining roots and alveoli suggest some mesiodistal compression. The large alveoli of the anterior teeth suggest the presence of substantial canines and incisors.

## Femur KNM-ER 1472

KNM-ER 1472, a right femur, was discovered as a number of fragments by Dr. J. Harris. It shows some features that are also seen in the better preserved left femur, KNM-ER 1481, but other features, such as the apparently very straight shaft and the bony process on the anterior aspect of the greater trochanter, require further evaluation.

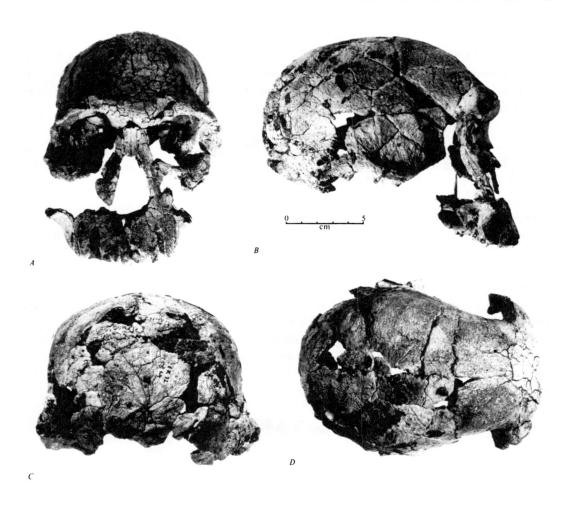

图 3. 颅骨 KNM-ER 1470。a，前面观；b，侧面观；c，后面观；d，上面观。

腭浅、宽而短，唇边缘接近笔直，这使人想起了大型南方古猿。然而，腭宽度与长度的比例偏大，这又与已知的南方古猿材料有着明显的不同。白齿和前白齿齿冠没有保存下来，但是残存的牙根和齿槽表明其受到了来自近中远侧的挤压。前牙的巨大齿槽表明其具有相当大的犬齿和门齿。

## 股骨 KNM-ER 1472

KNM-ER 1472 是一件右侧股骨，它被哈里斯博士发现时是一堆破片。该标本具有的某些特征在保存相对较好的左侧股骨 KNM-ER 1481 中也有体现，但是其他特征，例如非常笔直的骨干和大转子前面的骨质突起等，还需要进一步评估。

315

## Femoral Fragment KNM-ER 1475

The proximal fragment of femur, KNM-ER 1475, was discovered by Mr. Kamoya Kimeu. Its condition is such that a final taxonomic identification will be difficult and it is therefore included only tentatively in this report. This fragment shows some features such as a short, more nearly cylindrical neck, which are not seen in the femurs of *Australopithecus*.

## Associated Skeleton KNM-ER 1481

A complete left femur, KNM-ER 1481, associated with both ends of a left tibia and the distal end of a left fibula were also discovered by Dr. J. Harris.

The femur (see Fig. 4) is characterized by a very slender shaft with relatively large epiphyses. The head of the femur is large and set on a robust cylindrical neck which takes off from the shaft at a more obtuse angle than in known *Australopithecus* femurs. There is a marked insertion for gluteus maximus and the proximal region of the shaft is slightly flattened antero-posteriorly. The femoro-condylar angle is within the range of *Homo sapiens*. When the femur is compared with a restricted sample of modern African bones, there are marked similarities in those morphological features that are widely considered characteristic of modern *H. sapiens*. The fragments of tibia and fibula also resemble *H. sapiens* and no features call for specific comment at this preliminary stage of study.

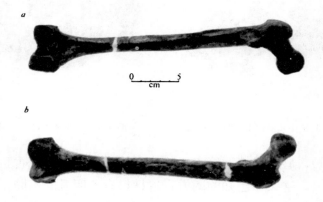

Fig. 4. Left femur KNM-ER 1481. *a*, Posterior aspect; *b*, anterior aspect.

## *Homo* or *Australopithecus*?

The taxonomic status of the material is not absolutely clear, and detailed comparative studies which should help to clarify this problem have yet to be concluded. The endocranial capacity and the morphology of the calvaria of KNM-ER 1470 are characters that suggest inclusion within the genus *Homo*, but the maxilla and facial region are unlike those of any known form of hominid. Only the flat fronted wide palate is suggestive of *Australopithecus*, but its extreme shortening and its shallow nature cannot be matched in existing collections representing this genus. The postcranial elements cannot readily be distinguished from *H. sapiens* if one considers the range of variation known for this species.

### 股骨破片 KNM-ER 1475

股骨近端的破片，KNM-ER 1475，由卡莫亚·基梅乌先生发现。鉴于该标本的情况，很难对其进行最终的分类学鉴定，因此在本文中只是暂且将其列出。该破片的一些特征，例如短的、接近圆柱形的颈部等特征在南方古猿的股骨中都不曾出现。

### 相关联的骨骼 KNM-ER 1481

哈里斯博士还发现了一根完整的左侧股骨 KNM-ER 1481，这根股骨与同时发现的左侧胫骨两端以及左侧腓骨远端相关联。

该股骨（见图4）的特征是具有很细长的骨体以及相对较大的骨骺。股骨头部大，长在一个粗壮的从骨体生出的圆柱状颈上，该颈部与骨体形成的钝角比已知的南方古猿股骨的要大。臀大肌有一个明显的插入，骨体的近端区域在前后方向上有些扁平。股骨髁突与股骨的角度属于智人的范畴。当把该股骨与一个特定的现代非洲骨骼标本进行比较时，普遍认为它们在形态学特征上与现代智人的特点有显著相似性。胫骨和腓骨破片也与智人相似，就目前的初步研究阶段来看，还没有需要特别讨论的特征。

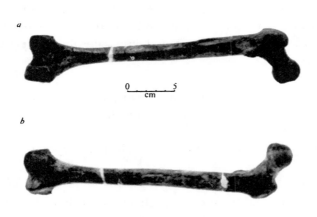

图 4. 左侧股骨 KNM-ER 1481。a，后面观；b，前面观。

## 是人还是南方古猿？

该材料的分类学位置还不十分清楚，有助于阐明该问题的详细比较学研究尚未得出结论。KNM-ER 1470 的颅容量和颅顶形态学特征表明其属于人属，但是其上颌骨和面部区域又不像任何已知的人科动物。只有前移的宽阔腭表明其可能属于南方古猿，但是它极短且浅的特征却又不能与现存的代表此属的标本相匹配。如果考虑到智人种已知的变异范围，其颅后骨骼结构无法与智人明确地区别开。

The East Rudolf area has provided evidence of the robust, specialized form of *Australopithecus* from levels which span close to 2 m.y. (2.8 m.y.-1.0 m.y.)[1]; throughout this period the morphology of this hominid is distinctive in both cranial and postcranial elements. The cranial capacity of the robust australopithecine from Olduvai Gorge, *A. boisei*, has been estimated for OH 5 to be 530 cm[3] (ref. 9); this is the same value as that estimated by Holloway for the only specimen in South Africa of *A. robustus* which provides clear evidence of cranial capacity[9]. Holloway has also found the mean cranial capacity of six specimens of the small gracile *A. africanus* from South Africa[10] to be 422 cm[3]. Thus, to include the 1470 cranium from East Rudolf within the genus *Australopithecus* would require an extraordinary range of variation of endocranial volume for this genus. This seems unacceptable and also other morphological considerations argue strongly against such an attribution.

The Olduvai Gorge has produced evidence of an hominine, *H. habilis*; the estimated endocranial volumes for three specimens referred to this species are 633, 652 and 684 cm[3] (ref. 10). The Olduvai material is only known from deposits that are stratigraphically above a basalt dated at 1.96 m.y. (ref. 11). At present therefore there does not seem to be any compelling reason for attributing to this species the earlier, larger brained, cranium from East Rudolf.

The 1470 cranium is quite distinctive from *H. erectus* which is not certainly known from deposits of equivalent Pleistocene age. It could be argued that the new material represents an early form of *H. erectus*, but at present there is insufficient evidence to justify this assertion.

There is no direct association of the cranial and postcranial parts at present, and until such evidence becomes available, the femora and fragment of tibia and fibula are only provisionally assigned to the same species as the cranium, KNM-ER 1470. Differences from the distinctive *Australopithecus* postcranial elements seem to support this inferred association.

For the present, I propose that the specimens should be attributed to *Homo* sp. indet. rather than remain in total suspense. There does not seem to be any basis for attribution to *Australopithecus* and to consider a new genus would be, in my mind, both unnecessary and self defeating in the endeavor to understand the origins of man.

I should like to congratulate Mr. Ngeneo and Dr. Harris for finding these important discoveries. Dr. Bernard Wood spent many long hours at the site screening for fragments and assisted my wife, Meave, and Dr. Alan Walker in the painstaking reconstruction work. I thank them all. The support of the National Geographic Society, the National Science Foundation, the W. H. Donner Foundation and the National Museum of Kenya is gratefully acknowledged.

(**242**, 447-450; 1973)

鲁道夫湖以东地区将近 200 万年跨度（距今 280 万到 100 万年）的地层中出土了粗壮种南方古猿这一特化类群存在的证据[1]；这整个时期里，这种人科动物在颅骨和颅后骨骼结构的形态方面都是独特的。奥杜威峡谷发现的一种粗壮型南方古猿——南方古猿鲍氏种 OH5 的颅容量估计为 530 cm³（参考文献 9）；这与霍洛韦估计的南非唯一一个能提供明确的颅容量数据的南方古猿粗壮种的数值相同[9]。霍洛韦还计算了在南非[10]发现的小型纤细南方古猿非洲种的六个标本的颅容量，其平均值为 422 cm³。因此，要将鲁道夫湖以东发现的 1470 号颅骨纳入南方古猿属中，就要求该属的颅容量具有更大的变异范围。这似乎并不能为人们所接受，另外还有其他的形态学因素也强烈反对这种分类。

奥杜威峡谷已经出土了一种人类——能人的化石；估计三个被归入该种的标本的颅腔容量分别为 633 cm³、652 cm³ 和 684 cm³（参考文献 10）。我们仅仅知道奥杜威标本是从年代为距今 196 万年的玄武岩之上的地层堆积物中得到的（参考文献 11）。因此现在似乎还没有令人信服的理由可以将该标本划分到这种鲁道夫湖以东发现的更早期的、具有较大大脑的颅骨的物种中去。

1470 号颅骨与从更新世同期沉积物中采集到的研究不充分的直立人非常不同。可以这样说，这件新标本代表了直立人的一种早期形式，但是现在还没有足够的证据来证实这种说法。

目前这具颅骨和颅后部分没有直接的联系，除非出现相反证据，否则只能暂时将股骨和胫骨、腓骨的破片与颅骨 KNM-ER 1470 归为同一种。新标本与独特的南方古猿颅后骨骼结构之间存在的差异似乎支持这种推测出的联系。

目前，我提议将该标本归入人属未定种，而非像原来那样完全悬而未决。我认为，将其划分为南方古猿似乎没有任何依据，而将其定义为一种新属既没有必要，而且在理解人类起源这一问题上也只会弄巧成拙。

我想祝贺恩格奈奥先生和哈里斯博士取得了这些重要的发现。伯纳德·伍德博士在遗址处花费了很长时间筛查骨骼破片，并协助我的妻子米芙和艾伦·沃克博士进行艰苦的重建工作。我要感谢他们所有人。对于国家地理学会、国家科学基金会、唐纳基金会和肯尼亚国家博物馆的支持，也表示衷心的感谢。

（刘皓芳 翻译；吴新智 崔娅铭 审稿）

**R. E. F. Leakey**
National Museums of Kenya, PO Box 40658, Nairobi

Received January 23, 1973.

---

References:

1. Leakey, R. E. F., *Nature*, **242**, 170 (1973).

2. Leakey, R. E. F., *Nature*, **231**, 241 (1971).

3. Leakey, R. E. F., *Nature*, **237**, 264 (1972).

4. Leakey, R. E. F., Mungai, J. M., and Walker, A. C., *Amer. J. Phys. Anthrop.*, **35**, 175 (1971).

5. Leakey, R. E. F., Mungai, J. M., and Walker, A. C., *Amer. J. Phys. Anthrop.*, **36**, 235 (1972).

6. Fitch, F. J., and Miller, J. A., *Nature*, **226**, 223 (1970).

7. Vondra, C., and Bowen, B., *Nature*, **242**, 391 (1973).

8. Maglio, V. J., *Nature*, **239**, 379 (1972).

9. Tobias, P. V., *The Brain in Hominid Evolution* (Columbia University Press, New York and London, 1971).

10. Holloway, R. L., *Science*, **168**, 966 (1970).

11. Curtis, G. H., and Hay, R. L., in *Calibration of Hominoid Evolution* (edit. by W. W. Bishop and J. A. Miller) (Scottish Academic Press, Edinburgh, 1972).

# Practical Application of Acupuncture Analgesia

S. B. Cheng and L. K. Ding

## Editor's Note

Around this time, the widespread use of acupuncture analgesia across China was drawing interest from the West. Here Chinese medical doctors S. B. Cheng and L. K. Ding sum up pros and cons for the use of the technique in surgery. The procedure, which is cheaper and carries fewer complications than analgesic drugs, works particularly well in patients with a confident outlook. But it fails to dull the nerves as effectively as drug analgesia, and only really works well in upper-body operations such as thyroidectomies and lung surgery. Given this, the duo suggests that acupuncture analgesia sometimes be considered an alternative but not a replacement to drug therapy.

---

Acupuncture analgesia can sometimes be considered as an alternative to drugs, but it cannot be considered as a universal replacement. There are certain cases, however, where acupuncture analgesia is better than drugs and this technique needs to be developed further in order to assess its true significance. In this article two Chinese doctors, one of whom has conducted twenty-four operations using acupuncture analgesia, assess the advantages and disadvantages of using the technique in surgery.

---

SINCE the reported success of the use of acupuncture analgesia in several hundred thousand operations in China, great interest in this type of analgesia has been aroused all over the world. In Japan, America and other nations, medical people have begun to investigate the application of acupuncture analgesia in their daily medical and clinical work. This article is an attempt to give some explanation of the technique in order to assist others who are experimenting with it. It is based on the personal experience of one of us who has used this type of analgesia in twenty-four operations—three mitral stenoses, five lobectomies, six gastrectomies and ten thyroidectomies.

Acupuncture analgesia uses no anaesthetic drugs. Instead it is based on Chinese traditional medical theory, *Ching-lo*, which states that by applying pressure to certain specific points on the body, these points (on the meridians) will become numb. Pressure is applied by using a certain method of needling so that pain is either dulled or removed altogether. Thus, in using this technique during surgical operations, sensation in the area in which the operation is to be performed can be dulled while the patient remains entirely conscious.

At present in China this technique is widely used in both urban and rural hospitals and in mobile medical clinics. It has been used for surgery on the brain, neck, chest, abdomen and limbs. In addition, it has been applied in obstetric operations and in operations on

# 针刺镇痛的实际应用

郑，丁

**编者按**

在这个时期，针刺镇痛在中国的广泛应用吸引了西方的关注。本文中中医师郑和丁总结了在手术中使用这项技术的利弊。这种技术与麻醉剂相比成本更低廉，带来的并发症更少，在有信心的患者身上发挥了特别好的功效。但是它并不像麻醉剂那样有效地使神经麻木，而且实际上只能在上半身的手术中发挥好的疗效，如甲状腺切除术和肺部手术。考虑这些，两位医师建议某些时候将针刺镇痛作为药物疗法的另一种选择而不是替代治疗。

---

针刺镇痛有时候可以作为药物的另一种选择，但是不能完全取代药物的作用。尽管确实在一些病例中针刺镇痛的效果要好于药物，但这门技术需要进一步的发展以评估其真正的重要意义。在这篇文章中，两位中国医生评估了在手术中使用这门技术的优点和缺点，其中一位已经用针刺镇痛施行了 24 例手术。

---

据报道在中国使用针刺镇痛成功进行了成百上千例手术，这种镇痛方法引起了全世界人们的广泛关注。在日本、美国和其他国家，医学工作人员已经开始研究将针刺镇痛应用到他们的日常医疗和临床工作中。本文试图对这门技术进行一些解释，以便于帮助那些正在研究这门技术的人。这主要来自于我们其中一位作者的个人经验，这位作者已经应用这种镇痛方法进行了 24 例手术——3 例二尖瓣狭窄、5 例肺叶切除术、6 例胃切除术和 10 例甲状腺切除术。

针刺镇痛不使用任何麻醉剂，而是基于传统中医学理论——经络，该理论认为将通过向身体上某些特定位点施压，这些点（位于经脉上）会变得麻木。压力的给予是通过一种特定的针刺方法，这样疼痛感就会变得迟钝或者完全消失。因此在手术中使用该技术就可以在患者保持神智完全清醒的状态下，使需要手术的部位的感觉变得迟钝。

目前该技术在中国的城市和乡村医院以及流动诊所均得到广泛使用。它已经被用于脑部、颈部、胸部、腹部和四肢的手术。此外它也被用于产科手术以及耳、鼻

the ears, nose and throat. Acupuncture has attained a definite place in Chinese medical practice and, when it can be used appropriately, has become the first choice of anaesthetic.

The use of acupuncture analgesia depends on the availability of properly trained manpower. A skilled medical team including anaesthetists is necessary. The team should be composed both of those who have expertise in the use of anaesthetic drugs and of those familiar with acupuncture analgesia. Those who have a thorough knowledge of both techniques are obviously the most valuable. Before the operation, one or two members of the team need to visit the patient to find out the patient's mental attitude, his desire to use this kind of analgesia and the nature of his illness. For their part, the team member or members should give a complete explanation of the anaesthesia technique to the patient.

In addition, the team of surgeons must be skilled, alert and capable. The doctors must be those whom the patient trusts, and they must have a thorough understanding of the patient's illness and mental attitude. Before the operation, they must give the patient a complete explanation of the surgical procedure and teach the patient to do the appropriate exercises such as deep breathing. The doctors must work quickly, steadily and accurately and must make the incisions and do suturing in the shortest possible time.

## Particular Applications

To illustrate the use of this technique in surgery, we shall describe its application in a thyroidectomy, where the best results have been obtained. Two preliminary steps are necessary. First, the consent of the patient must be obtained. In addition to explaining the procedures to him, it is highly recommended that a demonstration be performed on the patient before his operation. Second, the individuals who administer the analgesia must have a thorough understanding of the procedures. We suggest that the anaesthetists practise acupuncture on their own bodies in order to discover the various methods of using the needle, the different sensations acupuncture produces and the proper depth to which the needle needs to be inserted.

About a half hour before surgery, 50 mg pethidine or other sedative is given to the patient by injection. The acupuncture needles are then inserted at two points on the hand and forearm. The first point is called the *hu ku* and is located between the thumb and the forefinger on each hand. The needle is inserted to a depth of 0.5 inch or until the patient begins to feel sensations of aching, heaviness, fullness and numbness. The other point is the *nei kuan* which is located posteriorly about 2 inches above the wrist. The needle is inserted to a depth of 0.5 to 1 inch, again until similar sensations are felt. If the needles are placed in the proper position and are rotated in a circular manner for about 20 min, an analgesic effect will be induced. The ensuing surgical procedure must be light and fast. When the skin is cut, the technique of "flying knife–rapid cutting" must be used as some pain may be caused when the incision is made.

Acupuncture analgesia does not completely remove pain. For this reason, electric

和喉部的手术。针刺疗法在中医实践中的地位是不可否认的，而且运用恰当时，它势必成为麻醉的首选。

针刺镇痛的使用取决于经过合格训练的专业人员。而且还需要一个包括麻醉科医生在内的训练有素的医疗团队。这个团队的成员应该包括那些对于麻醉剂的使用有丰富经验的人和熟悉针刺镇痛的人。当然能够全面理解两种技术的人是最受欢迎的。手术前，该团队的一或两名成员需要访视患者以了解该患者的精神状态、他对于使用这种镇痛方法的诉求以及他的疾病的状况。他们的任务是向患者完整地解释这种镇痛方法。

此外，外科医生团队也要训练有素、机警并有足够的能力来完成手术。这些医生必须取得患者的信任，他们必须对患者的疾病和精神状态有充分的了解。手术之前他们必须向患者详细解释手术的过程并教会患者作适当的练习，比如深呼吸。医生的工作必须要迅速、稳定和准确，并且必须在尽可能短的时间内完成切口和缝合。

## 特 别 应 用

为了说明一下该技术在手术中的应用，我们将以其在甲状腺切除术中的应用为例，因为在这种手术中取得的效果最好。手术前的两个预备步骤很重要。首先，需要获得患者的知情同意。除了向他解释整个手术过程，我们强烈建议手术前在该患者身上进行一次演示。其次，施行针刺镇痛的术者必须熟练掌握整个过程。我们建议施针者在自己的身体上练习针刺技术以发现不同的用针方法、针刺产生的不同感受和针刺入的合适深度。

大约手术前半小时，给患者注射 50 mg 哌替啶或者其他镇静剂。然后将针刺入手和前臂上的两个点。第一个点被称为合谷，位于拇指和食指之间。针刺入的深度是 0.5 英寸或者直到患者出现疼痛、沉重、胀和麻木的感觉。另一个点被称为内关，位于腕掌侧正中向上 2 英寸。刺入的深度是 0.5 英寸到 1 英寸，也是直到患者出现类似的感觉为止。如果针刺的位置是准确的并且施行捻转手法大约 20 分钟，就能够产生镇痛效果。接下来的手术过程必须轻柔而且迅速。当切开皮肤时，必须使用"飞刀－快切"技术，因为切割时还是可能引起一定程度的疼痛。

针刺镇痛不能完全消除疼痛。出于这个原因，不能用电灼来止血。取而代之的

cauterization must not be used to stop bleeding. Instead, either ligation or pressure must be used. In addition, the patient must be warned that some uncomfortable feeling may be caused when the muscle is pulled around the neck and thyroid gland. The suturing procedure may also cause some pain and must be done as quickly as possible with sharp suture needles. If the level of pain increases, then the needles may be rotated again— or if that fails to bring relief, of course, drug anaesthesia may be resorted to. The whole operation should be performed very quickly to obtain the best results.

## Advantages

There are many advantages to the use of acupuncture analgesia. Here we shall discuss three. First, as we have mentioned, acupuncture analgesia, unlike drug anaesthesia, dulls the nerves without causing the patient to lose consciousness; thus, it allows the patient and doctor to cooperate with each other. For example, again in a thyroidectomy, the doctor can talk with the patient at any time, and by listening to the patient's voice can discover if any injury has been caused to the recurrent laryngeal nerve. Another example is found in cases which involve heart and lung surgery. After the opening incision has been made the doctor can direct the patient to do deep abdominal breathing in order to prevent a sudden shift in the mediastinum and to keep the lung inflated so as not to interfere with the operation and ventilation of the patient.

Second, by comparison with the use of anaesthetic drugs, there are fewer physiological and psychological complications. During operations using acupuncture, we have observed that the blood pressure, pulse and breathing remain regular. This is often not the case with drugs. After an operation with acupuncture analgesia, there are no side effects nor evidence of the complications which may follow operations done with drug anaesthesia. Moreover, because there are few physiological reactions, the patient recovers his normal physical and mental state very quickly. In addition, the patient is more psychologically fit after an operation using acupuncture analgesia. According to our observations, the patient has been aware of and understood the entire surgical process as he has been conscious during the operation; therefore, when the operation is finished, he feels the surgery has gone smoothly and has been quite safe. He is very happy with the results. Often, he immediately wants to get off the operating table, walk around and eat.

Third, acupuncture analgesia is more convenient and comparatively cheaper than other known techniques.

## Sometimes Inappropriate

One should not assume, however, that acupuncture analgesia is appropriate for all operations or a complete substitute for drug anaesthesia. Again according to our observations, the following factors impose limits on the use of this technique. First, acupuncture analgesia produces different results on different parts of the body. Our past experience has indicated that the results are better if the parts of the body involved are in the chest cavity and above. At present acupuncture analgesia is used in operations

方法是结扎或者压迫。此外，必须预先告知患者当牵拉颈部和甲状腺周围的肌肉时可能出现一些不适的感觉。缝合的过程也会产生一些疼痛，因此也需要用锋利的缝针尽可能快地完成。如果疼痛的程度加重了，需要再次捻转针灸针，如果这样还不能缓解疼痛，就需要加用麻醉剂了。整个手术过程必须非常快地进行以获得最好的效果。

优　　点

使用针刺镇痛有很多优点。这里我们只讨论三点。首先，正如我们所提过的，针刺镇痛在保持患者意识的情况下可以使神经麻木，这不同于麻醉剂麻醉。这样便于医生和患者间的合作。再以甲状腺切除术为例，医生能够随时与患者交谈，而通过听患者的声音就能够判断是否损伤了喉返神经。另一个例子就是心肺手术。在打开切口之后，医生能够指导患者进行深度的腹式呼吸以防止胸腔纵膈膜突然摆动。同时还能保持肺处于膨胀状态，这就不会干扰手术以及患者的呼吸。

其次，与使用麻醉剂相比，针刺镇痛的生理和心理并发症更少。利用针刺镇痛手术时，我们发现血压、脉搏和呼吸仍然保持平稳。这通常在药物麻醉时不容易实现。利用针刺镇痛进行手术后，不会出现药物麻醉所导致的副作用或者并发症。此外，由于出现的生理反应较少，患者容易迅速恢复正常的生理和心理状态。而且针刺镇痛手术后的患者心理更加健康。根据我们的研究发现，由于患者在手术中一直保持清醒，他们已经意识到并了解整个手术过程。因此，在手术结束以后他会觉得手术进行得很顺利而且非常安全。他会对结果非常满意。通常他们会立即想从手术床上下来，四处走动和吃饭。

第三，针刺镇痛相对已知的其他技术更加方便而且相对便宜。

有些时候不适用

但是我们不能认为针刺镇痛适于所有的手术，或者可以完全替代药物麻醉。同样根据我们的发现，下面的因素制约了这项技术的应用。首先，针刺镇痛在身体的不同部位产生的效果是不同的。我们过去的经验指出，对胸腔及其以上的身体部位使用针刺镇痛会取得更好的效果。目前，针刺镇痛已经用于头、颈和胸部的手术。正如前面所提及的，在甲状腺切除术中获得最满意的效果，因此我们用这种手术作

involving the head, neck and chest. As mentioned above, the best results have been achieved in thyroidectomies, so this type of surgery is being used for demonstration purposes. Other types of operation in which acupuncture analgesia has achieved good results are lung operations. In surgery on the abdomen and limbs, however, the results have been disappointing.

Second, the surgical cases must be selected carefully. When choosing a patient to undergo surgery with acupuncture analgesia, his illness must be considered. For example, in operations such as gastrectomies for gastric ulcers and pyloric stenosis, only if the operating time is short is it appropriate to use acupuncture analgesia. But for gastrectomies for stomach cancer in which a rather wide and long investigation is necessary, it is not wise to use acupuncture analgesia. For simple chest surgery such as localized pulmonary tuberculosis, acupuncture analgesia can be used. For exploratory surgery which takes time and in operations for widespread adhesions, it is, however, not advisable to use this technique. In conclusion, at the present time, cases should be chosen in which the nature of the disease is not too complicated and in which the operating time is 1 to 2 h.

Third, the emotional state of the patient must be considered. Because the success of the use of acupuncture analgesia depends on the willingness and understanding of the patient, this is a decisive factor. Before it is used, the entire procedure must be explained to the patient and his active cooperation must be enlisted. Thus, we select those who are emotionally stable, who have a high degree of confidence in the advantages of using acupuncture analgesia, and who are able to follow the doctor's requests and carry out his instructions. This kind of person is usually strong, energetic and young. Unsuitable types of patient include children under 10, who cannot cooperate with the doctor, and highly nervous individuals. In China, because thought preparation is thorough and deep, there are many people who have great faith in the doctors and nurses, and therefore many now volunteer for and even request acupuncture analgesia.

## Problems

Acupuncture analgesia in clinical use is still in the initial stages of development. Our experience indicates that several problems have arisen in its application.

Acupuncture analgesia does not dull the nerves as completely and effectively as drugs. Thus, it is not suitable for every operation. On some occasions when the first incision is made, when suturing commences and/or when the procedure is long, the pain threshold may be decreased so as to render the analgesic effect relatively ineffective. It is therefore necessary to have drug anaesthesia available in case it must be used to complete the operative procedure.

Acupuncture analgesia does not cause complete relaxation of the muscles. For example, in abdominal surgery, during the operation the stomach and intestines might be disturbed which could result in a nervous reflex tightening the muscles and hence pain to the patient. If this condition does arise, drug anaesthesia may have to be used.

为示范。其他针刺镇痛取得良好效果的就是肺部手术。但是从腹部和四肢的手术取得的效果来看，结果并不令人满意。

其次，手术病例的选择必须非常谨慎。当选择一个患者进行针刺镇痛手术时，必须要考虑他的病情。比如，在进行胃溃疡和幽门梗阻的胃部切除术时，只有手术时间短的患者才适合用针刺镇痛。而胃癌进行胃部切除术时，需要进行非常广泛和长时间的观察，因此并不适合用针刺镇痛。对于简单的胸部手术，比如局部肺结核，可以使用针刺镇痛。但是对于非常耗时的探查性手术和广泛粘连的手术，我们不建议使用这种技术。总之，目前应该选择疾病本身不是很复杂，并且手术时间在 1 小时到 2 小时之间的病例。

第三，必须考虑患者的情绪状态。因为针刺镇痛成功使用取决于患者的意愿和理解，这是一个决定因素。在使用前，必须向患者解释整个过程，而且必须获得其主动配合。因此我们选择那些情绪稳定、高度相信针刺镇痛的优势以及能够听从医生的要求并执行医生指令的患者。这类患者通常比较强壮、精力充沛并且年轻。不合适的患者包括不能和医生合作的 10 岁以下的儿童和高度紧张的患者。在中国，因为思想准备工作做得非常全面和深入，许多患者非常相信医生和护士，因此有很多人自愿甚至主动要求进行针刺镇痛。

## 问　　题

临床使用针刺镇痛仍处在发展的初始阶段。我们的经验表明在其应用过程中出现了一些问题。

针刺镇痛使神经麻木的作用不像药物那么完全和有效。因此它不适用于所有手术。有些情况下，当切开第一刀、开始缝合和（或）手术时间很长时，痛阈可能会下降导致镇痛的效果变得不理想。因此，有必要准备好麻醉剂，在必要的时候使用，以保证整个手术的完成。

针刺镇痛不能让肌肉完全放松。比如，在腹部手术中，胃和肠道受到刺激后可能导致产生神经反射使肌肉紧张，因此造成患者的疼痛。如果确实出现了这种情况就需要使用药物麻醉。

The theoretical investigation of the effects and uses of acupuncture analgesia is still in the early stages. The results of the use of this technique are only being brought to light through continued experience and experiments. Thus, at present, there is a method of systematic investigation to provide a firm basis for our work. We are now attempting to investigate the relationships between drugs and acupuncture analgesia. Although we believe acupuncture analgesia can be used widely, we feel it is misleading to say that it can and will replace the use of drug anaesthesia. At this stage we can only say that in certain cases acupuncture analgesia is better than drugs. Acupuncture analgesia is only a new anaesthetic technique, and in some contexts at least it may prove to be a better kind of anaesthetic skill. We believe that both acupuncture analgesia and drugs should be used in surgical work in order to further our understanding of the use of this new technique. We admit that it is a radical step to say it is possible merely to insert a needle, in the absence of drugs, to relieve pain. But at a time when the medical field is changing rapidly and new ideas are ever present, the importance of this development must not be neglected.

(**242**, 559-560; 1973)

S. B. Cheng and L. K. Ding
Chinese Medical Research Centre, 566-568 Nathan Road, Kowloon, Hong Kong

　　针刺镇痛的效果和应用的理论研究仍然处于早期阶段。使用该技术的效果只能通过后续的经验和试验才受到人们的关注。因此，目前需要一个系统的研究方法来给我们的工作提供坚实的基础。我们现在正在尝试研究药物麻醉和针刺镇痛之间的关系。尽管我们相信针刺镇痛能够被广泛应用，但是我们认为那种认为它能完全替代药物麻醉的说法是一种误导。现阶段，我们只能说在某些情况下针刺镇痛比药物好。针刺镇痛只是一种新的麻醉技术，而且，至少在某些情况下，它是一种比较好的麻醉方法。我们相信针刺镇痛和药物麻醉都应该在手术中使用以便于加深我们对这项新技术的理解。我们承认仅仅通过刺入一根针而不用药物就可以缓解疼痛是比较激进的。但是在这个医学领域变幻莫测、新想法不断涌现的年代，这种技术的重要性一定不能被忽视。

（毛晨晖 翻译；于天源 审稿）

# Experiments on Polishing of Diamond

J. Wilks

### Editor's Note

The interest of this contribution from John Wilks at Oxford is not so much in the specific findings—that polished diamond is microscopically rough—but in the way it touches on several themes in materials science that have become increasingly relevant in recent decades: the microscopic mechanisms of lubrication and friction, the microtopography of surfaces, and the quest for superhard materials. Wilks highlights the fact that polishing a solid surface is usually different to abrading it, involving local melting because of intense frictional heating. But as only diamond powder itself can polish diamond, abrasion must here be the mechanism: the powder chips the surface and leaves it rough in a way that depends on the orientation of the crystal planes.

---

Polished diamond surfaces have unusual properties because polishing of the brittle material generally proceeds by mechanical chipping.

---

DIAMONDS are shaped and polished to produce gem stones by methods which have remained essentially unchanged for several hundred years. Yet it is only recently that the physical basis of these operations has been studied, and their unusual features fully appreciated. This article outlines the principal features of the polishing process and describes some recent experiments which illustrate the very characteristic nature both of the process itself and the polished surfaces produced. We shall show that these perhaps unique properties result from the very hard and brittle nature of the diamond.

The usual method of polishing a diamond is to hold it either against the face of a rotating cast-iron wheel (or scaife) charged with a suspension of fine diamond powder in a light oil, or against the face of a wheel in which diamond powder is bonded into a metal matrix. One of the most striking features of this method is that if a cube face is prepared on the diamond, it turns out that the rate of removal of material during polishing with a bonded wheel in a direction parallel to a cube axis is about 100 times greater than if the same face is polished in a direction at 45° to a cube axis. Similar effects are observed on other faces, and even greater differences are evident when polishing on a cast-iron scaife, as the more resistant directions of the diamond tend to knock the powder out of the scaife.

In preparing a gem stone from a rough diamond it is necessary to remove a certain amount of material to position the facets before polishing them. Another unusual feature is that this removal of material is effected in almost the same way as polishing, except that larger sized diamond powder is used to remove material quickly. For most materials,

# 金刚石抛光实验

### 编者按

来自牛津的约翰·威尔克斯所做的贡献中令人感兴趣的不仅仅在于抛光的金刚石在显微镜下是粗糙的这一特定研究结果，还在于近几十年来它越来越多地涉及材料科学的若干主题：润滑和摩擦的微观机制、表面的微观形貌和对超硬物质的探求。威尔克斯强调固体表面的抛光与磨削是有区别的，抛光包括由强烈的摩擦热产生的局部熔化。但是只有金刚石粉本身能抛光金刚石，磨削一定是这种机制：粉末切削表面后，表面的粗糙情况在某种程度上取决于晶面的取向。

---

抛光的金刚石表面具有不同寻常的性质，因为这种脆性物质的抛光通常是通过机械切削来进行的。

---

在过去的几百年中，将金刚石加工成形和抛光以生产宝石所用的方法在本质上保持不变。一直到最近，这些操作的物理学基础才得到了研究，它们那不同寻常的特征也得到了充分的理解。本文概述了抛光过程的主要特征，并且描述了一些最近的实验，它们阐明了对于抛光过程本身和所产生的抛光表面都极有特征性的本性。我们将要说明，这些独特性质可能是由金刚石极硬且脆的本性所导致的。

抛光金刚石的常规方法是将金刚石抵在覆盖着细小金刚石粉末的轻油悬浊液的旋转铸铁轮（或磨光盘）表面上，或者是抵在表面嵌入金刚石粉末的金属基体的轮表面上。这种方法一个最令人吃惊的特征是，如果要在金刚石上磨制一个立方体表面，就会发现在用黏合了粉末的轮子进行的抛光过程中，平行于立方轴方向上的磨除速率约是同一表面在与立方轴呈 $45°$ 角方向上的速率的 100 倍。在其他面上也观测到了类似的效应，在用铸铁磨光盘进行抛光时甚至发现了更为显著的速率差异，因为在金刚石更具刚性的方向上更容易磨掉磨光盘上的粉末。

在把金刚石原料加工成宝石时，必须要在抛光定位刻面前切除一定量的余料。另一个不同寻常的特征就是这种材料的切除会产生与抛光几乎一样的效应，只不过为了快速切除会使用较大尺寸的金刚石粉末。对于大多数材料来说，抛光和通过磨

polishing and the removal of material by abrasion are quite different processes. Removal of material is generally achieved by the use of an abrasive powder in what is essentially a cutting process; the powder is harder than the specimen, and it either gouges out material, or sets up stresses which lead to cracking after it has moved on. By contrast, polishing is generally a smearing process, brought about by rubbing with a second material to produce high temperatures in the small regions of true contact between the asperities on the two surfaces; the high temperatures result in local melting of the asperities, which are then smoothed out. It follows that to polish a specimen, we must use polishing material with a higher melting point, so that on rubbing, the specimen melts and flows first. For further details of the general features of abrasion and polishing, see for example, Bowden and Tabor[1] and Cottrell[2].

In view of all this, one would expect to encounter difficulties both in removing material from diamonds and in polishing them. As far as the removal of material is concerned, there is no harder substance than diamond which can be used to produce abrasive cutting. In rubbing operations, the high thermal conductivity of diamond will tend to reduce the temperature of the hot spots at the areas of local contact, whereas high temperatures are required to effect even the conversion of diamond to graphite. Thus, conditions seem unfavorable for both abrasion and polishing, but in fact the traditional methods used by the diamond industry abrade and polish diamond quite successfully. The rate of abrasion is relatively low, but a high polish can readily be obtained, and a diamond surface may be worked to the standard of a good optical flat[3].

The first scientific experiments on the polishing process were made more than 50 years ago by Tolkowsky[4], who proposed that both abrasion and polishing proceed by mechanical chipping on a microscopic scale. This chipping will be controlled by the lie of the cleavage planes relative to the direction of abrasion, and will therefore occur more readily in some directions than others, thus giving rise to very considerable differences in rates of abrasion. To indicate the geometrical arrangement of the cleavage planes, Tolkowsky made use of a model of diamond built up from small identical octahedral and tetrahedral shaped blocks, and thus explained the variations of the hardness on both the cube and the dodecahedron planes[4,5].

Tolkowsky was principally interested in practical applications and his conclusions about how to polish and abrade diamonds soon found their way into the diamond trade, as did his other research on the best way to lay out the facets of a diamond so as to produce the well known brilliant cut. On the other hand, his account of the underlying mechanism was not widely published, and attracted little attention. His treatment was criticized on the grounds that diamond is certainly not built up of equally sized elementary blocks as in his model, but the essential function of the model is to indicate the positions of the cleavage planes—and this it does correctly. It now turns out, as the result of various experiments on diamond over the past 15 years, together with increasing knowledge of the nature of brittle materials, that Tolkowsky's views are essentially correct.

削来切除材料是相当不同的过程。原料的切除一般是通过使用磨料粉末以本质上是切削的过程来实现的；粉末比样品更坚硬，它们在移动中或者挖去原料，或者施加应力而使样品产生破裂。与此相反，抛光一般是一个涂抹的过程，通过用另一种材料进行摩擦，在两个表面的粗糙部位之间真正接触的小区域中产生高温，高温引起粗糙部位的局部熔融，继而使其变平滑。由此可知，为了将样品抛光，我们必须使用具有较高熔点的抛光材料，以便使样品在摩擦时首先熔融和流动。关于磨削与抛光过程一般特征的更详细资料可参见鲍登和泰伯 [1] 与科特雷尔 [2] 的文章。

考虑到上述这一切，可以预料人们在从金刚石上切除余料以及对其进行抛光时都会遇到困难。就原料的切除而言，不存在比金刚石更硬的物质可以用来进行磨削切削。在摩擦操作中，金刚石的热传导性高，将会倾向于降低局部接触区域中热位点的温度，而高温甚至是从金刚石到石墨的转化过程所必需的。因此，情况对于磨削和抛光似乎都是不利的，但事实上，金刚石工业所用的磨削和抛光金刚石的传统方法却是相当成功的。磨削速率相对来说较低，但是很容易获得高度抛光，而且金刚石表面可以作为一个良好的光学标准平面 [3]。

关于抛光过程的第一个科学实验是在 50 多年前由托尔考斯基 [4] 进行的，他提出，磨削和抛光过程都是通过微观尺度上的机械切削实现的。这一切削过程将会受到解理面的形貌相对于磨削方向的位置的控制，并且会因此在某些方向上比在另一些方向上更容易发生切削过程，从而导致颇为可观的磨削速率差异。为了说明解理面的几何排列方式，托尔考斯基使用了以同样的八面体和四面体形小块搭建的金刚石模型，并由此解释了立方体和十二面体平面上的硬度变化 [4,5]。

托尔考斯基主要关心实践应用，因而他关于如何抛光和磨削金刚石的结论很快就在金刚石行业得到应用，就像他另一个关于展示金刚石刻面的最佳方式的研究导致了广为人知的明亮琢型的产生一样。另一方面，他关于潜在机制的说明却没有得到广泛发表，因此没有引起多少注意。他的处理方法遭到了批评，根据是金刚石肯定不是像他的模型中那样由同样大小的基本模块搭建而成的，但是该模型的实质功能在于说明解理面的位置——而它正确地做到了。过去 15 年来关于金刚石的若干实验的结果，再加上对于脆性材料本性越来越多的了解，可以证实托尔考斯基的观点实质上是正确的。

One of the crucial features of the above experiment observed but not stressed by Tolkowsky[4], is that the rate of removal of material is proportional to the total number of revolutions of the polishing scaife but does not depend on its speed. This result, confirmed by Wilks and Wilks[5,6], shows that thermally activated processes play no significant part in the removal of material. The rubbing together of two materials produces heating at the areas of true local contact, and this excess temperature increases rapidly with the speed of rubbing[1]. The fact that the abrasion per revolution does not increase with rising speed of rubbing clearly demonstrates that local hot spots play no significant part in the wear process. In particular, it rules out the possibility that the diamond is worn away by either burning or conversion to graphite, as suggested by Seal[7]. On the other hand, one would expect the same amount of material to be removed by each revolution of the wheel if the abrasion proceeds by a mechanical chipping or cleavage process.

The conditions necessary for materials to fail by chipping or brittle fracture have been discussed by several authors, for example Kelly[8]. Kelly, Tyson and Cottrell[9] have considered whether an ideal crystal free of imperfections will fail plastically by shear or by brittle fracture under tension. They show that for face centred metals such as copper, gold and silver, the stress required to produce fracture is about 30 times greater than that to produce shear, and that failure always occurs by plastic deformation rather than cleavage. On the other hand, the calculations show that, of the substances considered, sodium chloride and diamond are most likely to fail by brittle fracture. The critical stresses for shear and cleavage in sodium chloride and diamond are approximately equal, but the calculations are not sufficiently refined to indicate which process is preferred. These calculations are, however, for ideal crystals and the essential question for real materials is whether the presence and motion of dislocations will permit plastic flow before fracture.

Dislocations in diamond have been observed by Evans[10] who prepared specimens of diamond by etching, and viewed the dislocations directly in the transmission electron microscope. They are also clearly delineated by the X-ray topograph techniques of Frank and Lang[11]. Calculations mentioned by Evans[12] suggest that the movement of the dislocations will be inhibited by the necessity of breaking carbon-carbon bonds. Their motion has been studied experimentally by Evans and Wild[12,13] who took specimens of diamond in the form of thin slabs, loaded them in the middle, and observed whether they failed by fracture or plastic deformation. They found that at low temperatures the beam always failed by fracture, but that an increasing amount of plastic flow was observed as the temperature exceeded 1,500°C. Hence dislocations in diamond may be quite mobile, but at room temperature are held back by obstacles which can only be overcome by considerable thermal activation. As the rates of abrasion and polish in the experiments referred to above were independent of the temperature of local hot spots, one concludes that the abrasion was not accompanied by any thermally activated motion of dislocations.

It is sometimes suggested that plastic flow in diamond may be produced by conditions of intense local pressure. The effect of pressure on brittle materials is sometimes surprising, for example it is possible to compress a slab of brittle material, such as rock salt, to half its

上述实验中托尔考斯基观察到了但并未强调的一个关键特征 [4]，就是切除材料的速率与抛光磨盘总转数成比例，而与其速率无关。这个结果得到了威尔克斯和威尔克斯 [5,6] 的确认，它表明热激发过程在材料切除中的作用并不重要。两种材料的相互摩擦使真正接触的局部区域产生了热，而且过剩温度随着摩擦速率的上升而快速增加 [1]。每转的磨削不随摩擦速率提高而增加这一事实清晰地证明局部热位点在磨削过程中不起重要作用。尤其是，它排除了西尔 [7] 的观点，即金刚石通过燃烧或转化为石墨而磨削的可能性。另一方面，人们可以预想，如果磨削是通过机械切削或解理过程而进行的，那么轮的每一转会切除相同量的材料。

若干位作者，比如凯利 [8]，已经讨论了关于材料通过切削或脆性断裂而破坏的必需条件。凯利、泰森和科特雷尔 [9] 曾考虑，毫无缺陷的理想晶体是否会通过切变或在张力下脆性断裂发生塑性破坏。他们指出，对于诸如铜、金和银等面心金属来说，产生断裂所需的应力是产生切变所需应力的约 30 倍，而且破坏的产生经常是由于塑性形变而不是解理。另一方面，计算表明，在所考虑的各种物质中，氯化钠和金刚石是最容易由于脆性断裂而破坏的。氯化钠与金刚石中切变和解理的临界应力是近似相等的，但是计算还没有精细到足以指出哪一过程是更为有利的。不过，这些计算都是针对理想晶体的，而对于真实材料的实质问题是，位错的存在和运动是否会允许先塑性流动后再断裂。

金刚石中的位错已被埃文斯 [10] 所观测到，他用蚀刻法制备金刚石样品，然后在透射电子显微镜下直接观察到了位错。弗兰克和兰 [11] 也用 X 射线照相技术对其进行了清晰的描述。埃文斯 [12] 所提到的计算指出位错的运动会因为必须要打破碳—碳键而被抑制。位错的运动已由埃文斯和维尔德 [12,13] 进行了实验研究，他们使用具有薄板形式的金刚石样品，在其中部加置负荷，然后观察它们是因断裂还是塑性形变而破坏。他们发现，低温时样品板总是会因断裂而破坏，但是当温度超过 1,500 ℃时，可以观测到塑性流动量的增加。因此金刚石中的位错可能具有相当的流动性，不过在室温时被某种阻碍所抑制，只有通过相当大的热激发才能克服这种阻碍。由于上面所提到的实验中的磨削和抛光速率与局部热位点的温度无关，有人断言，磨削并不伴随着任何位错的热激发运动。

不时有人提出，金刚石中的塑性流动可能是由强烈的局部压力而产生的。压力对于脆性材料的影响有时会是令人惊讶的，例如，将诸如岩盐等脆性材料的平板压

initial thickness without producing cracking[14], and Howes and Tolansky[15] have argued that the ring cracks produced by indenting diamond with steel spheres show evidence of plastic flow. Later studies by Lawn and Komatsu[16] of the region round such a crack, using X-ray topography, show no sign of plastic deformation, and Frank and Lawn[17] have since shown that the cracks may be described in terms of fracture processes.

We conclude that the mechanism of abrasion is one of mechanical chipping. This conclusion is supported by a study of the area around an abrasion mark, by Frank, Lawn, Lang and Wilks[18] using X-ray topography, which shows that the state of strain in the surface is consistent with stresses set up by fracture processes and not by plastic flow. We believe that there is no convincing evidence for the motion of dislocations in any of the relevant abrasion and polishing experiments, although claims to have observed plastic flow in diamond at room temperature have been made by Brookes[19] and by Gane and Cox[20]. Brooks indented a diamond surface with a Knoop indenter made of diamond and claimed that the form of the indentation indicated that plastic flow had occurred. A careful study of Brookes's indentations, however, show clear indications of brittle fracture (Fig. 1), which appear to have been obscured in the earlier micrographs. The observations of Gane and Cox were based on the study of thin diamond wedges pressed against each other, but their evidence is at best inconclusive. Even under these rather specialized conditions, there is no clear evidence that plastic flow and motion of dislocations took place.

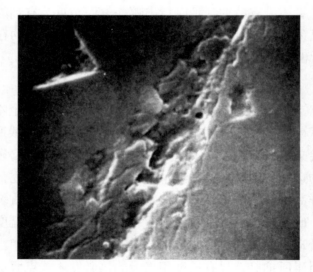

Fig. 1. Scanning electron microscope micrograph of a diamond surface indented with a Knoop indenter (×8,400).

We shall now describe three sets of experiments which confirm the fracture process and illustrates the unusual properties of polished diamond surfaces. In the first set a simple micro-abrasion tester[21] was used to study the variation of the rate of removal of material—in short the hardness of the diamond—with the orientation of the surface and the direction of polish. The hardness is often extremely sensitive to any change in the orientation of the facet being abraded. For example, Fig. 2 shows the relative rates

缩到其初始厚度的一半而不产生裂痕[14]是有可能的，而且豪斯和托兰斯基[15]认为，通过用钢球挤压金刚石而产生的环形裂纹可以作为塑性流动的证据。后来朗和小松[16]利用 X 射线照相法对这类裂纹周围的区域的研究指出没有这种塑性形变的迹象，弗兰克和朗[17]由此指出，可以按照断裂过程对裂纹加以描述。

我们断言磨削的机制是一种机械切削。这一结论为弗兰克、朗、兰和威尔克斯[18]用 X 射线照相法对磨削痕迹周围区域的研究所证实，该研究表明，表面的应变状态与断裂过程而非塑性流动所导致的应力相一致。我们相信，在任何有关磨削和抛光的实验中都不存在位错运动的可靠证据，尽管布鲁克斯[19]以及甘恩和考克斯[20]曾宣称在室温下观测到金刚石中的塑性流动。布鲁克斯用金刚石制成的努普压头挤压金刚石表面，并且宣称凹痕的形态表明曾发生过塑性流动。但是，对布鲁克斯凹痕的仔细研究可以看出清晰的脆性断裂迹象（图 1），它在以前的显微图像中可能一直都是模糊的。甘恩和考克斯的观测是基于对彼此挤压的小块楔形金刚石的研究，但是他们的证据充其量是不确定的。即便是在这些相当特殊的条件下，也不存在发生塑性流动和位错运动的明确证据。

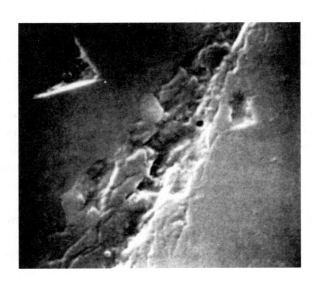

图 1. 用努普压头挤压金刚石表面得到的扫描电子显微图像（×8,400）。

现在我们要介绍三组实验，它们确证了断裂过程并且描绘出抛光后金刚石表面不同寻常的性质。第一组实验是用一个简单的微型磨削检测器来研究材料切除速率[21]——简而言之就是金刚石的硬度——随表面指向和抛光方向的变化。硬度通常对于磨削刻面的任何指向变化都极为敏感。例如，图 2 所示为通过使八面体平面偏

of removal of material on surfaces obtained by tilting an octahedron plane about the (011) axis indicated in the sketch plan. The crosses show the rate of removal of material for abrasion in the direction $A_x$, and the circles the rate in the direction $A_o$. We see that on a true octahedron plane the rate of removal in the direction $A_o$ is more than twice that in the direction $A_x$, but that a tilt of only about 1° is sufficient to reverse the relative hardness.

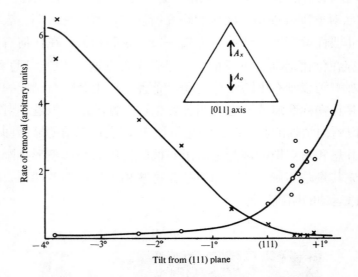

Fig. 2. The relative rates of removal of material by grinding on surfaces near to an octahedron plane. The symbols ○ and × correspond to the directions shown in the inset.

These orientation effects are not explained by Tolkowsky's treatment, which also has difficulty in discussing the octahedron face. The variation in rates of abrasion on cube and dodecahedron faces is explained by the lie of the cleavage planes which results in the production of a different structure by abrasion in different directions. As the cleavage planes run parallel to an octahedron face, the treatment seems to predict a uniform surface with no easy and hard directions of abrasion, in contrast with the measurements. To explain this point, we must consider the behavior of tilted octahedron facets.

A diamond surface which has been polished by a process of mechanical chipping will not be atomically flat but must consist of hills and valleys bounded by an irregular arrangement of cleavage planes as shown very schematically in Fig. 3A. It follows that abrasion proceeds by the removal of material from the tops or sides of the microhills. If Fig. 3A represents a section through an octahedron face, parallel to the directions $A_x$ and $A_o$, the lie of the cleavage planes is such that the most likely sites for the removal of material are the edges $a$ and $b$ (ref. 5). It also follows that the easiest direction of abrasion is $A_o$, and that most of the material is then removed from the edges $b$. If, on the other hand, a face is prepared inclined to the octahedron face by a small angle, the lie of the cleavage planes remains the same, so the structure of the microhills is as shown schematically in

340

离示图中所标出的（011）轴而得到的表面的材料切除的相对速率。叉形符号表示 $A_x$ 方向上由磨削所导致的材料切除速率，圆形符号则表示 $A_o$ 方向上的速率。我们看到在一个真正的八面体平面上，$A_o$ 方向上的切除速率比 $A_x$ 方向上的 2 倍还要大，但是只偏离 1° 就足以使相对硬度关系逆转。

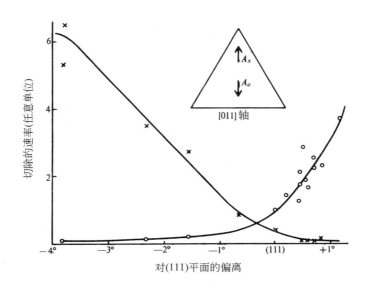

图 2. 在八面体平面附近的表面上碾磨所产生的材料切除的相对速率。符号 ○ 和 × 对应于插图中所示的方向。

托尔考斯基的处理方法并未解释这种指向效应，他的方法在讨论八面体的面时也是有困难的。在立方体表面和十二面体面上的磨削速率差异可以利用通过在不同方向上磨削而导致不同结构产生的解理面的形貌来解释。由于解理面趋向于与一个八面体的面平行，这种处理方法似乎预言了一个不存在磨削难易方向的均一表面，而这与测量结果是违背的。为了解释这一点，我们必须考虑偏离的八面体刻面的行为。

如同图 3A 中颇为概略地显示的那样，通过机械切削过程抛光后得到的一个金刚石表面不是平坦的，而是包含着由解理面无规则排布所围成的峰和谷。由此可知，磨削是通过从这些微小山峰的顶部和侧部切除材料而实现的。如果图 3A 表示通过八面体的一个面的截面，平行于 $A_x$ 和 $A_o$ 方向，那么解理面就会具有这样的形貌：最有可能发生材料切除的位置是边 $a$ 和 $b$（参考文献 5）。还可以知道最容易磨削的方向是 $A_o$，以及大部分材料因此是从 $b$ 边切除的。另一方面，如果令一个面与八面体的面倾斜成一个小角度，那么解理面的形貌仍保持原样，所以微小山峰的结构就如图 3B 中概略地显示的那样。从形貌的角度看，磨削轮一定会得到数量增加的 $b$ 类

Fig. 3*B*. Topographically, the abrading wheel must be presented with an increased number of *b* type edges, and the hardness correspondingly reduced. Similarly a tilt in the opposite direction increases the hardness.

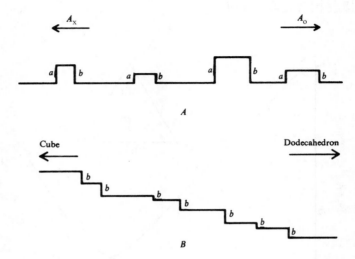

Fig. 3. Schematic diagrams of polished diamond surfaces (see text).

One also expects that the change in hardness with tilt may be very rapid. If the linear dimensions of the microhills are all of the same order of magnitude $h$, the average distance between hills in contact with the abrading wheel will be much larger because the areas of real contact are less than the nominal areas by factors of order $10^4$. Thus the distance between the hills may be of the order of $100\ h$, so that a tilt of $1°$ would be sufficient to change the topography of Fig. 3*A* to that of Fig. 3*B*, and thus approximately double the number of sites of easy abrasion. Similar arguments may be applied to account for the hardness of both true and tilted cube and dodecahedron faces. All the predictions that can be made from the model are in accord with experiment[5].

We have also made studies of the jagged nature of polished diamond surfaces, implied by our abrasion experiments, by observing the friction of diamond sliding on diamond in air. Some time ago Seal[7] showed that the friction of a polished cube surface varies with the azimuthal angle of sliding, with a four-fold symmetry. This result is at first surprising, as Bowden and Hanwell[22] have shown that diamond surfaces in air are covered by a strongly adsorbed film which reduces the friction by an order of magnitude below its value for clean surfaces in high vacuum. Thus even though the diamond surface is covered by a tenacious film of adsorbed gases, the symmetry of the diamond is projected through the film.

The friction between diamonds in air was first measured by Bowden and Young[23], and Bowden and Tabor[24] later pointed out that their results showed an approximate relation between the friction $\mu$ and the load $W$ of the form $\mu \propto W^{-1/3}$. They then suggested that

型的边，而硬度则相应地下降。类似地，相反方向上的偏离则会增加硬度。

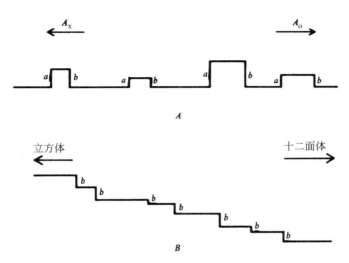

图 3. 抛光后金刚石表面的示意图（见正文）。

　　我们还可以预期硬度随偏离的变化会非常快。如果微小山峰的线性尺度全都具有同样的数量级 $h$，与磨削轮接触的山峰之间的平均距离就会大很多，因为真正的接触面积不到名义上的面积的 $10^{-4}$。因此山峰之间的距离可能具有 $100h$ 的数量级，才能使 $1°$ 的偏离就足以使图 $3A$ 中的形貌改变成图 $3B$ 中那样，并由此而使易磨削位置的数目近似翻了一倍。类似的论证可以用来解释正的与倾斜的立方体面和十二面体面的硬度。从这个模型所能得到的所有预言都与实验结果吻合 [5]。

　　我们还对磨削实验显示的抛光后金刚石表面的粗糙性质进行了研究，方法是观测在空气中金刚石在金刚石表面滑行时的摩擦力。一段时间之前，西尔 [7] 曾指出抛光立方体表面的摩擦力随着滑行方位角的变化而变化，并具有四重对称性。最初看来这个结果是令人惊讶的，因为鲍登和汉威尔 [22] 曾指出，空气中的金刚石表面为一层强烈吸附的薄膜所覆盖，它使摩擦力比起在高真空中清洁表面降了一个数量级。因此，即使金刚石表面被黏着性的吸附气体薄膜所覆盖，金刚石的对称性也会透过薄膜表现出来。

　　空气中的金刚石间摩擦力是由鲍登和扬 [23] 首先测得的，后来鲍登和泰伯指出，他们的结果表明摩擦力 $\mu$ 与负载 $W$ 之间具有形如 $\mu \propto W^{-1/3}$ 的近似关联。接着，他们提出，这种关联性会由于实际上的真实接触区域之间的附着过程而增加，而且这

this relation arose because of adhesion processes between the actual areas of true contact, and that this adhesion was responsible for the friction. Recent measurements by Casey and Wilks[25] show, however, that the friction is independent of the load over a wide range of loads, including the range of the earlier experiments. It therefore seems that the mechanism responsible for friction is not one of adhesion, a result which is confirmed by the fact that the friction remains unchanged when the diamond surface is lubricated with light oil.

The observed behavior of the friction is readily explained by a roughness (or ratchet) type mechanism associated with the jagged nature of a polished diamond surface. That is, the friction force arises from the work required to move the two diamond surfaces against the normal load as they are forced apart when asperities ride over each other. Some of this work will degenerate into heat when the jagged and irregular surfaces come together again, because the return motion will tend to be abrupt and irreversible. The work of separation is proportional to the load, so this type of mechanism leads to a value of the friction which is independent of the load. We believe that this mechanism accounts quite generally for the friction of diamond on diamond in air as discussed in more detail by Casey and Wilks[25]. The adsorbed film acts as a lubricant, which reduces adhesion and the high friction observed in a vacuum, but does not obscure the structure of the surface.

Fig. 4a shows the results of recent measurements on the friction of a diamond sliding over a polished cube surface which are similar to those of Seal[7]. The diamond surface had been polished in the usual way and was therefore covered by an array of fine polishing lines or grooves running parallel to a cube axis. Nevertheless, the friction shows a full four-fold symmetry, having the same value in directions parallel and perpendicular to the grooves. We then repolished a surface by abrasion in a hard direction at 45° to a cube axis, until the original polishing lines were replaced by a new set at 45° to the original direction. The friction on this new surface is shown in curve b; the friction has quite different values and exhibits only a two-fold symmetry, the lowest values being for directions parallel to the direction of polish.

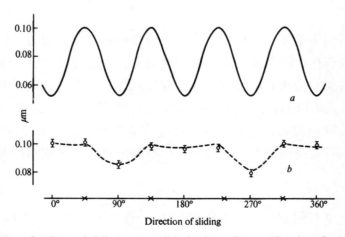

Fig. 4. The friction of a diamond sliding over a polished cube surface as a function of azimuthal angle. a, After polishing in the normal soft direction; b, after polishing in a hard direction.
The symbols × indicate the positions of the cube axes.

种附着就是摩擦力产生的原因。不过，凯西和威尔克斯最近的测量结果 [25] 表明，摩擦力在一个宽广的负载范围内是与负载无关的，其中包含着早期实验中的负载范围。于是，看起来附着机制并不是导致摩擦力产生的机制，这个结果被下面的事实所证实，即用轻油将金刚石表面润滑后摩擦力保持不变。

利用与抛光的金刚石表面粗糙性质有关的粗糙度（或棘齿）型机制，很容易解释已观测到的摩擦力行为。也就是说，摩擦力缘起于承担着正常负载的两个金刚石表面在其凹凸部分越过彼此被迫分离时所需要的功。这些功的一部分会在粗糙且不规则的表面再次靠拢时转化为热，因为返回运动会倾向于不连续和不可逆。这种分离功与负载成比例，因此这种机制导致摩擦力数值与负载无关。我们相信这种机制更普遍地解释了空气中金刚石间的摩擦力，如同凯西和威尔克斯 [25] 更为详细地讨论的那样。吸附膜承担润滑剂的作用，它减少了真空中所观测到的附着和强摩擦，但是并不掩盖表面的结构。

图 4a 显示了最近关于金刚石在抛光立方表面上滑行的摩擦力的测量结果，它与西尔的结果 [7] 类似。金刚石的表面已经用常规方式进行了抛光，从而为平行于立方轴的一排精细的抛光线或者说凹槽所覆盖。尽管如此，摩擦还呈现出完全的四重对称性，在平行于和垂直于凹槽的方向上具有相同的数值。接着，我们在与立方轴成 45° 角的硬方向用磨削方法对一个表面进行重新抛光，直到原来的抛光线被一组与原方向成 45° 角的新抛光线所取代。曲线 b 显示了这个新表面上的摩擦力；摩擦力具有不同的数值，而且只呈现出二重对称性，最低数值出现在与抛光方向平行的方向上。

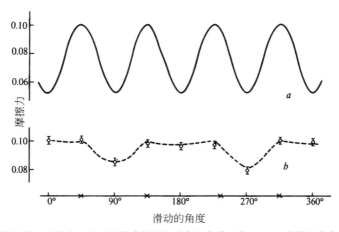

图 4. 金刚石在抛光的立方体表面滑动时的摩擦力作为方位角的函数。a，正常的软方向上的抛光后；b，硬方向上的抛光后。符号 × 表示立方轴的位置。

These results confirm that the topography of a polished surface is determined by mechanical chipping. Just as abrasion proceeds at different rates in different directions, because of the orientation of the cleavage planes, so surfaces prepared by polishing in different directions will have different structures. As discussed by Tolkowsky, a surface polished in the usual direction parallel to a cube axis will present a jagged surface with a four-fold symmetry. If, however, the diamond is polished in one of the hard directions, the surface structure will tend to take the form of grooving parallel to the direction of polish, with the two-fold symmetry shown in the friction measurements. We are at present extending our studies to observe the wear effects associated with repeated passes of the stylus over the same area of surface.

The third set of experiments are concerned with observing the surface structure of polished diamonds by using high resolution electron microscopy and carbon replica techniques. The structure turns out to be irregular and on a very small scale; therefore, particular care must be taken to ensure that the micrograph is in focus and free of astigmatism. Fig. 5 shows micrographs prepared under carefully controlled and similar conditions, except that the replica of Fig. 5a was taken from a freshly cleaved surface of mica, and those of Fig. 5b and c from polished surfaces of diamond. The greater contrast in the diamond micrographs indicates that the surface is much rougher than the mica and that the scale of the irregularities is of the order of 50 Å.

The micrographs in Fig. 5b and c were prepared from the same stone, using the same technique, but Fig. 5b was taken from a cube surface polished in the usual way, and Fig. 5c from a polished octahedron face. We have also observed similar structures on the cube and octahedron faces of a second diamond, and also a different characteristic structure on the dodecahedron faces. These results confirm the fact, well known to diamond polishers, that the quality of polish depends on the particular face being polished, as follows from the mechanical nature of the polishing process. One expects the surface structure to be delineated, at least to some extent, by cleavage planes. On a cube surface, the traces of these cleavage planes will lie at 45° to the direction of polish, and it is interesting to note that there are features lying in these directions. Further details of our results, together with details of the replication technique, will be published elsewhere.

Diamond is perhaps unique in that an apparently highly polished surface may in fact be mechanically rough on a microscopic scale, a result which is the consequence of its brittleness. We are at present applying these results to the use of diamond as cutting tools for machining metals, as both the rate of wear of the diamond, and the finish produced on the metal, depend sensitively on the surface structure of the tool. For example, the rate of wear of two single-diamond turning tools with identical external geometry, but fabricated so that the diamonds have different crystallographic orientations, show wear rates which are reproducible, and differ by a factor of 7 (ref. 26). The wear in this particular experiment, in which the diamonds turned an aluminum-silicon alloy of the type used to manufacture motor car pistons, was almost certainly controlled by the lie of the fracture planes as discussed above, and these are quite different in the two crystallographic

上述结果证实，抛光表面的形貌是由机械切削所决定的。正如磨削过程在不同方向上以不同速率进行一样，由于解理面的取向，通过不同方向上的抛光所制得的表面就会有不同的结构。根据托尔考斯基所讨论的，在平行于立方轴的常规方向上抛光的表面会呈现为具有四重对称性的粗糙表面。但是，如果将金刚石在某一个硬方向上抛光，表面结构将会倾向于形成平行于抛光方向的凹槽，并具有摩擦力测量中所显示的二重对称性。目前我们还将研究扩展到观测用铁针反复划过同一表面区域时所涉及的磨损效应。

第三组实验是利用高分辨电子显微技术和碳复型技术对抛光金刚石表面结构进行观测。研究表明该结构是不规则的并且具有很小的尺度；因此必须要特别小心以保证显微图像是清晰的而且没有受到像散的影响。图 5 显示了在类似条件下经谨慎控制所制备的显微图像，仅有的区别在于图 5a 的样品是云母的新鲜解理面，而图 5b 和 5c 则是抛光的金刚石表面。金刚石显微图像中更为鲜明的对比说明其表面比云母要粗糙很多，而且其不规则性的尺度具有 50 Å 的数量级。

图 5b 和 5c 中的显微图像是从同一块宝石以同样的技术得到的，不过图 5b 是来自以常规方式抛光的立方体表面，而图 5c 则是来自抛光的八面体表面。我们还曾在另一块金刚石立方体表面和八面体表面上观察到类似的结构，而且在十二面体表面上发现了不同的特征结构。这些结果确认了一个为金刚石抛光者所熟悉的事实，即抛光的质量取决于所抛光的特定的面，如同从抛光过程的机械性质中所得知的那样。人们期望至少在某种程度上表面结构可以用解理面来加以描述。在一个立方体表面上，这些解理面的交线会位于与抛光方向成 45° 角的方向，而且值得注意的是，在这些方向上存在着形貌特征。关于我们的结果的更多具体内容以及制样技术的细节，将会在其他文章中发表。

金刚石的独特在于它外观上高度抛光的表面可能实际上在显微镜尺度下却是机械粗糙的，这是其脆性所导致的后果。由于金刚石的磨损速率和金属表面的光亮效果都高度依赖于工具的表面结构，因此目前我们正在将这些结果运用在将金刚石制成金属加工的切割工具上。例如，两个具有相同外部几何形状但是制作成具有不同结晶学取向的单晶金刚石车刀，其磨损速率表现为可重现的，而且相差 7 倍（参考文献 26）。在这个特别的实验中，用两个结晶学取向完全不同的金刚石车刀车削一块用于制造汽车活塞的铝硅合金，其磨损几乎可以肯定是由上面所讨论的断裂面形

orientations. Further experiments are being continued on both the wear of diamonds and the finish they produce.

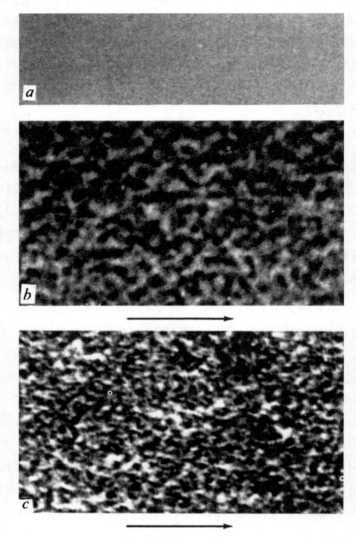

Fig. 5. Micrographs of replicas taken from *a*, cleaved mica; *b*, a polished cube face of diamond; *c*, a polished octahedron face of diamond. The arrows indicate the directions of polish. (× 1,000,000).

I thank Mr M. Casey for Figs. 1 and 4, Dr E. M. Wilks for Fig. 2, Dr D. Driver and Mr A. G. Thornton for the micrographs in Fig. 5, and the Science Research Council and De Beers Industrial Diamond Division for their support of this work.

(**243**, 15-18; 1973)

J. Wilks
Clarendon Laboratory, University of Oxford

貌所控制的。对于金刚石的磨损和它们所产生的光亮效果正进行进一步实验。

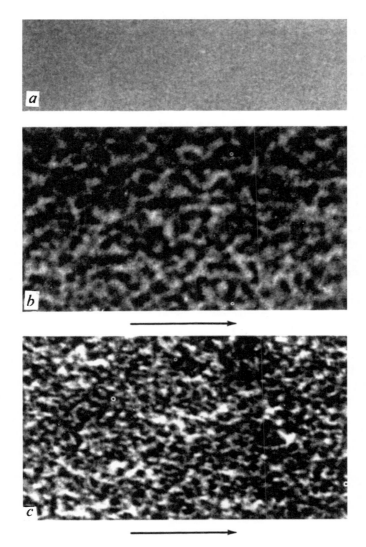

图 5. 样品的显微图像，a，取自解理的云母；b，取自抛光的金刚石立方表面；c，取自抛光的金刚石十二面体表面。箭头表示抛光方向。（×1,000,000）。

在此我要感谢凯西先生提供图 1 和图 4，感谢威尔克斯博士提供图 2，感谢德赖弗博士和桑顿先生提供图 5 中的显微图像，并且感谢科学研究理事会与戴比尔斯工业钻石部对这项研究的支持。

（王耀杨 翻译；郝伟 审稿）

References:

1. Bowden, F. P., and Tabor, D., *The Friction and Lubrication of Solids*, **1** (Clarendon, 1950); **2** (Clarendon, 1964).

2. Cottrell, A. H., *The Mechanical Properties of Matter* (Wiley, 1964).

3. Wilks, E. M., *J. Opt. Soc. Amer.*, **2**, 84 (1953).

4. Tolkowsky, M., thesis, Univ. London (1920).

5. Wilks, E. M., and Wilks, J., *J. Phys. D.*, **5**, 1902 (1972).

6. Wilks, E. M., and Wilks, J., *Phil. Mag.*, **38**, 158 (1959).

7. Seal, M., *Proc. Roy. Soc.*, **A248**, 379 (1958).

8. Kelly, A., *Strong Solids* (Clarendon, 1966).

9. Kelly, A., Tyson, W. R., and Cottrell, A. H., *Phil. Mag.*, **15**, 567 (1967).

10. Evans, T., *Physical Properties of Diamond* (edit. by Berman, R.), 116 (Clarendon, 1965).

11. Frank, F. C., and Lang, A. R., *Physical Properties of Diamond* (edit. by Berman, R.), 69 (Clarendon, 1965).

12. Evans, T., *Science and Technology of Industrial Diamonds*, **1** (edit. by Burls, J.), 105 (Industrial Diamond Information Bureau, London, 1966).

13. Evans, T., and Wild, R. K., *Phil. Mag.*, **12**, 479 (1965).

14. Bowden, F. P., and Tabor, D., *The Friction and Lubrication of Solids*, **2**, 118 (Clarendon, 1964).

15. Howes, V. R., and Tolansky, S., *Proc. Roy. Soc.*, **A230**, 287, 294 (1955).

16. Lawn, B. R., and Komatsu, H., *Phil. Mag.*, **14**. 689 (1966).

17. Frank, F. C., and Lawn, B. R., *Proc, Roy. Soc.* **A299**, 291 (1967).

18. Frank, F. C., Lawn, B. R., Lang, A. R., and Wilks, E. M., *Proc. Roy. Soc.*, **A301**, 239 (1967).

19. Brookes, C. A., *Nature*, **228**, 660 (1970).

20. Gane, N., and Cox, J. M., *J. Phys. D.*, **3**, 121 (1970).

21. Wilks, E. M., and Wilks, J., *The Physical Properties of Diamond* (edit. by Berman, R.), 221 (Clarendon, 1965).

22. Bowden, F. P., and Hanwell, A. E., *Proc. Roy. Soc.* **A295**, 233 (1966).

23. Bowden, F. P., and Young, J. E., *Proc. Roy. Soc.* **A208**, 444 (1951).

24. Bowden, F. P., and Tabor, D., *The Friction and Lubrication of Solids*, **2**, 169 (Clarendon, 1964).

25. Casey, M., and Wilks, J., *Diamond Research 1972* (Suppl. to *Ind. Diam. Rev.*), 6 (1972).

26. Casey, M., and Wilks, J., *Diamond Research 1972* (Suppl. to *Ind. Diam. Rev.*), 11 (1972).

# Tectono-eustatic Changes in Sea Level and Seafloor Spreading

N. C. Flemming and D. G. Roberts

## Editor's Note

Today there is general concern that the accumulation of carbon dioxide in the atmosphere will lead to a melting of ice in the Arctic and Antarctic and so increase sea level. This paper by two scientists from the National Institute of Oceanography in Britain raised the question whether the process of continental drift could substantially change sea level. The principle underlying this research is that the Earth's surface tends to be in "isostatic" equilibrium, meaning that the pressure exerted on the fluid mantle at great depths tends everywhere to be the same—in other words, continents exist only because they are less dense than the rocks that make up the sea bed in the great oceans.

This article describes a model for estimating eustatic changes and evidence for a correlation with seafloor spreading.

EUSTATIC changes in sea level are caused by a change in the form of the Earth's crust or in the total volume of ocean water[1]. The best examples of the latter are the short duration ($\sim 10^5$ yr) reversible changes caused by glacial advance and retreat during the Quaternary although there may also have been an increase in water volume by degassing from the mantle during the Mesozoic and Cainozoic[2,3]. Changes in sea level arising from changes in the form of the ocean basins are revealed in the geological record on continents as longer period ($\sim 10^7$ yr) transgressions and regressions that mark global changes in sea level[4,5], although the magnitude of the change may vary locally. Five principal factors[1,3,6] control sea level; of these, sediment deposition and trench formation may be neglected because the volumes are small or balanced by subduction. The most significant factors are (i) subsidence of the ocean crust, (ii) uplift of mid-ocean ridges and (iii) an increase or decrease in the length of the mid-ocean ridge system. These factors are, of course, controlled by sea-floor spreading and their relation to eustatic changes has been subject to speculation[5-13].

### Simple Quantitative Model

Here we present a model designed to estimate the magnitude of the eustatic change in sea level that would result from net alterations in the distribution of matter forming the continents and ocean floor, irrespective of the mechanisms involved. We assume a constant volume of water in the oceans and that there is no significant change in the average

# 构造–海平面变化和海底扩张

弗莱明，罗伯茨

编者按

现在，人们普遍关注的一个问题是大气中二氧化碳积累将会引起南、北极冰的融化，从而导致海平面上升。本文中，英国海洋科学研究所的两位科学家提出大陆漂移可能会使海平面发生很大程度变化的问题。开展此项研究的原理为，地球表面倾向于保持"均衡"平衡。这意味着对深部流体地幔所施加的压力在各处是相同的，换句话说，大陆之所以能够存在仅仅是因为它们的密度低于构成大洋海床的岩石密度。

---

本文阐述了一个估计全球海平面变化的模型以及海平面变化与海底扩张之间具有相关性的证据。

---

全球海平面变化是由地壳形态或大洋水总体积的变化引起的 [1]。后者的最好例子就是第四纪冰川进退所产生的短期（约 $10^5$ 年）可逆的变化，尽管中生代和新生代时期地幔的去气也可能使大洋水体积增加 [2,3]。在大陆的地质记录中，标志全球海平面变化的更长时期（约 $10^7$ 年）的海进和海退可以揭示因大洋盆地形状变化而引起的海平面变化 [4,5]，尽管其变化幅度因地而异。有五个主要因素控制着海平面变化 [1,3,6]，其中沉积物堆积和海沟形成所造成的影响可以忽略不计，因为它们的体积较小或者可以被俯冲作用所抵消。最重要的因素为：（1）大洋地壳的沉降，（2）洋中脊的抬升，（3）大洋中脊体系长度的增加或减少。当然，上述因素受海底扩张的控制，并且它们与海平面变化的关系仍属推测 [5-13]。

## 简单的定量模型

在本文中，我们提出了一个估算全球海平面变化幅度的模型。该模型只是依据形成大陆和洋底的物质分布的净变化，而不考虑其机理。我们假设大洋水的体积不变，地球平均半径、形状或转动均无明显改变。在一个平坦的、由现代体积的水

radius, shape or rotation of the Earth. On a smooth almost spherical Earth covered with the present volume of water, the ocean floor would be about 2,440 m below sea level, which would itself be about 240 m above present sea level[14,15].

Interaction between tectonics and sea level begins only when part of the lithosphere is raised above sea level; then any net vertical movement between the ocean floor and dry area will obviously produce a change in sea level. In particular, any increase in volume of solid crust above the water line must also be accompanied by an absolute lowering of sea level. In the context of plate tectonics, it is most meaningful to retain the distinction between continents and oceans in calculating departures from present continental areas and ocean depths. The global hypsographic curve[16,17] provides a convenient means of analysis (Fig. 1a) because constancy of water volume and rock density require that the total area representing crust and water volume must remain constant. To study a systematic series of deviations from the present curve, we varied the continent area ($x$) and maximum ocean depth ($y$) independently in 5% increments on either side of the present values, thereby defining forty-eight additional hypsographic curves. The base line for definition of the hypothetical continental areas was taken as the present area of continents at the altitude of present sea level, thus retaining the geophysical concept of a continent which may or may not be covered by water. Further, the profile of the continents was assumed to remain similar to the present profile and the oceanic part was altered by an amount proportional to its depth at all points, thereby preserving important features such as continental margins, mid-ocean ridges and satisfying fault distributions observed by Van Andel and Heath[18]; horizontal dimensions were altered in the proportion new oceanic area/old oceanic area.

From comparison with a new hypsographic curve (Fig. 1) we estimated the change in solid volume of the Earth beneath the ocean. This change was added to or subtracted from the volume of the continents above present sea level, and the new profile of the continents calculated using rules of proportionality similar to those used for the oceanic profiles.

Two further boundary conditions are necessary and define the range of variability possible without causing total submergence or extreme altitude. Total submergence of the continents occurs if the postulated increase in Earth volume below the oceans is greater than the total volume of continents above present sea level. Large decreases in solid volume below the ocean, or large decreases in continental area, require excessive increases in continental altitude. Peak continental altitudes greater than twice the present value have been disregarded on isostatic grounds and because uplift is unlikely to exceed erosion by a sufficient amount.

Typical hypsographic curves for two extreme conditions are shown in Fig. 1. For each of the generated curves, the ocean area was drawn in with constant ocean volume and the sea level derived to an accuracy limited by scale to ± 50 m. The resulting changes in sea level varied from the maximum rise of 240 m to a maximum fall of 800 to 1,000 m. Errors of about ± 20% were caused by difficulties in constructing the curves and measuring areas.

体所覆盖、几乎是球体的地球上，洋底在海平面下约 2,440 米，但海平面要比现代海平面高出约 240 米 [14,15]。

构造运动与海平面之间的相互作用仅仅开始于部分岩石圈升高并超过海平面的时候，此后洋底与陆地之间任何净垂向运动都将产生明显的海平面变化。特别是高出水面的固体地壳体积的增加必然会伴随着海平面的绝对降低。按照板块构造理论，重要的是要保持大陆和海洋之间的差别，这样才能计算出与现代大陆面积和大洋深度的偏离。由于水的体积和岩石密度的恒定性要求代表地壳和水体积的总面积保持不变，因此全球陆高海深曲线 [16,17] 可以提供一个简便的分析方法（图 1a）。为了研究与现代曲线的系统偏差，我们令陆地面积（$x$）和最大海深（$y$）相对于其现代的数值前后各自浮动 5%，从而得到另外 48 条陆高海深曲线。确定这些假定的大陆面积所使用的基线与限定现代大陆面积各处的海平面高度的基线一致，这样可以为大陆保留一个地球物理学上的概念，即大陆可以被水覆盖，也可以不被水覆盖。我们进一步假设大陆剖面与现代的相似，海洋部分的变化量与各处的深度成比例，因此可以保留诸如大陆边缘、洋中脊等的重要特征，并且与范安德尔和希思 [18] 所观察的断层分布一致。水平尺度随新、老海洋面积的比例变化而定。

通过与新的陆高海深曲线（图 1）比较，我们估算了海洋下面固体地球体积的变化。在现代海平面之上的大陆体积上加上或减去该变化，并利用类似于计算海洋剖面时所用的比例，计算出新的大陆剖面。

有另外两个边界条件必须要满足，并且要确定出不会发生全部淹没或极端高度的可能变化范围。如果假定的海面下地球体积的增加大于现代海面之上大陆的总体积，那么大陆将被全部淹没。海面下固体体积的明显减小或大陆面积的明显减小需要大幅增加大陆的高度。根据地壳均衡原理，大陆最高的海拔不应超过现代值的两倍，因为抬升过程会被侵蚀作用明显削弱使其超出侵蚀作用的量不太可能是一个足够大的量。

图 1 显示了在两个极端条件下的典型陆高海深曲线。对于生成的每一条曲线，海洋的面积都是根据固定的海洋体积和精度为 ±50 米的海平面确定的。产生的海平面变化范围为：最大上升幅度 240 米，最大下降幅度 800~1,000 米。约 ±20% 的误差是由曲线作图和面积测量的难度造成的。

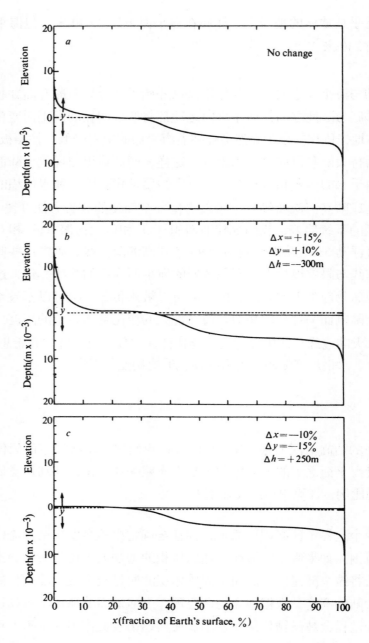

Fig. 1. *a*, The present hypsographic curve for the Earth[16,17]. *b*, Hypothetical hypsographic curve after increasing continental area at present sea level by 15% and increasing ocean depth by 10%. Note increased height of continents, and decrease of sea level by 300 m. *c*, Hypsographic curve resulting from decreasing continental area at present sea level by 10% and decreasing ocean depth by 15%. Although continents are not reduced below present sea level, the eustatic rise in sea level results in total inundation.

The model shows that small departures from the present proportion of continental area and ocean depth produce enormous changes in degree of flooding of continental margins (Fig. 2). For example, an extension of continental area results in a lowering of the mean

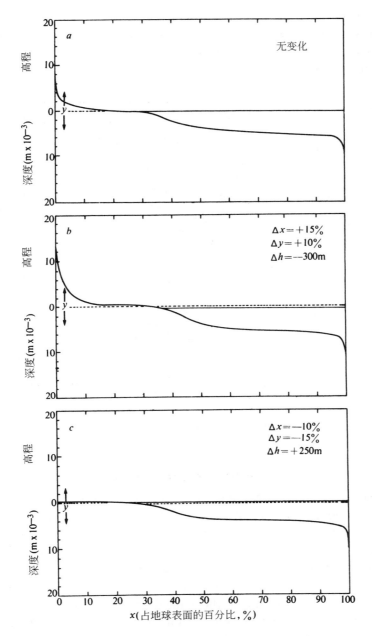

图 1. *a*，现代地球的陆高海深曲线 [16,17]。*b*，在现代海平面基础上，大陆面积增加 15% 和海洋深度增加 10% 后的陆高海深曲线。注意：大陆高度增加和海平面降低了 300 米。*c*，在现代海平面基础上，大陆面积减少 10% 和海洋深度减少 15% 后的陆高海深曲线。虽然大陆面积在现代海平面之下没有减少，但全球海平面上升导致大陆整体被淹。

该模型显示，与现代大陆面积和海洋深度比例的微小偏差都会对大陆边缘的淹没程度产生巨大影响（图 2）。例如，大陆面积的扩大会导致大陆平均高度降低和靠

height of continents, and an increase of land near present sea level with a necessary eustatic rise in sea level causing extensive trangression and shallow seas. An increase in continental area of 10% accompanied by a 6% decrease in mean ocean depth would submerge all continents.

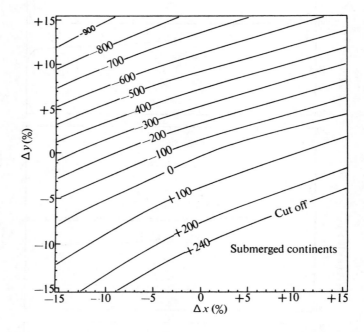

Fig. 2. Eustatic changes of sea level (m) relative to present sea level, contoured in terms of % change in continental area, $x$, and % change in ocean depth, $y$. For a rise of 240 m all continents are submerged.

## Changes and Discontinuities

The oceanic part of a plate steadily subsides as it spreads away from the mid-ocean ridge axis[3,19,20] and the aseismic continental margin undergoes a similar thermal subsidence that declines exponentially with a time constant of about $50 \times 10^{6}$ yr (ref. 21). Transgressions and regressions on young margins may be masked by this effect and are therefore likely to be best observed on margins older than 50 m.y. We have therefore examined the transgressions and regressions shown on Sleep's generalized subsidence curve[21] for the old, Triassic[22] Atlantic margin of the United States for correlations with events in independently derived spreading histories[23,24] for the North Atlantic Ocean (Fig. 3). Our comparison shows a good correlation between the Oligocene regression and deceleration in spreading at 45 m.y. and correlations between earlier eustatic changes and spreading discontinuities.

近现代海平面的陆地增加，同时，全球性海平面的升高必然会引起广泛的海进和浅海的形成。大陆面积增加10%以及伴随的平均海洋深度减少6%将会使所有的大陆被淹。

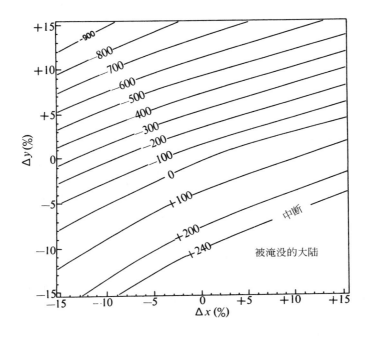

图 2. 相对现代海平面的全球海平面变化（米）。等值线是按照大陆面积变化百分数（$x$）和海洋深度变化百分数（$y$）来确定的。海平面升高 240 米，所有大陆将被淹没。

## 变化和不连续性

当一个板块的大洋部分由洋中脊向外扩散的时候，它会稳定沉降[3,19,20]。无震大陆边缘也会经历类似的热沉降，并且在大约 $50 \times 10^6$ 年的时间内其沉降速率呈指数减缓（参考文献 21）。海进和海退过程在年轻大陆边缘上会被此种效应所掩盖，因此在老于 5,000 万年的大陆边缘上才较有可能观察到。斯利普建立了古老三叠纪[22]美国大西洋边缘广义的沉降曲线[21]，我们对其所显示的海进和海退进行了研究，并将其与独立获得的北大西洋扩张史[23,24]中的事件进行了对比（图 3）。比较结果显示，渐新世的海退与 4,500 万年前洋中脊扩张速度的减慢有很好的对应关系。更早期的海平面变化与洋中脊扩张的不连续性之间也具有相关性。

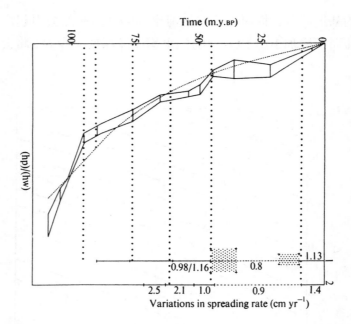

Fig. 3. Subsidence curve (---) for the Atlantic continental margin of the USA (from ref. 21). The depth normalized to the base of the Woodbine formation is plotted as a function of absolute age for wells on the East Coast. The error bars are 90% confidence limits. The subsidence curve is a 50 m.y. exponential constraint to fit data at the base of the Woodbine and at the surface. Kinks in the data correspond to eustatic changes. Spreading history of the North Atlantic derived independently is shown in column 1 (ref. 23) and column 2 (ref. 24). ..., possible correlations between eustatic change and spreading. Shaded area, transition from one spreading mode to another[23].

To check that this correlation does not reflect only the vertical movement of a particular plate, we have examined the Late Cretaceous and Cainozoic spreading histories of the major plates[25] for a global relationship. Global discontinuities in spreading have been postulated[23,25-28]; our comparison (Fig. 4) shows a global deceleration in spreading at about 45 m.y., an acceleration at 10 m.y., and other discontinuities between 55 and 60 m.y. and about 70 m.y. Comparison of the ages of these discontinuities and eustatic changes documented on continental margins (Fig. 4 and Fig. 5) shows (within the limitations of the data) that the Oligocene–Miocene spreading deceleration is associated with a regression preceded by a minor transgression. The Late Miocene transgression just precedes the 10 m.y. acceleration and a transgressive–regressive phase may correlate with the 60 m.y. discontinuity. We therefore suggest that eustatic changes are connected with contemporaneous global spreading discontinuities and that older transgressions such as the Cenomanian will probably be associated with similar discontinuities.

360

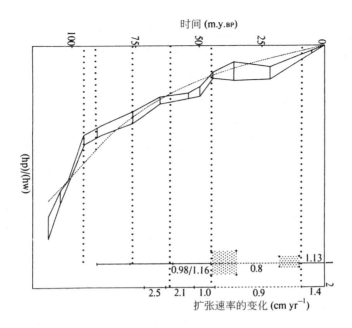

图 3. 美国大西洋大陆边缘的沉降曲线（---）（来自参考文献 21）。深度是根据忍冬属植物群分布的底界来标定的，并根据东海岸钻井所获得的绝对年龄作函数图像。误差线为 90% 的置信限。为了与忍冬属植物群分布底界以及地表的资料一致，在 5,000 万年中的沉降曲线受到约束，为指数形式。资料中的结点对应海平面的变化。独立获得的北大西洋扩张历史显示在第 1 栏（参考文献 23）和第 2 栏（参考文献 24）。…表示海平面变化和扩张之间可能的相关性。阴影区表示从一种扩张模式向另一种模式的转变[23]。

　　为了验证这种相关性不仅仅反映某个特定板块的垂向运动，我们研究了主要板块在晚白垩世和新生代的扩张历史 [25] 以及它们的全球关系。已有人提出扩张具有全球不连续性 [23,25-28]。我们的比较结果（图 4）显示，扩张在大约 4,500 万年前经历了一次全球性的减速，在 1,000 万年前经历了一次加速。扩张的不连续性还发生在 5,500 万年和 6,000 万年之间，以及大约 7,000 万年前。将上述不连续性的时代与在大陆边缘记录的海平面变化进行比较（图 4 和图 5），结果表明（在有限资料范围内）渐新世－中新世时期扩张的减速伴随着一次小海进之后的海退。晚中新世海进恰好发生在 1,000 万年前的加速扩张之前，而一个海进－海退序列可能与 6,000 万年前的扩张不连续性有关。因此，我们认为海平面变化与同期的全球扩张不连续性相关，譬如，森诺曼期古老海进可能与类似的不连续性相关。

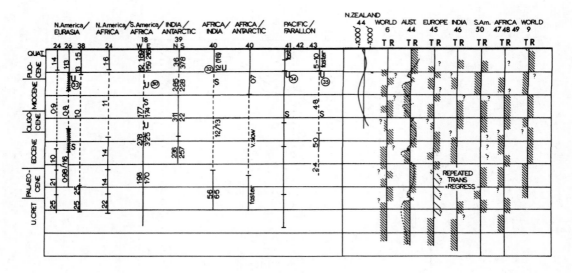

Fig. 4. Correlation between global discontinuities in spreading and global eustatic changes. ---, General reduction in spreading rate during the Oligocene and Miocene. Note correlation of uplift (U) and subsidence (S) with spreading rate changes and eustatic changes. Eustatic changes are shown as regressive (R) and transgressive phases (T) rather than curves showing interpreted amplitude of change. Circled numbers are references.

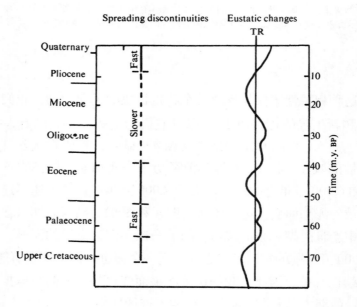

Fig. 5. Correlation between generalized global discontinuities in spreading and generalized global eustatic change (from Fig. 4). The eustatic change is necessarily approximate because of the limitations of the data.

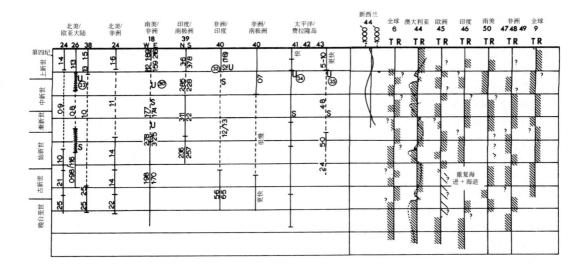

图 4. 海底扩张的全球不连续性与全球海平面变化之间的相关性。--- 表示渐新世和中新世时期扩张速度的普遍降低。注意抬升（U）和沉降（S）与扩张速率变化和海平面变化之间的相关性。海平面变化表示为海退（R）和海进（T），而不是用显示变化幅度的曲线表示。圆圈中数字为参考文献。

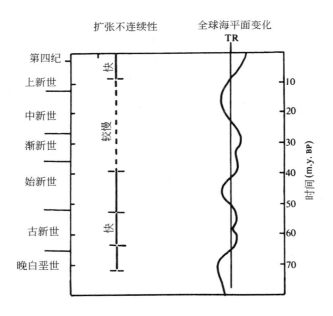

图 5. 扩张的全球不连续性和全球海平面变化之间的相关性（根据图4）。由于资料有限，全球海平面变化是近似的。

A relationship between mid-ocean ridge elevation changes and eustatic changes has been suggested[3-13] and the relationship between ridge elevation and spreading rate[29] has been supported by statistical evidence[20] showing that ridges spreading slower than 3 cm yr$^{-1}$ tend to be higher than faster ones. Decelerations in spreading should therefore be accompanied by uplift and accelerations by subsidence. But deep-sea drilling data[30] and spreading rates[18] for the southern Mid-Atlantic Ridge show the converse; the post 38 m.y. deceleration was followed by uplift in the Late Oligocene and subsidence in the Early Miocene; the ridge was uplifted to near its present elevation just before the 10 m.y. acceleration. Although these elevation changes correlate well with eustatic changes, the differences between the observed data and empirical model suggest that, at the slow (1.12 to 1.74 cm yr$^{-1}$) spreading rates on this ridge[18], effects such as phase changes[31] may also contribute to elevation changes. Other deep-sea drilling data[32-35] can also be interpreted to support uplift and subsidence accompanying spreading rate changes. The transgressive-regressive sequence may be due to elevation changes during the adjustment period observed at some discontinuities[26].

## General Implications

The paucity of deep sea drilling data does not permit us to estimate accurately eustatic changes caused by uplift and subsidence. But the southern Mid-Atlantic Ridge was uplifted[30] by between 500 and 1,000 m during the Late Miocene, a change of 25%. If we assume this uplift was not uniformly distributed over the South Atlantic[18] and that uplift on other ridges was not perfectly synchronous, we can reasonably consider a reduction in ocean depth of about 10%. A depth decrease of this order would, provided the continental area remained constant, result in a eustatic rise of about 500 m (Fig. 2) because the change depends on the prior form of the hypsographic curve. If the continental area decreased during uplift, the eustatic change would be rather less but more if the area increased. Estimates of a Middle Miocene transgression of 350 m[36] suggest our calculations are of the right order.

The maximum eustatic rise of 300 m (including 60 m for deglaciation) implies uplift of all marine features now above 300 m. The maximal fall of 800 to 1,000 m indicates that sub-aerial processes may have influenced the morphology of the outer shelf, upper slope and canyons. Such a fall might have exposed sills in semi-enclosed seas resulting in circulation changes and possibly in complete evaporation; a lowering of this order could, for example, have contributed to the drying out of the Mediterranean in the Miocene[37] (see Fig. 2).

We thank H. Charnock and A. S. Laughton for their comments on the manuscript. Peter Hunter drew the diagrams.

(**243**, 19-22; 1973)

N. C. Flemming and D. G. Roberts
National Institute of Oceanography, Godalming, Surrey

曾经有人提出洋中脊高度的变化与海平面变化之间有联系 [3-13]。洋中脊的高度与其扩张速度 [29] 之间的关系也已得到统计证据 [20] 的支持，即速度慢于 3 厘米 / 年的扩张洋脊要比扩张速度快的洋脊更高。因此，洋脊扩张减速应伴随其抬升，扩张加速伴随其沉降。然而，深海钻探数据 [30] 和南大西洋中脊的扩张速度 [18] 则显示相反的情况。3,800 万年前以后的减速跟随的是晚渐新世的抬升和早中新世的沉降。洋脊恰恰在 1,000 万年前的加速之前抬升到接近其现代的高度。虽然高度的变化与海平面变化有很好的对应关系，但观察数据和经验模型之间的差异说明，在南大西洋中脊扩张速度变慢时（1.12 厘米 / 年至 1.74 厘米 / 年）[18]，诸如相变等效应 [31] 也会导致其高度的变化。其他深海钻探资料 [32-35] 也支持洋脊的抬升和沉降伴随其扩张速度的变化而变化。海进－海退续发事件可归因于洋脊高度的变化，而洋脊高度的变化发生在调整阶段。这些调整阶段在某些不连续性中可以观察到 [26]。

## 普 遍 意 义

深海钻探资料的缺乏使我们不能精确估算由洋中脊抬升和沉降所引起的全球海平面变化。但南大西洋中脊在晚中新世时期抬升了 [30] 500 米至 1,000 米，变化了 25%。如果我们假设这一抬升运动在整个南大西洋中并不是均匀分布 [18]，并且其他洋中脊的抬升并不完全同期发生，那么我们可以合理地认为，海洋深度减少了大约 10%。若大陆面积保持不变，海洋深度这种程度的减少会使全球海平面升高约 500 米（图 2），因为海平面变化取决于陆高海深曲线早期的形态。如果大陆面积在洋中脊抬升时期减少，海平面的变化会很小；如果大陆面积增加，那么海平面变化将会增大。有人估计中新世中期海进幅度为 350 米 [36]，该估计值表明我们计算的数量级是正确的。

海平面升高的最大值为 300 米（包括因冰川消融而升高的 60 米），这意味着现在整个海洋地貌抬升 300 米以上。海平面下降最大幅度为 800 米至 1,000 米，这说明地表过程可以影响外陆架、上斜坡和峡谷的地貌。这种规模的海平面下降可以使半封闭海的海槛暴露，使其环流发生变化，并且可能导致海水完全蒸发。例如，这样规模的海平面下降可能是中新世地中海干枯的原因 [37]（参见图 2）。

我们感谢查诺克和劳顿对手稿的讨论，彼得·亨特为本文绘制了图表。

（李任伟 翻译；孟庆任 审稿）

Received October 12, 1972; revised February 12, 1973.

---

References:

1. Fairbridge, R. W., in *Physics and Chemistry of the Earth* (edit. by Ahrens, L. H., *et al.*), **5**, 99 (1961).

2. Revelle, R., *J. Mar. Res.*, **14**, 446 (1955).

3. Menard, H. W., *Earth Planet. Sci. Lett.*, **6**, 275 (1969).

4. Bucher, W. H., *The Deformation of the Earth's Crust* (Princeton Univ. Press, Princeton, 1933).

5. Hallam, A., *Amer. J. Sci.*, **261**, 397 (1963).

6. Leont'yer, O., *Oceanology*, **10**, 210 (1970).

7. Duff, P., *et al.*, *Cyclic Sedimentation* (Elsevier, Amsterdam, 1967).

8. Frerichs, W., *Geol. Soc. Amer. Bull.*, **81**, 3445 (1970).

9. Frerichs, W., and Shive, P., *Earth Planet. Sci. Lett.*, **12**, 406 (1971).

10. Hallam, A., *J. Geol.*, **79**, 129 (1971).

11. Vine, F., in *Abstracts of NATO Symposium "Continental Drift, Sea Floor Spreading and Plate Tectonics-Implications for the Earth Sciences"* (Newcastle, 1972).

12. Valentine, J. W., and Moores, E. M., *Nature*, **228**, 657 (1970).

13. Valentine, J. W., and Moores, E. M., *J. Geol.*, **80**, 167 (1972).

14. Menard, H. W., and Smith, S. M., *J. Geophys. Res.*, **71**, 4305 (1966).

15. Sverdrup, H. U., Johnson, M. W., and Fleming, R. H., *The Oceans* (Prentice-Hall, 1942).

16. Kossinna, E., *Handbuch der Geophysik* (edit. by Gutenberg, B.), **2**, 869 (1933).

17. Holmes, A., *Principles of Physical Geology* (Nelson, London, 1965).

18. Van Andel, Tj. H., and Heath, G. R., *Mar. Geophys. Res.*, **1**, 5 (1970).

19. Le Pichon, X., and Langseth, M. G., *Tectonophysics*, **8**, 319 (1969).

20. Sclater, J. G., *et al.*, *J. Geophys. Res.*, **76**, 7888 (1971).

21. Sleep, N., *Geophys. J.*, **24**, 325 (1971).

22. Emery, K. O., *et al.*, *Amer. Assoc. Petrol. Geol. Bull.*, **54**, 44 (1970).

23. Vogt, P., *et al.*, *Tectonophysics*, **12**, 211 (1971).

24. Pitman, W., and Talwani, M., *Geol. Soc. Amer. Bull.*, **83**, 619 (1972).

25. Le Pichon, X., *J. Geophys. Res.*, **73**, 3661 (1968).

26. Vogt, P., *et al.*, *Tectonophysics*, **8**, 285 (1969).

27. Schneider, E., and Vogt, P., *Nature*, **217**, 1212 (1968).

28. Ewing, M., and Ewing, J., *Science*, **156**, 1590 (1967).

29. Menard, H. W., *Science*, **157**, 923 (1967).

30. Maxwell, A. E., *et al.*, *Science*, **168**, 1047 (1970).

31. Torrance, K. E., and Turcotte, D. L., *J. Geophys. Res.*, **74**, 542 (1969).

32. Whitmarsh, R. B., *et al.*, *Geotimes*, **17**, 22 (1972).

33. Peterson, M. N. A., *et al.*, in *Initial Reports of the Deep Sea Drilling Project*, **2** (National Science Foundation, Washington, 1970).

34. Van Andel, Tj. H., and Heath, G. R., *Geotimes*, **16**, 12 (1971).

35. McManus. D. A., *et al.*, in *Initial Reports of the Deep Sea Drilling Project*, **5** (National Science Foundation, Washington, 1970).

36. Schofield, J. C., *Palaeogeog., Palaeoclim., Palaeoecol.*, **5**, 142 (1968).

37. Hsu, K. H., *et al.*, in *Initial Reports of the Deep Sea Drilling Project Leg XIII* (in the press).

38. Williams, C. A., and Mackenzie, D. P., *Nature*, **232**, 168 (1971).

39. Weissel, J., and Hayes, D. E., *Nature*, **231**, 518 (1971).

40. Mackenzie, D. P., and Sclater, J. G., *Geophys. J.*, **24**, 437 (1971).

41. Atwater, T., *Geol. Soc. Amer. Bull.*, **81**, 3513 (1972).

42. Francheteau, J., *et al.*, *Nature*, **226**, 746 (1970).

43. Herron, E. M., *Geol. Soc. Amer. Bull.*, **83**, 1671 (1972).

44. Glenie, R. C., *et al.*, *Palaeogeog., Palaeoclim., Palaeoecol.*, **5**, 141 (1968).

45. Larsonneur, C., in *Colloque sur la Géologie de la Manche, Mem. Bur. Geol.*, No. 79 (1972).

46. Sengupta, S., *Amer. Assoc. Petrol. Geol. Bull.*, **50**, 1001 (1966).

47. Short, K. C., and Stauble, A. J., *Amer. Assoc. Petrol. Geol. Bull.*, **51**, 761 (1967).

48. Haughton, S. H., *Stratigraphic History of Africa South of the Sahara*, 365 (Oliver and Boyd, London, 1963)

49. Furon, R., *Geology of Africa*, 377 (Oliver and Boyd, London, 1963).

50. Zambrano, J. J., and Urien, C. M., *J. Geophys. Res.*, **75**, 1363 (1970).

# Resonance Raman Spectroscopy of the Photoreceptor-like Pigment of *Halobacterium halobium*

R. Mendelsohn

## Editor's Note

The purple membrane of the salt-loving photosynthetic bacterium *Halobacterium halobium* (and related organisms) contains the protein bacteriorhodopsin, which uses the energy of absorbed light to drive hydrogen ions (protons) through its central channel, creating a gradient in acidity across the membrane that can be tapped for chemical energy. This system has become archetypal in the study of biological energy conversion and proton transfer, as well as attracting technological interest for solar energy. Here Richard Mendelsohn of King's College, London, uses spectroscopy to identify the fundamental process of light absorption by the light-sensitive chemical group in the core of the protein. The details of how photochemical changes in this group lead to the movement of protons are still being worked out.

Use of the resonance Raman technique has shown that the colour of the purple membrane pigment of *H. halobium* arises from an unprotonated Schiff base whose electron density is perturbed by further (electrostatic) interaction with a protein. The chromophore probably consists of a charge transfer complex between retinyllysine and an appropriate side chain of the protein.

RESONANCE Raman spectra have been reported for several molecules of biological interest, including haemoglobin[1,2], cytochrome C[2,3], rubredoxin[4] and several carotenes[5] and retinals[6,7]. The resonant enhancement of certain Raman-active vibrations occurs when molecules are excited by light of a wavelength lying within an electronic transition[8], and the effect provides a structural probe at unusually low solution concentration. Of particular importance to biological systems is the feasibility of *in situ* examination.

One potentially useful area of application for this technique is to photoreceptor pigments. The bathochromic shifts in visual pigments have not yet been satisfactorily explained. The absorption maxima of these pigments, in which there appears to be a Schiff base of 11-*cis* retinal with the ε-amino group of a lysine residue, vary from 430 to 562 nm (ref. 9). Solutions of the Schiff base itself, however, absorb near 360 or 440 nm, depending on whether the nitrogen atom is unprotonated or protonated, respectively. Thus another specific interaction occurs between protein and chromophore which

# 盐生盐杆菌中类感光色素的共振拉曼光谱

门德尔松

## 编者按

嗜盐光合细菌盐生盐杆菌（及相关生物）的紫膜中含有细菌视紫红质蛋白，能够利用所吸收光的能量，使氢离子（质子）穿过中央通道，在膜两侧产生酸度梯度，进而被开发为化学能。这个系统已成为研究生物能量转化和质子转移的原始模型，还引发了研究太阳能技术的兴趣。伦敦国王学院的理查德·门德尔松利用光谱确定了蛋白质中心光敏化学基团光吸收的基本过程。这些基团中光化学变化如何导致质子转移的细节仍需进一步阐明。

共振拉曼技术的使用表明，盐生盐杆菌紫膜色素的颜色来自于一种未质子化的席夫碱，该碱的电子密度受到蛋白质的远程（静电）相互作用的干扰。发色团可能包含一个由视黄基赖氨酸与蛋白质的适当支链构成的电荷转移复合体。

共振拉曼光谱已被报道应用于多种具有生物学意义的分子，其中包括血红蛋白[1,2]、细胞色素 C[2,3]、红素氧还蛋白[4]，以及几种胡萝卜烯[5]和视黄醛[6,7]。分子在受到能引起电子跃迁的波长的光的激发时，其特征拉曼活性振动就会共振增强[8]，这种效应提供了一种极低浓度下的结构探针。对于生物体系来说尤为重要的是它使原位检测变得可行。

感光色素就是这种技术的潜在应用领域之一。视色素的红移现象目前尚没有令人满意的解释。这些色素的最大吸收峰位于 430 nm 到 562 nm（参考文献 9），显示其中含有由赖氨酸残基中的 ε− 氨基基团和 11− 顺式视黄醛所形成的席夫碱。而席夫碱的溶液，根据氮原子未被质子化与质子化的不同，其对应的吸收峰分别位于 360 nm 和 440 nm 附近。由此，蛋白质与发色基团之间的另一特定相互作用的出现，

perturbs the chromophore absorption band and gives rise to pigment colour[10]. Several theories proposed to explain visual pigment spectra have been reviewed by Abrahamson and Ostroy[11]. The two most important ones are those of: (1) Morton *et al.*[12,13], which assumes that the primary bond is a protonated Schiff base in which the bathochromic shifts are provided by negatively charged groups appropriately positioned adjacent to the polyene chain; (2) the Dartnall formulation[9], which assumes that the primary bond is an unprotonated Schiff base, with secondary shifts caused by an optimally placed pair of charges, producing massive dipoles in the polyene. Little experimental evidence is available with which to test either description.

Because of the anticipated extensive photochemical changes associated with the shining of intense laser radiation on a sample containing rhodopsin, I decided to examine initially the photoreceptor-like pigment of *Halobacterium halobium*. The "purple membrane" fragment containing the pigment offered several advantages for a laser-Raman spectroscopic study. (*a*) The primary structure of the chromophore is retinyllysine, the evidence being much the same as that for rhodopsin[14]. (*b*) Unlike rhodopsin, the pigment does not bleach or undergo photochemical changes on even prolonged exposure to intense (>200 mW) laser light, but simply undergoes a reversible spectral shift from $\lambda_{max}=558$ nm to $\lambda_{max}=570$ nm on exposure to red or blue light respectively[14]. (*c*) The membrane is easily handled at room temperature in aqueous suspension.

The purple membrane used in the study described here was the gift of Drs D. Oesterhelt and A. E. Blaurock.

Cells of *Halobacterium halobium* were grown and the purple membrane fragments isolated as previously described[14]. Suspensions of membrane used for Raman spectroscopy had an optical density of 3.0 at $\lambda_{max}$.

Raman spectra of purple membrane fragments excited with 4880 Å and 5145 Å radiation are shown in Fig. 1. The most intense vibration in each spectrum occurs at 1,531 cm$^{-1}$ and about fifteen other peaks have also been distinguished. The only significant difference in the two spectra is the relative intensity of the 1,568 cm$^{-1}$ vibration compared with that at 1,531 cm$^{-1}$. The former appears about four times more intense when excited by 4880 Å radiation than when excited by 5145 Å excitation. This observation is explained below.

干扰了发色基团的吸收带，从而产生了色素的颜色 [10]。阿伯拉罕森和奥斯特罗伊 [11] 曾综述了几种解释视色素光谱的理论。其中最重要的两种是：（1）莫顿等 [12,13] 提出，假定主价键为质子化的席夫碱，其中多烯链邻近适当位置上的负电子基团导致了红移；（2）达特诺 [9] 的说法，假定主价键为未质子化的席夫碱，其中处于最优位置上的电子对引发二次频移，在多烯上生成大量偶极。几乎没有实验证据可用来验证任一理论。

由于对含视紫红质样品进行强激光照射会产生大量可预期的光化学变化，笔者决定首先研究盐生盐杆菌中的类感光色素。包含色素的"紫膜"碎片为激光-拉曼光谱的研究提供了几个有利条件。（$a$）发色基团的主要结构是视黄基赖氨酸，提供的证据对于视紫红质差不多同样有效 [14]。（$b$）与视紫红质不同，这种色素即使长期暴露在强烈（> 200 mW）激光中也不会脱色或发生光化学变化，当暴露在红光或蓝光中，在两种光之间只会发生可逆的光谱频移，由 $\lambda_{max}$ = 558 nm 移到 $\lambda_{max}$ = 570 nm[14]。（$c$）这种膜在室温下的水悬浮液中很容易处理。

这里描述的本研究中所用的紫膜，为厄斯特黑尔特和布劳罗克两位博士所赠。

培养盐生盐杆菌和分离紫膜碎片的方法如先前所述 [14]。用于拉曼光谱检测的膜悬浮液在最大吸收峰 $\lambda_{max}$ 处光密度为 3.0。

图 1 所示为分别以 4880 Å 和 5145 Å 的射线激发紫膜碎片的拉曼光谱。每张谱图中，都有一个位于 1,531 cm⁻¹ 处的最强振动，以及其他约十五个可分辨出的峰。两张谱图中唯一的显著区别，就是位于 1,568 cm⁻¹ 处的振动与 1,531 cm⁻¹ 处的相比，其相对强度不同。用 4880 Å 的射线激发时，1,568 cm⁻¹ 处的峰比用 5145 Å 的射线激发时强约四倍。下面将解释这一观测结果。

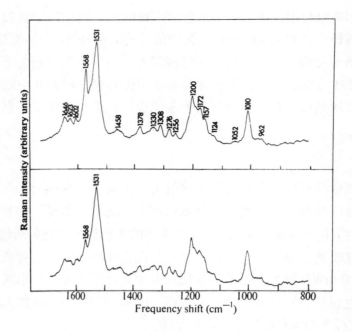

Fig. 1. Raman spectra of an aqueous suspension ($5.5 \times 10^{-5}$ M in the purple protein, $p$H 7.0, unbuffered) of purple membrane fragments obtained with a "Spex" 1401 Raman Spectrophotometer using: (Top) 100 mW of 4880 Å radiation from an $Ar^+$ laser. Resolution, 7 $cm^{-1}$; time constant 2 s; scanning rate 25 $cm^{-1}min^{-1}$; photon counting detection; 1 mm i.d. capillary cell, transverse excitation. (Bottom) 125 mW of 5145 Å radiation from an $Ar^+$ laser. Conditions as above. Polarization measurements indicated that all observed vibrations had depolarization ratios $0 \leq \rho \leq 0.3$. Spectra of membrane fragments suspended in 4 N NaCl solution are identical with those shown, as are spectra obtained in 0.05 M phosphate buffer ($p$H 7.0).

## Evidence for Resonance Enhancement

Several experiments showed that the observed spectra were resonance-enhanced. (*a*) The protein concentration as measured from the visible spectrum ($\varepsilon_{max}=54,000$ l/mol cm)[14] was $5.5 \times 10^{-5}$ M or two orders of magnitude less than that required to obtain ordinary protein Raman spectra[15]. (*b*) On bleaching the pigment with 0.1 M cetyltrimethyl-ammonium bromide ($p$H 7.9), a procedure which leaves the Schiff base intact but destroys the purple colour[14], no spectrum could be observed. (*c*) An excitation profile (variation of Raman intensity with excitation wavelength) experiment was carried out as follows. Samples of membrane were prepared containing 0.1 M $Na_2SO_4$ in which the non-resonant enhanced symmetric stretching vibration of the $SO_4^{2-}$ ion at 983 $cm^{-1}$ was used as an internal standard. The ratios of the intensities of the peaks at 1,531 and 1,568 $cm^{-1}$ to the intensity of the standard were determined as a function of excitation wavelength using six lines available from the argon ion laser, all of which lie on the high frequency side of the pigment absorption band. The results are shown in Fig. 2. It is clear that there is substantial deviation from the $1/\lambda^4$ law for intensity of scattered light, as the observed ratios would not vary with wavelength if this relationship were obeyed. The two vibrations studied appear to be enhanced by (vibronic) coupling to different components of the membrane absorption spectrum. The peak at 1,531 $cm^{-1}$ increases in relative intensity as

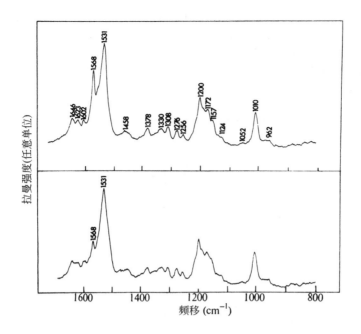

图1. 使用"Spex"1401型拉曼光谱仪，得到紫膜碎片水悬浮液（紫色蛋白质浓度为 $5.5 \times 10^{-5}$ M，pH 7.0，不含缓冲剂）的拉曼光谱图：（上图）100 mW $Ar^+$ 激光产生的 4880 Å 射线。分辨率 7 cm$^{-1}$；时间常数 2 s；扫描速率 25 cm$^{-1}$ · min$^{-1}$；光子计数检测；1 mm 内径的毛细管池，横向激发。（下图）125 mW $Ar^+$ 激光产生的 5145 Å 射线。其他条件同上。偏振测量指出，所有观测到的振动具有的退偏比值为 $0 \le \rho \le 0.3$。悬浮于 4 N NaCl 溶液中的膜碎片的谱图与所示谱图是一致的，在 0.05 M 磷酸盐缓冲溶液（pH 7.0）中得到同样的谱图。

## 共振增强的证据

若干实验表明观测到的谱图有共振增强。（a）通过可见光谱测定（$\varepsilon_{max} = 54,000$ L · mol$^{-1}$ · cm$^{-1}$）[14] 的蛋白质浓度为 $5.5 \times 10^{-5}$ M，或者说，比要获得正常的蛋白质拉曼光谱所需的浓度低两个数量级 [15]。（b）若使用 0.1 M 的溴化十六烷基三甲铵（pH 7.9）使色素脱色，这个过程可以使席夫碱保持完好但破坏紫色 [14]，导致不能观测到光谱。（c）激发曲线（拉曼强度随着激发波长的变化）实验步骤如下。在膜样品中加入 0.1 M 的 $Na_2SO_4$，以 $SO_4^{2-}$ 离子在 983 cm$^{-1}$ 处的没有共振增强的对称伸缩振动作为内标。测定以位于 1,531 cm$^{-1}$ 处和 1,568 cm$^{-1}$ 处峰强度与内标强度的比值作激发波长的函数；光源是氩离子激光，可以产生六条都位于色素吸收带高频端的谱线。结果如图2所示。很明显，确实存在着对于散射光强度的 $1/\lambda^4$ 定律的严重偏离，因为如果遵循该关系的话，所观测到的比值是不会随波长而变化的。所研究的两种振动看来是为膜吸收光谱中不同部分的（电子振动）耦合所增强的。随着激发光波长向着色素的 $\lambda_{max}$ 方向的增长，位于 1,531 cm$^{-1}$ 处峰的相对强度会增加。由此与主要

the exciting line increases in wavelength toward the pigment $\lambda_{max}$. It is therefore coupled to the main pigment absorption. The 1,568 cm$^{-1}$ band, however, is increased in relative intensity as the wavelength is decreased, and it is therefore not coupled to the visible component of the membrane spectrum but to an absorption located at shorter wavelength than the main band.

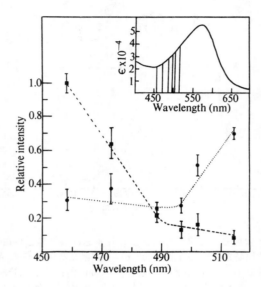

Fig. 2. Excitation profile results. ---, Ratio of the integrated intensities of 1,568 cm$^{-1}$ vibration compared with 983 cm$^{-1}$ vibration of SO$_4^{2-}$ ion used as internal standard. ..., Same ratio comparing the 1,531 cm$^{-1}$ vibration with the standard. ■ and ● , Experimental points, observed at the indicated laser wavelength. Error bars represent standard deviations based on four measurements. Insert, pigment absorption band of purple membrane. Vertical lines indicate positions of laser lines located at 457.9, 472.7, 488.0, 496.5, 501.7 and 514.5 nm. The visible absorption spectrum was recorded on a "Unicam" SP-800A spectrophotometer using cells of 2 mm path length.

All of the other vibrations (except that attributable to solvent O–H bending at 1,646 cm$^{-1}$) behave in a fashion similar to the 1,531 cm$^{-1}$ vibration and hence arise from coupling to the 560 nm band of the pigment.

## Analysis of Spectral Data

Spectral analysis is simplified by the fact that only chromophore vibrations are observed in the resonance Raman effect[1-3]. Protein vibrations are of insufficient intensity to be seen and therefore do not complicate the spectra. In this work the region 1,500-1700 cm$^{-1}$ which contains C=C and C=N stretching vibrations will be considered. The region below 1,500 cm$^{-1}$, which contains C–C stretching and C–H bending modes, will be discussed in a future publication.

Rimai and coworkers have made a detailed Raman spectroscopic study of various retinals[7] and their Schiff bases[6]. They found that those vibrational modes most strongly enhanced are contributed by C=C and C–C stretching in the conjugated chain, which occur near

374

色素吸收耦合起来。不过，位于 1,568 cm⁻¹ 附近的吸收带相对强度随着激发光波长减少而增加，因此不会与膜光谱的可见部分耦合，而是与位于比主吸收带波长短的吸收部分耦合。

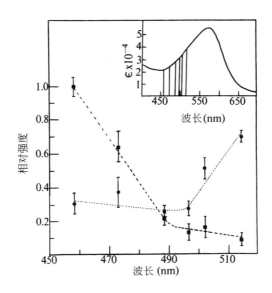

图 2. 激发曲线结果。---，1,568 cm⁻¹ 处振动峰强与作为内标的 SO₄²⁻ 在 983 cm⁻¹ 处振动峰强的比值。…，1,531 cm⁻¹ 处振动峰强与同样的内标峰强的比值。■ 和 ● 为在上述激光波长条件下观测到的实验值。误差线代表基于四次实验得到的标准偏差。插图为紫膜的色素吸收带。垂直线表示位于 457.9 nm、472.7 nm、488.0 nm、496.6 nm、501.7 nm 和 514.5 nm 的激光束。可见光吸收光谱是由 "Unicam" SP-800A 光谱仪使用 2 mm 路径长度的样品池得到的。

所有的其他振动（除了 1,646 cm⁻¹ 处归属为溶剂 O—H 的振动外）都具有与 1,531 cm⁻¹ 处振动类似的振动方式，因此也是由与色素 560 nm 处吸收带的耦合产生的。

## 光谱数据分析

在共振拉曼效应中只能观测到发色团的振动这一事实简化了谱图分析[1-3]。蛋白质振动的强度尚不足以被看到，因而不会使谱图复杂化。在本工作中要考虑的是包含 C=C 与 C=N 伸缩振动的 1,500～1,700 cm⁻¹ 区域。低于 1,500 cm⁻¹ 的包含 C—C 伸缩振动与 C—H 弯曲振动的区域，将会在以后的发表物中进行讨论。

里毛伊与他的同事们已经对各种视黄醛[7]及其席夫碱[6]的拉曼光谱进行了详细研究。他们发现，增强最明显的是在共轭链中的 C=C 和 C—C 伸缩振动，分别位

1,570 and 1,200 cm⁻¹, respectively. In addition, they identified C=O and C=N stretching vibrations in the range 1,600-1,670 cm⁻¹.

In Fig. 3*a* and *c*, the 1,500-1,700 cm⁻¹ region of the Raman spectra of unprotonated and protonated retinylhexylamine are shown. The C=N frequencies in this model Schiff base are expected to be similar to those of the pigment Schiff base and can be used to decide whether the nitrogen of the latter is protonated. In the unprotonated form (Fig. 3*a*), $\nu$ (C=N) occurs as a weak band near 1,623 cm⁻¹ while $\nu$ (C=C) appears strongly at 1,579 cm⁻¹. In protonated retinylhexylamine (Fig. 3*c*) the C=N stretching frequency is broadened and shifted to 1,645 cm⁻¹, while $\nu$ (C=C) is shifted to 1,559 cm⁻¹.

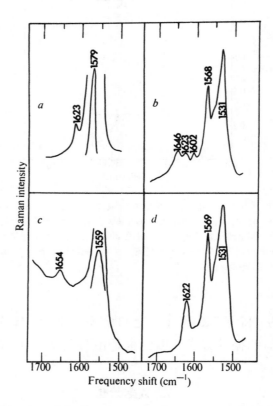

Fig. 3. 1,500-1,700 cm⁻¹ region of the Raman spectra of *a*, unprotonated retinylhexylamine ($10^{-3}$ M in C₆H₁₄ solution, $\lambda_{max}$=360 nm); *b*, purple membrane fragments in H₂O suspension (see Fig. 1 (top), caption); *c*, protonated retinylhexylamine ($10^{-4}$ M in acidified EtOH solution, $\lambda_{max}$=445 nm); *d*, purple membrane fragments in D₂O suspension (conditions as in Fig. 1 (top) except for solvent). All spectra recorded using 4880 Å radiation. The difference in concentration in *a* and *c* reflects the increased resonant enhancement as the retinylhexylamine absorption band is shifted into the visible region. There is little or no change in the Raman frequencies of this Schiff base as a function of solvent. The best spectra of unprotonated and protonated retinylhexylamine were obtained in the solvent indicated.

In Fig. 3*b*, the 1,500-1,700 cm⁻¹ range of the purple membrane spectrum is shown. This region is complicated by the presence of a weak solvent OH bending vibration at

于大约 1,570 cm⁻¹ 和 1,200 cm⁻¹ 处。另外，他们还在 1,600~1,670 cm⁻¹ 区域中指认出 C═O 和 C═N 的伸缩振动。

在图 3*a* 和 3*c* 中所示分别为未质子化的和质子化的视黄基己胺拉曼光谱图的 1,500~1,700 cm⁻¹ 区域。在这种形式的席夫碱中，预期 C═N 的振动频率会与视色素席夫碱中的相似，从而可用于确定后者中的氮原子是否被质子化。在未质子化的形式中（图 3*a*），*v*（C═N）为位于 1,623 cm⁻¹ 附近的一个弱吸收带，而位于 1,579 cm⁻¹ 处的 *v*（C═C）看起来很强。在质子化了的视黄基己胺中（图 3*c*），C═N 伸缩振动峰增宽并移向 1,645 cm⁻¹ 处，而 *v*（C═C）则移向 1,559 cm⁻¹ 处。

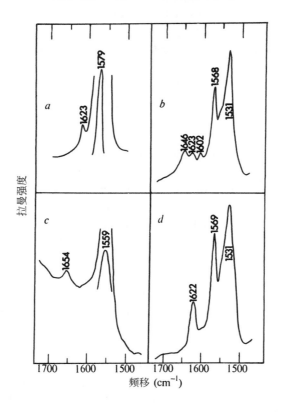

图 3. 拉曼光谱图的 1,500~1,700 cm⁻¹ 区域，其中 *a*，未质子化的视黄基己胺（浓度 10⁻³ M 的 C₆H₁₄ 溶液，λ_max = 360 nm）；*b*，紫膜碎片在水中的悬浮液（见图 1 的上图，图注）；*c*，质子化的视黄基己胺（浓度 10⁻⁴ M 的酸化乙醇溶液，λ_max = 445 nm）；*d*，紫膜碎片在 D₂O 中的悬浮液（除溶剂外，条件与图 1 的上图相同）。所有谱图都是在 4880 Å 光照射下记录的。在 *a* 和 *c* 之间的浓度差别反映出，共振增强在视黄基己胺的吸收带向可见光区域移动时变大。这种席夫碱在不同溶剂下其拉曼频率改变很少甚至没有变化。在已提到的溶剂中获得了未质子化和质子化的视黄基己胺的最佳谱图。

图 3*b* 中所示为紫膜光谱的 1,500~1,700 cm⁻¹ 区域。这个区域由于有 1,646 cm⁻¹ 处的溶剂 OH 产生的微弱的弯曲振动出现而复杂化了，不过位于 1,531 cm⁻¹、1,568 cm⁻¹、

$1,646$ cm$^{-1}$, although distinct peaks are seen at $1,531$, $1,568$, $1,602$, and $1,623$ cm$^{-1}$. The peak at $1,568$ cm$^{-1}$ is assigned to $v$ (C=C) of the Schiff base. The excitation profile results described above indicate that this vibration arises from retinyllysine other than that in the pigment. Whether this free Schiff base is significant to the structure of the pigment is not clear. On suspension of the purple membrane in D$_2$O, the $1,646$ cm$^{-1}$ band disappears as expected, while the vibration near $1,623$ cm$^{-1}$ becomes more prominent (Fig. 3*d*) than in the H$_2$O preparation. This band, assigned to C=N stretch of the Schiff base, appears at the same frequency as in unprotonated retinylhexylamine and strongly suggests that the Schiff base in the pigment itself is unprotonated.

The strongest peak in the purple membrane Raman spectrum at $1,531$ cm$^{-1}$ has no counterpart in the spectra of the model Schiff bases, all of which have intense C=C stretching vibrations above $1,550$ cm$^{-1}$. The intensity of the $1,531$ cm$^{-1}$ band implies strong vibronic coupling to the pigment absorption and it is suggested that, by its magnitude and position, the vibration is still due to retinal C=C stretch. The frequency decrease indicates that the $\pi$ electron density of the conjugated system has been perturbed and electrons removed from the C=C bonds. Such a process would reduce the C=C stretching force constants and lower $v$ (C=C).

The above observations indicate that pigment colour arises from an unprotonated Schiff base whose $\pi$ electron density is perturbed by further (electrostatic) interaction with the protein. Additional evidence for this description was obtained when it was noticed that the purple membrane $\lambda_{max}$ is highly solvent dependent (C. W. F. McClare, personal communication). Addition of a small amount of chloroform reversibly shifts $\lambda_{max}$ of the pigment to 500 nm and the main Raman frequency to $1,520$ cm$^{-1}$. The chloroform seems to penetrate to the chromophore and thereby perturbs its electronic arrangement.

The exact geometry of the purple membrane pigment must await a three-dimensional structure determination; however, one model which this study points to is that of a charge transfer complex[16] between retinyllysine and an appropriate side chain of the protein. Such interactions can account for the large shift in $\lambda_{max}$ (from 360 nm to ~560 nm) of the chromophore as well as the perturbation of chromophore vibration frequencies upon complex formation. In addition $\lambda_{max}$ in such complexes are quite solvent dependent[16], as observed in the present case. That such a mechanism is feasible has been shown by Ishigami *et al.*[17], who observed charge transfer between tryptophan and 9-*cis* retinal in acidified methanol solution ($\lambda_{max}$ of complex $=520$ nm). Furthermore, I have observed charge transfer between indole and *trans* retinal ($\lambda_{max}=625$ nm) in the same solvent. It is therefore quite conceivable that an appropriately positioned tryptophan residue on the protein interacts with the $\pi$ electrons of the Schiff base and produces the purple pigment colour.

A Raman spectroscopic study of rhodopsin and the intermediates present in its low temperature bleaching sequence would yield valuable information as to the nature of the Schiff base-protein interactions that determine pigment colour. The work described here

1,602 cm⁻¹ 和 1,623 cm⁻¹ 处的峰还是明显可见。位于 1,568 cm⁻¹ 处的峰归属于席夫碱的 $v$（C═C）。前面描述过的激发曲线实验结果指出，这种振动来自于视黄基赖氨酸，而不是色素中的振动。尚不清楚这种游离的席夫碱对于色素结构是否有重要意义。至于紫膜在 $D_2O$ 中的悬浮液，1,646 cm⁻¹ 处的吸收带如同预期那样地消失了，而 1,623 cm⁻¹ 附近的振动变得比水溶液中的更显著（图 3$d$）。这一归属于席夫碱中 C═N 伸缩振动的吸收带，显示与未质子化的视黄基己胺中振动频率相同，从而强烈暗示着色素中的席夫碱是未质子化的。

紫膜拉曼光谱中位于 1,531 cm⁻¹ 处的最强峰在模型席夫碱的谱图中找不到对应峰，后者在 1,550 cm⁻¹ 以上有很强的 C═C 伸缩振动峰。1,531 cm⁻¹ 吸收带的强度暗示着对于色素吸收存在强烈的电子振动耦合，并且指出，从其数值和位置来看，该振动仍是源于视黄基中的 C═C 伸缩。频率的降低意味着共轭系统中 π 电子密度受到扰动以及电子远离了 C═C 键。这一过程将会减小 C═C 伸缩的力常数并降低 $v$（C═C）。

上述观测指出，色素颜色来自于一种未质子化的席夫碱，该碱的 π 电子密度受到其与蛋白质的远程（静电力）相互作用干扰。当注意到紫膜的 $\lambda_{max}$ 是高度依赖于溶剂时（麦克莱尔，个人交流）就得到了支持这一陈述的另一证据。加入少量氯仿能够使色素的 $\lambda_{max}$ 可逆地移向 500 nm，而主拉曼频率移至 1,520 cm⁻¹ 处。氯仿似乎渗透进了发色团并以此干扰其电子排布。

紫膜色素的具体的几何形状还得等待其三维结构的确定；但是，本研究所针对的模型是一个由视黄基赖氨酸与蛋白质的适当支链构成的电荷转移复合体[16]。这种相互作用可以解释发色团 $\lambda_{max}$ 的巨大位移（从 360 nm 到约 560 nm），以及复合体形成后对发色团振动频率的干扰。此外，就目前所观测到的来说，这种复合体中的 $\lambda_{max}$ 是非常依赖于溶剂的[16]。石上等[17] 已经说明了这一机制的可能性，他在酸化的甲醇溶液中观测到色氨酸与 9-顺式视黄醛的电荷转移（该复合体的 $\lambda_{max}$ = 520 nm）。而且，笔者曾观测到吲哚与反式视黄醛（$\lambda_{max}$ = 625 nm）在相同溶剂中的电荷转移。因此，极有可能是处于蛋白质适当位置上的色氨酸残基与席夫碱的 π 电子相互作用并产生了紫色素的颜色。

对视紫红质及其在低温脱色过程中出现的中间体的拉曼光谱研究，能获得关于决定色素颜色的席夫碱 - 蛋白质相互作用本质的宝贵信息。本工作描述了这种研究

illustrates the feasibility of such studies and the power of the resonance Raman technique in providing a structural probe for the photoreceptor pigments.

I thank Drs A. E. Blaurock, W. R. Lieb, and C. W. F. McClare for detailed discussions. This work was supported by the National Research Council of Canada.

(**243**, 22-24; 1973)

R. Mendelsohn

Biophysics Department, King's College, 26-29 Drury Lane, London WC2B 5RL

Received February 2, 1973.

---

References:

1. Spiro, T. G., and Strekas, T. C., *Biochim. Biophys. Acta,* **263**, 830 (1972).

2. Spiro, T. G., and Strekas, T. C., *Proc. US Nat. Acad. Sci.,* **69**, 2622 (1972).

3. Spiro, T. G., and Strekas, T. C., *Biochim. Biophys. Acta,* **278**, 188 (1972).

4. Long, T. V., Loehr, T. M., Allkins, J. R., and Lovenberg, W., *J. Amer. Chem. Soc.,* **93**, 1809 (1971).

5. Rimai, L., Kilponen, R. G., and Gill, D., *J. Amer. Chem. Soc.,* **92**, 3824 (1970).

6. Heyde, M. E., Gill, D., Kilponen, R. G., and Rimai, L., *J, Amer. Chem. Soc.,* **93**, 6776 (1971).

7. Rimai, L., Gill, D., and Parsons, J. L., *J. Amer. Chem. Soc.,* **93**, 1353 (1971).

8. Behringer, J., in *Raman Spectroscopy* (edit. by Szymanski, H. A.) (Plenum Press, New York, 1967).

9. Dartnall, H. J. A., and Lythgoe, J. N., *Vision Res.,* **5**, 81 (1964).

10. Hubbard, R., *Nature,* **221**, 432 (1969).

11. Abrahamson, E. W., and Ostroy, S. E., *Prog. Biophys. Mol. Biol.,* **17**, 181 (1967).

12. Morton, R. A., and Pitt, G. A. J., *Biochem. J.,* **59**, 128 (1955).

13. Kropf, A., and Hubbard, R., *Ann. NY Acad. Sci.,* **74**, 266 (1958).

14. Oesterhelt, D., and Stoeckenius, W., *Nature New Biology,* **233**, 149 (1971).

15. Lord, R. C., and Mendelsohn, R., *J. Amer. Chem. Soc.,* **94**, 2133 (1972).

16. McGlynn, S. P., *Rad. Res. Suppl.,* **2**, 300 (1960).

17. Ishigami, M., Mieda, Y., and Mishima, K., *Biochim. Biophys. Acta,* **112**, 372 (1966).

的可行性，以及共振拉曼技术为感光色素提供结构探针的能力。

我要感谢布劳罗克、利布、麦克莱尔这几位博士所做的详细讨论。本研究由加拿大国家研究委员会赞助。

（王耀杨 翻译；李芝芬 审稿）

# Discontinuous Change in Earth's Spin Rate following Great Solar Storm of August 1972

J. Gribbin and S. Plagemann

## Editor's Note

Does solar activity influence how fast the Earth spins? The idea sounds unlikely, but in 1959, following one of the largest solar storms in recorded history, Andre Danjon reported an apparent sharp increase in the length of the day as measured by astronomical means. Here John Gribbin and Stephen Plagemann tested this controversial idea by taking advantage of an even larger solar storm in 1972. They found a similar effect: an abrupt change in the length of day correlated with an increase in cosmic rays from solar nuclear reactions. The authors speculated that these cosmic rays might influence the dynamics of the Earth's upper atmosphere, changing the Earth's rate of spin within a few days.

THE question of a link between changes in the Earth's spin rate and the activity of the Sun is of topical interest, and there is good evidence that the changing length of day is influenced by the mean level of solar activity[1,2]. The possibility of a one-to-one correlation between specific events on the Sun and specific changes in the length of day has remained more controversial, however, although there was a suggestion of such an effect associated with the great solar storm of 1959 (refs. 3-5). Specifically, Danjon suggested[3-5] that there was an increase in the length of day when the nucleonic component of solar cosmic rays increased; this was in addition to the usual steady increase in the length of day. Other observers questioned the reality of this effect (for a discussion of the controversy see ref. 6), and because the 1959 solar storm was the greatest recorded since the time of Galileo, there was no immediate hope of an independent test of Danjon's claim. In August 1972, however, an even greater disturbance occurred on the Sun[7-9]. It seemed to us that this might provide the ideal opportunity to resolve the controversy, and we have indeed found a discontinuous change in the length of day, and a change in the rate of change of the length of day (a glitch) immediately after that event. Changes in the length of day, and thus in the spin rate of the Earth, are revealed by regular measurements of Universal Time (UT) carried out at many observatories around the world. For our purpose, we are interested in UT2, the version of Universal Time with the effects of the Chandler Wobble and seasonal variations removed. The difference between Atomic Time (AT) and UT2 shows, on average, a monotonic increase as the Earth's spin slows down and the length of day increases.

In Fig. 1 we plot AT–UT2 for a period of one month on either side of the great solar storm of August 1972. The spot group associated with the flare activity built up from July 29, reaching a maximum size (covering 17° in longitude) on August 4. In Fig. 1, we have

# 1972年8月强太阳风暴过后地球自转速度的不连续变化

格里宾，普拉格曼

## 编者按

太阳活动是否会对地球的自转速度产生影响？答案似乎是否定的，但是在 1959 年，有史以来最强的太阳风暴之一爆发过后，安德烈·丹戎报道了通过天文学方法，测量出日长（译者注：地球自转一周的时间）发生了显著增长。在本文中，通过研究 1972 年的一次更大规模的太阳风暴，约翰·格里宾和斯蒂芬·普拉格曼对这个有争议的观点进行了检验。他们发现一个相似的效应：日长发生突变，与太阳核反应发出的宇宙射线增长相关。作者推断这些宇宙射线可能会对地球高层大气的动力学过程产生影响，在几天内改变地球的自转速度。

地球自转速度的变化与太阳活动的关系是当前的热点问题，目前已有充分的证据证明，日长变化受太阳平均活动强度的影响[1,2]。然而，太阳上发生的特定事件与日长的特定变化之间存在一一对应的相互关系的可能性仍有许多争议。尽管已有学者指出，1959 年的强太阳风暴曾对日长带来过这样的影响（参考文献 3~5）。特别指出的是，丹戎曾经提出[3-5]当太阳宇宙射线的核子组分增加时日长就会增加，这一增加是附加在日长的稳定增加之外的。其他学者则对该效应的真实性持怀疑态度（关于该争议的讨论见参考文献 6），而且由于 1959 年的强太阳风暴是自伽利略时代以来记录到的最强的一次，所以无法立即对丹戎的观点进行独立检验。然而，1972 年 8 月太阳上发生了一次更强的扰动[7-9]。对我们来说，这可能为解决该争议提供了一次理想的机会，我们也确实发现了日长的不连续变化，以及在该事件之后日长变化速率立即发生了改变（即突变）。世界各地的多个天文台对世界时（UT）的常规测定都揭示了日长的变化，以及由此而带来的地球自转速度的变化。对我们来说，我们感兴趣的是 UT2，即一种去除了钱德勒摆动以及季节性变化的影响的世界时。通常来说，随地球自转减慢即日长增加，原子时（AT）与 UT2 之间的差值显示为单调递增。

在图 1 中我们标出了 1972 年 8 月强太阳风暴爆发前后各一个月内，AT–UT2 的变化情况。与耀斑活动相关的黑子群于 7 月 29 日开始活跃，在 8 月 4 日达最大规模（日面经度跨越了 17°）。我们在图 1 中用箭头标志出了 8 月 3 日（JD 41532）的位

marked August 3 (JD 41532), the last day before the series of Forbush decreases which marked the solar activity[7], by an arrow. The expected change in spin rate and length of day is clearly visible; a similar plot using data for the six month period May to October 1972 shows (Fig. 2) that the jump is the largest such event recorded over that period. The change in slope indicated by the data of Fig. 2 is equally significant; this is qualitatively similar to the changes seen in pulsar spin rates during glitches, and we therefore borrow the term from the pulsar literature to describe this terrestrial process. At the time of the flare and sunspot activity, the slope flattens slightly, subsequently trending back towards a slope more typical of the data of the preceding three months over a period of several weeks.

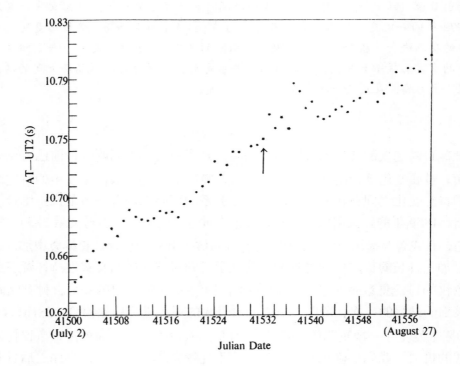

Fig. 1. Change in length of day for a period of one month on either side of date of great solar flare activity of August 1972. Arrow marks August 3, the last day before the flare activity. Large discontinuous change in AT–UT2 occurs on August 8.

These effects are not so dramatic that one would necessarily attribute them to an outside cause on the basis of these data alone, but they take on a greater significance in the light of out prediction, following Danjon, that just such a change should occur soon after a great solar flare. We are confident that the effect is real, and that the glitch was indeed caused by events associated with the solar activity of early August 1972.

置，这是福布什下降的前一天，福布什下降是太阳活动的标志[7]。从图中可以清楚地看到我们所预期的自转速度及日长的变化。我们还利用 1972 年 5~10 月这 6 个月的数据作了类似的图（图 2），如图所示，该跃变是这一时期内记录到的此类事件中最大的一次。图 2 数据所显示的斜率变化也同样显著，究其本质，它类似于脉冲星自转突快期间出现的自转速度的变化,因此我们借用描述脉冲星文献中的术语"突变"（glitch）来描述这一发生在地球上的情况。在太阳耀斑和太阳黑子活动期间，该斜率会略微变小，持续数周后，又回归至前三个月的数据所表现出的更加具有代表性的斜率上。

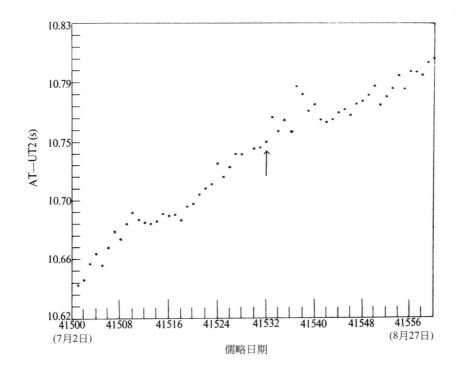

图 1. 1972 年 8 月强太阳耀斑活动发生日前后各一个月内日长的变化。箭头标示 8 月 3 日，是耀斑活动
发生的前一天。AT–UT2 的较大不连续变化出现在 8 月 8 日。

　　由于自转与日长并未发生很大的变化，所以我们不能仅凭这些数据就将其归因于太阳风暴这一外部因素。但是据我们预测，也正如丹戎所言，这些变化应该有更重要的意义，因为它们紧随强太阳耀斑活动发生。我们确信，这种效应是真实存在的，并且突变确实是由与 1972 年 8 月初的太阳活动相关的事件所引起。

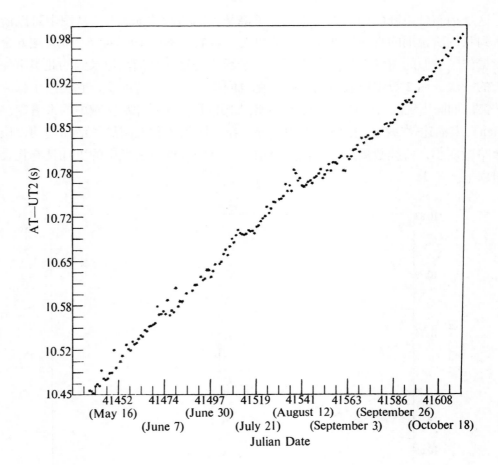

Fig. 2. As Fig. 1, for May to October 1972. The change in slope after the time of the great solar activity, and subsequent return towards the pre-flare slope, emphasize the importance of the event.

It is not difficult to envisage models which explain the delay of 5 days between commencement of the flare activity and the glitch. We will not discuss detailed mechanisms here, except to point out that solar phenomena are known to influence the large scale circulation of the Earth's atmosphere. For example, troughs in the circulation pattern at high latitudes are amplified when the level of solar cosmic rays reaching the Earth is high[10,11]. Like Schatzman[6], we believe that sudden variations in the length of day may be produced by meteorological phenomena induced by solar activity; in that case, it would be most unreasonable if it did not take a few days for these effects to show themselves in the AT–UT2 measurements.

We will discuss details of such a mechanism and further consequences of this discovery elsewhere. We thank the US Naval Observatory, Washington, for supplying the raw data used in the preparation of Figs. 1 and 2.

(**243**, 26-27; 1973)

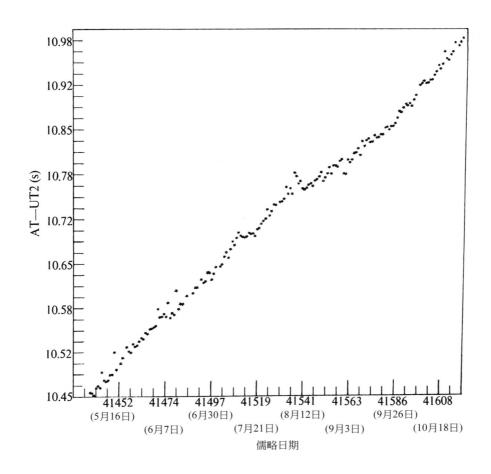

图 2. 1972 年 5~10 月 AT–UT2 的变化情况。强太阳活动后斜率发生变化，而随后又回归至耀斑发生前的斜率，这充分说明了该事件的重要性。

我们不难想出一个模型来解释为何耀斑活动开始到日长的突变发生之间有 5 天的滞后效应。在本文中我们不会讨论详细的机制问题，仅指出地球大气层的大尺度环流会受太阳活动的影响。例如，当到达地球的太阳宇宙射线水平较高时，高纬度地区环流模式中的低压槽就会加深 [10,11]。同沙茨曼 [6] 一样，我们认为日长的突然变化可能是由太阳活动导致的气象现象造成的。在这种情况下，AT–UT2 的测定结果中这类效应并未出现几天时间的滞后，那反而是最不合理的。

有关这一机制的详情以及该发现的进一步结果，我们将在其他文章中详细讨论。在准备绘制图 1 和图 2 的过程中，位于华盛顿的美国海军天文台向我们提供了原始数据，在此表示感谢。

（齐红艳 孙惠南 翻译；马宇蒨 审稿）

**John Gribbin\* and Stephen Plagemann†**
\*Nature, 4 Little Essex Street, London WC2R 3LF
†NASA Goddard Space Flight Center, Institute for Space Studies, 2880 Broadway, New York, NY 10025

Received March 26, 1973.

---

References:

1. Challinor, R. A., *Science*, **172**, 1022 (1971).

2. Gribbin, J., *Science*, **173**, 558 (1971).

3. Danjon, A., *CR Acad. Sci. Paris*, **254**, 2479 (1962).

4. Danjon, A., *CR Acad. Sci. Paris*, **254**, 3058 (1962).

5. Danjon, A., *Notes et Informations de l'Observatoire de Paris*, **8**, No. 7 (1962).

6. Schatzman, E., in *The Earth-Moon System* (edit. by Cameron, A. G. W., and Marsden, B. G.), 12 (Plenum, New York, 1966).

7. Pomerantz, M. A., and Duggal, S. P., *Nature*, **241**, 331 (1973).

8. Chupp, E. L., Forrest, D. J., Higbie, P. R., Surie, A. N., Tsai, C., and Dunphy, P. P., *Nature*, **241**, 333 (1973).

9. Mathews, T., and Lanzerotti, L. J., *Nature*, **241**, 335 (1973).

10. Macdonald, N. J., and Roberts, W. O., *J. Geophys. Res.*, **65**, 529 (1960).

11. Roberts, W. O., and Olsen, R. M., *J. Atmos. Sci.*, **30**, 135 (1973).

# Removal of Xenon and Radon from Contaminated Atmospheres with Dioxygenyl Hexafluoroantimonate, $O_2SbF_6$

L. Stein

## Editor's Note

Since the discovery in 1962 that the noble gases were not fully inert to the formation of chemical compounds (in a paper that *Nature* embarrassingly failed to publish through editorial dilatoriness), noble-gas chemistry had expanded considerably. Here Larry Stein of Argonne National Laboratory, one of the early pioneers in the field, puts it to practical use. He shows that both xenon and radon will react with a salt of "dioxygen", a chemical species instrumental to the discovery of xenon's chemical reactivity. Stein proposes that this salt be used to remove radioactive isotopes of xenon, and perhaps krypton, from the atmosphere contaminated by nuclear power plants and in uranium mines. The method was never applied in practice, presumably because of prohibitive cost.

RADIOACTIVE noble gases, such as $^{133}Xe$, $^{135}Xe$, $^{85}Kr$, and $^{88}Kr$, are formed in uranium fission and are released to the atmosphere by nuclear power plants and fuel reprocessing plants. Studies of the US Public Health Service have shown that a modern boiling-water reactor, for example, releases about 20 Ci of $^{85}Kr$ and 13,000 Ci of $^{133}Xe$ per year under normal operating conditions[1,2]. Under adverse operating conditions, the release rates may be much higher[1]. Of the physical methods for reducing these emissions[3-7], cryogenic distillation and charcoal adsorption are being developed for large-scale use.

Soon after the first noble gas compounds had been discovered[8-12], Pomeroy[13] suggested that chemical methods might be useful for trapping krypton and xenon isotopes. Slivnik[14] has studied reactions of krypton-xenon mixtures with fluorine for waste-gas treatment and has demonstrated that xenon can be separated from krypton by such reactions. Fluorine is not, however, a convenient reagent for this purpose, as it must be heated with the process gas, and the excess fluorine must be removed afterwards. I have shown that radon, the heaviest noble gas, can be collected by oxidation with liquid bromine trifluoride and solid halogen fluoride-metal fluoride complexes, such as $ClF_2SbF_6$, $BrF_2SbF_6$, $BrF_2BiF_6$, and $IF_4(SbF_6)_3$ (refs. 15 and 16). I report here further experiments with a dioxygenyl salt, $O_2SbF_6$, which reacts with radon and xenon at 25°C and which appears very promising as a reagent for removing both of these gases from contaminated atmospheres.

Dioxygenyl hexafluoroantimonate was prepared in 0.5-10 g amounts by photochemical reaction of oxygen, fluorine, and antimony pentafluoride[17]. Samples (0.5 g) of the

# 六氟合锑酸（Ⅴ）双氧盐（$O_2SbF_6$）去除污染大气中的氙和氡

斯坦

## 编者按

自从 1962 年发现稀有气体在化合物的形成中并不完全是惰性的（由于编辑方面的拖延，该文章很尴尬地未能在《自然》上发表），稀有气体化学取得了显著进展。在本文中，该领域的早期开拓者之一——阿贡国家实验室的拉里·斯坦，将其运用到实际应用中。他展示了氙（Xe）和氡（Rn）能与一个"双氧"盐反应，这种盐是一类有助于发现氙的化学反应活性的化学物质。斯坦建议使用这种盐去除受核电站和铀矿污染的大气中的放射性同位素氙，也许也能除去氪（Kr）。可能由于成本太高，这个方法从未应用于实践中。

放射性惰性气体，诸如 [133]Xe，[135]Xe，[85]Kr 和 [88]Kr，是在铀裂变过程中形成的，并由核电站与燃料再处理厂排放到大气之中。美国公共卫生署的研究显示，以现代沸水反应堆为例，它在正常工作条件下每年会释放出大约 20 Ci 的 [85]Kr 和 13,000 Ci 的 [133]Xe[1,2]。在不利的工作条件下，释放速率可能会更高 [1]。在减少上述排放的物理方法中 [3-7]，低温蒸馏和活性炭吸附正被开发为大规模应用。

在第一种稀有气体化合物被发现 [8-12] 后不久，波默罗伊 [13] 就提议，可以使用化学方法来捕集氪和氙的同位素。斯利弗尼克 [14] 就废气处理问题研究了氪－氙混合气体与氟的反应，并证明这种反应能够将氙从氪中分离出来。不过，要达到这个目的，氟并不是一种适宜的试剂，因为氟必须与废气共热，然后除去过量的氟。我曾指出，最重的稀有气体氡，可以通过用液态三氟化溴和固态卤素氟化物－金属氟化物复合物（例如 $ClF_2SbF_6$，$BrF_2SbF_6$，$BrF_2BiF_6$ 和 $IF_4(SbF_6)_3$）进行氧化来收集（参考文献 15, 16）。在本文中，我报道了用双氧基盐——$O_2SbF_6$ 进行的进一步实验。这种双氧基盐在 25℃时与氡和氙反应，并且似乎非常有希望成为一种能从污染大气中去除这两种气体的试剂。

通过氧、氟与五氟化锑之间的光化学反应制得 0.5~10 g 的六氟合锑（V）酸双氧盐 [17]。将该化合物样品（0.5 g，白色，结晶粉末）暴露于放在金属真空线上的

391

compound, a white, crystalline powder, were exposed to samples of radon, xenon and krypton in 300 ml. "Pyrex" bulbs on a metal vacuum line. Tracer $^{222}$Rn (8.1 mCi) reacted with the powder immediately at 23-25°C, forming a nonvolatile radon compound. Xenon at 10-200 mm pressure also reacted immediately, forming a pale-yellow, translucent xenon compound. Oxygen was shown to be liberated in the xenon reaction by the fact that the residual gas was not completely condensible at −195°C. No reaction of krypton at 485-700 mm pressure was observed from 23°C to 150°C.

Flow experiments were carried out with $O_2SbF_6$ powder and samples of air (0.33-0.76 l. at STP) which had been artificially contaminated with $^{222}$Rn and $^{133}$Xe. In each experiment, a rare gas/air mixture was passed through a glass U-tube packed with the powder, then through a trap cooled with liquid nitrogen to condense any unreacted radioisotope. The distribution of the radioisotope was afterwards determined by measuring the γ-emission of the U-tube and the cold trap. (The distribution of $^{133}$Xe was determined immediately; the distribution of $^{222}$Rn was determined after 3 hours, when $^{222}$Rn and its γ-emitting daughters $^{214}$Pb and $^{214}$Bi were known to be in radioactive equilibrium.) In three experiments with the radon isotope and with a bed of powder 5.0 cm long and 6.3 mm in diameter, all of the radon was absorbed. In 5 experiments with the xenon isotope and with a bed of powder 6.5 cm long and 5.5 mm in diameter, 67-100% of the xenon was absorbed (Table 1).

Table 1. Removal of Radon and Xenon from Air with $O_2SbF_6$ at 23-25°C

| Radioisotope | Conc. in air (mCi l.$^{-1}$) | Average flow rate (ml. min$^{-1}$) | Amount of radioisotope removed (%) |
|---|---|---|---|
| $^{222}$Rn | 13 | 12 | 100 |
| ,, | 15 | 15 | 100 |
| ,, | 24 | 12 | 100 |
| $^{133}$Xe | 9.8 | 15 | 67* |
| ,, | 7.9 | 13 | 100 |
| ,, | 2.0 | 14 | 100 |
| ,, | 3.2 | 13 | 98 |
| ,, | 4.3 | 14 | 100 |

* Flow rate poorly controlled at start of experiment.

Raman spectral studies have shown that the xenon product is $XeF^+Sb_2F_{11}^-$, a 1:2 xenon difluoride-antimony pentafluoride complex[18-20]. When xenon is added gradually to $O_2SbF_6$, a new band (characteristic of the xenon-fluorine stretching vibration of $XeF^+$ cation[15]) appears in the spectrum at 618 cm$^{-1}$. Shifts in the $SbF_6^-$ vibration frequencies also occur. The final spectrum contains prominent bands at 450, 618, 655, and 686 cm$^{-1}$.

300 ml"派热克斯"玻璃瓶内的氡、氙和氦样品中。在 23~25℃ 下，示踪剂 $^{222}$Rn（8.1 mCi）与该粉末迅速反应，产生了一种不挥发的氡化合物。氙在 10~200 mm 压强下也会迅速反应，形成一种浅黄色的、半透明的氙化合物。残余气体在 −195℃时不能完全冷凝，说明在氙的反应中释放出了氧气。在 485~700 mm 压强、23~150℃ 温度范围内，没有观测到氦的反应。

用 O₂SbF₆ 粉末与人为污染 $^{222}$Rn 和 $^{133}$Xe 的空气样品（标准状态下 0.33~0.76 l）进行了流动实验。每个实验中，稀有气体 / 空气混合物先经过一个填满该粉末的玻璃 U 形管，接着再经过一个液氮冷阱，冷凝未反应的放射性同位素。随后通过测定 U 形管和冷阱中的 γ 发射来确定放射性同位素的分布。（即刻确定 $^{133}$Xe 的分布；3 小时后确定 $^{222}$Rn 的分布，已知此时 $^{222}$Rn 与其 γ 发射子体 $^{214}$Pb 和 $^{214}$Bi 处于放射性平衡中。）在用氡同位素和长 5.0 cm、直径 6.3 mm 的粉末床进行的 3 次实验中，所有的氡都被吸收了。在用氙同位素和长 6.5 cm、直径 5.5 mm 的粉末床进行的 5 次实验中，67%~100% 的氙被吸收了（表 1）。

表 1. 23~25℃ 下 O₂SbF₆ 去除空气中的氙和氡

| 放射性同位素 | 空气中浓度（mCi·l⁻¹） | 平均流速（ml·min⁻¹） | 放射性同位素的去除量（%） |
|---|---|---|---|
| $^{222}$Rn | 13 | 12 | 100 |
| ,, | 15 | 15 | 100 |
| ,, | 24 | 12 | 100 |
| $^{133}$Xe | 9.8 | 15 | 67* |
| ,, | 7.9 | 13 | 100 |
| ,, | 2.0 | 14 | 100 |
| ,, | 3.2 | 13 | 98 |
| ,, | 4.3 | 14 | 100 |

\* 实验开始时流速控制不佳。

拉曼光谱研究显示，氙反应产物为 XeF⁺Sb₂F₁₁⁻，为二氟化氙 - 五氟化锑以 1 : 2 的比例形成的复合物 [18-20]。将氙逐渐加入到 O₂SbF₆ 中时，一个新的谱带（XeF⁺ 阳离子中氙 - 氟键特征性伸缩振动 [15]）出现在光谱的 618 cm⁻¹ 处，SbF₆⁻ 振动频率也发生改变。在最终的光谱中，主要谱带位于 450 cm⁻¹、618 cm⁻¹、655 cm⁻¹ 和 686 cm⁻¹ 处。

Mass spectrometric analyses of residual gases in experiments with krypton-xenon mixtures have shown that two molecules of oxygen are released for each atom of xenon absorbed as follows

$$Xe^{(g)} + 2O_2^+SbF_6^{-(s)} \rightarrow XeF^+Sb_2F_{11}^{-(s)} + 2O_2^{(g)}$$

No spectral or analytical data have been obtained for the trace amounts of radon product (no stable isotopes of radon are known, and the $^{222}Rn$ product is intensely radioactive), but radon probably forms an analogous 1:2 radon difluoride-antimony pentafluoride complex as follows

$$Rn^{(g)} + 2O_2^+SbF_6^{-(s)} \rightarrow RnF^+Sb_2F_{11}^{-(s)} + 2O_2^{(g)}$$

Mixtures of approximately three parts $O_2SbF_6$ and one part antimony pentafluoride by volume (grey powders, prepared in a dry box) react with radon but not with xenon. Dilution with antimony pentafluoride therefore lowers the free energy of $O_2SbF_6$ below the threshold for zenon oxidation but not below that for radon oxidation.

Equimolar mixtures of krypton and xenon were partly separated on passage through U-tubes packed with $O_2SbF_6$. The mixtures were passed through beds of the compound 5.8-6.0 cm long and 5.5 mm in diameter at 23-25°C and at total pressures of 20-160 mm. Gases emerging from the beds were collected and analysed by mass spectrometry. The first samples had the following range of composition: 45.5-49.6% $O_2$, 12.7-16.2% Xe, and 37.7-38.3% Kr. The percentage of oxygen fell and that of krypton and xenon rose as the $O_2SbF_6$ was depleted. The colour change of the powder, from white to yellow, could be used to indicate the amount depleted, as there was a sharp interface between coloured zones. Each time that gas was admitted, a blue-green fluorescence was noted in the $O_2SbF_6$. The source of this emission is not known at present, but it is probable that an excited xenon, oxygen, or ozone species is formed during the reaction.

More complete separation of krypton and xenon was achieved by shaking equimolar mixtures of the gases with $O_2SbF_6$ powder in "Pyrex" bulbs containing stirring vanes. The mixtures were shaken intermittently, by hand, at room temperature with excess amounts of the powder over periods of 3 to 24 h. Residual gases were then analysed by mass spectrometry, and the final gas mixtures were found to contain less than 2% xenon.

Because it has negligible vapour pressure at 25°C, and because oxygen is the gaseous product, the dioxygenyl compound appears to be a very "clean" reagent for air-purification purposes. It is less corrosive than such complex fluorides as $ClF_2SbF_6$, $BrF_2SbF_6$, and $BrF_2BiF_6$, and may be stored in glass or fluorinated plastic containers. Very little decomposition has been noted, for example, in samples that have been stored for 6-9 months in "Pyrex" bulbs and "Kel-F" test tubes. Some corrosion of "Kel-F" has been observed, however, by products formed in the reaction with xenon—probably excited

对用氪－氙混合物进行的实验中得到的残余气体质谱分析显示，每吸收一个氙原子释放出两个氧气分子，如下式所示：

$$Xe^{(g)} + 2O_2^+SbF_6^{-(s)} \rightarrow XeF^+Sb_2F_{11}^{-(s)} + 2O_2^{(g)}$$

对于痕量的氡产物（没有已知稳定的氡同位素，而且 $^{222}$Rn 产物具有强放射性），未得到光谱数据或分析数据，不过，氡很可能会形成一种类似于组成比为 1∶2 的二氟化氡－五氟化锑复合物，如下式所示：

$$Rn^{(g)} + 2O_2^+SbF_6^{-(s)} \rightarrow RnF^+Sb_2F_{11}^{-(s)} + 2O_2^{(g)}$$

大约三体积的 $O_2SbF_6$ 与一体积的五氟化锑（灰色粉末，保存在干燥盒中）组成的混合物可以与氡反应，但是不能和氙反应。因此，五氟化锑的稀释能够使 $O_2SbF_6$ 的自由能降低到氙氧化的阈值之下，但还没有低于氡氧化的阈值。

氪和氙的等摩尔混合物在通过装满了 $O_2SbF_6$ 的 U 形管之后发生了部分分离。在 23~25℃、总压强 20~160 mm 条件下，将混合气体通过长 5.8~6.0 cm、直径 5.5 mm 的混合物反应床。收集反应床中逸出的气体并用质谱法进行分析。第一份样品的组成范围如下：45.5%~49.6% $O_2$、12.7%~16.2% Xe 和 37.7%~38.3% Kr。随着 $O_2SbF_6$ 的消耗，氧的百分比下降，而氪和氙的百分比上升。粉末的颜色变化（从白到黄）可以用来指示消耗量，因为在有色区域之间存在着一个明显的分界面。每次加入气体后，就会在 $O_2SbF_6$ 中产生蓝绿色荧光。目前这种荧光发射的来源尚未明确，不过，很有可能是在反应过程中形成了一种激发态的氙、氧或者臭氧类物质。

在放有搅拌叶片的"派热克斯"玻璃瓶中振摇等摩尔的氪、氙气体与 $O_2SbF_6$ 粉末的混合物，可以对两种物质进行更完全的分离。在室温下，手工对混合物进行间歇性的振摇，使其与过量粉末反应 3~24 h。接着用质谱法分析残余气体，发现最终气体混合物中含有不到 2% 的氙。

由于 25℃时蒸汽压可忽略，再加上氧为气态产物，因此对于空气净化来说，双氧化合物似乎是一种非常"清洁的"试剂。与 $ClF_2SbF_6$，$BrF_2SbF_6$ 和 $BrF_2BiF_6$ 等复合氟化物相比，它的腐蚀性较小，并且可以储存在玻璃和氟化塑料容器中。如在"派热克斯"玻璃瓶和"Kel-F（聚三氟氯乙烯）"试管中储存了 6~9 个月的样品，只有很少量的分解。不过，通过与氙反应生成产物——可能为激发态的氙、氧或臭氧类物质，可观测到"Kel-F"受到一些腐蚀。混合物会被水分分解；因此在处理潮湿气

xenon, oxygen, or ozone species. The compound is decomposed by moisture; in treatment of wet gases, it must therefore be used in conjunction with a desiccant, such as silica gel or a molecular sieve.

The dioxygenyl compound can probably be used for such purposes as purifying radon-contaminated atmospheres in uranium mines; removing xenon isotopes from reactor and reprocessing plant off-gases; separating xenon from lighter noble gases; and analysing xenon and radon isotopes in air. In one of the methods which is being developed to reduce emissions from boiling-water reactors, large beds of charcoal are used to "hold up" radioisotopes[2,3]. Waste gases are passed through the beds at ambient temperature, and the noble gases are adsorbed and retained long enough for short-lived isotope to decay. (Xenon isotopes may be held for 20 days and krypton isotopes for about 1 day.) Small beds of $O_2SbF_6$ can probably be substituted for the large (100 to 200 ton) beds of charcoal to remove xenon isotopes from the waste gases completely.

Further research may disclose oxidants that can be used to collect krypton as well as radon and xenon. Krypton forms a simple fluoride, $KrF_2$, which is stable only at low temperatures, and a complex fluoride, $KrF_2.2SbF_5$, which is stable at 25°C (refs. 21, 22). (The latter is probably an ionic compound, $KrF^+Sb_2F_{11}^-$, analogous to $XeF^+Sb_2F_{11}^-$.) By substituting cations of very great oxidizing power for the $O_2^+$ cation in $O_2SbF_6$, it may be possible to prepare reagents that combine spontaneously with krypton to form this stable compound.

I thank J. G. Malm for information concerning the preparation of dioxygenyl hexafluoroantimonate and A. Engelkemeir for mass spectrometric analysis of gas mixtures. This work was performed under the auspices of the US Atomic Energy Commission.

(**243**, 30-32; 1973)

L. Stein

Chemistry Division, Argonne National Laboratory, 9700 S Cass Avenue, Argonne, Illinois 60439

Received January 31, 1973.

---

References:

1. Logsden, J. E., and Chissler, R. I., *Radioactive Waste Discharges to the Environment from Nuclear Power Facilities* (Public Health Service, US Department of Health, Education, and Welfare, March 1970).

2. Lewis, W. D., *et al.*, *Engineering for Resolution of the Energy-Environment Dilemma*, 68 and 192 (Committee on Power Plant Siting, National Academy of Engineering, Washington, DC, 1972).

3. Slansky, C. M., *At. Energy Rev.*, **9**, 423 (1971).

4. Knowles, D. J., and Gillespie, F. E., *Nucl. Safety*, **1**, 47 (1960).

5. Keilholtz, G. W., *Nucl. Safety*, **8**, 155 (1966).

6. Bendixsen, C. L., Offutt, G. F., and Wheeler, B. R., *Chem. Eng.*, 55 (1971).

7. Merriman, J. R., *et al.*, in *Proc. Symp. Treatment of Airborne Radioactive Wastes*, 303 (Int. At. Energy Agency, Vienna, 1968).

8. Bartlett, N., *Proc. Chem. Soc.*, 218 (1962).

9. Claassen, H. H., Selig, H., and Malm, J. G., *J. Amer. Chem. Soc.*, **84**, 3593 (1962).

体时，必须与硅胶或分子筛等干燥剂联用。

双氧化合物或许可以用于净化铀矿内氡污染的气体、从反应堆和再处理厂的废气中除去氙同位素、从较轻的稀有气体中分离氙以及分析空气中氙和氡的同位素等。减少沸水堆废气排放的方法之一是用大量的活性炭来"拦截"放射性同位素[2,3]。将废气通过处于室温下的反应床时，稀有气体被吸收，并且停留足够长的时间以确保短暂的同位素衰变。（氙同位素可以保持 20 天，而氡同位素需要大约一天。）要从废气中完全去除氙同位素，用 $O_2SbF_6$ 小反应床就能代替活性炭大反应床（100~200 吨）。

进一步研究可以揭示其他能够用来收集氪、氡和氙的氧化剂。氪形成一种只在低温下稳定的简单氟化物 $KrF_2$，和一种在 25℃稳定的复合氟化物 $KrF_2 \cdot 2SbF_5$（文献 21，22）。（后者可能是一种离子化合物，$KrF^+Sb_2F_{11}^-$，类似于 $XeF^+Sb_2F_{11}^-$）通过将 $O_2SbF_6$ 中的 $O_2^+$ 阳离子换成强氧化能力的阳离子，就有可能制备出能够与氡自发结合形成稳定化合物的试剂。

感谢马尔姆提供的关于六氟合锑酸（V）双氧盐的制备信息，以及恩格尔克迈尔提供的混合气体质谱分析的信息。本研究得到了美国原子能委员会的赞助。

（王耀杨 翻译；安俊岭 审稿）

Removal of Xenon and Radon from Contaminated Atmospheres with Dioxygenyl Hexafluoroantimonate, $O_2SbF_6$

10. Fields, P. R., Stein, L., and Zirin, M. H., *J. Amer. Chem. Soc.,* **84**, 4164 (1962).

11. Chernick, C. L., *et al., Science,* **138**, 136 (1962).

12. Grosse, A. V., Kirshenbaum, A. D., Streng, A. G., and Streng, L. V., *Science,* **139**, 1047 (1963).

13. Pomeroy, J. H., in *Noble Gas Compounds* (edit. by Hyman, H. H.), 123 (University of Chicago Press, Chicago, 1963).

14. Slivnik, J., in *Proc. of Symp. on Treatment of Airborne Radioactive Wastes,* 315 (Int. At. Energy Agency, Vienna, 1968).

15. Stein, L., *Science,* **175**, 1463 (1972).

16. Stein, L., *J. Inorg. Nucl. Chem.,* **35**, 39 (1973).

17. Shamir, J., and Binenboym, J., *Inorg. Chim. Acta,* **2**, 37 (1968).

18. Edwards, A. J., Holloway, J. H., and Peacock, R. D., *Proc. Chem. Soc.,* 275 (1963).

19. Sladky, F. O., Bulliner, P. A., and Bartlett, N., *J. Chem. Soc. (A),* 2179 (1969).

20. Baranov, G. S., Egorov, N. P., Sopikov, A. N., and Chaivanov, B. B., *Zh. Fiz. Khim.,* **46**, 18 (1972).

21. Selig, H., and Peacock, R. D., *J. Amer. Chem. Soc.,* **86**, 3895 (1964).

22. Selig, H., in *Halogen Chemistry* (edit. by Gutman, V.), **1**, 403 (Academic Press, London and New York, 1967).

# Cores of the Terrestrial Planets

K. E. Bullen

## Editor's Note

In the early 1970s we were just beginning to understand the properties of the planets of the Solar System, as the first unmanned space missions sent back data. In particular, the densities of the terrestrial planets systematically decreased going from Mercury outwards to Mars. Keith Bullen here makes an early attempt to explain this by invoking a change in mineral composition for mixtures of iron and iron oxides. The idea only partially worked, failing to account for the cores of Mercury and the Moon. We now have much better data and a far more sophisticated understanding of the conditions in the early Solar System and how the planets were assembled, rendering Bullen's model obsolete.

---

The compositions of the cores of the terrestrial planets have been re-examined following a calculation by O. G. Sorokhtin that the iron oxide $Fe_2O$ is stable at pressures reached in the Earth's core and his suggestion that the outer core may consist of $Fe_2O$. It is shown that the idea of an $Fe_2O$ outer core in the Earth can be fairly well reconciled with a common overall composition for the planets Earth, Venus and Mars in a way that avoids the main objections to the earlier phase-transition theory.

---

THE presently favoured theory that the Earth's outer core consists predominantly of iron (possibly alloyed) requires[1,2] the overall compositions of the planets Earth, Venus and Mars to be markedly different. It is difficult to reconcile this result with accretion theories of the origin of the planets[1-3].

In an early attempt at reconciliation, Ramsey[4] and myself[5] independently advanced a "phase-transition theory" which treated the Earth's outer core as a high-pressure modification of the lower mantle material. This theory agreed with a common overall composition for the three planets and fitted well the then available observational data on the masses and radii of Venus and Mars and the polar flattening of Mars. The theory later met with difficulties.

Revisions of the planetary observational data reduced the quality of the original fit. The most serious surviving discrepancy is that the preferred observational estimate[6] of the radius of Venus is now 6,052±10 km, as against 6,270 km predicted[7] on the phase-transition theory.

The original Earth models $A$ and $B$ (refs 8, 9) used in deriving models of the other planets

400

# 类地行星的核

布伦

编者按

在 20 世纪 70 年代早期，当第一艘无人飞船传回数据时，人们才刚刚开始理解太阳系行星的性质，特别是类地行星的密度从水星向外到火星逐渐减小。本文中，基斯·布伦进行了一次早期尝试，他用铁和氧化铁混合物中矿物成分的变化解释这个现象。这个想法只是部分成立，它不能解释水星和月球的核。我们现在已经有好得多的数据和对早期太阳系的条件以及对行星是怎样形成的有着更细致的理解，布伦的模型过时了。

---

根据索罗赫京的计算，在地核的压强下氧化铁 $Fe_2O$ 是稳定的，他提出类地行星的外核可能由 $Fe_2O$ 构成，据此我们重新检验了类地行星的核的组成。这里证明了地球外核由 $Fe_2O$ 构成的想法可以和地球、金星和火星共同的总体成分保持相当好的一致，避免了与早期提出的相变理论的主要矛盾。

---

现在普遍接受的理论认为地球外核主要是由铁（可能是合金）组成，这就要求[1,2]地球、金星和火星这些行星的总体成分有显著的不同。这和行星形成的吸积理论[1-3]难以协调。

在早期调和这一矛盾的尝试中，拉姆齐[4] 和我 [5] 都曾独立提出"相变理论"，这个理论认为地球外核为一种高压下变质了的下地幔物质。这个理论和其他三个行星的总体成分一致，而且和那时已有的金星及火星的质量和半径、火星的极向扁率的观测数据符合得很好。这理论后来遇到了困难。

对行星观测数据的修正降低了原先的拟合效果。最严重的偏差是：金星半径的最佳观测估计值[6] 为 $6,052 \pm 10$ km，和相变理论预测[7] 的 6,270 km 不一致。

人们用地球模型 A 和 B （参考文献 8，9）来推导其他行星的情况。然而这两个原

have had to be amended (see refs10, 11) to allow (among other things) for the reduction of the estimated Earth's central density[12] from about 18 to 13 g cm$^{-3}$, and of the estimated moment of inertia coefficient[13] for the Earth from 0.3336 to 0.3309. Both revisions have slightly worsened the fit with Venus and Mars.

Geochemists have found difficulty, principally on the question of the packing of oxygen atoms in the lower mantle material, in reconciling the proposed phase transition with the large density jump (in the ratio 0.7 or more) at the Earth's mantle-core boundary, $N$ say.

Transitory shock-wave experiments carried out in laboratories at high pressures have failed to supply positive evidence that a phase transition occurs at $N$.

## Alternative Model

Having regard to various uncertainties and questions of experimental interpretation, I think it is unsound to assert, as do some investigators, that the difficulties have "disproved" the theory—indeed the theory still has some notable followers. But the case against it is sufficiently strong to make it desirable to seek alternatives.

As a possible alternative, I propose a theory which avoids the principal difficulties of the phase-transition theory while retaining the important feature that the pressure $p_c$ at $N$ is critically involved in the changes of property at $N$. The theory incorporates a suggestion of O. G. Sorokhtin (personal communication) that the Earth's outer core consists of $Fe_2O$. Sorokhtin has calculated that this oxide, which is unstable at ordinary pressures, becomes stable at the pressures in the Earth's core and has a density-pressure relation matching that in the Earth's outer core.

In other respects, I have deviated substantially from Sorokhtin. Whereas he attributes the occurrence of $Fe_2O$ in the outer core to a breakdown of FeO into $Fe_2O$ and oxygen, I have associated the occurrence of the $Fe_2O$ with the equation $Fe_2O \rightleftharpoons FeO + Fe$, my reason being the extent of planetary fit that can be thereby achieved.

My proposal, which I refer to as the "$Fe_2O$ theory", envisages a model family of planets with the following properties:

All planets of the family are composed of two primary materials—a basic mantle material $X$, and $Fe_2O$. (This is subject to qualification below.) For present purposes, the composition of $X$ need not be specified, but $X$ is likely to include some FeO.

In all the planets, the ratio of the mass of $X$ to the mass $M$ of the planet is the same.

In those planets which contain $Fe_2O$, the $Fe_2O$ occurs as a distinct zone (the "outer" core) throughout which $p \geqslant p_c$, where $p$ is the pressure.

初的地球模型被指出必须进行修正（参考文献 10，11）：（其中）要允许地球中心密度的估算值 [12] 从大约 18 g·cm⁻³ 降到 13 g·cm⁻³，同时允许地球转动惯量系数的估算值 [13] 从 0.3336 降到 0.3309。这两个修正都对金星和火星的拟合造成了轻微的不良影响。

地球化学家在协调所提出的相变理论与地球核幔边界（如 $N$ 处）大的密度跳跃（比值为 0.7 或更大）时遇到了困难，困难主要在于氧原子在下地幔物质中的填充问题。

在实验室进行的高压下瞬变激波实验中，并未提供足以支持在 $N$ 处发生相变的正面证据。

## 替 代 模 型

针对实验解释存在的各种问题和不确定性，我认为像一些研究学者们那样作以下断言——这些困难"反驳"了这个理论是不合适的，实际上这个理论还有一些著名的追随者。但是反对这个理论的理由也是足够强的，这使我们有必要去寻找替代模型。

作为一种可能的替代模型，我提出了一种新理论，避免了相变理论的主要困难，同时保留了其重要特点，即 $N$ 处的压强 $P_c$ 和 $N$ 处的性质变化密切相关。该理论还包括了索罗赫京的意见（个人交流），他认为地球外核是由 $Fe_2O$ 组成的。索罗赫京计算得出这种在一般压强下不稳定的氧化物在地核压强下变得稳定，并且有和地球外核相匹配的密度–压强关系。

在其他方面，我和索罗赫京的观点大相径庭。尽管他将外核中 $Fe_2O$ 的产生归结为 $FeO$ 分解为 $Fe_2O$ 和氧原子，但我认为外核中 $Fe_2O$ 的产生与方程 $Fe_2O \rightleftharpoons FeO+Fe$ 有关，我的理由在于这样可以达到和行星拟合的程度。

我这个称为 "$Fe_2O$ 理论"的提议假设了一个具有以下性质的行星模型族：

该族的行星都由两种主要物质组成，一种是基本的地幔物质 $X$，另一种是 $Fe_2O$。（这是受到以下这些限制的）基于现在的目的，$X$ 的组成无需详细说明，但是其中可能包含一些 $FeO$。

在所有的行星中，$X$ 的质量和行星质量 $M$ 的比值是相同的。

在那些含有 $Fe_2O$ 的行星中，$Fe_2O$ 存在于 $p \geqslant p_c$ 的独立区域（地核的"外层"），其中 $p$ 是压强。

In those planets where the first two properties would entail $p<p_c$ in an $Fe_2O$ zone, some or all of the $Fe_2O$ has broken down into FeO and Fe. This FeO, which I refer to as $Y$, forms part of the mantle and is additional to any FeO that may be part of $X$. The Fe falls to form an "inner" core.

## Details of the Model

The second property secures a common overall composition for the family. The masses of $Y$ and Fe in any planet are such as would combine precisely to form $Fe_2O$ when $p \geqslant p_c$, and the ratio of the total mass of Fe, $Fe_2O$ and $Y$ to $M$ is the same for the whole family.

The family has three subsets—$H$, $J$, $K$, say (Fig. 1). The subset $H$ includes the smallest planets which have no $Fe_2O$ zones and thus no outer cores; they have mantles composed of $X$ and $Y$ mixed, and inner cores of Fe. The subset $K$ includes the largest planets which have mantles composed purely of $X$, outer cores of $Fe_2O$, and no inner cores. The subset $J$ consists of intermediate planets which have mantles composed of $X$ and some $Y$, outer cores of $Fe_2O$, and inner cores of Fe. For all the $J$ planets, $\rho=\rho_c$ at the top of the outer core. The core-mantle mass ratios are the same for all $H$ planets, and for all $K$ planets (but the ratio is different for $H$ and $K$).

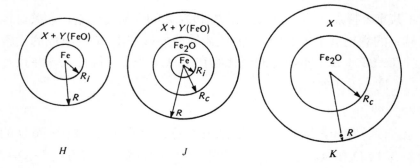

Fig. 1. Materials in the interiors of the three subsets ($H$, $J$, $K$) of terrestrial planets. The outermost zones, all containing the material $X$, are mantles. The $Fe_2O$ zones are referred to as "outer cores", the Fe zones as "inner cores".

Earth and Venus would correspond to members of $J$, Mars of $H$. Unfortunately, no known planets correspond to $K$, so that an observational test of the subset $K$ is not available. From evidence on the Earth, all $Fe_2O$ zones (outer cores) would be expected to be fluid, and Fe zones (inner cores) solid.

The $Fe_2O$ theory resembles the phase-transition theory in that all $J$ planets have the same (critical) pressure $p_c$ at the mantle-core boundaries, and all $H$ planets lack outer cores. To a considerable extent, it is this feature which enables both theories to go close to fitting a common overall composition for Earth, Venus and Mars. Differences in detail arise because, in planets smaller than Earth, the $Fe_2O$ theory entails larger iron (inner) cores than does the phase-transition theory.

在那些前两个性质限定了在 $Fe_2O$ 区域中 $p<p_c$ 的行星中，部分或全部的 $Fe_2O$ 已经被分解成 $FeO$ 和 $Fe$。这些 $FeO$，我称其为 $Y$，组成地幔的一部分，并且可能作为 $X$ 的一部分，即 $FeO$ 的补充。$Fe$ 则下落形成了"内"核。

## 模 型 细 节

第二个性质保证该模型族的行星有着相同的总体成分。在任何行星中 $Y$ 和 $Fe$ 的质量在 $p \geq p_c$ 时恰好形成 $Fe_2O$，而且 $Fe$、$Fe_2O$ 和 $Y$ 的质量之和与 $M$ 的比值在整个模型族中都是相同的。

该模型族有三个子集——$H$、$J$、$K$，如（图1）。子集 $H$ 包含那些最小的行星，它们没有 $Fe_2O$ 区域，因而没有外核；它们的幔由 $X$ 和 $Y$ 混合组成，内核由 $Fe$ 组成。子集 $K$ 包含那些最大的行星，它们的幔完全由 $X$ 组成，外核为 $Fe_2O$，没有内核。子集 $J$ 包含中等的行星，其幔由 $X$ 和一些 $Y$ 组成，外核为 $Fe_2O$，内核由 $Fe$ 组成。对于所有 $J$ 类行星，在外核顶层 $\rho=\rho_c$。对于所有的 $H$ 类以及所有 $K$ 类行星，它们各自内部的核－幔的质量比相同（但 $H$ 类和 $K$ 类行星的核－幔质量比是不同的）。

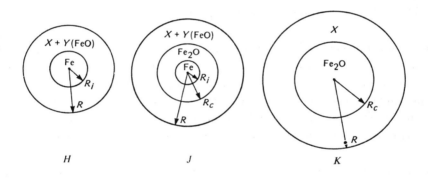

图 1. 三种类地行星模型族（$H$，$J$，$K$）内部的物质组成。最外层的地幔区域都含有 $X$ 物质。$Fe_2O$ 的区域称为"外核"，铁原子的区域称为"内核"。

地球和金星对应于 $J$ 类成员，火星对应于 $H$ 类成员。遗憾的是没有已知的行星属于 $K$ 类，所以无法对 $K$ 类行星进行观测检验。利用地球上的证据可以预期，所有的 $Fe_2O$ 区域（外核）为液态，$Fe$ 区域（内核）为固态。

这种 $Fe_2O$ 理论和相变理论的类似之处在于，所有 $J$ 类行星在核－幔边界有着相同的（临界）压强 $P_c$，并且所有的 $H$ 类行星都没有外核。在相当大的程度上，这个特点让两种理论都较为接近对地球、金星和火星共有的总体成分的拟合。出现细节上的区别是因为，对于比地球小的行星，$Fe_2O$ 理论所需要的铁（内）核比相变理论的大。

## Agreement with Observation

I have started from a simplified Earth model, taken to be a member of the subset $J$, in which the mean densities of the mantle, outer and inner cores are 4.5, 11 and 13 g cm$^{-3}$, respectively. I have provisionally neglected variations of density inside planetary zones and taken the ratio of the mean densities of $X$ and $Y$ as 0.7. For a first approximation, differences of compression between corresponding zones of the $J$ planets have also been neglected. Possible temperature differences between different planetary interiors, volume changes due to chemical interaction, and so on, in the mixing of $X$ and $Y$ in mantles, and the presence of nickel in cores have been neglected as likely to affect the essential numerical detail only slightly.

With these simplifications, the postulates formally determine numerical details for all the $J$ planets. In particular, a set of values of $M$, $R$ (radius of the planet), $R_c$ (radius of the outer core) and $R_i$ (radius of the inner core) is determined.

The observational mass of Venus[14] is $4.87 \times 10^{24}$ kg. For the $J$ planet with this mass, the simplified Fe$_2$O theory gives $R = 6,010$ km, $R_c = 2,710$ km, $R_i = 2,110$ km. Allowance for the neglected compression differences will increase this estimate of $R$ because Venus, being smaller, is less compressed than the Earth. Thus the Fe$_2$O theory fits the observed radius ($\sim 6,050$ km) of Venus as well as can be expected.

The value 600 km yielded for the thickness, $T$ say, of the (presumed fluid) Venus outer core is also interesting. It may be contrasted with the value exceeding 900 km (ref. 7) on the phase-transition theory and substantially larger values on theories which assume a predominantly iron outer core. By yielding the lowest value of $T$, the Fe$_2$O theory accounts best for the failure to observe a significant magnetic field around Venus; the presumed seat of the Earth's magnetic field (the Earth's outer core) is 2,200 km thick.

The postulates also determine the ratio of the mass of the inner core to the mass $M$ of any $H$ planet as approximately 0.15. For a particular $H$ planet of assigned mass, a first approximation to $R$ is then formally yielded if values are available for the mean densities, $\rho_1$ and $\rho_2$ say, of the core and mantle. For Mars, $M = 0.642 \times 10^{24}$ kg. For the $H$ planet with this value of $M$, taking $\rho_1$, $\rho_2 = 9.0$, 3.7 g cm$^{-3}$, the simplified Fe$_2$O theory gives $R = 3,354$ km; the yielded value of $R$ is increased by 10 km if the trial value of $\rho_1$ is decreased by about 1.0 g cm$^{-3}$, or of $\rho_2$ by about 0.03 g cm$^{-3}$. Thus uncertainties in the appropriate values of $\rho_1$ and $\rho_2$ could possibly permit raising $R$ to about 3,370 km, which is, however, less than the presently preferred observational value[3,15,16] of $3,388 \pm 5$ km.

When hydrostatic conditions are assumed throughout Mars and $\rho_1$ and $\rho_2$ are treated as constant, the Fe$_2$O theory yields $f = 1/191$ and $\delta = 18$ km, where $f$ and $\delta$ are, respectively, the polar flattening and the excess of the equatorial over the polar radius. These results agree closely with the observed $f$ and $\delta$ (see refs 3, 17). But allowance for density variation inside the mantle is likely to lower the calculated values to 1/200 (or even less) and 17 km.

## 与观测结果的吻合

我从一个简化的地球模型开始，假设它是子集 $J$ 中的成员，其幔、外核和内核的平均密度分别是 $4.5\ g\cdot cm^{-3}$、$11\ g\cdot cm^{-3}$ 和 $13\ g\cdot cm^{-3}$。我暂时忽略行星内部区域的密度变化，并将 $X$ 和 $Y$ 的平均密度比取为 0.7。作为一级近似，也忽略 $J$ 型行星中相应区域压缩的差异。在 $X$ 和 $Y$ 混合的地幔中，行星内部不同地方可能的温度差异和由于化学相互作用导致的体积变化之类的因素，以及核中镍的存在都被忽略了，因为它们可能对主要数值细节的影响甚微。

有了这些简化，对于所有 $J$ 类行星，这些假设从形式上确定了数值细节。特别是关于 $M$、$R$（行星的半径）、$R_c$（外核的半径）和 $R_i$（内核的半径）的一系列数值都被确定了。

金星的观测质量 [14] 为 $4.87\times10^{24}\ kg$。对于这个质量的 $J$ 类行星，简化的 $Fe_2O$ 理论得出 $R=6{,}010\ km$、$R_c=2{,}710\ km$ 和 $R_i=2{,}110\ km$。由于体积小的金星不如地球致密，模型中忽略了压缩率的不同，考虑压缩率的修正后将增加 $R$ 的估算值。因此 $Fe_2O$ 理论和金星观测半径（约 $6{,}050\ km$）符合得和预计的一样好。

假设金星外核为液体，同样有趣的是，我们得到其外核的厚度值 $T$ 为 $600\ km$。这可能与相变理论得到的超过 $900\ km$ 的值（参考文献 7）以及假设主要由铁构成外核的理论得出的大很多的值不同。通过估算 $T$ 的最小值，$Fe_2O$ 理论能很好地解释为何没能观测到明显的围绕金星的磁场；而由地球磁场数据推测（地球外核）的厚度为 $2{,}200\ km$。

这些假设也确定了任意 $H$ 类行星内核质量与总质量 $M$ 之比，大致为 0.15。对于一个特定质量的 $H$ 类行星，如果核和幔的平均密度值，即 $\rho_1$ 和 $\rho_2$ 已知，就可以推出 $R$ 的一级近似。对于火星，$M=0.642\times10^{24}\ kg$。对于这样质量的 $H$ 类行星，取 $\rho_1=9.0\ g\cdot cm^{-3}$，$\rho_2=3.7\ g\cdot cm^{-3}$，简化的 $Fe_2O$ 理论给出 $R=3{,}354\ km$，$R$ 值会随着试验参数 $\rho_1$ 降低 $1.0\ g\cdot cm^{-3}$ 而增加 $10\ km$，或者随着 $\rho_2$ 降低 $0.03\ g\cdot cm^{-3}$ 而增加 $10\ km$。于是 $\rho_1$ 和 $\rho_2$ 合适值的不确定性，可能允许将 $R$ 提高到 $3{,}370\ km$。然而，这仍然小于现在的最佳观测值 [3,15,16] $3{,}388\pm5\ km$。

当火星整体都采用了流体静力学条件的假设，并把 $\rho_1$ 和 $\rho_2$ 看作常数时，$Fe_2O$ 理论得到的极向扁率和赤道半径超过极向半径的值分别为 $f=1/191$ 和 $\delta=18\ km$。这些结果和观测到的 $f$ 和 $\delta$ 值（见参考文献 3、17）很接近。但是考虑地幔内部的密度变化之后，计算值很可能分别下降至 $1/200$（或者更少）和 $17\ km$。这些最新结果处

These last values are on the border[17] of the limits of error of the hydrostatic theory.

The phase-transition theory gives $R=3,390$ km and $f \approx 1/188$ (ref.18), assuming hydrostatic conditions. Thus the phase-transition theory gives the better fit with Mars unless the departures from hydrostatic conditions are considerable. This is principally because the $Fe_2O$ theory requires a larger core, radius $R_i \sim 1,400$ km. It is likely that seismic records taken on Mars will in due course provide an observational estimate of $R_i$ and so serve as a further test of the theories. (The gathering of seismic records on Venus is likely to be more difficult.)

Ironically, after the phase-transition theory had been shown to fit closely the then assumed observational estimate $R=3,390$ km for Mars, several investigators were disposed to reject that theory by insisting on observational values of 3,350 km or less[17]. A value of 3,350 km would fit the $Fe_2O$ theory extremely well.

Assuming, as usual, that the mantle and iron core of Mars are solid (ref. 19) the $Fe_2O$ theory, in common with the phase-transition theory, accounts satisfactorily for the failure to detect a magnetic field around Mars.

So the provisional calculations indicate that the $Fe_2O$ theory fits the observational $M$ and $R$ for Venus extremely well, and $M$, $R$ and $f$ for Mars moderately well. The theory also gives the closest agreement of all theories with the observational evidence on magnetic fields.

Like all theories that are not extremely *ad hoc*, the $Fe_2O$ theory does not fit the planet Mercury as Mercury now is, although the theory has an advantage over the phase-transition theory in requiring a substantially larger iron core. As I have previously suggested[20], Mercury, through its proximity to the Sun, has probably lost much of its primordial mantle by volatilization. The $Fe_2O$ theory would suggest that the primordial Mercury (assumed to belong to the subset $H$) was larger than Mars.

The low density of the Moon precludes it from belonging to the family of planets considered here. The $H$ planet with the Moon's mass would have an iron core of radius about 700 km, which is appreciably too large to fit evidence on the Moon's mean density and moment of inertia. Thus the $Fe_2O$ theory here merely confirms that the Moon must have had an exceptional origin.

I hope to present later calculations which take detailed account of compression and density variation inside the planetary zones.

(**243**, 68-70; 1973)

K. E. Bullen

Department of Geophysics and Astronomy, University of British Columbia, Canada, and University of Sydney, NSW 2006

于流体静力学理论的误差限上 [17]。

在流体静力学条件的假设下，相变理论给出 $R=3,390$ km 和 $f \approx 1/188$（参考文献 18）。因此除非偏离流体静力学条件较大，否则相变理论与火星符合得更好。这主要是因为 $Fe_2O$ 理论要求有一个较大的核，半径 $R_i$ 约为 1,400 km。火星上的地震记录有可能将在适当的时候提供一个 $R_i$ 的观测估计，成为对该理论的进一步检验。（搜集发生在金星上的地震记录可能更困难。）

具有讽刺意味的是，当相变理论被证明和当时的火星观测估计值 $R=3,390$ km 很接近时，一些学者打算拒绝那个理论，坚持认为观测值是 3,350 km 或者更小 [17]。3,350 km 这个数值和 $Fe_2O$ 理论符合得极好。

$Fe_2O$ 理论采用了和相变理论一样常见的假设，认为火星的幔和铁核都是固体（参考文献 19），这较好地解决了未能探测到火星周围磁场的问题。

所以暂时的计算结果表明 $Fe_2O$ 理论给出的结果和金星的观测 $M$ 和 $R$ 符合得极好，与火星的 $M$、$R$ 以及 $f$ 拟合得较好。这个理论也是所有理论中和磁场的观测证据符合得最好的。

像所有非极端特殊的理论一样，$Fe_2O$ 理论和现在的水星不符合，尽管这个理论相对相变理论而言，优势在于得到了更大的铁核。就像我以前提出的 [20]，水星由于接近太阳，可能已经通过蒸发损失了大量的原始地幔。$Fe_2O$ 理论可以推论出原始水星（假定它属于 $H$ 子集）比火星大。

月球的低密度将其排除在现在所讨论的这类行星家族之外。和月球同样质量的 $H$ 类行星会有一个大约 700 km 半径的铁核，这大到不能与月球的平均密度和转动惯量相符合。因此 $Fe_2O$ 理论只能确定月球肯定有一个特殊的起源。

我希望能够介绍详细考虑行星内部各区域的压缩率和密度变化细节的后续计算结果。

（冯翀 翻译；肖伟科 审稿）

Received January 29, 1973.

References:

1. Jeffreys, H., *Mon. Not. Roy. Astron. Soc., Geophys. Suppl.*, **4**, 62 (1937).

2. Bullen, K. E., *Rept. Austral. NZ Assoc. Adv. Sci.*, **23**, 25 (1937).

3. Cook, A. H., *Proc. Roy. Soc.*, A, **328**, 301 (1972).

4. Ramsey, W. H., *Mon. Not. Roy. Astron. Soc.*, **108**, 406 (1948).

5. Bullen, K. E., *Mon. Not. Roy. Astron. Soc.*, **109**, 457 (1949).

6. Dollfus, A., in *Surfaces and Interiors of Planets and Satellites*, 45 (Academic Press, London, 1970).

7. Bullen, K. E., *Mon. Not. Roy. Astron. Soc.*, **110**, 256 (1950).

8. Bullen, K. E., *Bull, Seismol. Soc. Amer.*, **32**, 19 (1942).

9. Bullen, K. E., *Mon. Not. Roy. Astron. Soc., Geophys. Suppl.*, **6**, 50 (1950).

10. Bullen, K. E., and Haddon, R. A., *Phys.Earth Planet. Int.*, **1**, 1 (1967).

11. Haddon, R. A., and Bullen, K. E., *Phys. Earth Planet. Int.*, **2**, 35 (1969).

12. Birch, F., *Geophys. J.*, **4**, 295 (1961).

13. Cook, A. H., *Space Sci. Rev.*, **2**, 355 (1963).

14. Anderson, J. D., *Jet Propulsion Lab. Tech. Rept.*, **32**, 816 (1967).

15. Bullen, K. E., *Nature*, **211**, 396 (1966).

16. Kliore, A., Cain, D. L., and Levy, G. S., in *Moon and Planets*, 226 (North-Holland, Amsterdam, 1967).

17. Bullen, K. E., *Mon. Not. Roy. Astron. Soc., Geophys. Suppl.*, **7**, 272 (1957).

18. Bullen, K. E., *Mon. Not. Roy. Astron. Soc.*, **109**, 689 (1949).

19. Bullen, K. E., *Mon. Not. Roy. Astron. Soc.* **133**, 229 (1966).

20. Bullen, K. E., *Nature*, **170**, 363 (1952).

# Physical State of the Earth's Core

J. A. Jacobs

## Editor's Note

**It had been long thought that convective motion in the liquid part of the Earth's iron core, which surrounds a solid innermost core, causes the geomagnetic field. But one study in 1971 found that the liquid core might be resistant to convection, implying that some other mechanism was needed to drive the field-generating flow. Here geophysicist John Jacobs questions that idea. He shows how a careful consideration of the possible crystalline forms of iron in the inner core (and their melting points), along with the presence of impurities such as nickel, might eliminate the "stable stratification" that would inhibit convection. Today it is believed that Jacobs was right, although the detailed structure and composition of the core are still debated.**

THE physical state of the Earth's core depends on its thermal regime. In any discussion of the Earth one begins with the simplest possible model, introducing additional complexities and sophistication later if necessary. I gave a possible evolution of the Earth leading to a solid mantle and inner core with a liquid outer core in 1953 based on two assumptions[1]. First, the mantle consists of silicates and the core of pure iron; second, in the core, the adiabatic temperature gradient is less than the melting point gradient. Higgins and Kennedy[2] re-estimated these gradients and found that in the outer core the adiabatic gradient was steeper than the melting point gradient, that is, my second assumption was not satisfied. If the actual temperature followed the adiabatic temperature of ref. 2 the outer core would also be solid. They thus concluded that the actual temperature gradient is much less than the adiabatic gradient in the outer core which would then be thermally stably stratified, thereby inhibiting radial convection which is necessary to drive the geomagnetic dynamo.

The immediate reaction to the work of Higgins and Kennedy was to accept their results at face value and try to invent ways and means to get around what they have since called the core paradox[3]. Thus Bullard and Gubbins[4] pointed out that a stable fluid can have internal wave motions and they carried out preliminary calculations which indicated that a body of fluid could possibly act as a dynamo, even when its motion is purely oscillatory. Busse[5], Malkus[6], and Elsasser[7] independently suggested that the outer core might consist of a slurry of fine Fe particles suspended in a Fe-rich liquid. There is, however, a critical limit to the solid grain sizes in order that they do not precipitate out faster than the core can stir them up. Malkus[6] has estimated that critical size is 1 μm for a convection-driven dynamo and 10 μm for a precession-driven dynamo. Such small grain sizes do not seem to be in accord with metallurgical experience. Reports of extremely low attention in the outer core also seem hard to reconcile with such a constitution.

# 地核的物理状态

雅各布斯

## 编者按

铁质地核最内层的固体核心被液态部分包围着。长期以来人们都认为地核液态部分的对流运动导致了地磁场。但是 1971 年的一项研究发现，地核的液态部分可能阻碍着对流，这意味着需要其他一些机制来驱动产生地磁场的对流。在本文中地球物理学家约翰·雅各布斯对这种看法提出了质疑。他展示了对内核中可能存在的一种铁的晶体结构（和它们的熔点）以及其包含的杂质（如镍）的仔细研究，说明它们是如何有可能消除那种可以抑制对流的"稳定分层"。现在人们相信雅各布斯是正确的，尽管对于地核的详细结构和组成仍存在争议。

地核的物理状态取决于其热状况。任何一个关于地球的论述都会从最简单的模型开始，除非确有必要，随后才会逐渐引入复杂而深入的内容。1953 年，基于两个假设，我提出了一种地球演化的可能性，该理论中地球有一个固态的地幔和内核及液态的外核 [1]。首先，假设地幔由硅酸盐组成，地核由纯铁组成；第二，假设在地核中，绝热温度梯度小于熔点梯度。希金斯和肯尼迪 [2] 重新估算了这些梯度的大小，并且发现在外核中绝热梯度比熔点梯度大，也就是说，我的第二个假设并不令人满意。如果实际的温度遵从参考文献 2 中的绝热温度，则其外核也将是固体。他们由此得出结论，外核中实际的温度梯度远小于绝热梯度，因而外核呈热稳定分层，抑制了驱动地磁发电机所必不可少的径向对流。

学界对希金斯和肯尼迪研究的第一反应是接受他们表象上的结论，并且试图找到途径和方法来回避他们所谓的地核悖论 [3]。因此，布拉德和格宾斯 [4] 指出，稳定的流体可能有内部的波动，并且他们的初步计算表明，流体很可能能够像发电机一样，即使当它完全做振荡运动时也是如此。布塞 [5]、马尔库斯 [6] 以及埃尔萨瑟 [7] 分别指出，外核可能由含有细铁粒子的富铁悬浮液组成。不过，固体微粒大小有一个临界值，以使其沉淀析出不快于地核对其的搅动。马尔库斯 [6] 推测，对于一个对流驱动的发电机而言，临界值是 1 μm；而对于进动驱动发电机，其临界值是 10 μm。这样小的微粒尺寸似乎并不符合冶金学经验。关于外核关注度极低的报道似乎也不认可这一结构。

413

It is important therefore to consider the results of Higgins and Kennedy objectively. Their melting point curve was obtained by extrapolating to high pressures low pressure experimental results which indicated a linear relationship between melting temperature and fractional change in volume[8]. Birch[9] has discussed the validity of such a procedure, stressing the fact that Fe exists in four crystalline forms ($\alpha$, $\gamma$, $\delta$, $\varepsilon$) and that present knowledge of the thermodynamic properties of the two denser phases ($\gamma$ and $\varepsilon$), which are those most likely to be applicable in the core of the Earth, is extremely rudimentary. The effect of these phase changes on the melting temperature of Fe is uncertain. Birch[9] estimates that $\gamma$-melting temperatures may be some 700°C above those estimated by Higgins and Kennedy, with $\varepsilon$-melting temperatures still higher. McLachlan and Ehlers[10] have presented a hypothetical melting point curve for the Earth's core, taking into consideration such phase changes. Verhoogen[11] has also criticized the melting temperatures of Higgins and Kennedy; in addition, significant structure calculations on the melting of Fe by Leppaluoto[12] are not consistent with the Kraut-Kennedy melting law[8].

Also, the core is not pure Fe but contains ~15% of some light alloying element. This not only modifies the phase relationships but also considerably lowers the melting temperature of the core. Hall and Murthy[13] have estimated that if the lighter alloying element is sulphur, at core pressures the melting temperature of the Fe-FeS eutectic is about 1,600°C lower than that of pure Fe. If the addition of sulphur is confined to the outer core and the inner core consists mainly of Fe-Ni with very little lighter components, there is yet another solution to the core paradox[14]. The presence of sulphur in the outer core may so reduce its liquidus below that of Fe that the adiabat of Higgins and Kennedy through the inner core/outer core boundary does not intersect it.

The adiabatic temperature gradient is given by

$$dT/dr = -\alpha g T/c_p \tag{1}$$

where r is the radius of the Earth, $\alpha$ the coefficient of thermal expansion, $g$ the acceleration due to gravity and $c_p$ the specific heat at constant pressure. Higgins and Kennedy estimated this gradient by two methods. Their first makes use of an equation derived by Valle[15] based on the Debye theory for solids—there is no reason to suppose that is can be applied to a liquid. In their second method, they transform equation (1) by writing

$$\Gamma = \alpha k_s/\rho c_p \tag{2}$$

where $k_s$ is the adiabatic incompressibility and $\rho$ the density. Thus

$$dT/dr = -gT\,\Gamma\rho/k_s = -gT\,\Gamma/\varphi \tag{3}$$

where $\varphi = k_s/\rho = V_p^2 - 4/3 V_s^2$ and $V_p$ and $V_s$ are the velocities of P and S waves and are

因此，客观地考虑希金斯和肯尼迪的结果变得相当重要。他们的熔点曲线是通过将低压下熔点温度和体积变化之间的线性关系 [8] 这一实验结果向高压外推而得到的。伯奇 [9] 讨论了这样一个过程的有效性，强调了铁存在四种结晶形式（α、γ、δ、ε）这一事实，并认为目前关于两种较密相（γ 和 ε）的热力学性质的认识是极为初步的，而这两种相最有可能适用于地核。相变对铁的熔点温度的影响并不明确。伯奇 [9] 推断，γ 相熔点温度可能比希金斯和肯尼迪估计的温度高约 700℃，ε 相熔点温度可能还要更高。考虑到相变，麦克拉克伦和埃勒斯 [10] 为地核描绘了一幅假想的熔点曲线。维胡吉安 [11] 也质疑希金斯和肯尼迪的熔点温度。另外，莱佩洛托 [12] 进行的关于铁熔点的重要结构计算同克劳特 – 肯尼迪的熔点定律 [8] 也不一致。

而且，地核并不是纯铁，而是包含了大约 15% 的其他轻合金元素。这不仅改变了相态关系，也大大降低了地核的熔点温度。霍尔和穆尔蒂 [13] 推测，如果更轻的合金元素是硫，在地核压力下，铁 – 硫化铁共晶的熔点温度大约比纯铁的熔点温度低 1,600℃，如果硫的添加仅仅局限于外核，并且内核主要包含铁 – 镍和极少量更轻的元素，那么仍然有其他方法来解释这个地核悖论 [14]。外核中的硫可能降低了它的液相线，使其低于铁的液相线，以至于希金斯和肯尼迪通过内核 / 外核边界的绝热线没有与之相交。

绝热温度梯度公式如下：

$$dT/dr = -\alpha g T/c_p \qquad (1)$$

其中 r 是地球半径，α 是热膨胀系数，$g$ 是重力产生的加速度，$c_p$ 是定压比热。希金斯和肯尼迪通过两种方法来估算这个梯度。第一种方法是使用瓦莱 [15] 推导出来的一个方程，该方程建立在德拜的固体理论上——还没有理由假设该理论可以应用于液体。在第二种方法中他们对方程（1）进行变换，令

$$\Gamma = \alpha k_s/\rho c_p \qquad (2)$$

其中 $k_s$ 是绝热不可压缩系数，ρ 是密度。因此

$$dT/dr = -g T \Gamma \rho/k_s = -g T \Gamma/\varphi \qquad (3)$$

其中 $\varphi = k_s/\rho = V_p^2 - 4/3 V_s^2$，$V_p$ 和 $V_s$ 是 P 波和 S 波的波速，由地震数据获得。很明显，

known from seismic data. It is clear that the adiabatic gradient is quite sensitive to the assumed value of $\Gamma$. There is no reason to identify it with Grüneisen's parameter $\gamma$ for a solid. Knopoff and Shapiro[16] have pointed out that for a liquid $\Gamma$ may be no more than a dimensionless combination of thermodynamic parameters. Birch[9] has also stressed the uncertainties in such estimates of the adiabatic gradient.

I have re-estimated[17] the adiabatic gradient in the core by a different method[18]—assuming that there is a linear relationship between $1/\alpha$ and pressure in analogy with Bullen's compressibility-pressure hypothesis[19]. There is no real reason to suppose that the use of such an empirical relationship is superior to any of the other methods. But my calculations indicate that in the core the adiabatic temperature gradient is still less than the melting point gradient of Higgins and Kennedy. More detailed calculations by Birch[9] have led to the same conclusion, that "the adiabat originating at the melting temperature of the inner core/outer core boundary lies entirely in the liquid phase". In view of all the uncertainties in the estimates of both the melting and adiabatic temperatures, it is impossible to say definitely which gradient is the steepest in the core. It thus seems unnecessary at the moment to try and circumvent the consequences of accepting the results of Higgins and Kennedy.

Birch[9] and myself[17] have concluded that actual temperatures in the core are probably very close to those of the melting temperature. If this is indeed the case, it raises the interesting possibility, which I have pointed out elsewhere[17], that perhaps the boundaries of the core may not be fixed, but may show slow variations with time. This could possibly explain Hide's bumps[20] at the core-mantle boundary, which may, if they exist, be temporal features of the Earth's interior.

(**243**, 113-114; 1973)

J. A. Jacobs
Institute of Earth and Planetary Physics, University of Alberta

Received May 3, 1973.

References:

1. Jacobs, J. A., *Nature*, **172**, 297 (1953).

2. Higgins, G., and Kennedy, G. C., *J. Geophys. Res.*, **76**, 1870 (1971).

3. Kennedy, G. C., and Higgins, G., *J. Geophys. Res.*, **78**, 900 (1973).

4. Bullard, E. C., and Gubbins, D., *Nature*, **232**, 548 (1971).

5. Busse, F. H., *J. Geophys. Res.*, **77**, 1589 (1972).

6. Malkus, W. V. R., *J. Geophys. Fluid Dyn.* (in the press).

7. Elsasser, W. M., *Core-Mantle Interface Conf.* (NASA, 1972).

8. Kraut, E. A., and Kennedy, G. C., *Phys. Rev.*, **151**, 668 (1966).

9. Birch, F., *Geophys. J.*, **29**, 373 (1972).

10. McLachlan, D., and Ehlers, E. G., *J. Geophys. Res.*, **76**, 2780 (1971).

11. Verhoogen, J., *Core-Mantle Interface Conf.* (NASA, 1972).

绝热梯度对 $\Gamma$ 的假设值非常敏感。还没有理由将它等同于用于固体的格吕奈森参数 $\gamma$。克诺波夫和夏皮罗[16]指出，对液体来说，$\Gamma$ 可能仅仅是一个无量纲的热力学参数的组合。伯奇[9]也强调了这样估算绝热梯度的不确定性。

我也用其他方法重新估算[17]了地核的绝热梯度[18]——假定 $1/\alpha$ 与压力之间存在线性关系，这也同布伦的压缩率—压力假设[19]类似。没有真正的理由认为使用这样一个经验性的关系优于任何其他方法。但是，我的计算表明，地核的绝热温度梯度仍然低于希金斯和肯尼迪的熔点梯度。伯奇[9]所做的更多的详细计算也得出了同样的结论，即"在内核/外核边界的熔点温度下所产生的绝热线完全处于液相"。鉴于对熔点温度和绝热温度的估算都存在不确定性，不可能明确指出，地核的哪个梯度最大。因此，目前似乎没有必要尝试和回避因接受希金斯和肯尼迪的结果而导致的后果。

伯奇[9]和我本人[17]认为地核的实际温度很可能非常接近熔点温度。如果情况的确如此，就产生了非常有趣的可能，正如我已经在其他文献中[17]指出的那样，或许地核的边界并不固定，而是可能随时间缓慢地变化着。这可能能够解释位于核幔边界的海德簸动[20]——如果它们确实存在，可能是地球内部随时间变化的特征。

（刘霞 翻译；吴庆举 审稿）

12. Leppaluoto, D. A., *Phys. Earth Planet. Int.*, **6**, 175 (1972).

13. Hall, H. T., and Murthy, V. R., *Core-Mantle Interface Conf.* (NASA, 1972).

14. Stacey, F. D., *Geophys. Surv.*, **1**, 99 (1972).

15. Valle, P. E., *Ann. Geofisica*, **5**, 41 (1952).

16. Knopoff, L., and Shapiro, J. N., *J. Geophys. Res.*, **74**, 1439 (1969).

17. Jacobs, J. A., *Nature*, **231**, 170 (1971).

18. Jacobs, J. A., *Canad. J. Phys.*, **31**, 370 (1953).

19. Bullen, K. E., *Nature*, **157**, 405 (1946).

20. Hide, R., *Nature*, **222**, 1055 (1969).

# Formation of the Earth's Core

H. G. Tolland

## Editor's Note

About one-fifth of the Earth is molten and lies at its core. At the centre of this annulus is a solid mass believed to consist primarily of iron. Little has been learned of the constitution of these structures in the past half-century, although the temperature gradients are now well constrained, while it is clear that the molten annulus is the seat of the Earth's magnetism. This paper discusses some of the ways in which this layered structure of the Earth may have been assembled.

SEGREGATION of the Earth into a metallic core and silicate mantle could have occurred during accretion[1-3] or later, but the idea of segregation during accretion encounters difficulties. I therefore consider the possibility of core formation after accretion from an initial homogeneous mixture of about 82% by volume of silicate and 18% of iron plus sulphide.

Core formation has often been regarded as a slow process which may not yet be complete[4-9]. Oversby and Ringwood challenge this[10], concluding, from a study of isotope ratios, that core formation must have been completed within $5\times10^8$ yr, and probably $10^8$ yr, of the Earth's formation. Further, the oldest known rocks, which presumably post-date core formation, are $3.9\times10^9$ yr old[11], quite close to the age of the Earth. These pieces of evidence suggest that core formation was rapid, being complete some $5\times10^8$ yr after the Earth's formation.

The proposed model envisages infall of core material through the silicates of the proto-Earth. The rate of infall of pieces of core material depends on their size and shape and on the silicate viscosity. Differential rate of fall leads to pieces meeting and coagulating with consequent acceleration. The infalling core material is most probably liquid, though the early stages of agglomeration may be assisted by welding of solid pieces. The proposed model differs from previous models[12] in that the role of convection during the period of core formation and interaction between infall and convective processes is taken into account.

The view of thermal history and mantle rheology upon which the theory is based is similar to that of Tozer[13-15], whose model is based on a rheology in which no absolute distinction is made between solid and liquid. Instead it considers the response of materials to small non-hydrostatic stresses which can be regarded as producing a permanent deformation of matter, though at a rate which varies enormously with temperature. For small departures from hydrostatic equilibrium the rheology can be expressed in terms of

# 地核的形成

托兰

## 编者按

地球约五分之一的物质处于熔融状态并分布在地核当中。这个环状区域的中心是固体，人们认为它主要由铁组成。尽管现在此区域的温度梯度被很好地限定下来，同时我们清楚熔融环状区域为地磁的发源地，但在过去的半个世纪里，人们对这些结构的组成仍然知之甚少。这篇文章讨论了地球这种分层结构可能的几种聚集方式。

地球分离成金属质的地核与硅质的地幔可能发生在地球吸积期间 [1-3]，也可能发生于其后，但是吸积期间发生分离的观点遇到了困难。因此，我考虑了这种可能性，即地核形成于吸积之后，并由体积分数 82% 的硅酸盐和 18% 的铁和硫化物组成的原始均匀混合物分离而来。

通常认为地核的形成是一个极为缓慢的过程，至今可能尚未完成 [4-9]。奥弗斯比和林伍德对这一观点提出了质疑 [10]，他们根据同位素比值研究结果，得出结论，地核的形成在地球形成后的 5 亿年甚至 1 亿年内就已经完成。另外，已知最古老岩石的年龄约为 39 亿年 [11]，这非常接近地球的年龄，而它很有可能形成于地核形成之后。上述证据表明，地核的形成是快速的，在地球形成后大约 5 亿年的时间里就已全部完成了。

本文提出的模型假设地核物质下沉穿过原始地球的硅质层进入地核。该下沉速度取决于其大小、形状以及硅质层的黏度。它们下沉速度的不同导致各片段的汇集和凝聚速度越来越快。尽管早期的凝聚得益于固体块的结合，但是向地心流入的地核物质极有可能是液态。本文提出的模型与前人模型 [12] 的不同之处在于，我们考虑了地核形成期间对流的作用以及沉降和对流过程之间的相互影响。

该理论所依据的热演化史以及地幔流变观点与托泽的观点 [13-15] 类似，他的模型是以流变学为基础建立的，在这种流变状态中没有绝对的固态和液态之分。相反，该模型考虑了不同物质对小的非静水压力的响应，一般认为这会导致物质发生永久变形，尽管其速率随温度的变化非常大。在与静压平衡状态偏离较小的情况下，流变性可用牛顿黏度表示。对流体中进行的对流过程本身将黏度值限制在了一个很窄

a Newtonian viscosity. In a convecting body the convection process itself places narrow limits on the value of viscosity. If the convecting region is hundreds of kilometres thick, the viscosity is essentially fixed at $10^{20}$ poise for any reasonable heat generation. This circumvents the objection[16] to infall theories that the mantle viscosity is too high.

The response time for the Earth to reach thermal equilibrium, at about 0.4 times the melting point, is a few times $10^8$ yr. This is very different from that expected on conduction theory and implies that the present thermal state is virtually decoupled both from the initial state and from any early thermal event such as rapid core formation.

The Earth's initial thermal state is unknown. Urey[4] has given chemical reasons for supposing that the Earth was never extensively melted. This condition must be met by any theory of core formation, even with rapid release of the energy of core formation ($1.5$-$2\times$ $10^{37}$ erg, refs. 16 and 17). Rapid convection enables this condition to be met.

I assume the present core to be essentially an Fe-S mix[18-20]. The low melting point of the Fe-S eutectic[21] and its insensitivity to pressure up to at least 30 kbar (ref. 22) compared with iron imply the first melt would occur throughout the proto-Earth at temperatures well below the melting point of iron. This allows core formation to start very soon after, or during, accretion even for cold accretion. This suggests the present thermal profile of the Earth may be much lower than is generally accepted on the basis of an iron or Fe-Si core or a conductive thermal history. It is in accord with the expected convective thermal history[13-15] and enables the condition that the Earth never melted to be more easily met.

Unlike previous models, the core material need not be molten for core formation to commence. This is because solid core material can fall through the silicates and agglomerate by welding on of other pieces. This process is quite efficient above "red-heat".

The time scale of core formation may be estimated using Stokes's law, $V_0=2a^2g(\rho-\sigma)/9\eta$. I assume $\rho-\sigma=4$, and neglect any effect arising from the fact that core material would be descending all around the Earth and any cooperative motion between the various pieces. For a sphere to traverse the mantle of viscosity $10^{20}$ poise in time $\sim10^8$ yr the terminal velocity would be $0.1 \rightarrow 1$ cm yr$^{-1}$ implying a radius of 100 to 1,000 m. Such large fragments of core material may not have been present initially but this is not necessary because agglomeration of core material from smaller "seeds" may be envisaged. For example, in a mantle containing 15% "core material" such seeds double in volume in falling approximately six times their initial radius. The time for this first doubling in volume is comparable to half the time taken to form the core.

Application of Stokes's law to a mantle of viscosity $10^{20}$ poise shows that to form the core in about $10^8$ yr the seed radius must be about 1 m whereas for a viscosity of $10^{26}$ poise this size is 1 km. In the latter case the existence of suitable seeds seems unlikely but in the former case there seems little difficulty in providing sufficient seeds because they need only

的范围内。倘若对流区厚达数百千米，对任何合理的产热来说，其黏度基本上都保持在 $10^{20}$ 泊左右。同时这也打消了反对意见 [16] 对下沉理论中地幔黏度过高的质疑。

地球达到热平衡所需的时间约是熔融时间的 0.4 倍，为数亿年。这与热传导理论的预期有很大不同，表明现今的热状态实质上与初始状态已大不相同，同时与其他早期的热事件（如地核的快速形成）也已大不相同。

我们不知道地球的初始热状态。尤里 [4] 给出了一些化学证据，证明地球从未发生过大规模的熔融。任何地核形成理论都应该满足这一条件，即使地核形成产生的能量（$1.5 \times 10^{37} \sim 2 \times 10^{37}\,erg$，参见文献 16 和 17）可快速释放也不例外。快速对流可以使这一条件得以满足。

假设现今的地核基本上是由 Fe-S 混合物组成的 [18-20]。相对于铁，Fe-S 共晶体 [21] 的低熔点以及在至少 30 kbar 压力下对压力不敏感（参见文献 22），表明整个原始地球上首次熔融时的温度远远低于铁的熔点。这就使得吸积完成后不久或吸积期间，甚至冷积期间，地核的形成过程能很快开始。这表明地球目前的热剖面温度可能远低于人们普遍接受的温度，这个温度是根据由铁或 Fe-Si 混合物构成的地核，或有着可传导性的热演化史得到的。这与预期的对流性的热演化史 [13-15] 一致，而且这使地球从未出现过熔融的情况更容易实现。

与前人的模型不同，在本模型中地核物质不必熔融，地核的形成过程就能开始。这是因为固态地核物质可以穿过硅质层下沉，并通过与其他结块聚合的方式凝结。该过程在"赤热"状态以上非常有效。

我们可以利用斯托克斯定律，$V_0 = 2a^2 g\,(\rho - \sigma)/9\eta$ 来估算地核形成的时标。假设 $\rho - \sigma = 4$，同时忽略地球上所有由于地核物质下沉引起的效应以及各碎块之间的协同运动。一个球体要用 1 亿年的时间穿过黏度为 $10^{20}$ 泊的地幔，其最终速度应为 $0.1 \sim 1\,cm \cdot yr^{-1}$，这意味着其半径大概在 $100 \sim 1,000\,m$ 之间。最初地核物质中可能并不存在如此大的碎块，不过这也没有关系，因为我们可以假设地核物质是由较小的"籽块"凝结而成的。例如，在含有 15% 的"地核物质"的地幔中，这样的小块体在下降距离达其最初半径的 6 倍时体积便可增大 1 倍。而体积首次增加 1 倍所需要的时间约是地核形成所需时间的一半。

黏度为 $10^{20}$ 泊的情况下，运用斯托克斯定律可知，为了保证地核在约 1 亿年的时间内形成，籽块的半径应为 1 m 左右，而当黏度为 $10^{26}$ 泊时，这个数值约为 1 km。后一种情形中，大小合适的籽块似乎不太可能存在，但对于前一种情况，提

be a small number which could be found on the upper limit in the initial size distribution of core material pieces.

The seeds would not grow indefinitely because core material would be swept up by other infalling pieces. Estimates of the average final size depend on the assumed initial number of seeds, which could be quite small. One seed in a column of several hundred sq km area suffices.

Convection will affect the infall process and be affected by it. Continental drift indicates the velocity of present-day convective motion is about 1 cm yr⁻¹. If mantle-wide convection is assumed during core formation and due allowance is made for the rapid release of gravitational energy in the region through which the core material is falling then convection is expected to have been much more rapid than today, perhaps by a factor as great as 1,000. The convective velocity could have been greater than the velocity of infall. This would alter the details of the core-forming process. But consideration of a convective cell suggests that the overall effect on the rate of core formation would be small since infalling material would descend more rapidly in some regions, less so in others.

Assuming marginal stability and neglecting the effect of the infall on the convective system, the convective pattern would be quite simple, for example, mantle wide of harmonic order 2, 3, 4, 5, changing rapidly as the core grows. But rapid release of gravitational energy implies conditions well above critical, so more modes could be excited. These could be quite complex. Other factors must be considered. Differential infall implies more gravitational energy released in the descending columns than in the ascending, implying a relative heating of the cooler, descending column. The heavy descending columns would lose more of their dense core material than any other part of the system, and thereby become the lightest part. There could be some kind of cooperative motion between the descending pieces of core material[23,24]; steady convection is not possible. Thus convection during core formation may either have been spasmodic, akin to turbulent in appearance, or in some way controlled by the motion of the infalling material in the convecting region.

There is no reason to assume heat transport by this convection is less efficient than by steady convection, but, if it is, the viscosity could be lowered giving more rapid convective movements and core formation. There would still be some viscosity effectively maintained by the convection itself.

When core formation is effectively complete a steady convection would be set up, bringing the Earth to thermal equilibrium in a few times $10^8$ yr. During that time the core and mantle would convect as separate systems, and both reach their present temperatures to within a few %. The assumed mantle wide convection may subsequently break down into several regions only some of which convect.

Tozer's proposed convective model predicts limited zones of high viscous dissipation with

供足够多的原始籽块似乎并不困难，因为这只是很小的数目，可以在地核物质块的原始尺寸分布上限中找到。

当然，籽块不会无限增大，因为地核物质还会受到其他下沉碎块的清扫作用。最终的平均尺寸取决于所假定籽块的原始数量，而这一数量是非常小的。在数百平方公里的范围内只要有一个籽块就足够了。

对流还会影响沉降过程，并受沉降过程的影响。大陆漂移意味着现今的对流速度约为 $1 \text{ cm} \cdot \text{yr}^{-1}$。倘若假设地核形成期间整个地幔都存在对流，由于需要保证地核物质下沉所穿过地区重力能的快速释放，因此当时的对流速度要远快于现在，可达到现在的 1,000 倍。对流的速度甚至要快于下降速度。而这将改变地核形成的具体过程。不过对对流元的研究表明，它对地核形成速率的总体影响很小，这是因为下沉物质在某些地区下降得很快，而另一些地区则较慢。


假设边缘是稳定的，并且忽略下沉作用对对流系统的影响，对流模式将变得极为简单，比如，地幔中广泛分布的 2、3、4、5 级谐波将随着地核的增长快速变化。而重力能的快速释放则意味着环境条件远在临界值之上，因此可能激发更多模式。这些模式可能非常复杂。另外的一些因素也需要考虑。差异沉降意味着下降柱中的物质所释放的重力能要高于上升柱，这意味着对较冷的下沉物质的相对加热。重的下沉柱要比系统的其他部分损失更多密度较大的地核物质，因而变成了最轻的部分。地核物质构成的下降块体之间也可能存在某种协同运动 [23,24]，因此不可能存在稳定对流。所以，地核形成期间对流的形式只能是间歇性的，表现上类似于湍流，或者是受对流区域内的下沉物质运动的控制。

没有理由假设通过这种对流进行热量传输的效率低于稳定的对流，但是，如果确实存在这种情况，要想使对流及地核形成得更快，那么地幔的黏度应当降低。另外，对流本身也会有效地维持一部分黏度。

地核完全形成后将形成一个稳定的对流，用几亿年的时间使地球达到热平衡状态。在此期间，地核与地幔将作为两个系统分别发生对流，并且很快在百分之几的精度内达到现今的温度。假定整个地幔范围内的对流可能分解为多个不同区域，而其中仅有部分区域处于对流状态。

托泽提出的对流模型预测了存在随着温度的升高和黏度的降低，高黏性耗散的

raised temperature and lowered viscosity[15]. These zones could have been established before core formation started. Early rapid agglomeration of core material would be favoured in such zones. During the principal stages of core formation such zones can be discounted since the convective pattern would not have been simple or steady. The model presented for the Earth is consistent with rapid core formation for viscosities up to about $10^{23}$ poise.

Core formation in Venus would presumably follow a similar pattern, though if the core contains little or no sulphur[20] agglomeration of core material by welding, not fusion of liquid drops, may have predominated. For the Moon and Mars with relatively smaller cores the transport of core material would have been speeded up by convection.

(**243**, 141-142; 1973)

H. G. Tolland

Department of Geophysics and Planetary Physics, School of Physics, The University, Newcastle upon Tyne NE1 7RU

Received March 26, 1973.

References:

1. Orowan, E., *Nature*, **222**, 867 (1969).

2. Turekian, K. K., and Clark, S. P., *Earth Planet. Sci. Lett.*, **6**, 346 (1969).

3. Anderson, D. L., and Hanks, T. C., *Nature*, **237**, 387 (1972).

4. Urey, H. C., *The Planets* (Yale Univ., 1952).

5. Munk, W. H., and Davies, D., in *Isotope and Cosmic Chemistry*, chapter 22 (edit. by Craig, H., Miller, S., and Wasserberg, G.) (North-Holland, Amsterdam, 1964).

6. Runcorn, S. K., *Nature*, **193**, 311 (1962).

7. Runcorn, S. K., in *Continental Drift*, chapter 1 (Academic Press, 1962).

8. Runcorn, S. K., *Nature*, **195**, 1248 (1962).

9. Runcorn, S. K., *Phil. Trans. Roy. Soc.*, **258**, 228 (1965).

10. Oversby, V. M., and Ringwood, A. E., *Nature*, **234**, 463 (1971).

11. Anon, *Nature*, **234**, 438 (1971).

12. Elsasser, W. M., in *Earth Science and Meteorites* (edit. by Geiss, L., and Goldberg, E.), chapter 1 (North-Holland, Amsterdam, 1963).

13. Tozer, D. C., in The *Earth's Mantle*, chapter 2 (Academic Press, London, 1967).

14. Tozer, D. C., *J. Geomag. Geoelect.*, **22**, 35 (1970).

15. Tozer, D. C., *Proc. Conf. Lunar Geophys.* (Lunar Science Institute, Houston 1971).

16. Lubimova, E. A., in *The Earth's Crust and Upper Mantle* (edit. by Hart, P. J.) (American Geophysical Union, Washington, 1969).

17. Birch, F., *J. Geophys. Res.*, **70**, 6217 (1965).

18. Mason, B., *Nature*, **211**, 616 (1966).

19. Rama Murthy, V., and Hall, H. T., *Phys. Earth Planet. Int.*, **2**, 276 (1970).

20. Lewis, J. S., *Earth Planet. Sci. Lett.*, **15**, 286 (1972).

21. Hansen, M., *Composition of Binary Alloys* (McGraw-Hill, 1958).

22. Brett, R., and Bell, P. M., *Earth Planet. Sci. Lett.*, **6**, 479 (1969).

23. Whitmore, R. L., *Brit. J. Appl. Phys.*, **6**, 239 (1955).

24. Kaye, B.H., and Boardman, R. P. *Interaction between Fluids and Particles* (Institution of Chemical Engineers, London, 1962).

有限区域 [15]。这些区域应该形成于地核开始形成之前。地核物质早期的快速凝聚可能更多地发生在这样的区域中。在地核形成的主要阶段，这些区域的作用可能要打折扣，因为对流模式可能不再是简单或稳定的。对于黏度高达 $10^{23}$ 泊的情况，该地球模型与地核的快速形成是一致的。

金星核的形成可能遵循类似的模式，只是，倘若其内核中仅有少量的硫甚至没有硫 [20]，内核物质可能通过聚结而非液滴的熔结成为主要的凝聚形式。对于核相对较小的月球和火星，对流作用将加速其内核物质的输运。

（齐红艳 翻译；赵俊猛 审稿）

# Properties of Ultra-high Modulus Linear Polyethylenes

G. Capaccio and I. M. Ward

## Editor's Note

Polymer fibres with a large Young's modulus—meaning that they are very stiff—have applications ranging from ropes and cables to guitar strings. While the strongest and stiffest such materials are advanced polymer formulations such as aramids, developed in the late 1960s, older and rather cheap materials such as nylon and polyethylene can be given a large modulus if stretched, which extends the chain-like molecules to something approaching their full length. Here Giancarlo Capaccio and Ian Ward of Leeds University report that high "draw ratios"—the amount of extension—during the preparation of polyethylene fibres can give them a modulus close to the maximum theoretically possible, showing the vast potential still to be exploited in these inexpensive materials.

WE have recently been studying the effect of molecular weight and molecular weight distribution on the cold drawing behaviour of linear polyethylene. Some of the results seem to be sufficiently unusual to warrant reporting at this stage.

Figure 1 shows the extensional moduli of two selected samples (sample 1: $\overline{M}_n$=6,180, $\overline{M}_w$=101,450; sample 2: $\overline{M}_n$=13,350, $\overline{M}_w$=67,800) as a function of the natural draw ratio. The extensional moduli were calculated from the 10 s isochronal stress-strain curves obtained from the creep response in a dead loading creep experiment at room temperature. The different natural draw ratios were obtained by varying the morphology of the initial material by adopting different initial quenching conditions. The details of the preparation are the subject of a patent application (Br. Pat. Appl. 10746/73 (filed 6.3.73)).

In agreement with previous work[1], it is clear that the extensional modulus is strongly dependent on the natural draw ratio. At the highest draw ratios the extensional moduli are by far the highest ever recorded for this polymer ($\sim 7 \times 10^{10}$ N m$^{-2}$) and almost approach the range of the theoretical moduli for fully extended polyethylene chains ($2.4 \times 10^{11}$ N m$^{-2}$, according to ref. 2). It also seems that up to draw ratio 30 the effects of molecular weight and molecular weight distribution on modulus are very small.

# 超高模量线型聚乙烯的性质

卡帕乔，沃德

*编者按*

高杨氏模量的聚合物纤维具有很高的刚性，其应用范围可从绳索、电缆到吉他弦。20 世纪 60 年代后期发展起来的高级聚合物类型（如芳纶）是这种材料中强度和刚度最大的。而一些较老、相当廉价的材料如尼龙和聚乙烯，当其分子链被拉伸至接近完全伸展时，也可被赋予很大的杨氏模量。在本文中，利兹大学的贾恩卡洛·卡帕乔和伊恩·沃德报道了在制备聚乙烯纤维时，高"拉伸比"，即大的拉伸程度，可以使聚乙烯的模量接近于理论预测的最大值，表明这些廉价材料有着尚待开拓的巨大潜力。

最近，我们一直在研究分子量和分子量分布对线型聚乙烯冷拉行为的影响。一些结果看上去很不寻常，值得在当下进行报道。

图 1 给出了两个选取样品 （样品 1：$\overline{M}_n$=6,180，$\overline{M}_w$=101,450；样品 2：$\overline{M}_n$=13,350，$\overline{M}_w$=67,800）的拉伸模量与自然拉伸比的关系。拉伸模量是根据 10 s 等时应力－应变曲线计算得到的，该曲线记录了室温下静荷载蠕变实验中材料的蠕变响应。不同的自然拉伸比是通过采取不同的初始淬冷条件以改变初始材料的形态而获得的。样品制备的细节是一项专利申请的主题（英国专利申请，10746/73（申请日期 1973 年 3 月 6 日））。

与先前的研究结果一致[1]，很明显，拉伸模量强烈地依赖于自然拉伸比。在最高拉伸比处，拉伸模量是迄今为止所报道的这种聚合物数据中最大的（约 $7 \times 10^{10}$ N·m$^{-2}$），而且几乎接近完全伸展的聚乙烯链的理论模量范围（$2.4 \times 10^{11}$ N·m$^{-2}$，见参考文献 2）。而且似乎直到拉伸比为 30 时，样品的分子量与分子量分布对模量的影响都很小。

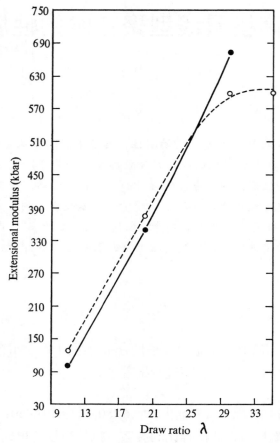

Fig. 1. Extensional moduli at two samples. ●——●, $\overline{M}_n=6,180$ and $\overline{M}_w=101,450$; ○---○, $\overline{M}_n=13,350$ and $\overline{M}_w=67,800$.

Differences in molecular weight and distribution do, however, give rise to structural differences between the samples which are revealed by their melting behaviour. The melting curves were measured on a Du Pont Thermal Analyser with a differential scanning calorimeter (DSC) cell and operated in a DSC heat mode. The results are shown in Fig. 2. Sample 1 shows a melting peak at about 137°C, which is typical of oriented linear polyethylenes in the lower draw ratio range hitherto examined[3]. Sample 2, on the other hand, shows a melting peak at 138.5°C, corresponding to the presence of extended chain material conventionally defined as extended chain crystallites (ref. 4 and D. C. Bassett, private communication).

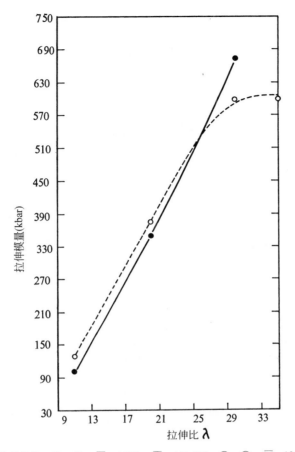

图 1. 两种样品的拉伸模量。●—●，$\overline{M}_\mathrm{n}$=6,180，$\overline{M}_\mathrm{w}$=101,450；○---○，$\overline{M}_\mathrm{n}$=13,350，$\overline{M}_\mathrm{w}$=67,800。

　　但是，分子量及其分布的差异确实导致了样品之间的结构差异，它们的熔融行为揭示了这一点。熔融曲线是在杜邦热分析仪的差示扫描量热（DSC）单元上采用 DSC 加热模式测得的。所得结果如图 2 所示。样品 1 的熔融峰大约位于 137℃，这是迄今为止所研究过的较低拉伸比范围内的取向线型聚乙烯的典型特征 [3]。另一方面，样品 2 的熔融峰位于 138.5℃，这对应于样品中存在伸展链材料，亦即我们通常所说的伸展链晶体（参考文献 4 以及与巴西特的私人交流）。

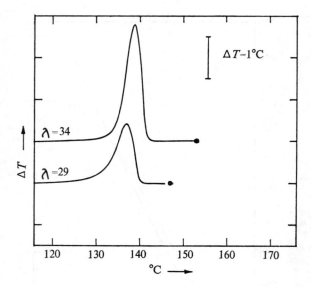

Fig. 2. Melting curves for two samples. Upper curve, sample 2; lower curve, sample 1.

It therefore seems from the results of the thermal analysis that extended chain crystallites can be produced by cold drawing, provided that polymers of suitable molecular weight and molecular weight distribution are chosen. It is also evident from the mechanical data that the presence of extended chain crystallization *per se* is not a necessary requirement for the production of high modulus material. We believe that this is because oriented non-crystalline extended chain molecules (tie molecules)[1,5] are just as effective in contributing to the overall stiffness.

A more complete account will be published elsewhere.

We thank Dr F. Jones, Department of Colour Chemistry, Leeds University, for undertaking the thermograms. One of us (G. C.) was supported by the Science Research Council.

(**243**, 143; 1973)

G. Capaccio and I. M. Ward
Department of Physics, University of Leeds

Received March 26, 1973.

References:

1. Andrews, J. M., and Ward, I. M., *J. Mat. Sci.*, **5**, 411 (1970).

2. Frank, F. C., *Proc. R. Soc.*, A, **319**, 127 (1970).

3. Glenz, W., Peterlin, A., and Wilke, W., *J. Polym. Sci.*, A–2, **9**, 1243 (1971).

4. Meinel, G., Morosoff, M., and Peterlin, A., *J. Polym. Sci.*, A–2, **8**, 1723 (1970).

5. Glenz, W., and Peterlin, A., *J. Macromol. Sci. Phys.*, B4, **3**, 473 (1970).

432

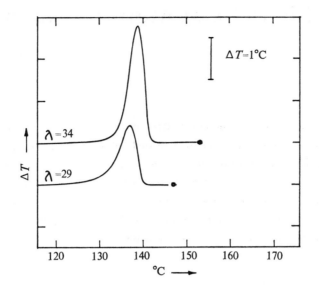

图 2. 两种样品的熔融曲线。上方曲线为样品 2；下方曲线为样品 1。

因此，从热分析的结果看来，如果选定具有适当分子量与分子量分布的聚合物，那么通过冷拉可以获得伸展链晶体。而由力学数据也可证明，伸展链结晶的存在本身并不是制造高模量材料的必要条件。我们相信，这是因为取向的非晶伸展链分子（系带分子）[1,5] 也能有效地对整体刚性做出贡献。

相关工作更为完整的描述将会另文发表。

我们要感谢利兹大学色彩化学系的琼斯博士，其承担了热分析图的工作。我们中的一位（贾恩卡洛·卡帕乔）得到了科学研究理事会的资助。

（王耀杨 翻译；陈尔强 审稿）

# Double Helix at Atomic Resolution

J. M. Rosenberg *et al.*

## Editor's Note

By this time, the double-helix structure of DNA proposed by Francis Crick and James Watson was not in doubt. All the same, no one had carried out X-ray crystallography at sufficiently high resolution to see the positions of the atoms directly. That is what Alexander Rich, a postdoctoral student of Linus Pauling, and his colleagues report here—not for DNA itself, but for a double-helical form of a small fragment of RNA. This offered the first direct view of a Watson–Crick base pair, and confirmed its structure beautifully. Nadrian Seeman, one of Rich's coauthors, went on to pioneer the use of DNA as a construction material for molecular nanotechnology.

The sodium salt of the dinucleoside phosphate adenosyl–3′, 5′–uridine phosphate crystallizes in the form of a right-handed antiparallel double helix with Watson–Crick hydrogen bonding between uracil and adenine. A sodium ion is located in the minor groove of the helix complexed to both uracil rings.

M ANY important functions in molecular biology are determined by antiparallel double helical nucleic acids with complementary base pairing between the two strands, as first described by Watson and Crick[1]. Although considerable work has been carried out on the structures of double helical nucleic acids[2-8], the fine details of their molecular architecture have never been available at atomic resolution. The X-ray diffraction patterns shown by fibres of DNA and RNA characteristically die out at resolution greater than about 3 Å. Because of this, there has been considerable discussion[9-13] about the actual nature of the detailed stereochemistry and hydrogen bonding in double helical DNA. One way to obtain additional information about these atomic details is to crystallize oligonucleotide fragments of known sequence which may form double helices in the crystal lattice. Here we report the single crystal X-ray analysis of the sodium salt of adenosyl–3′, 5′–uridine phosphate (ApU) which forms a right-handed antiparallel double helix in which the ribose phosphate backbones are held together by Watson–Crick hydrogen bonding between the adenine and uracil residues. This is the first crystal structure in which the atomic details of double helical nucleic acids can be visualized. In addition, this is the first single crystal structure showing Watson–Crick base pairing between adenine and uracil.

## Experiments

The sodium salt of ApU (Miles) was mixed stoichiometrically with bromotertiary butyl amine in a 40% solution of 2–methyl–2,4–pentanediol (MPD). A small volume of the solution was placed in equilibrium with a large reservoir of 60% MPD in a closed

# 原子分辨率的双螺旋

罗森堡等

## 编者按

直到现在，由弗朗西斯·克里克和詹姆斯·沃森提出的 DNA 双螺旋结构仍无可置疑。尽管如此，利用 X 射线晶体学的方法获得高分辨率结构以便直接观察原子位置的研究还没有人进行过。莱纳斯·鲍林的博士后亚历山大·里奇以及他的同事在本文中报道了一小段 RNA（而不是 DNA）的双螺旋结构。此项工作使人们第一次直接观察到沃森–克里克碱基配对，并且对其结构的正确性进行了精彩的证实。里奇的一位合作者纳德里安·西曼继而开创性地将 DNA 作为构建材料应用到了分子纳米技术中。

---

二核苷磷酸腺苷 –3′, 5′– 尿苷磷酸的钠盐以右手反向平行双螺旋的形式结晶，尿嘧啶和腺嘌呤之间形成沃森–克里克氢键。一个钠离子位于双螺旋的小沟，与两侧的两个尿嘧啶环结合。

---

分子生物学中的许多重要功能皆由两条链之间形成碱基互补配对的反向平行双螺旋核酸决定，沃森和克里克首次对其进行了描述 [1]。尽管人们对双螺旋核酸的结构已经开展过大量的研究 [2-8]，却还从未获得过精细的原子分辨率的分子结构。由 DNA 和 RNA 纤维获得的 X 射线衍射图样的分辨率无法超过 3 Å。基于这一现实，人们对双螺旋 DNA 中精细的立体化学结构及氢键形成的真实本质开展了诸多讨论 [9-13]。将已知序列的寡聚核苷酸片段进行结晶是获得更多 DNA 的原子结构细节的一种途径，它们可能在晶格中形成双螺旋结构。本文报道了由腺苷 –3′,5′– 尿苷磷酸（ApU）的钠盐所形成的右手反向平行双螺旋的单晶体 X 射线分析结果，其中的核糖磷酸骨架通过在腺嘌呤和尿嘧啶残基之间形成沃森–克里克氢键而结合在一起。这是第一个可以看到双螺旋核酸原子细节的晶体结构。此外，这也是第一个显示腺嘌呤和尿嘧啶之间的确能形成沃森–克里克碱基配对的单晶体结构。

## 实　验

在 40% 的 2– 甲基 –2,4– 戊二醇（MPD）溶液中，将 ApU（迈尔斯公司生产）的钠盐与三溴丁胺按化学反应计量比混合。在一个密闭容器中，将少量该混合物溶液置于含 60% MPD 的大体积溶液中在 4℃ 进行平衡。静置两周后，开始出现具有清

container which was stored at 4 . After standing for 2 weeks, small prismatic crystals with well-defined faces began to appear. Crystal growth continued slowly for several months and yielded crystals suitable for X-ray analysis. The amine was put into the solution in the hope that it might become the cation of the structure; however, subsequent analysis revealed that the sodium salt had crystallized rather than the bromoamine. A crystal measuring $0.2 \text{ mm} \times 0.15 \text{ mm} \times 0.05 \text{ mm}$ was mounted on the tip of a glass fibre for X-ray analysis. The crystal was found to be monoclinic, space group $P2_1$, with cell dimensions $a = 18.025$ Å, $b = 17.501$ Å, $c = 9.677$ Å, $\beta = 99.45°$. The crystal density measured in a density gradient was 1.53. In order to obtain a calculated density near the observed density, it was necessary to assume four molecules of $Na^+ApU^-$ and twenty-two water molecules in the unit cell. This surprisingly high degree of hydration was subsequently shown to be a low estimate as solution of the structure revealed twenty-four water molecules in the unit cell. Three-dimensional X-ray diffraction intensity data were collected out to a resolution of 0.8 Å, with a "Picker" FACS-1 diffractometer in an "Omega" step scan mode, using Nickel filtered CuKα radiation. The data were collected at 8 and were corrected for Lorentz and polarization effects; no absorption correction has been applied because of the low mass absorption coefficient (18.0).

## Solution of the Structure

Although there was no crystallographic two-fold axis in the lattice, the presence of a peak nearly 40% the height of the origin on the Harker section of the Patterson function suggested a non-crystallographic two-fold axis in the structure. From this we inferred the double helical nature of ApU. This peak was assumed to contain all vectors from each atom of one ApU molecule to the corresponding atom of the other independent molecule, symmetry related. From previous work with the protonated dinucleoside phosphate uridyl–3′,5′–adenosine phosphate[14] (UpA), it was known that resolution difference Patterson techniques were effective in discriminating vectors arising from two second-row atoms in a large structure. (Resolution difference Patterson techniques are those in which two Patterson or superposition functions, for example, multiple minimum functions or $N$-atom symmetry minimum functions, are compared. These two Pattersons are (1) the standard $F^2$ Patterson, calculated using all the diffraction data, and (2) a Patterson calculated only from the higher-order reflexions whose $F$s should contain a larger contribution from the heavier atoms sought as they are relatively denser near the atomic centres. The origins of both Pattersons are normalized to the same value. Peaks arising from heavy atom–heavy atom vectors ought to be relatively more prominent than overlapping light atom–light atom vectors in the second map. In this work, the first Patterson contained all the 1 Å data, and the second function contained the data in the shell between 1.5 Å and 1 Å.)

UpA contained seventy-seven first-row atoms. Thus, we hoped to locate the phosphorus atoms by using this vector as the basis vector of a Resolution Difference 2-Atom Symmetry Minimum Function[15,16] (RDSMF(2)). The RDSMF(2) initially indicated the wrong location for the phosphorus atoms, however, which was obvious when Fourier refinement procedures failed to reveal the structure. An $(E^2-1)$ Patterson ($E$ is the

晰表面的细小棱状晶体。晶体持续缓慢生长数月，最终形成适用于 X 射线分析的晶体。之所以在溶液中加入胺，是希望其成为结构中的阳离子；不过，之后的分析表明，形成晶体的是钠盐而非溴胺。一个大小为 0.2 mm×0.15 mm×0.05 mm 的晶体置于一玻璃纤维的尖端进行 X 射线分析。分析显示，晶体为单斜晶系，空间群为 P2₁，晶胞大小为：$a = 18.025$ Å，$b = 17.501$ Å，$c = 9.677$ Å，$\beta = 99.45°$。在密度梯度中测得晶体密度为 1.53。为了使计算出的密度值接近观测到的密度，我们必须假设在一个晶胞中含有 4 个分子的 Na⁺ApU⁻ 和 22 个分子的水。这种令人惊讶的高度水合现象被后来的结果证明仍然是被低估的，因为结构分析结果表明，一个晶胞含有 24 个分子的水。利用"皮克"式 FACS-1 衍射仪、采取"欧米茄"逐步扫描模式、以镍过滤的 CuKα 做光源，我们采集到了分辨率达到 0.8 Å 的三维 X 射线衍射强度数据。数据是在 8℃ 采集的并校正了洛伦兹和偏振效应；由于质量吸收系数比较低（18.0），所以没有进行吸收校正。

## 结 构 解 析

尽管晶格中没有晶体学二次轴，在帕特森函数的哈克截面上出现了约为初始高度 40% 的峰值，这提示在该结构中存在非晶体学二次轴。由此我们推断出了 ApU 的双螺旋本质。我们认为这一峰值包含了一个 ApU 分子中的每一原子到另一独立分子中相应原子的所有矢量，而且这些矢量是相关对称的。根据以前针对质子化尿苷–3′,5′–腺苷磷酸 [14]（UpA）这种二核苷磷酸的研究，人们已经知道，在辨别一个大的结构中源自两个第二排（编者注：应指元素周期表第三周期）原子的矢量时，分辨率差异帕特森技术是有效的。（分辨率差异帕特森技术是指将两种帕特森或叠加函数（如多个最小值函数或 N 原子对称最小函数）进行比较。这两种帕特森函数是：（1）标准 $F^2$ 帕特森函数，采用全部衍射数据计算所得；（2）仅利用较高次序的反射数据计算出的帕特森函数，其 $F$s 会包含更多所收集到的较重原子的权重，因为它们的原子中心附近相对更加致密。两种帕特森函数的初始值被归一化为相同的值。在第二张图上，源自重原子–重原子矢量的峰值应当比重叠的轻原子–轻原子向量相对更加明显。在本研究中，第一个帕特森函数包含了所有分辨率为 1 Å 的数据，而第二个函数包含了 1.5 Å 到 1 Å 之间的数据）

UpA 这种二核苷磷酸含有 77 个第一排（编者注：应指元素周期表第二周期）原子。因此，我们希望使用这一矢量作为"分辨率差异 2–原子对称最小函数"[15,16]（RDSMF(2)）的基矢量来定位磷原子。然而，RDSMF(2) 最初对磷原子的定位是错误的。当傅里叶优化程序无法揭示该结构时，这一点就变得显而易见了。因此我们

quasinormalized structure factor) was therefore calculated and the map and its Fourier coefficients were corrected for non-negativity and minimal bond lengths according to the procedure proposed by Karle and Hauptman[17]: (1) all negative points in the Patterson map and all points within a 0.9 Å radius of the origin were zeroed; (2) the map was Fourier transformed and all resultant $(E^2-1)$ coefficients less than $-1$ were raised to $-1$; (3) a new Patterson map was calculated from these coefficients, and the process was iterated until convergence was obtained at forty cycles. From the final amplitudes, a set of thermally sharpened $F$s were generated, and used to calculate Patterson functions. The RDSMF(2) calculated from these Pattersons revealed the proper phosphorus locations. Approximate phosphate orientations were derived from Patterson superpositions. Fourteen cycles of Fourier refinement using the corrected $E$s as Fourier amplitudes revealed the two molecules of ApU, the sodium ions and four water molecules. The other water molecules were located in a series of difference syntheses. The structure has been refined using isotropic thermal parameters and only the 1 Å observed data by full matrix least squares. The current $R$ factor is 0.091. (The discrepancy factor, $R$, is defined as $R = \sum \left\lVert F_o \rvert - \lvert F_c \right\rVert / \sum \lvert F_o \rvert$, where $\lvert F_o \rvert$ and $\lvert F_c \rvert$ are the amplitudes of the observed and calculated structure factors, respectively.) Because this is one of the larger non-centrosymmetric biological crystal structures solved without isomorphous replacement, we will expand on the details of the solution in a later publication.

## Structure

In the analysis of this structure, there are two striking features. The non-crystallographic pseudo two-fold axis mentioned above rotates one ApU molecule into the other, so that the structure forms a segment of a right-handed antiparallel double helix in which the bases are hydrogen bonded to each other in the Watson–Crick manner, as shown in Figs. 1 and 2. This is the familiar hydrogen bonding between adenine and uracil which is believed to occur quite generally in double helical nucleic acids. Nonetheless, this type of hydrogen bonding had never been seen previously in single crystal X-ray analysis. It should be noted that the two-fold axis to which we are referring lies half-way between the base planes, rather than in those planes. Axes in the planes are the ones usually discussed in the literature, but the periodic nature of double helices generates symmetry elements at both locations.

计算了一种（$E^2-1$）帕特森函数（$E$ 是准归一化的结构因子），并根据卡勒和豪普特曼[17] 提出的流程，将其图谱和傅里叶系数校正为非负值和最小键长：（1）帕特森图谱上的所有负点及距原点 0.9 Å 半径以内所有的点都被归零；（2）对该图谱进行傅里叶变换，产生的所有（$E^2-1$）系数小于 –1 的都被提到 –1；（3）根据这些系数计算出一个新的帕特森图谱，重复该过程，直到第 40 轮得到收敛解为止。从最后的振幅中，产生了一组热锐化的 $F$s，并用于计算帕特森函数。从这些帕特森函数中计算得到的 RDSMF(2) 揭示了正确的磷原子位置。磷原子的大致取向是通过帕特森叠加得到的。使用校正过的 $E$s 作为傅里叶振幅，进行 14 次傅里叶优化后，两分子 ApU、钠离子和 4 个水分子的位置得以确定。其他水分子是通过一系列的差值合成而被定位的。使用各向同性热参数和仅 1 Å 的观察数据，通过全矩阵最小二乘法，我们对该结构进行了优化。目前得到的 R 因子为 0.091。（偏离因子 R 被定义为：$R = \sum ||F_o| - |F_c|| / \sum |F_o|$，其中 $|F_o|$ 和 $|F_c|$ 分别是观测到的和计算得到的结构因子的振幅。）因为这是没有用同晶置换解析的、较大的非中心对称生物晶体结构之一，我们将在以后发表的文章中交代解析方法的细节。

## 结　　构

经过分析，我们发现该结构有两个显著的特征。上文提到的非晶体学伪二次轴使一个 ApU 分子旋转到另一个 ApU 上方，因而该结构形成了一个右手反向平行双螺旋片段，其中的碱基以沃森－克里克方式相互形成氢键，如图 1 和 2 所示。这种存在于腺嘌呤和尿嘧啶之间的氢键为人们所熟知，它被认为相当普遍地出现在双螺旋的核酸分子中。尽管如此，这种氢键之前从未在单晶体的 X 射线分析中被观察到。应当注意的是，我们所说的二重轴位于两个碱基平面的中间线上，而非位于每一个碱基平面之中。位于碱基平面内的那个轴在文献中经常被讨论到，但是双螺旋的周期性本质使得在这两个位置上都能产生出对称元素。

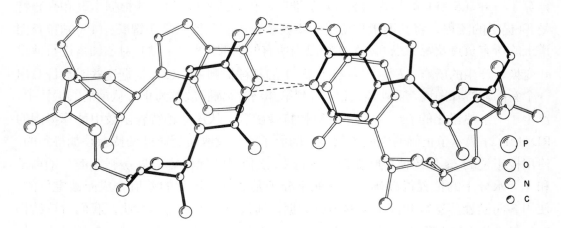

Fig. 1. View of the crystal structure perpendicular to the base planes showing hydrogen bonding (dashed lines) as well as the base stacking interactions. The darkest portions of the figure are those nearest the viewer. The rotational relationship is easily seen by comparing the front (black) and rear (white) glycosidic bonds.

The other prominent feature was that the crystal was heavily hydrated, so that the ApU molecules are surrounded by large numbers of water molecules. This observation, coupled with the non-crystallographic nature of the two-fold axis, leads us to believe that the double helical nature of ApU is a function of the molecules themselves, rather than crystal packing forces.

The separation between the base pairs is 3.4 Å and, as can be seen in Fig. 1, there is a considerable degree of stacking in the structure. The NH...O hydrogen bonds between the N6 amino group of adenine and the O4 carbonyl oxygen of uracil (see Fig. 3 for the numbering scheme) have bond lengths of 2.95 Å and 2.91 Å. The NH...N hydrogen bonds between uracil N3 and adenine N1 have lengths of 2.82 Å and 2.86 Å. The important distances across the base pairs between the two ribose carbon atoms Cl' of the glycosidic linkage, are 10.50 Å and 10.53 Å. Similar distances to these have been obtained by analysis of single crystals of intermolecular complexes of purine and pyrimidine derivatives[18] but this is the first time that these distances have been observed in a molecule which forms a fragment of a double helix.

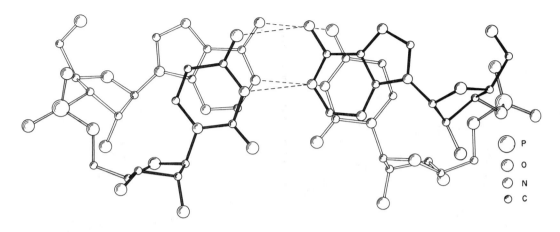

图 1. 从垂直于碱基平面的方向观察晶体结构可以显示氢键（虚线）以及碱基堆积相互作用。图中颜色最深的部分距离观察者最近。通过比较前面的（黑色）和后面的（白色）糖苷键，可以很容易看出碱基之间的旋转关系。

另一个显著的特征是该晶体被高度水合，使得 ApU 分子被大量水分子包围。这一结果结合非晶体学二次轴的性质使我们相信，ApU 的双螺旋本质源于分子本身的作用，而非晶体学堆积所致。

碱基对之间的距离是 3.4 Å，如图 1 所示，该结构中有相当程度的堆积。在腺嘌呤的 N6 氨基与尿嘧啶的 O4 羧基氧（碱基上各个原子的编号规则见图 3）之间的 NH⋯O 氢键的键长分别为 2.95 Å 和 2.91 Å。尿嘧啶 N3 和腺嘌呤 N1 之间的 NH⋯N 氢键长分别为 2.82 Å 和 2.86 Å。另外一对重要的距离是横跨碱基对、参与糖苷键形成的两个核糖碳原子 C1′ 之间的，分别是 10.50 Å 和 10.53 Å。（译者注：这里的两个距离应该是指图 3 中的上面那对碱基之间的和下面那对碱基之间的相关原子之间距离）人们曾经通过分析嘌呤和嘧啶衍生物的分子间复合物的单晶体，得到过类似的距离 [18]；但在形成了双螺旋片段的分子中测得这些距离，还是第一次。

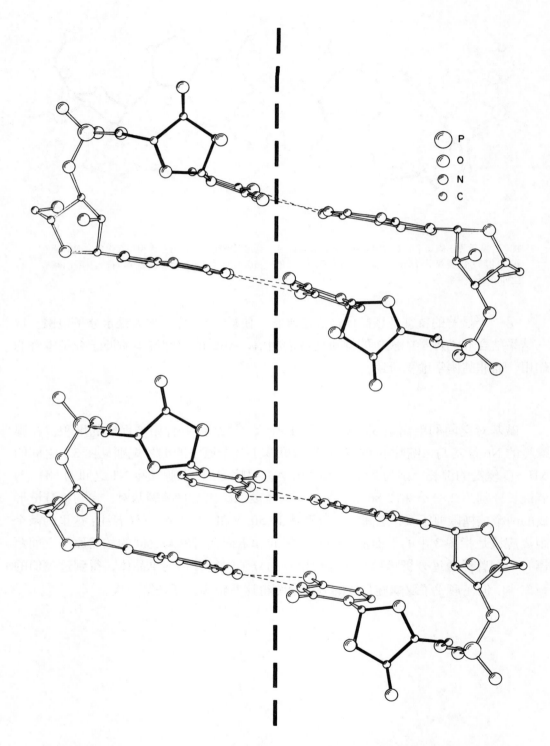

Fig. 2. Comparison of the structures of ApU (upper) and RNA 11 (lower). This view is approximately perpendicular to the helix axis which is indicated by the vertical dashed line.

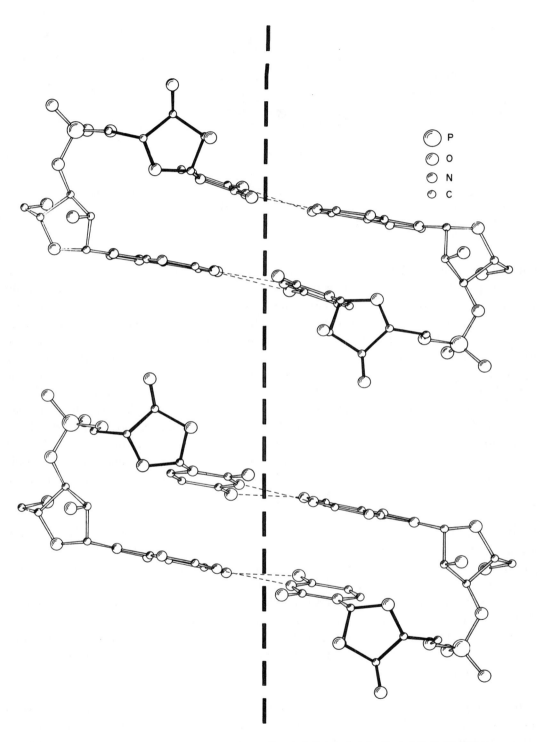

图 2. ApU（上方）和 RNA 11（下方）的结构比较。观察角度大致垂直于竖直虚线所示的螺旋轴。

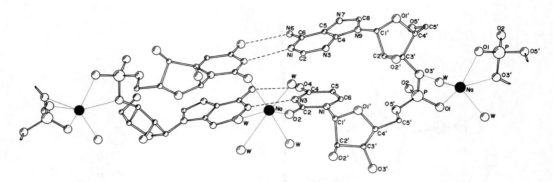

Fig. 3. Perspective view of the structure as seen from the minor groove showing the numbering scheme and the coordination of the sodium ions. Both sodium ions (●) have distorted octahedral coordination involving water molecules and other oxygens. The central sodium ion is 2.36 Å from the uracil O2 atoms.

The helical form of the molecules can be seen in Fig. 1 in which one is looking in a direction perpendicular to the base pair plane. There is clearly a rotational relationship between the glycosidic bonds (C1′ to adenine N9 or C1′ to uracil N1) of the front and rear base pairs. Another view of the structure parallel to the stacked hydrogen bonded bases is shown in Fig. 2. The right-handed helical rotation can readily be seen by observing the orientations of adjoining ribose residues on the ribose phosphate chain. This structure is similar to that which has been deduced from studying double-stranded viral RNA. The naturally occurring material is called RNA 11. Fig. 2 shows similar views of ApU and RNA 11, where the dashed vertical line represents the approximate helix axis. The continued extension of the ApU nucleotide pairs would generate a right-handed double-stranded helix similar to RNA 11. It is important to note that although the helical parameters of RNA 11 can be derived directly from an X-ray analysis of the fibre, the positions of the atomic centres are of necessity inferred from data derived from single crystal studies of small molecules rather than from direct observation.

Although the two molecules of ApU in the asymmetric unit are very similar, they are not quite identical. The bond lengths and angles are all within expected range. The conformations of the ribose residues are all 3′-endo[19], and the nucleosides are orientated in the anticonformation[20], with torsion angles about the glycosidic bonds[19] of 2° and 7° for the adenosine residues, and 29° and 30° for the uridines. Comparison with the protonated UpA structure[21,22] suggests that discrepancies between adenine and uracil torsion angles are caused by the differences between the 3′ and 5′ ends of the molecule as the same pattern was obtained with respect to the 3′ and 5′ ends in that molecule which had the opposite base sequence.

In the protonated structure UpA, it was noted that there were short distances between adenosine C8 and O5′, as well as uridine C6 and O5′ (ref. 14). At that time, it was suggested that this might be a result of an intramolecular attraction which, if of a general nature, would help stabilize the anticonformation of the nucleotide. Accordingly, the

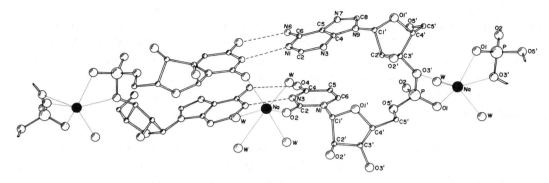

图 3. 从（DNA 双螺旋的）小沟上观察到的透视结构图，显示了核苷酸中原子的编号和钠离子形成的配位结构。两个钠离子（●）均参与形成扭曲的八面体配位，参与成键的原子还有水分子和其他氧原子。位于中心的那个钠离子距离尿嘧啶的 O2 原子的距离是 2.36 Å。

从图 1 中可以看到这些分子的螺旋形态，在此图中，读者的观察方向与碱基对平面垂直。图中前方和后方的碱基对的糖苷键（C1′ 到腺嘌呤 N9 或 C1′ 到尿嘧啶 N1）之间存在明显的旋转关系。图 2 则显示了从平行于以氢键连接的堆积碱基的方向观察到的结构。通过观察核糖磷酸链上的相邻核糖残基的取向，我们可以很容易地看出该分子的右手螺旋结构。这一结构与研究双链病毒 RNA 推导出的结构相似。这种天然形成的分子被称为 RNA 11。图 2 显示了 ApU 和 RNA 11 之间的类似结构，其中垂直的虚线表示近似的螺旋轴。ApU 核苷酸对的持续延伸将会形成一个类似于 RNA 11 的右手双螺旋。值得注意的是，尽管 RNA 11 的螺旋参数可以从 RNA 纤维的 X 射线分析中直接得到，但是其中那些原子中心的位置必须从小分子的单晶体研究数据中得到，而无法直接观察到。

尽管在不对称单元中的两分子 ApU 非常相似，但它们并非完全相同。它们的键长和键角均在预期范围内。核糖残基的构象均为 3′- 内向 [19]，而核苷基团的取向则为反向构象 [20]，其中糖苷键 [19] 对于腺苷残基的扭转角为 2º 和 7º，对于尿嘧啶则为 29º 和 30º。与质子化的 UpA 结构 [21,22] 进行比较表明，腺嘌呤和尿嘧啶在扭转角上的差异是由于分子的 3′ 和 5′ 端之间的差异而引起的；因为在具有相反碱基序列的分子中也观察到了类似的 3′ 和 5′ 端的差异。

在 UpA 的质子化结构中，人们注意到了腺苷的 C8 和 O5′ 之间以及尿嘧啶的 C6 和 O5′ 之间的距离都很短（文献 14）。当时有人提出，这可能是分子内吸引的结果。如果这种吸引力普遍存在的话，它有助于核苷酸反向构象的稳定。因此，人们怀着

related distances in this structure were examined with great interest. Three of the four independent distances were greater than or equal to 3.3 Å; thus, there was no evidence of any interaction. But the distance between one adenine C8 and its ribose O5′ was 3.07 Å. As this O5′ is not covalently linked to a phosphorus atom, the phenomenon may not be relevant to the nucleotides in a helical polynucleotide chain. Nevertheless, for non-helical and 3′ terminal nucleic acid structures, this interaction may yet be seen to play an important role.

The individual double helical fragments are separated in the crystal lattice by a spacing of 3.4 Å, with considerable overlapping of the adenine residues. Besides this intermolecular base stacking, the other important interaction in the direction perpendicular to the base pairs involves the proximity of O1′ of both adenosine riboses with uracil rings. A similar type of interaction was found to be important in the crystal structure of UpA[21,22].

The crystal structure can be visualized as a rod-like entity. The central portions of these rods contain the stacked base pairs. These are flanked by the ribose phosphate backbones, both of which in turn are surrounded by the solvent structure. The large amount of water allows the crystal structure to assume a conformation which is minimally perturbed by lattice interactions. Thus, the double helical structure which we observe here bears a marked resemblance to those structures proposed for solvated polynucleotides. It should be noted in passing, however, that the water is held rather firmly, as the intensity data were collected from the crystal while it was mounted in air.

The ribose phosphate chains are packed together with the phosphate groups facing each other. In the layer between the ribose phosphate moieties are sodium ions which are found in two distinct sites: one, complexed between phosphate groups, and the other, surprisingly, bound to the uracil residues. The sodium ions and their ligands are shown in Fig. 3. The sodium ion in the centre is located on the pseudo two-fold axis in the minor groove of the helix with octahedral coordination which includes the free O2 atoms of the uracils; the remaining ligands are water molecules. As shown in Fig. 3, the other sodium ion rests on an intermolecular pseudo-dyad axis, also exhibiting octahedral coordination, which includes two adenosyl O3′ atoms and two phosphate oxygen atoms.

The stability of the sodium ion position between two phosphate groups is readily understood on electrostatic grounds. What is not so obvious is why the second sodium ion is complexed to the two uracils in the minor groove of the helix. Five angstroms away from this site there is another position between two phosphate groups which could comfortably accommodate the sodium ion and is occupied only by solvent. It is possible that the structure is stabilized considerably by the sodium ion in the minor groove site. Should this prove to be of more general occurrence in other crystals containing A–U sequences, it is possible that this type of coordination may be of importance in polynucleotide structure and function.

浓厚的兴趣对该结构中的相关距离进行了研究。在 4 种独立距离中，有 3 种大于或等于 3.3 Å；因此，没有证据表明发生了任何相互作用。但腺嘌呤的 C8 与其核糖 O5′ 的距离是 3.07 Å，由于这个 O5′ 与磷原子并非共价相连，这一现象可能与核苷酸是否位于螺旋状的多聚核苷酸链上无关。尽管如此，对于非螺旋的和有 3′ 端的核酸结构而言，这种相互作用可能仍然起着重要作用。

每一个双螺旋片段都以 3.4 Å 的距离分布在晶格上，其腺嘌呤残基之间存在相当程度的重叠。除了这种分子之间的碱基堆积外，另一种重要的相互作用存在于碱基对的垂直方向上，由两个腺苷的核糖中的 O1′ 与两个尿嘧啶环之间的相互接近而产生。人们发现在 UpA 晶体中有一种类似的相互作用也十分重要 [21,22]。

晶体结构可以被看作是一种类似杆状的实体。这些杆状实体的中心部分为堆积的碱基对，两侧为核糖磷酸骨架，而这两条核糖磷酸骨架又被溶剂结构所包围。大量的水的存在使得晶体结构呈现出一种构象，该构象可以使晶格之间的扰动降到最低。因此，我们这里所观察到的双螺旋结构与那些溶剂化的多聚核苷酸的结构之间存在显著的相似性。不过，应当顺便提出的是，核酸分子相当牢固地结合了水，因为晶体的衍射强度数据是将其置于空气中时采集的。

核糖磷酸链组装在一起，磷酸基团两两相对。在两个核糖磷酸的中间层内，钠离子存在于两个位点：其一是络合在磷酸基团之间，另一个则是出乎意料地与尿嘧啶残基络合。钠离子及其配体见图 3。钠离子位于双螺旋小沟的伪二次轴上，以其为中心，可以与包括尿嘧啶的自由 O2 原子和水分子形成八面体配位 。如图 3 所示，另一个钠离子位于分子内的伪二次对称轴上，同样以八面体配位形式存在，参与配位的包括两个腺苷的 O3′ 原子和两个磷酸基团上的氧原子。

从静电学角度就能很容易地理解钠离子可以稳定存在于两个磷酸基团之间。然而，我们不清楚的是为何第二个钠离子与螺旋小沟的两个尿嘧啶络合。距离这一位点 5Å 处，在两个磷酸基团之间有另一位点，完全可以容纳钠离子，但是该位点仅被溶剂分子所占据。该结构的稳定性很大程度上可能是通过位于小沟上的钠离子而实现的。如果能证明在其他包含 A–U 序列的晶体中这一现象也常见的话，这种类型的配位可能对多聚核苷酸的结构和功能起重要的作用。

As noted above, one of the most significant features of the organization of the crystal structure of ApU is that the two independent molecules in the asymmetric unit have very similar but not quite identical conformations. Thus, they are related by a pseudo two-fold rotation axis while in an antiparallel double helical polynucleotide there is presumed to be a true two-fold axis which relates the backbones of the two antiparallel chains. We do not completely understand why the crystal structure of ApU did not adopt a true two-fold axis. In this regard, however, we recently discovered that the closely related dinucleoside phosphate, guanosyl-3′, 5′-cytidyl phosphate does indeed form a right-handed antiparallel double helix in the crystalline state in which this two-fold axis is crystallographic (unpublished results of R. O. Day, N. C. Seeman, J. M. R., and A. R.). This recent observation lends support to our earlier emphasis on the importance of the pseudo two-fold axis in the present crystal structure.

Among the significant facts which we learn by analysing double helical fragments are the important detailed parameters determining the conformation of the polynucleotide chain, especially those parts dealing with the geometry of the phosphate group. The structure of the ribose phosphate chain is of central importance in understanding the physical properties and behavior of polynucleotide chains[23]. This information should prove valuable in interpreting the details of the molecular structure in polynucleotide double helices, as well as in the more complex forms of RNA such as those observed in tRNA[24].

This research was supported by grants from the National Institutes of Health, the National Science Foundation and the American Cancer Society. N. C. S. is a postdoctorate fellow of the Damon Runyon Foundation, J. M. R. is a predoctoral trainee of the National Institutes of Health, F. L. S. is a postdoctoral fellow of the American Cancer Society, H. B. N. was an NIH postdoctoral fellow.

We thank Bob Rosenstein, Roberta Ogilvie Day, Don Hatfield, Sung-Hou Kim and Gary Quigley for useful discussions and encouragement, and John Genova and Tim O'Meara for technical assistance.

(**243**, 150-154; 1973)

John M. Rosenberg, Nadrian C. Seeman, Jung Ja Park Kim, F. L. Suddath, Hugh B. Nicholas and Alexander Rich
Department of Biology, Massachusetts Institute of Technology, Cambridge, Massachusetts 02139

Received January 3, 1973.

References:

1. Watson, J. D., and Crick, F. H. C., *Nature*, **171**, 737 (1953).

2. Fuller, W., Wilkins, M. H. F., Wilson, H. R., and Hamilton, L. D., *J. Mol. Biol.*, **12**, 60 (1965).

3. Langridge, R., and Gomatos, P. J., *Science*, **141**, 694 (1963).

4. Tomita, K., and Richa, A., *Nature*, **201**, 1160 (1964).

5. Arnott, S., Dover, S. D., and Wonacott, A. J., *Acta Cryst.*, B, **25**, 2192 (1969).

6. Rich, A., Davies, D. R., Crick, F. H. C., and Watson, J. D., *J. Mol. Biol.*, **3**, 71 (1961).

正如以上所言，ApU 晶体结构组织的最显著的特征是，位于不对称单元中的两个独立分子之间具有非常相似但不完全相同的构象。因此，尽管在这里它们是以一条伪二重旋转轴相关联，但当处于一条反向平行的双螺旋多聚核苷酸中时，应该有一条真正的二重轴把两条反向平行链的骨架关联起来。我们还没有完全理解为何 ApU 的晶体结构没有采用真正的二重轴。不过，关于这一点，我们最近发现与之密切相关的二核苷磷酸，鸟苷 –3′,5′– 胞苷磷酸在晶体状态下确实形成了右手反向平行双螺旋，且形成的是晶体学二次轴（戴、西曼、罗森堡和里奇的未发表成果）。此前我们强调了伪二次轴对该晶体结构的重要性，这一近期结果支持了我们的结论。

我们通过分析双螺旋片段所得到的重要结果有，确定多聚核苷链构象的重要详细参数，特别是关于磷酸基团几何结构的部分。核糖磷酸链的结构对于理解多聚核苷酸链的物理性质和行为都至关重要 [23]。对于解释多聚核苷酸双螺旋以及形式更为复杂的 RNA 中的（如在 tRNA 中观察到的）分子结构细节，这些信息将会非常有价值 [24]。

此研究得到了国立卫生研究院、国家科学基金会和美国癌症协会的经费资助。西曼是戴蒙·鲁尼恩基金会的博士后学者，罗森堡是国立卫生研究院的博士前实习生，苏达茨是美国癌症协会的博士后学者，尼古拉斯是国立卫生研究院的博士后学者。

在此我们感谢鲍勃·罗森斯坦、罗伯塔·奥格尔维·戴、唐·哈特菲尔德、金圣浩和加里·奎格利的有益讨论和鼓励，以及约翰·吉诺瓦和蒂姆·奥马拉的技术支持。

（周志华 翻译；昌增益 审稿）

7. Arnott, S., Hukins, D. W. L., and Dover, S. D., *Biochem. Biophys. Res. Comm.*, **48**, 1392 (1972).

8. Arnott, S., and Hukins, D. W. L., *Biochem. Biophys. Res. Comm.*, **47**, 1504 (1972).

9. Donahue, J., *Science*, **165**, 1091 (1969).

10. Wilkins, M. H. F., Arnott, S., Marvin, D. A., and Hamilton, L. D., *Science*, **167**, 1693 (1970).

11. Crick, F. H. C., *Science*, **167**, 1694 (1970).

12. Arnott, S., *Science*, **167**, 1694 (1970).

13. Donahue, J., *Science*, **167**, 1700 (1970).

14. Seeman, N. C., Sussman, J. L., Berman, H. M., and Kim, S.-H., *Nature New Biology*, **233**, 90 (1971).

15. Corfield, P. W. R., and Rosenstein, R. D., *Trans. Amer. Cryst. Assoc.*, **2**, 17 (1966).

16. Seeman, N. C., thesis, Univ. Pittsburgh (1970).

17. Karle, J., and Hauptman, H., *Acta Cryst.*, **17**, 392 (1964).

18. Voet, D., and Rich, A., *Prog. Nucl. Acid. Res. Mol. Biol.*, **10**, 183 (1970).

19. Sunderalingam, M., *Biopolymers*, **7**, 821 (1969).

20. Donahue, J., and Trueblood, K. N., *J. Mol. Biol.*, **2**, 363 (1960).

21. Sussman, J. L., Seeman, N. C., Kim, S.-H., and Berman, H. M., *J. Mol. Biol.*, **66**, 403 (1972).

22. Rubin, J., Brennan, T., and Sundaralingam, M., *Biochemistry*, **11**, 3112 (1972).

23. Kim, S. -H., Berman, H. M., Seeman, N. C., and Newton, M. D., *Acta Cryst.* (in the press).

24. Kim, S. H., Quigley, G. J., Suddath, F. L., MacPherson, A., Sneden, D., Kim, J. J. P., Weinzierl, J., and Rich, A., *Science*, **179**, 285 (1973).

# Eukaryotes-Prokaryotes Divergence Estimated by 5S Ribosomal RNA Sequences

M. Kimura and T. Ohta

## Editor's Note

This brave stab at estimating one of the earliest but most crucial events in evolution marks an early attempt at using comparative molecular data to calibrate evolutionary history. Motoo Kimura and Tomoko Ohta compared sequences from 5S ribosomal RNA—one of the most "conserved" of all genetic sequences, meaning that it differs little across species—to estimate the divergence date between eukaryotes (such as humans and yeast) and prokaryotes (here two bacterial species). The estimate of two billion years would not surprise anyone today, but it caused some surprise then by implying that yeast is more closely related to humans than to bacteria.

D ATING the principal events in the history of life on the Earth is an interesting subject in evolutionary studies. Here we estimate the time of divergence of the eukaryotes and the prokaryotes through comparative studies of 5S ribosomal RNA sequences, coupled with those of cytochrome *c*. By prokaryotes we mean primitive forms having no true nucleus (bacteria and blue-green algae), while by eukaryotes we mean higher nucleated organisms such as plants and animals including yeasts and fungi. The principle we use in our estimation is that the rate of nucleotide substitutions in the course of evolution is constant per year per site for each informational macromolecule as long as the structure and function of the molecule remain unaltered.

To estimate the evolutionary distances (number of mutant substitutions) among 5S rRNA sequences, we made the alignment shown in Fig.1, using published data[1-3] on human, yeast and bacterial (*Escherichia coli* and *Pseudomonas fluorescens*) sequences. To arrive at this alignment, previous attempts[1,3] involving two or three sequences were helpful. The alignment is made in such a way that the number of matches between sequences is maximized while keeping the gaps inserted as few as possible. It involves a trial and error process, shifting various regions, and counting the number of nucleotides by which the two sequences agree with each other, followed by calculation of probability that this or better agreement occurs by chance. Figure 1 shows clearly (as was noted already by others) the marked conservative nature of this molecule as shown by the fact that only a small number of gaps need be inserted to obtain homology. The observed differences between sequences in terms of the fraction of different sites are given in Table 1. The mutational distance, that is, the average number of nucleotide substitutions per site, was estimated using the formula

$$K = -\frac{3}{4}\ln(1-(\frac{4}{3}\lambda))$$

# 通过5S核糖体RNA序列估计真核生物–原核生物分化

木村资生，太田朋子

*编者按*

*对进化中最早但是最关键事件的估计，这种大胆的尝试标志着应用比较的分子数据来标定进化历史的早期努力。5S 核糖体 RNA（5S rRNA）序列是最保守的遗传序列之一，其在物种之间差异很小。通过比较该序列，木村资生和太田朋子对真核生物（例如人类和酵母）与原核生物（本文中以两种细菌为例）之间的差异进行了估算。如今，对"二十亿年"的估计恐怕不会令人惊讶，但是研究显示酵母与人类的关系比其与细菌的关系更近却让大家感到意外。*

确定地球生命史中重要事件的发生年代是进化研究中一个有趣的课题。在此我们通过对 5S rRNA 序列的比较研究，外加对细胞色素 *c* 的研究，估计了真核生物和原核生物分离的时间。对于原核生物，我们是指没有真正细胞核的简单构造（如细菌和蓝–绿藻），而对于真核生物，我们是指高等有细胞核的生物，如植物和动物，包括酵母和真菌。我们在估计中使用的原则是，只要分子的结构和功能保持不变，那么对于每个信息大分子而言，在进化过程中，每年每个位点的核苷酸替代率是恒定的。

为了估计 5S rRNA 序列的进化距离（突变替代的数量），我们用已发表的人类、酵母和细菌（大肠杆菌和荧光假单胞菌）的数据[1-3]进行了序列比对，如图 1 所示。为了获得这个比对，之前涉及两到三个序列比对的尝试[1,3]是有帮助的。这个比对是按照将两个序列间匹配的数量最大化同时又使插入的间隙数尽可能少的原则建立的。这是一个试错的过程，移动各个区域，记录两个序列之间一致的核苷酸数量，接下来计算当前结果的概率或随机出现的更好的一致性的概率。图 1 明确显示了（正如其他人已经注意到的）该分子显著的保守性，事实上只需插入少量间隙就能获得同源性。表 1 以差异位点所占序列比例的形式给出了序列之间的差异。突变距离，也就是每个位点的核苷酸替代的平均数量，通过公式

$$K = -\frac{3}{4} \ln\left(1 - \left(\frac{4}{3}\lambda\right)\right)$$

where $\lambda$ is the fraction of sites by which two homologous sequences differ. The formula was derived under the assumptions that in the course of evolution nucleotide substitutions occur spatially at random and with uniform probabilities and that each of the four bases (A, C, G, U) mutates to any of the remaining three with equal probability. (For details see ref. 4.) The equivalent formula has been previously derived by Jukes and Cantor[5]. We should also note that Dayhoff's[3] empirical relationship tabulated in her Table 11–3 is practically equivalent to this formula especially for the purpose of comparing different $K$ values.

| | |
|---|---|
| Human | – G– UCUACGGCC– AUACCACCCUGAACGCGCCCGAUCUCGUCUGAU– CUCGGAAGCUAAGCAG |
| Yeast | – G– GUUGCGGCC– AUACCAUCUAGAAAGCACCGUUCUCCGUCCGAUAACCUGUAGUUAAGCUG |
| E. coli | UGCCUGGCGGCC– GUAGCGCGGUGGGUCCCACCUGACCCCAUGCCGAACUCAGAAGUGAAACGC |
| P. fluorescens | UGUUCUUUGACGAGUAGUGGCAUUGGAACACCUGAUCCCAUCCCGAACUCAGAGGUGAAACGA |

GGUCGGGCCUG– GUUAGUACUUGGAUGGGGAGACCGCCUGGGAAUACCGGGUGCUGUAG– GCUU
GUAAGAGCCUGACCGAGUAGUGUAGUGGGGUGACCAUACGCGAAACCUAGGUGCUGCA– – AUCU
CGUAGCGCC– – – GAUGGUAGUGUG– – GGGUCUCCCCAUGCGAGAGUAGGGAACUGCCAGGCAU
UGCAUCGCC– – – GAUGGUAGUGUG– – GGGUUUCCCCAUGUCAAGAUCUCG– ACCAUAGAGCAU

Fig. 1. Alignment of 5S rRNA sequences.

Table 1. Fraction of Different Sites between 5S rRNA Sequences

| | Yeast | E. coli | P. fluorescens |
|---|---|---|---|
| Human | 0.395 | 0.457 | 0.478 |
| Yeast | | 0.474 | 0.565 |
| E. coli | | | 0.319 |

The average mutational distance between the eukaryotes (man, yeast) and the prokaryotes (E. coli, P. fluorescens) turned out to be

$$K_{eu-pro}=0.817\pm0.158$$

where the standard error was obtained from four observations (comparisons). On the other hand, the corresponding quantity between the human and yeast was

$$K_{h-y}=0.561\pm0.095$$

where the error is a theoretical one computed by equation (5) in ref. 4. It may be interesting to note here that yeast is more closely related to man than to the bacteria, supporting the thesis (compare ref. 6) that the division between the eukaryotes and prokaryotes is more basic than divisions within eukaryotes. The remoteness of the eukaryotes-prokaryotes divergence relative to the human-yeast divergence can be estimated by the ratio $K_{eu-pro}/K_{h-y}$ which is approximately 1.5. This is much lower than the corresponding estimate of McLaughlin and Dayhoff[7] who obtained the ratio 2.6 using data on cytochrome $c$, $c_2$ and tRNA sequences. It is also lower than the corresponding estimate, ~2, obtained by Jukes (1969) (quoted in ref.7). Hoping to resolve this discrepancy

454

来估计，其中 λ 是两个同源序列相异位点的比例。这个公式基于如下假设得出：进化过程中核苷酸替代在空间上以相同概率随机发生，并且四种碱基（腺嘌呤、胞嘧啶、鸟嘌呤、尿嘧啶）中的每一种都能以相等的概率突变成其他三种中的任何一种（详细信息请看参考文献4）。之前朱克斯和康托尔就已推导出此当量公式[5]。我们也应当注意到，戴霍夫[3] 在她的表 11-3 中列出的经验关系实际上和这个公式等价，尤其是当用于比较不同 K 值时。

```
人类          – G– UCUACGGCC– AUACCACCCUGAACGCGCCCGAUCUCGUCUGAU– CUCGGAAGCUAAGCAG
酵母          – G– GUUGCGGCC– AUACCAUCUAGAAAGCACCGUUCUCCGUCGAUAACCUGUAGUUAAGCUG
大肠杆菌      UGCCUGGCGGCC– GUAGCGCGGUGGUCCCACCUGACCCCAUGCCGAACUCAGAAGUGAAACGC
荧光假单胞菌  UGUUCUUUGACGAGUAGUGGCAUUGGAACACCUGAUCCCAUCCCGAACUCAGAGGUGAAACGA

              GGUCGGGCCUG– GUUAGUACUUGGAUGGGAGACCGCCUGGGAAUACCGGGUGCUGUAG– GCUU
              GUAAGAGCCUGACGAGUAGUGUUAGUGGGUGACCAUACGCGAAACCUAGGUGCUGCA– – AUCU
              CGUAGCGCC– – – GAUGGUAGUGUG– GGGUCUCCCCAUGCGAGAGUAGGGAACUGCCAGGCAU
              UGCAUCGCC– – – GAUGGUAGUGUG– GGGUUUCCCCAUGUGAGAGUAGGGAACUGCCAGGCAU
```

图 1. 5S rRNA 序列的比对图

表 1. 5S rRNA 序列间差异位点的比例

|  | 酵母 | 大肠杆菌 | 荧光假单胞菌 |
|---|---|---|---|
| 人类 | 0.395 | 0.457 | 0.478 |
| 酵母 |  | 0.474 | 0.565 |
| 大肠杆菌 |  |  | 0.319 |

真核生物（人、酵母）和原核生物（大肠杆菌、荧光假单胞菌）间的平均突变距离就是

$$K_{真核-原核}=0.817\pm0.158$$

其中，标准差由四组观察结果（比较）获得。另一方面，人和酵母菌之间相对应的值为

$$K_{人-酵母}=0.561\pm0.095$$

其中，误差是由参考文献 4 中的方程（5）计算出的一个理论值。此处有个有趣的现象值得注意，相比与细菌的关系，酵母和人的关系更近一些，这支持了真核生物和原核生物之间的差异比真核生物内的差异更为根本这一论点（对照参考文献6）。真核生物-原核生物之间的差异相对于人-酵母之间差异的遥远程度可以通过比值 $K_{真核-原核}/K_{人-酵母}$ 来估计，大约是 1.5。这比麦克劳克林和戴霍夫相应的估计[7] 低很多，他们用细胞色素 $c$、$c_2$ 和转运 RNA（tRNA）序列数据得出的比值为 2.6。这也比朱克斯（1969）（在参考文献 7 中引用）得出来的约等于 2 的估计值要低。我们用麦克

we calculated the evolutionary distances using the same data[3] on tRNA as McLaughlin and Dayhoff[7] but restricting our treatment only to paired regions. The reason for doing this is that it seems as if there is no excess of highly conserved regions (as inferred from our statistical analysis of the frequency distribution of the number of evolutionary changes per site in the alignment of Fig. 1), so that evolutionary change appears to be uniform over the entire sequence and in this respect 5S rRNA might be more similar to the paired than unpaired regions of tRNA. The evolutionary distances turned out to be $K_1 = 0.836 \pm 0.136$ for the eukaryotes-prokaryotes divergence but $K_2 = 0.420 \pm 0.029$ for the average of rat-yeast (tRNA$^{Ser}$) and wheat-yeast (tRNA$^{Phe}$) divergences. It may be seen that although $K_1$ is comparable to $K_{eu-pro}$, $K_2$ is clearly lower than $K_{h-y}$, so that the ratio $K_1/K_2 = 1.99$ is still considerably higher than $K_{eu-pro}/K_{h-y} = 1.46$. It is possible that the difference is due to sampling error, with the true value lying somewhere between these two. At any rate we should take these estimates as tentative (including the problem that might arise because of the multiplicity of ribosomal genes). There is some reason to believe, however, that our estimate of 1.5 is consistent with the fossil records as explained below.

From comparative studies of cytochrome $c$ sequences among eukaryotes, we can estimate the remoteness of the human-yeast divergence relative to the mammal-fish divergence. This allows us to estimate the absolute time of the human-yeast divergence as it is known from classical palaeontological studies that the common ancestor of the fish and the mammals goes back to some 400 m.y. (compare refs 8 and 9). From a number of comparisons involving various species of fish and mammals (data taken from ref. 3), we obtained the results that the mutational distance (in terms of the number of amino acid substitutions) between mammals and yeast is about three times that between mammals and the fish. This puts the time of the human-yeast divergence back to about $1.2 \times 10^9$ yr. This agrees with Dickerson[10] who obtained $1,200 \pm 75$ m.y. as the estimated date of the branch point for animals/plants/protists. We should note here that we avoided using the cytochrome $c_2$ sequence of the bacterium *Rhodospirillum rubrum* to estimate the prokaryotes-eukaryotes divergence, because there seems to be some difference in function between cytochromes $c$ and $c_2$ (compare ref. 7).

Multiplying $1.2 \times 10^9$ yr by the ratio $K_{eu-pro}/K_{h-y} \approx 1.5$, we arrive at the result that the divergence between the eukaryotes and prokaryotes goes back to some $1.8 \times 10^9$ yr. Recent studies on Precambrian fossils (compare ref.11) suggest that the eukaryotes evolved from prokaryotes at some point between the Bitter Springs formation ($10^9$ yr old) and the Gunflint formation ($2 \times 10^9$ yr old). With additional relevant data forthcoming (for example, ref. 12) we hope that the studies of molecular evolution will soon supply a more accurate date.

We tentatively conclude that the eukaryotes diverged from prokaryotes nearly $2 \times 10^9$ yr ago, thus opening up the way toward "higher organisms".

We thank Dr. K. Miura and Mr. H. Komiya for calling our attention to the relevant literature on 5S rRNA sequences and Drs. T. Maruyama, S. Takemura and S. Kondo for

劳克林和戴霍夫 [7] 使用过的同一组 tRNA 数据 [3] 计算了进化距离，但是我们的处理只限定在配对区域，希望可以解决这个差异。这样做的原因是看起来好像没有额外的高度保守区（正如通过比对图 1 中每个位点的进化改变数的频度分布进行的统计分析推测出的一样），所以在整个序列上进化改变似乎是均衡的，并且在这方面 5S rRNA 和 tRNA 的未配对区相比可能和配对区更相似。对于真核生物－原核生物之间的差异，进化距离为 $K_1=0.836 \pm 0.136$，而对大鼠－酵母（色氨酸 tRNA）和小麦－酵母（苯丙氨酸 tRNA）之间差异的平均值，进化距离为 $K_2=0.420 \pm 0.029$。可以看出，尽管 $K_1$ 和 $K_{真核-原核}$ 相当，$K_2$ 却明显比 $K_{人-酵母}$ 小，所以比值 $K_1/K_2=1.99$ 仍然比 $K_{真核-原核}/K_{人-酵母}=1.46$ 高很多。这个差异有可能是采样误差造成的，真实值可能介于二者之间。至少我们应该将这些作为初步估计值（可能存在由核糖体基因多样性而产生的问题）。然而有理由相信，我们估计的 1.5 是同下面阐述的化石数据相符的。

通过真核生物间细胞色素 $c$ 序列的比较研究，我们能够估计人－酵母之间的差异相对于哺乳动物－鱼差异的遥远程度。经典的古生物学研究表明鱼和哺乳动物的共同祖先出现在 4 亿年前（对照参考文献 8 和 9），这使我们能估计出人－酵母菌趋异的绝对时间。通过对各种鱼类物种和哺乳类物种的大量比较（数据来自参考文献 3），我们得到了哺乳动物和酵母之间的突变距离（依据氨基酸替代的数量）是哺乳动物和鱼之间突变距离的三倍的结果。这将人和酵母分离的时间推到了 12 亿年前。这和迪克森 [10] 得到的动物、植物和原生生物的分支点是 $1,200 \pm 75$ 百万年的结论相符。在此我们应该注明，我们没有使用细菌中的红螺菌的细胞色素 $c_2$ 来估计原核生物－真核生物的分离，因为细胞色素 $c$ 和细胞色素 $c_2$ 在功能上似乎有些不同（对照参考文献 7）。

用 $1.2 \times 10^9$ 年乘以比例 $K_{真核-原核}/K_{人-酵母} \approx 1.5$，我们得出真核生物和原核生物的分离发生在大约 $1.8 \times 10^9$ 年前的结论。最近对前寒武纪化石的研究（对照参考文献 11）表明，在苦泉地层（年龄为 $10^9$ 年）和加拿大冈弗林特地层（年龄为 $2 \times 10^9$ 年）之间的某个时候，真核生物从原核生物进化而来。结合将来更多的相关数据（例如参考文献 12），我们希望不久后分子进化的研究将提供一个更加准确的日期。

我们暂且推断大约 $2 \times 10^9$ 年前真核生物从原核生物分离，从此走上了通向"高等生物"的道路。

感谢三浦博士和小宫先生引起我们对 5S rRNA 序列相关文章的关注，感谢丸山

457

helpful discussions.

(*Nature New Biology*, **243**, 199–200; 1973)

**Motoo Kimura and Tomoko Ohta**
National Institute of Genetics, Shizuoka-ken 411, Mishima

Received December 29, 1972; revised March 5, 1973.

---

References:

1. DuBuy, B., and Weissman, S. M., *J. Biol. Chem.*, **246**, 747 (1971).

2. Hindley, J., and Page, S. M., *FEBS Lett.*, **26**, 157 (1972).

3. Dayhoff, M. O., *Atlas of Protein Sequence and Structure 1972* (National Biomedical Research Foundation, Washington, DC, 1972).

4. Kimura, M., and Ohta, T., *J. Mol. Evol.*, **2**, 87 (1972).

5. Jukes, T. H., and Cantor, C. R., in *Mammalian Protein Metabolism* (edit. by Munro, H. N.), 21 (Academic Press, New York, 1969).

6. Margulis, L., *Origin of Eukaryotic Cells* (Yale Univ. Press, New Haven and London, 1970).

7. McLaughlin, P. J., and Dayhoff, M. O., *Science*, **168**, 1469 (1970).

8. Romer, A. S., *The Procession of Life* (Weidenfeld and Nicolson, London, 1968).

9. McAlester, A. L., *The History of Life* (Prentice-Hall, Englewood Cliffs, 1968).

10. Dickerson, R. E., *J. Mol. Evol.*, **1**, 26 (1971).

11. Barghoorn, E. S., *Sci. Amer.*, **224**, 30 (1971).

12. Brownlee, G. G., Cartwright, E., McShane, T., and Williamson, R., *FEBS Lett.*, **25**, 8 (1972).

博士、武村博士和绀户博士的宝贵讨论。

（邓铭瑞 翻译；陈新文 陈继征 审稿）

# Isolation and Genetic Localization of Three φX174 Promoter Regions

C. Chen *et al.*

## Editor's Note

Four years before the φX174 bacteriophage became the first DNA-based organism to have its genome completely sequenced, Cheng-Yien Chen and colleagues had used restriction enzymes (which cut DNA at sequence-specific locations) to produce a genetic map of this model molecular biology system. Importantly, they managed to isolate and localize three promoter regions (DNA segments that facilitate the transcription of a particular gene) by clever use of a "protective" RNA polymerase protein that let them digest away the exposed, unwanted nucleic acid. Three decades later the φX174 bacteriophage was to court attention again, when researchers reported that they had synthetically assembled its genome from scratch.

SPECIFIC sequences of nucleic acids such as ribosome binding sites[1] (W. Gilbert, cited in ref. 2) and portions of the promoter region[3,4] have been isolated by protecting those sequences with the relevant protein or organelle and digesting away the exposed nucleic acid. We have isolated specific sequences from the promoter regions in bacteriophage φX174 replicative form (RF) DNA using RNA polymerase as the protecting protein. We wish to describe that isolation and the procedures used to localize these RNA-polymerase-protected sequences within the φX174 genome.

We have previously described the use of restriction enzymes to cleave φX174 DNA into specific fragments[5,6] and the genetic assay used to order these fragments with respect to the φX174 recombination map[7]. The φX genome is separated into 11-14 specific pieces using either of the *Haemophilus* restriction enzymes, endonuclease R[5,8] or endonuclease Z[6]. Our approach has been to determine which restriction fragments contain sequences protected by RNA polymerase. As most of the restriction fragments have been ordered with respect to the φX174 genetic map (manuscript in preparation), this localizes the protected sequences within the map as well.

Two procedures were used to identify DNA fragments bearing sequences protected by RNA polymerase. In the first, *Escherichia coli* RNA polymerase was bound to [3]H-labelled φX174 RFI (covalently closed circular DNA). After extensive digestion with pancreatic DNase, the fraction of the DNA protected by RNA polymerase was isolated. The protected [3]H-DNA was then hybridized to purified [32]P-labelled restriction fragments of φX174 RF immobilized on nitrocellulose filters. Retention of [3]H counts indicated the presence of homologous sequences within that particular specific restriction fragment.

# 三个ΦX174启动子区的分离和基因定位

陈等

## 编者按

在 $\phi$X174 噬菌体成为首个被完整测序的基于 DNA 的生物有机体的四年前，陈成印（音译）和他的同事们就已经使用限制性内切酶（在序列特异性位点切开 DNA）得到了这个模式分子生物学系统的遗传图谱。重要的是，他们巧妙地运用一种"保护性"RNA 聚合酶蛋白，通过消化掉暴露的、不需要的核酸，分离和定位了三个启动子区域（帮助特定基因进行转录的 DNA 片段）。三十年后，当研究者们报道了他们从头合成组装了 $\phi$X174 噬菌体的基因组时，它再次引起了人们的关注。

通过相关蛋白或细胞器保护 DNA 序列并消化掉暴露的核酸，若干特异核酸序列已经被确定，例如核糖体结合位点 [1]（吉尔伯特，引自参考文献 2）和部分启动子区域 [3,4]。我们已经利用 RNA 聚合酶作为保护蛋白，从噬菌体 $\phi$X174 复制型（RF）DNA 的启动子区域中分离到了特定序列。我们想叙述一下这一分离的过程，以及在 $\phi$X174 基因组中定位这些 RNA 聚合酶保护序列的步骤。

之前，我们已经对采用限制性内切酶将 $\phi$X174 DNA 切割成特定片段 [5,6]，及根据 $\phi$X174 重组图谱将这些片段进行排序的遗传分析 [7] 进行过描述。使用嗜血杆菌限制性内切酶、核酸内切酶 R[5,8] 或者核酸内切酶 Z[6] 均可将 $\phi$X 基因组切割成 11~14 个特定的片段。我们的方法可以确定哪个限制性片段含有被 RNA 聚合酶所保护的序列。由于绝大多数限制性片段已经根据 $\phi$X174 基因图谱进行了排序（论文撰写中），因此我们的方法也能同样在图谱中定位被（RNA 聚合酶）保护的片段。

鉴定含有 RNA 聚合酶保护序列的 DNA 片段需要两个过程。首先，让大肠杆菌 RNA 聚合酶与 [3]H 标记的 $\phi$X174 RFI（共价闭合环状 DNA）结合。经过胰 DNA 酶的充分消化后，RNA 聚合酶保护的 DNA 片段就被分离出来了。受保护的 [3]H–DNA 随后与固定在硝酸纤维素滤膜上的 [32]P 标记的纯化 $\phi$X174 RF 限制性片段进行杂交。留在滤膜上的 DNA 的 [3]H 计数表明与特定的限制性片段的同源序列的存在。

461

About 1.9% of φX174 RFI is protected from DNase digestion by RNA polymerase. The DNA-RNA polymerase complex formed is quite stable because an excess of cold RF during digestion does not change the fraction of labelled DNA protected. The sites which can be protected by RNA polymerase are saturated, as increasing the ratio of RNA polymerase to DNA beyond 4 μg polymerase to 0.02 μg DNA (our standard conditions) does not increase the amount of DNA protected.

Assuming the average chain length of a protected site is thirty-five base pairs long[3], the resistant counts represent approximately three to four such sites per genome. The protected ³H-labelled DNA sequences were eluted from a nitrocellulose filter with 0.2% SDS and hybridized to a set of filters loaded with purified restriction fragments of φX174 RF produced by endonuclease R and to a separate set of filters containing the fragments produced by endonuclease Z. The RNA polymerase protected DNA hybridized to filters bearing endonuclease R fragments r2, r4 and r6 and to endonuclease Z fragments z1,z2 and z3 (Table 1).

Table 1. Protection of DNA

| Fragments on filter from band | % ³H bound* | Fragments on filter from band | % ³H bound† |
|---|---|---|---|
| r1 | 0.74 | z1 | 6.0 |
| r2 | 6.2 | z2 | 3.7 |
| r3 | 0.97 | z3 | 3.4 |
| r4 | 4.0 | z4 | 0.7 |
| r5 | 0.77 | z5 | 0.6 |
| r6 | 2.4 | z6 | 0.9 |
| r7 | 0.93 | z7 | 0.6 |
| r8 | 0.92 | z8 | 0.9 |
| r9 | 0.80 | z9 | 0.2 |
| RFII | 18.6 | RFII | 18.6 |

* A blank filter background of 0.39% has been subtracted.
† A blank filter background of 0.35% has been subtracted.

Hybridization of RNA-polymerase-protected ³H-labelled φX174 RF DNA to specific ³²P-labelled, endonuclease R and Z fragments. The preparation of ³²P-RFI, endonuclease R and Z digestions, electrophoresis and autoradiography have been described previously[5,6]. The ³²P endo Z and endo R fragments were eluted from the bands of dry gel in 2×SSC at 65°C for 24 h (N. Axelrod, personal communication). Equimolar amounts of the ³²P restriction fragments were immobilized on the membrane filters (25 mm) (Schleicher and Schuell, B6). Each fragment was made up to 20 ml at a final concentration of 0.1×SSC. After heating at 100°C for 5 min and quickly quenching in the ice bath, each fragment was immobilized on a B6 filter according to the method of Raskas and Green[18]. The ³H-RFI-DNA-RNA polymerase complexes were produced as follows. The reaction mixture contained 0.02 μg of ³H-RFI-DNA (about 75,000 c.p.m.) (prepared as in ref. 6), 20 μg of RNA polymerase and 0.1 mM each of ATP and GTP in 0.5 ml of buffer A (8 mM MgCl₂, 50 mM KCl, 20 mM Tris, pH 7.9, 0.1 mM dithiothreitol). The RNA polymerase had been purified through a glycerol gradient centrifugation as in the method of Burgess[16]. Acrylamide gels had verified that sigma factor was present in our preparation. After 5 min at 37°C, 10 μg of unlabelled RFI-DNA, followed by 200 μg of pancreatic DNase, was added and the digestion was continued for 40 min. The mixture was chilled, diluted with

受 RNA 聚合酶保护而免于被 DNA 酶消化的 φX174RFI 大约有 1.9%。形成的 DNA–RNA 聚合酶复合物非常稳定，因为消化过程中过量的冷 RF 也改变不了被标记的受保护 DNA 的比例。受 RNA 聚合酶保护的位点已经达到饱和，将 RNA 聚合酶与 DNA 的比例增加到超过 4 μg 聚合酶比 0.02 μg DNA（我们的标准条件）也不能增加受保护 DNA 的数量。

假设受保护位点的平均链长是 35 个碱基对 [3]，那么每个基因组中这样的抗消化位点的数量大约为 3 到 4 个。用 0.2% SDS 将 3H 标记的受保护 DNA 序列从硝酸纤维素膜上洗脱下来，然后将其分别与含有纯化的由核酸内切酶 R 制备的 φX174RF 限制性片段的滤膜及负载了由核酸内切酶 Z 制备的片段的滤膜进行杂交。RNA 聚合酶保护的 DNA 与负载了核酸内切酶 R 片段 r2、r4 和 r6 以及核酸内切酶 Z 片段 z1、z2 和 z3 的滤膜进行杂交（表 1）。

表 1. DNA 的保护

| 滤膜上来自条带的片段 | 3H 结合比例 %* | 滤膜上来自条带的片段 | 3H 结合比例 %† |
|---|---|---|---|
| r1 | 0.74 | z1 | 6.0 |
| r2 | 6.2 | z2 | 3.7 |
| r3 | 0.97 | z3 | 3.4 |
| r4 | 4.0 | z4 | 0.7 |
| r5 | 0.77 | z5 | 0.6 |
| r6 | 2.4 | z6 | 0.9 |
| r7 | 0.93 | z7 | 0.6 |
| r8 | 0.92 | z8 | 0.9 |
| r9 | 0.80 | z9 | 0.2 |
| RFII | 18.6 | RFII | 18.6 |

\* 减去了 0.39% 的空白滤膜本底。

† 减去了 0.35% 的空白滤膜本底。

RNA 聚合酶保护的 3H 标记的 φX174RF DNA 与特异性 32P 标记的核酸内切酶 R 和 Z 片段的杂交。32P–RFI 的制备、内切酶 R 和 Z 的消化、电泳以及放射自显影的方法如前所述 [5,6]。在 2×SSC 65℃条件下，经过 24 小时的洗脱，从干燥胶条带中获得 32P 标记的内切酶 R 和 Z 的片段（阿克塞尔罗德，个人交流）。在滤膜（25 mm）上固定等摩尔的 32P 限制性片段（施莱克尔和许尔，B6）。每个片段溶解于终浓度 0.1×SSC 的缓冲液中，最终体积 20 ml。100℃ 加热 5 分钟后在冰浴中快速冷却，然后根据拉斯卡斯和格林的方法 [18] 将每个片段固定在 B6 滤膜上。3H–RFI–DNA–RNA 聚合酶复合物的制备方法如下：反应混合物是 0.5 ml 缓冲液 A（8 mM MgCl₂，50 mM KCl，20 mM Tris，pH7.9，0.1 mM 二硫苏糖醇）中含有 0.02 μg 的 3H–RFI–DNA（大约 75,000 c.p.m.）（制备方法按照文献 6），20 μg 的 RNA 聚合酶，ATP 和 GTP 各 0.1 mM 的。RNA 聚合酶按照伯吉斯的方法用甘油梯度离心纯化 [16]。丙烯酰胺凝胶的实验结果证实，在我们的制备物中存在西格玛因子。经过 37℃下 5 分钟，加入 10 μg 没有标记的 RFI–DNA，随后加入 200 μg 胰 DNA 酶并继续消化 40 分钟。反应混合物经过冷的缓冲液 A 冷却稀释，其中的复合物被收集到硝酸纤维素膜上（密理博，HA）。用 0.2% 的 SDS 将受保护的序列从滤膜上洗脱下来。在

cold buffer A and the complexes were collected on a nitrocellulose filter ("Millipore", HA). The protected sequences were freed from the filter by treatment with 0.2% SDS. An aliquot (430 c.p.m.) of the protected sequences was heated at 100°C for 5 min and quickly quenched in ice and hybridized to each filter containing $^{32}$P endo Z and endo R fragments. The filters were then counted with a Packard Tri-Carb scintillation counter in a toluene-based scintillation fluid. The percentage of the $^3$H bound was calculated as the fraction of input counts bound minus the percentage of counts bound to a blank filter. The counts were determined from 100 min counts and were reproducible in four different experiments.

The second procedure used to identify DNA fragments bearing RNA-polymerase-protected sequences was to bind RNA polymerase to $^{32}$P-labelled restriction fragments of φX174 RF and then to pass the reaction mixture through a nitrocellulose filter which should retain only the RNA polymerase-$^{32}$P-labelled DNA fragment complex[9]. The filtrate was then electrophoresed in 3% polyacrylamide gels to determine which DNA fragments were missing. The gel was then fractionated and counted to obtain quantitative data on the recovery of each restriction fragment. The recoveries of these fragments compared with fragments which were not reacted with RNA polymerase showed that fragments r2, r4 and r6 were retained by the filter (Fig. 1). A similar experiment with restriction fragments produced by endonuclease Z showed that fragments z1, z2 and z3 were retained by filtration.

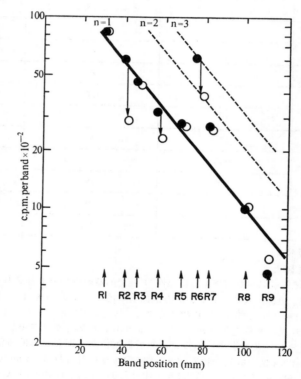

Fig. 1. Quantitative determination of fragment recovery with and without RNA polymerase binding before nitrocellulose filtration. A sample of 200 μl of $^{32}$P-φX RF DNA (2.6×10$^5$ c.p.m., 0.08 μg) was digested with endonuclease R[5]. RNA polymerase (32 μg) was then mixed with 100 μl of the endo R limit digest of the RF to give a final volume of 200 μl in buffer A (8 mM MgCl$_2$, 50 mM KCl, 20 mM Tris, $p$H 7.9, 0.1 mM dithiothreitol) and 0.1 mM each of ATP and GTP. After 5 min at 37°C the reaction mixture

100℃下将一部分（430 c.p.m.）受保护序列加热 5 分钟，并迅速在冰上冷却，将其分别与含有 $^{32}P$ 标记的内切酶 Z 和内切酶 R 片段的滤膜杂交。所得滤膜随后在甲苯为基础的闪烁液中用 Packard Tri–Carb 型闪烁计数器计数。投入的计数比例减去空白滤膜的计数比例就是 $^3H$ 的结合比例。所有数值经由 100 分钟计数确定，并且在四个不同的实验中具有可重复性。

鉴定含有 RNA 聚合酶保护序列的 DNA 片段的第二步是将 RNA 聚合酶结合到 $^{32}P$ 标记的 φX174RF 限制性片段上，将反应混合物通过硝酸纤维素滤膜后仅会留下 RNA 聚合酶 –$^{32}P$ 标记 DNA 片段的复合物 [9]。将滤过物在 3% 的聚丙烯酰胺凝胶中进行电泳，以确定哪些 DNA 片段丢失了。随后将凝胶分成几部分并计数，获得回收后每个限制性片段的定量数据。通过将这些回收后的片段与没有和 RNA 聚合酶反应的片段进行比较，得知被滤膜拦截的片段为 r2、r4 和 r6（图 1）。用核酸内切酶 Z 制备得到的限制性片段的类似实验显示，片段 z1、z2 和 z3 被滤膜拦截。

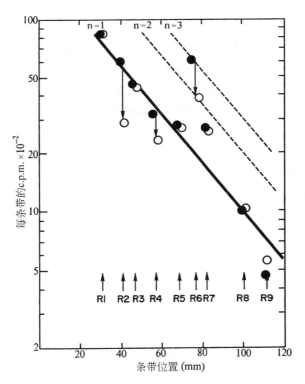

图 1. 在硝酸纤维素膜过滤前使用和不用 RNA 聚合酶的条件下，回收各片段的定量计数。200 µl 的 $^{32}P$–φX174 RF DNA 样本（$2.6 \times 10^5$ c.p.m.，0.08 µg）用核酸内切酶 R 进行消化 [5]。RNA 聚合酶（32 µg）随后与 100µl RF 的内切酶 R 限制性消化产物混合并加入含 0.1 mM ATP 和 GTP 的缓冲液 A（8 mM MgCl$_2$，50 mM KCl，20 mM Tris，pH 7.9，0.1 mM 二硫苏糖醇），使总体积为 200 µl。37℃作用 5 分钟后，将反应混合物用硝酸纤维素膜过滤（密理博，HA）。滤过物约 150 µl，进行电泳 [5]。剩余的 100µl RF 的内

was passed through a nitrocellulose filter ("Millipore", HA). The filtrate containing approximately 150 μl was subjected to electrophoresis[5]. The remaining 100 μl of the endo R limit digest of RF was treated as above except that RNA polymerase was omitted. After electrophoresis the gels were dried on a filter paper, cut into 1 mm segments and counted with a scintillation counter. The tracking dye migrated 142 mm. The integrated counts in the various bands were plotted (log scale) against mobilities (band position in mm). Band R6 has been shown to contain three unresolved fragments of about the same size[5] and so has three times (n=3) the number of counts as those bands containing a single fragment (n=1). Band R7 as those bands containing a single fragment (n=1). Band R7 contains two unresolved fragments (n=2). ●, No RNA-P; ○, plus RNA-P.

The data from these experiments are consistent with the restriction fragment map for φX174. That is, each r fragment containing sequences protected by RNA polymerase overlaps with a z fragment also shown to contain such a sequence (Fig. 2).

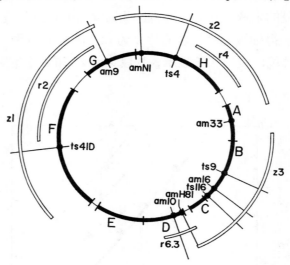

Fig. 2. Locations on the genetic map of φX174 of restriction fragments containing sequences protected by RNA polymerase. The order of eight φX174 genes (A through H) has been determined by genetic recombination[15]. The gene sizes shown on this map were calculated from published estimates of the molecular weights of the corresponding gene products[19-21]. (The assignments of sizes for genes A, B, C and E are uncertain; however, the exact sizes of these genes do not affect the general picture presented here.) As the estimated gene sizes add up to 90% of the total genome size (5,500 nucleotide pairs), the remaining 10% has been arbitrarily distributed as intergenic spacers. Fragments z1, z2 and z3 have been mapped by the genetic assay for DNA fragments[5-7,22] and contain the indicated genetic sites. Fragment r2 is homologous to z1 by hybridization, but does not contain any of the genetic sites shown. A different endonuclease R fragment (r1) contains the site F$ts$41D and extends counterclockwise beyond the end of z1. Therefore, r2 must lie between the sites F$ts$41D and G$am$9 as shown. Fragment r4 is homologous to z2 by hybridization. Also, r4 is adjacent to a fragment (r3) containing the site $am$33 in gene A. So r4 must be located in the region indicated. (We know that r4 and r3 are adjacent because electrophoresis of an endonuclease R digest of phage S13 RF gives the normal φX174 pattern of fragments except that r4, r3 and r5 (gene B) are missing and are replaced by a single large fragment.) Band R6 has been shown to contain three fragments[5] (named r6.1, r6.2 and r6.3) which have been partially resolved on prolonged electrophoresis. Fragments r6.1 and r6.2 contain genetic sites within cistrons G and H; therefore, fragment r6.3 (containing the indicated sites in cistron D) must be the component of band R6 which shares a polymerase protected sequence with fragment z3.

466

切酶 R 的限制性消化产物也按如上步骤处理，只是不加入 RNA 聚合酶。电泳后，将凝胶放在一张滤纸上干燥，切成 1 mm 的片段后用闪烁计数器计数。示踪染料迁移了 142 mm。将不同条带上计数值的整数（取对数值）对迁移率（条带位置，单位 mm）作图。条带 R6 含有三种大小几乎相同的不能分解的片段 [5]，因此它们的计数是那些都含有单一的片段（n=1）条带的三倍（n=3）。条带 R7 含有两个不能分解的片段（n=2）。●没有 RNA 聚合酶；○加入 RNA 聚合酶。

这些实验获得的数据与 φX174 的限制性片段图谱一致。也就是说，每个含有 RNA 聚合酶保护序列的 r 片段与同样显示含有这些序列的 z 片段有重叠（图 2）。

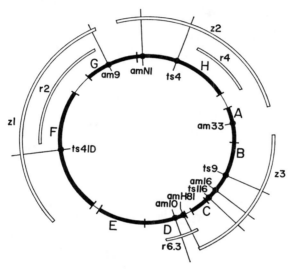

图 2. φX174 遗传图谱上含 RNA 聚合酶保护序列的限制性片段的定位。应用基因重组技术已经确定了 8 个 φX174 基因的顺序（A 到 H）[15]。本图中显示的基因大小是根据已发表的相应基因产物的分子量的估计值计算出来的 [19-21]。（基因 A，B，C 和 E 的大小尚未确定；但是，这些基因的准确大小不会影响这里显示的总体图像。）由于估计的基因大小占到了整个基因组大小的 90%（5,500 个核苷酸对），剩余的 10% 是随意分布于基因之间的间隔。片段 z1，z2 和 z3 已经通过 DNA 片段的遗传分析定位于图上 [5-7,22]，并含有所显示的基因位点。杂交显示片段 r2 与 z1 同源，但是不含有任何显示的基因位点。另一个不同的核酸内切酶 R 片段（r1）含有位点 Fts41D，并逆时针延伸超出 z1 的末端。因此，r2 肯定位于如图所示的 Fts41D 和 Gam9 位点之间。片段 r4 通过杂交定位与 z2 同源。而且，r4 与基因 A 中含有位点 am33 的片段（r3）相邻。因此，r4 肯定位于图中所示的区域。（我们知道 r4 和 r3 相邻，因为除了 r4，r3 和 r5（基因 B）丢失并被一个大的单片段替代以外，噬菌体 S13 RF 的核酸内切酶 R 消化产物的电泳显示正常的 φX174 片段分布类型。）条带 R6 含有在延时电泳中部分显示的三个片段 [5]（称为 r6.1，r6.2 和 r6.3）。片段 r6.1 和 r6.2 含有位于顺反子 G 和 H 内的基因位点；因此，片段 r6.3（含有图中顺反子 D 中所示的位点）肯定是条带 R6 的组成部分，并且与片段 z3 共享一个聚合酶保护序列。

The RNA polymerase DNA fragment complexes were also visualized in the electron microscope. RNA polymerase was reacted with purified restriction fragments r2 and z1 and stained by the Kleinschmidt procedure for microscopy. When r2 was mixed with RNA polymerase the structures shown in Fig. 3a, b, and c were seen. Polymerase was seen bound only at the end of r2, although not every r2 fragment had an enzyme molecule associated with it. On the other hand, when RNA polymerase was mixed with fragment z1 all the binding seen was internal, about one-third of the way from the end (Fig. 3d, e and f). These fragments have not been placed precisely enough with respect to the recombination map to be sure which end of r2 contains the sequences protected by RNA polymerase.

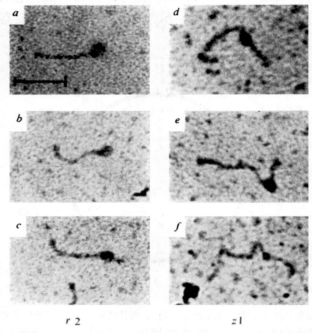

Fig. 3. Electron microscopic pictures of RNA polymerase-restriction fragment mixtures. RNA polymerase was bound to the fragments r2 (a, b, c) and z1 (d, e, f) as described in Fig. 1. The RNA polymerase-DNA fragments were prepared for microscopy according to Kleinschmidt's procedure, as modified by Davis and Davidson[17]. Grids containing DNA-RNA polymerase complexes were stained with uranyl acetate and then photographed at a magnification of 20,000 with an AEI model EM6B electron microscope. The bar represents 0.2 μm.

It is clear that RNA polymerase when reacted with DNA in this way protects specific sequences from nuclease digestion. It seems likely to us that these sequences contain the start sites[10] within the promoter regions. RNA polymerase in the presence of ATP and GTP presumably becomes associated with the DNA at entry sites[10] and then drifts to the start site where it is prevented from synthesizing mRNA by the absence of all four triphosphates. It has been shown that the sequences from bacteriophage fd protected in a similar fashion by RNA polymerase contain sequences which specify the initial nucleotides in the *in vivo* messages[3]. Rüger[11] showed that similar sites from T4 phage DNA still serve as a template for RNA polymerase. There is no clear evidence, however, that every sequence protected in this fashion by RNA polymerase contains a start site.

也可在电子显微镜下对 RNA 聚合酶 –DNA 片段复合物进行观察。将 RNA 聚合酶与纯化的限制性片段 r2 和 z1 进行反应，并用克莱因施密特方法染色后于显微镜下观察。当 r2 与 RNA 聚合酶混合时，看到了图 3a、b 和 c 所示的结构。聚合酶仅仅结合到 r2 的末端，尽管不是每个 r2 片段都有结合的酶分子。另一方面，当 RNA 聚合酶与片段 z1 混合时，所有可见的结合都位于中间，距末端大约 1/3 处（图 3d、e、f）。对根据重组图谱确定 r2 的哪一端含有 RNA 聚合酶保护序列而言，这些片段的定位还不够精确。

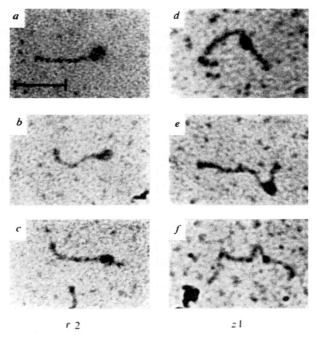

图 3. RNA 聚合酶 – 限制性片段复合物的电子显微镜照片。正如图 1 所示，RNA 聚合酶同片段 r2（a、b、c）和 z1（d、e、f）结合。用于显微观察的 RNA 聚合酶 – DNA 片段按照戴维斯和戴维森改良的克莱因施密特法制备 [17]。用醋酸双氧铀对含有 DNA–RNA 聚合酶复合物的样品载网进行染色，然后用 AEI 型 EM6B 电子显微镜在放大 20000 倍时照相。图例标尺表示 0.2 μm。

很清楚的是，当 RNA 聚合酶以这种方式与 DNA 反应时，可以保护特定的序列免受核酸酶消化。在我们看来，这些序列在启动子区可能含有起始位点 [10]。在 ATP 和 GTP 存在时，RNA 聚合酶可能在进入位点开始与 DNA 相互作用 [10]，然后漂移到起始位点，在那里因为没有四种三磷酸盐而无法合成 mRNA。研究显示，被类似 RNA 聚合酶方式保护的、来自噬菌体 fd 的序列含有在体内信息传递中起到起始核苷酸作用的序列 [3]。吕格尔 [11] 指出 T4 噬菌体 DNA 的类似位点也能作为 RNA 聚合酶的模板。但是，没有明确的证据表明每个被 RNA 聚合酶以这种方式保护的序列都含有起始位点。

Previous studies of the *in vivo* and *in vitro* transcription products of φX174[12,13] and fd[14] have suggested the existence of multiple sites for message initiation and termination. These sites, however, were not ordered with respect to the genetic map. Studies on φX174 *in vivo* translation[15] led to the conclusion that synthesis was initiated with the cistron A and D products. We have now mapped three φX174 sequences which are protected by RNA polymerase. These sequences lie within restriction fragments which span the beginnings of cistrons A, D and G (Fig. 2). However, our data do not prove that these protected sequences are in fact located at the beginnings of the cistrons.

It is interesting that sequences can be isolated from *E. coli* DNA by protection with *E. coli* RNA polymerase which will hybridize to these same restriction fragments from φX174 RF DNA (Table 2) which we have shown to contain the φX174 sequences protected by RNA polymerase. Apparently *E.* coli DNA contains some promoter regions which have start sites similar to those found in φX174 RF DNA.

Table 2. Hybridization of $^3$H-labelled *E. coli* DNA Sequences Protected by RNA Polymerase to Specific $^{32}$P-labelled Endonuclease R and Z Fragments

| Fragments on Filter | % $^3$H bound* | Fragments on filter | % $^3$H bound† |
|---|---|---|---|
| r1 | 0.58 | z1 | 1.44 |
| r2 | 1.4 | z2 | 1.15 |
| r3 | 0.47 | z3 | 1.11 |
| r4 | 1.1 | z4 | 0.45 |
| r5 | 0.54 | z5 | 0.50 |
| r6 | 1.2 | z6 | 0.56 |
| r7 | 0.028 | z7 | 0.46 |
| r8 | 0.6 | z8 | 0.58 |
| r9 | 0.58 | z9 | 0.38 |
| RFII | 6.7 | RFII | 6.7 |

* A blank filter background of 0.21% has been subtracted.

† A blank filter background of 0.18% has been subtracted. See legend to Table 1 for the procedures used.

The hybridization data in the two tables indicate a different degree of hybridization with the various restriction fragments. These are reproducible differences. This suggests that the φX174 promoter regions are not necessarily identical. It may be possible to use these techniques to divide promoter regions into several classes. The overlap between r6.3 and z3 containing an RNA-polymerase-protected sequence is less than 100 nucleotide pairs long. This overlap fragment has been isolated from φ174 RF cleaved simultaneously by endonucleases R and Z and has been shown to contain a genetic site (D*am*H81) near the beginning of cistron D (J. H. Middleton, unpublished results).

之前有关 φX174[12,13] 和 fd[14] 的体内和体外转录产物的研究提示存在多个信息起始和终止的位点。但是，这些位点并不是按照遗传图谱排列的。φX174 体内翻译的研究 [15] 得出结论，合成起始于顺反子 A 和 D 的产物。我们目前已经定位了 3 个受 RNA 聚合酶保护的 φX174 序列。这些序列位于跨越顺反子 A，D 和 G 起点的限制性片段内（图 2）。但是，我们的数据还不能证明这些受保护的序列实际就是位于这些顺反子的起点处。

有意思的是，用大肠杆菌 RNA 聚合酶进行保护也能从大肠杆菌的 DNA 中分离出相应序列，这些序列能够与已经证实的同样受 RNA 聚合酶保护的 φX174 序列的 φX174 RF DNA（表 2）限制性片段进行杂交。显然大肠杆菌 DNA 的某些启动子区含有与 φX174 RF DNA 类似的起始位点。

表 2. 受 RNA 聚合酶保护的 $^3$H 标记大肠杆菌 DNA 序列与特异 $^{32}$P 标记的核酸内切酶 R 和 Z 片段的杂交

| 滤膜上的片段 | $^3$H 结合比例 %* | 滤膜上的片段 | $^3$H 结合比例 %† |
|---|---|---|---|
| r1 | 0.58 | z1 | 1.44 |
| r2 | 1.4 | z2 | 1.15 |
| r3 | 0.47 | z3 | 1.11 |
| r4 | 1.1 | z4 | 0.45 |
| r5 | 0.54 | z5 | 0.50 |
| r6 | 1.2 | z6 | 0.56 |
| r7 | 0.028 | z7 | 0.46 |
| r8 | 0.6 | z8 | 0.58 |
| r9 | 0.58 | z9 | 0.38 |
| RFII | 6.7 | RFII | 6.7 |

* 减去了 0.21% 的空白滤膜本底。
† 减去了 0.18% 的空白滤膜本底。使用的方法见表 1 注。

两张表格中的杂交数据表明，不同的限制性片段存在不同程度的杂交。这些差异都是可重复的。这提示 φX174 的启动子区域不是完全相同的。用这些技术有可能将启动子区分成不同种类。含有受 RNA 聚合酶保护序列的 r6.3 和 z3 之间的重叠少于 100 个核苷酸对。这个重叠的片段已经从同时被核酸内切酶 R 和 Z 消化的 φX174 RF 中分离出来了，并且经证实在靠近顺反子 D 的起始处含有一个遗传位点（DamH81）（米德尔顿，未发表的结果）。

We thank June H. Middleton for stocks of endonulease R and endonuclease Z. This work was supported by US Public Health Service grants from the National Institute of Allergy and Infectious Diseases.

(*Nature New Biology*, **243**, 233–236; 1973)

**Cheng-Yien Chen, Clyde A. Hutchison, III and Marshall Hall Edgell**
Department of Bacteriology and Immunology and Curriculum in Genetics, School of Medicine, University of North Carolina, Chapel Hill, North Carolina 27514

Received December 14, 1972; revised March 7, 1973.

References:

1. Steitz, J. A., *Nature*, **224**, 957 (1969).
2. von Hippel, P. H., and McGhee, J. P., *Ann. Rev. Biochem.*, **41**, 231 (1972).
3. Okamoto, T., Sugiura, M., and Takanami, M., *Nature New Biology*, **237**, 108 (1972).
4. Heyden, B., Nüsslein, C., and Schaller, H., *Nature New Biology*, **240**, 9 (1972).
5. Edgell, M. H., Hutchison, C. A., III, and Sclair, M., *J. Virol.*, **9**, 574 (1972).
6. Middleton, J. H., Edgell, M. H., and Hutchison, C. A., III, *J. Virol.*, **10**, 42 (1972).
7. Hutchison, C. A., III, and Edgell, M. H., *J. Virol.*, **8**, 181 (1970).
8. Smith, H. O., and Wilcox, K. W., *J. Mol. Biol.*, **51**, 379 (1970).
9. Jones, O. W., and Berg, P., *J. Mol. Biol.*, **22**, 199 (1966)
10. Blattner, F. R., Dahlberg, J. E., Boetliger, J. K., Fiandt, M., and Szybalski, W., *Nature New Biology*, **237**, 232 (1972).
11. Rüger, W., *Biochim. Biophys. Acta,* **238**, 202 (1971).
12. Sedat, J. W., and Sinsheimer, R. L., *Cold Spring Harbor Symp. Quant. Biol.*, **35**, 163 (1970).
13. Hayashi, Y., and Hayashi, M., *Cold Spring Harbor Symp. Quant. Biol.*, **35**, 171 (1970).
14. Okamoto, T., Sugiura, M., and Takanami, M., *J. Mol. Biol.*, **45**, 101 (1969).
15. Benbow, R. M., Hutchison, C. A., III, Fabricant, J. D., and Sinsheimer, R. L., *J. Virol.*, **7**, 549 (1971).
16. Burgess, R. R., *J. Biochem.*, **244**, 6160 (1969).
17. Davis, R. W., and Davidson, N., *Proc. US Nat. Acad. Sci.*, **60**, 243 (1968).
18. Raskas, H. J., and Green, M., in *Methods in Virology* (edit. by Maramorosch, K., and Koprowsky, H.), **5**, 247 (1971).
19. Burgess, A. B., and Denhardt, D. T., *J. Mol. Biol.*, **44**, 377 (1969).
20. Godson, G. N., *J. Mol. Biol.*, **57**, 541 (1971).
21. Benbow, R. M., Mayol, R. F., Picchi, J. C., and Sinsheimer, R. L., *J. Virol.*, **10**, 99 (1972).
22. Hutchison, C. A., III, Middleton, J. H., and Edgell, M. H., *Biophys. J.*, **12** (abstracts), 31a (1972).

我们感谢米德尔顿供给核酸内切酶 R 和 Z。本工作得到了美国国家过敏与传染病研究所的公共卫生服务资金的资助。

（毛晨晖 翻译；曾长青 审稿）

# Tree-ring Calibration of Radiocarbon Dates and the Chronology of Ancient Egypt

R. M. Clark and C. Renfrew

## Editor's Note

Radiocarbon dating was common in archaeology and palaeoclimatology by the 1970s. But it was known that the apparent ages deduced from the activity of radioactive [14]C in the samples—which decays steadily when the organic constituents stop incorporating [14]C from the atmosphere—are not equivalent to the real ages, because the concentration of [14]C has varied over time. This led to discussion of how to calibrate radiocarbon dates. Here R. M. Clark and Colin Renfrew assess the use of the calendar system of ancient Egypt as a reference. They show that both radiocarbon dates of Egyptian artefacts and the Egyptian calendar correlate in the same way with tree-ring dates, implying consistency between the historical records and radiocarbon dates.

The historical calendar of Ancient Egypt is the only independent chronology for testing the bristlecone pine calibration of the radiocarbon time scale from 3000 to 1800 BC. Here a statistical approach is used to compare the functions relating the Egyptian historical dates to the corresponding radiocarbon dates and the bristlecone pine tree-ring dates to the corresponding radiocarbon dates, and it is concluded that the calibrated radiocarbon dates for Egypt do not differ significantly from the historical dates in the time period considered, although the errors associated with these preclude a precise comparison. The accord gives qualified support for both systems and invalidates some published objections to the use of a calibrated time scale in prehistoric archaeology.

THREE radiocarbon laboratories, at La Jolla, Philadelphia and Tucson[1-3], have obtained radiocarbon dates over the past decade for specimens of bristlecone pine already dated dendrochronologically[4], thereby allowing the "correction" of the radiocarbon scale. The calibration curve produced by Suess[5] is now widely used for this purpose. Its precise form has been questioned by some workers[6], especially the validity of the "kinks" or short-term fluctuations in the curve, and the nature of these short-term fluctuations in the atmospheric concentration of radiocarbon remains a problem[7]. In some quarters doubt has been expressed over the reality and magnitude of the first order deviation itself[8].

The historical calendar of Ancient Egypt has been used several times for checking the value of the radiocarbon method[9] although more recently the divergence between the radiocarbon dates and the historical chronology has given grounds for disquiet[10,11]. The discrepancies are reduced by applying the bristlecone pine calibration to the Egyptian

474

# 放射性碳年代的树轮校正及古埃及年表

到 20 世纪 70 年代，放射性碳定年方法在考古学和古气候学上就已经得到了普遍应用。但是，由于大气中 $^{14}C$ 浓度随时间发生变化，由样本 $^{14}C$ 放射性活度——当有机成分停止从大气中吸收 $^{14}C$ 时，样本中 $^{14}C$ 则会稳定衰变——推断出的表观年龄与样本的真实年龄不符。这导致了如何对放射性碳年代进行校正的讨论。本文中克拉克和科林·伦弗鲁评估了利用古埃及历法系统作为 $^{14}C$ 年代校正参考的有效性。结果表明埃及文物的 $^{14}C$ 年代和埃及历法均与树轮年代具有相同的相关关系，这意味着历史记录与放射性碳年代具有一致性。

---

古埃及历史历法是检验从公元前 3000 年到公元前 1800 年时间尺度上刺果松放射性碳年代校正有效性的唯一独立年表。本文利用统计方法通过埃及历史年代和相应的放射性碳年代的相关函数与刺果松树轮年代和相应的放射性碳年代之间相关函数的对比，得出如下结论：尽管相关误差妨碍精确比较，但校正后的埃及放射性碳年代在研究时段内与历史学年代没有显著差异。这种一致性在一定程度上支持了这两个校正系统，使一些已发表的反对在史前考古学中使用校正年代标尺的论断变得无效。

---

过去几十年，分别位于拉霍亚、费城和图森的三个放射性碳实验室 [1–3]，已经获得了经树木年轮断代法标记了年代的刺果松标本的放射性碳年代 [4]，因此我们得以"校正"放射性碳年代标尺。由苏斯 [5] 建立的校正曲线现在广泛用于放射性碳年代的校正。但它的精确模式受到一些研究者 [6] 的质疑，特别是曲线中的"扭结"或短尺度波动的有效性。并且这种大气中放射性碳含量短时间波动的实质仍是悬而未决的问题 [7]。在某些方面，主要是一阶方差本身的真实性和幅度方面存在质疑 [8]。

尽管最近放射性碳年代和古埃及历史年表不一致使人们利用古埃及历法校正放射性碳年代感到忧虑 [10,11]，但之前古埃及历史历法已多次用来检验放射性碳年代的结果 [9]。虽然使用刺果松校正埃及放射性碳年代减小了这种差异 [12–15]，但一些学者

radiocarbon dates[12-15], but some scholars have suggested that this now makes these Egyptian dates systematically too old instead of too recent. One worker has indeed advocated the calibration of radiocarbon dates from archaeological samples by reference to the Egyptian dates alone and without regard to the bristlecone pine[8,16].

Sufficient data are available to permit a statistical investigation of both problems, taking into account the experimental errors in the radiocarbon determinations. The time range selected covers the period from the beginning of the Egyptian historical chronology (about 3100 BC) to the first secure and astronomically verifiable Egyptian historical date (1872 BC).

## Calibration Function

Any calibration curve based on tree rings is derived ultimately from the analysis of a series of tree-ring-dated wood samples, where each sample has both a tree-ring date (generally assumed to establish a date in calendar years with a probable error of less than two or three years), and a radiocarbon date with its attendant standard error arising chiefly from counting problems. Similarly, the historical data used for any check on the dendrochronological calibration arise from a series of samples each having, as well as a radiocarbon date (with standard error), a date in calendar years assigned on the basis of its observed archaeological context and the appropriate historical calendar.

Here we investigate the proposition that the calibration relationship connecting radiocarbon dates and their corresponding "true" dates is the same in both sets of data. If this proposition is correct, it would lend support to the use of bristlecone pine radiocarbon dates to calibrate radiocarbon dates relevant to prehistoric material in general.

Our method assumes that the calibration relationship is of the form $y = f(x) + \varepsilon$ where $y$ denotes the radiocarbon date of a sample, $x$ its corresponding "true" date (as determined dendrochronologically or archaeologically), $\varepsilon$ the random measurement error in the radiocarbon date, and $f$ the unknown "calibration function". This function is approximated by fitting a suitable smoothing function $g$, using a weighted least-squares procedure. The hypothesis is then tested by standard statistical methods, essentially by comparing the goodness-of-fit of a single smoothing function $g$ fitted to the whole data, with that of two smoothing functions of the same type fitted separately to the two sets of data. If a common curve fits just as well as two separate curves, one may conclude that there is only one calibration curve for both the Egyptian and bristlecone pine data. As the choice of type of smoothing function may be crucial, this method has the important advantage of enabling several possible such functions to be easily compared.

Earlier workers have approached this problem by fitting a smoothing function $g$ to the bristlecone pine data alone, and then matching the observations from individual Egyptian samples against that curve. This can be done in two ways: (a) by comparing , for each Egyptian radiocarbon date, the corresponding calendar date(s) as calibrated against $g$ with the assigned historical date for that sample; (b) by comparing, for each Egyptian historical

认为利用这一方法使这些埃及年代系统偏老而不是年轻。一名研究者明确主张通过只参考埃及年代而不考虑刺果松来校正考古样本的放射性年代[8,16]。

有足够的数据允许我们在考虑放射性碳定年过程中的实验误差的同时，在统计学上研究以上的问题。本研究选择的时间段涵盖了从埃及历史年表的开始（约公元前3100年）到第一次确切的并通过天文学考证的埃及历史年代（公元前1872年）这一时间段。

## 校 正 函 数

任何基于树轮的校正曲线最终都是从分析一系列标明树轮年代的树木样本中得出的，每个样本都有一个树轮年代（一般假定在日历年中确定一个概差小于两年或三年的年代），和一个主要由计数问题产生标准误差的放射性碳年代。同样，用于树轮校正检验的历史数据也来自一一系列样本，这些样本除具有放射性碳年代（带标准误差）外，同时也具有基于考古学背景观察和合适的历史学年表给定的日历年代。

这里我们探讨放射性碳年代和其相应"真实"年代在两组数据中具有相同的校正关系这一命题。如果这一命题正确，那么它通常会支持使用刺果松放射性碳年代来校正与史前物质相关的放射性碳年代。

我们的方法假设校正关系式为 $y = f(x) + \varepsilon$，$y$ 代表样本的放射性碳年代，$x$ 代表其相应的"真实"年代（由树木年代学或考古学确定），$\varepsilon$ 为放射性碳年代的随机测量误差，$f$ 代表未知"校正函数"。利用加权最小二乘法拟合平滑函数 $g$ 对校正函数进行模拟。然后通过标准统计学方法验证假设，主要是通过对比符合总体数据的单一平滑函数 $g$ 的吻合度与分别符合两组不同数据的两个同类型的平滑函数的吻合度来验证。如果一条共同的曲线恰好如两条单独的曲线那样与数据拟合得很好，就可以得出，对于埃及和刺果松数据只有一条校正曲线。由于平滑函数类型的选择可能是关键，这种方法的重要优势是使几种可能的此类函数之间易于比较。

早期工作者已着手研究这个问题，他们拟合只符合刺果松数据的平滑函数 $g$，然后对比不同埃及样本的观测值与曲线值。这可以通过两种方法实现：(a) 对每个埃及放射性碳年代，将由平滑函数 $g$ 校正得到的日历年代与样本给定的历史年代进行对比；(b) 对每个埃及历史年代，比较 $g$ 预测的放射性碳年代与实际观测到的放

date, the corresponding radiocarbon date as predicted by g with the date actually observed (see Fig. 1). In both cases it must be remembered that the smoothing function g is only an estimate of the calibration function f, and therefore has its own associated standard error.

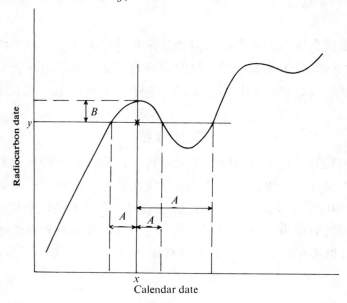

Fig. 1. Methods (a) and (b) of matching a typical Egyptian sample against a fitted calibration curve. Method (a) considers the discrepancies A between the estimated and known calendar dates; method (b) considers the discrepancy B between the observed and predicted radiocarbon date. ×, Plotted point corresponding to Egyptian sample; ——, calibration curve.

In such a procedure method (b) is preferable to (a) for two reasons. (i) It avoids the possibility of several calendar dates corresponding to a single radiocarbon date if there are "kinks" in the calibration curve (see Fig. 1). (ii) The comparison of predicted and observed radiocarbon dates is preferable to the comparison of predicted and observed calendar dates, for it is the radiocarbon dates which are subject to random errors of known magnitude. The errors associated with the tree-ring dates themselves are thought to be small[4], whereas those involved in assigning precise historical contexts of samples of Egyptian material are difficult to quantify or treat statistically.

Recent workers[12,14] using method (a) have not correctly allowed for the standard error of a calibrated radiocarbon date. Such a standard error depends not only on that of the radiocarbon date itself, but also on the nature and precision of the smoothing function near the point of calibration. An important disadvantage of Suess's calibration curve[5] is that, as it is not determined by explicit reproducible methods, its precision cannot be reliably assessed.

A crucial problem is the choice of type of smoothing function g. Among those already applied to radiocarbon determinations for samples of known age are linear functions[17], periodic functions[18], polynomials[19], and the visual fitting of a subjectively-drawn curve[5].

射性碳年代（见图 1）。在两种情况下，必须注意平滑函数 $g$ 只是对校正函数 $f$ 的一个估计，因此其本身带有相关的标准误差。

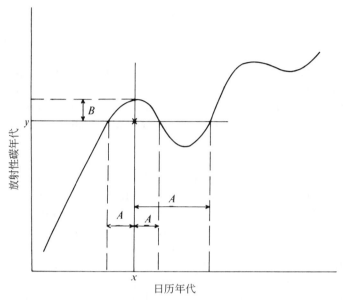

图 1. 对比一个典型埃及样本与校正曲线的方法（a）和（b）。方法（a）考虑了估测的和已知的日历年代之间的偏差 $A$；方法（b）考虑了观测的和预测的放射性碳年代间的偏差 $B$。×，对应埃及样本绘制点；——，校正曲线。

在这一过程中，方法（b）比（a）更可取，原因有：(1) 如果在曲线中存在"扭结"（见图 1），其避免了几个日历年代与单一放射性碳年代对应的可能性；(2) 预测和观察放射性碳年代之间的比较比预测和观测日历年代的比较更可取，因为放射性碳年代常受大小已知的随机误差影响。树轮年代本身相关的误差被认为很小 [4]，而涉及给定埃及样本的精确历史学背景的误差却难于确定或进行统计处理。

近来使用方法（a）的研究者 [12,14] 没有正确考虑校正后放射性碳年代的标准误差。这种标准误差不仅依赖放射性碳定年本身的标准误差，也受校正点附近平滑函数性质和精确度的影响。苏斯校正曲线 [5] 的重要不足是由于其不是通过明确的可重复的方法确定的，它的准确性不能进行可靠的评估。

一个关键问题是平滑函数 $g$ 类型的选择。用于对已知年代的样本的放射性碳年代进行校正的函数包括线性函数 [17]、周期函数 [18]、多项式 [19] 和主观绘制曲线的视

There is no universally valid criterion for preferring a particular approach, and indeed it is relevant to consider some of the general criteria which might be thought desirable in a smoothing function.

(1) It should be derived by a reproducible and non-arbitrary method.
(2) There should be an objective method of testing whether the curve is an adequate fit to the data.
(3) The fitted smoothing function should in fact be an adequate fit to the data.
(4) There should be an objective estimate of the error in the fitted smoothing function.
(5) The smoothing function need not, however, possess the same general properties (such as continuity, smoothness) as the calibration function, although they may be desirable.

The choice of smoothing function will naturally depend on the purpose of the smoothing. In the case presented here, the smoothing is intended to facilitate the comparison of the Egyptian and bristlecone pine dates. We are not claiming to have produced a universal all-purpose calibration curve relevant to this time period. The production of a suitable calibration curve for use by archaeologists is a related problem at present under investigation. The physical background may well require that the calibration function $f$ should have a bounded continuous first derivative, while the smoothing function $g$ need not necessarily be constrained to have this property. For the present purpose, a discontinuous function, such as a series of unconnected straight lines, may be statistically convenient and quite valid, even if it would not be satisfactory as a calibration curve.

## Evaluation of the Data

The data for our analysis consisted of the assigned historical dates, and the corresponding radiocarbon dates with their associated standard errors, for fifty-two Egyptian samples relevant to the time period 3100-1800 BC (calendar years), comprising fifty-one radiocarbon dates given by Berger[20] and Edwards[21], with the subsequent corrections[22] noted, and one extra sample (BM 236) found to be paired with UCLA 1208 (ref. 22). We also used the tree-ring date and radiocarbon date corresponding to each of fifty-seven specimens of bristlecone pine relevant to this time period, obtained from the list set out by Houtermans[18]. These specimens were dendrochronologically dated by the Laboratory of Tree-Ring Research, University of Arizona, and their radiocarbon dates determined by Suess at the La Jolla laboratory. Concerning the standard errors of these radiocarbon measurements, Houtermans[18] states only that they range from 4 to 7 per mil, and so we decided, in the absence of more specific information, to assign to these radiocarbon dates a common standard error of 5.5 per mil or 45.5 yr, the midpoint of the range.

In constructing a calibration curve, or comparing one proposed curve against another, the magnitude of the errors of measurement is of course important, as this determines how well a given smoothing function $g$ approximates the unknown calibration function $f$. So, before fitting any smoothing function, it is essential to verify the quoted measurement errors whenever possible.

觉拟合 [5]。这里没有倾向于某一特殊方法的统一有效的标准，事实上，这与平滑函数中被认为应具有的一些一般标准的考量有关。

（1）它应该通过可重复的并且非随机的方法得到。

（2）应有一个客观的方法检验曲线是否充分符合数据。

（3）拟合的平滑函数事实上应该充分符合数据。

（4）对符合的平滑函数中的误差应该有一个客观的评估。

（5）然而，平滑函数不需要像校正函数一样具有同样的完整性（如连续性、平滑性），虽然具有这些性质可能更好。

平滑函数的选择本质上依赖于平滑的目的。在这里出现的实例中，平滑是为了便于比较埃及年代和刺果松年代。我们并不是说已建立了与这个时期相关的统一的适用于所有用途的校正曲线。为考古学家提供合适的校正曲线是目前研究的相关问题。物理背景完全可以要求校正函数 $f$ 应该具有有界连续的一阶导数，而平滑函数 $g$ 并不一定非得要有这个性质。对目前的用途，一个不连续的函数，如一系列间断的直线，可能在统计学上相当便利和有效，即使作为校正曲线它可能并不令人满意。

## 数据的评价

我们用于分析的数据包括 52 个埃及样本的给定历史年代和相应带有标准误差的放射性碳年代，这 52 个样本与公元前 3100 年到公元前 1800 年（日历年龄）时间段有关，包含 51 个由伯杰 [20] 和爱德华兹 [21] 给出的放射性碳年代及随后标记的校正 [22]，还有一特殊样本（BM 236）发现与 UCLA 1208 一致（参考文献 22）。我们也使用了从豪特曼斯 [18] 始创的列表中，与这个时期相关的 57 个刺果松样本的树轮年代和放射性碳年代。这些样本由美国亚利桑那州大学树木年轮研究实验室进行树木年轮断代，样本的放射性碳年代是由苏斯在拉霍亚实验室测定的。关于这些放射性碳测量的标准误差，豪特曼斯 [18] 只是描述它们的范围在千分之四到千分之七，因此在缺少更具体信息的条件下，我们指定这些放射性碳年代的统一标准误差为千分之五点五或 45.5 年，也就是误差范围的中值。

在构建校正曲线，或对比两条拟定曲线时，测量误差的大小当然很重要，因为这决定了给定平滑函数 $g$ 与未知的校正函数 $f$ 的近似程度。因此，在拟定任何平滑函数前，尽可能地验证所引用数据的测量误差是必要的。

The standard error of 45.5 yr assigned to the La Jolla radiocarbon dates is at least partially verified by the estimated error variance, namely 2,263 on eleven degrees of freedom, obtained by Clark and Renfrew[17] by considering the differences[23] between replicate radiocarbon determinations carried out by the La Jolla laboratory on samples of wood from Auvernier, Switzerland. These Auvernier samples, however, were not of wood of the bristlecone pine, and so the quoted variance may not necessarily represent the precision of the La Jolla laboratory with bristlecone pine samples.

As many of the Egyptian samples were divided and analysed by both the BM and UCLA laboratories, the comparison allows the evaluation of interlaboratory variations, and hence of the published standard errors which the laboratories associate with their determinations.

Examination of the twenty-five paired differences so obtained showed that there was no systematic difference between these laboratories, but that the paired differences showed significantly greater variation than that expected due to measurement errors, the corresponding $x^2$ value being significant at the 0.2% level. This implies that either the real measurement errors are greater than believed, or that there were some gross (non-counting) errors in some of the dates, or both. The standard errors of measurement would have to be 20% to 40% greater than the quoted standard errors in order to explain the full observed discrepancy.

McKerrell[8] has also concluded that there is no evidence of a systematic difference between these laboratories, but failed to note the excessive variation in the paired differences. The inclusion of two pairs omitted by McKerrell and the use of a more sensitive test does, however, document the excessive variability in the paired differences.

Some impression may be gained of the reliability of the ascription to the samples of a historical context by the Egyptologists concerned, together with the variation in the age of the samples when buried, by comparing the measured radiocarbon dates of samples from different archaeological contexts reported as approximately contemporary. Several analyses are available from different contexts assigned archaeologically to the same period. If these archaeological assignations are correct, the differences in the radiocarbon dates for them should be no greater than would arise from the laboratory measurement errors alone. The question here is not simply the major one of the validity of the Egyptian historical calendar[11,21,24] but the more practical one of the precision with which these historical dates may be assigned, assuming for the moment their correctness, to the specific samples in question, on the basis of their stratigraphic contexts.

Ten groups of dates were considered, where all the samples within each group were supposedly of the same historical date, and their radiocarbon dates determined by the same laboratory. In three of these groups, the range of the corresponding radiocarbon dates was significantly greater than could be explained by measurement errors. Table 1 summarizes the results of the ten significance tests performed using Table 22 of Pearson and Hartley[25].

由拉霍亚放射性碳年代确定的 45.5 年的标准误差至少部分通过估计误差范围而得到了验证，也即在自由度为 11 水平上的 2,263，这是由克拉克和伦弗鲁 [17] 考虑拉霍亚实验室重复测定来自瑞士奥韦尼耶的木头样本的放射性碳年代之间的差异 [23] 获得的。然而，这些奥韦尼耶木头样本不是刺果松木，因此引用的差异不一定代表拉霍亚实验室刺果松样本的精度。

因为对许多埃及样本进行了分样，并且分别在 BM 和 UCLA 的实验室进行了分析，对比分析可以对实验室间的差异以及已发表的与实验室测定有关的标准偏差进行评价。

检查这样获得的 25 个对差异显示实验室间没有系统差异，但由于测量误差，对差异的幅度比预期的大很多，对应 $x^2$ 值在 0.2% 的水平显著。这意味实际测量误差比认为的大，或者一些年代有明显（非计数）误差，或两者都有。为解释观察到的全部差异，测量的标准误差可能比引用的标准误差大 20%~40%。

麦克雷尔 [8] 也得出没有证据表明实验室间存在系统差异的结论，但他没注意到对差异中的超大变化。但是，数据中收录的被麦克雷尔省略的两对数据和更敏感的增量测试的使用记录了对差异中的超大变化。

通过比较约同时代不同考古背景下样品的放射性碳年代，我们对一些样本的历史背景（如埃及古物学者关心的那样）归属以及样品埋藏年龄的可靠性会获得一些了解。存在几种对不同背景样品的分析结果，这些样品被认为处于考古上指定的同时代。如果这些考古学指定是正确的，那它们放射性碳年代的差异不应该比单独由实验室测量产生的误差大。这一问题不仅是埃及历史学历法有效性的主要问题 [11,21,24]，也是基于地层背景赋予所研究样品历史年代（暂且假设这些年代是正确的）的准确性这一更实际的问题。

我们考虑了十组年代，每组中所有样本据推测属于相同的历史年代，放射性碳年代也在同一实验室测定。在其中三组中，相应放射性碳年代的范围显著高于测量误差可解释的范围。表 1 总结了皮尔逊和哈特利 [25]（表 22）对十组数据进行显著性检验的结果。

Table 1. Significance of Range of Radiocarbon Dates of Supposedly Contemporaneous
Egyptian Samples

| Historical date | BM | UCLA |
|---|---|---|
| 3025 BC | * (4) | — |
| 3000 BC | — | ns (2) |
| 2950 BC | ns | — |
| 2650 BC | † (4) | ns (2) |
| 2600 BC | ns (3) | — |
| 2335 BC | ns (2) | ns (2) |
| 2000 BC | ns (5) | ‡ (4) |

—, No dates available; ns, not significant at 5% level; *, significant at 5% level; †, significant at 0.1% level; ‡, significant well beyond the 0.1% level (about 0.001%). Number in parentheses is number of samples in each group.

These results imply (i) that some of measurement errors are greater than indicated by the laboratories, or (ii) that certain groups of samples are not in fact contemporaneous (which was assumed in these tests), or (iii) there are gross errors in some of the radiocarbon dates. If the measurement errors were increased by 40%, as suggested previously, the two most significant groups would still show significantly large ranges. The observed discrepancies cannot be explained simply by increasing the standard error of measurement to the extent suggested by the interlaboratory comparison. But the four samples given an historical date of 2650 BC and the five corresponding to 2000 BC were of different materials (such as wood, linen, reed), and these samples might not be of identical age, even when they were buried.

It is concluded that some of the information concerning the fifty-two Egyptian samples is grossly in error: either some "true" dates, or some radiocarbon dates, or their associated standard errors. This has not previously been demonstrated by a systematic statistical analysis, although Michael and Ralph[26] and Säve-Söderbergh and Olsson[27] have used qualitative comparisons to draw similar conclusions, the latter pointing to uncertainties in some cases about the archaeological date. There does not seem to be any independent objective method of deciding, on the basis of existing data, which pieces of information are wrong and by how much. We suspect that in some cases difficulties in stratigraphic interpretation have led to error. Admittedly, the assigned Egyptian historical dates are not claimed to be exact, but there seems to be no objective way of quantifying their lack of precision.

These results alone show clearly that the attempt to use the Egyptian historical dates as the basis for a "calibration" of the radiocarbon chronology, quite independent of the bristlecone pine dendrochronology[16], is not well founded.

These discrepancies make the Egyptian data less suitable for a check on the bristlecone

表 1. 一系列推测为同时代的埃及样本的放射性碳年代的显著性

| 历史年代 | BM | UCLA |
|---|---|---|
| 公元前 3025 | *（4） | — |
| 公元前 3000 | — | ns（2） |
| 公元前 2950 | ns | — |
| 公元前 2650 | †（4） | ns（2） |
| 公元前 2600 | ns（3） | — |
| 公元前 2335 | ns（2） | ns（2） |
| 公元前 2000 | ns（5） | ‡（4） |

—，未获得年代；ns，在 5% 的水平上不显著；*，在 5% 的水平显著；†，在 0.1% 的水平上显著；‡，在远超过 0.1%（约 0.001%）的水平显著。括号中的数字是每组中样本的数目。

这些结果表明（1）一些测量误差大于实验室所给出的误差，或（2）某些组样本实际上不是同一时代的（这些测试中它们被认为处于同一时代），或（3）一些放射性碳年代存在严重误差。如果测试误差增加 40%，如同前面所建议的，差异最显著的两组仍显示具有显著的变化幅度。观察到的差异不能简单地用测量标准误差增加到了实验室间比较所指示的误差程度来解释。但给定历史年代为公元前 2650 的四个样本，以及对应公元前 2000 的五个样本是不同材料的样本（如木头、亚麻、芦苇），这些样本的真实年龄可能不同，甚至它们被埋藏时的年龄就不相同。

我们推断 52 个埃及样本的一些相关信息存在严重错误：或者是一些"真实"年代，或一些放射性碳年代，或它们的相关标准误差。这一点在以前没有通过系统统计学分析得到论证，尽管迈克尔和拉尔夫 [26] 以及塞韦－瑟德贝里和奥尔森 [27] 已通过定性对比得出相似的结论，后一组研究人员指出一些情况下考古学年代具有不确定性。好像没有任何独立客观的方法能基于现有数据判断其中哪些信息是错误的以及错误程度有多严重。我们怀疑在一些情况下，地层解释的困难导致了历史年代的误差。不可否认，虽然样品赋予的埃及历史年代并不完全确定是准确的，但好像没有客观方法对它们缺乏的准确性进行定量分析。

这些结果清楚地表明试图用埃及历史学年代为基础"校正"放射性碳年表，即完全独立于刺果松树木年轮断代法 [16]，不是很有依据。

这些差异使埃及年表的数据远未像期望的那样适合检验刺果松的年龄校正结果。

pine calibration than might be hoped. Both Berger[20] and McKerrell[16], however, have based comments on the calibration upon an examination of these Egyptian data, and it is important to consider such claims. In what follows analyses are therefore conducted on the provisional assumption that the assigned historical dates for the Egyptian samples are without error, and that the discrepancies observed are simply the result of high measurement errors of their radiocarbon dates. Although, as already noted, this assumption is not strictly warranted, it should not affect the conclusions unless the historical dates are very seriously in error, as the *F*-values in Table 2 are not near the critical values.

Table 2. Comparison of Goodness-of-Fit of Various Smoothing Functions Applied to Egyptian, Bristlecone Pine and the Combined Data

| Type of curve | Bristlecone pine data | | Egyptian data | | Combined data | | *F*-value | Degrees of freedom |
|---|---|---|---|---|---|---|---|---|
| | Residual s.s. | m.s.e. | Residual s.s. | m.s.e. | Residual s.s. | m.s.e. | | |
| Linear | 310,319.72 | 75.11 | 337,186.78 | 82.12 | 661,938.08 | 78.65 | 1.08 | 2,34 |
| Quadratic | 291,545.86 | 73.47 | 333,640.54 | 82.51 | 657,691.58 | 78.76 | 1.63 | 3,34 |
| Cubic | 266,432.82 | 70.90 | 333,599.58 | 83.37 | 627,952.14 | 77.33 | 1.05 | 4,34 |
| Quartic | 266,371.64 | 71.57 | 320,793.39 | 82.62 | 625,044.44 | 77.52 | 1.14 | 5,34 |
| Eighth degree polynomial | 214,232.53 | 66.80 | 298,367.62 | 83.30 | 602,018.40 | 77.58 | 1.49 | 9,34 |
| Fourteenth degree polynomial | 167,840.19 | 63.21 | 270,739.99 | 85.54 | 543,762.94 | 76.05 | 1.05 | 15,34 |
| Seven connected lines | 151,717.62 | 55.64 | 300,483.77 | 82.64 | 539,256.58 | 73.07 | 1.64 | 8,34 |

Residual s.s., weighted residual sum of squares; m.s.e., mean-square-error. *F*-value is the value of the standard *F*-statistic for testing the hypothesis of a common calibration curve of the given type. Items *a*, *b* and *c* of Table 3 are given in the first, third and fifth columns respectively.

## Statistical Analysis

The problem of testing the hypothesis of a common calibration curve for the bristlecone pine and Egyptian data can be recognized as a special case of testing a sub-hypothesis in a general linear model, for which standard statistical techniques are available[28]. In order to apply these techniques, it was necessary to assume, at least provisionally, that the calendar dates assigned to all Egyptian and bristlecone pine samples were without error, and that the errors of measurement of the radiocarbon dates were normally distributed. It was also assumed that the standard errors of all radiocarbon dates used were equal to $k$ times the corresponding reported standard errors. The factor $k$, initially unspecified but later estimated from the data, allows for possible underestimation by all three laboratories of their overall measurement error. As has been noted elsewhere[29,30], the reported standard error refers only to "counting error", which is only part of the overall measurement error. The preceding analysis of paired differences indicates that such underestimation of the real measurement errors could be substantial.

然而，伯杰[20]和麦克雷尔[16]把对校正的评价建立在埃及数据的检验上，而对这些论断进行思考是很重要的。因此，下文中的分析是基于以下临时假设进行的，即埃及样本指定的历史学年代没有错误，观察到的差异只是简单的放射性碳年代测量的高误差的结果。尽管，正如前面提到的那样，这个假设没有严格的根据，但这一假设不会对结论产生影响，除非历史学年代有严重的误差，因为表 2 中的 $F$ 值并不接近临界值。

表 2. 埃及、刺果松和综合数据的各种平滑函数的吻合度比较

| 曲线类型 | 刺果松数据 | | 埃及数据 | | 综合数据 | | $F$ 值 | 自由度 |
|---|---|---|---|---|---|---|---|---|
| | 残差 s.s. | m.s.e. | 残差 s.s. | m.s.e. | 残差 s.s. | m.s.e. | | |
| 线性 | 310,319.72 | 75.11 | 337,186.78 | 82.12 | 661,938.08 | 78.65 | 1.08 | 2,34 |
| 二次方程式 | 291,545.86 | 73.47 | 333,640.54 | 82.51 | 657,691.58 | 78.76 | 1.63 | 3,34 |
| 立方 | 266,432.82 | 70.90 | 333,599.58 | 83.37 | 627,952.14 | 77.33 | 1.05 | 4,34 |
| 四次方 | 266,371.64 | 71.57 | 320,793.39 | 82.62 | 625,044.44 | 77.52 | 1.14 | 5,34 |
| 八次多项式 | 214,232.53 | 66.80 | 298,367.62 | 83.30 | 602,018.40 | 77.58 | 1.49 | 9,34 |
| 十四次多项式 | 167,840.19 | 63.21 | 270,739.99 | 85.54 | 543,762.94 | 76.05 | 1.05 | 15,34 |
| 七段连接线 | 151,717.62 | 55.64 | 300,483.77 | 82.64 | 539,256.58 | 73.07 | 1.64 | 8,34 |

残差 s.s.，加权残差平方和；m.s.e.，平均平方误差。$F$ 值是测试给定类型具有共同校正曲线假设的标准 $F$ 统计量。表 3 的 $a$、$b$ 和 $c$ 分别在第一、第三和第五栏给出。

## 统 计 分 析

检验刺果松和埃及样本存在共同校正曲线的假设可被看作是检验一般线性模型中子假设的一个特殊实例，对线性模型可以使用标准统计技术[28]。为了利用这些统计技术，假设（至少暂时的）所有埃及和刺果松样本给定的日历年代没有错误，并且放射性碳年代的测量误差呈正态分布是必要的。同时，假设使用的所有放射性碳年代的标准误差等于对应报告标准误差的 $k$ 倍。$k$ 因子最初不确定，而后可基于数据的估计获得，$k$ 因子的列入考虑了三个实验室对总体测量误差可能存在低估。正如在其他研究中指出的那样[29,30]，报告的标准误差只是指"计数误差"，其只是真实总体测量误差的一部分。先前对差异的分析表明这种对真实测量误差低估的可能性很大。

Two types of smoothing function $g$ were fitted to the data over the range 3100-1800 BC, using the method of weighted least-squares to allow for the differing precision of the radio carbon measurements. As the weights used in this procedure depend only on the relative magnitudes of the standard errors of the radiocarbon dates, the weights can be chosen without knowing the actual value of the factor $k$. First, a single $m$th degree polynomial was chosen, giving in fact fourteen curves corresponding to the various values of $m$ up to a maximum of 14 imposed by the limits of computer accuracy. Second, $g$ was assumed to comprise seven straight lines constrained to be continuous at the six corresponding join-points (see Fig. 2). The number of line-segments was restricted to seven because of computer capacity and the location of the resulting six join-points was estimated statistically without reference to Suess's curve.

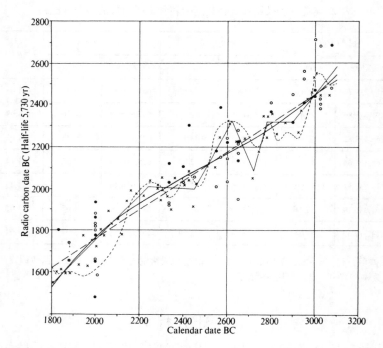

Fig. 2. Relationship between radiocarbon dates and calendar dates, showing the curve published by Suess ---, and three of the smoothing functions fitted by weighted least-squares: — —, straight line; ——, fourth-degree polynomial; ——, piecewise linear curve. Plotted points represent data used in this analysis: ×, bristlecone pine (LJ); ○, Egyptian (BM); ●, Egyptian (UCLA).

Amongst the Egyptian data, in most cases there was more than one radiocarbon date corresponding to each of the eighteen distinct historical dates. For the purposes of curve-fitting, each group of radiocarbon dates corresponding to each historical date could be replaced by a weighted mean radiocarbon date. The residual variation after fitting any smoothing function $g$ to these data can therefore be partitioned into two components. The first component involves the deviations of the weighted groups-means from the fitted function, whereas the second component represents the within-groups variation for these radiocarbon determinations of supposedly contemporary Egyptian samples. Being the

用两类平滑函数 $g$ 对公元前 3100 年到公元前 1800 年范围内的数据进行拟合，用加权最小二乘法来考虑放射性碳测量的不同精度。由于这个过程中使用的加权只依赖于放射性碳年代的标准误差的相对大小，因此可以在不知道 $k$ 因子真实值的情况下选择加权。第一，选择单一 $m$ 次多项式，实际上给出了对应于不同 $m$ 值的 14 条曲线，这也是计算机准确性所限定的最大值。第二，假设 $g$ 是由 7 条限制于 6 个对应连接点的连续直线组成的(见图 2)。由于计算机容量限制，线段的数目限制为 7，所产生的 6 个连接点的位置是在不参考苏斯曲线情况下通过统计估计得到的。

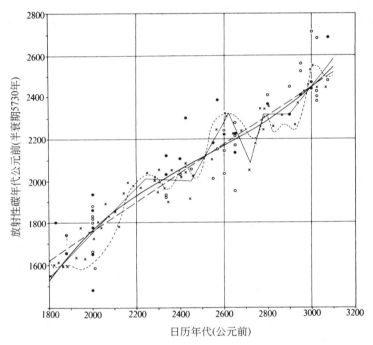

图 2. 放射性碳年代与日历年代间的关系，---- 显示苏斯发表的曲线，加权最小二乘法拟合的三个平滑函数：— —，直线；——，四次多项式；——，分段线性曲线。绘制点代表此分析所用的数据：×，刺果松 (LJ)；○，埃及 (BM)；●，埃及 (UCLA)。

在埃及数据中，多数情况下，18 个不同历史年代中的每一个都对应多个放射性碳年代。为进行曲线拟合，对应于不同历史时期的每组放射性碳年代数据可以由放射性碳年代的加权平均值来代替。在这些数据拟合任何平滑函数 $g$ 后的残差可以分为两个组分。第一组分与来自拟合函数加权组平均值的偏差有关，而第二组分代表对假定同时代的埃及样品进行放射性碳年代判定时的组内偏差。由于第二组分在所有拟合函数中相同，因此，其测量的是埃及数据的固有变化，没有任何曲线拟合可减少这一固有变化。

same for all fitted functions, this second component measures the intrinsic variability of the Egyptian data, which no amount of curve-fitting can reduce.

The corresponding analysis of variance is given in Table 3 for the case where the function $g$ is simply a straight line. The weighted least-squares procedure is exactly equivalent to transforming the data so that the transformed radiocarbon dates have a common error variance and then performing a standard least-squares analysis of the transformed data. In this particular case, the weights were chosen so that this common error variance was equal to $(45.5\ k)^2$. Item $e$ in Table 3 is an unbiased estimate of this variance, even if the fitted straight line is not an adequate fit to the data and even if our hypothesis is incorrect. It follows then that the factor $k$ must be at least 1.5 and possibly 1.8, implying that the true standard errors of the radiocarbon dates must be at least 50% and possibly 80% greater than the quoted standard errors. This reinforces the doubts expressed earlier concerning the validity of the Egyptian data.

Table 3. Analysis of Variance due to Fitting Linear Smoothing Functions

| Source of variation | Degrees of freedom | Sum of squares | Mean-square |
|---|---|---|---|
| Deviation of weighted group means from Egyptian line | 16 | 111,724.76 | 6,983 $d$ |
| Within-groups (Egyptian) | 34 | 225,462.02 | 6,631 $e$ |
| Total residuals from Egyptian line | 50 | 337,186.78 $b$ | 6,744 |
| Residuals from bristlecone pine line | 55 | 310,319.72 $a$ | 5,642 $f$ |
| Difference between lines | 2 | 14,431.58 | 7,216 $g$ |
| Residuals from common line | 107 | 661,938.08 $c$ | |
| Regression due to common line | 1 | 5,895,145.74 | |
| Total | 108 | 6,557,083.82 | |

In Table 3, comparison of items $d$ and $f$ with $e$, using the appropriate $F$-tests, shows that a straight line is in fact an adequate fit over the time range to both the Egyptian and bristlecone pine data separately. Moreover, comparison of items $g$ and $e$, yielding the low $F$-value of 1.08, indicates that a single straight line fits the combined data just as well as these two separate lines. In other words, the hypothesis of a common calibration curve (in this case, a straight line) is well supported.

Similar tables of analysis of variance may be constructed for each fitted smoothing function, simply by substituting the value of items $a$, $b$ and $c$ given in Table 2, and using the well-known structure of analysis-of-variance tables. The resulting $F$-values for testing the hypothesis of a common calibration function are listed in Table 2. In all the cases considered, this hypothesis was supported, as testified by the low $F$-values. Table 2 also gives a comparison of the goodness-of-fit of the various smoothing functions when fitted to the combined data or to either the bristlecone pine or Egyptian data separately.

平滑函数 $g$ 是简单直线所对应的方差分析见表3。最小加权二乘法过程实际上等同于数据转换，以便使转换后放射性碳数据有一个共同的误差方差，然后对转化后的数据进行标准最小二乘分析。在这个特别的例子中，选择加权使共同的误差方差等于 $(45.5 \, k)^2$。表3中的 $e$ 是对方差的无偏差估计，即使拟合的直线与数据不十分吻合以及我们的假设是错误的。由此得出的结论是 $k$ 因子必须至少为1.5，也可能是1.8，指示放射性碳年代的真实标准误差至少比引用标准误差大50%，也可能是80%。这加强了人们先前对有关埃及数据有效性的怀疑。

表 3. 拟合线性平滑函数产生的方差分析

| 方差的来源 | 自由度 | 平方和 | 均方 |
|---|---|---|---|
| 埃及线的加权组平均值差异 | 16 | 111,724.76 | 6,983 $d$ |
| 组内（埃及） | 34 | 225,462.02 | 6,631 $e$ |
| 埃及线总残差 | 50 | 337,186.78 $b$ | 6,744 |
| 刺果松线残差 | 55 | 310,319.72 $a$ | 5,642 $f$ |
| 线间差异 | 2 | 14,431.58 | 7,216 $g$ |
| 共同线残差 | 107 | 661,938.08 $c$ | |
| 共同线的回归 | 1 | 5,895,145.74 | |
| 合计 | 108 | 6,557,083.82 | |

表3中，用合适的 $F$ 检验，$d$ 和 $f$ 与 $e$ 的对比显示，事实上一条直线足以在埃及和刺果松数据的时间范围分别对其进行拟合。此外，$g$ 和 $e$ 的对比，得出低 $F$ 值1.08，表明，恰像两条单独曲线那样，单一直线可与综合数据吻合得一样好。换句话说，共同校正曲线（在这个例子中，一条直线）的假设得到了很好的支持。

利用著名的方差分析表结构，简单地通过替代表2中的 $a$、$b$ 和 $c$ 值，对每个拟合平滑函数可以建立相似的方差分析表。用于检验存在共同校正函数假设的 $F$ 值列于表2。在设想的所有情况下，如低 $F$ 值所验证的那样，这一假设得到支持。表2也比较了各种平滑函数与综合数据拟合或分别与刺果松或埃及数据拟合时的吻合度。

If the assigned historical dates of the Egyptian samples were not correct, then the various $F$-statistics would have only an approximate $F$-distribution, rather than the exact $F$-distribution assumed in the preceding significance tests. But, provided these dates are not very seriously in error, our conclusions remain the same, because the computed $F$-values are comparatively distant from the critical values. As there is no objective measure of the precision of these estimated dates, no completely objective statistical test of the hypothesis is possible, using the given data. Method (a) seems to overcome the problem by calibrating the Egyptian radiocarbon dates using a calibration curve based on bristlecone pine observations only, but there is then no objective way of comparing those calibrated dates with the assigned historical dates. Some assumption concerning the precision of these dates is thus necessary for any analysis, and our assumption facilitates the comparison of several smoothing functions. The remaining assumptions are likely to be at least approximately correct and, in any case, the analysis would be only marginally affected by small departures from them.

## Validity of the Time Scales

Detailed analysis of the Egyptian data shows that, if major experimental errors be discounted, either the standard errors associated with the radiocarbon dates have been grossly underestimated, or some of the calendar dates assigned to samples on stratigraphic evidence are seriously in error, or both. It would therefore be ill-advised to use the Egyptian data to construct a calibration curve independent of the bristlecone pine chronology, although this has been suggested by McKerrell.

These deficiencies in the Egyptian data unfortunately preclude any completely objective statistical analysis, or any exact comparison of the two time scales. We claim, however, that our analysis is the most precise comparison possible in the circumstances. A more exacting test of the comparability of the two data sets could only be obtained with better data, and in particular better Egyptian data.

Nonetheless, although the comparison is not as precise as is desirable, the available information indicates that the hypothesis of a common calibration curve for the bristlecone pine and Egyptian data over the time period 3100 to 1800 BC is not contradicted, and suggestions to the contrary are not well founded. The conjunction of the bristlecone-pine-calibrated Egyptian radiocarbon dates and the historical dates for Ancient Egypt from 3100 to 1800 BC carries with it the implication that, within the error limits discussed, both chronological systems are correct. It seems unlikely that the Egyptian historical calendar, as reconstructed by Egyptologists today, and the bristlecone pine calibration of radiocarbon dates should be in error in precisely the same way over this range, so as to yield closely comparable yet erroneous calibration functions.

Our analysis thus lends support to the general validity of both the radiocarbon calibration and the Egyptian historical chronology. Further accurate work on Egyptian material is still required to reduce the level of error and thus to make the comparison more sensitive. But the present harmony gives some grounds for optimism concerning the validity of the

如果埃及样本指定的历史年代是错误的，那么不同 $F$ 统计量将只有一个近似的 $F$ 分布，而不是先前显著性检验中假设的准确 $F$ 分布。但是，由于计算出的 $F$ 值远离临界值，如果这些年代不存在非常严重的错误，我们的结论是相同的。因为没有对这些估计年代准确性的客观估量，所以利用既定数据对这一假设进行完全的客观统计检验是不可能的。虽然通过利用只基于刺果松观测的校正曲线对埃及放射性碳年代进行了校正，方法（a）似乎克服了这一问题，但没有客观方法来实现校正年龄和给定历史年代的对比。因此，关于这些年代的准确性的一些假设对任何分析都是必要的，我们的假设有助于几个平滑函数的比较。其余的假设可能至少近似正确，不管怎样，分析只受小偏差的轻微影响。

## 时间尺度的有效性

埃及数据的详细分析显示，如果不考虑主要实验误差，要么是与放射性碳定年有关的标准误差被严重低估，要么是基于地层证据给定的一些样本的日历年代存在严重错误，或二者皆有。因此，独立于刺果松年代学，利用埃及数据构建校正曲线是不明智的，尽管麦克雷尔曾经这样建议过。

遗憾的是，埃及数据中的这些缺陷限制了任何完全的客观统计分析，或两个时间尺度的任何准确比较。然而，我们敢说，我们的分析可能是在这种情况下最准确的比较。两个数据集更准确的相似性检验只能在有更好的数据，特别是有更好的埃及数据时才能实现。

然而，虽然对比不如期望的准确，但可得到的信息表明在从公元前3100年到公元前1800年期间的刺果松和埃及数据具有共同的校正曲线的假设并没被否定，并且与此相反的观点也没有充分的理由。刺果松校正的埃及放射性碳年代和从公元前3100年到公元前1800年间的古埃及历史学年代的契合本身就意味着在讨论的误差范围内，两个年代学系统都是正确的。现代埃及考古工作者重建的埃及古日历和刺果松校正的放射性碳年代似乎不太可能恰好以相同的方式在这个时间范围内被弄错了，以致产生非常类似但错误的校正函数。

因此，我们的分析支持放射性碳校正和埃及历史年代学的一般有效性。不过仍然需要对埃及物质进行更准确的研究以减小误差水平，使比较变得更灵敏。但总的来说，在有关刺果松校正应用于史前研究的有效性方面，目前的一致性为乐观看法

bristlecone pine calibration as applied to prehistoric studies in general.

(**243**, 266-270; 1973)

**R. M. Clark\* and C. Renfrew†**
\* Department of Probability and Statistics, University of Sheffield
† Department of Archaeology, University of Southampton

Received November 24, 1972; revised February 7, 1973.

---

References:

1. Suess, H. E., *Proc. Symp. on Radioactive Dating and Methods of Low-Level Counting, Monaco, 1967*, 143 (IAEA, Vienna, 1967).

2. Damon, P. E., Long, A., and Grey, D. C., in *Radiocarbon Variations and Absolute Chronology* (edit. by Olsson, I. U.), 615 (John Wiley, New York, 1970).

3. Ralph, E. K., and Michael, H. N., in *Radiocarbon Variations and Absolute Chronology* (edit. by Olsson, I. U.), 619 (John Wiley, New York, 1970).

4. Ferguson, C. W., *Tree-Ring Bulletin*, **29**, 3 (1969).

5. Suess, H. E., in *Radiocarbon Variations and Absolute Chronology* (edit. by Olsson, I. U.), Plate I (John Wiley, New York, 1970).

6. Barker, H., *Nature*, **231**, 270 (1971).

7. Baxter, M. S., and Walton, A., *Proc. Roy. Soc. London*, A, **321**, 105 (1971).

8. Mckerrell, H., *Scottish Archaeological Forum*, **3**, 73 (1971).

9. Libby, W. F., *Radiocarbon Dating*, 10, Fig. 1 (Chicago University Press, 1949).

10. Libby, W. F., *Science*, **140**, 278 (1963).

11. Smith, H. S., *Antiquity*, **38**, 32 (1964).

12. Suess, H. E., *Zeit. f. Physik*, **202**, 1 (1967).

13. Renfrew, C., *World Archaeology*, **2**, 199 (1970).

14. Vogel, J. C., *Helinium*, **9**, 19 (1969).

15. Derricourt, R., *J. Near Eastern Studies*, **30**, 271 (1971).

16. McKerrell, H., *Proc. Prehist. Soc.*, **38**, 286 (1972).

17. Clark, R. M., and Renfrew, C., *Archaeometry*, **14**, 5 (1972).

18. Houtermans, J. C., thesis, Univ. Berne (1971).

19. Wendland, W. M., and Donley, D. L., *Earth Planet. Sci. Lett.*, **11**, 135 (1971).

20. Berger, R., *Phil. Trans. Roy. Soc.*, **A269**, 23 (1970).

21. Edwards, I. E. S., *Phil. Trans. Roy. Soc.*, **A269**, 11 (1970).

22. Barker, H., Burleigh, R., and Meeks, N., *Radiocarbon*, **11**, 281 (1969).

23. Suess, H. E., *Antiquity*, **44**, 91 (1970).

24. Hayes, W. C., Rowton, M. B., and Stubbings, F. H., *Cambridge Ancient History*, **1**, ch. 6 (1962).

25. Pearson, E. S., and Hartley, H. O., *Biometrika Tables for Statisticians* (second ed.), **1** (1958).

26. Michael, H. N., and Ralph, E. K., in *Radiocarbon Variations and Absolute Chronology* (edit. by Olsson, I. U.), 109 (Wiley, New York, 1970).

27. Säve-Söderbergh, T., and Olsson, I. U., in *Radiocarbon Variations and Absolute Chronology* (edit. by Olsson, I. U.), 35 (Wiley, New York, 1970).

28. Searle, S. R., *Linear Models* (Wiley, New York, 1971).

29. Neustupny , E., in *Radiocarbon Variations and Absolute Chronology* (edit. by Olsson, I. U.), 23 (Wiley, New York, 1970).

30. Hultin, E., *Etnologiska Studier*, **32**, 185 (1972).

提供了一些支持。

（李梅 翻译；许冰 审稿）

# Redshift of OQ 172

E. J. Wampler *et al.*

## Editor's Notes

**Quasars are among the most distant objects in the universe, which is demonstrated by the degree to which the light they emit is reddened. This paper reports the discovery of one of the more distant quasars. Quasars are now believed to be galaxies containing massive black holes which generate intense radiation by sucking in neighbouring matter. In the 1970s, however, it was still possible for people to argue that the redshift of quasars was a consequence of their great mass.**

WE report the discovery of a second QSO with a redshift greater than 3. Spectra taken at the 120-inch at Lick Observatory[1] give $z=3.53$ for OQ172. Carswell and Strittmatter[2] have found the redshift of OH471 to be $z=3.40$. Our attention was drawn to the object by the work of Gent *et al.*[3] on Molonglo radio sources. Accurate radio coordinates for OQ172 were communicated to us ahead of publication by C. Hazard and H. Gent. They are:

$$\alpha \ (1950) \ 14 \ h \ 42 \ min \ 50.48 \ s$$
$$\delta \ (1950) \ 10° \ 11' \ 12.4''$$

A finding chart for OQ172 is given by Véron[4], who notes that it is a "blue stellar object". From our inspection of the Palomar Sky Survey plates we agree with Véron's assessment of the colour of OQ172, although Gent *et al.*[3] list it as stellar, that is an object with neutral colours. Radio fluxes for OQ172 are available from ref. 5, where the spectral index is given as −0.09 between 178 and 1,400 MHz. The tabulated fluxes at 1,400, 2,695 and 5,009 MHz are 2.42, 1.96 and 1.22 f.u., respectively[5]. The radio spectrum is therefore very flat and extends to high frequencies.

Figure 1 shows a spectrum of OQ172 obtained with the Cassegrain ITS system[6] at Lick Observatory. This spectrum is a composite formed by adding data from spectra obtained on different nights. Consequently the signal-to-noise ratio in the spectrum varies as a function of wavelength. It is particularly poor in the $\lambda6000$–$\lambda6500$ region where we have only one spectrum, to the red of $\lambda7200$ Å where OH emission features increase the radiation from the night sky, and shortward of 3500 Å where the atmospheric extinction becomes troublesome. In the spectral region between 4000 Å and 6000 Å the signal-to-noise ratio is good; most of the strong features present here are real and can be seen on the several individual spectra. The two strong emission features near $\lambda5540$ and $\lambda7015$ have been identified with Ly-$\alpha$ $\lambda1216$ and CIV $\lambda1549$. The measured wavelength of the emission peaks corresponds to a redshift of 3.56 for Ly-$\alpha$ and 3.53 for CIV. The very strong absorption in the blue wing of the feature identified as Ly-$\alpha$ has probably shifted

# 类星体OQ172的红移

万普勒等

编者按

类星体是宇宙中最遥远的天体之一，这一点可以用它们所发出光的红化大小来证明。本文报道了最遥远的类星体之一的发现，尽管现在人们认为类星体是含有大质量黑洞的星系，黑洞通过吞噬周围物质而产生强烈的辐射，不过在 20 世纪 70 年代，当时的人们仍可能会认为，类星体的红移是其巨大质量的结果。

我们报道的是第二颗红移超过 3 的类星体的发现。在利克天文台用 120 英寸望远镜得到的光谱 [1] 给出 OQ172 的红移为 $z = 3.53$。卡斯韦尔和斯特里特马特 [2] 发现 OH471 的红移为 $z = 3.40$。由于金特等人 [3] 对莫隆格勒射电源的研究，我们也开始关注这个天体。在哈泽德和金特的论文发表前，他们就将精确的射电坐标告诉了我们。它们是：

$$\alpha \ (1950) \ 14 \ h \ 42 \ min \ 50.48 \ s$$
$$\delta \ (1950) \ 10° \ 11' \ 12.4''$$

韦龙 [4] 提供了 OQ172 的证认图，他注意到那是一个"蓝色的恒星状天体"。尽管金特等人 [3] 将它列为恒星，但是根据我们在帕洛玛巡天底片中查阅的结果，我们赞同韦龙对 OQ172 颜色的评估，即它是一个具有中性颜色的天体。参考文献 5 中给 出了 OQ172 的射电流量，并给出 178 MHz 和 1,400 MHz 之间的谱指数为 –0.09。1,400 MHz、2,695 MHz 和 5,009 MHz 处的流量分别为 2.42、1.96 和 1.22 流量单位 [5]，因此射电频谱非常平坦并延伸到高频段。

图 1 显示了使用利克天文台的卡塞格林 ITS 系统获得的 OQ172 的光谱 [6]。这条光谱是由不同夜晚得到的光谱数据叠加而成的，因此光谱中的信噪比是波长的函数。在 6,000~6,500 Å 光谱区，由于信噪比特别糟糕，我们只有一条光谱。在 λ7200 Å 的红端，OH 发射的辉光增加了夜空的辐射；而 3500 Å 处的短波端大气消光又成了棘手问题。在 4000 Å 到 6000 Å 之间的光谱区，信噪比很好；这里显示的大部分强谱线特征都是实际存在的，并且能在若干单独的光谱中看到。邻近 λ5540 Å 和 λ7015 Å 的两个强的发射特征已被确认为 Ly–α λ1216 和 CIV λ1549。对于 Ly–α，测量的发射线峰值波长对应 3.56 的红移，CIV 对应的红移为 3.53。被证认为 Ly–α 的蓝端线翼的极强吸收特征可能使观测波长移向真实峰位置的红端。为此，我们认为

the measured wavelength to the red of the true peak. For this reason we do not regard the slight difference in the measured redshifts of the lines as being significant. We found no other acceptable fit to the observed ratio of wavelengths that could not be rejected because of the absence of other strong lines in observed spectral regions. The presence of many strong absorption lines would also suggest a large redshift, say $z \gtrsim 2$. We therefore conclude that the emission line redshift is near 3.53. The position of several features assuming a redshift of 3.53 have been marked on Fig. 1.

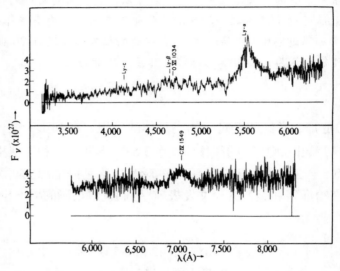

Fig. 1. Image tube scanner spectrum of OQ172. Units of $F\nu$ are erg cm$^{-2}$ s$^{-1}$ Hz$^{-1}$.

It is common for large redshift QSOs to have absorption features; OQ172 seems to have one of the richest absorption spectra known. The heavy absorption shortward of Ly-$\alpha$ increases the difficulty of identifying emission features in that spectral region. There is some indication of emission at the expected position of Ly-$\beta$ and OVI but spectra with higher resolution will be needed to reduce the line blending and establish the continuum level before any such identification can be regarded as secure. In any case, there is no doubt that the continuum radiation remains strong far to the violet of the position of the Lyman edge in the emission line redshift system, a surprising result for an object with such strong absorption features. The strongest lines near the Ly-$\alpha$ emission peak have the correct separation to be identified with the CIV $\lambda1549$ doublet at $z=2.56$, raising the possibility that the absorption line systems have a much lower redshift than the emission line system. The Lyman continuum absorption associated with these features would then begin at the extreme violet end of our data where the signal-to-noise ratio is poor. It is also possible, in a gas with little turbulent motion, to have a substantially higher optical depth in Ly-$\alpha$ than in the Lyman continuum. One could therefore have strong, narrow, Ly-$\alpha$ absorption features without having appreciable absorption in the Lyman continuum. A programme to obtain higher resolution spectra of this object is now under way and should help resolve some of these questions.

观测到的谱线红移的微小差异并不重要。由于在观测的光谱范围内缺乏其他强线，我们没有找到其他不能被排除的、与观测到的波长比符合的拟合。很多强吸收谱线的存在也暗示着高红移，比如 $z \geqslant 2$。我们由此得出结论，发射线红移大约为 3.53。图 1 中标注了假定红移为 3.53 时的一些特征谱线的位置。

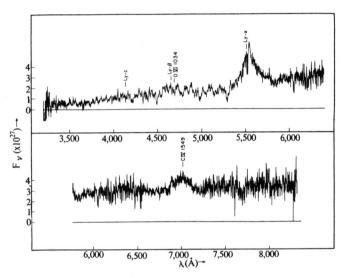

图 1. OQ172 的显像管扫描器（ITS）光谱。$Fv$ 的单位为 $erg \cdot cm^{-2} \cdot s^{-1} \cdot Hz^{-1}$。

　　高红移的类星体通常具有吸收特征；OQ172 似乎是拥有已知最丰富吸收谱的类星体之一。Ly–α 短波端的强吸收增加了在该波段识别发射特征的难度。在 Ly–β 和 OVI 的预期位置存在某些发射迹象，但是需要更高分辨率的光谱以减少谱线的重叠并确定连续谱，这样的证认才是可靠的。但无论如何，在远离发射线红移系统的莱曼吸收边紫端的连续谱辐射无疑仍然是很强的，这对于一个有如此强吸收特征的天体来说是个惊人的结果。在 Ly–α 发射附近有合理间距的最强的吸收谱线被证认为 $z = 2.56$ 的 CIV λ1549 双线。这提高了一种可能性，即吸收线系的红移比发射线系低得多。伴随这些特征的莱曼连续谱吸收始于我们所得数据的极紫端，那里的信噪比很糟糕。在几乎不存在湍流运动的气体中，Ly–α 的光深可能比莱曼连续谱大得多。因此，在没有可观测的莱曼连续谱吸收的情况下，可以观测到强而窄的 Ly–α 吸收特征峰。获得该天体更高分辨率的光谱的工作正在进行，它将有助于解决这其中的一些问题。

OQ172 is very bright. It was estimated by Véron[4] to be magnitude 17.5. Our calibrated spectra, which should be accurate to ±20%, indicate that the V magnitude of the continuum is about 17.9. The strong continuum level, extending well into the ultraviolet, is in agreement with the blue classification given to OQ172 by Véron[4]. Although it is bright at short radio wavelengths it is too faint to appear in the 4C catalogue, otherwise it satisfies all the normal criteria for classification as a QSS. Other, similar objects presumably exist and could be discovered by the proper survey techniques without requiring highly accurate radio positions.

This research has been supported, in part, with grants from the National Science Foundation, the National Aeronautics and Space Administration and NATO.

(**243**; 336-337; 1973)

E. J. Wampler*, L. B. Robinson*, J. A. Baldwin* and E. M. Burbidge†
*Lick Observatory, Board of Studies in Astronomy and Astrophysics,University of California, Santa Cruz
†Royal Greenwich Observatory, Herstmonceux Castle

Received May 14, 1973.

References:
1. Fitch, L. T., Dixon, R. S., and Kraus, J. D., *Astron. J.*, 74, 612 (1969).

2. Carswell, R. F., and Strittmatter, P. A., *Nature*, 242, 394(1973).

3. Gent, H., Crowther, J. H., Adgie, R. L., Hoskins, D. G., Murdoch, H. S., Hazard, C., and Jauncey, D. L., *Nature*, 241, 261 (1973).

4. Véron, M. P., *Astron. Astrophys.*, 11, 1 (1971).

5. Witzel, A., Véron, P., and Véron, M. P., *Astron. Astrophys.*, 11, 171 (1971).

6. Robinson, L. B., and Wampler, E. J., *Publ. Astron. Soc. Pacific*, 84, 161 (1972).

OQ172 非常明亮。按照韦龙 [4] 的估计，其亮度为 17.5 等。我们定标过的光谱可以精确到 ±20%，它显示连续谱的 V 星等大约为 17.9 等。充分延伸到紫外区域的强连续谱与韦龙将 OQ172 归类为蓝色 [4] 一致。尽管它在短波长的射电波段很亮，但它在其他波长看还是太暗了，所以没有出现在 4C 星表中，否则它会符合归类为类星射电源的全部常规判据。在不要求高精度射电位置的情况下，利用恰当的巡天技术，可能发现还存在其他类似的天体。

此项研究部分得到了国家科学基金会、美国国家航空航天局、北大西洋公约组织的资助。

（王耀杨 翻译；吴学兵 审稿）

# Depression of Freezing Point by Glycoproteins from an Antarctic Fish

R. E. Feeney and R. Hofmann

## Editor's Note

Fish living in polar waters risk having their blood and cell fluids freeze. In the late 1960s it was found that their blood contains "antifreeze" proteins that reduce the freezing point. One possibility was that these act like other solutes which suppress freezing, such as salt or sugar, simply by their physical presence and not their chemical nature—a so-called colligative property. But here Robert Feeney and R. Hofmann in Zürich, Switzerland, show that this cannot be so for antifreeze proteins from two types of Antarctic fishes. They conclude that these proteins must be exerting more specific effects, perhaps by altering the way ice crystals grow. Modern research now focuses on how antifreeze proteins' surface structure affects ice nucleation.

SCHOLANDER and colleagues[1-3] observed that the blood sera of some polar fishes contain a substance of high molecular weight which lowers the freezing point. The general properties and structures of a family of several glycoproteins with this characteristic have recently been described in Antarctic fishes[4-14]. These "antifreeze" glycoproteins (AFGP) consist of repeating units of the triglycopeptide Ala-Ala-Thr-o-disaccharide. Three active glycoproteins have been characterized; these differ only in polymer length, with molecular weights ranging from 10,500 to 21,000 g mol$^{-1}$ as determined by ultracentrifugation, light scattering, or osmotic pressure[6,11]. According to the freezing point depression, however, the apparent molecular weight is only 20 g mol$^{-1}$, a value equivalent to >500 times the depression calculated from the molecular weights.

The blood sera of two species of Antarctic fish, *Trematomus borchgrevinki* and *Dissostichus mawsoni*, freeze at approximately −2.0°C, slightly below the temperature of the ice-salt water mixture in Antarctica[5]. Approximately one-third of the depression of the freezing point is caused by the AFGP, the remainder by dialysable substances of low molecular weight[5]. We have examined the rates of development of ice crystals and possible equilibria between ice crystals and aqueous phases, using differential thermal analysis (DTA) and direct microscopic observations of freezing and melting, respectively. The AFGP was purified from *T. borchgrevinki* serum as described previously[6,10].

The DTA experiments were carried out in aluminium vessels in a Mettler vacuum thermal analyser. Controls of water or solutions of 1% chicken ovomucoid[15] (a glycoprotein containing approximately 25% carbohydrate) in water and the solutions containing 1% AFGP froze at the same temperatures and had similar freezing and melting curves. Freezing of small volumes (10 λ) of such solutions usually occurred between −15 and

# 一种南极鱼类的糖蛋白具有降低凝固点的作用

菲尼，霍夫曼

## 编者按

生活在极地海域中的鱼类有血液和细胞内液体凝固的危险。在 20 世纪 60 年代后期，人们发现它们的血液中含有一种可以降低血液凝固点的"抗冻"蛋白。有可能像盐或糖这类溶质一样，仅依靠其物理特性（即所谓的依数特性）而非化学性质来阻碍结冰。但是本文中的瑞士苏黎世的罗伯特·菲尼和霍夫曼发现的两种南极鱼类的抗冻蛋白的作用机理却并非如此。他们认为这类蛋白或许是通过改变冰晶的生长方式而发挥其独特的抗冻作用。当代的研究主要集中在抗冻蛋白的表面结构如何影响冰晶成核。

朔兰德和他的同事们[1-3]发现某些极地鱼类的血清中含有一种可以降低凝固点的大分子量物质。最近报道了南极鱼类中具有这种性质的这一家族的几种糖蛋白的结构和一般性质[4-14]。这些"抗冻"糖蛋白（AFGP）是由三糖肽丙氨酸-丙氨酸-苏氨酸-邻-二糖的重复单位组成。已经对三种活性糖蛋白做了鉴定，通过超速离心、光散射或者渗透压的方法测定出它们之间唯一的区别就是聚合长度不同，它们的分子量在 10,500 g/mol 到 21,000 g/mol 范围内[6,11]。然而根据凝固点下降的程度，其表观分子量仅为 20 g/mol，这个数值相当于比实际分子量下降了 500 多倍。

博氏肩孔南极鱼和鳞头犬牙南极鱼这两种南极鱼的血清凝固点大约为 -2.0℃，略低于南极冰盐水混合物的温度[5]。凝固点的降低，其中将近 1/3 是由抗冻糖蛋白引起的，其余的是由一些可透析的小分子量物质引起的[5]。我们已经通过示差热分析 (DTA) 以及显微镜直接观察凝固和融化状态的方法分别研究了冰晶的形成速率以及冰晶和水相之间可能存在的平衡关系。从博氏肩孔南极鱼血清中提纯的抗冻糖蛋白在先前的文章已有描述[6,10]。

示差热分析实验是在梅特勒真空热分析仪的铝管中进行的。将对照水或者含有 1% 蛋清粘蛋白[15]（一种含有大约 25% 碳水化合物的糖蛋白）的水溶液和含有 1% 抗冻糖蛋白的水溶液在相同的温度下冻结，并得到相似的冻融曲线。通常情况下，小体积（10λ）的这种溶液在 -15℃ 至 -20℃ 时发生凝固，这取决于水的纯度以及实

−20°C, depending on the purity of the water and the experimental rates of lowering the temperature. The freezing temperatures in these conditions are usually considered to be related to the rates of nucleation and not to their freezing temperatures in equilibrium with ice. These experiments did not, therefore, indicate that the AFGP functions by inhibiting nucleation, that is, by inhibiting the initial formation of points of crystallization.

Direct observations of melting and freezing in volumes of approximately 50 λ at closely controlled temperatures were made with a Zeiss Universal polarization microscope (magnification 90) equipped with a photographic camera and a television screen monitor. The microscope slides were double-celled, with a compartment on each side of a centre divider. The whole slide was cooled by a slow flow of cold nitrogen gas and the temperature was maintained by heat supplied to the centre of the slide by a heating element in the divider. The thermocouple was Pt-PtRh, positioned in the centre of the slide. The apparatus was calibrated by determining the melting and freezing temperatures of pure water. A series of eight experiments was done and each experiment had five to twenty separate melting and thawing trials. Results of a typical experiment are summarized in Table 1.

Table 1. Freezing and Melting of Water and Solution of Antifreeze Glycoproteins in Water

| Temperature adjustments | Observed changes | |
|---|---|---|
| °C phase | In water containing ice crystals | In water solution of 1% antifreeze glycoproteins containing ice crystals |
| 0.0 holding | Melt and freeze | Crystals melt |
| −0.1 lowering | Frozen | Crystals do not melt, liquid does not freeze |
| −0.7 lowering | Frozen | |
| −0.8 holding | Frozen | Crystals grow, new crystals form until all solution frozen |
| −0.7 raising | Frozen | All frozen, no melting |
| −0.1 raising | Frozen | |
| 0.0 holding | Melt and freeze | Melt |

Water and antifreeze glycoprotein solution was initially frozen at −3°C and then allowed to melt at +0.1°C until 5-10% of solution remained as ice crystals. The temperature was then adjusted to 0.0°C and periodically lowered and then raised as indicated. The times at each temperature intermediate between freezing and melting were 5-10 min. All observations were made microscopically as described in the text.

In one series of trials, solutions of egg white ovomucoid were used in the control well of the microscope slide. The AFGP and the ovomucoid were both tested as 1% solutions in water. In all trials, both the melting and freezing point of the ovomucoid solution were −0.02±0.01°C. The melting point of an AFGP frozen solution or of ice crystals in AFGP solution was −0.01°C, and the freezing point of the solution containing ice crystals was −0.80°C. In another series of trials, a solution of AFGP containing a few crystals of ice froze at −0.78°C and melted at 0.00°C. After freezing, the sample was melted at +1°C

验时温度降低的速率。一般认为这种情况下的凝固温度与成核速率有关，而与冰水均衡态的凝固温度无关。因此，这些实验并没有揭示出抗冻糖蛋白对成核的抑制作用，也就是对最初结晶点形成的抑制。

通过配备照相机和电视显示屏的蔡司全能偏光显微镜（放大倍数为 90 倍），我们可以在严格控温的条件下直接观察到大约 50 λ 的体积中的融化与凝固过程。显微镜载片是一个双室的结构，在中心分隔物的两侧分别有一个小室。整个载片是通过缓慢施加的冷氮气流进行冷却的，并通过载片分隔物上带有的加热元件对载片中心部位进行加热以维持温度。载片中心处的热电偶为 Pt–PtRh。此仪器是通过测量纯水融化温度和凝固温度来进行校准的。现在已经完成了一个系列的 8 个实验，每个实验都有 5 到 20 个独立的融化和融解试验。表 1 中总结了其中一个典型实验的结果。

表 1. 水和抗冻糖蛋白水溶液的凝固和融化

| 温度调节 ℃状态 | 观察到的变化 | |
|---|---|---|
| | 含有冰晶的水 | 含有冰晶的 1% 抗冻糖蛋白水溶液 |
| 0.0 维持 | 融化和凝固 | 晶体融化 |
| −0.1 降低 | 冻结 | 晶体不融化，液体不凝固 |
| −0.7 降低 | 冻结 | |
| −0.8 维持 | 冻结 | 晶体生长，新的晶体开始形成，直至所有液体全部冻结 |
| −0.7 升高 | 冻结 | 全部冻结，没有融化 |
| −0.1 升高 | 冻结 | |
| 0.0 维持 | 融化和凝固 | 融化 |

水和抗冻糖蛋白溶液事先在 −3℃ 冻结，然后在 +0.1℃ 下开始融化直至 5%~10% 的溶液以冰晶形式存在为止。接着将温度调整到 0.0℃ 并如表所示周期性地降低温度之后再升高。每个融化和冻结温度之间的时间间隔为 5~10 min。所有的结果都是通过文中所述的显微观察得到的。

在一系列的试验中，显微镜载片的对照室中使用的是蛋清粘蛋白溶液。检测的抗冻糖蛋白和蛋清粘蛋白都是浓度为 1% 的水溶液。在所有的试验中，蛋清粘蛋白溶液的熔点和凝固点都是 −0.02 ± 0.01℃。抗冻糖蛋白冷冻溶液或者抗冻糖蛋白溶液中冰晶的熔点为 −0.01℃，而含有冰晶的溶液的凝固点为 −0.80℃。在另外一系列试验中，含有少量冰晶的抗冻糖蛋白溶液在 −0.78℃ 凝固，在 0.00℃ 融化。在凝固后，样品在 +1℃ 时开始融化，直至仅仅剩余一点冰晶（大约 0.1% 的溶液含有晶体）。然

until only a small bundle of crystals remained (approximately 0.1% of the solution had crystals). The sample was then adjusted to −0.60°C and held at this temperature for 300 min. No growth or melting of the crystals occurred. Similar observations were made when the FPDG solutions containing ice crystals were maintained at a temperature slightly less than the melting point (−0.10°C) or slightly more than the freezing point (−0.70°C).

From our experiments we conclude that: (1) Ice formed in a solution of AFGP seems to be normal ice—that is, it melts at 0°C. (2) Freezing and melting of AFGP solutions occur at rates similar to those at which water freezes and melts when equivalent amounts of heat are applied or removed at the respective melting or freezing temperatures. Thus there was no evidence indicating a comparatively rapid development of crystals in AFGP solutions as described by Hargens[16]. (3) It is not possible to prove a mechanism involving nucleation from the DTA experiments on kinetic effects. There are, therefore, no unusual "supercooling effects" as are commonly found in solutions in which initiation of freezing is very slow in the absence of crystals. The data indicate that there is no significant kinetic effect involved in the overall freezing mechanism.

The pronounced hysteresis and absence of equilibrium between the melting and freezing of solutions of AFGP are consistent with a mechanism which is not based on colligative properties. Models for the mechanism could include those postulating effects on either the structure or growth of ice crystals or the structure of water. If a model concerning ice is correct, the mechanism would most likely involve the development of ice crystals[10,17] after nucleation. If the model concerning the structure of water is correct, the mechanism could involve either the structuring of water itself or some intermediate state. The fact that ice crystals in AFGP solutions have normal melting points lends credence to the latter model.

We thank Dr Hansa Ahrends for supervising the DTA experiments and for his advice and suggestions, the Mettler Corp. for assistance, and Dr Richard Criddle for discussions and suggestions regarding the mechanism of action. The investigation was supported by funds from the Eidgenössische Technische Hochschule. R. E. F. was on sabbatical leave from the University of California, Davis.

(**243**, 357-359; 1973)

R. E. Feeney and R. Hofmann

Laboratorium für Festkörperphysik, Eidgenössische Technische Hochschule, Zürich, Hönggerberg, CH-8049 Zürich

Received January 23, 1972.

---

References:

1. Scholander, P. F., Flagg, W., Walters, V., and Irving, L., *Physiol. Zool.*, **26**, 67 (1953).

2. Scholander, P. F., van Dam, L., Kanwisher, J. W., Hammel, H. T., and Gordon, M. S., *J. Cell Comp. Physiol.*, **49**, 5 (1957).

3. Gordon, M. S., Amdur, B. H., and Scholander, P. F., *Biol. Bull.*, **122**, 52 (1962).

后把样品溶液的温度调整到 –0.60℃，并保持在这个温度 300 min，结果没有发生新的冰晶的生长或冰晶的融化。当含有冰晶的凝固点降低糖蛋白（FPDG）溶液保持在一个略低于其熔点（–0.10℃）或者略高于其凝固点（–0.70℃）的温度时，我们发现了类似的现象。

从这些实验中我们得到如下的结论：（1）抗冻糖蛋白溶液中形成的冰晶看来是正常的冰，也就是说，其熔点为 0℃。（2）在各自的融化或凝固温度时给予或去除等量的热量，抗冻糖蛋白溶液和水的凝固及融化发生的速度相近。因此，并没有证据显示哈根斯所报道的抗冻糖蛋白溶液中结晶速度相对较快[16]。（3）通过示差热分析实验从动力学效应方面来证明冰晶的成核机制是不可能的。因此，并不存在非同寻常的"过冷效应"。"过冷效应"通常出现在没有晶体时其凝固起始的过程非常缓慢的溶液中，数据显示在整个凝固机理中并没有显著的动力学效应。

抗冻糖蛋白溶液的融化和凝固之间具有明显的滞后并且缺乏平衡，这与其发生的不依据于依数性特征的机理一致。此机理的模型应该包括那些对冰晶的结构或生长，或者对水的结构所提出的假设效应。如果关于冰的模型是正确的，那么这个机理就有可能会涉及成核后冰晶的生长过程[10,17]。如果关于水的结构的模型是正确的，那么这个机理可能会涉及水本身的结构，或者某种中间状态。抗冻糖蛋白溶液中的冰晶具有正常的熔点，基于这一事实，我们倾向于第二种模型。

我们感谢汉萨·阿伦茨博士对示差热分析实验的指导以及他提出的意见和建议，感谢梅特勒公司的协助，感谢理查德·克里德尔博士在作用机理方面所做的讨论和给出的建议。该项研究是菲尼在加州大学戴维斯分校休学术年假期间，受到苏黎世联邦理工学院的基金资助完成的。

（刘振明 翻译；黄晓航 审稿）

4. De Vries, A. L., and Wohlschlag, D. E., *Science*, **163**, 1073 (1969).

5. Komatsu, S. K., thesis, Univ. California, Davis (1969).

6. DeVries, A. L., Komatsu, S. K., and Feeney, R. E., *J. Biol. Chem.*, **245**, 2901 (1970).

7. Komatsu, S. K., DeVries, A. L., and Feeney, R. E., *J. Biol. Chem.*, **245**, 2909 (1970).

8. DeVries, A. L., Vandenheede, J., and Feeney, R. E., *J. Biol. Chem.*, **246**, 305(1971).

9. Shier, W. T., Lin, Y., and DeVries, A. L., *Biochem. Biophys. Acta*, **263**, 406 (1972).

10. Vandenheede, J. R., Ahmed, A. I., and Feeney, R. E., *J. Biol. Chem.*, **247**, 7885 (1972).

11. Feeney, R. E., Vandenheede, J., and Osuga, D. T., *Naturwissenschaften*, **59**, 22 (1972).

12. DeVries, A. L., in *Fish Physiology* (edit. by Hoar and Randall), **6**, 157 (Academic Press, New York, 1969).

13. Chuba, J. V., Kuhns, W. J., Nigrelli, R. F., Vandenheede, J., Osuga, D. T., and Feeney, R. E., *Nature*, **242**, 342 (1973).

14. DeVries, A. L., *Science*, **172**, 1152 (1971).

15. Feeney, R. E., and Allison, R. G., *Evolutionary Biochemistry of Proteins* (Wiley-Interscience, New York, 1969).

16. Hargens, A. R., *Science*, **176**, 184 (1972).

17. Scholander, P. F., and Maggert, J. E., *Cryobiology*, **8**, 371 (1971).

# Muscular Contraction and Cell Motility

H. E. Huxley

## Editor's Note

One of the early triumphs of molecular biology was the working out of the mechanism of muscular contraction. Much of the work was done by Hugh Huxley at the Medical Research Council Laboratory of Molecular Biology at Cambridge. This paper describes Huxley's views on muscular contraction (which are still regarded as essentially correct) and also his preliminary views on a mechanism by which cells are able to move themselves relative to others.

This article is based on a lecture given at the Thirteenth International Congress of Cell Biology, University of Sussex, September 3-8, 1972.

IT has become apparent during the past few years that close similarities exist in a number of instances between some of the proteins directly involved in contraction in striated muscle, and proteins present in certain non-muscle cells in which movement occurs. The question therefore arises whether all these systems share a common basic mechanism, and if so, whether the current picture of the contracting mechanism in striated muscle, which is a fairly detailed one in some respects, can cast any light on these other motile mechanisms, which are less well understood.

Here I first describe certain aspects of the muscle mechanism, especially structural ones, which seem to me particularly relevant to more general questions of motility. Next, I review a number of recent studies which demonstrate in a very decisive way that the similarities between the proteins concerned are ones that relate to the most basic properties and interactions used in the muscle mechanism. Finally, I point out that these considerations suggest a definite mechanism for certain kinds of cell motility. This general type of mechanism ("active shearing") has been suggested by others before[1-3] (though not always in very explicit terms) but it does not seem to have gained general acceptance.

According to the sliding filament model of muscle contraction striated muscles consist of overlapping arrays of actin and myosin filaments which can slide past each other when the muscle changes length. The individual filaments, and the arrays which they form because of their in-register arrangement, remain virtually constant in length. The active sliding force between the filaments is developed by cross-bridges on the thick myosin-containing filaments. These represent the biologically active ends of individual myosin molecules, which can attach to, and exert a longitudinal force on, the thin actin-containing filaments alongside. A cross-bridge is believed to act in a cyclical manner, pulling an actin filament

# 肌肉收缩与细胞运动

赫胥黎

编者按

分子生物学早期的重大成就之一是阐明了肌肉收缩的机理。其中许多工作都是由剑桥大学医学研究理事会分子生物学实验室的休·赫胥黎教授完成的。这篇论文阐述了赫胥黎有关肌肉收缩的观点（目前为止仍被认为是基本正确的），也包含了他对于细胞相对运动的一些初步的想法。

---

本文是基于我在"第十三届国际细胞生物学大会"（1972年9月3日到8日，萨塞克斯大学）上的报告完成的。

---

在过去的几年中，人们发现在许多情况下，横纹肌细胞中与收缩直接相关的蛋白质与发生运动的某些非肌细胞中的蛋白质之间存在着惊人的相似性。我们因此提出疑问，这些系统是否都有着共同的基本机制？如果是的话，目前在某些方面对于横纹肌收缩机理已经相当详尽的研究能否为那些了解相对较少的其他运动机制的研究带来一些启示呢？

在这篇文章中，我首先对肌肉机制的某些方面进行了介绍，尤其是肌肉的结构——我认为这与运动的普遍性问题特别相关。接着，我回顾了近来的很多研究，结果都非常明确地证明，人们所关注的蛋白质之间的相似性与肌肉运动机制中最基本的性质和相互作用有关。最后，我认为这些观点提示了特定种类细胞运动的明确机制。虽然这个普遍性的机制（"主动剪切"）在以前也曾被其他人提到过 [1-3]（尽管有时表述地不够明确），但似乎尚未得到广泛认可。

根据肌肉收缩的肌丝滑动模型，横纹肌由一系列互相重叠的肌动蛋白纤维（细肌丝）和肌球蛋白纤维（粗肌丝）排列组成，当肌肉长度改变时这些纤维可以发生相对滑动。不过每条纤维以及由它们有序排布形成的阵列事实上保持着恒定的长度。这种纤维间的主动滑动力来自含肌球蛋白的粗肌丝上的横桥。横桥代表了个体肌球蛋白分子的生物活性末端，它可以结合在附近的细肌丝上并且对其施加一个纵向力。横桥被认为是以循环往复的方式发挥功能的，其每次循环可以将肌动蛋白纤维向 A

511

along towards the centre of an A-band for a distance which is probably of the order of 50 to 100 Å, then releasing and reattaching to the actin filament at another point, initially further away from the centre of the A-band and going through the cycle again. A continuous movement of the actin filament is thus produced by the asynchronous action of all the cross-bridges acting upon it from the myosin filaments alongside.

The mechanism requires that the molecules of myosin and actin are assembled in their respective filaments with the appropriate structural polarity. As the cross-bridges have to move so as to draw the actin filaments towards the centre of the A-band, they must be oriented so that they pull in one direction in one half A-band and in the opposite direction in the other half. Thus all the myosin molecules must be oriented in one sense in one half of the length of each thick filament, and in the opposite sense in the other half. This is indeed found to be the case in practice[4]. Also myosin molecules are able to assemble *in vitro* into filaments with this important and characteristic reversal of polarity half way along their length. A similar requirement applies to the actin filaments. Highly specific interactions between an actin monomer and a myosin cross-bridge require that the interacting groups on the two molecules always have the appropriate mutual orientation. Thus actin filaments which interact with opposite ends of a myosin filament must contain actin monomers with opposite polarity. In practice, it is found that all the actin monomers along a given actin filament have the same polarity, and that the polarity reverses at the Z-lines. Thus the actin filaments are attached on either side of the Z-lines with opposite polarity[4].

This means that the direction of the relative force experienced by an actin filament when it interacts with appropriately oriented myosin filaments is specified by the structural polarity of the actin filament itself. Consequently, if an actin filament were attached to some other cellular structure with the same polarity as actin filaments are attached to Z-lines, then the attachment point would experience a force pulling it in the direction of the actin filament. Again, as the force exerted on an actin filament must always be in the same direction, such a filament (or group of similarity polarized filaments) might be maintained in motion over significant distances by interaction with myosin filaments[4], whose orientation could be selected and perhaps enforced by the actin. These considerations are obviously relevant to mechanisms for cell motility and will be discussed again later.

A second characteristic of the sliding filament mechanism as it appears to work in practice is that the relative force between myosin and actin is developed as the result either of an active change in the angle of attachment of the head of the myosin molecules (the $S_1$ subunit) to the actin filament (Fig. 1), or of an active change in the shape of the $S_1$ subunit, the attachment to actin remaining rigidly fixed[5]. That is, the relative sliding force appears not to be generated by changes elsewhere in the myosin molecule or filament, not, for example, by an active change in the orientation of the $S_1$ head generated at the link to the $S_2$ part of the molecule. The arguments supporting this view, which I believe are very powerful are somewhat involved, and the original papers should be consulted[4,6,7]. In essence, they derive mainly from X-ray diffraction and electron microscope evidence that

带的中心拉动约 50~100 Å 的距离，然后与肌动蛋白纤维脱离，并重新结合到距离 A 带中心更远的另一个位点上，然后重复上述循环。通过肌球蛋白纤维上的所有横桥的异步运动，便可以产生肌动蛋白纤维的连续滑动。

上述机制要求肌动蛋白与肌球蛋白分子在装配的时候以合适的结构极性形成各自的纤维。由于横桥需要通过移动把肌动蛋白纤维向 A 带中心拉动，因此横桥排布必然是具有方向性的，这样才可以使 A 带中一半的横桥向一个方向拉动，而另一半则向相反方向拉动。由此可以推断出，粗肌丝上的肌球蛋白分子肯定是一半沿着一个方向排布，另一半则沿着相反方向排布。事实的确如此 [4]。实验证明肌球蛋白分子可以在体外沿其轴方向组装成这种重要而且颇具特点的逆转极性纤维。同样的，肌动蛋白纤维也具有极性特征。肌动蛋白分子单体与肌球蛋白横桥之间高度特异性的相互作用要求这两种分子上相互作用的基团总是具有适当的极性取向。因此，如果两条肌球蛋白纤维具有方向相反的末端，那么与之相互作用的肌动蛋白纤维必然含有极性相反的肌动蛋白单体。事实上，实验表明在一条给定的肌动蛋白纤维上所有的肌动蛋白单体都具有相同的极性。不过，在 Z 线的位置，肌动蛋白纤维的极性会调转过来。因此，肌肉中肌动蛋白纤维是以相反的极性结合在 Z 线两侧的 [4]。

这就意味着当肌动蛋白纤维与适当取向的肌球蛋白纤维相互作用时，产生的相对作用力的方向是一定的，且由肌动蛋白纤维本身的结构极性所决定。因此，如同肌动蛋白纤维结合到 Z 线，当肌动蛋白纤维结合到与之相同极性的其他细胞结构时，该连接位点将会承受一个与肌动蛋白纤维极性取向相同的拉力。同样地，由于这些施加在肌动蛋白纤维上的拉力必须总是朝着同一个方向，因此这样一条纤维（或一组具有相同极性的纤维）就可以通过与肌球蛋白纤维的相互作用而持续滑动较远的距离 [4]。这种滑动的方向当然也是由肌动蛋白所选择或是强制决定的。上述这些观点与细胞运动机制显著相关并将在后文中再次讨论。

在实际研究中发现的肌丝滑动机制的第二个问题是滑动动力的来源。实验表明肌球蛋白与肌动蛋白的连接保持固定不变，两者间的相对滑动力来源于肌球蛋白分子头部（$S_1$ 亚基）与肌动蛋白纤维结合角度的主动变化（图 1），或者来源于 $S_1$ 亚基形状的主动变化 [5]。也就是说，相对滑动力不是通过肌球蛋白分子本身或肌球蛋白纤维上其他部位的改变而产生的，例如，不是通过改变 $S_1$ 与 $S_2$ 的连接处使 $S_1$ 头部取向产生主动变化。我认为一些支持上述观点的论据很有说服力，在此处或多或少会提到，具体内容可参考它们的原始文献 [4,6,7]。其实，这些结论主要来源于 X 射线衍射和电子显微镜观察到的结果，即肌球蛋白分子的头部与粗肌丝主链结合的部

the attachment of the heads of the myosin molecules to the backbone of the thick filament is very flexible, whereas their attachment to the actin filaments (in the rigor configuration) is a very rigid one.

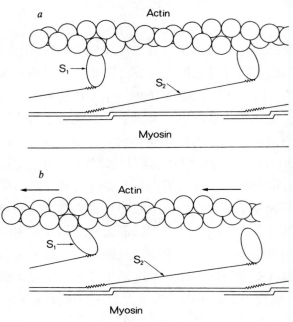

Fig. 1. Active change in angle of attachment of cross-bridges ($S_1$ subunits) to actin filaments could produce relative sliding movement between filaments maintained at constant lateral separation (for small changes in muscle length) by long range force balance. Bridges can act asynchronously as subunit and helical periodicities differ in the actin and myosin filaments. Only one of the two $S_1$ subunits in each myosin molecule is shown. a, Left hand bridge has just attached; other bridge is already partly tilted. b, Left hand bridge has just come to the end of its working stroke; other bridge has already detached, and will probably not be able to attach to this actin filament again until further sliding brings helically arranged sites on actin into favourable orientation.

If this picture is correct, it follows that the basic contractile mechanism is represented by the interacting complex of thin filament and attached myosin head, and that the exact mode of assembly of myosin molecules into filaments, provided their appropriate polarity is maintained, may be capable of some variation. Even amongst striated muscles, variations are observed in non-vertebrate species, and it is perfectly possible that myosin may be organized in quite different forms in other situations whilst the same myosin head-actin filament interaction is still maintained.

A third feature of the sliding filament mechanism in striated muscle is concerned with the exact mode of attachment of the myosin head to the actin filaments. At present, no means are available to arrest the working stroke of the cross-bridge, or to prevent subsequent dissociation in the presence of ATP. In the absence of ATP, however, the myosin cross-bridges remain attached to the actin filament and the muscle is then in rigor. In an *in vitro* system, actin filaments can be "decorated" in the absence of ATP, by the

位具有很好的柔性，而其与肌动蛋白纤维结合的部分（在精确的构型中）则是一个刚性结构。

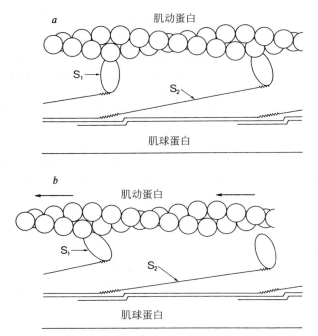

图 1. 横桥（$S_1$ 亚基）与肌动蛋白纤维结合角度的主动变化使肌丝间（在肌肉长度发生微小变化的情况下，长程力的平衡使肌丝间保持恒定的间隔）发生相对滑动。由于肌动蛋白纤维与肌球蛋白纤维的亚基及螺旋周期不同，横桥可以异步方式发挥作用。图中只显示了每个肌球蛋白中两个 $S_1$ 亚单位中的一个。($a$) 左边的横桥处于刚与肌动蛋白结合的状态；另一个横桥则已经处于部分倾斜的状态。($b$) 左边的横桥已经接近其摆动过程的末尾；另一个横桥则处于刚从肌动蛋白纤维上解离的状态，并且如果没有进一步的滑动使肌动蛋白上螺旋型排列的位点呈现一个适当的取向，那么这个横桥可能就不会再与该肌动蛋白纤维结合了。

如果这幅图所描述的机制是正确的话，那么由此我们可以得出肌肉收缩的基本原理就是通过细肌丝与结合在它上面的肌球蛋白头部形成具有相互作用的复合物来实现的。同样的，我们还可以得出，如果要维持纤维适当的极性，肌球蛋白分子组装成肌丝纤维的精确模型可能存在某些可变之处。即使都是横纹肌，不同的无脊椎动物物种之间肌球蛋白的组装模式也有所不同，并且很有可能在某些情况下，肌球蛋白可通过一种完全不同的形式组装而仍保持原有的肌球蛋白头部–肌动蛋白的相互作用。

横纹肌肌丝滑动模型的第三个特点是肌球蛋白头部与肌动蛋白纤维之间精确的结合方式。目前，还没有一种办法可以捕捉到横桥的摆动过程，也不能在 ATP 存在的情况下阻止随后横桥与细肌丝的解离。然而，当没有 ATP 存在时，肌球蛋白的横桥会保持与肌动蛋白纤维结合的状态，之后肌肉会处于僵直状态。在一个体外实验系统中，在没有 ATP 的情况下，肌动蛋白纤维可以被肌球蛋白分子、重酶解肌球蛋

attachment of molecules of myosin or of heavy meromyosin (HMM) or of subfragment 1 (S[1]). Suggestion of an "angled" configuration of the attached myosin heads was given by the visual appearance of "arrowheads" on decorated thin filaments, but the first good evidence was provided by electron microscope studies of thin sections of glycerinated insect flight muscle, and of the X-ray diagrams given by it in rigor and in the relaxed state[8]. More detailed studies of the negatively stained decorated filaments by the three-dimensional image reconstruction technique[9] have shown that not only are the myosin S[1] subunits (which appear as somewhat elongated structure of dimensions very approximately 150 Å×40 Å×30 Å) tilted at an angle of about 45° to the long axis of the actin filaments, but they are slewed round in a characteristic way, that is rotated by about 45° in a plane parallel to the axis of the actin filament and perpendicular to the plane in which they are tilting. It is this combination of tilting and slewing, together with the distinctive shape of the myosin heads, which gives rise to the very characteristic "arrowhead" appearance (Fig. 2), which would not arise from a straightforward "tilted" attachment. We do not at present know the functional significance of this peculiar feature of the attachment (the tilt itself is, of course, what we should expect to find at the end of the working stroke if the initial attachment was perpendicular, and is in the right direction); but it is diagnostic of a very specific structural interaction and of a very specific shape of the attached molecule. It has been found in many cases, as I will describe, that proteins which may be involved in non-muscular motility can form complexes of virtually identical structure.

A final feature of the contraction mechanism in striated muscle is concerned with regulation of activity, that is with switching contractile activity on and off. This is effected by preventing the attachment of the myosin heads to actin in a relaxed muscle, and allowing it to take place when the muscle is activated. Attachment to actin is a necessary part of the biochemical cycle in which ATP is split and force developed by the actin-myosin system. In its absence, ATP splitting, by the myosin alone, takes place very slowly and no tension is developed by the sliding filament system. Indeed, the filaments will slide past each other passively under the action of relatively small external forces.

白（HMM）或亚片段 1（S₁）的结合所"修饰"。修饰后的肌动蛋白纤维呈现出"箭头"的形状，表明肌球蛋白头部是以一定角度结合的。首次证明这个结论的有力证据来自对甘油处理过的昆虫飞行肌超薄切片的电子显微镜研究，以及飞行肌紧张和放松状态时的 X 射线照片 [8]。更细致的研究来自于利用三维图像重构技术对修饰后的肌动蛋白纤维负染样品的观察 [9]。其结果显示，肌球蛋白 S₁ 亚基（看起来是一个细长的结构，三维尺寸约为 150 Å × 40 Å × 30 Å）一方面以与肌动蛋白纤维纵轴方向呈 45 度的角度与其结合，另一方面又以一种特殊的方式缠绕，即其在平行于肌动蛋白横轴的平面内，垂直于倾斜面旋转 45 度角。正是这种倾斜加缠绕式的排列，加之肌球蛋白头部独特的形状，使得整个复合物呈非常独特的"箭头"外观（图 2），这种外观不可能由直接的倾斜连接所导致。目前我们尚不清楚这种奇特的结合方式在功能上的意义（当然，如果肌球蛋白与肌动蛋白开始结合的状态是垂直的，并且其方向也是正确的，那么这种在摆动过程结束时产生的倾斜状态很可能是我们所期望的），不过此类结合方式可以用来鉴定特定的结构相互作用和结合分子的特定形状。正如我将要描述的那样，许多例子表明，和非肌细胞的运动有关的蛋白质也可以形成与上述结构几乎完全相同的复合物。

横纹肌收缩机制的最后一个特点与其活性的调节有关，即收缩活性开启与关闭的切换。这是通过阻止肌球蛋白的头部与肌动蛋白结合从而使肌肉处于放松状态，以及通过允许两者结合从而使肌肉处于兴奋状态来实现。肌球蛋白与肌动蛋白结合是生化循环的一个必要步骤，在这个循环里，ATP 水解，肌动蛋白 – 肌球蛋白系统相互作用产生动力。在肌动蛋白不存在，仅肌球蛋白存在的条件下，ATP 的水解过程变得非常缓慢，不可能通过肌丝滑动系统产生张力。实际上，在较小的外力作用下，这些纤维之间也会被动地发生相对滑动。

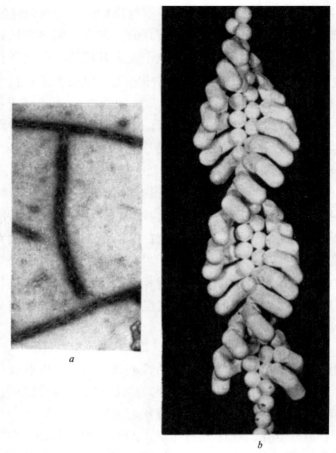

Fig. 2. *a*. Electron micrograph of negatively stained preparation of actin filaments "decorated" with myosin subfragment 1, showing well developed "arrowhead" formations (×138,600). *b*, Simplified model of "decorated" actin filament, based on 3-D reconstruction results; the $S_1$ subunits are attached to the central core of helically arranged actin subunits in a characteristically tilted and slewed configuration, and it is this that leads to the appearance of arrowheads.

In a relaxed muscle, the concentration of free calcium is kept at a very low value (probably less than $10^{-7}$ to $10^{-8}$ M) by the action of the calcium pump in the sarcoplasmic reticulum. Upon activation, calcium is released so that the level of free calcium rises (probably to $10^{-6}$ to $10^{-5}$ M) and attachment of myosin to actin can take place. In vertebrate striated muscle, this change is effected by the tropomyosin-troponin system in the actin-containing filaments[10], which prevents attachment of myosin in the absence of free calcium, but allows it to take place in its presence, possibly by a steric blocking mechanism dependent on changes in position of tropomyosin. In molluscan muscles, however (including the striated muscle of *Pecten*), regulation is effected by changes in the myosin molecules to which calcium ions become bound upon activation[11]. The distribution of these two types of regulation, or combinations of them, between species is a subject of very active current research[12]. Nevertheless, all systems so far investigated share the common feature that they are operated by changes in the concentration of free calcium ions over the critical range of $10^{-7}$ to $10^{-5}$ M.

518

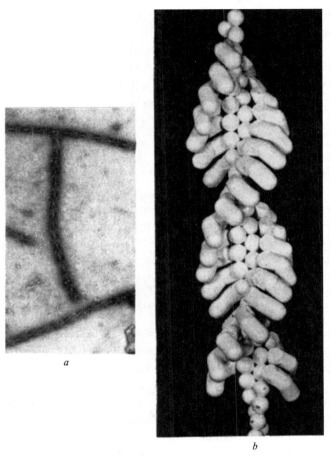

图 2.（$a$）经负染处理的肌动蛋白纤维被肌球蛋白$S_1$亚基"修饰"后的电子显微照片。图中可以非常清楚地观察到"箭头"形状（放大138,600倍）。（$b$）根据三维图像重构结果制作的被"修饰"肌动蛋白纤维的简化模型。肌动蛋白分子呈螺旋状排列，$S_1$亚基以一种特别的倾斜加缠绕的方式与其中心核结合。这种独特的结合方式导致了"箭头"形状的形成。

在松弛的肌肉中，由于肌质网中钙泵的作用，游离钙离子的浓度保持在一个非常低的水平（可能低于 $10^{-7}\sim10^{-8}$ M）。一旦被激活，钙离子从肌质网中释放，胞内游离钙离子的浓度升高（可能升至 $10^{-6}\sim10^{-5}$ M），此时肌球蛋白可以与肌动蛋白结合。在脊椎动物的横纹肌中，这种变化由肌动蛋白纤维中的原肌球蛋白 – 肌钙蛋白系统产生 [10]。当没有游离钙离子时，肌球蛋白与肌动蛋白的结合被抑制；而当游离钙离子存在时，可能由于原肌球蛋白的位置发生变化，引起空间位阻的改变，从而允许肌球蛋白与肌动蛋白结合。然而在软体动物的肌肉中（包括螺类的横纹肌），钙离子的调节功能是通过激活后直接与肌球蛋白结合令其发生变化来实现的 [11]。关于不同物种中这两种调节方式的分工或者协同的问题是当前非常活跃的研究领域之一 [12]。然而，在目前已经研究过的物种中，所有的系统都具有一个共同特点，即游离钙离子浓度变化的临界范围是 $10^{-5}\sim10^{-7}$ M。

If one is primarily interested in the molecular mechanism of contraction, then striated muscle is the best system to work with, because of its high degree of order, because of the high concentration and relatively large amounts of the contractile proteins in it, and because of its great robustness and stability, which allow it to be manipulated with ease and fixed for electron microscope examination in a state close to its native one by relatively crude techniques. We must now consider, however, whether the same basic mechanism appears anywhere else in nature, even, in the first instance, in as closely related a system as smooth muscle.

There is no difficulty here with the kind of smooth muscles found, for example, in the adductor and retractors of bivalves; these have been shown to contain abundant thick and thin filaments[13], and the reason that striations are absent is the simple one, suggested by Jean Hanson and myself[14], that the filaments are not arranged in register. It is vertebrate smooth muscle which has until recently presented much more difficulty, as for many years only thin filaments could be seen by electron microscopy and only actin reflexions picked up by X-ray diffraction, in spite of the fact that both actin and myosin were obviously present from biochemical observations.

In the past few years, however, several groups of workers have shown that the form of the myosin component in vertebrate smooth muscles is very dependent on the physical and chemical environment of the muscle; and Lowy et al.[15,16] have found that with appropriate conditions before and during fixation, prominent and plentiful ribbon shaped structures can be seen amongst the actin filaments. They have also shown that there is good X-ray evidence for this form of myosin aggregate in comparable specimens before fixation. Some workers believe that cylindrical filaments represent the more natural form of the myosin assembly in smooth muscle, but I think everyone now agrees that myosin is present in smooth muscle in the form of large aggregates and that this probably represents its form when involved in contraction.

The actin component and the regulatory protein system appear to be virtually the same as in vertebrate striated muscle, and the main difference detectable in the purified proteins from smooth muscle lies in the solubility properties of the myosin, that is, its inability to form aggregates with itself at physiological ionic strength except in special conditions. We do not know the functional significance of this, but it is undoubtedly responsible for the difficulties which have occurred in detecting the myosin component by X-ray diffraction and electron microscopy. However, I do not think that there are any serious doubts now that contraction takes place in smooth muscle by the same basic molecular mechanism as in striated muscle and by an essentially similar sliding filament process, although the overall structural organization may be somewhat different.

## Non-muscular Systems

Before I consider how some of the other motile systems might function mechanically, it will be helpful to review briefly some of the more recent findings on their protein

对于主要对收缩的分子机制感兴趣的人们来说，横纹肌是最理想的研究系统。因为它具有高度有序的结构、含有浓度高且相对大量的与收缩系统有关的蛋白质以及高度的稳健性和稳定性，便于人们对它进行各种操作，可以通过相对粗糙的技术固定并保持其接近天然的状态以用于电子显微镜的观察。然而，现在我们必须要考虑横纹肌的这种基本机制是否同样出现在自然界中的其他系统，与横纹肌紧密相关的平滑肌是我们要考察的第一个系统。

我们很容易便可以找出一些平滑肌的例子，比如双壳类动物的内收肌和牵缩肌。这些肌肉中也含有丰富的粗肌丝和细肌丝[13]，却没有横纹。在琼·汉森和我[14]看来，缺乏横纹的原因很简单，主要由于这些肌丝没有像在横纹肌中那样高度有序地排列。最近的研究表明，研究脊椎动物平滑肌的难度大得多。多年来，虽然生化实验的结果表明其中显然同时含有肌动蛋白和肌球蛋白，但是人们通过电子显微镜只能观察到其中的细肌丝，通过 X 射线衍射实验也只能检测到肌动蛋白的反射信号。

然而，最近几年，多个研究组的研究结果表明，脊椎动物平滑肌中的肌球蛋白的存在形式高度依赖于肌肉所处的物理和化学环境。洛伊等人[15,16]发现在固定前和固定过程中保持适当的条件，便可以观察到肌动蛋白纤维中分布着大量明显的带状结构。通过 X 射线衍射实验，他们证明了这种固定后所观察到的肌球蛋白的聚集方式与固定前的样品是一致的。过去一些研究人员认为圆柱形纤维更接近于平滑肌中肌球蛋白组装的天然形式，但是我想现在每个人都会认同平滑肌中肌球蛋白以大的聚集体的形式存在的观点。并且，这种大的聚集体可能代表着肌球蛋白参与平滑肌收缩时的状态。

平滑肌中的肌动蛋白组分以及调节蛋白系统几乎与脊椎动物横纹肌中是一样的，其主要不同是可监测到从平滑肌中纯化出的肌球蛋白的溶解度的改变，即在生理离子强度下，肌球蛋白不能自发形成聚集体，只有在特殊条件下才能自发形成。我们不知道这种性质在功能方面的意义，但是毫无疑问，肌球蛋白的这种性质使得人们很难用 X 射线衍射和电子显微镜的方法对其进行观察。虽然平滑肌与横纹肌的总体结构的组织方式有些许不同，但是我认为目前没有任何可靠的理由去怀疑，在平滑肌中发生的收缩与在横纹肌中发生的收缩具有相同的基本分子机制并经过了相似的肌丝滑动过程。

## 非 肌 系 统

在考虑其他的运动体系可能的作用机理之前，很有必要首先简单回顾一下最近对这些体系的蛋白质组分的研究结果。这样做的目的并非评判许多先行者的研究，

components. This account cannot do justice to many of the pioneers, but very often technical advances have now made it possible to characterize these proteins much more fully and relate them to the proteins from muscle in a decisive way; and this latter evidence is easier to summarize in a short article.

First, consider the amoeba *Acanthamoeba castellanii*, which has the capacity for typical amoeboid movement. Weihing and Korn[17-19] have extracted an actin-like protein from this organism, which is virtually identical to muscle actin in every respect that can be investigated. It forms the same double helical filaments when examined by negative staining in the electron microscope, and these give exactly the same arrowhead structures when combined with muscle myosin, showing that the myosin-binding sites are oriented in a closely similar way[20]. The amoeba actin can activate the ATPase activity of muscle myosin, possibly to a lesser extent than muscle actin can, and this can be regulated by the tropomyosin-troponin system of rabbit muscle[21]. When the molecule is cleaved by cyanogen bromide, three large peptides can be isolated which are almost identical in amino acid composition to the three corresponding cyanogen bromide peptides from muscle actin[19]. As in muscle actin, one of these peptides contains the rare amino acid 3-methylhistidine. Additionally, amoeba actin contains one residue of ε-N-dimethyllysine and small amounts of ε-n-monomethyllysine.

Next consider the slime mould *Physarum polycephalum*, which shows very active cytoplasmic streaming. It has been shown by Hatano *et al.*[22-24] that an actin-like protein can be extracted from this organism, which shows the same double helical structure as muscle actin in the electron microscope. As in muscle actin, the monomeric form has one mol of bound ATP which is dephosphorylated to ADP when the actin polymerizes in the presence of salts. Adelman and Taylor[25] have shown that slime mould actin can activate the ATPase activity of muscle myosin, and Nachmias *et al.*[26] have shown that the actin can combine with rabbit muscle myosin subfragment 1 to give arrowheads very closely similar to those characteristic of muscle actin. Again, this shows a very specific structural relationship in the complex.

Next consider blood platelets, which undergo a kind of contraction during clot retraction. Several groups of workers[27-30] have shown that the protein known as thrombosthenin A is closely similar to muscle actin in its structure, in its ability to form arrowhead complexes with muscle myosin (usually HMM), in its ability to activate muscle myosin ATPase, in its ability to allow its activating activity to be regulated by the tropomyosin-troponin system, and in its content of 3-methylhistidine.

Again, consider nerve cells actively growing and extending in tissue culture. Fine and Bray[31] have shown that no less than 20% of all the "soluble" protein in developing chick neurones behaves like actin on an SDS gel. This protein forms the characteristic arrowheads with HMM and shows remarkable chemical similarity to muscle actin on two-dimensional electrophoresis diagrams; of fourteen methionine labelled peptides, ten coincided with ones from muscle actin, showing close homology though not necessarily

而是因为技术的进步使得我们现在可以对这些蛋白质的特征有更清楚的认识，并且以一种更明确的方式将它们与肌肉系统中的蛋白质联系起来，而且后者的证据更易于在短的文章中进行总结。

首先来了解一下可以进行典型的阿米巴运动的变形虫卡氏棘阿米巴。魏和科恩 [17-19] 从这种生物中分离出了一种肌动蛋白样的蛋白质，并发现其与肌肉中的肌动蛋白在研究过的各个方面都几乎完全相同。利用电子显微镜观察负染后的样品可以看到其形成了同样的双螺旋纤维，并且当其与肌肉肌球蛋白结合后也可以形成与肌肉系统完全相同的"箭头"形状，表明该肌动蛋白上肌球蛋白结合位点的结合方式也与肌肉中高度相似 [20]。阿米巴肌动蛋白还可以激活肌肉肌球蛋白的 ATP 酶的活性（效果比肌肉肌动蛋白稍弱），这个过程同样可以被兔肌肉中的原肌球蛋白 – 肌钙蛋白系统所调节 [21]。阿米巴肌动蛋白可以被溴化氰切割成三个大的肽段，它们与使用同样方法切割肌肉肌动蛋白所得到的多肽在氨基酸组成上几乎完全一致 [19]。就像肌肉肌动蛋白一样，其中一条多肽含有稀有氨基酸残基 3– 甲基组氨酸。此外，阿米巴肌动蛋白中还含有一个 $\epsilon$–$N$– 二甲基赖氨酸残基和少量 $\epsilon$–$N$– 单甲基赖氨酸。

接下来我们来了解一下黏菌中的多头绒泡菌，它具有非常活跃的胞质环流。波多野等人 [22-24] 证明可以从这种生物中分离出一种肌动蛋白样的蛋白质，使用电子显微镜也可以观察到其具有与肌肉肌动蛋白相同的双螺旋结构。与肌肉肌动蛋白一样，这种蛋白质的单体上结合一摩尔的 ATP 分子，并且在一定盐浓度下单体发生多聚化，ATP 便会脱去磷酸水解为 ADP。阿德尔曼和泰勒 [25] 证明了这种黏菌肌动蛋白同样可以激活肌肉肌球蛋白的 ATP 酶活性，而纳赫米尔斯等人 [26] 则证明这种肌动蛋白可以与兔肌球蛋白 S1 亚基结合并形成"箭头"结构，这与肌肉中肌动蛋白的特征非常相似。这些结果再一次表明这些运动相关的蛋白质复合物具有高度特异的结构相关性。

接下来我们再了解一下可以在血液凝结过程中收缩的血小板。多个研究小组 [27-30] 的结果表明血栓收缩蛋白 A 与肌肉中的肌动蛋白在结构上具有很高的相似性——其可以与肌肉肌球蛋白（一般为重酶解肌球蛋白）形成"箭头"状复合物，也可以激活肌肉肌球蛋白 ATP 酶的活性，并且这种活性可以被原肌球蛋白 – 肌钙蛋白系统所调节，此外血栓收缩蛋白 A 也含有 3– 甲基组氨酸。

我们再来看看在组织培养液中活跃生长并向外延伸的神经细胞。法恩和布雷 [31] 证明在正在发育的鸡神经元中，至少有 20% 的"可溶性"蛋白质在 SDS –聚丙烯酰胺凝胶中的电泳行为与肌动蛋白很相似。这种蛋白质可以与重酶解肌球蛋白结合形成典型的"箭头"结构，并且在双向电泳图谱中显示出与肌肉肌动蛋白具有非常高的化学相似性——在十四个甲硫氨酸标记的肽链中有十个与肌肉肌动蛋白一致，显

complete identity.

Further examples could be given, but I think cases mentioned are sufficient to show decisively that in a number of widely different cells exhibiting different forms of motile activity, a protein closely similar to muscle actin by rather strict criteria is present in significant amounts. And in many cases, the protein can be identified in the cell *in situ*, as bundles of filaments of the appropriate diameter, which can be "decorated" by HMM, and which are in a position where they might be associated with movement[32-34].

In addition to non-muscle actins, myosin-like proteins have also been found in many of these same cells possessing motile activity, and in several instances the protein in question has been identified by rather strict criteria.

In the slime mould *Physarum polycephalum*, Hatano *et al.*[35-37] have isolated a protein which has similar ATPase and actin-combining activities to muscle myosin, the same very characteristic form (being a long rod-shaped molecule with a globular region at one end), and a similar sedimentation constant to muscle myosin (~6.05). Interestingly, the protein differs from striated muscle myosin in being soluble at physiological ionic strength. Adelman and Taylor[25] showed that its molecular weight was close to that of muscle myosin, about 460,000. Nachmias[38,39] showed that the slime mould myosin would attach in the characteristic arrowhead configuration both to slime mould actin and to muscle actin, and also[40] that in the presence of millimolar concentrations of calcium the myosin would assemble itself into rather short but essentially similar bipolar filamentous aggregates like those of muscle myosin.

In the case of blood platelets, Bettex-Gallard *et al.*[41] and Booyse *et al.*[42] have shown that the other component of thrombosthenin is a myosin-like protein, having calcium and magnesium-activated ATPase activity and a molecular weight of approximately 540,000. Adelstein *et al.*[28] have shown that this molecule contains large polypeptide chains of chain weight 200,000, just like muscle myosin, and chains of 16 to 18,000 molecular weight, analogous to the light chains of muscle myosin. The platelet myosin will form excellent arrowhead structures with actin, and will also assemble itself into the characteristic bipolar aggregates at low ionic strength.

In the case of the amoeba *Acanthamoeba*, however, Pollard and Korn[43] have found that, although a myosin like component can be identified in the sense of having ATPase activity and actin-binding ability, this protein is rather different from muscle myosin in other respects, having a much lower molecular weight (~200,000) and lacking the ability to form filaments. This particular species of amoeba may, of course, be a special case, and it should be remembered that myosin-like filaments have been seen in other amoeba (for example, in *Chaos chaos*[44,45] and in *Proteus*[46,47]).

Thus there are a number of instances where it has been demonstrated quite decisively that cells showing various forms of motility contain proteins which behave in many

示其与肌动蛋白具有很高的同源性，不过完全的一致性是不必要的。

类似的例子还可以举出很多，不过我想上面提到的这些例子已经有力地证明了在各种具有不同运动能力的细胞中，都在严格标准下存在相当数量的与肌肉肌动蛋白高度相似的蛋白质。在许多例子中，人们发现这种蛋白质能在细胞中被原位鉴定出，它们是具有适当直径的束状纤维，可以被重酶解肌球蛋白"修饰"，且这些蛋白质通常可能分布在与运动相关的位置 [32-34]。

除了肌动蛋白，在许多具有运动能力的非肌细胞中还发现了肌球蛋白样的蛋白质，并且在一些例子中，研究人员是按照相当严格的标准进行鉴定的。

波多野等人 [35-37] 从多头绒泡菌（一种黏菌）中分离出了一种蛋白质，其具有类似肌肉肌球蛋白的 ATP 酶活性并可与肌动蛋白结合。这种蛋白质与肌肉肌球蛋白一样具有典型的形态（长棒型分子，一侧末端有一个球形头部），且沉降常数（~6.05）也相似。有意思的是，与横纹肌中的肌球蛋白不同，这种蛋白质在其生理离子强度的溶液中，处于溶解状态。阿德尔曼和泰勒 [25] 证明该蛋白的分子量约为 460,000，与肌肉肌球蛋白的分子量近似。纳赫米尔斯 [38,39] 证明这种黏菌肌球蛋白可以附着在黏菌肌动蛋白和肌肉肌动蛋白上形成典型的"箭头"结构，而且在毫摩尔浓度的钙离子存在时，这种肌球蛋白可以自组装成本质上与肌肉肌球蛋白形成的聚合物类似的双极性纤维状短聚集体 [40]。

贝泰－加拉尔等人 [41] 以及博伊兹等人 [42] 发现血小板血栓收缩蛋白中的另一种组分为肌球蛋白样的蛋白质。该蛋白质具有可被钙离子和镁离子激活的 ATP 酶活性，其分子量大约为 540,000。阿德尔斯坦等人 [28] 证明这个分子与肌肉肌球蛋白一样，含有分子量为 200,000 的多肽链和分子量 16,000~18,000 的类似于肌肉肌球蛋白轻链的小肽链。血小板肌球蛋白可以和肌动蛋白结合形成完美的"箭头"结构，也可以在低离子强度的溶液中自组装成特征性的双极性聚集体。

然而，在对变形虫卡氏棘阿米巴的研究中，波拉德和科恩 [43] 发现尽管鉴定出一个肌球蛋白样的成分，它具有 ATP 酶的活性和与肌动蛋白结合的能力，但是该蛋白其他方面的特征却与肌肉肌球蛋白大为不同，其分子量只有约 200,000，远低于肌肉肌球蛋白的分子量，并且这种蛋白不能够形成纤维。当然，这种变形虫可能是变形虫的一个特例，值得注意的是，在其他的一些变形虫中已经观察到肌球蛋白样的纤维（例如在多核变形虫 [44,45] 和变形杆菌 [46,47] 中）。

综上所述，众多的例子都很确切的证明，具有不同运动形式的细胞却都含有某些在许多关键方面与肌肉中的肌球蛋白和肌动蛋白性质极其相似的蛋白质。涉及以

crucial respects exactly like actin and myosin from muscle. The resemblance is particularly significant in those properties concerned with the activating effect of actin on the ATPase activity of the myosin and with the precise structural form of the actin-myosin complex, as these are so directly linked to the contraction mechanism in striated muscle. It is difficult to believe that such close homology would exist unless the same basic mechanism was involved in each case.

Indeed, one can take this argument a stage further and suggest that the actin filament-myosin head interaction was developed as a motile mechanism very early in evolution, and that cells have been using it ever since, with a high degree of conservation of the essential protein interactions involved. As multicellular organisms developed, certain cells specialized in producing more extensive and more powerful movements, and the contractile proteins in them became organized into the large structures required to integrate the smaller scale motile processes into directed forces. But the same basic molecular mechanism was retained.

In striated muscle, it has been shown that the mechanism depends on the development of a relative shearing force between filaments of actin and myosin. Because so many of the underlying structural and biochemical features of this interaction are shared by the more primitive systems, it seems highly probable, to say the least, that these systems must also operate by an active shearing mechanism, in which sliding forces are developed between polarized actin filaments and some form of myosin assembly. For example, in cases where cytoplasmic streaming is taking place next to a stationary cortical gel layer, one might suppose that actin filaments, attached to the inner cell surface and lying approximately parallel to it, with appropriate structural polarity, generate an active shearing force by their interaction with assemblies of myosin molecules in the more fluid cytoplasm, which is therefore propelled along, carrying with it other cell organelles. If the myosin assemblies, which could be quite small, contained two sets of myosin molecules with opposite polarity (either in the form of bipolar filaments, or perhaps as "face-polar" sheets as described in smooth muscle by Lowy et al.[48] and Small and Squire[49]), then the second set could interact with actin filaments of appropriate polarity in solution, and propel those along too. Alternatively, the location of the actin and myosin assemblies could be interchanged.

Cell organelles could be moved more directly by means of attached actin filaments, which could interact with myosin in large or even very small assemblies and propel themselves along in a manner which I suggested some years ago[4], or by the interactions described above.

Where a cell, for instance in tissue culture, is moving over a substratum, it is clear that one part must be anchored to the support and that another part of the cell must move relative to that attachment site and form new attachment sites of its own. As attachment sites on and between cells often show filaments trailing back from them, it is natural to suggest that those filaments represent one component of an active shearing system, say, actin, and that the other components are in the cytoplasm and therefore can flow forward over

下两方面的相似是非常重要的：肌动蛋白对肌球蛋白 ATP 酶活性的激活，以及肌动蛋白－肌球蛋白复合物的精确结构，因为这两点与横纹肌的收缩机制直接相关。我们很难相信如果不是基于某种共同的机制，这些高度同源的分子如何会在每个例子中都存在。

其实，可以将上述讨论继续推进一个阶段，认为在进化早期肌动蛋白纤维－肌球蛋白头部的相互作用已经发展成为了一种运动机制，细胞自此一直使用这种机制，并使这种基本的蛋白质相互作用在进化中高度保守。随着多细胞生物的出现，某些细胞特化为能够产生更大范围更有力运动的特定细胞，其细胞内与收缩有关的蛋白质也组织成更大的结构以便把小尺度的运动整合成为定向的力量。但是，在这个过程中，同一种基本分子机制被保留了下来。

人们已经证明，在横纹肌中这种机制取决于肌动蛋白和肌球蛋白纤维之间的相对剪切力的产生。因为在这种相互作用中如此多的潜在结构和生化特性都为更多原初系统所共有，至少可以说，很有可能的是这些系统也通过一种主动剪切机制来运行，在这种机制中，在极化的肌动蛋白纤维和以某种形式组装的肌球蛋白之间产生了滑动力。例如，当胞质环流发生在稳定的皮质凝胶层附近时，我们可以假设具有适当结构极性的、附着在细胞内表面并与之大致平行的肌动蛋白纤维，可以通过与肌球蛋白聚合体的相互作用在流动性更高的细胞质中产生一个主动的剪切力，从而驱使并携带其他细胞器进行环流。当肌球蛋白聚合体（可以非常小）包含两组具有相反极性的肌球蛋白分子时（可能是以双极性纤维的形式存在，也可能以洛伊等人 [48] 和斯莫尔、斯夸尔 [49] 描述的在平滑肌中的"面极性"层的形式存在），第二组肌球蛋白也可以与细胞质中具有适当极性的肌动蛋白纤维相互作用，推动胞质环流。在上述机制中，肌动蛋白和肌球蛋白聚合体的位置可以相互轮流交换。

细胞器可以更直接地通过连接在它上面的肌动蛋白纤维实现移动。这些肌动蛋白纤维可以与或大或小的肌球蛋白聚集体相互作用，从而通过某种方式驱动它们移动（我在几年前便提出了这种方式 [4]），或者通过上文所述的相互作用方式运动。

当细胞在某种基质上运动时（例如在组织培养物中），可以肯定的是，细胞中的其中一部分必须锚定在基质支持物上，而另一部分必定对这些附着位点做相对移动，并形成自己新的附着位点。由于在细胞上和细胞间的附着位点上经常可以观察到来自它们的拖尾的纤维，我们很自然的认为这些纤维是剪切系统中的某种组分，比如肌动蛋白，而另一个组分（此处指肌球蛋白，译者注）则因存在于细胞质中而得以

the attached filaments. The filament attachment sites, perhaps analogous to fragments of Z-lines, would pass through the membrane and anchor to the substratum. As the front part of the cell was pushed forward by the internal pressure generated by the cytoplasmic stream, fresh attachment sites for actin filaments might be laid down at the leading edge. As actin filaments polymerized onto these (with appropriate polarity) they would be pulled back by shearing forces developed with the cytoplasm. This might give rise to the appearance of "ruffling" and backwards flow of the unattached membrane of moving cells. When the attachment sites became anchored to the substratum, however, the cell as a whole could then move forward as before over the attachment point (Fig. 3). (See also Bray, *Nature New Biology*, in the press.)

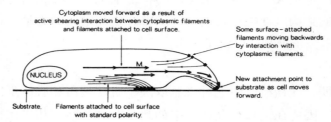

Fig. 3. Diagrammatic representation of a mechanism by which active shearing forces developed between two sets of filaments could produce cytoplasmic streaming and cell movement.

The character of encounters with other cells would depend on whether the external attachment sites on the two interacting cells could attach to each other, or only to a third, freely movable site on the opposing membrane. In the latter case, the attachment sites between cells would be drawn to their edge, sustained overlap could not occur, and indeed the entire actin complement of that region of the cell might become tied up in such junctions, leading to "contact inhibition"[50]. In the former, then, overgrowth could occur. Whilst these latter suggestions are entirely speculative, the force of the earlier arguments may make them worth considering and testing.

Another problem, about which there is very little experimental evidence at present, concerns the regulation mechanisms used in non-muscular motile systems. Because activity in muscle is controlled by small changes in calcium concentration, it would be reasonable to look for similar changes, and for the necessary calcium sequestering structures, in other motile systems. Evidence for the presence of elements of the troponin-tropomyosin system in slime mould[51] and in platelets[52] has recently been described, and evidence for the presence of calcium-sequestering structures has been described in *Spirostomum*[53] and *Physarum*[54].

Finally, I should mention that there are now numerous other instances where actin-like filaments have been implicated in cell movement, though the evidence does not have the decisive character of the examples I have given earlier. In many of these, particularly in the cases of various types of morphogenetic movement, biochemical identification of

向前流动越过附着的纤维。这些纤维的附着位点，可能与肌节中的 Z 线相似，会穿过细胞膜并锚定在基质上。当细胞的前端被胞质环流产生的内部压力推动向前移动时，一些新的肌动蛋白纤维附着位点也相应地在细胞前沿形成。当肌动蛋白纤维以适当的极性聚合到附着位点时，它们也会被胞质环流产生的剪切力拉向后方。这可能引发"波缘运动"，并使未与基质附着的细胞膜逆向流动。然而，一旦附着位点锚定到了基质上，细胞便可以作为一个整体向附着位点移动了（图 3）。（同样可参考布雷即将发表在《自然新生物》上的论文。）

利用"肌丝滑动"进行细胞运动的可能机制

图 3. 两组纤维间产生的主动剪切力引起胞质环流和细胞运动的机制。

当细胞在运动中与其他细胞相遇时，其特征取决于两个相遇细胞的外部附着点是彼此直接结合还是与对方膜上可自由移动的第三附着位点结合。在后一种情况下，细胞间的附着位点会被拖到细胞的边缘，而不会发生持续互相重叠的情况，实际上细胞该区域内的肌动蛋白补充因接触而停止，从而导致"接触抑制"[50]。而在前一种情况下，细胞则可能出现过度生长。虽然后面这些想法完全来自推断，但之前的讨论说明这些推断是值得认真考虑和进一步验证的。

另外一个问题是，目前对于非肌运动系统中的调节机理仍缺乏实验证据。由于肌肉活动是通过钙离子浓度的细微变化来调节的，所以我们理应在其他的运动系统中寻找类似的变化和螯合钙离子的必需结构。最近有人报道黏菌 [51] 和血小板 [52] 中含有原肌球蛋白 – 肌钙蛋白系统的组分，并且在旋口虫 [53] 和绒泡菌 [54] 中也发现了螯合钙离子的结构存在的证据。

最后，我想指出的是，尽管并不能像在我以前给出的例子一样具有明确的特征，但是现在有大量其他的证据表明肌动蛋白样纤维与细胞运动关系密切。在许多例子中，尤其是在各种形态发生运动中，要想用生化手段鉴定肌动蛋白是非常困难的。

actin will be difficult. There are, however, several instances where actin has been identified by arrowhead formation with HMM[55]. This is a very specific test for an actin-like protein (though not necessarily for its location in polymerized form unless actin-like filaments can be seen in the same position in untreated material). For example, Perry *et al.*[56] showed that a ring of filaments, just below the surface of the cleavage furrow at the newt egg, would bind HMM to give arrowhead complexes. This ring of filaments has been described by several workers on jellyfish eggs[57,58], and also on the eggs of a polychaete worm[58] and on the ciliate *Nassula*[59] as a contractile structure which, by decreasing its diameter, is responsible for at least a large part of the cleavage process. Two opposing sets of actin filament, linked by myosin, could have this property.

Tilney and Mooseker[60] have shown that filaments located in the microvilli forming the brush border of epithelial cells of chicken intestine also give arrowheads with HMM, behave like actin on SDS gels and, especially interestingly, appear clearly to be anchored to the cell membrane; thus they may aid transport by some kind of pumping action.

In summary then, there seems to be good evidence that several types of cell movement are brought about by molecular mechanisms which use proteins very similar to actin and myosin in muscle. A strong presumption exists, therefore, that active sliding or shearing mechanisms are involved. This possibility needs to be explored in each case, especially by structural and mechanical studies on the detailed processes involved.

(**243**, 445-449; 1973)

**H. E. Huxley**
MRC Laboratory of Molecular Biology, Hills Road, Cambridge CB2 2QH

References:

1. Jarosch, R., *Biochim. Biophys. Acta,* **25**, 204 (1957).

2. Jarosch, R., *Protoplasma,* **7**, 478 (1956).

3. Kamiya, N., and Kuroda, K., *Bot. Mag. (Tokyo)*, **69**, 544 (1956).

4. Huxley, H. E., *J. Mol. Biol.,* **37**, 507 (1963).

5. Huxley, H. E., *Science,* **164**, 1356 (1969).

6. Huxley, H. E., and Brown. W., *J. Mol. Biol.,* **30**, 383 (1967).

7. Huxley, H. E., *J. Mol. Biol.,* **37**, 507 (1968).

8. Reedy, M. K., Holmes, K. C., and Tregear, R. T., *Nature,* **207**, 1276 (1965).

9. Moore, P. B., Huxley, H. E., and DeRosier, D., *J. Mol. Biol.,* **50**, 279 (1970).

10. Ebashi, S., and Endo, M., *Prog. Biophys. Mol. Biol.,* **18**, 123 (1968).

11. Kendrick-Jones, J., Lehman, W., and Szent-Gyorgyi, A. G., *J. Mol. Biol.,* **54**, 313 (1970).

12. Lehman, W., Kendrick-Jones, J., and Szent-Gyorgyi, A. G., *Cold Spring Harbor Symp. Quant. Biol.,* **37**, 319 (1972).

13. Lowy, J., and Hanson, J., *Physiol. Rev.,* **42**, Suppl. 5, 34 (1962).

14. Hanson, J., and Huxley, H. E., *Symp. Soc. Exp. Biol.,* **9**, 228 (1955).

15. Lowy, J., and Small, J. V., *Nature,* **227**, 46 (1970).

16. Lowy, J., Poulsen, F., and Vibert, P., *Nature,* **225**, 1053 (1970).

17. Weihing, R., and Korn, E. D., *Biochem. Biophys. Res. Comm.,* **35**, 906 (1969).

18. Weihing, R., and Korn, E. D., *Biochemistry,* **10**, 590 (1971).

不过，在一些实例中，肌动蛋白通过与重酶解肌球蛋白形成箭头状结构而被鉴定出来 [55]。对于肌动蛋白样的蛋白质来说，这是一个非常特异性的检验（检测它在聚合体中的位置不是必要的，除非能够在未经处理的材料的相同位置观察到肌动蛋白样纤维）。例如，佩里等人 [56] 证明，在蝾螈卵裂沟表面下的环状纤维可以与重酶解肌球蛋白结合并形成箭头状复合物。在水母卵 [57,58]、多毛虫卵 [58] 和蓝色纤毛虫卵 [59] 的研究中，该环状纤维被认为是收缩性结构，通过缩小直径在卵裂过程中发挥主要作用。由肌球蛋白连接的两组极性相反的肌动蛋白纤维可能具有这种性质。

蒂尔尼和穆斯科尔 [60] 证明了鸡肠上皮刷状边缘的微绒毛中的纤维也可以与重酶解肌球蛋白结合形成箭头状结构，且其在 SDS– 聚丙烯酰胺凝胶中的特征与肌动蛋白的特征相似。尤其有意思的是，该纤维明显已锚定在细胞膜上。因此，它可能通过某种泵的机制帮助物质转运。

总之，似乎有很好的证据表明不同类型的细胞运动都是通过类似于肌肉中肌动蛋白 – 肌球蛋白系统的分子机制来产生的。因此，我们可以作出一个有力的假设，主动滑动和剪切机制也包含在细胞运动的分子机制中。这一假设还有待在各个实验中进一步验证，尤其需要对涉及的相关精细过程进行结构以及机理方面的研究。

（张锦彬 翻译；周筠梅 审稿）

19. Weihing, R., and Korn, E. D., *Biochemistry*, **11**, 1538 (1972).

20. Pollard, T. D., Shelton, E., Weihing, R., and Korn, E. D., *J. Mol. Biol.*, **50**, 91 (1970).

21. Eisenberg. E., and Weihing, R. R., *Nature*, **228**, 1092 (1970).

22. Hatano, S., and Oosawa, F., *Biochim. Biophys. Acta*, **154**, 507 (1966).

23. Hatano, S., and Oosawa, F., *J. Cell. Physiol.*, **68**, 197 (1966).

24. Hatano, S., Totsuka, T., and Oosawa, F., *Biochim. Biophys. Acta*, **140**, 109 (1967).

25. Adelman, M. R., and Taylor, E. W., *Biochemistry*, **8**, 4964 (1969).

26. Nachmias, V. T., Huxley, H. E., and Kessler, D., *J. Mol. Biol.*, **50**, 83 (1970).

27. Bettex-Gallard, M., and Lüscher, E. F., *Adv. in Protein Chem.*, **20**, 1 (1965).

28. Adelstein, R. S., Pollard, T. D., and Kuehl, W. M., *Proc. US Nat. Acad. Sci.*, **68**, 2703 (1971).

29. Zucker-Franklin, D., and Grasky, G., *J. Clin. Invest.*, **51**, 49 (1972).

30. Adelstein, R. S., and Conti, M. A., *Cold Spring Harbor Symp. Quant. Biol.*, **37** (in the press).

31. Fine, R. E., and Bray, D., *Nature*, **234**, 115 (1971).

32. Wessells, N. K., Spooner, B. S., Ash, J. F., Bradley, M. O., Ludena, M. A., Taylor, E. L., Wrenn, J. T., and Yamada, K. M., *Science*, **171**, 135 (1971).

33. Spooner, B. S., Yamada, K. M., and Wessells, N. K., *J. Cell Biol.*, **49**, 595 (1971).

34. Goldman, R. D., and Knipe, D. M., *Cold Spring Harbor Symp. Quant. Biol.*, **37**, 523 (1972).

35. Hatano, S., and Tazawa, M., *Biochim. Biophys. Acta*, **154**, 507 (1968).

36. Hatano, S., and Ohnuma, J., *Biochim. Biophys. Acta*, **205**, 110 (1970).

37. Hatano, S., and Takahashi, K., *J. Mechanochem. Cell. Motility*, **1**, 7 (1971).

38. Nachmias, V. T., and Ingram, W. C., *Science*, **170**, 743 (1970).

39. Nachmias, V. T., *J. Cell Biol.*, **52**, 648 (1972).

40. Nachmias, V. T., *Proc. US Nat. Acad. Sci.*, **69**, 2011 (1972).

41. Bettex-Gallard, M., Portzehl, H., and Lüscher, E. F., *Nature*, **193**, 777 (1962).

42. Booyse, F. M., Hoveke, T. P., Zschocke, D., and Rafelson, M. E., *J. Biol. Chem.*, **246**, 4291 (1971).

43. Pollard, T. D., and Korn, E. D., *Cold Spring Harbor Symp. Quant. Biol.*, **37** (in the press).

44. Nachmias, V. T., *J. Cell Biol.*, **23**, 183 (1964).

45. Nachmias, V. T., *J. Cell Biol.*, **38**, 40 (1968).

46. Wolpert, L., Thompson, C. M., and O'Neill, C. H., in *Primitive Motile Systems*, **143** (Academic Press, NY, 1964).

47. Pollard, T. D., and Ito, S., *J. Cell Biol.*, **46**, 267 (1970).

48. Small, J. V., Lowy, J., and Squire, J. M., *Proc. First Europ. Biophys. Congr.*, *Baden*, EX1/5 (1971).

49. Small, J. V., and Squire, J. M., *J. Mol. Biol.*, **67**, 117 (1972).

50. Abercrombie, M., *Exp. Cell Res.*, suppl., **8**, 188 (1961).

51. Tanaka, H., and Hatano, S., *Biochim. Biophys. Acta*, **257**, 445 (1972).

52. Cohen, I., and Cohen, C., *J. Mol. Biol.*, **68**, 383 (1972).

53. Ettienne, E. M., *J. Gen. Physiol.*, **56**, 168 (1970).

54. Braatz, R., and Komnick, H., *Cytobiologie*, **2**, 457 (1970).

55. Ishikawa, H., Bischoff, R., and Holtzer, H., *J. Cell Biol.*, **43**, 312 (1969).

56. Perry, M. M., John, H. A., and Thomas, N. S. T., *Exp. Cell Res.*, **65**, 249 (1971).

57. Schroeder, T. E., *Exp. Cell Res.*, **53**, 272 (1968).

58. Szollosi, D., *J. Cell Biol.*, **44**, 192 (1970).

59. Tucker, J. B., *J. Cell Sci.*, **8**, 557 (1971).

60. Tilney, L. G., and Mooseker, M., *Proc. US Nat. Acad. Sci.*, **68**, 2611 (1971).

# Effect of Low-level Radioactive Silver on Photographic Emulsions

E. Ehn *et al.*

## Editor's Note

With the growth of the nuclear industry from the 1950s onwards, generalized radioactive contamination became a matter of general concern. There are, however, particular problems of an unexpected character. This paper draws attention to the possibility that photographic emulsions, and in particular those used for taking X-ray photographs, might be affected by radioactive silver, which does not occur naturally and whose only source is irradiated nuclear fuel. This calculation, so far as it goes, concludes that the fogging of photographic emulsions is unlikely to be a serious problem.

LINDNER *et al.*[1] described the detection of low levels of radioactivity in silver bullion bars. Because this silver may be used in the manufacture of photographic emulsions the effects of the radioactivity are obviously of concern to photographic film manufacturers. We consider here the storage of photographic materials containing silver of the radioactivity level ($10^{-4}$ μCi/g silver) given by Lindner *et al.*

We illustrate this point by calculating the rate of fogging that would result in a highly sensitive X-ray film for materials testing. Typically, such a film will be coated with about 2.3 mg of silver cm$^{-2}$. The silver bromide grains will have a diameter of about 1.5 μm. If such a film is irradiated with about 80 mR of γ-rays (0.3–2 MeV) an increase in optical density of about 0.3 will be the result. In a normal environment background, dose rate from cosmic radiation and radioactivity in the surroundings will be 80–100 mR yr$^{-1}$. Film manufacturers and users will rule out a film which, during storage, has obtained a fog level of optical density 0.3.

The film we describe will have about $3.5 \times 10^8$ grains cm$^{-2}$. With $10^{-4}$ μCi g$^{-1}$ silver one will have a radioactive decay in $2.7 \times 10^5$ grains cm$^{-2}$ yr$^{-1}$. Thus about one per thousand of the grains will be directly involved in each year. If every radioactive decay involved one grain only, there would be no serious fogging, but the question "How many are involved?" is not a trivial one.

As a first step, the decay of $^{110m}$Ag can be simplified. We will assume: for βs 0.087 MeV (61%), 0.529 MeV (36%) and 1.5 MeV (0.6%); for γs 0.67 MeV (127%), 0.88 MeV (139%) and 1.4 MeV(38%). The 0.087 MeV β-rays will only involve one grain. The amount of silver involved with the 0.529 βs we will leave open.

# 低放射水平的银对感光乳剂的影响

恩等

## 编者按

随着 20 世纪 50 年代以来核工业的发展，普遍的放射性污染受到人们的广泛关注。不过，也存在着一些特征难以预见的特殊问题。这篇论文关注的是感光乳剂，尤其是那些用于 X 射线照相的感光乳剂，它们或许会受到放射性银（天然中不存在，唯一来源是辐照性核燃料）的影响。目前看来，据计算结果推断，感光乳剂的灰雾不太可能成为严重问题。

林德纳等 [1] 描述了银锭中低水平放射性的检测方法。由于这种银有可能用来制造摄影感光乳剂，所以很显然其放射性的影响令胶片制造商感到担忧。本文中，我们考虑了在林德纳等给出的放射性水平（$10^{-4}$ μCi·g$^{-1}$ 的银）下含银照相材料的储存问题。

我们通过计算高感 X 射线胶片用于材料检测时的灰雾速率来探讨这个问题。一般情况下，这类胶片上覆盖的银大约为 2.3 mg·cm$^{-2}$。溴化银颗粒的直径约为 1.5 μm。如果用强度为 80 mR 左右的 γ 射线（0.3~2 MeV）照射这张胶片，光密度会增加 0.3 左右。在正常环境背景下，从宇宙辐射和本地放射性接受的剂量率为 80~100 mR·yr$^{-1}$。而在储存过程中，胶片制造商和用户会剔除那些灰雾水平达到光密度 0.3 的胶片。

我们描述的胶片每平方厘米大约有 $3.5 \times 10^8$ 个颗粒。$10^{-4}$ μCi·g$^{-1}$ 的银可以导致每年每平方厘米 $2.7 \times 10^5$ 个颗粒发生放射性衰变。因而每年直接参与衰变的颗粒数约为颗粒总数的千分之一。如果每次放射性衰变只有一个颗粒参与，那就不会存在严重的灰雾问题了。可是"到底有多少颗粒参与衰变？"并不是小问题。

第一步，可将 $^{110m}$Ag 的衰变进行简化。我们假定 3 种 β 射线——0.087 MeV (61%)、0.529 MeV (36%) 和 1.5 MeV (0.6%)，以 及 3 种 γ 射 线 ——0.67 MeV (127%)、0.88 MeV (139%) 和 1.4 MeV (38%) 情况下的变化。可知，0.087 MeV 的 β 射线只涉及一个颗粒。至于 0.529 MeV 的 β 射线涉及的银的数量，则暂不确定。

To calculate the effect of the γs we assume that the film is stacked with fifty sheets per cm thickness. If film and polyester film base were to be ground together, we would get a substance with a density of about 1.5 g cm$^{-3}$ and with absorption coefficients $\mu_s$ of 0.105 cm$^{-1}$ (0.67 MeV), 0.090 cm$^{-1}$ (0.88 MeV), and 0.072 cm$^{-1}$ (1.4 MeV). The radioactivity of this substance would be 0.43 d.p.s. per cm$^3$, and result in a photon emission $S_v$ of 0.56 s$^{-1}$ cm$^{-3}$ (0.67 MeV), 0.61 s$^{-1}$ cm$^{-3}$ (0.88 MeV) and 0.167 s$^{-1}$ cm$^{-3}$ (1.4 MeV). The photon flux in the centre of an infinite slab source of homogeneous activity is

$$\varphi = BS_v[1-E_2(\mu_s d)]/\mu_s$$

where $B$ is the build-up factor, $E_2(\mu_s d)$ is the exponential integral of the second order and the thickness of the slab is $2d$. If $d$ is about 15 cm, $\mu_s d$ will be >1; $E_2(\mu_s d)\sim 0.1$, so that $[1-E_2(\mu_s d)]$ can be neglected. Neglecting the build-up factor for the time being we obtain

$$\varphi \sim S_v/\mu_s$$

and with the data given we obtain photon fluxes of 5.3 s$^{-1}$ cm$^{-2}$ (0.67 MeV); 6.8 s$^{-1}$ cm$^{-2}$ (0.88 MeV); and 2.3 s$^{-1}$ cm$^{-2}$ (1.4 MeV) to give dose rates of $7\times10^{-6}$ R h$^{-1}$ (0.67 MeV); $12\times10^{-6}$ R h$^{-1}$ (0.88 MeV); and $6\times10^{-6}$ R h$^{-1}$ (1.4 MeV). Adding these fluxes gives a dose rate of 210 mR yr$^{-1}$. This result is obtained without taking a build-up factor of, perhaps, 2–5 into consideration. Strong fogging in this case is evident.

Workers requiring very sensitive emulsions must hope that the case described by Lindner *et al.* will be an isolated incident. Or will we have to purchase low-level counting equipment for raw materials control?

(**243**, 460; 1973)

**Erik Ehn, Arne Lundh and Olle Staaf**
Ceaverken AB, 15200 Strängnäs, Sweden

Received February 19, 1973.

References:

1. Lindner, L., Brinkman, G. A., and Schimmel, A., *Nature*, **240**, 463 (1972).

2. Rockwell, T., III, *Reactor Shielding Design Manual* (McGraw-Hill, New York, 1956).

在计算 γ 射线的效应时，我们假设每厘米厚度的胶片由 50 层堆叠而成。如果将胶片和聚酯片基叠放在一起，我们会得到一种密度约为 1.5 g·cm$^{-3}$ 的物质，其吸收系数 $\mu_s$ 为 0.105 cm$^{-1}$ (0.67 MeV)、0.090 cm$^{-1}$ (0.88 MeV) 和 0.072 cm$^{-1}$ (1.4 MeV)。这种物质的放射性是每立方厘米 0.43 d.p.s.，并导致 $S_v$ 为 0.56 s$^{-1}$·cm$^{-3}$ (0.67 MeV)、0.61 s$^{-1}$·cm$^{-3}$ (0.88 MeV) 和 0.167 s$^{-1}$·cm$^{-3}$ (1.4 MeV) 的光子发射。位于放射性均匀分布的无限平面源中心的光子流量为：

$$\varphi = BS_v[1-E_2(\mu_s d)]/\mu_s$$

其中 $B$ 为累积因子，$E_2(\mu_s d)$ 是二阶指数积分，平板厚度为 $2d$。当 $d$ 在 15 cm 左右时，将有 $\mu_s d > 1$；因 $E_2(\mu_s d) \sim 0.1$，故而 $[1-E_2(\mu_s d)]$ 可以忽略。暂时忽略累积因子，就可得到：

$$\varphi \sim S_v/\mu_s$$

我们还可以利用给定的数据求得光子流量分别为：5.3 s$^{-1}$·cm$^{-2}$ (0.67 MeV)、6.8 s$^{-1}$·cm$^{-2}$ (0.88 MeV)，以及 2.3 s$^{-1}$·cm$^{-2}$ (1.4 MeV)。进而得出剂量率为 $7 \times 10^{-6}$ R·h$^{-1}$(0.67 MeV)、$12 \times 10^{-6}$ R·h$^{-1}$ (0.88 MeV) 和 $6 \times 10^{-6}$ R·h$^{-1}$ (1.4 MeV)。将上述光子流量累加起来，得到剂量率为 210 mR·yr$^{-1}$。这个结果是在不考虑累积因子（可能为 2~5）的前提下得到的。显然在这种情况下将出现强灰雾现象。

需要高感乳剂的工人一定希望林德纳等所描述的情况是一个孤立事件。否则我们将有必要为监控原材料添置低强度计数设备？

*（王耀杨 翻译；宋心琦 审稿）*

# Effect of Lithium on Brain Dopamine

E. Friedman and S. Gershon

## Editor's Note

Lithium's anti-manic properties were first noted in 1949, when Australian medical officer John Cade reported its calming effects on guinea pigs and humans. 21 years later it was licensed for the treatment of bipolar disorder in the United States, and although it remains in widespread use, its mode of action remains unclear. Here Eitan Friedman and Samuel Gershon describe how treating rat brain slices with chronic lithium inhibits dopamine production. The finding correlates with the observation that chronic treatment is needed to lessen manic behavior, and suggests that dopamine metabolism is impaired in patients with bipolar disorder. Today, lithium's effects on dopamine are accepted, but other potential key players in the process have also emerged.

THE efficacy of lithium ion in the therapy of mania is now established[1,2], and much speculation about its mode of action has involved its effects on brain catecholamine metabolism. Treatment with lithium ion increases the turnover rate of whole brain noradrenaline[2-4]; increases intraneuronal while decreasing extraneuronal metabolism of noradrenaline[3,4]; increases uptake of noradrenaline by synaptosomes[5], and reduces the rate of release of $^3$H-noradrenaline caused by electrical stimulation of striatal slices[6]. The influence of lithium ion on brain dopamine, however, is less fully documented. Here we describe the effect of chronic lithium chloride treatment on dopamine synthesis in striatal brain slices.

Male albino Sprague-Dawley rats (180 to 200 g) were housed four per cage in a regime of 12 h light and 12 h darkness and fed lab chow and water *ad lib*. Lithium chloride, dissolved in distilled water (0.7% w/v) or an equal volume of isotonic sodium chloride, was administered intraperitoneally (i.p.) as acute or chronic daily injections. Animals were killed 60 min after the last injection, the brains were quickly removed, rinsed in ice-cold Krebs-Henseleit physiological solution and the striatum was dissected out as described by Glowinski and Iversen[7]. Striatal slices (0.4 mm thick) were prepared using the slicing guide described by McIlwain[8] and placed in flasks containing 2 ml. of oxygenated cold physiological solution. Incubations were carried out at 37°C in an atmosphere of 95% $O_2$-5% $CO_2$. After a 10 min preincubation, 3,5-$^3$H-tyrosine (New England Nuclear Corp.) was added to each flask to give a final concentration of $8.15 \times 10^{-6}$ M tyrosine and the incubations were continued for a further 45 min. The tissue and incubation media were rapidly separated by filtration and the tissue slices were washed twice with cold physiological solution. The tissue was homogenized in 0.4 N perchloric acid and the media and washings were acidified to give a final 0.4 normality with perchloric acid. The samples were centrifuged and cold tyrosine and dopamine were added to the supernatant as carriers. Labelled and endogenous tyrosine and dopamine were isolated on "Dowex"

538

# 锂对于大脑中多巴胺的作用

弗里德曼，格申

## 编者按

锂的抗躁狂性质在 1949 年被首次提出，当时澳大利亚卫生官员约翰·凯德报道了它对豚鼠和人体的镇静作用。21 年后，它在美国获得批准用于治疗双相情感障碍，尽管一直被广泛使用，其作用机制仍然不清楚。在本文中，埃坦·弗里德曼和塞缪尔·格申描述了如何用慢性锂处理大鼠脑片抑制多巴胺的产生。减轻躁狂行为需长期治疗，本文中的发现与这一观察结果相关，并提示双相情感障碍患者的多巴胺代谢受损。今天，人们不但认可了锂对多巴胺的影响，还揭示出了此过程中其他潜在关键参与者。

现在锂离子治疗狂躁症的疗效得到了确认 [1,2]，很多关于其作用机制的推测都与它对大脑儿茶酚胺代谢的影响有关。用锂离子治疗能够增加全脑去甲肾上腺素的转换率 [2-4]，增加神经细胞内去甲肾上腺素代谢的同时降低神经细胞外去甲肾上腺素的代谢 [3,4]，增加突触小体对去甲肾上腺素的摄取 [5]，并降低纹状体切片因电刺激引起的 $^3$H–去甲肾上腺素释放的速率 [6]。然而，关于锂离子对大脑多巴胺的影响，却较少被详细记录。我们在本文中描述长期氯化锂治疗对纹状体脑切片中多巴胺合成的影响。

白化的雄性 SD 大鼠（180 g 到 200 g），每 4 只一笼，光照周期为 12 h 光照，12 h 黑暗，自由摄取食物水分。氯化锂溶解于蒸馏水（0.7% w/v）或者等体积的等渗氯化钠溶液中，急性腹腔注射或每日慢性腹腔注射。最后一次注射 60 分钟后处死动物，快速取出脑部，在以冰冷却的克雷布斯－亨泽莱特生理溶液中冲洗，按照格洛温斯基和艾弗森所描述的方法 [7] 解剖分离出纹状体。用麦基尔韦恩描述的方法 [8] 制备纹状体切片（厚度：0.4 mm），并置于盛有 2 ml 充氧冷生理溶液的烧瓶中。在含 95% $O_2$–5% $CO_2$ 的气体中 37℃进行孵育。在 10 分钟预培养后，向每个烧瓶中加入 3,5–$^3$H–酪氨酸（新英格兰核公司），使酪氨酸终浓度达到 $8.15 \times 10^{-6}$ M，再继续孵育 45 分钟。通过过滤快速分离组织与培养液，用冷的生理溶液清洗组织切片两次。在 0.4 N 的高氯酸中将组织匀浆，并用高氯酸酸化培养液和洗液，使终浓度为 0.4 N。离心样品，并向上清液中加入冷的酪氨酸和多巴胺作为载体。被标记的内源性酪氨酸和多巴胺用"Dowex"50–4X 色谱柱（$K^+$ 型）进行分离，按照内夫等人 [9] 所描述的方法用氧化铝进行纯化。利用液体闪烁光谱方法对酪氨酸和多巴胺样品进行放射

50-4X columns ($K^+$ form) followed by purification with alumina as described by Neff *et al.*[9]. Aliquots of the tyrosine and dopamine were taken for radioactive determination by liquid scintillation spectroscopy. Endogenous amines were determined fluorometrically by methods described previously[10,11]. Fluorescence was read in the Aminco Bowman spectrofluorometer. Plasma lithium concentrations were determined by atomic absorption spectrometry.

Acute injections of lithium chloride in doses of 2 to 4 mequiv $kg^{-1}$ did not affect endogenous dopamine nor the synthesis of $^3$H-dopamine in striatal slices (Table 1). Daily administration of lithium chloride, 1 and 2 mequiv $kg^{-1}$ for 14 days, inhibited striatal dopamine synthesis by 34 and 62% respectively (Table 1). These doses caused a slight but insignificant decrease in endogenous dopamine. There was no alteration in tyrosine specific activity. Serum lithium concentrations of 0.54 to 1.7 mequiv $l.^{-1}$ resulted from the chronic treatment; these levels are within the range associated with lithium therapy. The *in vitro* addition of 4 to 18 mequiv $l.^{-1}$ of lithium ion, or the replacement of similar amounts of sodium by lithium in the media incubating striatal slices obtained from saline-treated rats, did not affect dopamine synthesis (Table 2).

Table 1. Effect of LiCl on Dopamine Synthesis in Striatal Slices

| Treatment | | $N^*$ | Dose (mequiv $kg^{-1}$) | Plasma $Li^+$ (mequiv $l.^{-1}$) | Dopamine ($\mu g\ g^{-1}$) | $^3$H-Dopamine (c.p.m. $mg^{-1}$) |
|---|---|---|---|---|---|---|
| Acute | NaCl | 16 | — | — | 4.21±0.08 | 1,063±21 |
| | LiCl | 10 | 2 | 1.65 | 4.34±0.05 | 1,108±28 |
| | LiCl | 10 | 4 | 2.84 | 4.28±0.06 | 1,162±31 |
| Chronic | NaCl | 8 | | | 4.02±0.07 | 1,160±44 |
| | LiCl | 8 | 1 | 0.64 | 3.89±0.07 | 761±25† |
| | LiCl | 8 | 2 | 1.52 | 3.82±0.05 | 445±24‡ |

\* Number of animals; each provided duplicate striatal samples.
† $P<0.005$.
‡ $P<0.001$.

Table 2. Effect of *in vitro* LiCl or Replacement of Na by Li ion on Striatal Dopamine Synthesis

| Concentration of $Li^+$ (mequiv $l.^{-1}$) | $N^*$ | $^3$H-Dopamine (c.p.m. $mg^{-1}$) |
|---|---|---|
| Added to control media | 6 | 948±24 |
| 4 | 4 | 1,028±34 |
| 6 | 4 | 1,006±29 |
| Replacement of Na | 6 | |
| 4 | 4 | 959±28 |
| 6 | 4 | 1,078±31 |
| 18 | 4 | 992±32 |

*Number of animals; each provided duplicate striatal samples.

性测定。按照以前描述的荧光方法测定内源性胺类 [10,11]。用 Aminco-Bowman 荧光分光计读取荧光信号。用原子吸收光谱方法测定血浆锂浓度。

急性注射剂量为 2~4 mEq/kg 的氯化锂，既不影响纹状体切片中内源性多巴胺，也不影响纹状体切片中 $^3$H– 多巴胺的合成（表 1）。每天给予氯化锂 1~2 mEq/kg，连续 14 天，对纹状体多巴胺合成的抑制分别为 34% 和 62%（表 1）。这些剂量使得内源性多巴胺略有下降但无统计学意义。酪氨酸的比活性并无改变。长期治疗造成血清锂浓度在 0.54~1.7 mEq/L 范围；这个浓度水平在锂治疗相关浓度范围之内。在培养液中加入 4~18 mEq/L 锂离子，或者是用等量的锂取代培养液中的钠，孵育经生理盐水处理的大鼠纹状体切片，不会影响多巴胺的合成（表 2）。

表 1. LiCl 对纹状体切片中多巴胺合成的影响

| 处理方法 | | $N^*$ | 剂量 (mEq/kg) | 血浆 Li$^+$ (mEq/L) | 多巴胺 ($\mu$g/g) | $^3$H– 多巴胺 (c.p.m. mg$^{-1}$) |
|---|---|---|---|---|---|---|
| 急性 | NaCl | 16 | — | — | $4.21 \pm 0.08$ | $1,063 \pm 21$ |
| | LiCl | 10 | 2 | 1.65 | $4.34 \pm 0.05$ | $1,108 \pm 28$ |
| | LiCl | 10 | 4 | 2.84 | $4.28 \pm 0.06$ | $1,162 \pm 31$ |
| 慢性 | NaCl | 8 | | | $4.02 \pm 0.07$ | $1,160 \pm 44$ |
| | LiCl | 8 | 1 | 0.64 | $3.89 \pm 0.07$ | $761 \pm 25$† |
| | LiCl | 8 | 2 | 1.52 | $3.82 \pm 0.05$ | $445 \pm 24$‡ |

* 动物数量，每只提供两份相同的纹状体样品。
† $P < 0.005$
‡ $P < 0.001$

表 2. LiCl 或以锂离子取代钠离子对离体纹状体多巴胺合成的影响

| Li$^+$的浓度 (mEq/L) | $N^*$ | $^3$H– 多巴胺 (c.p.m. mg$^{-1}$) |
|---|---|---|
| 加入对照培养液 | 6 | $948 \pm 24$ |
| 4 | 4 | $1,028 \pm 34$ |
| 6 | 4 | $1,006 \pm 29$ |
| 取代 Na | 6 | |
| 4 | 4 | $959 \pm 28$ |
| 6 | 4 | $1,078 \pm 31$ |
| 18 | 4 | $992 \pm 32$ |

* 动物数量，每只提供两份相同的纹状体样品。

Thus the inhibition of dopamine synthesis by lithium ion seems to require chronic treatment. High lithium concentrations produced by either an acute injection or by *in vitro* addition of lithium ion are insufficient to inhibit synthesis. These conclusions correlate with the clinical observations that lithium's anti-manic action requires 1 to 2 weeks of daily medication. Our results agree with the observed decrease of dopamine excretion in manic patients undergoing lithium treatment[12]. Although the clinical results may reflect the effect of lithium on the peripheral disposition of dopamine, the data reported here suggest that central dopamine metabolism is altered in the same direction by lithium treatment.

Corrodi *et al.*[14] also found a slight but significant decrease in whole brain dopamine turnover in rats treated with lithium for 3 weeks, judged on the basis of the rate of dopamine decline observed after injection of $\alpha$-methyl-$p$-tyrosine. They have further found, using the histochemical fluorescence method, an increase in tubero-infundibular dopamine turnover. On the other hand, Ho *et al.*[15] found no alteration in dopamine turnover rates in four brain regions after 4 weeks of treatment with lithium. They used the synthesis inhibition method for estimating dopamine turnover. Although differences in methods and treatment time may have contributed to the discrepancy in these results, the fact that different brain regions were studied may be more significant, especially as we have been concerned only with the corpus striatum.

Messiha *et al.* reported increased urinary levels of dopamine during manic states[12], while others have described the induction of hypomanic and manic behavior by L-dopa in depressed patients with prior episodes of mania[13]. Thus, the inhibition of striatal dopamine synthesis may play some part in the psychomotor action of lithium in mania, or this element may exert some more fundamental action on the disorder itself.

(**243**, 520-521; 1973)

Eitan Friedman and Samuel Gershon

Neuropsychopharmacology Research Unit, New York University Medical Center, 550 First Avenue, New York, New York 10016

Received January 16; revised March 9, 1973.

References:

1. Schou, M., *J. Psychiat. Res.*, **6**, 67 (1968).
2. Gershon, S., *Ann. Rev. Med.*, **23**, 439 (1972).
3. Stern, D. N., Fieve, R. R., Neff, N. H., and Costa, E., *Psychopharmacologia*, **14**, 315 (1969).
4. Schildkraut, J. J., Logue, M. A., and Dodge, G. A., *Psychopharmacologia*, **14**, 135 (1969).
5. Dolburn, R., Goodwin, F., Bunney, W., and Davis, J., *Nature*, **215**, 1395 (1967).
6. Katz, R. I., Chase, T. N., and Kopin, I. J., *Science*, **169**, 466 (1968).
7. Glowinski, J., and Iversen, L. L., *J. Neurochem.*, **13**, 655 (1966).
8. McIlwain, H., *Biochem. J.*, **78**, 213 (1961).
9. Neff, N. H., Spano, P. F., Groppetti, A., Wang, C. T., and Costa, E., *J. Pharmacol. Exp. Ther.*, **170**, 701 (1971).
10. Laverty, R., and Taylor, K. M., *Anal. Biochem.*, **22**, 269 (1968).
11. Udenfriend, S., *Molecular Biology Series* (edit. by Kaplan, N. O., and Scheraga, H. A.), 129 (Academic Press, New York, 1962).
12. Messiha, F., Agallianos, D., and Clower, C., *Nature*, **225**, 868 (1970).
13. Murphy, D. L., Brodie, H. K. H., Goodwin, F. K., and Bunney, jun., W. E., *Nature*, **229**, 135 (1971).
14. Corrodi, H., Fuxe, K., and Schou, M., *Life Sci.*, **8**, 643 (1969).
15. Ho, A. K. S., Loh, H. H., Craves, F., Hitzemann, R. J., and Gershon, S., *Europ. J. Pharmacol.*, **10**, 72 (1970).

　　由此看来，通过锂离子对多巴胺合成进行抑制似乎需要长期治疗。由急性注射或者体外加入锂离子所产生的高锂浓度，不足以抑制其合成。这些结论与临床观察相关：锂离子的抗躁狂作用，需要每天服药一至两周才能实现。我们的结果与所观察到的接受锂治疗的躁狂症患者多巴胺分泌减少一致[12]。尽管临床结果可能反映的是锂对多巴胺的外周处置效果，但这里报道的数据表明锂治疗使得中枢多巴胺代谢以相同的方向发生变化。

　　科罗迪等人[14]也发现，接受锂治疗3周的大鼠全脑多巴胺转换出现轻微但有统计学意义的下降；这是基于在注射 $\alpha$-甲基-$p$-酪氨酸后观察到多巴胺下降速率得出的判断。运用组织化学荧光方法，他们还进一步发现下丘脑漏斗节结部位多巴胺转换率的增加。另一方面，何等人[15]发现，经过4周锂治疗后，4个脑区中的多巴胺转换率没有发生变化。他们使用合成抑制方法来估算多巴胺转换。尽管检测方法和治疗时间的不同对这些结果的差异可能有影响，实际上对不同脑区的研究可能更有意义，特别是一直以来我们只关心纹状体。

　　梅西亚等人报道了躁狂状态下尿液中多巴胺水平增加[12]，而其他人描述了对躁狂发作前的抑郁患者用 L- 多巴治疗可诱发轻躁狂和躁狂行为[13]。由此看来，纹状体多巴胺合成的抑制可能在锂对躁狂症的心理运动作用中扮演某种角色，或者这种元素对障碍本身可能产生更为基础的作用。

（王耀杨 翻译；李素霞 审稿）

# L-Glutamic Acid Decarboxylase in Parkinson's Disease: Effect of L-Dopa Therapy

K. G. Lloyd and O. Hornykiewicz

## Editor's Note

**Parkinson's disease is caused by a malfunction of the pathways in the brain leading to the synthesis of a substance called dopamine, which occurs in two optically active forms: laevo and dextro. The former, known as L-dopa, is used as a means of treating Parkinsonism and appears to have a beneficial effect on the development of symptoms of the disease. This paper is an attempt to unravel what happens when L-dopa is administered to patients. That it is inconclusive is perhaps not surprising, given that the problem is still unresolved.**

IN Parkinson's disease severe decreases occur in striatal L-dopa decarboxylase, putaminal synaptosomal uptake of dopamine, and dopamine and homovanillic acid concentrations in the nigro-striato-pallidal complex[1-4]. In addition, L-glutamic decarboxylase (GAD) activity is decreased in the caudate nucleus[5]. The experiments described here were performed to further evaluate this finding and to determine the effect (if any) of L-dopa therapy.

Human or rat brains were dissected and stored on dry ice as previously described[6]. Human material was obtained at autopsy from either control (no known neurological disorder) or Parkinsonian patients. Nine Parkinsonian patients received L-dopa until they died; two others did not receive L-dopa therapy. The patient groups were well matched with respect to age (means: control=68 yr; Parkinsonian=67 yr), sex (controls: ten males and three females; Parkinsonian: nine males and two females) and interval between death and freezing of the tissue (4–21 h for the controls, and 4–17 h for the Parkinsonian patients). None of these parameters had any apparent influence on GAD activity[4].

For the animal experiments, male albino Wistar rats (250–275 g) were fed an aqueous suspension of L-dopa by way of a stomach tube on the following regimen: days 1–37, 50 mg per rat per day; days 38–88, 100 mg per rat per day; days 89–109, 2×100 mg per rat per day. Controls were fed the suspension fluid (water) according to the same schedule. Animals were killed at days 37, 88 and 109. The striata were immediately removed and frozen.

GAD activity was estimated as described for L-dopa decarboxylase[6]. In brief, brain tissue was homogenized in ice-cold isotonic dextrose and incubated at $p$H 7.0 (37°C, 60 min) in the presence of pyridoxal phosphate (0.6 mM) and L-glutamic acid (2.5 mM containing 0.4 µCi DL-glutamic acid-1-$^{14}$C). The carbon dioxide formed was trapped

# 帕金森氏症中的L–谷氨酸脱羧酶：L–多巴的治疗效果

劳埃德，霍尼基维茨

*编者按*

*帕金森氏症是由于大脑中被称作多巴胺的一种物质的合成通路出现功能障碍所致，多巴胺以两种光学活性形式存在——左旋和右旋。前者，就是我们所说的L–多巴，用于帕金森氏症的治疗，并且对疾病症状的发展产生有益的影响。这篇文章试图阐明患者服用L–多巴后的反应。由于该问题仍未解决，此处未得出结论也就不足为奇了。*

在帕金森氏症中，纹状体L–多巴脱羧酶，壳核突触小体对多巴胺的摄取以及黑质–纹状体–苍白球复合体的多巴胺和高香草酸浓度均严重减少 [1-4]。此外，尾状核中的L–谷氨酸脱羧酶（GAD）的活性也降低 [5]。此实验的目的就是要进一步评估这个研究发现，并确定L–多巴的治疗效果（如果有效的话）。

按照以前描述的方法，将人或大鼠的脑取出并保存于干冰中 [6]。人体材料来自对照（不患有已知的神经性疾病）或者帕金森氏症患者的尸体。9 位帕金森氏症患者在死亡前均一直接受L–多巴治疗，另外 2 例没有接受L–多巴治疗。两组患者在年龄（平均年龄：对照患者 = 68 岁，帕金森氏症患者 = 67 岁），性别（对照患者：10 男 3 女，帕金森氏症患者：9 男 2 女）以及从死亡到组织冷冻之间的时间间隔（对照患者为 4~21 小时，帕金森氏症患者为 4~17 小时）等方面都匹配得非常好。上述参数对 GAD 活性都没有任何明显的影响 [4]。

对于动物实验，雄性白化 Wistar 大鼠（250~275 g）通过胃管喂食 L–多巴的水性悬浊液，具体方案如下：第 1~37 天，每天每鼠 50 mg；第 38~88 天，每天每鼠 100 mg；第 89~109 天，每天每鼠 $2 \times 100$ mg。根据同样的方案，用空白悬浊液（水）喂养对照组。分别在第 37，88 和 109 天时处死动物，立即将纹状体取出并进行冷冻。

按照以前描述过的测定 L–多巴脱羧酶的方法来评估 GAD 的活性 [6]。简言之，将脑组织在冰冷的等渗葡萄糖溶液中匀浆，在含有磷酸吡哆醛（0.6mM）和 L–谷氨酸（2.5 mM，含有 0.4 μCi 的 DL–谷氨酸 –1–$^{14}$C），pH 7.0 的溶液中进行孵育（37℃，

in hyamine hydroxide and assayed for radioactivity. Blanks contained *p*-bromo-*m*-hydroxybenzyloxyamine, a potent inactivator of pyridoxal phosphate[7].

The GAD activity in the striatum and substantia nigra of the non-dopa treated Parkinsonian patients was less than 50% of the control mean (Table 1), in agreement with a previous report[1]. In other brain regions GAD activity was within the range of the control values. In the brains of patients who received L-dopa for 8 months or less, GAD activity was significantly lower than in the controls (Table 1). In the caudate nucleus, putamen, substantia nigra, and globus pallidus of patients who received L-dopa continuously for 1 yr or longer, however, GAD activity was within the range of the controls, being significantly greater than that of patients treated for a shorter time. The GAD activity in other brain regions was only slightly higher in patients with the more prolonged L-dopa treatment.

Table 1. Activity of L-Glutamic Acid Decarboxylase in Discrete Brain Regions of Control Patients and Patients with Parkinson's Disease

| Caudate nucleus | Putamen | Pallidum externum | Substantia nigra | Temporal cortex |
|---|---|---|---|---|
| *A*, Control patients | | | | |
| 1,318±185 (13) | 1,243±220 (13) | 1,106±306 (13) | 1,273±297 (13) | 1,024±154 (13) |
| *B*, Patients with Parkinson's disease 1. No L-dopa therapy | | | | |
| 641 (2) | 583 (2) | 776 (2) | 526 (2) | 663 (2) |
| 2. L-Dopa therapy for 8 months or less (average dose: 3 g day$^{-1}$) | | | | |
| 339±53 (4)* | 249±24 (4)* | 504±50 (4) | 300±102 (4)† | 292±101 (3)* |
| 3. L-Dopa therapy for 1 yr or longer (average dose: 4 g day$^{-1}$) | | | | |
| 1,172±173 (5) ‡ | 887±95 (5)§ | 1,210±109 (5)§ | 1,210±110 (4)§ | 407±67* |

Patients on L-dopa received the drug for different periods in daily oral doses ranging from 2 to 6 g. Enzyme activity (mean±s.e.m.) is expressed as nmol carbon dioxide produced per 100 mg of protein per 2 h. (Number of cases in parentheses.) Brain tissue was homogenized in ice-cold isotonic dextrose and incubated for 20 min (37°C) in the presence of phosphate buffer (*p*H 7.0) and 0.6 mM pyridoxal phosphate. L-Glutamic acid was then added (final concentration of 2.5 mM containing 0.4 μCi DL-glutamic acid-$^{14}$COOH) and after 2 h the reaction was terminated by addition of acid. The evolved carbon dioxide was trapped in hyamine hydroxide and then assayed for radioactivity.
* Significantly different from group *A* ($P<0.01$).
† Significantly different from group *A* ($P<0.001$).
‡ Significantly different from group *B*, 2 ($P<0.05$).
§ Significantly different from group *B*, 2 ($P<0.001$).

In the rats treated chronically with oral L-dopa, after administration of L-dopa for 37 and 38 days the striatal GAD activity was not different from control (Table 2). After 109 days, however, striatal GAD activity was significantly greater than in either those rats which had received lower doses of L-dopa for a shorter period, or the controls. Thus, it was possible to replicate, in controlled laboratory conditions, the increase in striatal GAD activity observed in Parkinsonian patients chronically treated with L-dopa.

60 分钟）。用氢氧化甲基苄氧乙胺吸收生成的二氧化碳，并检测其放射性。空白中含有 $p$-溴-$m$-羟基苯甲氧基羟胺，是磷酸吡哆醛的强力灭活剂 [7]。

在未接受多巴治疗的帕金森氏症患者的纹状体和黑质中，GAD 活性低于对照平均值的 50%（参见表 1），与之前的报道一致 [1]。在其他脑区中，GAD 活性处于对照组的范围之内。在接受 L-多巴治疗等于或少于 8 个月的患者脑中，GAD 活性明显低于对照组（参见表 1）。对于连续接受 L-多巴治疗 1 年及以上的患者,其尾状核、壳核、黑质和苍白球中 GAD 活性处于对照组的活性范围之内，显著高于接受治疗时间较短的患者。接受更长时间 L-多巴治疗的患者其他脑区 GAD 活性只是略高一点而已。

表 1. 对照患者与帕金森氏症患者不同脑区中 L- 谷氨酸脱羧酶的活性

| 尾状核 | 壳核 | 苍白球外层 | 黑质 | 颞叶皮质 |
| --- | --- | --- | --- | --- |
| *A*，对照患者 | | | | |
| $1,318 \pm 185(13)$ | $1,243 \pm 220(13)$ | $1,106 \pm 306(13)$ | $1,273 \pm 297(13)$ | $1,024 \pm 154(13)$ |
| *B*，帕金森氏症患者<br>1. 未接受 L-多巴治疗 | | | | |
| 641(2) | 583(2) | 776(2) | 526(2) | 663(2) |
| 2．L-多巴治疗等于或不足八个月（平均剂量：每天 3 g） | | | | |
| $339 \pm 53(4)*$ | $249 \pm 24(4)*$ | $504 \pm 50(4)$ | $300 \pm 102(4)\dagger$ | $292 \pm 101(3)*$ |
| 3．L-多巴治疗一年或更久（平均剂量：每天 4 g） | | | | |
| $1,172 \pm 173(5)\ddagger$ | $887 \pm 95(5)\S$ | $1,210 \pm 109(5)\S$ | $1,210 \pm 110(4)\S$ | $407 \pm 67*$ |

不同治疗周期的患者的 L-多巴日口服剂量为 2~6 g。酶活性（平均值 ± 标准差）以每 2 小时 100 mg 蛋白质产生的二氧化碳纳摩尔数表示（括号中为案例数）。脑组织在冰冷的等渗葡萄糖溶液中匀浆，在含有磷酸盐缓冲液（pH 7.0）和 0.6 mM 磷酸吡哆醛的溶液中孵育 20 分钟（37℃）。之后加入 L- 谷氨酸（终浓度为 2.5 mM，含 0.4 μCi 的 DL- 谷氨酸 -$^{14}$COOH【译注：即具有放射活性的消旋谷氨酸进行示踪，引入放射性原子为 $^{14}$C，取代位置是羧基碳原子，放射性强度为 0.4 μCi】），2 小时后加入酸终止反应。用氢氧化甲基苄氧乙胺吸收生成的二氧化碳，并检测其放射活性。
\* 与 A 组结果相比，差异有统计学意义（$P<0.01$）
† 与 A 组结果相比，差异有统计学意义（$P<0.001$）
‡ 与 B，2 组结果相比，差异有统计学意义（$P<0.05$）
§ 与 B，2 组结果相比，差异有统计学意义（$P<0.001$）

在接受 37 和 38 天 L-多巴治疗后，长期口服 L-多巴的大鼠纹状体 GAD 活性与对照组没有差异（表 2）。但是，经过 109 天治疗后的大鼠纹状体 GAD 活性显著高于那些接受较短时间较低剂量 L-多巴治疗的大鼠或者对照组。由此看来，在可控制的实验室条件下，长期接受 L-多巴治疗的帕金森氏症患者纹状体 GAD 活性增加是可重复的。

Table 2. Effect of Chronic Oral L-Dopa Administration on the GAD Activity of the Rat Striatum

| Duration of L-dopa administration (days) | L-Glutamic acid decarboxylase activity | | |
|---|---|---|---|
| | Mean±s.e.m. | No. of animals | % of control |
| Control | 7,399±950 | 7 | 100.0 |
| 37 days | 7,360±853 | 7 | 99.5 |
| 88 days | 7,012 | 2 | 94.8 |
| 109 days | 11,310±839 | 5 | 152.8*† |

Rats were fed an L-dopa suspension (on the regimen described in detail in the text) by means of a metal stomach tube at 1600 h (days 1–88) or at 0800 and 2000 h (days 89–109). Enzymic activity expressed as nmol carbon dioxide produced per 100 mg of protein per 2 h. Age-matched sham-treated control animals were killed with each experimental group and GAD values did not differ between groups; hence all control values were combined. Assay conditions as in Table 1.

* Significantly different from controls, $P<0.002$.
† Significantly different from 37+88 day groups, $P<0.005$.

The GAD activity of the substantia nigra and globus pallidus, but not striatum, in Parkinsonism was reported to be subnormal compared with the frontal cortex[8,9]. Absolute GAD activity was, however, decreased throughout the brain compared with controls. Moreover, there was no indication of whether or not L-dopa had been administered. We find that in Parkinson's disease there is a definite decrease in the activity of striatal GAD and that its amelioration by L-dopa therapy is dependent upon the daily dose of L-dopa and the duration of its administration. This implies that the striatal GAD-L-dopa relationship depends on the concentration of dopamine present. In fact, in rats the increase in striatal GAD induced by L-dopa was dose-dependent. In addition, the L-dopa-treated patients with highest GAD activities were treated for longer (1 year or longer) and received, as a group, a higher dose of L-dopa (Table 1). It has also been shown that the striatal dopamine concentration of chronically L-dopa treated patients is markedly higher than in non-dopa treated patients[5,12,13]. Correspondingly, the more chronically treated group of Parkinsonian patients had an average concentration of striatal dopamine (caudate nucleus: 1.6 μg g⁻¹) distinctly higher than in the group treated for 8 months or less (caudate nucleus: 0.7 μg g⁻¹).

What is the mechanism of the L-dopa-induced increase in GAD activity? Although large diencephalic lesions in experimental animals decrease GAD activity in the substantia nigra and globus pallidus[8,10], no such lesions are apparent in Parkinson's disease[11]. Thus the decrease in GAD activity in Parkinson's disease may be secondary to the severe degeneration of the nigrostriatal dopamine pathway. These GAD-containing neurones could be under a continuous "trophic" influence of the dopaminergic system; degeneration of the dopaminergic pathway might then result in a biochemical "atrophy" of the GAD neurones. Replenishment of striatal dopamine by L-dopa[4,14] possibly reverses the biochemical atrophy of the GAD-containing neurones, a process that may well require prolonged administration of L-dopa.

表 2. 长期口服 L-多巴对大鼠纹状体 GAD 活性的影响

| 给予 L-多巴的持续时间（天） | L-谷氨酸脱羧酶活性 | | |
|---|---|---|---|
| | 平均值 ± 标准误 | 动物数量 | 与对照的百分比 |
| 对照 | 7,399 ± 950 | 7 | 100.0 |
| 37 天 | 7,360 ± 853 | 7 | 99.5 |
| 88 天 | 7,012 | 2 | 94.8 |
| 109 天 | 11,310 ± 839 | 5 | 152.8*† |

通过金属胃管给大鼠喂以 L-多巴悬浊液（文中已具体描述了施用方案），给药时间为 16:00 点（第 1~88 天）或者 08:00 点与 20:00 点（第 89~109 天）。酶活性以每 2 小时内 100 mg 蛋白质所产生的二氧化碳纳摩尔数表示。处死与每个实验组年龄匹配的假饲对照动物后，发现各组间 GAD 值没有差异；因此将全部对照组数据进行合并。分析条件如表 1。

* 与对照组相比，差异具有统计学意义，$P < 0.002$。

† 与 37 + 88 天实验组相比，差异具有统计学意义，$P < 0.005$。

据报道，帕金森氏症患者的黑质和苍白球的 GAD 活性低于额叶皮质，而纹状体的结果并非如此 [8,9]。不过，与对照组相比，整个脑中的绝对 GAD 活性下降。此外，也没有迹象表明患者是否服用过 L-多巴。我们发现，在帕金森氏症中纹状体 GAD 活性有明确降低，并且 L-多巴治疗效果取决于每天使用的剂量与持续时间。这意味着，纹状体 GAD 与 L-多巴的关系取决于多巴胺的实际浓度。实际上，由 L-多巴引起的大鼠纹状体 GAD 增加是剂量依赖性的。另外，在接受 L-多巴治疗的患者中，GAD 活性最高的患者（作为一个组）接受的治疗时间较长（1 年或更久），而且服用 L-多巴的剂量也较大（参见表 1）。还可以看出，接受长期 L-多巴治疗的患者纹状体多巴胺浓度显著高于未接受多巴治疗的患者 [5,12,13]。相应的，接受治疗时间更长的帕金森氏症患者组纹状体多巴胺的平均浓度（尾状核：1.6 µg/g）明显高于接受 8 个月或更短时间治疗的患者组（尾状核：0.7 µg/g）。

由 L-多巴诱导 GAD 活性增加的机制是什么？尽管实验动物的间脑大面积损伤会降低黑质和苍白球的 GAD 活性 [8,10]，但帕金森氏症却没有出现上述损伤 [11]。因此，帕金森氏症的 GAD 活性降低，可能是继发于黑质纹状体多巴胺通路严重退化。这些含有 GAD 的神经元可能受多巴胺能系统的持续"营养"影响；多巴胺能通路的退化可能导致 GAD 神经元的生化性"萎缩"。通过 L-多巴补充纹状体多巴胺 [4,14]，有可能逆转含 GAD 神经元的生化性萎缩，这一过程很可能需要长期服用 L-多巴。

Dopamine might act by removing a repression of GAD synthesis. This is an attractive but possibly incomplete explanation because of the long latency before striatal GAD activity increases. Relatively high concentrations of striatal dopamine may be needed, a process requiring a considerable time. This is supported by the lengthy period of L-dopa administration required to increase striatal GAD activity in rat brain.

An alternative hypothesis is an enhanced synthesis of GAD apoenzyme in compensation for decreased cofactor availability as a result of Schiff base formation with L-dopa[15,16]. Such an *in vivo* formation of Schiff base would not be reflected *in vitro* where an optimal concentration of pyridoxal phosphate is added. Signs of vitamin $B_6$ deficiency are not, however, apparent during chronic L-dopa therapy, making this a rather unlikely hypothesis.

The increase in striatal GAD activity during chronic L-dopa therapy may have an important clinical correlate as it conspicuously parallels the ameliorative effect of L-dopa on Parkinsonian tremor (which may take from several weeks to months to develop[17]). So far the anti-tremor effect of L-dopa has been without any known neurochemical correlate; our observations suggest that a GABA-containing neurone system may be involved. In this context, a new GABA-like compound has recently been reported to exert a specific anti-tremor effect in Parkinsonian patients[18].

The *p*-bromo-*m*-hydroxybenzyloxyamine was supplied by Dr J. M. Smith jun., of Lederle Laboratories, Pearl River, New York. This work was supported by the Clarke Institute of Psychiatry and Eaton Laboratories, Norwich, New York.

(**243**, 521-523; 1973)

K. G. Lloyd and O. Hornykiewicz

Department of Psychopharmacology, Clarke Institute of Psychiatry, and Department of Pharmacology, University of Toronto, Toronto, Ontario

Received February 14; revised March 18, 1973.

References:

1. Hornykiewicz, O., in *Handbook of Neurochemistry* (edit. by Lajtha, A.), 7, 465 (Plenum, New York, 1972).

2. Lloyd, K. G., and Hornykiewicz, O., *Science*, **170**, 1212 (1970).

3. Lloyd, K. G., and Hornykiewicz, O., *Fifth International Congress on Pharmacology* (Abstract) (1972).

4. Lloyd, K. G., thesis, Univ. Toronto (1972).

5. Bernheimer, H., and Hornykiewicz, O., *Arch. Exp. Path.*, **243**, 295 (1962).

6. Lloyd, K. G., and Hornykiewicz, O., *J. Neurochem.*, **19**, 1549(1972).

7. Perkinson, E. N., and DaVanzo, J. P., *Biochem. Pharmacol.*, **17**, 2498 (1968).

8. McGeer, E. G., McGeer, P. L., Wada, J. A., and Jung, E., *Brain Res.*, **32**, 425 (1971).

9. McGeer, P. L., McGeer, E. G., and Wada, J. A., *Neurology*, **21**, 1000 (1971).

10. Kim, J. S., Bak, I. J., Hassler, R., and Okada, Y., *Exp. Brain Res.*, **14**, 95 (1971).

11. Greenfield, J. G., *Neuropathology*, 530 (Arnold, London, 1958).

12. Davidson, L., Lloyd, K. G., Dankova, J., and Hornykiewicz, O., *Experientia*, **27**, 1048 (1971).

多巴胺可能通过解除 GAD 合成抑制起作用。虽然这个解释很有吸引力，但考虑到纹状体 GAD 活性增加前有很长的潜伏期，这个解释可能还是不完整。纹状体多巴胺可能需要达到相当高的浓度，而这个过程需要相当长的时间。大鼠脑纹状体 GAD 活性增加需要长期服用 L–多巴的事实支持这一观点。

另外一种假说是，增强 GAD 脱辅基酶的合成弥补了由于 L–多巴合成席夫碱而导致可用的辅因子减少 [15,16]。这种在"体内"形成的席夫碱的过程，在体外实验中即使加入最适浓度的磷酸吡哆醛后也不能反映出来。然而，L–多巴长期治疗并未导致维生素 $B_6$ 缺乏的体征，使得这一假说不可能成立。

在 L–多巴长期治疗期间，纹状体 GAD 活性增加可能与临床有重要的关联，因为它与 L–多巴明显改善帕金森氏症患者颤抖呈现显著的平行关系（这可能要花上几个星期至几个月的时间 [17]）。目前为止，L–多巴的抗震颤作用与任何已知的神经化学物质都不相关；我们的观察表明这一过程可能会涉及含 γ–氨基丁酸（GABA）的神经元系统。基于这一说法，最近报道了一种新的 GABA 样化合物，其对帕金森氏症患者具有特异性的抗震颤作用 [18]。

*p*–溴–*m*–羟基苯甲氧基羟胺由纽约珀尔里弗莱德利实验室的小史密斯博士所提供。这项研究由纽约诺威奇克拉克精神病研究所和伊顿实验室提供支持。

（王耀杨 翻译；李素霞 审稿）

13. Rinne, U. K., Sonninen, V., and Hyyppa, M., *Life Sci.*, **10**, (I) 549 (1971).

14. Lloyd, K. G., and Hornykiewicz, O., in *Treatment of Parkinsonism* (edit. by Calne, D. B.) (Raven Press, New York, 1973).

15. Schott, H. F., and Clark, W. G., *J. Biol. Chem.*, **196**, 449 (1952).

16. Kurtz, D. S., and Kanfer, J. N., *J. Neurochem.*, **18**, 2235 (1971).

17. Barbeau, A., *J. Canad. Med. Assoc.*, **101**, 791 (1969).

18. Curci, P., and Prandi, G., *Rev. Farmacol. Terap.*, **111**, 197 (1972).

# Neutral Mutations

B. Charlesworth

## Editor's Note

**Mutations are changes in the structure of a gene brought about by the replacement of one nucleotide by another. Motoo Kimura, a Japanese geneticist, argued strongly in a book with his student Tomoko Ohta that most mutations that occur in living things have no effect on the fitness of the organism and so are neutral in the process of natural selection. In mid 1970s this was a controversial idea, but experience has shown it to be valid in many circumstances.**

*THEORETICAL Aspects of Population Genetics*\*. This is an excellent book, which should be read by everyone interested in population genetics. The authors are two of the world's outstanding theoretical geneticists, and this book is essentially an account of their contributions to the field over the past five years or so. It is admirably clear and concise; the non-mathematically minded are catered for by the relegation of most of the mathematical proofs to an appendix. In chapter 1, the problem of the fixation of mutant genes is treated; this is used in chapter 2 in discussing the interpretation of observations on the rate of evolution as measured from protein sequence data. Later chapters deal with the concept of effective population size, the theory of genetic load, two-locus problems, the maintenance of variability in populations, and the adaptive significance of sex.

Kimura and Ohta believe that most nucleotide substitutions in evolution are due to the random fixation of selectively neutral alleles, and that protein polymorphisms revealed by electrophoresis merely represent a transient phase of this molecular evolution. Most of the mathematical results described in this book have been developed in order to show that this theory can account for the known facts of protein variation and evolution. Kimura and Ohta do a very good job of presenting this view, and only the most dyed-in-the-wool pan-selectionist can fail to be impressed. Nevertheless, there are some facts which are hard to fit into a neutral scheme of things, notably Prakash and Lewontin's discovery of non-random associations between inversions and protein variants in *Drosophila pseudoobscura*. It is a pity that these observations are not discussed in this book.

Many criticisms have, of course, been levelled against the authors' arguments for neutral mutations. In this book, most of them are dealt with quite convincingly. There does, however, seem to be an inconsistency which is hard to overcome. Kimura and Ohta show that, on the neutral mutation theory, the rate of amino acid substitution in evolution is equal to the rate of origin by mutation of new alleles affecting protein structure. If the data from proteins which have been sequenced are taken as representative, the average

---

\* By M. Kimura and T. Ohta. Pp. ix+219. (Princeton University: Princeton, New Jersey, 1971.) $12.50.

# 中性突变

查尔斯沃思

编者按

突变是一种核苷酸被另一种核苷酸置换而造成的基因结构的改变。日本遗传学者木村资生与他的学生太田朋子在书中强有力地论证了：生物中的绝大多数突变都不会对生物体的适应度造成影响，这些突变在自然选择过程中是中性的。尽管在20世纪70年代中期这是一个很有争议的观点，但是实验显示它在多数情况下都是正确的。

《群体遗传学理论》*是一本极好的图书，每一个对群体遗传学感兴趣的读者都应该阅读它。这本书的作者是世界上两位杰出的理论遗传学家，这本书主要讲述了他们过去五年里在这个领域所做出的贡献。本书内容非常清晰、精炼，大多数的数学证据都降低了难度，使数学手段成为附属工具，从而迎合了非数学思维模式。第1章处理了突变基因的固定的问题；第2章对进化速率观测结果的阐释进行讨论，这用到了第1章的内容，其中进化速率是根据蛋白质序列数据测得的。接下来的章节阐述了有效群体大小的概念、遗传负荷理论、双基因座问题、群体多样性的维护以及性别的适应意义。

木村和太田认为进化中的大多数核苷酸置换是由于可选择的中性等位基因的随机固定，通过电泳显示出来的蛋白质的多态现象仅仅描绘了这个分子进化的一个瞬间相。为了说明这个理论可用来解释蛋白质的变异和进化这些已知的事实，书中描述的大部分数学结果都有所改进。木村和太田非常好地提出了这个观点，只有极少数顽固的泛自由选择论者才能够不为所动。然而，还存在一些不符合中性进化理论框架的事实，特别是普拉卡什和列万廷发现的拟暗果蝇中倒位和蛋白质变异之间存在的非随机关系。令人遗憾的是这些观察结果并没有在这本书中被讨论。

许多批判不可避免地将矛头指向了作者的中性突变论点。在这本书中，大多数对立观点都被令人信服地处理了。然而，似乎还是存在一个很难克服的矛盾。木村和太田表示，中性突变理论认为，在进化中氨基酸被取代的速率与新的等位基因突变影响蛋白质结构的速率相等。如果将蛋白质的序列信息认为是具有代表性的话，

---

* 作者是木村资生和太田朋子。ix+219页。（普林斯顿大学：普林斯顿，新泽西，1971年。）12.50美元。

rate of mutation to neutral alleles per locus per generation can be computed. Kimura and Ohta find that this rate is less than one-tenth the order of magnitude of the mutation rates per locus measured experimentally in higher organisms. These mutation rates are based almost exclusively on rates of mutation to deleterious alleles. They therefore conclude that "this suggests that the neutral mutations constitute a rather small fraction of the total mutations".

Now the rate of neutral mutation for the whole genome can be estimated by multiplying the rate per nucleotide site by the total number of sites in the genome, calculated from the DNA content of sperm. For man, Kimura and Ohta estimate that between sixty and seventy-five neutral mutations occur per genome per generation. They argue that this means that "nucleotide substitution has an appreciable effect on fitness in only a small fraction of DNA sites", otherwise "the mutational load must be unbearably high for human populations".

This is a puzzling contradiction, which is difficult to resolve without serious damage to some other parts of the case for neutral mutations. For example, if one assumes that much of the DNA is functionless, the argument that most amino acid substitutions cannot be adaptive (because there would otherwise be too high a substitutional load) loses its force. Perhaps Kimura and Ohta would argue that observed mutation rates are biased in favour of loci which are known to have mutated and which therefore must have higher than average mutation rates. This can be tested by measuring mutation rates for electro-phoretically detectable loci. Some data of this sort have been published by Mukai and by Kojima, and these agree quite well with usual mutation rates.

I would emphasize again that this is an important and well-written book. The question of the possible selective neutrality of most protein variation is one of the most interesting in contemporary biology. Kimura and Ohta have greatly refined the mathematical tools needed for tackling this problem, and have made us all much more critical in our attitude towards evidence in favour of selection. This book is a valuable account of their work.

(**243**, 551-552; 1973)

我们就可以计算出每代每个基因座中性等位基因的平均突变率。木村和太田发现这个速率比通过实验在高等生物上测量出的每个基因座的突变率的十分之一还低。这些突变率几乎是完全以有害等位基因的突变率为基础的。他们因此得出结论"这些结果证明中性突变在全部突变中只占相当小的一部分"。

现在，可以根据精子 DNA 含量计算基因组核苷酸位点总数，再通过每个核苷酸位点的突变率与基因组核苷酸位点总数的乘积，估算出整个基因组的中性突变率。根据木村和太田的估计，人的每个基因组每代会出现 60 到 75 个中性突变。他们认为这意味着"核苷酸置换仅在小部分的 DNA 位点上才能显著地影响适应度"，否则"人类种群的突变负荷就会高得不可忍受"。

要想解决这个令人迷惑的矛盾而不严重破坏中性突变理论的其他方面是十分困难的。例如，如果假设大多数 DNA 都是没有功能的，那么关于大多数氨基酸置换不能被适应（因为那将出现过高的替代负荷）的论点就失去了它的说服力。也许木村和太田会认为观察到的突变率都偏好于一些已知突变的位点，因此它们本身就具有高于平均水平的突变率。这可以通过检测可被电泳检测到的基因座的突变率来测定。这方面的一些相关数据向井和小岛已经发表，并且与通常的突变率相当吻合。

我想再次强调一下，这是一本非常重要且写得很好的书。多数蛋白的可选择的中性突变是当代生物学界最有意思的问题之一。木村和太田很好的优化了解决这个难题所需要的数学工具，并且使我们所有人对支持选择理论的证据产生了更为批判的态度。这本书是对他们工作的一个有价值的报道。

（姜薇 翻译；梁前进 审稿）

# Relative and Latitudinal Motion of Atlantic Hot Spots

K. Burke et al.

## Editor's Note

**"Hotspots" on the Earth's surface are regions of volcanic activity where molten magma rises to the crust. Canadian geophysicist John Tuzo Wilson proposed that these may be the heads of hot plumes rising by convection from deep within the mantle. Here he and his coworkers ask whether hotspots are fixed or in relative motion. This can be assessed by looking at the persistent traces that hotspots leave over time, namely island chains formed from blobs of magma. The researchers reconstruct hotspot motions over the past 180 million years, and conclude that while in general they don't retain their relative positions, some small groups do so. Hotspot motions offer clues about the patterns of mantle convection, which are still debated today.**

---

Although not all hot spots are fixed with respect to one another, the members of small groups of them seem to be fixed internally.

---

THE hypothesis that hot spots[1] and their underlying plumes[2] all remain fixed with respect to one another, and perhaps also to the Earth's spin axis and axial dipolar magnetic field, has recently received attention[3-5]. Atwater and Molnar[6] have shown, by rotating plates back to their 13 and 38 m.y. position, that some hot spots (notably Iceland and St Paul/Amsterdam) have probably moved with respect to one another during this time. Using a different approach we present here evidence that during the past 120 m.y. some hot spots have moved significantly with respect to each other and to the magnetic field.

We use the term "hot spot" to describe succinctly a class of localized volcanism and associated uplift characteristically found within plates (Hawaii and Tibesti, for example), but also found on divergent plate boundaries (Iceland, for example). The term is used to describe the surface feature, with no intended implications about processes below the surface, in the same way as the term "island arc" is used. In the ocean a hot spot trace is a volcanic ridge or line of seamounts which leads away from a hot spot and which is considered to have been progressively generated as the plate moved relatively over or away from the underlying source of the hot spot. Where a hot spot occurs on a spreading ridge axis, a trace is generated on each plate. The former presence of a hot spot on continental crust is expressed by relatively localized alkaline volcanic piles or subvolcanic alkaline intrusives, sometimes accompanied by more extensive flood basalts. The former position of a hot spot at any time in the past is marked by the point of that age on its trace.

# 大西洋热点的相对运动和纬向运动

伯克等

编者按

地球表面的"热点"是指那些有熔融岩浆上升至地壳的火山活动区域。加拿大地球物理学家约翰·图佐·威尔逊提出，这些热点可能是地幔深处对流而上升的热地幔柱头。在本文中，他和他的同事们就热点是固定的还是处于相对移动状态这一问题进行了探究。这可以通过查看热点随时间的连续轨迹进行估算，也就是说，岛链是由岩浆团形成的。研究者们对过去 1.8 亿年以来的热点运动进行了重建，结果表明，尽管大体上它们的相对位置并不是保持不变的，但是有些小群体成员之间的相对位置是保持不变的。热点的运动情况为地幔对流模式提供了线索，这个问题在当今仍未有定论。

虽然并不是所有热点的相对位置都是固定的，但其中的小群体的成员之间的相对位置却似乎是固定的。

最近一项假说受到了广泛关注，该假说认为，热点[1]（及其下伏地幔柱[2]）相互之间保持固定，而且它们相对于地球自转轴及其轴向偶极磁场可能也是固定的[3-5]。阿特沃特和莫尔纳[6]通过将板块恢复至 1,300 万年前和 3,800 万年前的位置表明，在该时期内，某些热点（最明显的是冰岛和圣保罗/阿姆斯特丹热点）彼此间极有可能发生过相对移动。本文我们将利用不同的方法来证明，在过去的 1.2 亿年中有些热点相互之间以及相对于磁场均发生了明显的移动。

我们使用"热点"这一术语来简单地表示一类局部化火山作用及相关的隆起，其主要见于板块内部（比如夏威夷和提贝斯提山），不过也可见于离散板块边界（比如冰岛）。该术语用于描述表层特征，并不包含表层以下任何过程的信息，与术语"岛弧"的用法类似。在大洋中，一条热点迹线就是起源于热点的一个火山脊或者一条海山链，并且，它们是随着板块相对于下伏热点源的移离而逐渐形成的。当扩张脊轴上有热点形成时，两侧的板块上都会形成一条迹线。陆壳上热点的早期表现为相对局部的碱性火山堆积体或碱性次火山侵入体，有时还会伴随有大量的溢流玄武岩。某热点在过去某时间点上的位置就是热点迹线上年龄为该时间的那一点。

# Misfit

Figure. 1 is a reconstruction of the Atlantic ocean and its surrounding continents about 120 m.y. ago[7], and five selected Atlantic hot spots which possess comparatively well defined traces are plotted on it at the positions that they occupied at that time. If hot spots stay fixed with respect to each other, it should be possible to superimpose the same hot spots in their present relative positions on their positions 120 m.y. ago. It is not possible to do this, and the misfit is conveniently represented by keeping one hot spot fixed, and plotting the others in their present positions relative to it. We have chosen to keep the Colorado Seamount hot spot fixed for the purposes of illustration, as it has a trace on the North American plate, and the reference frame on Fig. 1 is with respect to present North America. Although the Azores hot spot does plot at the relative position it occupied 120 m.y. ago, the three others shown from the South Atlantic fall about 20° beyond their positions at that time. This indicates that relative motion between them and the two northern hot spots has occurred at an average rate of 1.8 cm yr$^{-1}$ during the past 120 m.y., in a direction approximately perpendicular to the general direction of relative plate motion.

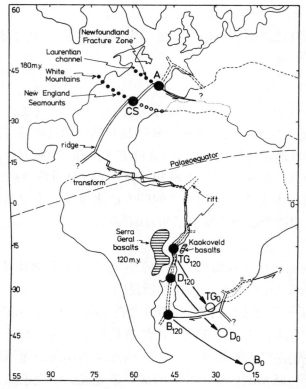

Fig. 1. Sketch of configuration of Atlantic continents, with schematic plate boundaries, for about 120 m.y. ago (from ref. 7); reference frame fixed to North America. ●, Positions of five hot spots at this time as given by their traces; •, earlier parts of traces of the two northern hot spots; ○, an interpolated older trace (see text); ◯, present positions of the southern hot spots relative to Colorado Seamount hot spot kept fixed at its position relative to North America 120 m.y. ago. A, Azores; CS, Colorado Seamount; TG, Tristan da Cunha/Gough; D, Discovery Seamounts; B4, Bouvet. Large arrows indicate total motion of the three southern hot spots between 120 m.y. ago and the present relative to Colorado Seamount hot spot. Palaeoequator is around average pole at 69° N 180° W with respect to North America.

## 非吻合性

图 1 是对 1.2 亿年前大西洋及其周边大陆的重建图 [7]，选定的五个大西洋热点均具有相对比较确定的迹线，并且已经标出它们当时所在的位置。倘若热点相互之间是固定不动的，那么，同一热点现今的相对位置应该能够与 1.2 亿年前的相对位置相吻合。然而这一点现在却做不到，并且我们通过保持某一热点固定，然后将其他热点相对于该热点的现今位置在图上画出，就可以很容易地发现这种非吻合性现象。为了说明该问题，我们选择科罗拉多海山热点作为固定热点，因为它在北美板块上有一条迹线，而且图 1 的参照系又是现今的北美洲。虽然亚速尔群岛热点确实位于 1.2 亿年前它所在的相对位置上，但南大西洋的其他三个热点则均落在了当时位置之外约 20° 的地方。这说明在过去的 1.2 亿年中，它们与北部两个热点之间发生了相对运动，平均速率为 1.8 厘米 / 年，其方向大致与板块相对运动的总体方向垂直。

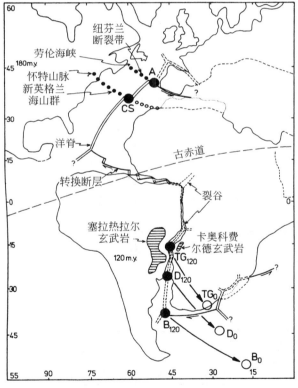

图 1. 1.2 亿年前大西洋板块轮廓的示意图。其中给出了大致的板块边界示意图（据参考文献 7），参照系相对于北美洲固定。●，代表根据其迹线得到的该时期 5 个热点的位置；●，表示北部两个热点的早期部分迹线；○，为插入的一条较老的迹线（见正文）；○，代表当前南部热点相对于科罗拉多海山热点的位置，其中科罗拉多海山热点相对于北美洲的位置与 1.2 亿年前保持一致。A，亚速尔群岛；CS，科罗拉多海山；TG，特里斯坦－达库尼亚 / 高夫；D，发现号海山；B4，布韦岛。大箭头指示南部三个热点从 1.2 亿年前至今相对于科罗拉多海山热点的总体移动方向。相对于北美洲，古地磁极平均位置为 69°N 180°W，古赤道环绕着古地磁极。

Data used to plot the hot spot positions on Fig. 1, and for subsequent parts of this paper, are listed in Table 1. The positions of the two northern hot spots at 120 m.y. ago were picked from maps of seafloor age in the central Atlantic[7,8]. A certain amount of interpolation has been necessary for the Colorado Seamount hot spot traces. The early part is well defined only on the western side, and the later part only on the eastern side of the Mid-Atlantic ridge, but the age ranges of the partial traces overlap, so the interpolation is valid. Some authors (for example ref. 9) prefer to generate the New England (Kelvin) and Corner Rise seamounts from the Azores hot spot. We do not favour this, because partial closure of the central Atlantic by appropriate rotations[8] connects the Corner Rise seamounts with a point of the same age on the trace of seamounts running east from Colorado Seamount.

Table 1. Position and Palaeolatitude Data for Some Atlantic Hot Spots

| Hot spot | Trace | Position of hot spot 120 m.y. ago | Present coordinates of hot spot | Present coordinates of hot spot position 120 m.y. ago | Palaeolatitude of position of hot spot | |
|---|---|---|---|---|---|---|
| | | | | | 120 m.y. ago | 180 m.y. ago |
| Azores | Newfoundland Ridge (or "Fracture Zone"); (eastern trace in tectonized area) | South-east corner of Grand Banks | 38° N 27° W | 41.5° N 48° W | 26° N | 29-30° N |
| Colorado Seamount | New England Seamounts; Corner Rise Seamounts; ill defined to present Mid-Atlantic Ridge | South-eastern New England Seamounts on Bermuda discontinuity | 34° N 37.5° W | 36.5° N 59° W | 25° N | 25-27° N |
| Colorado Seamount | Interpolated from continental margin to Great Meteor Seamount; Cruiser Seamount–Mid-Atlantic Ridge | Just west of Azores— interpolated | 34° N 37.5° W | 29° N 19° W | 25.5°N | |
| Tristan da Cunha | Rio Grande Rise | Florianapolis | 37° S 12.5° W | 27° S 48° W | 29° S | |
| Gough Island | Walvis Ridge | Cape Fria | 40° S 10° W | 18.5° S 11.5° E | 30° S | |
| Discovery Seamounts | Poorly defined line of seamounts | Luderitz | 47° S 6.5° W | 27° S 14° E | 39° S | |
| Discovery Seamounts | None known except one seamount just off continental margin | East of Montevideo | 47° S 6.5° W | 35.5° S 53° W | 38° S | |
| Bouvet Island | Meteor Seamount chain | South of Cape Agulhas | 54.5° S 3.5° E | 35° S 18° E | 48° S | |
| Bouvet Island | North Falkland Plateau; ill defined to east | South-west Argentine Basin—interpolated | 54.5° S 3.5° E | 45° S 59° W | 48.5° S | |

The relative motion between the five hot spots is set out in Table 2, showing in quantitative form what we show diagrammatically in Fig. 1. The large motion between the two groups of hot spots is clear, but there does not appear to have been significant motion between the hot spots in each group.

图 1 以及本文后续部分所绘的热点位置所采用的有关数据列于表 1。1.2 亿年前北部两个热点的位置来自大西洋中部的海底年龄图 [7,8]。有必要对科罗拉多海山热点迹线进行一定的插值。其早期部分仅在大西洋中脊的西侧非常明确，而之后的部分仅在大西洋中脊东侧比较明显，但部分迹线的年龄范围相重叠，因此我们作的插值是有效的。有些学者（例如参考文献 9）倾向于认为新英格兰（凯尔文）海山和角隆海山形成于亚速尔群岛热点。我们不赞同该观点，因为，适当的旋转将角隆海山与从科罗拉多海山向东延伸的海山迹线上相同年龄的热点连在了一起，使大西洋中部形成半封闭状态 [8]。

表 1. 大西洋部分热点的位置及其古纬度资料

| 热点 | 迹线 | 1.2 亿年前热点的位置 | 现今的热点坐标 | 1.2 亿年前热点位置的现今坐标 | 热点位置的古纬度 | |
|---|---|---|---|---|---|---|
| | | | | | 1.2 亿年前 | 1.8 亿年前 |
| 亚速尔群岛 | 纽芬兰海岭（"断裂带"）；（构造区域的东部迹线） | 格兰德班克东南角 | 38°N 27°W | 41.5°N 48°W | 26°N | 29~30°N |
| 科罗拉多海山 | 新英格兰海山；角隆海山；与现代大西洋中脊的界线不明确 | 新英格兰东南部，百慕大沉积间断面上 | 34°N 37.5°W | 36.5°N 59°W | 25°N | 25~27°N |
| 科罗拉多海山 | 在大陆边缘与流星号海山之间做插值；巡洋舰号，海山—大西洋中脊 | 紧邻亚速尔群岛西部——插值 | 34°N 37.5°W | 29°N 19°W | 25.5°N | |
| 特里斯坦－达库尼亚群岛 | 里奥格兰德海隆 | 佛罗里安纳波利斯 | 37°S 12.5°W | 27°S 48°W | 29°S | |
| 高夫岛 | 沃尔维斯海岭 | 弗里亚角 | 40°S 10°W | 18.5°S 11.5°E | 30°S | |
| 发现号海山 | 海山群的界线非常不清楚 | 吕德里茨 | 47°S 6.5°W | 27°S 14°E | 39°S | |
| 发现号海山 | 除大陆边缘附近的一座海山外，其他均未知 | 蒙得维的亚东部 | 47°S 6.5°W | 35.5°S 53°W | 38°S | |
| 布韦岛 | 流星号海山链 | 厄加勒斯角南部 | 54.5°S 3.5°E | 35°S 18°W | 48°S | |
| 布韦岛 | 北福克兰高原；东部边界不清楚 | 阿根廷盆地西南——插值 | 54.5°S 3.5°E | 45°S 59°W | 48.5°S | |

五个热点之间的相对运动情况见表 2，以量化的形式表示出了图 1 所示结果。两组热点之间的大规模运动是很清楚的，但每组热点内部之间却似乎并未发生明显的运动。

Table 2. Great Circle Distances between Hot Spots

| Hot Spots | 180 m.y. | 120 m.y. | Present | Difference between 120 m.y. and present |
|---|---|---|---|---|
| Azores–Colorado Seamount | 10 | 10 | 9 | −1 |
| Colorado Seamount–Tristan da Cunha | — | 57 | 75.5  77 | +20±2 |
| Colorado Seamount–Gough Island | — | | 79 | |
| Gough Island-Discovery Seamounts | — | 9 | (7 to) 10.5 | −2 to +1.5 |
| Gough Island–Bouvet | — | 19 | 16.5  18.5 | −2.5  −0.5 |
| Tristan da Cunha–Bouvet | — | | 20.5 | +1.5 |
| Discovery Seamounts–Bouvet | — | 9.5 | 10 | +0.5 |

All measurements in degrees (1degree ≈ 110 km).

## Relative Motion

The average rate of relative motion between the two groups has been about 1.8 cm yr$^{-1}$, but this rate has not been constant. Points representing particular ages on the traces from Colorado Seamount and Tristan/Gough can be picked from maps of seafloor age in the central[7,8] and southern[10,11] Atlantic. This identification of the age points along the two traces assumes that the two hot spots have stayed approximately on the axis of the spreading ridge, and is justified because hot spot traces extend away on both sides of the spreading ridge. Data are given in Table 3 and the change in great circle distance with time is shown in Fig. 2. Although the shape of the curve showing the relative motion is crudely exponential, we do not attach significance to this, since it only concerns the motion between two of many hot spot groups. We think, however, that the variations in the rate of motion are significant, and this rate has varied between about 5 cm yr$^{-1}$ (100 to 80 m.y.) and about 0.5 cm yr$^{-1}$ (25 to 0 m.y.). It is intriguing that the time of maximum rate of relative motion coincides with a time of world wide accelerated spreading rates[7], but we have not been able to confirm this correlation for any other hot spots.

Table 3. Increments of Motion between Tristan/Gough and Colorado Seamount Hot Spots

| Age (m.y.) | Present coordinates of hot spot position at ages given | | | | Great circle distance (degrees) | Rate of motion cm yr$^{-1}$ |
|---|---|---|---|---|---|---|
| | Walvis Ridge–Gough | | Colorado Seamount eastwards | | | |
| 120 | 18.5° S | 11.5° E | 29° N | 19° W | 57 | 2.8 |
| 100 | 25° S | 6° E | 29-29.5° N | 23-24° W | 62 | 4.1 to 5.0 |
| 80 | 32° S | 2° E | 30-31.5° N | 29° W | 69.5-71 | 1.6 to 3.3 |
| 70 | 34° S | 3° W | 32.5° N | 30° W | 72.5 | 1.4 |
| 50 | 36° S | 5.5° W | 33° N | 32° W | 75 | 1.3 |
| 25 | 40° S | 10° W | 34° N | 35° W | 78 | 0.44 |
| 0 | 40° S | 10° W | 34° N | 37.5° W | 79 | |

表 2. 热点之间的大圆距离

| 热点 | 1.8 亿年前 | 1.2 亿年前 | 现今 | 1.2 亿年前与现今的距离之差 |
|---|---|---|---|---|
| 亚速尔群岛—科罗拉多海山 | 10 | 10 | 9 | −1 |
| 科罗拉多海山—特里斯坦 – 达库尼亚 | — | 57 | 75.5 77 | +20 ± 2 |
| 科罗拉多海山—高夫岛 | — | | 79 | |
| 高夫岛—发现号海山 | — | 9 | (7~)10.5 | −2~+1.5 |
| 高夫岛—布韦岛 | — | 19 | 16.5 18.5 | −2.5 −0.5 |
| 特里斯坦 – 达库尼亚—布韦岛 | — | | 20.5 | +1.5 |
| 发现号海山—布韦岛 | — | 9.5 | 10 | +0.5 |

所有测定结果的单位均为度（1 度 ≈ 110 千米）。

## 相 对 运 动

两组热点之间相对运动的平均速率约为 1.8 厘米 / 年，不过该速率并不是一成不变。从大西洋中部 [7,8] 和南部 [10,11] 的海底年龄图上可以得到从科罗拉多海山和特里斯坦 / 高夫延伸出来的迹线上代表特定年龄的点。这两条迹线上年龄点确定的前提是，假设两个热点大致位于扩张脊脊轴上，而这点已经得到了证明，因为所有的热点迹线均沿扩张脊两侧向远处延伸。相关数据见表 3，大圆距离随时间的变化见图 2。虽然表示相对运动的曲线形状大致呈指数形式，然而我们认为这点无关紧要，因为它仅关系到许多热点组中的两组之间的运动。不过我们认为，运动速率的变化非常重要，而其速率变化在 5 厘米 / 年（距今 1 亿年到 8,000 万年前）和 0.5 厘米 / 年（2,500 万年前至今）之间。有趣的是，最大相对运动速率发生的时间与全球扩张速率加速的时间一致 [7]，但我们却未能证明对于其他热点也存在这样的相关性。

表 3. 特里斯坦 / 高夫热点和科罗拉多海山热点之间运动的增量

| 年龄（百万年） | 给定年龄下热点位置的现今坐标 | | | | 大圆距离（度） | 运动速率（厘米 / 年） |
|---|---|---|---|---|---|---|
| | 沃尔维斯海岭—高夫 | | 科罗拉多海山向东 | | | |
| 120 | 18.5°S | 11.5°E | 29°N | 19°W | 57 | 2.8 |
| 100 | 25°S | 6°E | 29~29.5°N | 23~24°W | 62 | 4.1~5.0 |
| 80 | 32°S | 2°E | 30~31.5°N | 29°W | 69.5~71 | 1.6~3.3 |
| 70 | 34°S | 3°W | 32.5°N | 30°W | 72.5 | 1.4 |
| 50 | 36°S | 5.5°W | 33°N | 32°W | 75 | 1.3 |
| 25 | 40°S | 10°W | 34°N | 35°W | 78 | 0.44 |
| 0 | 40°S | 10°W | 34°N | 37.5°W | 79 | |

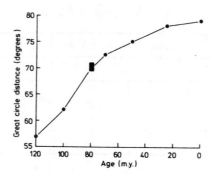

Fig. 2. Great circle motion between Colorado Seamount and Tristan/Gough hot spots during the past 120 m.y.

We take the Mascarene/Chagos-Laccadive Ridge and most of the Ninety-East Ridge to have been produced during the past 65 m.y. by the two hot spots now at Mauritius/Réunion and St Paul/Amsterdam Islands respectively. Tentative age data at two places along each of these traces[12,13] suggest that at present these two hot spots have the same separation as they had 65 m.y. ago (about 25°), but that their separation was slightly greater (about 29°) 25 m.y. ago. No significant motion between the Mauritius/Réunion and the Tristan/Gough hot spots can be detected for the past 12 m.y. (ref. 14); the motion between. 12 m.y. and 65 m.y. ago must amount to about 6° towards each other, on the basis of established plate motions[15].

Ideally, palaeomagnetic data can be used to establish how the relative motion between the hot spots has been distributed with respect to the magnetic field and by inference to the spin axis. We have estimated average palaeomagnetic poles for various plates at particular times from data contained in a recent compilation[16]. We used only non-redundant poles in reliability category *A*, and only if the age of any pole is well defined to within 10 m.y. of the age required (exceptionally 20 m.y. for the 180 m.y. and 120 m.y. ages), and we excluded poles from areas that may have suffered subsequent tectonic displacement. As the poles selected have restricted age ranges, any possible polar wandering as distinct from plate motion can be neglected for each age (but not between). Known plate rotations[8,15,17,18] can then be applied to the groups of poles of each age, and a combined pole defined, which can then be similarly rotated to give a consistent result for each plate.

Palaeolatitudes derived from the average pole for 180 m.y., and perhaps the other average poles, may have errors larger than the differences we are attempting to detect as the selected data scatter over significant areas, up to 15 to 20° across. But as the average poles for 180 and 120 m.y. have been selected and then deliberately rotated so as to be compatible with total subsequent plate motion for those plates involved, palaeolatitudes derived from them may be more reliable than those obtained from separate average poles for each plate, which do not coincide when subsequent plate motion is removed. The average palaeomagnetic poles given in Table 4 should be regarded as present estimates, and only for the restricted age ranges given. No motion of the African plate with respect to the dipole field is required by the palaeomagnetic data for the past 25 m.y. (ref. 19).

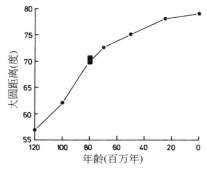

图 2. 在过去 1.2 亿年中，科罗拉多海山热点与特里斯坦 / 高夫热点之间的大圆运动。

我们认为，马斯克林 / 查戈斯－拉克代夫海岭及东经九十度海岭的大部都是在过去 6,500 万年中分别由位于现今毛里求斯 / 留尼汪岛和圣保罗 / 阿姆斯特丹群岛的两个热点形成的。从两地沿各条迹线[12,13]测定的初步年龄资料表明，现今这两个热点之间的距离与 6,500 万年前相同（约 25°），不过 2,500 万年前，两者之间的分离则略大一些（约 29°）。过去 1,200 万年中，在毛里求斯 / 留尼旺岛和特里斯坦 / 高夫这两个热点之间没有探测到明显的运动（参考文献 14），根据已知的板块运动情况[15]推算，在 1,200 万年前到 6,500 万年前这段时间，它们则应该相互靠近了大约 6°。

理论上来说，古地磁资料可用于确定热点之间的相对运动相对于磁场的分布情况并推断出其相对于自转轴的分布情况。根据新近出版的一本文集中的资料[16]，我们估算了特定时期不同板块古地磁极的平均位置，其中仅采用可靠性目录 A 中的非随机磁极，并且只要磁极的确定年龄与所要求的年龄之差在 1,000 万年以内（对于 1.8 亿年和 1.2 亿年的磁极放宽至 2,000 万年），其中我们还剔除了那些后来可能曾发生过构造位移的地区内的磁极。由于所选用的地磁极具有严格的年龄范围，因此对每个年代来说，其在板块运动之外可能存在的地磁极迁移可忽略不计（但不同年龄之间的相对迁移不可忽略）。那么已知的板块旋转[8,15,17,18]就可用于每个年龄的地磁极组中，从而确定出组合地磁极，而由组合地磁极再经过类似的旋转又可得出与每个板块相一致的结果。

根据 1.8 亿年前的古地磁极平均位置以及其他古地磁极平均位置得到的古纬度所存在的误差，可能比我们利用所选定的分布在各重要地区的数据资料所测定的值误差还要大，达 15°~20°。但是，1.8 亿年前和 1.2 亿年前的古地磁极平均位置被选定以后，我们又对其作了适当的旋转，使之与后来这些相关板块发生的总体运动可以协调起来，因此，相对于根据各个分散板块上的古地磁极平均位置所得到的值来说，由此得到的古纬度值可能更可靠一些，因为在消除了后来的板块运动影响之后，各板块的古地磁极平均位置并不相符。表 4 给出的古地磁极平均位置应该看成现今估测值，并且仅限于所给定的年龄范围内。根据过去 2,500 万年的古地磁数据，非洲板块相对于磁偶极场未作任何运动（参考文献 19）。

Table 4. Average Palaeomagnetic Poles

| Plate | Age (m.y.) | | | | |
|---|---|---|---|---|---|
| | 180 | 120 | 65-60 | 50 | 25 |
| Africa | 67.5° N 104° W | 55° S 74° E | — | — | 90° N |
| North America | 72.5° N 94° E | 69° N 180° W | (77° N 114° E?) 85° N 163° W (ref. 5) | — | — |
| South America | — | 83.5° S 113° W | — | — | — |
| India | — | — | 32° S 100° E | — | — |
| Indo-Australia | — | — | — | 70° S 54° E | 76° S 89° E |
| Eurasia | — | — | 77° N 150° E? | — | ? |

Seventeen poles for the Eurasian plate 60 m.y. ago are almost all closely grouped, but the average pole they define is not compatible with an average pole for North America[5] when the appropriate North Atlantic motion[8] is removed (Table 4, in brackets). Three poles in the Eurasian group plot 20° away from the main group, and their position is more compatible with the North American pole. In view of this uncertainty, we have not used the 60 m.y. poles to define palaeolatitudes for the Atlantic hot spots, as the error is potentially as much as 20°. Phillips and Forsyth[20] have previously discussed this discrepancy.

Palaeolatitudes derived from average poles are probably of variable reliability and only relatively small changes in one or more of the average pole positions may make a great deal of difference to the inferred motion of particular hot spots with respect to the magnetic field and the spin axis. The palaeolatitudes we derive show that all the hot spots have moved differing amounts with respect to the magnetic field for at least some parts of the last 120 m.y., but the precise amounts for each hot spot we regard as less certain.

Palaeolatitudes of the Atlantic hot spot positions 120 m.y. ago, and for the two northern hot spots at 180 m.y. ago, are given in Table 1. The discrepancies between the palaeolatitudes at 120 m.y. and the present latitudes of the hot spots are set out in Table 5, and shown graphically in Fig. 3. First, the results show that the total motion between the two groups of hot spots with respect to latitude is nearly as great as their motion with respect to each other during the past 120 m.y., indicating that aggregate relative longitudinal motion has been subordinate, at least for these particular hot spots (see also Fig. 1). Second, each group of hot spots has moved an approximately equal distance away from the equator toward the poles of their respective hemispheres. Duncan and others[3] showed that Eurasian palaeomagnetic data for 60 m.y. ago can be interpreted as indicating a large northward motion of the Iceland hot spot (about 20°) since this time. In view of the uncertainty in the palaeomagnetic data, we would suggest that although relative northward motion of this hot spot is probable, the amount of motion may be more modest. We estimate from known plate motions[8], allowing for uncertainty across the Labrador Sea, that the Iceland hot spot has not moved more than 5° away from the

表 4. 古地磁极平均位置

| 板块 | 年龄（百万年） | | | | |
|---|---|---|---|---|---|
| | 180 | 120 | 65~60 | 50 | 25 |
| 非洲板块 | 67.5°N 104°W | 55°S 74°E | — | — | 90°N |
| 北美板块 | 72.5°N 94°E | 69°N 180°W | (77°N 114°E?)<br>85°N 163°W（参考文献 5） | — | — |
| 南美板块 | — | 83.5°S 113°W | — | — | — |
| 印度板块 | — | — | 32°S 100°E | — | — |
| 印度–澳大利亚板块 | — | — | — | 70°S 54°E | 76°S 89°E |
| 欧亚板块 | — | — | 77°N 150°E ? | — | ? |

6,000 万年前欧亚板块上的 17 个地磁极几乎都紧密聚合在一起，然而当我们将北大西洋板块发生的相关运动 [8] 去除以后，根据它们确定出的地磁极平均位置却与北美板块的地磁极平均位置 [5] 不一致（表 4 括号内）。欧亚板块地磁极组中有三个地磁极与主体地磁极组偏离出 20°，而其位置与北美地磁极更接近。考虑到这种不确定性，我们并未采用 6,000 万年前的地磁极资料来确定大西洋热点的古纬度值，因为其误差可能会高达 20°。菲利普斯和福赛思 [20] 之前曾对该差异作过讨论。

根据地磁极平均位置得出的古纬度值可靠性可能不稳定，而且，即使仅有一个或几个磁极平均位置发生微小的变化都可能会导致所推断出的特定热点相对于磁场和自转轴的运动出现巨大差异。我们得到的古纬度表明，在过去 1.2 亿年中，至少有些时候，各热点相对于磁场的运动距离是互不相同的，不过尚不能确定具体每个热点的准确运动距离。

大西洋热点 1.2 亿年前的古纬度位置以及北部两个热点 1.8 亿年前的位置见表 1。热点在 1.2 亿年前的古纬度位置与其现今纬度之间的差异列于表 5，并示于图 3。首先，结果表明，在过去 1.2 亿年中，两组热点之间总的相对运动在纬度上的差异几乎与它们之间的相对运动相当，说明经向的相对运动是次要的，至少对这些特定的热点来说是这样（亦见于图 1）。其次，每组热点从赤道向各自半球的极点运动的距离基本相等。邓肯等人 [3] 证实，可以认为 6,000 万年前的欧亚古地磁资料表明冰岛热点自那时起就开始大规模向北运动（约有 20°）。考虑到古地磁资料的不确定性，我们认为，尽管该热点向北相对运动的可能性很大，但其运动的距离则可能较小。根据已知的板块运动资料 [8]，考虑到拉布拉多海一线的不确定性，我们认为，在过去的 6,000 万年中，冰岛热点相对亚速尔群岛热点和科罗拉多海山热点向北移动了

Azores and Colorado Seamount hot spots during the past 60 m.y. On the basis of the North American average palaeomagnetic pole[5], this indicates no more than about 8° of northward motion of the Iceland hot spot during this time.

Table 5. Latitudinal Motion of Hot Spots

| Hot spot (trace east or west) | Latitude/palaeolatitude change from 120 m.y. to present | Differences between hot spots (degrees) |
|---|---|---|
| Azores (W) | 12° N | +3 to +3.5 |
| Colorado Seamount (W) | 9° N | |
| Colorado Seamount (E) | 8.5° N | +16.5 to +19 |
| Gough (E) | 10° S | 0 to −2 |
| Discovery Seamount (E) | 8° S | −1.5 to −3 |
| Bouvet (E) | 6.5° S | |
| Tristan da Cunha (W) | 8° S | — |
| Discovery Seamount (W) | 9° S | — |
| Bouvet (W) | 6° S | — |

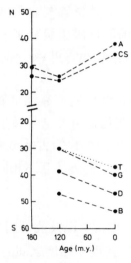

Fig. 3. Latitudinal motion between five Atlantic hot spots during the past 180 m.y. Letters identifying hot spots are as in Fig. 1.

## More Hot Spots

We have attempted to extend this study to the two hot spots of Mauritius/Réunion and St Paul/Amsterdam Islands. The palaeomagnetic data perhaps suggest that Mauritius/Réunion has moved northwards about 10° in the past 65 m.y. and that all or almost all of this relative motion occurred before 25 m.y. ago. On the same basis St Paul/Amsterdam has moved northwards about 16° since 65 m.y. ago. If a very tentative estimate is made of its position 50 m.y. ago, extrapolating from a point suggested to be 45 m.y. old[13] and using the Australian palaeomagnetic pole, it is possible that the overall relative northward motion of this hot spot may have reversed for a while between 50 and 25 m.y. ago.

不到 5°。根据北美平均古地磁极资料 [5] 来看，这一时期冰岛热点向北运动的距离不超过 8°。

表 5. 热点的纬向运动

| 热点（迹线向东或向西） | 从 1.2 亿年前至今发生的<br>纬度 / 古纬度变化 | 热点之间的纬度差异（度） |
|---|---|---|
| 亚速尔群岛（W）<br>科罗拉多海山（W） | 12°N<br>9°N | +3 ~ +3.5 |
| 科罗拉多海山（E）<br>高夫岛（E）<br>发现号海山（E）<br>布韦岛（E） | 8.5°N<br>10°S<br>8°S<br>6.5°S | +16.5 ~ +19<br>0 ~ −2<br>−1.5 ~ −3 |
| 特里斯坦－达库尼亚（W）<br>发现号海山（W）<br>布韦岛（W） | 8°S<br>9°S<br>6°S | —<br>—<br>— |

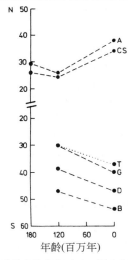

图 3. 过去 1.8 亿年中，5 个大西洋热点的纬向运动。图中字母所代表的热点与图 1 中的一致。

## 更多热点

我们希望将本研究扩展至位于毛里求斯 / 留尼汪岛和圣保罗 / 阿姆斯特丹群岛的这两个热点。古地磁资料表明，在过去的 6,500 万年中，毛里求斯 / 留尼汪岛热点可能已向北移动了约 10°，而且所有或几乎所有的这种相对运动都发生在 2,500 万年前。同理可知，在过去的 6,500 万年中，圣保罗 / 阿姆斯特丹热点向北移动了约 16°。倘若从一个年龄约为 4,500 万年的点出发 [13]，利用澳大利亚古地磁极对其在 5,000 万年前的位置作初步估算，那么在 5,000 万年前到 2,500 万年前之间，该热点在总体向北做相对运动的前提下，曾有段时间可能是做反向运动的。

The only other hot spot for which data are available is Hawaii; the palaeomagnetic data cannot resolve any motion of this hot spot in the past 70 m.y. (ref. 4), but the equatorial sedimentation data[4] perhaps suggest it has moved slightly southwards[21], perhaps up to 5° in the past 40 m.y. By implication, the other hot spots on the Pacific plate which seem to be approximately fixed with respect to Hawaii[2,4] may be moving in a similar manner.

McElhinny[5] showed that the apparent motion of the Iceland hot spot with respect to the magnetic field[3] is more likely to be due to relative motion between hot spots than to a rotation of the mantle containing fixed plumes with respect to the lithosphere as a whole[3,22]. Our conclusion that some groups of hot spots have moved significantly with respect to each other confirms this suggestion. The rate of motion between two small groups of hot spots is comparable with rates of plate motion, and has varied by an order of magnitude over the past 120 m.y.; the maximum rate of separation for these two groups appears to coincide with a temporary global increase in spreading rates[7]. The two or three hot spots within each of these two groups do not, however, seem to have moved significantly with respect to their partners for the maximum lengths of time that they can be observed (180 and 120 m.y.). While moving apart and remaining essentially fixed internally, the two groups of Atlantic hot spots seem to have rotated somewhat relative to one another (Fig. 1). Differential motion of hot spots with respect to the magnetic field and spin axis occurs and for the few hot spots we have studied it seems to have been predominantly in a poleward direction, though not all seem to move toward the pole of the hemisphere in which they occur. The poleward motion may also be intermittent, and even reversible. Data from other hot spots are desirable, but it is unfortunate that although there are many hot spots[23], there are few, if any, others that have clearly marked traces with well defined ages along them and that can be observed for comparable periods of time to those in the central and southern Atlantic.

## Satisfactory Hypothesis

We think that the idea that deep mantle plumes[2,24] underlie hot spots is at present the only satisfactory hypothesis available to account for hot spots, especially to explain their persistence as discrete localized anomalies, in some cases for 180 m.y. This is particularly the case for those hot spots which are on the axes of spreading ridges, and which have remained so for long periods; these are epitomized by the hot spots on the axis of the central and southern Mid-Atlantic Ridge. Although these hot spots have moved with respect to one another, and to the position of the spreading ridge at 120 m.y. ago (Fig. 1), they are still on, or near[14], the axis. The jumping of a restricted length of spreading ridge axis is probably a related phenomenon, and in several cases this is clearly associated with hot spots. It may occur repeatedly in a consistent direction, and this leads to apparent asymmetrical spreading[25]. Examples of ridge axis jumping occur at the Galapagos[26,27], St Paul/Amsterdam Islands[15], south of Australia[25], and in Iceland[28]. The inference we make is that whatever is under the hot spots controls the position of the ridge, and not the reverse; the presence of underlying deep mantle plumes seems to us the only available hypothesis that will account for this.

其他热点中唯一有资料可用的是夏威夷热点，从古地磁资料分析来看，并未发现该热点在过去 7,000 万年中发生过任何运动（参考文献 4），不过赤道附近的沉积资料 [4] 表明，该热点有略微的南移 [21]，在过去 4,000 万年中可能移动了 5° 左右，也就是说，太平洋板块上看似与夏威夷热点的相对位置基本保持不变的其他热点 [2,4] 可能也发生了类似的运动情况。

麦克尔希尼 [5] 指出，冰岛热点相对于磁场的视运动 [3] 更有可能是由热点之间的相对运动造成的，而非包含地幔柱的地幔相对于整个岩石圈 [3,22] 的旋转所致。而我们得出的结论——有的热点组之间相对运动明显——恰好证明了这一观点。两个小的热点组之间的运动速率与板块运动速率相当，且在过去的 1.2 亿年中变化了一个数量级，两组之间的最大分离速率与全球扩张速率暂时性加快 [7] 同时发生。然而即便在可观测的最大时间尺度（1.8 亿年和 1.2 亿年）内，各组内部的两个或三个热点之间似乎也没有发生明显的移动。在组与组之间相互分离而组内各点之间又基本固定的情况下，两组大西洋热点可能发生了相对旋转（图 1）。各热点相对于磁场和自转轴作不同的运动，而对于我们所研究的几个热点来说，似乎主要是向极运动，不过并不是所有的热点都向其所在半球的极点运动。向极运动也可能是间歇性的，有时甚至会反向运动。其他热点的有关资料也非常值得研究，然而遗憾的是，虽然热点有很多 [23]，但具有清晰的迹线且年龄确定，同时又与中大西洋和南大西洋热点同时期的、能够观测到的却少之又少（如果有的话）。

## 符合要求的假说

我们认为，深层地幔柱 [2,24] 位于热点之下的观点是当前唯一符合要求的、能够解释热点的假说，尤其是可以解释为什么作为分散的、小范围的异常体，它们能够延续至今，要知道它们中有的已有 1.8 亿年的历史了。而扩张脊脊轴上的热点尤其如此，并且它们长久以来一直处于这种状态下，其中以大西洋中脊的中部和南部脊轴上的热点最为典型。尽管这些热点相互之间以及相对于 1.2 亿年前的扩张脊（图 1）都发生了相对运动，但它们仍位于脊轴上，或处于脊轴附近 [14]。受限制的扩张脊脊轴有限长度的跃迁很可能就是由此产生的一种相关现象，并且在有些情况下该现象明显与热点有关。该现象可能会在相同方向上重复发生，由此导致明显的不对称扩张 [25]。在加拉帕戈斯 [26,27]、圣保罗／阿姆斯特丹群岛 [15]、澳大利亚南部 [25] 以及冰岛 [28] 等地都有脊轴跃迁的实例。我们得出的推论就是，无论是什么位于热点下方，它们都控制着洋脊的位置，而非相反；对我们而言，唯一可以解释这一点的似乎就是下伏深地幔柱的存在。

We suggest that within small groups of hot spots, the hypothesis that they are fixed with respect to one another may be valid, especially for short periods of a few tens of millions of years, but which hot spots belong to a particular internally fixed group may be hard to prove. The hypothesis that all hot spots are fixed with respect to one another and form an independent global reference frame is, however, clearly not valid.

The groups of hot spots that we have shown to remain essentially fixed internally have an approximate maximum horizontal dimension of 2,000 km. This is of the same order as the large swells that occur in East Africa and the Red Sea area, which are about 1,500 km across. We interpret the pattern of alkaline volcanism on abrupt topographic and structural uplifts each about 200 km across within these swells as showing the presence of four or five hot spots in each swell. The Cameroon zone also defines an ellipse about 1,500 km across and contains at least six discrete hot spots on uplifts, although a large overall topographic swell is not present. Apart from these examples, it is difficult to make a similar grouping of many of the remainder of the 120 hot spots we recognize, although some tentative suggestions can be made. Menard[29] has recently demonstrated the occurrence of low amplitude positive topographic anomalies 1,000 to 2,000 km across, and without obvious associated hot spots, in the North-east Pacific. We point out that similar large swells without associated hot spot volcanism are especially prominent in southern Africa, although the amplitude of these features is larger, and all but one are in continental lithosphere.

It may be that the large scale swells and internally fixed groups of hot spots reflect conditions at a depth comparable to their horizontal dimensions, and that the smaller uplifts and hot spots, of which there might be only one in some large swells (Hawaii?), reflect conditions at shallower depths. We speculate that the large swell may represent a broad, very slowly upwelling column, and that the smaller uplifts and hot spots within them represent smaller, more strongly heated and more rapidly rising columns within the large slowly rising column. The implications of the poleward motion of the few hot spots we have examined are not clear to us, and we think speculation on this is perhaps unjustified until well distributed data from other hot spots become available. If it is accepted that deep mantle plumes[2,24] underlie hot spots, then information relating to processes at the core-mantle boundary, and perhaps in the core, might eventually be extracted from the distribution and relative motion of hot spots. Our observations of the motion of some hot spots during the past 120 m.y. indicate that, if hot spots relate to mantle convection, this convection is probably highly complex and perhaps unlikely to be successfully modelled in terms of a small number of Rayleigh–Benard cells.

We thank Dr. E. Irving for advice and suggestions.

(**245**, 133-137; 1973)

Kevin Burke, W. S. F. Kidd and J. Tuzo Wilson
Erindale College, University of Toronto, Mississauga Road, Mississauga, Ontario

我们认为在小的热点组内部，关于各热点的相对位置保持固定不变的假说应该是合理的，特别是在几千万年的短期时间内，但是哪些热点属于一个特定的内部固定的组，这一点可能很难确定。然而，所有热点相互之间均保持固定不变且形成独立的全球参照系这一假说，则很显然是不成立的。

我们已证明，内部基本保持固定不变的各热点组中，最大的水平尺度约为 2,000 千米。这与发生在东非和红海地区的大规模隆起的尺度在同一个数量级上，其尺度约为 1,500 千米。在这些隆起中，存在直径约为 200 千米的陡峭地形和结构的小隆起，我们认为，这些小隆起上的碱性火山作用形式表明在每个隆起中存在四到五个热点。喀麦隆带也是跨度约 1,500 千米的一个椭圆，虽然它并不具有一个总体的地形隆起，但隆起上至少存在 6 个分散的热点。除上述实例外，对于我们所确定出的 120 个热点中的其他热点来说，虽然可从中得出一些初步结论，但要对它们进行类似的分组却很难。梅纳德[29] 最近在东北太平洋发现了规模约 1,000 ~ 2,000 千米的低起伏正地形异常体的存在，且与热点之间没有明显的相关关系。应当指出的是，类似的与热点火山作用无关的大规模隆起在非洲南部尤为显著，只是其起伏更大一些，并且它们中只有一个不在陆地岩石圈之内。

可能的情况是，大规模的隆起以及组内固定的热点组反映了与其水平尺度大小相当的深度上的环境，而较小的隆起和热点（有些大规模隆起中可能仅有一个这样的小隆起或热点，如夏威夷？）则反映了较浅深度上的环境。我们推测，大规模的隆起可能代表着宽广而缓慢的柱状上升流，而其内部较小的隆起和热点则代表在大的缓慢柱状上升流之内的、规模较小但更炽热、上升更快的柱状上升流。我们对所检测到的少数热点向极运动的指示意义尚不清楚，因此，我们认为在取得其他热点的分布资料之前，据此所得的推测可能是不合理的。倘若认可热点之下存在深地幔柱[2,24]，那么或许可从热点的分布及其相对运动情况中提取出有关核幔边界甚至地核内部所发生的过程信息。我们对某些热点在过去 1.2 亿年中运动情况的观测结果表明，倘若热点与地幔对流有关，那么该对流作用应该是高度复杂的，因而是不可能作几个瑞利 – 贝纳德涡旋就能模拟出来的。

感谢欧文博士对本文提出的意见和建议。

（齐红艳 孙惠南 翻译；李三忠 审稿）

Received June 19, 1973.

References:

1. Wilson, J. T., *Can. J. Phys.*, **41**, 863 (1963).

2. Morgan, W. J., *Bull. Am. Ass. Petrol. Geol.*, **56**, 203 (1972).

3. Duncan, R. A., Petersen, N., and Hargraves, R. B., *Nature*, **239**, 82 (1972).

4. Clague, D. A., and Jarrard, R. D., *Geol. Soc. Am. Bull.*, **84**, 1135 (1973).

5. McElhinny, M. W., *Nature*, **241**, 523 (1973).

6. Molnar, P., and Atwater, T., *EOS-Trans. Am. Geophys. Un.*, **54**, 240 (1973).

7. Larson, R. L., and Pitman, W. C., *Geol. Soc. Am. Bull.*, **83**, 3645 (1972).

8. Pitman, W. C., and Talwani, M., *Geol. Soc. Am. Bull.*, **83**, 619 (1972).

9. Coney, P. J., *Nature*, **233**, 462 (1971).

10. Ladd, J. W., Dickson, G. O., and Pitman, W. C. *The South Atlantic* (edit. by Nairn, A. E. M., and Stehli, F. G.) (Plenum, New York, in the press).

11. Mascle, J., and Phillips, J. D., *Nature*, **240**, 80 (1972).

12. Joides, Deep Sea Drilling Project, Leg 22, *Geotimes*, **17** (6), 15 (1972).

13. Joides, Deep Sea Drilling Project, Leg 26, *Geotimes*, **18** (3), 16 (1973).

14. Burke, K., and Wilson, J. T., *Nature*, **239**, 387 (1972).

15. McKenzie, D., and Sclater, J. G., *Geophys. J. R. astr. Soc.*, **24**, 437 (1971).

16. Hicken, A., Irving, E., Law, L. K., and Hastie, J., *Publ. Earth Phys. Branch, Energy Mines Resources, Ottawa*, **45**, 1 (1972).

17. Le Pichon, X., and Fox, P. J., *J. Geophys. Res.*, **76**, 6294 (1971).

18. Bullard, E. C., Everett, J. E., and Smith, A. G., *Phil. Trans. R. Soc.*, **A258**, 41 (1965).

19. Piper, J. D. A., and Richardson, A., *Geophys. J. R. astr. Soc.*, **29**, 147 (1972).

20. Phillips, J. D., and Forsyth, D., *Geol. Soc. Am. Bull.*, **83**, 1579 (1972).

21. Clague, D. A., and Jarrard, R. D., *EOS-Trans. Am. Geophys. Un.*, **54**, 238 (1973).

22. Deffeyes, K., *EOS-Trans. Am. Geophys. Un.*, **54**, 238 (1973).

23. Kidd, W. S. F., Burke, K., and Wilson, J. T., *EOS-Trans. Am. Geophys. Un.*, **54**, 238 (1973).

24. Deffeyes, K. S., *Nature*, **240**, 539 (1972).

25. Weissel, J. K., and Hayes, D. E., *Nature*, **231**, 578 (1971).

26. Holden, J. C., and Dietz, R. S., *Nature*, **235**, 266 (1972).

27. Hey, R. N., Johnson, G. L., and Lowrie, A., *EOS-Trans. Am. Geophys. Un.*, **54**, 244 (1973).

28. Ward, P. L., *Geol. Soc. Am. Bull.*, **82**, 2991 (1971).

29. Menard, H. W., *EOS-Trans. Am. Geophys. Un.*, **54**, 239 (1973).

# Black Hole Explosions?

## Editor's Note

**It was realized more than two hundred years ago that there is a critical mass and radius beyond which light cannot escape the gravitational field of an object—such an object becomes a "black hole". This idea was rigorously validated by the theory of general relativity. Here Stephen Hawking shows that black holes have effective temperatures that are inversely related to their mass, and should therefore radiate photons and neutrinos from their event horizons—they are not fully "black". As this radiation proceeds, the black hole loses mass. Finally it emits large quantities of X-rays and gamma-rays, and disappears in an explosion. "Hawking radiation" from black holes is now widely expected, but has not yet been seen.**

QUANTUM gravitational effects are usually ignored in calculations of the formation and evolution of black holes. The justification for this is that the radius of curvature of space-time outside the event horizon is very large compared to the Planck length $(G\hbar/c^3)^{1/2} \approx 10^{-33}$ cm, the length scale on which quantum fluctuations of the metric are expected to be of order unity. This means that the energy density of particles created by the gravitational field is small compared to the space-time curvature. Even though quantum effects may be small locally, they may still, however, add up to produce a significant effect over the lifetime of the Universe $\approx 10^{17}$ s which is very long compared to the Planck time $\approx 10^{-43}$ s. The purpose of this letter is to show that this indeed may be the case: it seems that any black hole will create and emit particles such as neutrinos or photons at just the rate that one would expect if the black hole was a body with a temperature of $(\kappa/2\pi)$ $(\hbar/2k) \approx 10^{-6}$ $(M_\odot/M)K$ where $\kappa$ is the surface gravity of the black hole[1]. As a black hole emits this thermal radiation one would expect it to lose mass. This in turn would increase the surface gravity and so increase the rate of emission. The black hole would therefore have a finite life of the order of $10^{71}$ $(M_\odot/M)^{-3}$ s. For a black hole of solar mass this is much longer than the age of the Universe. There might, however, be much smaller black holes which were formed by fluctuations in the early Universe[2]. Any such black hole of mass less than $10^{15}$ g would have evaporated by now. Near the end of its life the rate of emission would be very high and about $10^{30}$ erg would be released in the last 0.1 s. This is a fairly small explosion by astronomical standards but it is equivalent to about 1 million 1 Mton hydrogen bombs.

To see how this thermal emission arises, consider (for simplicity) a massless Hermitean scalar field $\phi$ which obeys the covariant wave equation $\phi_{;\,ab}g^{ab} = 0$ in an asymptotically flat space time containing a star which collapses to produce a black hole. The Heisenberg operator $\phi$ can be expressed as

# 黑洞爆炸?

## 编者按

人们在两百多年前就已经意识到，对于给定的半径有一个临界质量，当物体的质量超出临界质量时，其引力场就强到甚至连光都不能逃脱——这样的物体变成了"黑洞"。这一想法在广义相对论中得到了严格验证。本文中，斯蒂芬·霍金向我们表明黑洞有跟其质量成反比的等效温度，因此它必须从其事件视界向外辐射光子和中微子——即它们并不完全是"黑"的。黑洞在辐射过程中会损失质量，最终释放出大量的 X 射线和伽马射线，并在一次爆炸之后消失。虽然目前还没有直接观测到，但人们普遍相信黑洞存在"霍金辐射"。

在计算黑洞的形成和演化时，一般可忽略量子引力效应。这一点的合理性在于，在事件视界外的时空曲率半径远大于普朗克长度 $(G\hbar/c^3)^{1/2} \approx 10^{-33}$ cm，而在此尺度上预期度规的量子涨落是 1 的量级。这意味着由引力场产生的粒子的能量密度和时空曲率相比要小。虽然量子效应在局部很小，然而它们仍然可能在宇宙的寿命 $\approx 10^{17}$ s 内积累产生重大的影响，这个时间远长于普朗克时间 $\approx 10^{-43}$ s。这篇快报的目的是说明，似乎任何黑洞都将以预期的速率产生和发射粒子，如中微子或光子，正如同黑洞是一个温度为 $(\kappa/2\pi)(\hbar/2k) \approx 10^{-6} (M_\odot/M)$ K 的物体所表现的那样，其中 $\kappa$ 是黑洞的表面引力 [1]。当黑洞发射这类热辐射时，我们预期它将损失质量。这本身将增大它的表面引力，因而增大其发射速率。从此，黑洞将具有 $10^{71}(M_\odot/M)^{-3}$ s 量级的有限寿命。对于太阳质量的黑洞，这将比宇宙年龄更长。然而，可能存在许多较小的黑洞，它们是由早期宇宙中的涨落形成的 [2]。任何这类质量小于 $10^{15}$ g 的黑洞到现在都应该蒸发殆尽了。在接近它生命终了时，其粒子发射速率将非常高，在最后 0.1 s 将释放约 $10^{30}$ erg 能量。以天文学的标准来看，这是一个相当小的爆炸，但它相当于大约一百万个 100 万吨量级的氢弹爆炸。

为了解释黑洞热辐射是如何产生的，为简单起见，在一个包含由一颗恒星塌缩形成的一个黑洞的渐近平直时空中，考虑一个无质量的厄米标量场 $\varphi$，且它遵守协变波动方程 $\varphi_{;ab}g^{ab} = 0$。海森堡算符 $\varphi$ 可表示为：

$$\phi = \sum_i \{f_i a_i + \bar{f}_i a_i^+\}$$

where the $f_i$ are a complete orthonormal family of complex valued solutions of the wave equation $f_{i;ab} g^{ab} = 0$ which are asymptotically ingoing and positive frequency—they contain only positive frequencies on past null infinity $I^{-}$[3,4,5]. The position-independent operators $a_i$ and $a_i^+$ are interpreted as annihilation and creation operators respectively for incoming scalar particles. Thus the initial vacuum state, the state containing no incoming scalar particles, is defined by $a_i |0_-\rangle = 0$ for all $i$. The operator $\phi$ can also be expressed in terms of solutions which represent outgoing waves and waves crossing the event horizon:

$$\phi = \sum_i \{p_i b_i + \bar{p}_i b_i^+ + q_i c_i + \bar{q}_i c_i^+\}$$

where the $p_i$ are solutions of the wave equation which are zero on the event horizon and are asymptotically outgoing, positive frequency waves (positive frequency on future null infinity $I^+$) and the $q_i$ are solutions which contain no outgoing component (they are zero on $I^+$). For the present purposes it is not necessary that the $q_i$ are positive frequency on the horizon even if that could be defined. Because fields of zero rest mass are completely determined by their values on $I^-$, the $p_i$ and the $q_i$ can be expressed as linear combinations of the $f_i$ and the $\bar{f}_i$:

$$p_i = \sum_j \{\alpha_{ij} f_j + \beta_{ij} \bar{f}_j\} \text{ and so on}$$

The $\beta_{ij}$ will not be zero because the time dependence of the metric during the collapse will cause a certain amount of mixing of positive and negative frequencies. Equating the two expressions for $\phi$, one finds that the $b_i$, which are the annihilation operators for outgoing scalar particles, can be expressed as a linear combination of the ingoing annihilation and creation operators $a_i$ and $a_i^+$

$$b_i = \sum_j \{\bar{\alpha}_{ij} a_j - \bar{\beta}_{ij} a_j^+\}$$

Thus when there are no incoming particles the expectation value of the number operator $b_i^+ b_i$ of the $i$th outgoing state is

$$\langle 0_- |b_i^+ b_i| 0_-\rangle = \sum_j |\beta_{ij}|^2$$

The number of particles created and emitted to infinity in a gravitational collapse can therefore be determined by calculating the coefficients $\beta_{ij}$. Consider a simple example in which the collapse is spherically symmetric. The angular dependence of the solution of the wave equation can then be expressed in terms of the spherical harmonics $Y_{lm}$ and the dependence on retarded or advanced time $u$, $v$ can be taken to have the form $\omega^{-1/2} \exp(i\omega u)$ (here the continuum normalisation is used). Outgoing solutions $p_{lm\omega}$ will now be expressed as an integral over incoming fields with the same $l$ and $m$:

$$p_\omega = \int \{\alpha_{\omega\omega'} f_{\omega'} + \beta_{\omega\omega'} \bar{f}_{\omega'}\} d\omega'$$

$$\phi = \sum_i \{f_i a_i + \bar{f}_i a_i^+\}$$

其中，$f_i$ 是波动方程 $f_{i;ab}g^{ab}=0$ 的一族渐近向内、频率为正且完备正交归一复数解，它们在过去类光无穷远 $I^{-[3,4,5]}$ 只含有正频率。对于入射的标量粒子，位置无关的算符 $a_i$ 和 $a_i^+$ 分别解释为湮灭和产生算符。因此对于所有的 $i$，初始真空态，即不含有向内传播的标量粒子的态，可定义为 $a_i|0_-\rangle = 0$。算符 $\phi$ 也可以用代表向外的波和穿过事件视界的波的解表示：

$$\phi = \sum_i \{p_i b_i + \bar{p}_i b_i^+ + q_i c_i + \bar{q}_i c_i^+\}$$

其中，$p_i$ 是波动方程的解，它们在视界上为零且是渐近向外的正频波（在未来类光无穷远 $I^+$ 为正频率），而 $q_i$ 是不含向外成分的解（它们在 $I^+$ 为零）。就现在的目的而言，即使可以被定义，$q_i$ 在视界处也不一定是正频的。因为零静止质量的场完全被它们在 $I^-$ 的值确定，$p_i$ 和 $q_i$ 可以表示为 $f_i$ 和 $\bar{f}_i$ 的线性组合：

$$p_i = \sum_j \{\alpha_{ij} f_j + \beta_{ij} \bar{f}_j\} \ \text{等}$$

因为在塌缩期间度规的时间依赖性将导致一定量的正频和负频的混合，所以 $\beta_{ij}$ 将不为零。令 $\phi$ 的两个表达式相等，可以发现向外传播标量粒子的湮灭算符 $b_i$ 可以表示为向内湮灭和产生算符 $a_i$ 和 $a_i^+$ 的线性叠加，即：

$$b_i = \sum_j \{\bar{\alpha}_{ij} a_j - \bar{\beta}_{ij} a_j^+\}$$

于是在没有向内态的粒子时，第 $i$ 个向外态的粒子数算符 $b_i^+ b_i$ 的期望值为：

$$\langle 0_- |b_i^+ b_i| 0_-\rangle = \sum_j |\beta_{ij}|^2$$

因此，在一次引力塌缩中产生并发射到无穷远的粒子的数目可以通过计算系数 $\beta_{ij}$ 确定。考虑一个简单的例子，塌缩是球对称的。波动方程的解对角度的依赖可以用球谐函数 $Y_{lm}$ 表示，对推迟或超前时间 $u$、$v$ 的依赖可以取为 $\omega^{-1/2} \exp(i\omega u)$（这里使用了连续归一化）。向外的解 $p_{lm\omega}$ 现在可以表示为对相同 $l$ 和 $m$ 的向内的场的积分：

$$p_\omega = \int \{\alpha_{\omega\omega'} f_{\omega'} + \beta_{\omega\omega'} \bar{f}_{\omega'}\} d\omega'$$

(The *lm* suffixes have been dropped.) To calculate $\alpha_{\omega\omega'}$ and $\beta_{\omega\omega'}$ consider a wave which has a positive frequency $\omega$ on $I^+$ propagating backwards through spacetime with nothing crossing the event horizon. Part of this wave will be scattered by the curvature of the static Schwarzschild solution outside the black hole and will end up on $I^-$ with the same frequency $\omega$. This will give a $\delta(\omega-\omega')$ behaviour in $\alpha_{\omega\omega'}$. Another part of the wave will propagate backwards into the star, through the origin and out again onto $I^-$. These waves will have a very large blue shift and will reach $I^-$ with asymptotic form

$$C\omega^{-1/2} \exp \{-i\omega\kappa^{-1} \log (v_0-v) + i\omega v\} \; \textit{for } v < v_0$$

and zero for $v \geq v_0$ , where $v_0$ is the last advanced time at which a particle can leave $I^-$, pass through the origin and escape to $I^+$. Taking Fourier transforms, one finds that for large $\omega'$, $\alpha_{\omega\omega'}$ and $\beta_{\omega\omega'}$ have the form:

$$\alpha_{\omega\omega'} \approx C \exp [i(\omega-\omega')v_0](\omega'/\omega)^{1/2} \cdot \Gamma(1-i\omega/\kappa) [-i(\omega-\omega')]^{-1+i\omega/\kappa}$$

$$\beta_{\omega\omega'} \approx C \exp [i(\omega+\omega')v_0](\omega'/\omega)^{1/2} \cdot \Gamma(1-i\omega/\kappa) [-i(\omega+\omega')]^{-1+i\omega/\kappa}$$

The total number of outgoing particles created in the frequency range $\omega \rightarrow \omega+d\omega$ is $d\omega \int_0^\infty |\beta_{\omega\omega'}|^2 d\omega'$. From the above expression it can be seen that this is infinite. By considering outgoing wave packets which are peaked at a frequency $\omega$ and at late retarded times one can see that this infinite number of particles corresponds to a steady rate of emission at late retarded times. One can estimate this rate in the following way. The part of the wave from $I^+$ which enters the star at late retarded times is almost the same as the part that would have crossed the past event horizon of the Schwarzschild solution had it existed. The probability flux in a wave packet peaked at $\omega$ is roughly proportional to $\int_{\omega_1'}^{\omega_2'}\{ |\alpha_{\omega\omega'}|^2 - |\beta_{\omega\omega'}|^2 \} \, d\omega$ where $\omega_2' \gg \omega_1' \gg 0$. In the expressions given above for $\alpha_{\omega\omega'}$ and $\beta_{\omega\omega'}$ there is a logarithmic singularity in the factors $[-i(\omega-\omega')]^{-1+i\omega/\kappa}$ and $[-i(\omega+\omega')]^{-1+i\omega/\kappa}$. Value of the expressions on different sheets differ by factors of $\exp(2\pi n\omega\kappa^{-1})$. To obtain the correct ratio of $\alpha_{\omega\omega'}$ to $\beta_{\omega\omega'}$ one has to continue $[-i(\omega+\omega')]^{-1+i\omega/\kappa}$ in the upper half $\omega'$ plane round the singularity and then replace $\omega'$ by $-\omega'$. This means that, for large $\omega'$,

$$|\alpha_{\omega\omega'}| = \exp (\pi\omega/\kappa)|\beta_{\omega\omega'}|$$

From this it follows that the number of particles emitted in this wave packet mode is $(\exp(2\pi\omega/\kappa)-1)^{-1}$ times the number of particles that would have been absorbed from a similar wave packet incident on the black hole from $I^-$. But this is just the relation between absorption and emission cross sections that one would expect from a body with a temperature in geometric units of $\kappa/2\pi$. Similar results hold for massless fields of any integer spin. For half integer spin one again gets a similar result except that the emission cross section is $(\exp(2\pi\omega/\kappa)+1)^{-1}$ times the absorption cross section as one would expect for thermal emission of fermions. These results do not seem to depend on the assumption of exact spherical symmetry which merely simplifies the calculation.

582

这里略去了 $lm$ 下标。为计算 $\alpha_{\omega\omega'}$ 和 $\beta_{\omega\omega'}$，考虑一个在 $I^+$ 为正频 $\omega$，在时空中反向传播的不穿过视界的波。这个波的一部分将被黑洞外的静态史瓦西解的曲率散射并将在 $I^-$ 上以相同的频率 $\omega$ 终止。这将导致 $\alpha_{\omega\omega'}$ 的 $\delta(\omega-\omega')$ 行为。这个波的另外一部分将向后传播到恒星中，通过原点然后向外再到 $I^-$。这些波将有非常大的蓝移，并将以渐近形式接近 $I^-$：

$$C\omega^{-1/2}\exp\{-i\omega\kappa^{-1}\log(v_0-v)+i\omega v\}，当\ v<v_0\ 时$$

当 $v \geqslant v_0$ 时，这个蓝移值为 0。其中，$v_0$ 是最后的超前时间，此时的粒子尚可脱离 $I^-$，通过原点并逃向 $I^+$。作傅里叶变换可以发现对于大的 $\omega'$，$\alpha_{\omega\omega'}$ 和 $\beta_{\omega\omega'}$ 有如下形式：

$$\alpha_{\omega\omega'}\approx C\exp[i(\omega-\omega')v_0](\omega'/\omega)^{1/2}\cdot\Gamma(1-i\omega/\kappa)[-i(\omega-\omega')]^{-1+i\omega/\kappa}$$

$$\beta_{\omega\omega'}\approx C\exp[i(\omega+\omega')v_0](\omega'/\omega)^{1/2}\cdot\Gamma(1-i\omega/\kappa)[-i(\omega+\omega')]^{-1+i\omega/\kappa}$$

在频率范围 $\omega\to\omega+d\omega$ 产生的向外粒子的总数为 $d\omega\int_0^\infty|\beta_{\omega\omega'}|^2d\omega'$，并由上面的表达式可以看出这个量是无限的。通过考虑在较晚的推迟时间的、峰值频率 $\omega$ 的向外波包，可以看到这个无限的粒子数对应于较晚推迟时间的一个稳态发射率。可以通过以下方法估计这个发射率。波中来自 $I^+$ 的在较晚推迟时间进入恒星的部分（如果这部分存在的话）和穿过史瓦西解的过去视界的部分几乎相同，峰值在 $\omega$ 处的波包中的概率流大致正比于 $\int_{\omega_1'}^{\omega_2'}\{|\alpha_{\omega\omega'}|^2-|\beta_{\omega\omega'}|^2\}d\omega$，其中，$\omega_2'\gg\omega_1'>0$。在上面给出的 $\alpha_{\omega\omega'}$ 和 $\beta_{\omega\omega'}$ 的表达式中，$[-i(\omega-\omega')]^{-1+i\omega/\kappa}$ 和 $[-i(\omega+\omega')]^{-1+i\omega/\kappa}$ 因子中有一个对数奇点。这个表达式在不同面上的值相差一个 $\exp(2\pi n\omega\kappa^{-1})$ 因子。为得到正确的 $\alpha_{\omega\omega'}$ 和 $\beta_{\omega\omega'}$ 的比值，必须在上半 $\omega'$ 平面围绕奇点对 $[-i(\omega+\omega')]^{-1+i\omega/\kappa}$ 进行延拓并将 $\omega'$ 换为 $-\omega'$。这意味着对于大的 $\omega'$：

$$|\alpha_{\omega\omega'}|=\exp(\pi\omega/\kappa)|\beta_{\omega\omega'}|$$

由此可得，这个波包模式中发射的粒子数是从 $I^-$ 入射到黑洞上的类似波包中已被吸收的粒子数的 $[\exp(2\pi\omega/\kappa)-1]^{-1}$ 倍，但这正是根据几何单位下温度为 $\kappa/2\pi$ 的物体所预期的吸收和发射截面之间的关系。类似结果对任何整数自旋的无质量场也同样成立。对半整数自旋，正如我们对费米子的热辐射所预期的那样，也能得到类似结果，只是发射截面是吸收截面的 $[\exp(2\pi\omega/\kappa)+1]^{-1}$ 倍，这些结果似乎并不依赖于只是为了简化计算而采取的精确球对称性假设。

Beckenstein[6] suggested on thermodynamic grounds that some multiple of $\kappa$ should be regarded as the temperature of a black hole. He did not, however, suggest that a black hole could emit particles as well as absorb them. For this reason Bardeen, Carter and I considered that the thermodynamical similarity between $\kappa$ and temperature was only an analogy. The present result seems to indicate, however, that there may be more to it than this. Of course this calculation ignores the back reaction of the particles on the metric, and quantum fluctuations on the metric. These might alter the picture.

Further details of this work will be published elsewhere. The author is very grateful to G. W. Gibbons for discussions and help.

(**248**, 30-31; 1974)

**S. W. Hawking**
Department of Applied Mathematics and Theoretical Physics and Institute of Astronomy, University of Cambridge

Received January 17, 1974.

References:

1. Bardeen, J. M., Carter, B., and Hawking, S. W., *Commun. math. Phys.*, **31**, 161–170 (1973).

2. Hawking, S. W., *Mon. Not. R. astr. Soc.*, **152**, 75-78 (1971).

3. Penrose, R., in *Relativity, Groups and Topology* (edit. by de Witt, C. M., and de Witt, B. S). Les Houches Summer School, 1963 (Gordon and Breach, New York, 1964).

4. Hawking, S. W., and Ellis, G. F. R., *The Large-Scale Structure of Space-Time* (Cambridge University Press, London 1973).

5. Hawking, S. W., in *Black Holes* (edit. by de Witt, C. M., and de Witt, B. S), Les Houches Summer School, 1972 (Gordon and Breach, New York, 1973).

6. Beckenstein, J. D., *Phys. Rev.*, D7, 2333–2346 (1973).

贝肯斯坦[6]在热力学基础上提出，$\kappa$的某个倍数应该被看作黑洞的温度。然而，他并未提出，黑洞可以像吸收粒子一样发射粒子。因此，巴丁、卡特和我曾经认为，$\kappa$和温度之间的热力学的相似性只是一种类比。然而，目前的结果似乎表明，可能存在比这更多的内容。当然，这个计算忽略了粒子对度规的反作用以及度规本身的量子涨落，这些不排除会改变这个物理图像。

这项工作的进一步细节将在其他地方发表。作者非常感谢吉本斯给予的建议和帮助。

（沈乃澂 翻译；肖伟科 审稿）

# Further Evidence of Lower Pleistocene Hominids from East Rudolf, North Kenya, 1973

R. E. F. Leakey

## Editor's Note

After six years of work at East Rudolf, Richard Leakey and his team had found evidence for two kinds of hominid. The first was a robust australopithecine found throughout the deposits and showing relatively little change. The second was a primitive but more evolutionarily variable form of *Homo*, perhaps exemplified by the spectacular skull "1470" Leakey described in 1973. This latest report suggested a hominid of a third kind, with *Homo*-like dentition but a smaller cranium, perhaps similar to the "gracile" australopithecines from Sterkfontein. The increasing wealth of hominid remains, the disputes over attributions to *Homo habilis* and australopithecines, together with the possibility of marked sexual dimorphism, only served to deepen the mysteries of human origin.

---

Twenty new hominid specimens were recovered from the East Rudolf area in 1973. New evidence suggests the presence of at least three hominid lineages in the Plio-Pleistocene of East Africa.

---

THIS is a report of the 1973 field season at East Rudolf, Kenya, where the East Rudolf Research Project (formerly Expedition) has now concluded its sixth year of operations. Eighty-seven specimens of fossil hominid were collected[1] from the area during 1968–72; a further twenty specimens were recovered between June and September 1973 from the Upper, Lower and Ileret Members of the Koobi Fora Formation[2]. Exploration to the south of Koobi Fora was begun in 1972 and continued in 1973. No hominids have yet been found in the limited exposures of the Kubi Algi Formation. A notice of two specimens—KNM-ER 1510 and 1590—that were previously[1] mentioned only by number, is included in this report. The 1973 hominids are not here attributed to genera as there are still no clear generic diagnoses available for fossil hominids. With a few exceptions, previous attributions for the East Rudolf hominid collection remain satisfactory.

Archaeological investigation during 1973 was extended under the direction of G. Ll. Isaac, with J. C. W. Harris who conducted major excavations at several sites in the Upper Member of areas 130 and 131. Limited excavation, but extensive prospecting, in the Lower Member produced sufficient results to support further searching for artefacts below the KBS Tuff.

586

# 1973年在肯尼亚北部鲁道夫湖以东下更新统发现更多人科动物证据

利基

**编者按**

理查德·利基及其研究小组在鲁道夫湖以东经过六年的研究工作，发现了两种人科动物的证据。其一是一种粗壮型南方古猿，他在整个沉积序列中都出现并且变化相对较小。其二是一种原始的但具备更多进步特征的人属类型，也许利基1973年所描述的引人注目的"1470"头骨就是其典型代表。这篇最新报道提出了第三种人科动物，他具有与人属相似的齿系，但颅骨更小，可能与在斯泰克方丹发现的"纤细型"南方古猿相似。随着人科动物化石的增加，将其归入能人还是南方古猿尚存争议，还有可能存在的明显性双形，这些都只能使人类起源的疑团更加扑朔迷离。

1973年在鲁道夫湖以东地区发掘出了20件新的人科动物标本。新证据表明在东非地区的上新世–更新世时期至少存在三个人科动物支系。

本文是有关1973年在肯尼亚鲁道夫湖以东野外挖掘的报告，鲁道夫湖以东研究项目组（前身是探险队）已经结束了在那里第六个年头的工作。在1968~1972年间，已经从该地区采集到了87件人科动物化石标本[1]；另外还有20件标本是在1973年6~9月之间从库比福勒组的上段、下段以及伊莱雷特段[2]发掘出来的。对库比福勒南部地区的调查始于1972年，并且在1973年持续进行。目前为止，还没有在库比阿尔及组有限出露的地层中发现过人科动物化石。本次报告对KNM–ER 1510和1590这两件标本也做了简报，而在此之前[1]，只提到过这两件标本的数字编号。由于现在尚无明确的对人科动物化石进行属一级划分的鉴定标准，所以在本文中，并未将1973年发现的人科动物鉴定到属。除个别例外，先前对鲁道夫湖以东采集到的人科动物标本的归属仍然适用。

在艾萨克的指导下，1973年的考古调查工作得到拓展，哈里斯重点在130和131区域的上段的几个遗址进行了发掘。尽管在下段进行的发掘工作较少，但很有前景，发掘结果充分表明在KBS凝灰岩下有进一步寻找人工制品的必要。

During the palaeontological survey, which was supervised by J. M. Harris, all identifiable fragments from certain horizons were collected; new species were recorded and some primate remains were recovered during a limited survey of the Kubi Algi Formation. A detailed account of the East Rudolf fauna will be presented upon conclusion of current studies, but there are clear indications that at times the palaeoenvironment differed from that of the lower part of the Shungura Formation of the Omo Valley in Ethiopia.

In the geological studies, emphasis was placed on microstratigraphy and palaeo-environmental reconstruction. B. Bowen supervised a study of the Lower and Upper Members of areas 130 and 131 which included confirming the stratigraphic relationships of the cranium KNM-ER 1470. The complete section of the Koobi Fora Formation exposed in area 102 was studied by a group from Dartmouth College, New Hampshire, under G. Johnson. A. K. Behrensmeyer completed a preliminary geological investigation of the hominid sites, noting depositional environments and possible association of fauna; further studies are planned.

I. Findlater extended mapping of tuffaceous horizons to the south of Koobi Fora and collected samples for isotope dating. A series of dates has been obtained from material collected during 1972 (unpublished work at Miller, Findlater, Fitch and Watkins). Palaeomagnetic studies complement those of 1972 and there are sufficient data for internal correlations to be made[3].

## Hominid Collection

Specimen KNM-ER 1590, reported previously[1], consists of dental and cranial fragments which were collected from area 12, some meters below the KBS Tuff. Both parietals, fragments of frontal and other pieces of cranial vault, the left deciduous c and $dm^2$, the left and right unerupted C, $P^3$ and $P^4$, and the erupted left and right $M^1$ and left $M^2$ were recovered. Although the cranium is immature, it was large with a cranial capacity as great as that determined for KNM-ER 1470. The parietals may show some deformation but, in any event, they suggest that the cranium was wide with a sagittal keel.

KNM-ER 1510, also reported previously[1], includes cranial and mandibular fragments. The specimen is poorly mineralised and further geological investigation at the site indicates a Holocene rather than an early Pleistocene provenance as originally thought.

The 1973 hominids and their stratigraphical positions are listed in Table 1. Specimens from area 123 are rare, and their stratigraphical position relative to the Upper and Lower Members of the Koobi Fora Formation needs clarification.

在哈里斯指导下的古生物调查中，收集了所有在特定地层中的可鉴定的化石残片；在库比阿尔及组地层中发现了新物种，并且发现了一些灵长类化石。对于鲁道夫湖以东动物群的详细报告将在本项研究的结论部分中给出，但是有明显迹象表明当时的古环境与埃塞俄比亚奥莫河谷的上古拉组下部是不同的。

在地质学研究方面，重点关注了微观地层学和古环境的重建。鲍恩指导了对130区和131区的上下段地层的研究，包括对产出 KNM–ER 1470 头骨的地层关系的确认。由约翰逊带领，来自新罕布什尔州达特茅斯学院的研究小组对 102 区出露完好的库比福勒组的地层剖面进行了研究。贝伦斯迈耶对人科动物化石地点做了初步地质调查，并记录了沉积环境和可能伴生的动物群；进一步的研究已做好了安排。

芬勒特将对凝灰岩层的绘图工作扩展到了库比福勒以南，并且采集了同位素测年样品。从 1972 年间采集到的材料中已经获得了一系列年代数据（米勒、芬勒特、菲奇和沃特金斯未发表的工作）。古地磁学研究补充了 1972 年的研究数据，现在已经有足够多数据来相互印证[3]。

## 人科动物标本

此前报道过的 KNM–ER 1590 号标本[1]包括牙齿和颅骨残片是采自 12 区的 KBS 凝灰岩之下数米处。发现的材料包括如下解剖部位：两侧顶骨、额骨及头盖骨残片，左侧乳犬齿和第二上乳臼齿（$dm^2$），未萌出的左、右 C，$P^3$ 及 $P^4$，已萌出的左右 $M^1$ 及左 $M^2$。尽管颅骨并未发育成熟，但是其颅容量却与已知的 KNM–ER 1470 号标本的一样大。虽然其顶骨可能有些变形，但无论如何，它们都表明了这是个很宽且具有矢状嵴的颅骨。

KNM–ER 1510 号标本此前也报道过[1]，该标本包括颅骨和下颌骨残片。这个标本石化程度很浅，后来对遗址的地质调查结果表明，含该标本的地层时代属于全新世，而非最初认为的早更新世。

表 1 中列出了 1973 年发现的人科动物标本及其地层位置。从 123 区出土的标本很少，其与库比福勒组的上、下段地层的相对位置关系还需要进一步澄清。

Table 1. 1973 hominid collection from East Rudolf

| KNM-ER NO. | Specimen | Area | Member |
|---|---|---|---|
| 1800 | Cranial fragments | 130 | Lower |
| 1801 | Left mandible, $P_4$, $M_1$, $M_3$ | 131 | Lower |
| 1802 | Left mandible, $P_4$-$M_2$ and right $P_3$-$M_2$ | 131 | Lower |
| 1803 | Right mandible fragment | 131 | Lower |
| 1804 | Right maxilla, $P^3$-$M^2$ | 104 | Upper |
| 1805 | Cranium and mandible | 130 | Upper |
| 1806 | Mandible | 130 | Upper |
| 1807 | Right femur shaft | 103 | Upper |
| 1808 | Associated skeletal and cranial fragments | 103 | Upper |
| 1809 | Right femur shaft | 127 | Lower |
| 1810 | Proximal left tibia | 123 | ?Lower |
| 1811 | Left mandible fragment | 123 | ?Lower |
| 1812 | Right mandible fragment and left $I_1$ and $M_1$ | 123 | Lower |
| 1813 | Cranium | 123 | ?Lower |
| 1814 | Maxillary fragments | 127 | Upper |
| 1815 | Right talus | 1 | Upper |
| 1816 | Immature fragmented mandible | 6A | Upper |
| 1817 | Right mandible | 1 | Upper |
| 1818 | $I^1$ | 6A | Upper |
| 1819 | $M_3$ | 3 | Upper |
| 1820 | Left mandible with $M_1$ | 103 | Upper |

A well preserved mandible (Fig. 1), KNM-ER 1802, was discovered by J. Harris *in situ* below the KBS Tuff in area 131. The dentition is only slightly worn, and fragments of both $M_3$ crowns suggest that death occurred before full eruption. The canines and incisors are represented by roots and by alveoli filled with matrix. The mandible shows some interesting features—moulding of the mandibular body, absence of a strong post-incisive planum, the development of a slight inferior mandibular torus and the distinct eversion of the mandibular body when viewed from below.

表 1. 1973 年从鲁道夫湖以东发掘的人科动物标本

| KNM–ER NO. | 标本 | 区 | 段 |
|---|---|---|---|
| 1800 | 颅骨残片 | 130 | 下 |
| 1801 | 左下颌骨，$P_4$，$M_1$，$M_3$ | 131 | 下 |
| 1802 | 左下颌骨，$P_4$–$M_2$ 及右 $P_3$–$M_2$ | 131 | 下 |
| 1803 | 右下颌骨残片 | 131 | 下 |
| 1804 | 右上颌骨，$P^3$–$M^2$ | 104 | 上 |
| 1805 | 颅骨和下颌骨 | 130 | 上 |
| 1806 | 下颌骨 | 130 | 上 |
| 1807 | 右股骨骨干 | 103 | 上 |
| 1808 | 关联的体骨和颅骨残片 | 103 | 上 |
| 1809 | 右股骨骨干 | 127 | 下 |
| 1810 | 左胫骨近端 | 123 | ？下 |
| 1811 | 左下颌骨残片 | 123 | ？下 |
| 1812 | 右下颌骨残片、左 $I_1$ 和 $M_1$ | 123 | 下 |
| 1813 | 颅骨 | 123 | ？下 |
| 1814 | 上颌骨残片 | 127 | 上 |
| 1815 | 右距骨 | 1 | 上 |
| 1816 | 未发育完全的残破下颌骨 | 6A | 上 |
| 1817 | 右下颌骨 | 1 | 上 |
| 1818 | $I^1$ | 6A | 上 |
| 1819 | $M_3$ | 3 | 上 |
| 1820 | 左下颌骨带 $M_1$ | 103 | 上 |

哈里斯在 131 区 KBS 凝灰岩之下就地发现了一件保存很好的下颌骨 KNM–ER 1802（图 1）。其齿系只有轻微磨损，两侧的 $M_3$ 牙冠残片表明该个体是在牙齿未完全萌出之前就已死亡。犬齿和门齿只保留着牙根和充满沉积物的齿槽。该下颌骨显示出了一些很有趣的特征——下颌体的形状，不存在明显的门齿后平面，轻微发育的下颌圆枕，以及从下面看时下颌体呈独特的外翻形式。

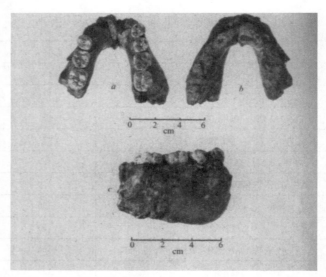

Fig. 1. Mandible, KNM-ER 1802. *a*, Superior view; *b*, inferior view; *c*, right lateral view.

A weathered mandible, KNM-ER 1801, bears some resemblances to KNM-ER 1802, but its worn dentition and loss of surface bone prevent direct comparisons. The relative proportions of the molars and premolars may have been exaggerated by interstitial wear.

A crushed maxillary fragment, KNM-ER 1804, with $P^3$-$M^2$ preserved was discovered by R. Holloway. The teeth are complete but worn.

A skull (cranium with associated mandible), KNM-ER 1805, was discovered by P. Abell *in situ* in the BBS Tuff complex in area 130. The specimen is heavily encrusted with a hard matrix and will require careful preparation before its morphology is revealed. Comments here are thus preliminary. The cranium is in pieces which fit together. After preparation, it should be possible to determine the endocranial capacity; at present, a volume of 600-700 cm$^3$ is suggested. The supraorbital region, much of the face and the greater part of the basi-cranium have not been preserved. The postorbital region is preserved and the minimum breadth is approximately 90 mm. No distinct temporal lines cross the frontal area although they can be discerned and are still apart at the bregma. There are distinct parasagittal crests. The nuchal attachments are very distinctive and protrude to form a wide bony shelf. The palate is intact; all the teeth are preserved except for the right $P^4$ and the left $I^1$. The mandible, small and distinctly robust, is represented by both sides of the body but, except for the right $M_2$ and $M_3$, the tooth crowns are missing. The ascending rami are not preserved. The right $M_3$ and $M_2$ are well worn but small. The upper dentition shows wear on all the teeth, including $M^3$.

A large mandible, KNM-ER 1806, was discovered by Meave Leakey at the same site and horizon as was KNM-ER 1805. There are no tooth crowns preserved and the ascending

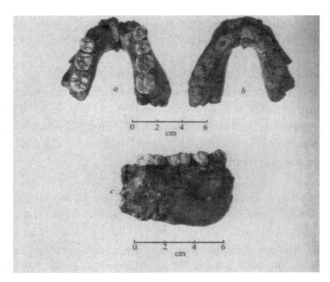

图 1. 下颌骨，KNM–ER 1802。*a*，上面视；*b*，下面视；*c*，右侧面视。

KNM–ER 1801 号标本是一个遭受风化的下颌骨，与 KNM–ER 1802 号标本有些许相像之处，但其严重磨耗的牙系及骨骼表面的破损使得我们无法进行直接比较。臼齿和前臼齿列的相对比例可能被齿间隙磨损放大了。

KNM–ER 1804 是霍洛韦发现的一个压碎了的、保存有 $P^3$–$M^2$ 的上颌骨残片。其齿列完整但磨耗严重。

KNM–ER 1805 是一个头骨（带有相连的下颌骨及颅骨），由埃布尔在 130 区的 BBS 混杂凝灰岩中就地发现。该标本外面包裹着厚厚的坚硬围岩，要想揭示其形态特征，还需要进行认真细致的修理。因此，此处所做讨论只是初步认识。该颅骨虽支离破碎，但可以拼接到一起。经过修理之后，应该可以确定其颅容量；目前，可以认为其颅容量为 600~700 cm³。眶上区域、面部大部分以及颅底绝大部分都没有保存下来。眶后区域保存下来了，其最小宽度约为 90 mm。尽管颞线依稀可辨，但在额区表现不明显，并且在前囟处仍然是分开的。有明显的副矢状嵴。项肌附着区明显而突出，形成了一个宽的骨质架。腭骨完好；除了右 $P^4$ 和左 $I^1$，其余牙齿都保存完好。下颌骨小且非常粗壮，左、右下颌体都保存下来了，除右 $M_2$ 和 $M_3$ 之外，其余牙齿齿冠都缺失了。下颌上升支没有保存下来。右 $M_3$ 和 $M_2$ 深度磨耗，并且很小。上齿系的所有牙齿都有磨耗，$M^3$ 也不例外。

KNM–ER 1806 是一个巨大的下颌骨，由米芙·利基在发现 KNM–ER 1805 的同一地点和同一地层发现。该下颌骨没有任何齿冠保存下来，上升支也丢失了，其他

rami are missing in this otherwise complete specimen. The mandible is typical of the large East Rudolf hominid that I have previously attributed to *Australopithecus*.

A fragmented specimen, KNM-ER 1808, was discovered in area 103 by Kamoya Kimeu. The specimen includes maxillary and mandibular teeth, cranial and mandibular fragments, a fragment of atlas vertebra, the distal half of a femur lacking the condyles, a large segment of humerus and other postcranial fragments. There is little doubt that the various pieces are from one individual and further sieving and excavation will be undertaken in the hope of recovering more material.

A cranium, KNM-ER 1813 (Fig. 2), was discovered *in situ* by Kamoya Kimeu in area 123. The specimen was fragmented but has been partially reconstructed. Plastic deformation is evident. The cranium is partly covered with a thin coat of matrix and considerable preparation is needed before a detailed description can be attempted. The endo-cranial volume is likely to be small; a figure of approximately 500 cm$^3$ is suggested on the basis of comparative external measurements. Other interesting features include the curvature of the frontals, a postglabella sulcus and the small dentition. The maxilla has well preserved teeth, P$^3$–M$^3$, on the left side, but on the right side only the tooth roots and the complete crown of M$^3$ remain. Both canines and lateral incisors are present but the central incisors seem to have been lost before fossilisation. Both sides of the maxilla fit together to give the form of the dental arcade. The right maxillary fragment includes the malar region and connects with the lateral margin of the right orbit.

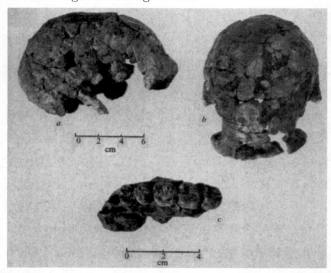

Fig. 2. Cranium, KNM-ER 1813. *a*, Right lateral view; *b*, superior view; *c*, occlusal view of left side of palate.

Other specimens recovered during 1973 are listed in Table 1 and will be described in detail after studies are completed.

方面都很完整。该下颌骨具有我此前归入南方古猿的鲁道夫湖以东出土的巨大人科动物的典型特征。

KNM–ER 1808 是一个破碎的标本，由卡莫亚·基梅乌在 103 区发现。该标本包括上、下颌牙齿、颅骨和下颌骨残片，寰椎残片，缺少股骨髁的股骨远端、一大段肱骨和其他颅后骨残片，几乎可以肯定这些残片均来自于同一个个体。为了得到更多材料，我们将进行进一步的筛洗和挖掘工作。

颅骨 KNM–ER 1813（图 2）由卡莫亚·基梅乌在 123 区就地发现。虽然该标本都裂成了碎片，但是已经被部分地修复好了。塑性变形明显。该颅骨的一部分被薄层沉积物所覆盖，在对其进行详细描述之前，需要大量的修理工作。其颅容量可能比较小；根据其外部尺寸的比较，可以估计出其数值约为 500 cm$^3$。其他有趣的特征包括：额骨的曲率、眉间后槽和小的牙齿。上颌骨上有保存很好的左 P$^3$–M$^3$，但是右齿列只有牙根和 M$^3$ 齿冠残存。犬齿和侧门齿都在，但是中门齿似乎在石化之前就已经丢失了。上颌骨的两侧可以拼接到一起，从而可看出齿弓的形状。右上颌骨残片包括颧骨部及与右眼眶侧边相连的部分。

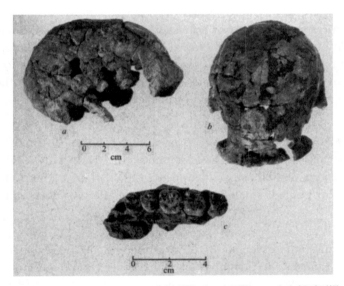

图 2. 颅骨，KNM–ER 1813。*a*，右侧面视；*b*，上面视；*c*，左上颌嚼面视。

1973 年间挖掘的其他标本都在表 1 中列出，并将在相关研究完成以后再做详细描述。

## Significance of the 1973 Collection

In previous reports[1,4-7], the East Rudolf hominids were assigned to *Australopithecus*, *Homo* or indeterminate (the last category included both very fragmentary specimens and those of uncertain taxonomic rank).

The East Rudolf specimens that have been attributed to *Australopithecus* span a period of time from 3 million years to just over 1 million years with apparently little morphological change. This form is likely to be the same species as *A. boisei*[8]; it also shows similarities with *A. robustus* from southern Africa. A Pliocene origin is suggested for this specialised group.

Specimens attributed to *Homo* have been recovered from deposits covering a similar time span, but these show greater morphological variability. Those recovered from the Ileret Member seem to differ from those recovered from the Lower Member of the Koobi Fora Formation. The suggestion that a large brained, fully bipedal hominid was living at East Rudolf 3 million years ago was put forward after the 1972 discoveries[7]. This point of view is supported by the cranial fragments, KNM-ER 1590, also from below the KBS Tuff, and this specimen is provisionally attributed to *Homo*.

The 1973 collection from East Rudolf raises many questions. The new mandible, KNM-ER 1802, could be considered as belonging to the same genus and species as KNM-ER 1470 and 1590. There are striking similarities between the dental characters of KNM-ER 1802 and some specimens from Olduvai Gorge such as the type mandible of *Homo habilis*, OH 7. Although the suggested cranial capacity for *H. habilis* is appreciably smaller than that determined for KNM-ER 1470, the discrepancy may be due to the fragmentary material upon which the former estimates were made. I consider that the evidence for a 'small brained' form of *Homo* during the Lower Pleistocene is tenuous.

The cranium, KNM-ER 1813, may prove to be quite distinct from the robust australopithecines and from *Homo*, as represented by KNM-ER 1470. The dentition is 'hominine', yet the cranial capacity appears small. The cranium has some of the features seen in the gracile, small brained, hominid *Australopithecus africanus* Dart, from Sterkfontein.

I have previously questioned the validity of a distinct gracile species of *Australopithecus*[6], but this new evidence reopens the possibility of its existence. Some authors[9,10] have suggested that *Homo habilis*, particularly OH 24, shows features typical of *Australopithecus africanus*. My suggestion here, that *H. habilis* may have affinities with KNM-ER 1470 and 1590, refers only to OH 7 and OH 16. Features of the calvarium of OH 24 show similarities with KNM-ER 1813. The size and morphology of the teeth of the two specimens are alike and the cranial capacities may also be comparable[11,12].

The skull KNM-ER 1805 is undoubtedly important, but its interpretation is enigmatic.

596

## 1973 年所采集标本的意义

在之前的报道中 [1,4-7]，鲁道夫湖以东的人科动物化石被归入到了南方古猿、人属或分类未定（后者既包括破碎的标本，也有分类位置不明的标本）。

鲁道夫湖以东发现的标本被归入南方古猿，其分布时间在距今 300 万到 100 万年，期间几乎未曾发生显著形态变化。这类南方古猿与南方古猿鲍氏种 [8] 相同；同时也显示了与南非的南方古猿粗壮种的相似性。有人提出这一特定类群起源于上新世。

出土人属化石的地层时代与上述时间段相似，但是这些标本的形态变异较大。从伊莱雷特段地层出土的标本似乎与从库比福勒组下段地层出土的标本有所不同。在 1972 年的发现 [7] 之后，有人提出 300 万年前在鲁道夫湖以东生活着一种脑量较大并且能完全直立行走的人科动物。这种观点也得到同样是从 KBS 凝灰岩层下出土的 KNM–ER 1590 号颅骨残片的支持，该标本暂时被归入人属。

1973 年在鲁道夫湖以东采集的标本引发了更多问题。可以认为新发现的下颌骨 KNM–ER 1802 与 KNM–ER 1470 和 1590 属于同一属种。KNM–ER 1802 和奥杜威峡谷出土的一些标本，例如能人种的模式标本 OH 7，在牙齿特征方面有着惊人的相似之处。尽管先前提出能人颅容量要明显小于 KNM–ER 1470 的脑量，这一偏差可能是由于前者颅容量的估算是基于残破化石材料的缘故。我认为，那些有关早更新世期间的人属具有"小容量大脑"的证据非常缺乏说服力。

颅骨 KNM–ER 1813 可以证明其与粗壮型的南方古猿及 KNM–ER 1470 号标本所代表的人属都非常不同。该标本的齿系具有"人亚科"的特征，但是其颅容量却显得很小。该颅骨所具有的某些特征与发现于斯泰克方丹的南方古猿非洲种相似，后者是一种纤细且脑量较小的人科动物。

我以前质疑过这种独特的南方古猿纤细种的有效性 [6]，但是这个新证据重新提供了其存在的可能性。有些作者 [9,10] 曾提出，能人，尤其是 OH 24，显示出了典型的南方古猿非洲种的特征。我的观点是，能人可能与 KNM–ER 1470 和 1590 具有亲缘关系，这里所说的能人只是指 OH 7 和 OH 16。OH 24 的颅骨与 KNM–ER 1813 具有相似性。这两个标本的牙齿尺寸和形态特征都很相像，颅容量可能也相当 [11,12]。

头骨 KNM–ER 1805 无疑很重要，但是对于它的解释还是一个谜。其相对较大

Its relatively large cranium bears sagittal and nuchal crests but has small teeth; this combination is in contrast to all the specimens previously recovered from East Rudolf.

In any consideration of the affinities of the East Rudolf hominids, the question of sexual dimorphism must not be overlooked. There does seem to be evidence for quite marked sexual dimorphism in one hominid group as demonstrated by the East Rudolf crania, KNM-ER 406 and 732[5]. Unfortunately both crania lack teeth so that the dental characteristics of the alleged female are far from clear.

The possibility of more than two contemporary hominid lineages in the Plio-Pleistocene of East Africa may now have to be recognised, whereas previously one, or at most, two forms were assumed. The attribution of isolated teeth may thus become even more difficult than it is now. Postcranial identifications likewise may be difficult, although the proximal femoral material continues to suggest a morphological dichotomy.

I suggest the following as a basis of nomenclature for Plio-Pleistocene hominids. One genus would include much of the material currently referred to *Australopithecus robustus* and *A. boisei*. A second genus would incorporate many of the gracile specimens from Sterkfontein presently referred to *A. africanus*, perhaps certain specimens from East Rudolf including KNM-ER 1813, and possibly some from Olduvai such as OH 24. A third genus, *Homo*, would incorporate specimens such as KNM-ER 1470 and 1590 from East Rudolf and possibly OH 7 and OH 16 from Olduvai. Some material from South Africa might also be considered within this last category together with later specimens from Olduvai and East Rudolf. The unusual mandible KNM-ER 1482[1], together with the specimen from the Omo area referred to *Paraustralopithecus*[13] and certain other specimens from Omo which are contemporary with the three groups just mentioned, could be considered a fourth form—a remnant of an earlier population that disappeared during the early Pleistocene. All these forms may be traced back well beyond the Plio-Pleistocene boundary.

These remarks are necessarily speculative. A more detailed review of hominid systematics is being prepared in collaboration with B. A. Wood. The wealth of data now available presents a new era in the study of early man. The complexities of dealing with the enlarged sample are challenging, and isolated studies on specific specimens must be replaced by exhaustive studies on all the fossil hominid evidence.

I should like to express appreciation for the financial backing provided by the National Geographic Society, the National Science Foundation, the W. H. Donner Foundation and others. The support and encouragement of the National Museums of Kenya and the Kenya Government made the research possible. Members of the East Rudolf Research Project are too numerous to thank individually but all play a part in a successful field season and are thanked along with those who made important discoveries. I would also

的颅骨具有矢状嵴和项嵴，但是牙齿却很小；这种组合与以前在鲁道夫湖以东发现的所有标本都形成了鲜明对比。

无论从哪方面考虑鲁道夫湖以东人科动物的亲缘关系，其性双形都是一个不容忽视的问题。似乎确能证明有一组人科动物，如鲁道夫湖以东发现的颅骨 KNM–ER 406 和 732 所展示的那样[5]，具有相当明显的性双形现象。遗憾的是，这两具颅骨都缺失牙齿，所以对所推断的女性个体的牙齿特征仍很不清楚。

现在必须承认，在上新世–更新世时期，东非地区同时生活着两种以上的人科动物，但此前，只推断有一种，最多两种。因此现在要将这些单个牙齿进行归类就变得更加困难了。尽管股骨近端总能表明形态上的歧异性，但对头后骨骼的鉴定也同样困难。

如下是我提出的有关上新世–更新世人科动物命名的基本框架。第一个属，包括目前被归入南方古猿粗壮种和南方古猿鲍氏种的大部分标本。第二个属，包含大量发现于斯泰克方丹的现被归入南方古猿非洲种的纤细类型的标本，也许还包括鲁道夫湖以东发现的一些标本，例如 KNM–ER 1813，甚至还有在奥杜威发现的某些标本，例如 OH 24。第三个属就是人属，该属包含鲁道夫湖以东出土的标本 KNM–ER 1470 和 1590，可能还有奥杜威出土的 OH 7 和 OH 16；也可以考虑将南非发现的一些标本以及后来从奥杜威和鲁道夫湖以东发现的标本一起都归入第三个属中。不寻常的下颌骨 KNM–ER 1482[1] 以及从奥莫地区发现的被归入傍人 [13] 的标本及某些其他标本与上述三个属同时代，可以考虑将它们一起归入第四种类型——消亡于早更新世的早期类群的孑遗分子。所有这些类型都可以追溯到上新世–更新世界限之前。

以上论述都是有必要深思的。我正在与伍德共同准备一份更详细的有关人科动物系统分类的综述。现在拥有的大量数据为研究早期人类开辟了新纪元。处理这些新增加标本的复杂程度很具有挑战性，必须停止对特定标本进行孤立的研究，而代之以对所有人科动物化石证据进行彻底详尽的研究。

我想对国家地理学会、国家科学基金会、唐纳基金会和其他组织提供的经济资助表示感谢。感谢肯尼亚国家博物馆和肯尼亚政府提供的支持与鼓励使我们的研究得以顺利进行。由于鲁道夫湖以东研究项目组的成员太多，无法一一致谢，但是我得说所有人都在成功的野外发掘工作中起了相当重要的作用，并同时感谢获得重要

express thanks to my wife Meave who, as always, provided invaluable assistance both at the museum and in the field.

(**248**, 653-656; 1974)

**R. E. F. Leakey**
National Museums of Kenya, PO Box 40658, Nairobi

Received January 9, 1974.

---

References:

1. Leakey, R. E. F., *Nature*, **242**, 170 (1973).

2. Bowen, B. E., and Vondra, C. F., *Nature*, **242**, 391 (1973).

3. Brock, A., and Isaac, G. Ll., *Nature*, **247**, 344 (1974).

4. Leakey, R. E. F., *Nature*, **226**, 223 (1970).

5. Leakey, R. E. F., *Nature*, **231**, 241 (1971).

6. Leakey, R. E. F., *Nature*, **237**, 264 (1972).

7. Leakey, R. E. F., *Nature*, **242**, 447 (1973).

8. Tobias, P. V., *Olduvai Gorge*, **2** (Cambridge University Press, 1967).

9. Robinson, J. T., *Nature*, **205**, 121 (1965).

10. Anon., *Nature*, **232**, 294 (1971).

11. Leakey, M. D., Clarke, R. J., and Leakey, L. S. B., *Nature*, **232**, 308 (1971).

12. *Nature*, **239**, 469 (1972).

13. Arambourg, C., and Coppens, Y., *C. r. hebd. Séanc. Acad. Sci., Paris*, **265**, 589 (1967).

发现的人员。我还要感谢我的妻子米芙一如既往地在博物馆和野外工作方面所提供的宝贵帮助。

（刘皓芳 翻译；同号文 审稿）

# Stratospheric Sink for Chlorofluoromethanes: Chlorine Atom-Catalysed Destruction of Ozone

M. J. Molina and F. S. Rowland

## Editor's Note

In this paper, one of the most prescient and important *Nature* has published, Mario Molina and F. Sherwood Rowland point out that chlorofluorocarbons (CFCs), widely used as refrigerants and aerosol propellant, will accumulate in the atmosphere because of their chemical inertness. But when they reach the upper atmosphere, the researchers say, ultraviolet sunlight may photochemically split the compounds to create highly reactive free radicals. These may then react with and destroy stratospheric ozone, which acts as a partial barrier to the penetration of harmful UV rays to the Earth's surface. This prediction was verified 11 years later, leading to an international phase-out of CFCs. The work earned Molina and Rowland the 1995 Nobel Prize in Chemistry.

---

Chlorofluoromethanes are being added to the environment in steadily increasing amounts. These compounds are chemically inert and may remain in the atmosphere for 40-150 years, and concentrations can be expected to reach 10 to 30 times present levels. Photodissociation of the chlorofluoromethanes in the stratosphere produces significant amounts of chlorine atoms, and leads to the destruction of atmospheric ozone.

---

HALOGENATED aliphatic hydrocarbons have been added to the natural environment in steadily increasing amounts over several decades as a consequence of their growing use, chiefly as aerosol propellants and as refrigerants[1,2]. Two chlorofluoromethanes, $CF_2Cl_2$ and $CFCl_3$, have been detected throughout the troposphere in amounts (about 10 and 6 parts per $10^{11}$ by volume, respectively) roughly corresponding to the integrated world industrial production to date[3-5,31]. The chemical inertness and high volatility which make these materials suitable for technological use also mean that they remain in the atmosphere for a long time. There are no obvious rapid sinks for their removal, and they may be useful as inert tracers of atmospheric motions[4-6]. We have attempted to calculate the probable sinks and lifetimes for these molecules. The most important sink for atmospheric $CFCl_3$ and $CF_2Cl_2$ seems to be stratospheric photolytic dissociation to $CFCl_2+Cl$ and to $CF_2Cl+Cl$, respectively, at altitudes of 20-40 km. Each of the reactions creates two odd-electron species—one Cl atom and one free radical. The dissociated chlorofluoromethanes can be traced to their ultimate sinks. An extensive catalytic chain reaction leading to the net destruction of $O_3$ and $O$ occurs in the stratosphere:

# 氟氯甲烷的平流层汇：氯原子
# 催化破坏臭氧过程

莫利纳，罗兰

## 编者按

本文是《自然》发表的最有预见性、最具影响力的文章之一，马里奥·莫利纳和舍伍德·罗兰指出，广泛应用于制冷剂和喷雾推进剂的氯氟烃（CFCs），由于其化学惰性会在大气中积累。研究表明，当到达大气层上层时，紫外线可能会使此化合物发生光化学裂解，生成高活性的自由基。这些自由基会与平流层臭氧发生反应，使之发生破坏，而臭氧层恰恰担当着保护地球表面免受有害紫外线照射的部分屏障作用。这个预言在 11 年后被证实，并且引领了一场逐步淘汰氯氟烃的全球化变革。这项研究也使得莫利纳和罗兰获得 1995 年的诺贝尔化学奖。

---

氟氯甲烷正以稳定增长的量被排放到环境中。这些化合物具有化学惰性，可以在大气中停留 40~150 年，预计其浓度能够达到目前水平的 10~30 倍。平流层中氟氯甲烷的光解可以产生大量氯原子，并会导致大气中臭氧的破坏。

---

在过去的几十年中，卤代脂肪烃的应用日益广泛，主要是作为喷雾推进剂和制冷剂，并以稳定增长的数量被排放到自然环境中[1,2]。目前已检测到两种氟氯甲烷（$CF_2Cl_2$ 和 $CFCl_3$）分布在整个对流层中（体积分数分别为 $10/10^{11}$ 和 $6/10^{11}$），数量上大致相当于迄今为止全世界工业的总产量[3-5,31]。这些物质所具有的化学惰性和高挥发性使其可应用于各种技术，但也意味着它们会在大气中停留很长时间。由于没有什么显著快速清除过程除去它们，因而可以用作大气运动的惰性示踪剂[4-6]。我们曾试图计算这些分子可能的汇及其寿命。对于大气中的 $CFCl_3$ 和 $CF_2Cl_2$ 来说，最重要的汇看来就是发生在海拔 20~40 km 的平流层中的光解离反应，产物分别是 $CFCl_2$ + Cl 和 $CF_2Cl$ + Cl。每个反应都会产生两种奇电子物质——Cl 原子和自由基。离解的氟氯甲烷可以示踪其最终汇。广泛的催化链反应导致平流层中发生着 $O_3$ 与 O 的净损失：

$$Cl + O_3 \rightarrow ClO + O_2 \tag{1}$$
$$ClO + O \rightarrow Cl + O_2 \tag{2}$$

This has important chemical consequences. Under most conditions in the Earth's atmospheric ozone layer, (2) is the slower of the reactions because there is a much lower concentration of O than of $O_3$. The odd chlorine chain (Cl, ClO) can be compared with the odd nitrogen chain (NO, $NO_2$) which is believed to be intimately involved in the regulation of the present level of $O_3$ in the atmosphere[7-10]. At stratospheric temperatures, ClO reacts with O six times faster than $NO_2$ reacts with O (refs 11, 12). Consequently, the Cl–ClO chain can be considerably more efficient than the NO–$NO_2$ chain in the catalytic conversion of $O_3 + O \rightarrow 2O_2$ per unit time per reacting chain[13].

## Photolytic Sink

Both $CFCl_3$ and $CF_2Cl_2$ absorb radiation in the far ultraviolet[14], and stratospheric photolysis will occur mainly in the "window" at 1,750-2,200 Å between the more intense absorptions of the Schumann–Runge regions of $O_2$ and the Hartley bands of $O_3$. We have extended measurements of absorption coefficients for the chlorofluoromethanes to cover the range 2,000-2,270 Å. Calculations of the rate of photolysis of molecules at a given altitude at these wavelengths is complicated by the intense narrow band structure in the Schumann–Runge region, and the effective rates of vertical diffusion of molecules at these altitudes are also subject to substantial uncertainties. Vertical mixing is frequently modelled through the use of "eddy" diffusion coefficients[10,15-18], which are presumably relatively insensitive to the molecular weight of the diffusing species. Calculated using a time independent one-dimensional vertical diffusion model with eddy diffusion coefficients of magnitude $K \sim (3\times10^3) -10^4$ cm$^2$ s$^{-1}$ at altitudes 20-40 km (refs 10, 15-18), the atmospheric lifetimes of $CFCl_3$ and $CF_2Cl_2$ fall into the range of 40-150 yr. The time required for approach toward a steady state is thus measured in decades, and the concentrations of chlorofluoromethanes in the atmosphere can be expected to reach saturation values of 10-30 times the present levels, assuming constant injection at current rates, and no other major sinks. (The atmospheric content is now equivalent to about five years world production at current rates.) Lifetimes in excess of $> 10$ and $> 30$ yr can already be estimated from the known industrial production rates and atmospheric concentrations[3,5], and so the stratospheric photochemical sink will be important even if other sinks are discovered.

Our calculation of photodissociation rates is modelled after those of Kockarts[19] and Brinkmann[20], and is globally averaged for diurnal and zenith angle effects. The photodissociation rates at an altitude of 30 km are estimated to be $3\times10^{-7}$ s$^{-1}$ for $CFCl_3$ and $3\times10^{-8}$ s$^{-1}$ for $CF_2Cl_2$, decreasing for each by about a factor of $10^{-2}$ at 20 km. The appropriate solar ultraviolet intensities at an altitude of 30 km may be uncertain by a factor of 2 or 3 (ref. 21) and we have therefore calculated lifetimes for photodissociation rates differing from the above by factors of 3 or more. The competition between photodissociation and upward diffusion reduces the relative concentration of chlorofluoromethane at higher altitudes and the concentrations should be very low above

$$Cl + O_3 \rightarrow ClO + O_2 \tag{1}$$
$$ClO + O \rightarrow Cl + O_2 \tag{2}$$

它具有重要的化学结果。在地球大气臭氧层中的大多数条件下（2）是较慢的反应，因为 O 的浓度比 $O_3$ 低得多。奇氯链（Cl 和 ClO）作用可与奇氮链（NO 和 $NO_2$）相当，后者被确信与调控当前大气 $O_3$ 含量密切相关[7-10]。在平流层温度下，ClO 与 O 的反应比 $NO_2$ 与 O 的反应快 6 倍（参考文献 11 和 12）。因此，在 $O_3 + O \rightarrow 2O_2$ 的催化转变过程中，单位时间内每个反应链中 Cl–ClO 链比 NO–$NO_2$ 链更为高效[13]。

## 光 解 汇

$CFCl_3$ 和 $CF_2Cl_2$ 都能吸收远紫外辐射[14]，平流层光解主要发生在波长为 1,750~2,200 Å 的"窗口"区域，即吸收更为强烈的 $O_2$ 的舒曼 – 龙格区与 $O_3$ 的哈特利带之间。我们把对氟氯甲烷吸收系数的测量推广到覆盖 2,000~2,270 Å 区域。舒曼 – 龙格区域中的强窄带结构使计算分子在特定高度、这段波长下的光解反应速率变得复杂，分子在这些高度发生垂直扩散的有效速率往往也有很大的不确定性。常常利用假定对于扩散物种分子质量相对不敏感的"湍流"扩散系数为垂直混合建模[10,15-18]。应用一个与时间无关的一维垂直扩散模型进行计算，取高度 20~40 km 处湍流扩散系数 $K$ 约为 $(3 \times 10^3)$~$10^4$ $cm^2 \cdot s^{-1}$（参考文献 10、15~18），得到 $CFCl_3$ 和 $CF_2Cl_2$ 在大气中的寿命范围处于 40~150 年。由此测得要达到稳态所需的时间是几十年，假设以目前速率持续向大气中排入氟氯甲烷，并且没有其他重要汇的话，那么可以预期，大气中氟氯甲烷的浓度将可以达到的饱和值是目前水平的 10~30 倍（现在，大气中的含量已相当于目前生产速率下全世界 5 年的总产量）。利用已知的工业生产率和大气浓度可以估算出寿命超过 10 年和 30 年的氟氯甲烷量[3,5]，因此，即使是发现了其他汇，平流层光化学清除过程也仍将是很重要的。

我们计算光解离反应速率时仿照了科卡茨[19] 和布林克曼[20] 的计算，并且做了天顶角效应和每天的全球平均计算。在 30 km 高度，估算出 $CFCl_3$ 的光解离反应速率为 $3 \times 10^{-7}$ $s^{-1}$，$CF_2Cl_2$ 则是 $3 \times 10^{-8}$ $s^{-1}$，在 20 km 处，它们都下降到原来的 1/100 左右。在 30 km 处适宜太阳紫外强度可能具有 2 或 3 倍的不确定性（参考文献 21），我们由此计算出与上部光解离反应速率不同（3 倍或者更大）时的寿命。光解离反应与向上扩散之间的竞争减少了氟氯甲烷在较高海拔处的相对浓度，因而在 50 km 以上的浓度应该是非常低的。破坏的峰值与 Cl 原子形成出现在 25~35 km 处，

50 km. The peak rate of destruction, and formation of Cl atoms, occurs at 25-35 km, in the region of high ozone concentration. The rates of formation of Cl atoms at different altitudes, and the chlorofluoromethane atmospheric lifetimes are sensitive to the assumed eddy diffusion coefficients, as well as to the photodissociation rates.

The major chain processes in the stratosphere involving species with odd numbers of electrons belong to the H (H, OH, $HO_2$), N (NO, $NO_2$), and Cl (Cl, ClO) series. ($ClO_2$ is rapidly decomposed and its concentration is negligible relative to Cl plus ClO.) These odd-electron chains can only be terminated by interaction with one another, although other reactions can convert one series to another. At most altitudes, the first reaction for converting the Cl–ClO odd-electron chain to an even-electron species containing chlorine is the abstraction of H from $CH_4$, which transfers the odd-electron character to the $CH_3$ radical:

$$Cl + CH_4 \rightarrow HCl + CH_3 \tag{3}$$

At stratospheric temperatures the rate constant for Cl atoms[22], for (3) is about $10^{-3}$ times as fast as (1) and the $O_3/CH_4$ concentration ratio can make the rate of (3) less than that of (1) by another factor of 10. The Cl atom chain can be renewed by the reaction of OH with HCl (ref. 23):

$$OH + HCl \rightarrow H_2O + Cl \tag{4}$$

Ultraviolet dissociation by absorption in the range 1,750-2,200 Å can also occur at the higher altitudes. The reaction rate of (4) in the stratosphere depends on the concentration of OH, which is known only roughly. In our estimates, termination of the Cl–ClO chain results from downward diffusion of the longer lived species in the chain (ClO, HCl) and eventual removal by tropospheric processes. The rate of termination thus also depends on diffusion processes and estimates will vary with the choice of eddy diffusion coefficients.

Possible terminations involving the Cl series with itself (for example, Cl + ClO $\rightarrow$ $Cl_2O$) or with one of the others (for example, Cl + NO $\rightarrow$ NOCl) normally lead to molecules with appreciable absorption coefficients at longer wavelengths, which are very rapidly dissociated again by the much more intense solar fluxes available there. Thus, even if a molecule which temporarily terminates two chains is formed, at least one of which involves the Cl series, the terminating molecule is rapidly photolysed and both chains are regenerated again.

Under most stratospheric conditions, the slow reactions in both the Cl–ClO and NO–$NO_2$ chains occur between O atoms and ClO and $NO_2$ molecules. The two chains are interconnected:

$$ClO + NO \rightarrow Cl + NO_2 \tag{5}$$

The rate of this reaction in the stratosphere is frequently comparable to that of reaction (2). The overall effect is complex and depends on the relative concentrations of $ClO_x$, $NO_x$, $O_3$, O and OH. Reaction (1) is so rapid that the ClO/Cl ratio is usually > 10, even when

即高臭氧浓度的区域。Cl 原子在不同海拔高度的形成速率以及氟氯甲烷在大气中的寿命，对于假定的湍流扩散系数与光解离反应速率都很敏感。

在平流层中，主要链反应过程涉及的奇数电子种类属于 H 系列（H、OH 和 HO₂）、N 系列（NO 和 NO₂）和 Cl 系列（Cl 和 ClO）。（ClO₂ 分解快速，它的浓度相对于 Cl 与 ClO 之和来说是可以忽略的。）这些奇电子链过程只能靠彼此间相互作用才会终止，不过其他一些反应能使其从一个系列转变到另一个。在大部分高度，将 Cl–ClO 奇电子链转换到一种含氯偶电子物质的第一个反应都是从 CH₄ 中抽提 H，从而将奇电子性质转移给 CH₃ 自由基：

$$Cl + CH_4 \rightarrow HCl + CH_3 \qquad (3)$$

在平流层温度下，对于反应（3）而言 Cl 原子[22] 速率常数约为反应（1）的 $10^{-3}$，而 O₃/CH₄ 浓度比可以使反应（3）的速率降至（1）的 $10^{-4}$。Cl 原子链可以通过 OH 与 HCl 的反应恢复（参考文献 23）：

$$OH + HCl \rightarrow H_2O + Cl \qquad (4)$$

通过吸收 1,750~2,200 Å 波长范围的光而产生的紫外离解反应也能在较高海拔处发生。反应（4）在平流层中的速率取决于只是大概知道的 OH 浓度。在我们的估计中，Cl–ClO 链的终止是由于链中寿命更长的种类（ClO 和 HCl）向下扩散以及对流层过程最终将其消除所导致。因此，终止速率也取决于扩散过程，并且估算结果会随着湍流扩散系数的选取有所变化。

Cl 系列与自身（例如 Cl + ClO → Cl₂O）或其他系列之一（例如 Cl + NO → NOCl）参与的可能终止反应通常会在较长波段产生具有明显吸收系数的分子，它们会因受到所在场所中的强太阳流作用而再次极快地离解。因此，即使形成了一个临时终止两个链（其中至少一个链涉及 Cl 系列）的分子，这个终止分子也会快速地光解，使两个链得以再生。

在大多数平流层条件下，Cl–ClO 链与 NO–NO₂ 链中的慢反应在 O 原子与 ClO、NO₂ 分子之间发生。两个链偶联起来：

$$ClO + NO \rightarrow Cl + NO_2 \qquad (5)$$

平流层中这个反应的速率往往可以与反应（2）的相当。总体效果是复杂的，而且取决于 $ClO_x$、$NO_x$、O₃、O 和 OH 的相对浓度。反应（1）非常快，即使是反应（2）和

Cl is produced by both reaction (2) and reaction (5), so that the overall rate of reaction (2) is not directly affected by the occurrence of reaction (5). As soon as Cl is produced, however, HCl can form by reactions (1) or (3), resulting in the temporary termination of the Cl atom chain. Whether or not the chain is then restarted depends primarily on the concentration of OH. There are substantial ranges of stratospheric altitudes in which neither reaction (3) nor reaction (5) seriously impedes the chain process of reactions (1) and (2).

The initial photolytic reaction produces one Cl atom from each of the parent molecules, plus a $CX_3$ radical (X may be F or Cl). The detailed chemistry of $CX_3$ radicals in $O_2$ or air is not completely known, but in the laboratory a phosgene-type molecule, $CX_2O$, is rapidly produced and another X atom—probably Cl (or ClO)—is released from $CFCl_2$ or $CF_2Cl$[24,25]. $CX_2O$ may also photolyse in the atmosphere to give a third and fourth free halogen atom. Thus, each molecule of $CFCl_3$ initially photolysed probably leads to between two and three Cl atom chains, and $CF_2Cl_2$ probably produces two Cl atom chains when it is photolysed. Initial calculations suggest that F atom chains will be much shorter than Cl atom chains because the reaction of abstraction from $CH_4$ is much faster for F atoms[26], whereas the reaction between OH and HF is 17 kcalorie $mol^{-1}$ endothermic and will not occur in the stratosphere. We have not yet attempted to analyse the subsequent reaction paths of HF.

## Production Rates

The 1972 world production rates for $CFCl_3$ and $CF_2Cl_2$ are about 0.3 and 0.5 Mton $yr^{-1}$ respectively[1,2,5], and are steadily increasing (by 8.7% per year for total fluorocarbons in the United States from 1961-71) (ref. 1). We have not included any estimates for other chlorinated aliphatic hydrocarbons also found in the atmosphere, such as $CCl_4$ (refs 3 and 4), $CHCl_3$, $C_2Cl_4$ and $C_2HCl_3$ for which there is no evidence for long residence times in the atmosphere[27]. If the stratospheric photolytic sink is the only major sink for $CFCl_3$ and $CF_2Cl_2$, then the 1972 production rates correspond at steady state to globally averaged destruction rates of about $0.8\times10^7$ and $1.5\times10^7$ molecules $cm^{-2} s^{-1}$ and formation rates of Cl atoms of about $2\times10^7$ and $3\times10^7$ atoms $cm^{-2} s^{-1}$, respectively. The total rate of production of $5\times10^7$ Cl atoms $cm^{-2} s^{-1}$ from the two processes is of the order of the estimated natural flux of NO molecules ($2.5-15\times10^7$ NO molecules $cm^{-2} s^{-1}$) involved in the natural ozone cycle[9-12], and of the $5\times10^7$ NO molecules $cm^{-2} s^{-1}$ whose introduction around 25 km from stratospheric aviation is estimated would cause a 6% reduction in the total $O_3$ column[10].

Photolysis of these chlorofluoromethanes does not occur in the troposphere because the molecules are transparent to wavelengths longer than 2,900 Å. In fact the measured absorption coefficients for $CFCl_3$ and $CF_2Cl_2$ are falling rapidly at wavelengths longer than 2,000 Å (ref. 14). The reaction between OH and $CH_4$ is believed to be important in the troposphere[17,28], but the corresponding Cl atom abstraction reaction (for example, OH + $CFCl_3 \rightarrow HOCl + CFCl_2$) is highly endothermic and is negligible under all atmospheric

（5）共同生成 Cl 时，ClO/Cl 的比值通常还是要 >10，因此反应（2）的总速率并不直接受反应（5）发生的影响。不过，一旦生成了 Cl，就可以通过反应（1）或（3）生成 HCl，进而导致 Cl 原子链的临时终止。接下来链能否重新开始主要取决于 OH 的浓度。在平流层高度内存在着一个较大的范围，在这个范围内反应（3）和（5）都不会严重阻碍反应（1）和（2）的链反应过程。

初期光解反应在每组母体分子中产生一个 Cl 原子和一个 $CX_3$ 自由基（X 可以是 F 或者 Cl）。对于 $CX_3$ 自由基在氧气或空气中的详细化学性质还不是完全了解，不过在实验室中，可以快速生成一个光气型的分子 $CX_2O$，还有另一个 X 原子——可能是 Cl（或 ClO）——从 $CFCl_2$ 或 $CF_2Cl$ 中释放出来[24,25]。$CX_2O$ 还可以在大气中光解，释放出第三个和第四个自由卤原子。因此，每个初期光解的 $CFCl_3$ 分子有可能引发两到三个 Cl 原子链，而 $CF_2Cl_2$ 可能在光解时产生两个 Cl 原子链。初期计算指出，F 原子链比 Cl 原子链要短很多，因为对于 F 原子来说，从 $CH_4$ 中的抽提反应要快得多[26]，而 OH 与 HF 之间的反应吸热量为 $17 \text{ kcal} \cdot \text{mol}^{-1}$，因而不会在平流层中发生。我们尚未试图分析 HF 的后续反应途径。

## 生 成 率

1972 年, $CFCl_3$ 和 $CF_2Cl_2$ 的全世界生产率分别约为每年 0.3 Mton 和 0.5 Mton[1,2,5]，而且还在稳定增长（美国在 1961~1971 年间碳氟化合物总产量的增长速率为每年 8.7%）（参考文献 1）。我们没有将任何其他也在大气中发现的氯代脂肪烃，例如 $CCl_4$（参考文献 3 和 4）、$CHCl_3$、$C_2Cl_4$ 和 $C_2HCl_3$ 等的估计量包含进来，因为还没有证据显示它们在大气中有很长的停留时间[27]。如果平流层光解汇是 $CFCl_3$ 和 $CF_2Cl_2$ 仅有的主要汇的话，那 1972 年的生成率为稳定态，相当于全球分解速率分别约为每平方厘米每秒 $0.8 \times 10^7$ 和 $1.5 \times 10^7$ 个分子，而 Cl 原子的生成率分别约为每平方厘米每秒 $2 \times 10^7$ 和 $3 \times 10^7$ 个分子。来自两个过程的 Cl 原子的总生成速率为每平方厘米每秒 $5 \times 10^7$ 个原子，已达到了参与天然臭氧循环的 NO 分子自然通量估计值（每平方厘米每秒 $2.5 \times 10^7 \sim 15 \times 10^7$ 个分子）的水平[9-12]，而由于平流层飞行向约 25 km 高空排入的每平方厘米每秒 $5 \times 10^7$ 个 NO 分子，估计将会导致臭氧总体积减少 6%[10]。

上述氟氯甲烷的光解反应不会在对流层中发生，因为这些分子在波长超过 2,900 Å 的辐射下是透明的。实际上，测量到的 $CFCl_3$ 和 $CF_2Cl_2$ 的吸收系数在波长超过 2,000 Å 之后快速下降（参考文献 14）。OH 与 $CH_4$ 之间的反应在对流层是重要的[17,28]，不过相应的 Cl 原子抽提反应（例如 $OH + CFCl_3 \rightarrow HOCl + CFCl_2$）要吸收大量热，因此在所有大气条件中都是可以忽略的。$CFCl_3$ 和 $CF_2Cl_2$ 在水中的

conditions. Neither $CFCl_3$ nor $CF_2Cl_2$ is very soluble in water, and they are not removed by rainout in the troposphere. Details of biological interactions of these molecules in the environment are very scarce because they do not occur naturally (except possibly in minute quantities from volcanic eruptions)[29], but rapid biological removal seems unlikely. The relative insolubility in water together with their chemical stability (especially toward hydrolysis)[30] indicates that these molecules will not be rapidly removed by dissolution in the ocean, and the few measurements made so far indicate equilibrium between the ocean surface and air, and therefore a major oceanic sink cannot be inferred[3].

It seems quite clear that the atmosphere has only a finite capacity for absorbing Cl atoms produced in the stratosphere, and that important consequences may result. This capacity is probably not sufficient in steady state even for the present rate of introduction of chlorofluoromethanes. More accurate estimates of this absorptive capacity need to be made in the immediate future in order to ascertain the levels of possible onset of environmental problems.

As with most $NO_x$ calculations, our calculations have been based entirely on reactions in the gas phase, and essentially nothing is known of possible heterogeneous reactions of Cl atoms with particulate matter in the stratosphere. One important corollary of these calculations is that the full impact of the photodissociation of $CF_2Cl_2$ and $CFCl_3$ is not immediately felt after their introduction at ground level because of the delay required for upward diffusion up to and above 25 km. If any Cl atom effect on atmospheric $O_3$ concentration were to be observed from this source, the effect could be expected to intensify for some time thereafter. A lengthy period (of the order of calculated atmospheric lifetimes) may thus be required for natural moderation, even if the amount of Cl introduced into the stratosphere is reduced in the future.

This research has been supported by the US Atomic Energy Commission. We acknowledge a helpful discussion with Professor H. S. Johnston.

(**249**, 810-812; 1974)

Mario J. Molina & F. S. Rowland
Department of Chemistry, University of California, Irvine, California 92664

Received January 21; revised March 21, 1974.

---

References:

1. *Chemical Marketing Reporter*, August 21, 1972.

2. *Chemistry in the Economy* (American Chemical Society, Washington, DC, 1973).

3. Lovelock, J. E., Maggs, R. J., and Wade, R. J., *Nature*, **241**, 194 (1973).

4. Wilkniss, P. E., Lamontagne, R. A., Larson, R. E., Swinnerton, J. W., Dickson, C. R., and Thompson, T., *Nature*, **245**, 45 (1973).

5. Su, C.-W., and Goldberg, E. D., *Nature*, **245**, 27 (1973).

6. Machta, L., Proceedings of the Second IUTAM-IUGG Symposium on Turbulent Diffusion in Environmental Pollution (Charlottesville, 1973).

7. Crutzen, P. J., *J. Geophys. Res.*, **30**, 7311 (1971).

溶解性都不大，因而不能通过雨水冲刷将它们从对流层中清除。关于这些分子在环境中的生物学相互作用的了解还远远不够，因为自然条件下这种作用不会发生（仅有的例外是在来自火山喷发物的微量产物中）[29]，不过看来不大可能有快速的生物学清除方法。在水中的相对不溶性以及它们的化学稳定性（尤其是对于水解反应来说）[30] 意味着这些分子不会通过溶于海洋中而被快速清除，目前为止为数不多的观测指出海面与空气之间存在平衡，因而不能断定存在一种重要的海洋转换过程 [3]。

看来十分清楚的是，大气对于平流层产生的 Cl 原子只有有限的吸收能力，而这可能导致重要的结果。即使是对目前氟氯甲烷的排放速率来说，这一吸收能力可能也不足以保持稳态。为了确定这一环境问题可能爆发的程度，需要在不久的将来对这种吸收能力进行更为精确的评估。

如同大多数针对 $NO_x$ 的计算一样，我们的计算也是完全基于气相中的反应，对于 Cl 原子与平流层中颗粒物之间可能发生的非均相反应，基本上还一无所知。这些计算得出的一个重要推论是，$CF_2Cl_2$ 和 $CFCl_3$ 光解反应导致的全部影响并不是在以地表水平排放到环境中之后就立刻体现出来的，因为向上扩散到 25 km 及更高的过程需要一段延迟时间。如果能够观测到从这个来源的 Cl 原子对于大气 $O_3$ 浓度的所有影响，那么可以预期，这一影响在一段时间之后会加强。因此即使未来排入平流层的 Cl 原子数量有所减少，自然调节过程也可能需要一个漫长的周期（计算的大气寿命的量级）。

这项研究一直受到美国原子能委员会的支持。我们还要感谢约翰斯顿教授提供的有益建议。

（王耀杨 翻译；安俊岭 审稿）

8. Johnston, H., *Science*, **173**, 517 (1971).

9. Johnston, H. S., Proceedings of the First Survey Conference, Climatic Impact Assessment Program, US Department of Transport, 90 (1972).

10. McElroy, M. B., Wofsy, S. C., Penner, J. E., and McConnell, J. C., *J. Atmos. Sci.*, **31**, 287 (1974).

11. Bemand, P. P., Clyne, M. A. A., and Watson, R. J., *J. Chem. Soc., Faraday I*, **69**, 1356 (1973).

12. Hampson, R., *et al.*, *Chemical Kinetics Data Survey VI*, National Bureau of Standard Interim Report 73-207 (1973).

13. Stolarski, R. S., and Cicerone, R. J., International Association of Geomagnetism and Aeronomy (Kyoto, Japan, 1973); see also *Can. J. Chem.*, (in the press).

14. Doucet, J., Sauvageau, P., and Sandorfy, C., *J. Chem. Phys.*, **58**, 3708 (1973).

15. McConnell, J. C., and McElroy, M. B., *J. Atmos. Sci.*, **30**, 1465 (1973).

16. Schütz, K., Junge, C., Beck, R., and Albrecht, B., *J. Geophys. Res.*, **75**, 2230 (1970).

17. Wofsy, S. C., McConnell, J. C., and McElroy, M. B., *J. Geophys. Res.*, **77**, 4477 (1972).

18. Wofsy, S. C., and McElroy, M. B., *J. Geophys. Res.*, **78**, 2619 (1973).

19. Kockarts, G., in *Mesospheric Models and Related Experiments* (edit. by Fiocco, G.), 168, Reidel, Dodrrecht (1971).

20. Brinkmann, R., *ibid.*, 89.

21. Hudson, R. D., and Mahle, S. H., *J. Geophys. Res.*, **77**, 2902 (1972).

22. Clyne, M. A. A., and Walker, R. F., *J. Chem. Soc., Faraday I*, **69**, 1547 (1973).

23. Takacs, G. A., and Glass, G. P., *J. Phys. Chem.*, **77**, 1948 (1973).

24. Marsh, D., and Heicklen, J., *J. Phys. Chem.*, **69**, 4410 (1965).

25. Heicklen, J., *Adv. Photochem.*, 7, 57 (1969).

26. Homann, K. H., Solomon, W. C., Warnatz, J., Wagner, H. G., and Zetzch, C., *Ber. Bunsenges. phys. Chem.*, 74, 585 (1970).

27. Murray, A. J., and Riley, J. P., *Nature*, **242**, 37 (1973).

28. Levy, H., *Planet. Space Sci.*, **20**, 919 (1972); **21**, 575 (1973).

29. Stoiber, R. E., Leggett, D. C., Jenkins, T. F., Murrmann, R. P., and Rose, W. J., *Bull. Geol. Soc. Am.*, **82**, 2299 (1971).

30. Hudlicky, M., *Chemistry of Organic Fluorine Compounds*, 340 (MacMillan, New York, 1962).

31. Lovelock, J. E., *Nature*, **230**, 379 (1971).

# Kinky Helix

F. H. C. Crick and A. Klug

## Editor's Note

**DNA in eukaryotes is tightly packaged in chromatin, in which it is wound around disk-shaped proteins called histones. This implies that the elegant double helix of Watson and Crick must be severely distorted. Here Crick, together with biochemist Aaron Klug, suggests that this distortion might involve sharp kinks in the chain, rather than smooth bends. Their argument is purely one of chemical plausibility, and it turned out to be incorrect in detail, although DNA is quite sharply bent in some situations in the cell. But the precise structure of chromatin remains unclear, although it seems apparent that this structure and its regulation are central to the way genes are activated.**

---

DNA in chromatin is highly folded. Is it kinked? And does it kink in other situations?

---

CHROMATIN is the name given to chromosomal material extracted from the nuclei of cells of higher organisms. It consists mainly of DNA and a set of small rather basic proteins called histones. Other proteins and RNA are present in lesser amounts (see for example ref. 1). Early X-ray work (for review see ref. 2) suggested that there was a structure in chromatin which repeated at intervals of about 100 Å. More recent work using nucleases[3,4] has shown that the DNA in chromatin exists in some regular fold which repeats every 200 base pairs, the best value currently being $205\pm15$ base pairs[5].

The most cogent model for chromatin has been put forward by Kornberg[6] who suggested that the basic structure consists of a string of beads each containing two each of the four major histones, each bead being associated with about 200 base pairs of DNA. Linear arrangements of beads (in a partly extended form) were first seen in the electron microscope by Olins and Olins[7] and called by them *v*-bodies. The exact diameter of a bead in the wet state is rather uncertain but it is probably in the region of 100 Å. Kornberg's model suggested that DNA, when associated with histone, is folded to about one-seventh of its length. This is the value deduced by Griffith[8] from electron micrographs of the mini-chromosome of the virus SV40. A similar value has been obtained by Oudet *et al.*[9] from measurements on adenovirus 2. Other compact models have been proposed by van Holde *et al.*[10] and Baldwin *et al.*[11].

Thus the DNA in chromatin, even at this first level of structure, must be folded considerably since its length is contracted to about one-seventh. Moreover, the basic repeat of 200 base pairs (which is 680 Å long in the B form of DNA) must be folded into a fairly limited space having the dimensions of about 100 Å$^3$ (ref. 6).

# 有扭结的螺旋

克里克，克卢格

## 编者按

真核生物的DNA在染色质中是紧密包装的，围绕在被称为组蛋白的盘状蛋白质周围。这意味着沃森和克里克提出的优美的双螺旋结构会受到严重扭曲。在本文中，克里克与生物化学家阿龙·克卢格一起提出，这种扭曲可能涉及DNA链的急剧扭结，而不是平滑的弯曲。他们的论证只是在化学上说得通，结果证明在细节上是错误的，虽然在某些情况下，细胞内的DNA会发生非常急剧的弯曲。迄今为止，染色质的精确结构尚不为人所知，但显而易见的是，该结构及其调控作用对基因的激活极其重要。

染色质中的DNA是高度折叠的。它是有扭结的么？在其他条件下它会发生扭结么？

染色质是指从高等生物的细胞核中提取的染色体物质。它主要由 DNA 和被称为组蛋白的一组碱性小蛋白组成，其他蛋白质和 RNA 少量存在（实例见参考文献 1）。早期的 X 射线研究（综述见参考文献 2）表明：在染色质中存在一种重复出现的结构，重复间隔大约为 100 Å。近期用核酸酶做的研究 [3,4] 已经表明：染色质中的 DNA 是规则折叠的，每 200 个碱基对为一个重复单位，目前的最佳值为 205±15 个碱基对 [5]。

科恩伯格 [6] 提出的染色质模型是最有说服力的。他认为其基本结构是一串珠粒，每颗珠粒含有四种主要组蛋白中的两个分子，每粒珠子与长度约为 200 个碱基对的 DNA 相连接。奥林斯和奥林斯 [7] 最先用电子显微镜观察到珠粒的线性排列（呈部分延伸状），并把它命名为 ν 小体（译者注：核小体）。在潮湿状态下，一个珠粒的准确直径尚未确定，不过可能是在 100 Å 的范围内。科恩伯格的模型表明，当与组蛋白结合时，DNA 折叠成其自身长度的七分之一。这个数值是由格里菲思 [8] 根据病毒 SV40 的微小染色体的电子显微照片推断出来的。乌代等人 [9] 对腺病毒 2 进行的测量也获得了相似的数值。范霍尔德等人 [10] 和鲍德温等人 [11] 还提出了其他的紧凑模型。

因此染色质中的 DNA 即便是在其结构的第一层次上，也必定是高度折叠的，因为其长度被压缩到了原来的约七分之一。而且，含 200 个碱基对的基本重复单位（在 B 型 DNA 中的长度为 680 Å）一定是被折叠到一个相当有限的空间内，其尺寸约为 100 Å³（参考文献 6）。

We have found it very difficult to estimate just how much energy is required to bend DNA "smoothly" to a small radius of curvature, say 30-50 Å, bearing in mind that these numbers are not many times greater than the diameter of the DNA double helix, which is about 20 Å, and that bending a helix destroys its symmetry. We have formed the impression that the energy might be rather high. We therefore asked ourselves whether the folded DNA may consist of relatively straight stretches joined by large kinks. This paper describes a certain type of kink which can be built rather nicely and has interesting properties.

## The Stereochemistry of a Kink

No doubt other types of kink could be built, but we have concentrated on one special type which we consider to be rather plausible. We have assumed that all the base pairs of the double helix are left intact (so that no energy is lost by unpairing them), that the straight parts of the DNA on each side of the kink remain in the normal B form, but that at the kink one base pair is completely unstacked from the adjacent one. Thus at each kink the energy of stacking of one base pair on another is lost. Naturally all bond distances and angles (including dihedral angles) have to be stereochemically acceptable.

We find that, given these assumptions, one can convincingly build a neat kink, having a large angle of kink, in one way only; or, more strictly, in a family of ways all very similar to each other. The double helix is bent towards the side of the minor groove. This can be seen in the photograph of one such model shown in Fig. 1.

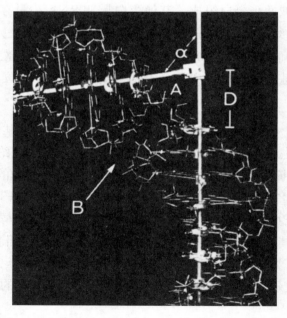

Fig. 1. General view of a model of a kink, taken from the side. For this model $d = 0$, $\alpha = 98°$, $D = 8$ Å and $\theta = 23°$ (see text). The two short lengths of backbone, connecting the two stretches of straight helix, can be seen at A. The region of van der Waals contacts between backbones, which limit the kink angle $\alpha$, is near B.

我们发现很难估计究竟需要多少能量才能将DNA"平滑地"弯曲成一个很小的曲率半径，例如30~50 Å。要知道，这些数值并非比DNA双螺旋的直径（大约20 Å）大许多倍，并且这样弯曲螺旋会破坏它的对称性。我们已经形成了一种想法：这需要的能量也许会相当高。因此我们曾经自问：这种折叠的DNA是否可能由相对笔直的舒展部分通过很大的扭结连接形成。本文描述了某一特定类型的扭结，这种扭结恰好可以完美构建，并具有令人感兴趣的性质。

## 一个扭结的立体化学

尽管其他类型的扭结无疑也可以构建形成，但我们只关注一个特殊的类型，因为我们认为它比较合理。我们假设：DNA双螺旋中所有的碱基对都保持完好无损（即没有未配对碱基的能量损失），在扭结每一侧DNA的笔直部分都保持正常的B型，但是在扭结处，一个碱基对与相邻碱基对完全不是相互堆积的。因此，在每个扭结处，就损失了把一个碱基对堆积到另一个碱基对上的能量。当然，所有的键长和键角（包括二面角）都必须是立体化学上能接受的。

我们发现，根据这些假设，可以令人信服地构建出一个具有很大扭结角度的纯扭结，但是只能以一种方式做到；或者更严格地说，可以用一类彼此非常相似的方式做到。其双螺旋弯向小沟的一侧，我们可以在图1所示的照片中看到一个这样的模型。

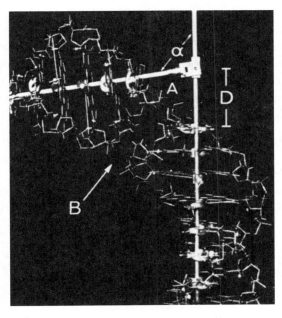

图 1. 从侧面观察的一个扭结模型的整体图。此模型的 $d = 0$，$\alpha = 98°$，$D = 8$ Å，$\theta = 23°$（见正文）。连接两段直螺旋的两段比较短的骨架在 A 处可见。骨架之间的范德华作用区域使扭结角度 $\alpha$ 受到限制，在 B 处可见。

The structure can be built with an approximation to a dyad axis passing through the kink, though we cannot see any strong reason why such symmetry is essential in chromatin. A partial view looking along the pseudo-dyad is shown in Fig. 2.

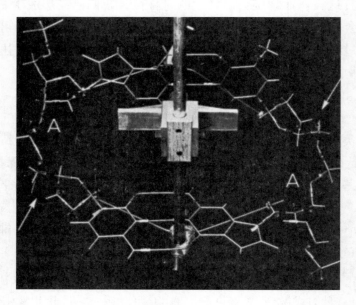

Fig. 2. View of part of the model of Fig. 1 taken approximately looking down the pseudo-dyad. It shows two base pairs, one on either side of the kink. The rest of the model has been blanked out for easier viewing. The two arrows point to the $C_4'$–$C_5'$ bonds at which the chain conformation is changed by kinking—see Fig. 3. The letters A correspond to the region marked A in Fig. 1.

To our surprise the configuration of the backbone at the kink can be made similar to that of the normal backbone of the B form except that the conformation at the $C_4'$–$C_5'$ bond in the sugar is rotated 120° about this bond, going from one of the possible staggered configurations to another one as shown in Fig. 3. (We have arbitrarily kept the same pucker of the sugar ring as is found in the B form of DNA.)

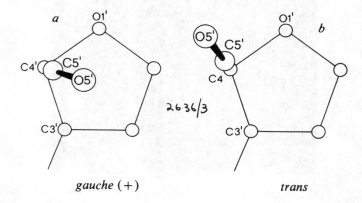

Fig. 3. Diagrams of the deoxyribose ring showing the approximate conformation at the $C_4'$–$C_5'$ bond (a) in the normal straight B form of DNA, and (b) in the proposed kink; the two sugars affected are marked in Fig. 2.

这种结构可以用一个二重轴通过扭结来近似构建，虽然我们不知道为什么在染色质中这样的对称性是必不可少的。沿假二重轴方向看的局部图示于图 2。

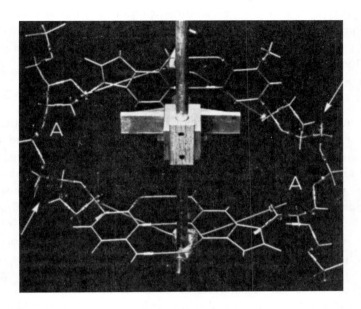

图 2. 从近似俯视假二重轴的角度拍摄到的图 1 模型的局部视图。图中显示了两个碱基对，在扭结的两侧各有一个碱基对。为了便于观察，模型的其他部分被屏蔽掉。两个箭头指向 $C_4' - C_5'$ 键，在这里扭结使链的构象发生变化（见图 3）。两个字母 A 与图 1 中标记的 A 区相对应。

令我们惊奇的是，扭结处的骨架构型可以做得与 B 型的正常骨架相似，只不过糖中 $C_4' - C_5'$ 键的构象绕此键旋转了 120°，使其从一种可能的交错构型转变为另外一种，如图 3 所示。（我们故意保存了与 B 型 DNA 中存在的相同的糖环折叠。）

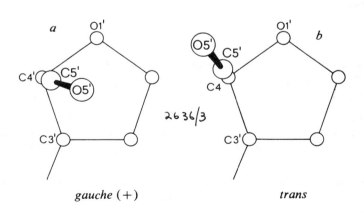

图 3. 脱氧核糖环示意图，显示在 $C_4' - C_5'$ 糖键处的近似构象：($a$) 在正常的直线 B 型 DNA 中和 ($b$) 在假设的扭结中；受影响的两个糖分子在图 2 中已经标明。

The structure of the backbone at the kink is not one of the preferred configurations that have been listed[12,13] since these involve a weak $CH \cdots O$ close contact between the hydrogen attached to either $C_6$ of a pyrimidine or $C_8$ of a purine and the $O_5{}'$ of the sugar, and by its very nature the type of kink we have assumed cannot have this at every position. In our model this contact is absent for one base of each of the base pairs immediately adjacent to the kink. As explained above, however, the backbone configuration is sufficiently close to that of the B form of DNA (except for the torsion angle about $C_4{}'-C_5{}'$) that we feel it is acceptable stereochemically.

The nature of the base pairs on either side of the kink is immaterial to the model though presumably the energy required to unstack these base pairs will depend to some extent on their composition. We have found it difficult to estimate the free energy involved. It is probably a few kilocalories. It is obviously desirable that this figure should be determined as accurately as possible since the ease of making kinks depends on just how big it is. Another important question is how much a DNA double helix can be bent before it kinks. If we denote the mean curvature by $\kappa$ (where $\kappa$ equals the reciprocal of the radius of curvature) then we would expect the energy of deformation of a uniformly bent helix, per unit length, to increase at least as fast as $\kappa^2$. For a kinked helix, on the other hand, this energy increases only as $\kappa$. In this case $\kappa$ is the mean "curvature" of the segmented double helix which is proportional to the number of kinks per unit length. Thus, as is intuitively obvious, at small $\kappa$ the double helix will bend, while at large $\kappa$ it will kink. The value we should like to know is the radius of curvature at which it changes from bending to kinking.

There is probably an appreciable activation energy to the process of making a kink since the $C_4{}'-C_5{}'$ bond must pass through the eclipsed configuration. For this reason we consider kinks of this type with a kink angle of about half the full 100° to be unlikely.

## Common Features of the Family

A number of very similar structures can be built along these lines and it is not obvious which is to be preferred. They all have certain features in common.

(1) The axes of the two straight parts of the DNA do not necessarily intersect exactly, but may be separated by only a small distance, $d$, typically about 1 Å or less. Note that $d$ has a sign. (2) The angle between the two axes, $\alpha$ (projected, if necessary, on to a plane perpendicular to the line joining their points of nearest approach) is easily made more than 90° but approaches 100° with difficulty. The model shown in Fig. 1 has $\alpha = 98°$. At the maximum angle (for any particular model) the backbone of one straight part starts to touch the backbone of the other chain of the other straight part. This contact, marked B in Fig. 1 has a (local) dyad axis. (3) If we define the kink point as the point where the local helix axes, on either side of the kink, intersect (or, if they do not intersect, then the midpoint of the shortest straight line between the axes) then the distance, D, from the kink point to the plane of the nearest base pair is appreciable and typically in the region of 7-8 Å.

扭结处的骨架结构并不是已经列举的优选构型 [12,13] 之一，因为这些优选的构型包含一个弱的 CH···O 紧密接触，这种紧密接触在嘧啶 $C_6$ 或者嘌呤 $C_8$ 上的氢与糖环上的 $O_5'$ 之间形成。而我们所设想的扭结类型，正是由于其本身性质，不可能在每个位置上都有这样的紧密接触。在我们的模型里，在紧邻扭结的每一个碱基对中，有一个碱基里不存在这种紧密接触。然而，正如上面所解释的那样，扭结的骨架构型与 B 型 DNA 的构型十分相似（除了绕 $C_4'$–$C_5'$ 键的扭角外），因此我们认为其在立体化学上是合理的。

扭结两侧的碱基对的性质对模型并不重要，尽管从理论上推测将碱基去堆积化所需的能量在一定程度上会依赖于碱基的组成。我们发现很难估计这个过程所涉及的自由能，也许只是几个千卡。显然最好是可以尽可能精确地测定自由能，因为扭结形成的容易程度恰恰取决于其所需能量的大小。另外一个重要的问题是：一个 DNA 双螺旋在其发生扭结前，能够弯曲的程度是多少。如果我们用 κ 代表平均曲率（这里的 κ 等于曲率半径的倒数），那么我们可以推测，一个均匀弯曲的双螺旋的形变能量，在单位长度上至少会以 $κ^2$ 的速度增加。而另一方面，对于扭结的双螺旋而言，这个能量仅以 κ 的速度增加。在这种情况下，κ 是指分段的双螺旋的平均"曲率"，它与单位长度上的扭结数成比例。因此，在直观上非常明显的是，当 κ 值小的时候，双螺旋会弯曲；而当 κ 值大的时候，双螺旋会形成扭结。我们想要知道从弯曲变成扭结时的曲率半径。

在发生扭结的过程中，可能需要数量可观的活化能，因为 $C_4'$–$C_5'$ 键必须经过重叠构型。正因如此，我们认为：这种类型的扭结不太可能具有约为完整 100° 一半的扭结角度。

### 扭结家族的共同特征

一些非常类似的结构都可以按着这些规则进行构建，而其中究竟哪一个结构更可取，这一点还不是很明显。它们都拥有某些共同特征。

（1）DNA 两个直线部分的轴不一定准确地相交，而或许只由一个很小的距离 $d$ 分隔开，典型的间距为 1Å 或更小。请注意，$d$ 是有符号的。（2）两轴之间的角度 $α$（必要时，可以将两个轴投影到一个平面上，该平面垂直于两轴之间最靠近点间的连接线）可以很容易地做到大于 90°，但很难达到 100°。图 1 中所示的模型的 $α$ 值为 98°。在角度最大的时候（对于任何特殊的模型来说都是如此），一条链直线部分的骨架就开始接触到另一条链直线部分的骨架。这种接触标示于图 1 中的 B 点，它具有一个（局部的）二重轴。（3）如果我们把扭结位点定义为扭结两侧的两个局部双螺旋两轴间的交点（或者，如果它们不相交，则把扭结位点定义为两个螺旋轴之间最短直线的中点），那么从扭结位点到最近碱基对所在平面的距离 D 就是可以估算的，其典型数值在 7~8 Å 这个区间内。

To introduce our fourth point we must first consider the relationship between three successive straight portions; that is, two kinks in succession. We assume that every kink is exactly the same. The structure formed will depend on the precise number of base pairs between the kinks. (It should be remembered that the B form of DNA has an exact repeat after ten pairs.) For example, if there are ten (or a multiple of ten) base pairs between two kinks, the structure will bend round into, very roughly, three sides of a square. If there are five base pairs between kinks (or an odd multiple of five) then the structure will approximate to a zig-zag. In short the dihedral angle for three successive straight portions will depend on the exact number of base pairs between the two adjacent kinks.

We can now state our fourth point. (4) The kink imparts a small negative twist to the DNA. This is most easily grasped by imagining that the kink is made in two steps; first, the two base pairs to be unstacked are unstacked in the axial direction without kinking the backbone—this reduces the twist of 36° between these residues to about 10-20°—and second, that this extended structure is then kinked. The result is that if successive kinks are made at intervals of $10n$ base pairs (where $n$ is an integer) the DNA instead of folding back to form a "circle" follows instead a left-handed helix, though naturally a kinked helix made of straight segments (see Fig. 4).

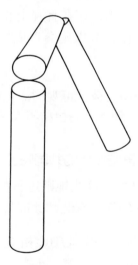

Fig. 4. Each cylinder represents a length of straight double helix. When there are ten base pairs (or an integer multiple of ten base pairs) in the middle stretch the kink has a left-handed configuration, as shown. The dihedral angle used in this paper is zero for the *cis* conformation. Its sign agrees with the usual convention that positive values less than 180° correspond to a right-handed configuration.

The exact dihedral angle associated with three successive straight stretches depends somewhat on the precise details of the kink but is typically about $(m.36°-\theta)$ where $m$ is the number of base pairs between the two kinks and $\theta$, the dihedral correction angle, is not far from 15-20°. A very small rotational deformation of the straight portions could, however, alter this figure a little so the exact value in chromatin (if it does indeed consist of kinked

为了介绍我们的第四点，我们首先要考虑三段连续直线部分之间的关系；也就是说，两个连续的扭结。我们假定每个扭结都是完全相同的。所形成的结构依赖于扭结之间碱基对的精确数目。（应该记住的是，B 型 DNA 在 10 个碱基对以后有完全相同的重复片段）。例如，如果在两个扭结之间存在 10（或者 10 的倍数）个碱基对，那么这个结构会粗略的弯曲环绕成正方形的三个边。如果在两个扭结之间存在 5（或者 5 的奇数倍数）个碱基对，那么这个结构大体上近似于一个锯齿的形状。简言之，三段连续直线部分的二面角会依赖于两个相邻扭结之间的碱基对的准确数目。

现在我们可以陈述我们的第四点了。（4）扭结带给 DNA 一点负面的小扭曲。如果设想扭结是通过两个步骤形成的，就可以很容易地理解这一点：首先，即将被拆开的两个碱基对沿轴线方向拆开，骨架并不发生扭结——这使得这些残基之间的扭曲角度从 36° 减少到大约 10°~20°。第二步，这种在空间上延伸了的结构接着就发生扭结。其结果是，如果连续的扭结在 10$n$（$n$ 为整数）个碱基对的间隔上形成，那么 DNA 就不反方向折叠形成一个"环"，而形成左手螺旋，虽然在自然情况下，扭结的螺旋是由直线的片段形成的（见图 4）。

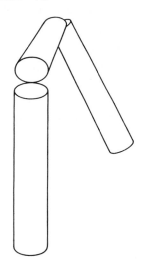

图 4. 每一个圆柱体代表一段直线形双螺旋。当中间呈直线舒展的部分含有 10 个碱基对（或 10 个碱基对的整数倍）时，扭结具有左手构型，如图所示。本文中，为顺式构象所用的二面角为 0。其符号与通常的惯例一致，小于 180° 的正值对应右手构型。

与三段连续直线舒展的片段相关的二面角的准确数值在一定程度上取决于扭结的精确细节，但其典型的数值约为（$m \times 36° - \theta$），$m$ 是两个扭结之间的碱基对数目，$\theta$ 是二面角的修正值，大约为 15°~20°。然而，这些直线部分发生的一些微小的旋转性变形，会使得此结构发生少许的改变，因此二面角在染色质中的精确数值（如

helices) will probably be imposed by the histones.

(5) For any model there is a smallest number of base pairs between two adjacent kinks. For models of this family this number is usually three. In particular, the model illustrated in Fig. 1, for which $\alpha = 98°$, can be built with three base pairs between two kinks but not with only two base pairs there. This is probably true for all models of this type for which $\alpha$ is greater than 90°. A model with three base pairs between two kinks exposes these base pairs rather effectively.

It is easy to see that six parameters are needed to describe the relationship between any two (equal) stretches of straight double helix. If these stretches are related by a dyad axis through the kink point then only four parameters are required. These can conveniently be taken to be the four used above: $d$, $\alpha$, $D$ and $\theta$.

Another family of models can be made with the kink on the side of the major groove, but such structures have a smaller angle of kink and seem rather awkward to build. We have not explored them further. A rather different type of kink, in which a base pair is undone, has been suggested by Gourévitch et al.[14]

## The Occurrence of Kinks

The idea that the fold of DNA in chromatin was based on a unit of 10 base pairs was originally suggested to us by experimental evidence discovered by our colleague, Dr. Markus Noll. Noll[15] has shown that the digestion of native chromatin with the nuclease DNase I produces nicks in the DNA which tend to be spaced multiples of 10 bases apart. This suggests that the DNA is folded in a highly regular way and is probably mainly on the outside of the structure[6,15]. More recent work by Noll and Kornberg (unpublished) using micrococcal nuclease points to a structural repeat at intervals of 20 base pairs. Thus a rather neat model for the most compact (wet) form of chromatin can be made in which the DNA is kinked through about 95-100° every 20 base pairs, giving a shallow kinked helix having 10 straight stretches of DNA in each 100 Å repeat. The middle stretches of this repeat would be largely protected by the histones of the bead, the flanking stretches less so. Whether this very simple model is basically correct remains to be seen.

Obviously we should ask whether DNA is kinked in other situations. One interesting possibility is that when the *lac* repressor binds to the operator site on the DNA the double helix becomes kinked. It has been shown by Wang, Barkley and Bourgeois[16] that this binding unwinds the helix by a small angle, either about 40°, or, more likely, about 90° (the value depending on the amount of unwinding assumed to be produced by the standard agent, ethidium bromide). As they point out, this is too small to allow the formation of a Gierer-type loop[17]. It is, however, just what one would expect from a small number of kinks since each kink of the kind we have described unwinds the double helix by about 15° to 25°. For example, an attractive zig-zag model can be imagined with four kinks, each spaced about five base pairs apart. This model places the two sequences related by a dyad,

果染色质确实是由发生了扭结的螺旋组成的话）很有可能是由组蛋白决定的。

（5）对于任何一个模型而言，相邻两个扭结之间总存在着最小数目的碱基对。对于这类模型而言，其最小数目通常是 3 个。特别是在图 1 中所示的模型（其 $\alpha$ 值为 98°），可以在两个扭结之间用 3 个碱基对进行构建，但仅用 2 个碱基对就不行。这个规律可能适用于这一类 $\alpha$ 值大于 90° 的所有模型。在两个扭结之间有 3 个碱基对的模型显示了碱基对的高效性。

我们可以很容易发现，在描述任意两条（相同的）直线双螺旋片段之间的关系时，需要有六个参数。如果这些片段由通过扭结位点的二重轴相联系，那么只需四个参数就可以。这些参数可以方便地采用上面已经采用过的四个参数：$d$，$\alpha$，$D$ 和 $\theta$。

另一类模型可以由在大沟一侧发生的扭结来构建。但这类结构的扭结角度比较小，似乎难于构建。我们没有进一步对其进行研究。古雷维奇等人 [14] 提出了一种非常不同的扭结类型，其中的一个碱基对是解开的。

## 扭结的发生

染色质中的 DNA 折叠是基于一个 10 个碱基对的单元发生的，这个观点最早是由我们的同事马库斯·诺尔博士根据他所发现的实验证据向我们提出的。诺尔 [15] 发现，用核酸酶 DNase I 对天然的染色质进行消化，使 DNA 上产生了一些切口，这些切口之间的间隔趋近于为 10 的倍数个碱基。这提示 DNA 是以一种高度规则的方式折叠的，并且切割可能主要发生在染色质结构的外侧 [6,15]。最近由诺尔和科恩伯格利用微球菌核酸酶进行的研究（尚未发表）表明，染色质结构的重复是以 20 个碱基对为间隔。由此可以为染色质最紧密的（湿的）形式构建一个比较简洁的模型，其中 DNA 每隔 20 个碱基对发生大约95°～100° 的扭结，形成一个浅的有扭结的螺旋，在每隔 100 Å 的重复间距上，有 10 个 DNA 的直线形片段。这个重复结构的中间片段大部分受到珠粒的组蛋白的保护，而两侧的段落受到较少保护。这个非常简单的模型是否基本正确，还有待证实。

显而易见，我们应该提出这样的问题：DNA 在其他情况下是否也发生扭结。一个有趣的可能性是：当乳糖阻遏子结合在 DNA 上的操纵子位点时，双螺旋就发生扭结。王、巴克利和布儒瓦等 [16] 证明：这种结合使螺旋以一个小的角度解旋，要么大约为 40°，更可能的是大约 90°（这个数值依赖于解旋的程度，通常假定解旋是由标准试剂溴化乙啶引起的）。正如他们指出的那样，这个数值太小，不容许吉勒型环 [17] 的形成。但这恰好是人们从少数扭结中期望看到的情况，因为在我们描述的那种类型中，每个扭结只能使双螺旋以大约 15°～25° 的角解旋。例如，可以设想一个有四个扭结的漂亮锯齿状模型，每个扭结之间相隔大约 5 个碱基对。该模型将两条序列通过二重轴相联系，每条序列具有六个连续的碱基对，分别安插在第一个和最后一个扭结

each of six consecutive base pairs, on either side of the first and last kinks (see Fig. 5). In this position, being near a kink, they are more exposed than they would be in a stretch of unkinked DNA.

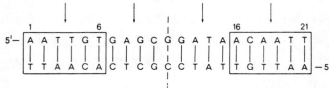

Fig. 5. The minimal base sequence of the *lac* operon, taken from Gilbert and Maxam[18]. The dotted line marks the pseudodyad in the base sequence. The two sets of consecutive base pairs, related by the dyad, are boxed. The arrows show one choice of positions where kinks might occur.

In essence, kinking may be a way of partly exposing a small group of base pairs without too great an expenditure of energy. The exposed side of each of these base pairs is that normally in the major groove. The kink has the effect of displacing one of the phosphate-sugar backbones which normally make up the two sides of this groove. The specific pattern of hydrogen bonding sites in the major groove is thus made more accessible for a few base pairs on either side of a kink. A kink may therefore turn out to be a preferred configuration of DNA when it is interacting specifically with a protein.

Kinks may be suspected in all cases where double-stranded DNA has been shown to adopt a more compact state than the normal double helix. Obvious examples are the folded chromosomes of *Escherichia coli*[19,20] (and no doubt other prokaryotes), the folded DNA in viruses, the $\psi$ phase of naked DNA discovered by Lerman[21] and the shortened form of DNA in alcoholic solutions as described by Lang[22].

One should also ask whether kinks occur spontaneously, as a result of thermal motion, in double-stranded DNA in solution. The frequency at which this occurs clearly depends on the free energy difference involved. If this were, say, about 4 kcalorie then there should be one kink in about 800 base pairs which could be appreciable. Such kinks would occur mainly between A–T pairs. If the free energy were as high as 6 kcalorie this would produce one kink in about every 22,000 base pairs, which would be more difficult to detect.

At the present we have no compelling evidence which shows that DNA in chromatin is kinked rather than bent nor that kinks exist in DNA in other contexts. Nevertheless our model seems to us sufficiently attractive to be worth presenting now for consideration by other workers in the field. Kinks, if they occur, have at least two possible advantages. It has always been a puzzle how to construct hierarchies of helices in a neat way, since bending an existing helix necessarily distorts its regular structure. This distortion becomes more acute as the basic helix is coiled at higher and higher levels. A kink allows such deformations to be local rather than diffuse and makes it easier to build hierarchical models which are neat stereochemically. The other advantage is that, at a kink, several base pairs may be more easily available for specific interaction with a protein. If kinks in

的两侧（参见图 5）。在这个位置上，由于靠近扭结，它们比在一段无扭结的 DNA 上更加的暴露。

图 5. 乳糖操纵子的最小碱基序列，来自吉尔伯特和马克萨姆的文章[18]。虚线标记的是碱基序列中的假二重轴。方框标记由二重轴联系的两组连续的碱基对。箭头表示扭结可能发生的位置。

从本质上说，扭结也许是一种不用消耗太多能量就可以暴露一小组碱基对的方式。正常情况下这些碱基对被暴露的一侧位于大沟中。大沟的两侧通常是由磷酸－糖骨架构成的，扭结使其中一个骨架发生移位。于是，大沟中氢键位点的特殊分布由此对扭结两侧的一些碱基对变得更易接近。因此，当 DNA 与一个蛋白发生特异性的相互作用时，扭结也许就成了 DNA 的一种优选构型。

当双链 DNA 被证实采用了比正常双螺旋更为紧凑的形态时，扭结都有可能存在。明显的例子有：大肠杆菌（无疑还有其他原核生物）的折叠染色体[19,20]，病毒中的折叠了的 DNA，列尔曼[21] 发现的裸露 DNA 的 $\psi$ 相，以及兰[22] 所描述的酒精溶液中 DNA 的缩短形式。

人们应该还会提出这样的问题：在双链 DNA 的溶液中，扭结是否会由于热运动而自发地产生。这种扭结发生的频率明显依赖于所涉及自由能的差别。比方说，如果该自由能大约是 4 千卡路里，那么可以估计，在大约 800 个碱基对上应该有一个扭结。这样的扭结主要发生在 A–T 碱基对之间。如果自由能高达 6 千卡路里，那么大约每 22,000 个碱基对上会产生一个扭结，这将更加难以察觉。

目前我们还没有令人信服的证据表明染色质中的 DNA 是扭结而不是弯曲，以及在其他环境下 DNA 中存在扭结。但不管怎样，我们的模型对我们来说具有足够的吸引力，值得现在呈现出来，供本领域内其他研究者参考。扭结如果发生的话，至少有两个可能的优点。一直以来让人困惑的是：如何以简洁的方式构建不同层次的螺旋结构，因为使已经存在的螺旋弯曲，必然导致其规则结构的扭曲。随着基本的螺旋在越来越高的层次上卷曲，这种扭曲变得越来越剧烈。扭结允许这样的扭曲在局部发生，而不是扩散开来；并且使构建立体化学上简洁合理的各层次模型变得更容易。另外一个优点是：在扭结处，有几个碱基对可能会更为容易地与蛋白质发

DNA exist they will surely prove to be important.

We thank our colleagues Drs. R. D. Kornberg, M. Noll and J. O. Thomas for communicating their results to us before publication. We also thank them and our other colleagues for many useful discussions on chromatin structure.

(**255**, 530-533; 1975)

F. H. C. Crick and A. Klug
Medical Research Council Laboratory of Molecular Biology, Hills Road, Cambridge, UK

Received April 25; accepted May 6, 1975.

---

References:

1. *Histones and Nucleohistones* (edit. by Philips, D. M. P.) (Plenum, London and New York, 1971).
2. Pardon, J. F., Richards, B. M., and Cotter, R. I., *Cold Spring Harb. Symp. Quant. Biol.*, **38**, 75-81 (1974).
3. Hewish, D. R., and Burgoyne, L. A., *Biochem. Biophys. Res. Commun.*, **52**, 504-510 (1973).
4. Burgoyne, L. A., Hewish, D. R., and Mobbs, J., *Biochem. J.*, **143**, 67-72 (1974).
5. Noll, M., *Nature*, **251**, 249-251 (1974).
6. Kornberg, R. D., *Science*, **184**, 868-871 (1974).
7. Olins, D. E., and Olins, A. L., *Science*, **183**, 330-332 (1974).
8. Griffith, J., *Science*, **187**, 1202-1203 (1975).
9. Oudet, P., Gross-Bellard. M., and Chambon, P., *Cell*, **4**, 281-299 (1975).
10. Van Holde, K. E., Sahasrabuddhe, B., and Shaw, R., *Nucleic Acid Res.*, **1**, 1579-1586 (1974).
11. Baldwin, J. P., Boseley, P. G., Bradbury, E. M., and Ibel, K., *Nature*, **253**, 245-249 (1975).
12. Arnott, S., and Hukins, D. W. L., *Nature*, **224**, 886-888 (1969).
13. Sundaralingam, M., *Biopolymers*, **7**, 821-869 (1969).
14. Gourévitch, M., *et al.*, *Biochemie*, **56**, 967-985 (1974).
15. Noll, M., *Nucleic Acid Res.*, **1**, 1573-1578 (1974).
16. Wang, J. C., Barkley, M. D., and Bourgeois, S., *Nature*, **251**, 247-249 (1974).
17. Gierer, A., *Nature*, **212**, 1480-1481 (1966).
18. Gilbert, W. and Maxam, A., *Proc. Natl. Acad. Sci. U.S.A.*, **70**, 3581-3584 (1973).
19. Pettijohn, D. E., and Hecht, R., *Cold Spring Harb. Symp. Quant. Biol.*, **38**, 31-41 (1974).
20. Worcel, A., Burgi, E., Robinton, J., and Carlson, C. L., *Cold Spring Harb. Symp. Quant. Biol.*, **38**, 43-51 (1974).
21. Lerman, L., *Cold Spring Harb. Symp. Quant. Biol.*, **38**, 59-73 (1974).
22. Lang, D., *J. Molec. Biol.*, **78**, 247-254 (1973).

生特异性相互作用。如果 DNA 中存在扭结，它们一定会被证明是很重要的。

我们感谢我们的同事科恩伯格、诺尔和托马斯博士在论文发表之前与我们交流他们的研究成果。我们也感谢他们以及我们的其他同事关于染色质结构的许多有益讨论。

（刘振明 翻译；顾孝诚 审稿）

# Continuous Cultures of Fused Cells Secreting Antibody of Predefined Specificity

G. Köhler and C. Milstein

## Editor's Note

Antibodies are the chemical agents (with well-known but complex molecular structure) that help vertebrate animals to defend themselves against infection and other foreign agents. In principle, antibodies against agents the body has not previously encountered would be invaluable in protecting the lives of human beings. This paper by César Milstein and Georges Köhler describes a technique for making antibodies specific against arbitrary protein structures, so providing a means of defence against unknown or as yet non-existent infectious agents. Such general-purpose antibodies (now known as monoclonal antibodies) are now widely used in research and in the practice of medicine. Milstein and Köhler shared the Nobel Prize in Physiology or Medicine (with Niels K. Jerne) in 1984.

THE manufacture of predefined specific antibodies by means of permanent tissue culture cell lines is of general interest. There are at present a considerable number of permanent cultures of myeloma cells[1,2] and screening procedures have been used to reveal antibody activity in some of them. This, however, is not a satisfactory source of monoclonal antibodies of predefined specificity. We describe here the derivation of a number of tissue culture cell lines which secrete anti-sheep red blood cell (SRBC) antibodies. The cell lines are made by fusion of a mouse myeloma and mouse spleen cells from an immunised donor. To understand the expression and interactions of the Ig chains from the parental lines, fusion experiments between two known mouse myeloma lines were carried out.

Each immunoglobulin chain results from the integrated expression of one of several $V$ and $C$ genes coding respectively for its variable and constant sections. Each cell expresses only one of the two possible alleles (allelic exclusion; reviewed in ref. 3). When two antibody-producing cells are fused, the products of both parental lines are expressed[4,5], and although the light and heavy chains of both parental lines are randomly joined, no evidence of scrambling of $V$ and $C$ sections is observed[4]. These results, obtained in an heterologous system involving cells of rat and mouse origin, have now been confirmed by fusing two myeloma cells of the same mouse strain, and provide the background for the derivation and understanding of antibody-secreting hybrid lines in which one of the parental cells is an antibody-producing spleen cell.

# 可分泌特异性抗体的融合细胞的连续培养

克勒，米尔斯坦

编者按

抗体是一种众所周知但分子结构复杂的化学物质，它帮助脊椎动物抵御感染及其他异物。原则上讲，抗体能够对抗机体先前没有遇到过的物质，对保护人类的生命极具价值。塞萨尔·米尔斯坦和乔治斯·克勒的这篇文章描述了一种制备针对任意蛋白结构的特异性抗体的技术，因此也提供了一种抵御未知的或迄今为止尚不存在的传染源的手段。这种通用抗体（现称为单克隆抗体）如今已被广泛应用于研究和医疗实践。米尔斯坦和克勒（与尼尔斯·杰尼）因此在 1984 年共同获得诺贝尔生理学暨医学奖。

通过对细胞系进行持续的组织培养来生产符合人们预期的特异性抗体的方法引起了人们的广泛关注。现在已经建立起了数量可观的可以永久培养的骨髓瘤细胞系[1,2]，并且还建立了多种筛选流程用于检测其中是否存在抗体活性。然而，这种方法无法提供令人满意的符合人们预期的特异性单克隆抗体。本文中，我们描述了一些可以分泌抗绵羊红细胞（SRBC）抗体的组织培养细胞系的制备过程。这些细胞系是通过融合小鼠骨髓瘤细胞和小鼠脾细胞（来自经过免疫的小鼠）的方法建立起来的。为了了解亲本细胞系中免疫球蛋白（Ig）链的表达和相互作用关系，我们使用了两个已知的小鼠骨髓瘤细胞系进行融合实验。

免疫球蛋白的每条链都是通过一个 $V$ 基因（编码可变区）与一个 $C$ 基因（编码恒定区）经过整合之后表达的。每个细胞只能表达两个可能的等位基因中的一个（等位基因排斥，详见参考文献 3 中所做的综述）。当两个都能够分泌抗体的细胞融合到一起之后，则两个亲本细胞系各自编码的抗体都会得到表达[4,5]。不过，虽然两个亲本细胞系中的轻链和重链都是随机组合的，但是在融合细胞中并没有发现扰乱 $V$ 片段和 $C$ 片段之间连接的现象[4]。这些实验结果最初来自于由大鼠细胞和小鼠细胞组成的异源系统，现在已经在来源于同一个小鼠品系的两个骨髓瘤融合细胞系中得到证实。这些结果也为了解分泌抗体的杂交系的来源提供了基础，因为该杂交系亲本细胞之一是可分泌抗体的脾细胞。

631

Two myeloma cell lines of BALB/c origin were used. PlBul is resistant to 5-bromo-2'-deoxyuridine[4], does not grow in selective medium (HAT, ref. 6) and secretes a myeloma protein, Adj PC5, which is an IgG2A($\kappa$), (ref. 1). Synthesis is not balanced and free light chains are also secreted. The second cell line, P3-X63Ag8, prepared from P3 cells[2], is resistant to 20 μg ml$^{-1}$ 8-azaguanine and does not grow in HAT medium. The protein secreted (MOPC 21) is an IgG1($\kappa$) which has been fully sequenced[7,8]. Equal numbers of cells from each parental line were fused using inactivated Sendai virus[9] and samples containing $2 \times 10^5$ cells were grown in selective medium in separate dishes. Four out of ten dishes showed growth in selective medium and these were taken as independent hybrid lines, probably derived from single fusion events. The karyotype of the hybrid cells after 5 months in culture was just under the sum of the two parental lines (Table 1). Figure 1 shows the isoelectric focusing[10] (IEF) pattern of the secreted products of different lines. The hybrid cells (samples *c-h* in Fig. 1) give a much more complex pattern than either parent (*a* and *b*) or a mixture of the parental lines (*m*). The important feature of the new pattern is the presence of extra bands (Fig. 1, arrows). These new bands, however, do not seem to be the result of differences in primary structure; this is indicated by the IEF pattern of the products after reduction to separate the heavy and light chains (Fig. 1*B*). The IEF pattern of chains of the hybrid clones (Fig. 1*B*, *g*) is equivalent to the sum of the IEF pattern (*a* and *b*) of chains of the parental clones with no evidence of extra products. We conclude that, as previously shown with interspecies hybrids[4,5], new Ig molecules are produced as a result of mixed association between heavy and light chains from the two parents. This process is intracellular as a mixed cell population does not give rise to such hybrid molecules (compare *m* and *g*, Fig. 1*A*). The individual cells must therefore be able to express both isotypes. This result shows that in hybrid cells the expression of one isotype and idiotype does not exclude the expression of another: both heavy chain isotypes ($\gamma$1 and $\gamma$2a) and both $V_H$ and both $V_L$ regions (idiotypes) are expressed. There are no allotypic markers for the $C_\kappa$ region to provide direct proof for the expression of both parental $C_\kappa$ regions. But this is indicated by the phenotypic link between the *V* and *C* regions.

Table 1. Number of chromosomes in parental and hybrid cell lines

| Cell line | Number of chromosomes per cell | Mean |
| --- | --- | --- |
| P3-X67Ag8 | 66,65,65,65,65 | 65 |
| P1Bul | Ref. 4 | 55 |
| Mouse spleen cells | – | 40 |
| Hy-B(P1-P3) | 112,110,104,104,102 | 106 |
| Sp-1/7-2 | 93,90,89,89,87 | 90 |
| Sp-2/3-3 | 97,98,96,96,94,88 | 95 |

在实验中我们使用了两个 BALB/c 小鼠来源的骨髓瘤细胞系。P1Bul 细胞具有 5-溴-2'-脱氧尿嘧啶抗性 [4]，在选择性培养基（HAT，参考文献 6）中不生长，并且可以分泌一种骨髓瘤蛋白——Adj PC5，属于 IgG2A（κ）亚型（参考文献 1）。这种蛋白的轻、重链合成并不是均衡的，也可以检测到分泌的游离免疫球蛋白轻链。另一个细胞系 P3-X63Ag8 来自于 P3 细胞 [2]，可以耐受 20 μg·ml⁻¹ 的 8-氮鸟嘌呤，并且不能在 HAT 培养基中生长。这个细胞分泌的蛋白（MOPC 21）属于 IgG1（κ）亚型，并且已经测出其全序列 [7,8]。利用灭活的仙台病毒 [9] 将相同数量的亲本细胞融合后，再将 $2 \times 10^5$ 个融合后的细胞分别接种在含有选择性培养基的不同培养皿中。结果含选择性培养基的 10 个培养皿中有 4 个培养皿上有融合细胞生长，这些被认为是独立的杂交细胞系，它们可能来自单一的细胞融合。经过 5 个月的培养后，这些杂交细胞的染色体组型被证明是其两个亲本细胞系相加的结果（表 1）。图 1 显示的是不同细胞系分泌产物的等电聚焦 [10]（IEF）图谱。其中，杂交细胞（图 1 中样品 c~h）的图谱比其两个亲本（a 和 b）或者两个亲本的混合样品（m）都要更加复杂。这种新图谱的一个重要特点就是产生了一些额外的条带（图 1 中箭头所示）。然而，我们发现这些新的条带似乎并不是因为蛋白质一级结构的不同而导致的；这一点可通过用还原剂处理样品（以便分开抗体的重链和轻链）后的还原产物的等电聚焦图谱看出（图 1B）。杂交细胞克隆（图 1B，g）的肽链的等电聚焦图谱与其两个亲本细胞克隆的肽链（a 和 b）的等电聚焦图谱之和相同，并且没有多余的产物。由此我们得出结论，与之前在不同物种来源的细胞间进行的融合实验一样 [4,5]，新的免疫球蛋白分子是两个亲本的重链和轻链相互组合的产物。由于单纯地将两种细胞混合并不能产生这种杂交分子（比较图 1A 中 m 和 g），因此这一过程应该发生在细胞内。相应地，每个融合细胞都应该能够表达这两种同种型。这一结果表明，在杂交细胞中一种同种型或独特型的表达并不会排斥另一种的表达——两种重链同种型（γ1 和 γ2a）以及重链可变区（$V_H$）和轻链可变区（$V_L$）（独特型）都有表达。由于缺乏链恒定区（$C_κ$）的同种异型标记，因此我们无法提供直接的证据证明两个亲本的 $C_κ$ 区都有表达。不过由于 V 区和 C 区是连接在一起的，因此可以间接证明这一结论。

表 1. 亲本细胞系和杂交细胞系中染色体的数量

| 细胞系 | 每个细胞的染色体数量 | 平均值 |
| --- | --- | --- |
| P3-X67Ag8 | 66, 65, 65, 65, 65 | 65 |
| P1Bul | 参考文献4 | 55 |
| 小鼠脾细胞 | — | 40 |
| Hy-B (P1-P3) | 112, 110, 104, 104, 102 | 106 |
| Sp-1/7-2 | 93, 90, 89, 89, 87 | 90 |
| Sp-2/3-3 | 97, 98, 96, 96, 94, 88 | 95 |

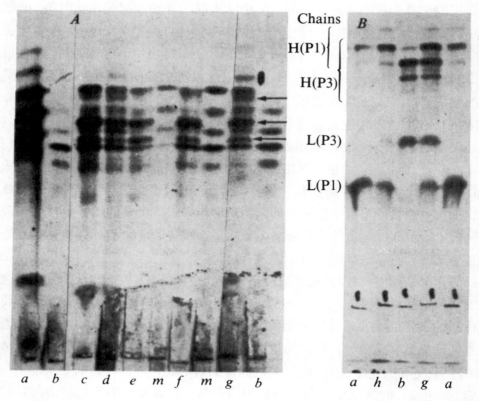

Fig. 1. Autoradiograph of labelled components secreted by the parental and hybrid cell lines analysed by IEF before (*A*) and after reduction (*B*). Cells were incubated in the presence of [14]C-lysine[14] and the supernatant applied on polyacrylamide slabs. *A*, *p*H range 6.0 (bottom) to 8.0 (top) in 4 M urea. *B*, *p*H range 5.0 (bottom) to 9.0 (top) in 6 M urea; the supernatant was incubated for 20 min at 37°C in the presence of 8 M urea, 1.5 M mercaptoethanol and 0.1 M potassium phosphate *p*H 8.0 before being applied to the right slab. Supernatants from parental cell lines in: *a*, P1Bu1; *b*, P3-X67Ag8; and *m*, mixture of equal number of P1Bu1 and P3-X67Ag8 cells. Supernatants from two independently derived hybrid lines are shown: *c-f*, four subclones from Hy-3; *g* and *h*, two subclones from Hy-B. Fusion was carried out[4,9] using 10[6] cells of each parental line and 4,000 haemagglutination units inactivated Sendai virus (Searle). Cells were divided into ten equal samples and grown separately in selective medium (HAT medium, ref. 6). Medium was changed every 3 d. Successful hybrid lines were obtained in four of the cultures, and all gave similar IEF patterns. Hy-B and Hy-3 were further cloned in soft agar[14]. L, Light; H, heavy.

Figure 1*A* shows that clones derived from different hybridisation experiments and from subclones of one line are indistinguishable. This has also been observed in other experiments (data not shown). Variants were, however, found in a survey of 100 subclones. The difference is often associated with changes in the ratios of the different chains and occasionally with the total disappearance of one or other of the chains. Such events are best visualised on IEF analysis of the separated chains (for example, Fig. 1*h*, in which the heavy chain of P3 is no longer observed). The important point that no new chains are detected by IEF complements a previous study[4] of a rat–mouse hybrid line in which scrambling of *V* and *C* regions from the light chains of rat and mouse was not observed.

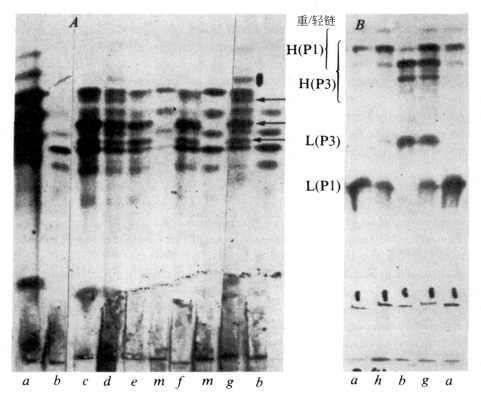

图 1. 放射性标记的亲本细胞系和杂交细胞系分泌产物在被还原前（*A*）和还原后（*B*）经过等电聚焦电泳分析后的放射自显影图像。细胞均培养在含有 [14]C–赖氨酸[14] 的培养基中，细胞培养上清被加到聚丙烯酰胺胶上。*A*，pH 范围为 6.0（底部）到 8.0（顶部），尿素浓度为 4 M。*B*，pH 范围为 5.0（底部）到 9.0（顶部），尿素浓度为 6 M。细胞培养上清先在含有 8 M 尿素、1.5 M 巯基乙醇的 0.1 M 磷酸钾缓冲液（pH 8.0）中 37℃ 孵育 20 分钟，再加到胶上。亲本细胞系上清为：*a*，P1Bul；*b*，P3-X67Ag8；*m*，P1Bul 和 P3-X67Ag8 细胞等量混合物。分别得到的两个杂交系上清为：*c~f*，Hy-3 的 4 个亚克隆；*g* 和 *h*，Hy-B 的 2 个亚克隆。各用 $10^8$ 个细胞的亲本细胞以及 4,000 血凝反应单位的灭活仙台病毒（瑟尔公司）进行细胞融合实验[4,9]。融合完成后，细胞被分为均等的 10 份并分别接种到选择性培养基（HAT 培养基，参考文献 6）中。培养基每 3 天换 1 次。最终在 4 个培养皿中获得了成功融合的杂交系，并且它们具有相似的等电聚焦图谱。Hy-B 和 Hy-3 则是在软琼脂中进一步克隆得到[14]。L 代表轻链，H 代表重链。

　　图 1*A* 显示出来源于不同杂交实验的克隆以及同一个细胞系的不同亚克隆是无法区别的。这在其他实验中也曾经被观察到（数据未显示）。然而，通过对 100 个亚克隆进行分析，我们发现了一些变异体。这种区别通常与不同肽链的比例变化有关，偶尔会发现有一种或另一种肽链完全消失。这种情况在等电聚焦实验分析单个肽链时得到了最好的体现（例如，图 1*h* 中，P3 的重链消失了）。在等电聚焦中观察不到新的条带这点很重要，这印证了早先在大鼠－小鼠杂交细胞系中所得到的类似的结论[4]，在这个细胞系中观察不到来自大鼠和小鼠轻链的 *V* 区和 *C* 区发生错误连接。在这个研究中，两个亲本的轻链具有相同的 $C_\kappa$ 区，因此无法检测融合细胞中 $V_L$–$C_L$ 是否错误

In this study, both light chains have identical $C_\kappa$ regions and therefore scrambled $V_L–C_L$ molecules would be undetected. On the other hand, the heavy chains are of different subclasses and we expect scrambled $V_H–C_H$ to be detectable by IEF. They were not observed in the clones studied and if they occur must do so at a lower frequency. We conclude that in syngeneic cell hybrids (as well as in interspecies cell hybrids) $V–C$ integration is not the result of cytoplasmic events. Integration as a result of DNA translocation or rearrangement during transcription is also suggested by the presence of integrated mRNA molecules[11] and by the existence of defective heavy chains in which a deletion of $V$ and $C$ sections seems to take place in already committed cells[12].

The cell line P3-X63Ag8 described above dies when exposed to HAT medium. Spleen cells from an immunised mouse also die in growth medium. When both cells are fused by Sendai virus and the resulting mixture is grown in HAT medium, surviving clones can be observed to grow and become established after a few weeks. We have used SRBC as immunogen, which enabled us, after culturing the fused lines, to determine the presence of specific antibody-producing cells by a plaque assay technique[13] (Fig. 2a). The hybrid cells were cloned in soft agar[14] and clones producing antibody were easily detected by an overlay of SRBC and complement (Fig. 2b). Individual clones were isolated and shown to retain their phenotype as almost all the clones of the derived purified line are capable of lysing SRBC (Fig. 2c). The clones were visible to the naked eye (for example, Fig. 2d). Both direct and indirect plaque assays[13] have been used to detect specific clones and representative clones of both types have been characterised and studied.

The derived lines (Sp hybrids) are hybrid cell lines for the following reasons. They grow in selective medium. Their karyotype after 4 months in culture (Table 1) is a little smaller than the sum of the two parental lines but more than twice the chromosome number of normal BALB/c cells, indicating that the lines are not the result of fusion between spleen cells. In addition the lines contain a metacentric chromosome also present in the parental P3-X67Ag8. Finally, the secreted immunoglobulins contain MOPC 21 protein in addition to new, unknown components. The latter presumably represent the chains derived from the specific anti-SRBC antibody. Figure 3A shows the IEF pattern of the material secreted by two such Sp hybrid clones. The IEF bands derived from the parental P3 line are visible in the pattern of the hybrid cells, although obscured by the presence of a number of new bands. The pattern is very complex, but the complexity of hybrids of this type is likely to result from the random recombination of chains (see above, Fig. 1). Indeed, IEF patterns of the reduced material secreted by the spleen-P3 hybrid clones gave a simpler pattern of Ig chains. The heavy and light chains of the P3 parental line became prominent, and new bands were apparent.

连接。另一方面，两个亲本的重链属于不同的亚型，因此我们预测可以通过等电聚焦实验来确定是否发生了 $V_H$–$C_H$ 的错误连接。在我们研究的克隆中，并没有检测到这种错误连接的发生，即使错误连接确实发生，其概率也是非常低的。我们的结论是，在同源性细胞杂交实验中（不同物种间的细胞杂交也是一样的），$V$–$C$ 的整合并不是发生在细胞质中的事件的结果，而是在转录的过程中 DNA 发生易位或者重排导致的。整合 mRNA 分子的发现 [11]，以及在已经定型的细胞中 $V$ 片段或 $C$ 片段缺失的重链（存在功能缺陷）的发现 [12] 都支持了这一结论。

上述 P3-X63Ag8 细胞系在 HAT 培养基中不能存活。从免疫后的小鼠中获得的脾细胞也会在生长培养基中死去。当这两种细胞在仙台病毒的作用下发生融合后则可以在 HAT 培养基中生长，几周后观察到存活下来的克隆生长并固定下来。我们使用绵羊红细胞作为免疫原刺激小鼠，这使我们可以在获得融合细胞之后，用空斑实验技术 [13] 来检测是否存在可以产生特异性抗体的细胞（图 2a）。我们将杂交细胞在软琼脂中进行了克隆 [14]，并且通过覆盖绵羊红细胞和补体便可以很容易地挑出那些可以产生抗体的克隆（图 2b）。单个克隆被分离出来之后仍然能保持其表型，几乎所有的来源于纯化细胞系的克隆都具有裂解绵羊红细胞的能力（图 2c）。这些克隆是肉眼可见的（例如图 2d）。经过直接和间接空斑实验 [13] 来检测特定的克隆，这两种方法检测出的代表性克隆被挑选出来用于进一步的研究。

以下原因证明上述筛选出来的细胞系（Sp 杂交体）是杂交细胞系。首先它们可以在选择性培养基中生长。其次，培养 4 个月后，它们的核型比两个亲本细胞系之和稍小，但比正常的 BALB/c 小鼠细胞的两倍要多。这表明杂交细胞不是由两个脾细胞之间的融合产生的。此外，杂交细胞中含有一个中着丝粒染色体，这也存在于其亲本细胞 P3-X67Ag8 中。最后，杂交细胞分泌的免疫球蛋白中除了含有 MOPC 21 蛋白外，还含有新的未知组分。后者可能表明杂交细胞分泌的抗体来自于亲本细胞中的特异性抗绵羊红细胞抗体。图 3A 显示了两种 Sp 杂交细胞克隆分泌物质的等电聚焦图谱。在杂交细胞中，来自于亲本 P3 细胞系的条带依然可见，尽管一些新产生的条带使其变得模糊。等电聚焦的图谱非常复杂，不过杂交细胞中的条带的复杂情况似乎来源于亲本肽链的随机重组（见上文，图 1）。确实，脾细胞 P3 杂交细胞克隆分泌的样品被还原后，免疫球蛋白链的图谱更简单一些。亲本 P3 细胞系的轻链和重链成为主要的条带，而其他新产生的条带也变得更明显了。

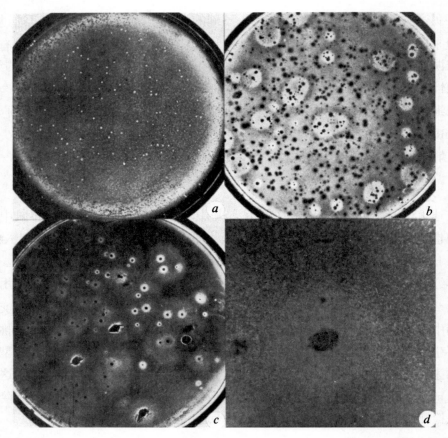

Fig. 2. Isolation of an anti-SRBC antibody-secreting cell clone. Activity was revealed by a halo of haemolysed SRBC. Direct plaques given by: *a*, 6,000 hybrid cells Sp-1; *b*, clones grown in soft agar from an inoculum of 2,000 Sp-1 cells; *c*, recloning of one of the positive clones Sp-1/7; *d*, higher magnification of a positive clone. Myeloma cells ($10^7$ P3-X67Ag8) were fused to $10^8$ spleen cells from an immunised BALB/c mouse. Mice were immunised by intraperitoneal injection of 0.2 ml packed SRBC diluted 1:10, boosted after 1 month and the spleens collected 4 d later. After fusion, cells (Sp-1) were grown for 8 d in HAT medium, changed at 1-3 d intervals. Cells were then grown in Dulbecco modified Eagle's medium, supplemented for 2 weeks with hypoxanthine and thymidine. Forty days after fusion the presence of anti-SRBC activity was revealed as shown in *a*. The ratio of plaque forming cells/total number of hybrid cells was 1/30. This hybrid cell population was cloned in soft agar (50% cloning efficiency). A modified plaque assay was used to reveal positive clones shown in *b-d* as follows. When cell clones had reached a suitable size, they were overlaid in sterile conditions with 2 ml 0.6% agarose in phosphate-buffered saline containing 25 μl packed SRBC and 0.2 ml fresh guinea pig serum (absorbed with SRBC) as source of complement. *b*, Taken after overnight incubation at 37°C. The ratio of positive/total number of clones was 1/33. A suitable positive clone was picked out and grown in suspension. This clone was called Sp-1/7, and was recloned as shown in *c*; over 90% of the clones gave positive lysis. A second experiment in which $10^6$ P3-X67Ag8 cells were fused with $10^8$ spleen cells was the source of a clone giving rise to indirect plaques (clone Sp-2/3-3). Indirect plaques were produced by the addition of 1:20 sheep anti-MOPC 21 antibody to the agarose overlay.

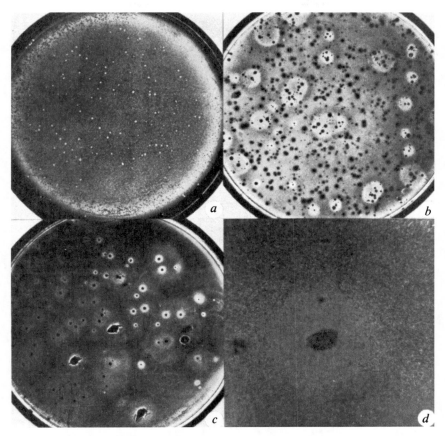

图 2. 可分泌抗绵羊红细胞抗体的细胞克隆的分离。在细胞克隆周围由溶解的红细胞形成的圆环大小代表了其所分泌的抗体的活性大小。直接空斑实验：a，6,000 个 Sp-1 杂交细胞；b，转接在软琼脂中的 2,000 个 Sp-1 细胞形成的克隆；c，对其中一个阳性克隆 Sp-1/7 进行再次克隆；d，阳性克隆的高倍放大图像。$10^7$ 个骨髓瘤细胞（P3-X67Ag8）与 $10^8$ 个从免疫后的 BALB/c 小鼠中获得的脾细胞进行融合。首次免疫向小鼠腹膜内注射 0.2 ml 绵羊红细胞（1：10 稀释），然后在一个月后再加强免疫一次，并于 4 天后收集脾细胞。经过融合后，将细胞（Sp-1）接种在 HAT 培养基中培养 8 天，期间每 1~3 天换液一次。然后将细胞在 DMEM 培养基中培养，并在接下来的两周内补充添加次黄嘌呤和胸腺嘧啶。40 天后，使用如图 a 所示的方法检测抗绵羊红细胞抗体的活性。空斑形成细胞数与总杂交细胞数之比为 1/30。这些杂交细胞群体被接种到软琼脂中进行克隆（克隆效率为 50%）。一种改良的空斑实验被用于阳性克隆的选择，如图 b~d 所示。当细胞克隆长到合适的大小时，在无菌环境下加入 2ml 含 0.6% 琼脂的磷酸盐缓冲液中（其中含有 25 μl 绵羊红细胞和 0.2 ml 新鲜豚鼠血清作为补体成分的来源）铺平板。b，37℃ 孵育过夜后的图像。阳性克隆占总克隆的 1/33。挑选出来一个合适的阳性克隆并悬浮培养。将该克隆命名为 Sp-1/7，如图 c 所示再次克隆。超过 90% 的克隆都具有裂解绵羊红细胞的能力。另一个实验使用了 $10^6$ 个 P3-X67Ag8 细胞和 $10^8$ 个脾细胞进行融合，所获得的融合细胞被用于间接空斑实验（克隆命名为 Sp-2/3-3）。在间接空斑实验中，1：20 稀释的绵羊抗 MOPC 21 细胞抗体被加到融合细胞克隆上层。

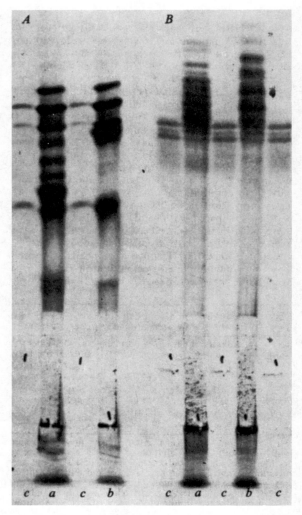

Fig. 3. Autoradiograph of labelled components secreted by anti-SRBC specific hybrid lines. Fractionation before (B) and after (A) reduction was by IEF. pH gradient was 5.0 (bottom) to 9.0 (top) in the presence of 6 M urea. Other conditions as in Fig. 1. Supernatants from: a, hybrid clone Sp-1/7-2; b, hybrid clone Sp-2/3-3; c, myeloma line P3-X67Ag8.

The hybrid Sp-1 gave direct plaques and this suggested that it produces an IgM antibody. This is confirmed in Fig. 4 which shows the inhibition of SRBC lysis by a specific anti-IgM antibody. IEF techniques usually do not reveal 19S IgM molecules. IgM is therefore unlikely to be present in the unreduced sample a (Fig. 3B) but μ chains should contribute to the pattern obtained after reduction (sample a, Fig. 3A).

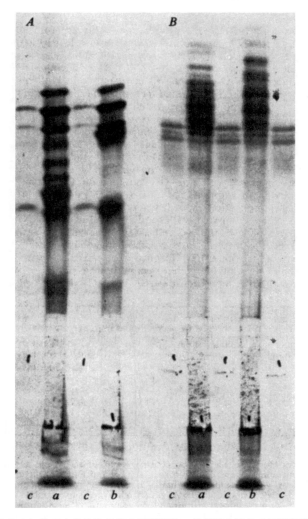

图 3. 抗绵羊红细胞杂交细胞系分泌物的放射自显影图片。使用等电聚焦分析还原前（*B*）和还原后（*A*）的样品。pH 梯度从 5.0（底部）到 9.0（顶部），尿素浓度为 6 M。其他条件与图 1 中相同。*a*，Sp-1/7-2 细胞培养上清；*b*，Sp-2/3-3 细胞培养上清；*c*，骨髓瘤细胞 P3-X67Ag8 细胞培养上清。

杂交细胞 Sp-1 可以直接形成空斑，这表明其可以产生 IgM 抗体。图 4 也进一步证明了这一点：特异性抗 IgM 的抗体可以抑制绵羊红细胞的裂解。等电聚焦实验通常不能分辨 19S 的 IgM 分子。因此，在非还原的样品 *a* 中（图 3*B*）IgM 应该没有显现出来，不过在还原之后 μ 链应该会显示在图中（样品 *a*，图 3*A*）。

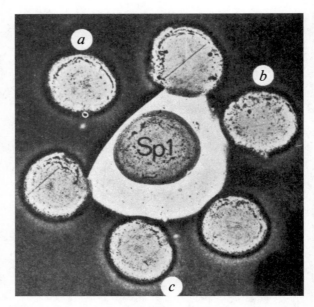

Fig. 4. Inhibition of haemolysis by antibody secreted by hybrid clone Sp-1/7-2. The reaction was in a 9-cm Petri dish with a layer of 5 ml 0.6% agarose in phosphate-buffered saline containing 1/80 (v/v) SRBC. Centre well contains 2.5 μl 20 times concentrated culture medium of clone Sp-1/7-2 and 2.5 μl mouse serum. *a*, Sheep specific anti-mouse macroglobulin (MOPC 104E, Dr. Feinstein); *b*, sheep anti-MOPC 21 (P3) IgGl absorbed with Adj PC-5; *c*, sheep anti-Adj PC-5 (IgG2a) absorbed with MOPC 21. After overnight incubation at room temperature the plate was developed with guinea pig serum diluted 1:10 in Dulbecco's medium without serum.

The above results show that cell fusion techniques are a powerful tool to produce specific antibody directed against a predetermined antigen. It further shows that it is possible to isolate hybrid lines producing different antibodies directed against the same antigen and carrying different effector functions (direct and indirect plaque).

The uncloned population of P3-spleen hybrid cells seems quite heterogeneous. Using suitable detection procedures it should be possible to isolate tissue culture cell lines making different classes of antibody. To facilitate our studies we have used a myeloma parental line which itself produced an Ig. Variants in which one of the parental chains is no longer expressed seem fairly common in the case of P1-P3 hybrids (Fig. 1*h*). Therefore selection of lines in which only the specific antibody chains are expressed seems reasonably simple. Alternatively, non-producing variants of myeloma lines could be used for fusion.

We used SRBC as antigen. Three different fusion experiments were successful in producing a large number of antibody-producing cells. Three weeks after the initial fusion, 33/1,086 clones (3%) were positive by the direct plaque assay. The cloning efficiency in the experiment was 50%. In another experiment, however, the proportion of positive clones was considerably lower (about 0.2%). In a third experiment the hybrid population was studied by limiting dilution analysis. From 157 independent hybrids, as many as 15 had anti-SRBC activity. The proportion of positive over negative clones is remarkably

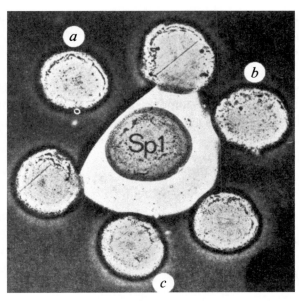

图 4. 杂交细胞克隆 Sp-1/7-2 分泌的抗体抑制红细胞溶解。反应在 9 cm 培养皿中进行。在 5 ml 0.6% 的琼脂糖（溶解在 PBS 中）中按 1/80（体积比）加入了绵羊红细胞。中间的孔中含有 2.5 μl 20 倍浓缩的 Sp-1/7-2 培养上清和 2.5 μl 小鼠血清。a，绵羊抗小鼠巨球蛋白（MOPC 104E，范斯坦博士）；b，绵羊抗 MOPC 21（P3）IgG1 与 Adj PC-5 结合；c，绵羊抗 Adj PC-5（IgG2a）与 MOPC 21 结合。室温下过夜培养后，加入豚鼠血清（用无血清的杜尔贝科培养基稀释 10 倍）。

上述结果表明，细胞融合技术是一种制备针对某种特定抗原的特异性抗体的强有力的工具。并进一步表明这种技术可能分离出能够产生针对同一抗原的具有不同效应功能的抗体的杂交细胞系（直接空斑和间接空斑）。

未克隆的 P3–脾细胞杂交细胞似乎具有异质性。使用合适的检测方法应该可以将产生不同种类抗体的组织培养细胞系分离出来。为了方便研究，我们使用了一种自身可以分泌免疫球蛋白的骨髓瘤细胞作为亲本细胞。在 P1–P3 杂交中，变异体某一亲本链不再表达的现象似乎相当常见（图 1h）。因此，筛选那些只表达某种特异性抗体链的细胞系似乎会更简单一些。或者，那些不产生变异体的骨髓瘤细胞也可以用于融合实验。

在实验中我们使用绵羊红细胞作为抗原。三个不同的融合实验都成功地产生了大量抗体生成细胞。第一个实验发现，在最初融合之后三周，33/1086 克隆（3%）在直接空斑实验中呈阳性。这个实验的克隆效率为 50%。然而，在另一个实验中，阳性克隆率则相当低（约为 0.2%）。在第三个实验中，我们使用了有限稀释法对杂交细胞群体进行了分析。在 157 个独立的克隆中，有 15 个克隆具有抗绵羊红细胞的活性。阳性与阴性克隆之比非常高。这可能是因为免疫过后的脾细胞大大增强了杂

high. It is possible that spleen cells which have been triggered during immunisation are particularly successful in giving rise to viable hybrids. It remains to be seen whether similar results can be obtained using other antigenes.

The cells used in this study are all of BALB/c origin and the hybrid clones can be injected into BALB/c mice to produce solid tumours and serum having anti-SRBC activity. It is possible to hybridise antibody-producing cells from different origins[4,5]. Such cells can be grown *in vitro* in massive cultures to provide specific antibody. Such cultures could be valuable for medical and industrial use.

(**256**, 495-497; 1975)

G. Köhler & C. Milstein

MRC Laboratory of Molecular Biology, Hills Road, Cambridge CB2 2QH, UK

Received May 14; accepted June 26, 1975.

References:

1. Potter, M., *Physiol. Rev.*, **52**, 631-719 (1972).

2. Horibata, K., and Harris, A. W., *Expl Cell Res.*, **60**, 61-70 (1970).

3. Milstein, C., and Munro, A. J., in *Defence and Recognition* (edit. by Porter, R. R.), 199-228 (MTP Int. Rev. Sci., Butterworth, London, 1973).

4. Cotton, R. G. H., and Milstein, C., *Nature*, **244**, 42-43 (1973).

5. Schwaber, J., and Cohen, E. P., *Proc. Natl. Acad. Sci. U.S.A.*, **71**, 2203-2207 (1974).

6. Littlefield, J. W., *Science*, **145**, 709 (1964).

7. Svasti, J., and Milstein, C., *Biochem. J.*, **128**, 427-444 (1972).

8. Milstein, C., Adetugbo, K., Cowan, N. J., and Secher, D. S., *Progress in Immunology*, II, 1 (edit. by Brent, L., and Holborow, J.), 157-168 (North-Holland, Amsterdam, 1974).

9. Harris, H., and Watkins, J. F., *Nature*, **205**, 640-646 (1965).

10. Awdeh, A. L., Williamson, A. R., and Askonas, B. A., *Nature*, **219**, 66-67 (1968).

11. Milstein, C., Brownlee, G. G., Cartwright, E. M., Jarvis, J. M., and Proudfoot, N. J., *Nature*, **252**, 354-359 (1974).

12. Frangione, B., and Milstein, C., *Nature*, **244**, 597-599 (1969).

13. Jerne, N. K., and Nordin, A. A., *Science*, **140**, 405 (1963).

14. Cotton, R. G. H., Secher, D. S., and Milstein, C., *Eur. J. Immun.*, **3**, 135-140 (1973).

交细胞的存活能力。不过，使用其他抗原是否也能得到类似的结果仍有待进一步的研究。

本研究所用到的所有细胞都来自于 BALB/c 小鼠。将融合后产生的杂交克隆注射到 BALB/c 小鼠体内能够诱导实体瘤并产生抗绵羊红细胞活性的抗体血清。此外，也可以使用不同种属来源的抗体生成细胞进行融合实验 [4,5]。体外大规模培养这些细胞可以用于生产特异性抗体，而特异性抗体在医学和工业领域具有非常高的应用价值。

（张锦彬 翻译；胡卓伟 审稿）

# Plio-Pleistocene Hominid Discoveries in Hadar, Ethiopia

D. C. Johanson and M. Taieb

## Editor's Note

After just three field seasons exploring the Afar Triangle of Ethiopia, Maurice Taieb and colleague Donald Johanson could present AL 288-1, a partial skeleton of a very primitive form that lived more than three million years ago. At first, this skeleton was assigned, if tentatively, to *Australopithecus africanus*, because of resemblances to fossils from Sterkfontein, and other Hadar specimens were thought to be more like *Homo*. Eventually, the Hadar material was ascribed to a new taxon, *Australopithecus afarensis*. The significance of this find was that even the most primitive hominids walked as upright as modern humans. This alone guaranteed the status of AL 288-1 as a truly important fossil. But it was its nickname that made it iconic: "Lucy".

---

The International Afar Research Expedition has now recovered remains of twelve hominid individuals from geological deposits estimated to be ~3.0 Myr in Hadar, Ethiopia. A partial skeleton represents the most complete hominid known from this period. The collection suggests that *Homo* and *Australopithecus* coexisted as early as 3.0 Myr ago.

---

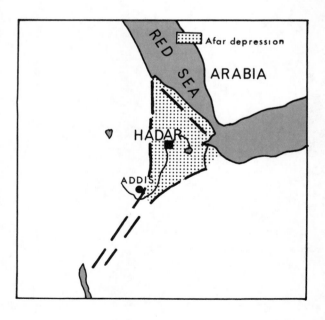

Fig. 1. Location of Hadar.

# 在埃塞俄比亚哈达尔发现的上新世–更新世时期的人科动物

约翰森，塔伊布

## 编者按

在埃塞俄比亚阿法尔三角区经过了仅仅三个野外工作季的发掘，莫里斯·塔伊布和同事唐纳德·约翰森就为大家展现了一个生活在超过 300 万年前的、形态非常原始的一具人类的不完整的骨架 AL 288–1。起初，由于认为它与斯泰克方丹的化石类似，因此被暂时归入南方古猿非洲种，而其他哈达尔的标本则被认为更像人属。最终，这具哈达尔的材料被归入一个新的分类单元——南方古猿阿法种。这个发现的意义在于，即使是最原始的人科动物，他们也跟现代人一样直立行走。单是这一点就足以确保 AL 288–1 作为一块真正重要的化石的地位。但是，使它成为标志性化石的却是它的外号——"露西"。

国际阿法尔研究探险队现已修复了 12 个人科动物个体的化石，这些化石均发现在埃塞俄比亚哈达尔的一处估计距今约 300 万年的地层堆积物中。其中一具不完整的骨架代表了现在已知的这一时期最完整的人科动物。该标本提示人属和南方古猿早在 300 万年前就同时存在着。

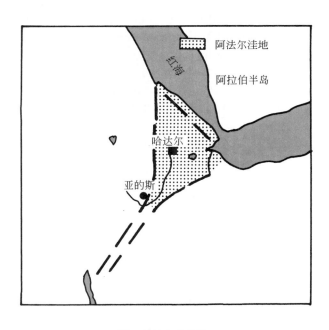

图 1. 哈达尔的位置

FOLLOWING a short reconnaissance expedition in 1972 (ref. 1) to the central Afar, one of us (M. T.) organised the International Afar Research Expedition. We have now codirected two field campaigns (September–December, 1973 and 1974 (refs 2 and 3)) in the area known as Hadar (see Fig. 1).

Although a number of other excellent fossil sites are known from the central Afar[4], Hadar was selected for intensive exploration for a number of reasons: first, the fossil vertebrate assemblage suggested a considerable antiquity (~3-4 Myr); second, the area is extremely rich in splendidly preserved fossils, deposited in low energy environments; third, the deposits are heavily dissected and characterised by clear marker-horizons which are laterally continuous; and fourth, the thick series of lake sediments contains a number of volcanic horizons available for absolute radiometric age determinations.

The Hadar site is located in the Afar depression in the west central Afar sedimentary basin[5] at 11°N and 40°30′E. It now encompasses ~42 km², but extension of study into adjacent, previously unexplored regions will substantially increase the area.

Preliminary palaeontological investigations, particularly of the suids and the elephants, have suggested a biostratigraphic correlation of the Hadar Formation with the Usno and the lower portion of the Shungura Formations[5,6]. Two radiometric K–Ar age determinations for a basalt support this with an age estimate of 3.0±0.2 Myr (ref. 5).

All hominid fossils (Table 1), and most of the vertebrate material, were surface finds, although some small scale excavation and sieving operations were undertaken. A painted marker was placed at each palaeontological locality, each located on a map and the geological section carefully examined to determine the horizon yielding fossil material (see Fig. 2). At each hominid locality, a topographical map and detailed stratigraphical sections were drawn. Samples of matrix adhering to fossil hominid specimens are undergoing mineralogical and sedimentological analyses for comparison with sediment samples taken at their collection points. Their completeness and lack of an ataxic abrasion[7] virtually precludes the possibility that the specimens were moved over great distances.

Table 1. Fossil hominid specimens from Hadar

| Afar locality (AL) | Date of discovery | Description |
|---|---|---|
| 1973 | | |
| 128–1 | 30 October | Left proximal femur fragment |
| 129–1a | 30 October | Right distal femur |
| 129–1b | 30 October | Right proximal tibia |
| 129–1c | 30 October | Right proximal femur fragment |
| 166–9 | 11 December | Left temporal fragment |
| 1974 | | |
| 188–1 | 16 October | Right mandibular corpus; $M_2$–$M_3$ |

648

1972 年，在一次赴阿法尔中部的短期勘察探险（参考文献 1）之后，我们的一名成员（塔伊布）便组织了国际阿法尔研究探险队。现在我们共同指导了两项野外活动（1973 年和 1974 年的 9~12 月（参考文献 2 和 3）），这两项活动都是在著名的哈达尔地区（见图 1）进行的。

尽管有许多其他极佳的化石遗址都是在阿法尔中部地区发现的 [4]，但是选在哈达尔开展集中的发掘工作是有很多原因的：第一，脊椎动物化石组合显示其时代相当古老（距今约 300 万到 400 万年）；第二，这里富含沉积在低能环境中并且保存得极好的化石；第三，这些沉积物被剧烈地切割，并在其侧面显示出连续的标志性地层；第四，厚厚的湖泊沉积物序列包含大量的可以用来测定绝对放射性年代的火山灰层。

哈达尔遗址的地理坐标为北纬 11° 东经 40° 30′，位于阿法尔沉积盆地中心区西部的阿法尔洼地 [5]。该遗址现在包含约 42 km² 的地域，不过对相邻的、以前未开发的地区进行的拓展研究实质上增加了其范围。

初步的古生物学研究，尤其是对猪类和大象的研究，已经提示了哈达尔组与乌斯诺组和上古拉组的下部之间存在生物地层相关性 [5,6]。对玄武岩进行了两次放射性 K–Ar 年代测定，估计其年代为距今 3.0±0.2 百万年，这进一步支持了该结论（参考文献 5）。

尽管进行了一些小范围的挖掘和筛查工作，但是所有的人科动物化石（表 1）和大部分脊椎动物材料都是在地表发现的。在每个古生物化石点都放置了一个涂色的标记，然后在地图上一一定位，并且对地质剖面进行了认真的调查以确定产出化石的地层（见图 2）。在每个人科动物化石点，都绘制了地形图和详细的地层剖面图。对人科动物化石表面黏附的围岩样本进行了矿物学和沉积学的分析，并将其与化石采集地的沉积物样本分析结果进行了对比。事实上，它们的完整性和未出现（与周围物质的）无序摩擦所产生的痕迹 [7] 排除了这些标本远距离搬运的可能性。

表 1. 来自哈达尔的人科动物化石标本

| 阿法尔地点（AL） | 发现日期 | 说明 |
|---|---|---|
| 1973 年 | | |
| 128–1 | 10 月 30 日 | 左股骨近端破片 |
| 129–1a | 10 月 30 日 | 右股骨远端 |
| 129–1b | 10 月 30 日 | 右胫骨近端 |
| 129–1c | 10 月 30 日 | 右股骨近端破片 |
| 166–9 | 12 月 11 日 | 左颞骨破片 |
| 1974 年 | | |
| 188–1 | 10 月 16 日 | 右下颌骨体；$M_2$~$M_3$ |

*Continued*

| Afar locality (AL) | Date of discovery | Description |
| --- | --- | --- |
| 198–1 | 18 October | Left mandibular corpus; C–$P_4$, dm, $M_1$–$M_2$ |
| 198–17a, b | 5 December | Left $I^1$ and $I^2$ |
| 198–18 | 5 December | Right $I_2$ |
| 199–1 | 17 October | Right maxilla; C–$M^3$ |
| 200–1a, b | 17 October | Complete maxilla; 16 teeth. Right $M_1$ |
| 211–1 | 20 October | Right proximal femur fragment |
| 228–1 | 27 October | Diaphysis of right femur |
| 241–14 | 22 December | Left lower molar |
| 266–1 | 16 November | Mandibular corpus; left $P_3$–$M_1$, right $P_3$–$M_3$ |
| 277–1 | 19 November | Left mandibular corpus; C–$M_2$ |
| 288–1 | 24 November | Partial skeleton: occipital and parietal fragments; mandibular corpus with left $P_3$, $M_3$, right $P_3$–$M_3$, mandibular condyles; right scapula fragment; right humerus; proximal and distal left humerus; proximal and distal right and left ulnae; proximal and distal right radius; distal left radius; left capitate; 2 phalanges; 6 thoracic vertebrae and fragments; 1 lumbar vertebra; sacrum; left innominate; left femur; proximal and distal right tibia; right talus right distal fibula; numerous rib fragments. |

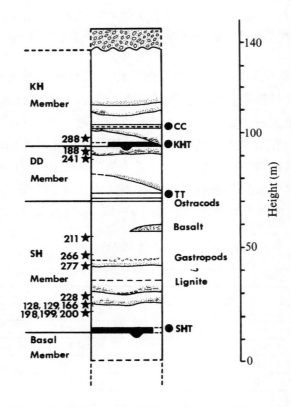

Fig.2. Stratigraphic positions of Hominid Horizons. ★ , Hominid levels; ● , marker beds.

| 阿法尔地点（AL） | 发现日期 | 说明 |
|---|---|---|
| 198–1 | 10月18日 | 左下颌骨体：$C\sim P_4$、dm、$M_1\sim M_2$ |
| 198–17a、b | 12月5日 | 左 $I^1$ 和 $I^2$ |
| 198–18 | 12月5日 | 右 $I_2$ |
| 199–1 | 10月17日 | 右上颌骨：$C\sim M^3$ |
| 200–1a、b | 10月17日 | 完整上颌骨：16颗牙齿。右 $M_1$ |
| 211–1 | 10月20日 | 右股骨近端破片 |
| 228–1 | 10月27日 | 右股骨骨干 |
| 241–14 | 12月22日 | 左下白齿 |
| 266–1 | 11月16日 | 下颌骨体：左 $P_3\sim M_1$、右 $P_3\sim M_3$ |
| 277–1 | 11月19日 | 左下颌骨体：$C\sim M_2$ |
| 288–1 | 11月24日 | 不完整的骨架：枕骨和顶骨破片；含左 $P_3$、$M_3$、右 $P_3\sim M_3$、两侧下颌髁突的下颌骨体；右肩胛骨破片；右肱骨；左肱骨近端和远端；左右尺骨近端和远端；右桡骨近端和远端；左桡骨远端；左头状骨；2块指骨；6块胸椎骨和破片；1块腰椎骨；骶骨；左髋骨；左股骨；右胫骨近端和远端；右距骨；右腓骨远端；许多肋骨破片。 |

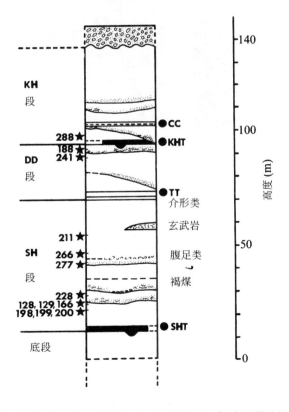

图2. 人科动物层的地层位置。★：人科动物层；●：标志性层位。

651

## 1973 Hominid Discoveries

The first discovery of fossil hominid remains in the Hadar region occurred on October 30, 1973, when four associated leg bone fragments (AL 128, 129) were collected from a mudstone horizon. These consist of fragmentary right and left proximal femora associated with a right proximal tibia and distal femur. Their proximity to one another, as well as the morphological and size similarities of the proximal femora, strongly suggest that they represent a single individual. This provides a complete knee which will greatly enhance our understanding of the biomechanics of this important joint in early hominids (see Fig. 3).

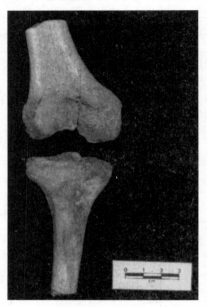

Fig. 3. Anterior view of AL 129-1a and 1c

Both proximal femora lack heads and necks. The left is best preserved with the shaft broken ~ 38.0 mm below the lesser trochanter. From the remaining portions of the femora it is clear that the neck is flattened anteroposteriorly and that its cross section is oval. There is an indication of trochanteric flare, the trochanteric fossa is well marked, a quadrate tubercle is clearly discernible, muscle markings are prominent on the greater trochanter, the spiral line is pronounced and the lesser trochanter is visible from the anterior aspect. Both fragments, particularly the right, exhibit some degree of predepositional crushing, which is suggestive of carnivore activity.

The distal femur is undistorted, and both condyles are complete and intact. It is small, with the lateral condyle measuring 39.0 mm anteroposteriorly and 18.9 mm mediolaterally. This fragment demonstrates a number of anatomical details which are intimately related to bipedal locomotion[8,9]: the bicondylar angle is rather high, the lateral lip of the patellar groove is raised and the lateral condyle flattened and elongated.

## 1973 年人科动物的发现

1973 年 10 月 30 日在哈达尔地区首次发现了人科动物化石，当时从一处泥岩层采集到了四个相关联的腿骨残段（AL 128 和 AL 129）。这些标本包括残断的左右股骨近端以及与其相关的右侧胫骨近端及股骨远端。它们彼此都很靠近，且股骨近端的形态和尺寸都很相似，这强有力地说明它们来自同一个体。该标本提供了一个完整的膝关节，这将大大增加我们对早期人科动物的这一重要关节的生物力学认识（见图 3）。

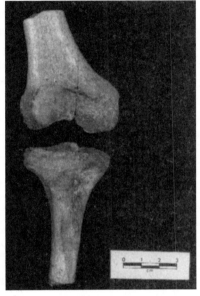

图 3. AL 129–1a 和 1c 的前面观。

两块股骨近端都缺少头部和颈部。左股骨近端保存最好，在小转子下约 38.0 mm 的骨干处有断裂。从股骨的其余部分看，股骨颈在前后方向上很明显是扁平的，其横截面呈椭圆形。有结节外展（编者注：现代人体解剖学中无法查到此解剖部位的对应译法。早期人科动物由于行走姿势不同可能存在大结节边缘外展的现象，故暂译如此）的迹象，转子窝很明显，可以很清楚地辨别出方形结节，肌肉纹理在大转子处非常明显，螺旋线突出，从前面可以看到小转子。两块残段，尤其是右侧残段，呈现出在沉积前就有一定程度破碎的现象，提示食肉动物的活动痕迹。

股骨远端未变形，两个髁突都是完整无损的。这块股骨远端很小，经测量，外侧髁前后方向上有 39.0 mm 长，内外方向上有 18.9 mm 长。该残段展示了许多与双足步行密切相关的解剖学细节特征 [8,9]：两个髁突所成角度非常大，髌骨沟的侧唇升高，外侧髁扁平且细长。

The associated proximal tibia is intact except for some slight abrasion around the periphery of the superior articular surface. It also is small, the total preserved articular surface measuring 50.7 mm mediolaterally and 33.0 mm anteroposteriorly. The tibial tuberosity is pronounced and is limited proximally by the transverse groove; the soleal line is distinct on the posterior surface of the shaft and the interosseous membrane attachment is indicated by a roughened line on the medial aspect of the shaft; the head is slightly retroflexed with only minor tibial torsion; and the intercondyloid eminence is prominent with well developed intercondyloid fossae.

A heavily eroded temporal fragment (AL 166‑9) constitutes the only other hominid discovery from the 1973 field season. The specimen derives from a sandstone horizon a few metres stratigraphically above the level of the postcranial material. The temporal has been extensively eroded, with most of the petrous portion broken away, and extensive pneumatisation is exposed in the mastoid and zygomatic regions. The mandibular fossa is broad and flat, bordered by a postglenoid process, but open anteriorly with only a slight articular tubercle. There is a prominent entoglenoid process on the medial wall which is broken exposing a large pneumatisation. The mastoid is large and globular. The external auditory meatus is oval in section with a thick tympanic plate.

## 1974 Hominid Discoveries

Our sample of the Hominidae has been greatly augmented with additional field work. The 1974 investigations yielded remains of 10 additional individuals represented by dental, cranial and postcranial elements, including a remarkably intact partial skeleton.

Stratigraphically just below the 1973 hominid discoveries, one complete (AL 200‑1) and one half maxilla (AL 199‑1) (see Fig. 4) were recovered by Ato Alemayehu Asfaw within 15 m of one another and from the same mudstone horizon.

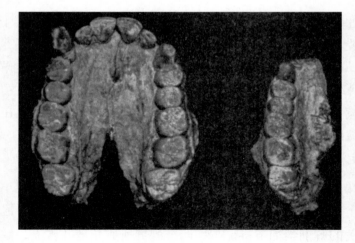

Fig.4. Occlusal views of AL 200‑1a and AL 199‑1

The AL 200 specimen is an undistorted palate with full dentition and an associated right

相关的胫骨近端除了在上关节面的边缘有轻微磨损外，其余部分都是完整的。这块胫骨近端也很小，经测量，保存下来的整个关节面在内外方向上长 50.7 mm，前后方向长 33.0 mm。胫骨粗隆突出，其近端以横股沟为界；比目鱼肌线在骨干的后表面上很明显，骨间膜的附着面可以从骨干中部粗糙的线迹看出来；由于胫骨有轻微的扭曲，其头部略显翻转；髁间隆起突出，髁间窝很发达。

一块严重磨损的颞骨破片（AL 166–9）是 1973 年野外工作中仅有的人科动物的其他发现。该标本来源于颅后化石产出层之上数米处的砂岩层。颞骨磨损的范围很大，岩部的大部分都断裂了，大量的气腔暴露在乳突区和颧突区。下颌窝宽阔平坦，后边是关节后突，但是前面仅有一细小的关节结节。在内侧壁有一个凸出的关节内突，内侧壁断裂，暴露出一个大的气腔。乳突大且呈球状。外耳道剖面呈椭圆形，具有很厚的鼓板。

## 1974 年人科动物的发现

接下来的野外工作大大增加了我们的人科动物标本的数量。1974 年的调查发现了另外 10 个个体的化石，包括齿系、颅骨和颅后等部分，还包括一具较完整的局部骨架。

就在 1973 年发现人科动物的地层之下，阿托·阿莱马耶胡·阿斯富发现并复原了一块完整的上颌骨（AL 200–1）和另外半块上颌骨（AL 199–1）（见图 4），它们之间相距近 15 m，且处于同一泥岩层。

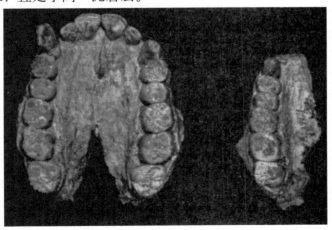

图 4. AL 200–1a 和 AL 199–1 的咬合面观。

AL 200 号标本是一个没有变形的带有整套齿系的上颌和一个相关联的右 M₁。

$M_1$. The general pattern of dental wear is interesting, in that the incisors exhibit extensive "ribbon like" wear and dentine exposure relative to the postcanine teeth. In addition, the canines and the $P^3$s have suffered antemortem enamel chippage on their buccal surfaces during the specimen's lifetime. The tooth rows of AL 200 are subparallel and the arch is relatively long. The anterior portion of the arch is broad to accommodate the large central incisors and marked diastemata occur between the lateral incisors and the canines. The palate is shallow, becoming somewhat deeper posteriorly.

In lateral view this specimen exhibits pronounced alveolar prognathism. The zygomatic root is situated above the first molar, the maxillary sinuses are large and the lower nasal margin is guttered.

The right half maxilla is smaller in size and is less complete, with $C–M^3$, as well as both incisor sockets and the $I^2$ root. The dentition is smaller than that of AL 200 (Table 2), but the similarity in morphological detail is striking. Although the incisors are lacking, it is apparent from the root sockets that the anterior portion of the arch was broad and somewhat squared-off as in AL 200. The specimen is broken close to the midline exposing the incisive canal. The palate is shallow and the greater palatine foramen is present. The inferior nasal margin is not sharp and in lateral view alveolar prognathism is well developed. The maxillary sinus is large and the zygomatic root is situated above the distal portion of the first molar.

Table 2. Dental measurements of AL 200–1a and AL 199–1 (mm)

| | Left | | Right | |
|---|---|---|---|---|
| AL 200–1a | Mesiodistal | Buccolingual | Mesiodistal | Buccolingual |
| $I^1$ | 10.8 | 8.3 | 10.9 | 8.5 |
| $I^2$ | 7.4 | 7.1 | 7.3 | 7.0 |
| C | 9.4 | 10.9 | 9.4 | 11.0 |
| $P^3$ | 9.0 | 12.2 | 8.9 | 12.2 |
| $P^4$ | 8.5 | 12.2 | 8.5 | 12.1 |
| $M^1$ | 11.8 | 13.1 | 11.8 | 13.2 |
| $M^2$ | 13.8 | 14.8 | 13.7 | 15.0 |
| $M^3$ | 14.2 | 15.0 | 14.3 | 15.0 |
| AL 199–1 | | | | |
| C | | | 8.7 | 9.3 |
| $P^3$ | | | 7.3 | 11.2 |
| $P^4$ | | | 7.1 | 11.2 |
| $M^1$ | | | 10.1 | 12.0 |
| $M^2$ | | | 11.7 | 13.5 |
| $M^3$ | | | 11.3 | (12.7) |

牙齿磨耗的总体模式很有趣，因为门齿呈现出大量的"带状"磨损而且其牙本质像颊齿一样暴露出来。此外，犬齿和 P³ 在颊面上存在着珐琅质剥落，这些剥落发生在个体生前。AL 200 的齿列接近平行，牙弓相对较长。牙弓的前部很宽可容下大的中门齿，侧门齿与犬齿之间有明显的齿隙。腭很浅，后部稍微变深。

从侧面观看，该样本显示出明显的牙槽前突。颧弓根部位于第一臼齿之上，上颌窦大，鼻腔的下沿呈沟状。

半块右侧上颌骨尺寸更小，也更不完整，保留有 C~M³，还有两个门齿槽和一个 I² 的牙根。其齿列比 AL 200 的要小（表 2），但是形态学细节上的相似性很明显。尽管缺少门齿，但从其牙根槽上可以明显看出牙弓的前部很宽，与 AL 200 的形状相似。该标本在靠近中线处断裂，暴露出门齿管。腭很浅，存在较大的腭孔。下鼻缘不清晰，从侧面看，牙槽前突很发达。上颌窦很大，颧弓根部位于第一臼齿远中部分的上方。

表 2. AL 200–1a 和 AL 199–1 的牙齿测量尺寸（mm）

| | 左 | | 右 | |
|---|---|---|---|---|
| AL 200–1a | 近中远中方向 | 颊舌方向 | 近中远中方向 | 颊舌方向 |
| I¹ | 10.8 | 8.3 | 10.9 | 8.5 |
| I² | 7.4 | 7.1 | 7.3 | 7.0 |
| C | 9.4 | 10.9 | 9.4 | 11.0 |
| P³ | 9.0 | 12.2 | 8.9 | 12.2 |
| P⁴ | 8.5 | 12.2 | 8.5 | 12.1 |
| M¹ | 11.8 | 13.1 | 11.8 | 13.2 |
| M² | 13.8 | 14.8 | 13.7 | 15.0 |
| M³ | 14.2 | 15.0 | 14.3 | 15.0 |
| AL 199–1 | | | | |
| C | | | 8.7 | 9.3 |
| P³ | | | 7.3 | 11.2 |
| P⁴ | | | 7.1 | 11.2 |
| M¹ | | | 10.1 | 12.0 |
| M² | | | 11.7 | 13.5 |
| M³ | | | 11.3 | (12.7) |

A partial mandible (AL 266-1) was located in a horizon of sandy clay, ~10m stratigraphically below the basalt flow[5]. This specimen includes the complete right corpus with $P_3$-$M_3$, the symphysis with canine and incisor roots, and a portion of the left corpus with $P_3$-$M_1$ (Table 3). The dentition is moderately worn with the third molar having just come into occlusion and showing only minor wear facets. The anterior portion of the dental arch is rounded and the dental rows are straight and slightly divergent posteriorly. The post-incisive planum is only moderately developed and the corpus in the region of $M_1$ is 21.7 mm thick and 31.0 mm deep.

Table 3 Dental measurements of AL 266-1 (mm)

| AL 266-1 | Left | | Right | |
|---|---|---|---|---|
| | Mesiodistal | Buccolingual | Mesiodistal | Buccolingual |
| $P_3$ | 9.1 | 10.1 | 9.2 | 10.1 |
| $P_4$ | 8.9 | 11.0 | 9.4 | 10.8 |
| $M_1$ | 12.1 | 11.9 | 12.1 | 12.0 |
| $M_2$ | | | 13.3 | 14.0 |
| $M_3$ | | | 15.3 | 13.7 |

A right mandibular fragment (AL 188-1) containing $M_2$-$M_3$ and roots of $P_3$-$M_1$, was collected from a sandstone horizon immediately below KHT. The molars are heavily worn. The mandible exhibits some wind abrasion, but it is possible to estimate a thickness of 20.7 mm and a depth of ~ 32.0 mm in the region of $M_1$.

AL 277-1, a fragmentary left mandible containing C-$M_2$ and sockets for $I_1$-$I_2$, is derived from a sandstone horizon. It is broken just to the right of the midline and distal to $M_2$. The occlusal wear is heavy with the canine worn flat. Anteriorly the fragment gives the impression of being deep, measuring ~41.0 mm just distal to $P_3$. A prominent post-incisive planum is present, as well as a slight inferior mandibular torus. The inferior surface of the symphysis is flattened and has distinct mental spines. The corpus exhibits slight eversion.

An interesting left half mandible (AL 198-1) was recovered from a mudstone horizon, stratigraphically equivalent to AL 199 and AL 200. The specimen is broken near the midline with the $I_1$ socket and the root for $I_2$ preserved. The C-$P_4$ and $M_1$-$M_2$ are present, with a retained deciduous molar located distal to the $P_4$. The deciduous nature of this tooth is confirmed by a radiograph demonstrating a widely divergent root system. Substantial occlusal wear is evident on $P_4$-$M_2$. the corpus is broken just distal to $M_2$, exposing a portion of the mesial root of $M_3$ immediately superior to the mandibular canal. The mandible is lightly built, being 16.0 mm thick and 31.9 mm deep at $M_1$. It exhibits some modelling and the inferior margin is thin and not bulbous.

不完整的下颌骨（AL 266–1）是在砂质黏土层中发现的，在地层上位于玄武岩熔体层下约 10 m 处[5]。该标本包括带有 $P_3$~$M_3$ 的完整右下颌骨体、带有犬齿根和门齿根的联合部，以及带有 $P_3$~$M_1$ 的部分左侧主体（表 3）。齿列中度磨损，第三臼齿刚刚达到咬合面，仅显示出微小的磨损面。牙弓前部呈圆形，齿列直，只是在后部稍微有些分散。门齿后平面中等发育，$M_1$ 处的下颌体厚 21.7 mm，深 31.0 mm。

表 3. AL 266–1 的牙齿测量尺寸（mm）

| AL 266–1 | 左 | | 右 | |
|---|---|---|---|---|
| | 近中远中方向 | 颊舌方向 | 近中远中方向 | 颊舌方向 |
| $P_3$ | 9.1 | 10.1 | 9.2 | 10.1 |
| $P_4$ | 8.9 | 11.0 | 9.4 | 10.8 |
| $M_1$ | 12.1 | 11.9 | 12.1 | 12.0 |
| $M_2$ | | | 13.3 | 14.0 |
| $M_3$ | | | 15.3 | 13.7 |

带有 $M_2$~$M_3$ 和 $P_3$~$M_1$ 齿根的右下颌骨破片（AL 188–1）是从紧挨着 KHT 下部的砂岩层中采集到的。其臼齿磨损严重。下颌骨显示出某种程度的风化，但是可以估计出在 $M_1$ 处的厚度为 20.7 mm，深度约为 32.0 mm。

AL 277–1 是一块带有 C~$M_2$ 和 $I_1$~$I_2$ 牙槽的残破不全的左下颌骨，它们是从砂岩层挖掘出来的。在中线右侧及 $M_2$ 之后发生了断裂。咬合面磨损严重，犬齿已经磨平。前部断裂让人感觉下颌骨深，$P_3$ 远端深约 41.0 mm。突出的门齿后平面保存下来，还有一个明显的下颌圆枕。联合部的下表面变平，具有明显的颏棘。下颌骨显示出轻微的外翻现象。

在泥岩中发现并复原了一块有趣的左半部分下颌骨（AL 198–1），其位置在地层上与 AL 199 和 AL 200 相当。该标本在接近中线处断裂，$I_1$ 牙槽和 $I_2$ 牙根保存下来。C~$P_4$ 和 $M_1$~$M_2$ 也保存下来，还有一个位于 $P_4$ 之后的乳臼齿。这颗牙的乳牙性质得到了 X 光照片的证实，显示其牙根分叉。大量的咬合磨损在 $P_4$~$M_2$ 上表现得很明显。下颌骨体在 $M_2$ 之后断裂，暴露出一部分紧挨在下颌管之上的 $M_3$ 的近中牙根。下颌骨较纤细，在 $M_1$ 处有 16.0 mm 厚、31.9 mm 深。它显示出一定的形态，下缘薄而不鼓。

During screening operations, three additional teeth were located at this locality: a right $I_2$ (AL 198–18), a left $I^2$ (AL 198–17a) and a left $I^1$ (AL 198–17b). The interproximal facets on the upper incisors match perfectly, suggesting that they are from the same individual. Because of the close association of these teeth with the AL 198 mandible, we tentatively assign them to the same individual.

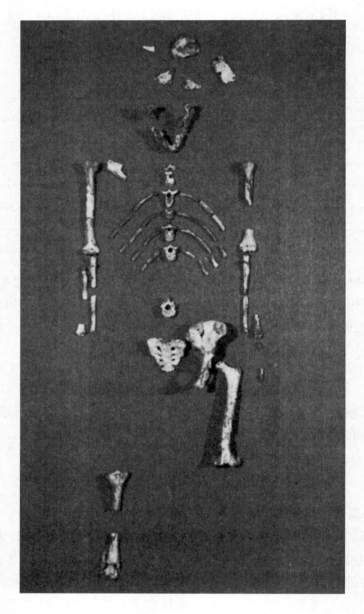

Fig .5. Partial skeleton (AL 288–1) from Hadar

Stratigraphically just below the basalt flow a fragmentary right proximal femur (AL 211–1) was collected. The specimen is somewhat abraded with the head and neck missing and

筛选工作期间，在该地点发现了另外三颗牙齿，包括：一颗右 $I_2$（AL 198–18）、一颗左 $I^2$（AL 198–17a）和一颗左 $I^1$（AL 198–17b）。上门齿的牙间面很匹配，说明它们来自同一个体。由于这些牙与下颌骨 AL 198 出于同一层，所以我们暂时将它们划分到同一个体。

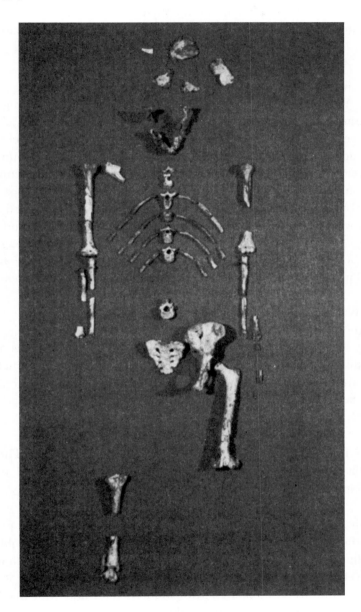

图 5. 来自哈达尔的不完整的骨架（AL 288–1）

就在地层上位于玄武岩熔体之下的位置，采集到了一块残破不全的右侧股骨近端（AL 211–1）。该标本轻微磨损，其头部和颈部缺失，大转子大部分被保存下来。

most of the greater trochanter. The neck is very flattened, no trochanteric flare is present, the intertrochanteric line is weakly expressed, the spiral line is well developed and the lesser trochanter is not visible from the anterior aspect. The specimen is quite large and fairly robust.

AL 228-1 is a distal portion of a femoral diaphysis recovered from a sandstone. It is not large, but exhibits strong development of the linea aspera. It is smaller than AL 129-1A.

## The Partial Skeleton

The discovery on November 24 of a partial skeleton (AL 288-1; see Fig. 5) eroding from sand represents the most outstanding hominid specimen collected during the 1974 field season. The stratigraphic horizon yielding the skeleton is situated just above the KHT, which has not yet been dated. Fossil preservation at this locality is excellent, remains of delicate items such as crocodile and turtle eggs and crab claws being found. It is obvious that this discovery provides us with a unique opportunity for reconstructing the anatomy of an early hominid in far more detail than has been previously possible. Extensive descriptive and comparative studies are projected for the AL 288 partial skeleton and will provide us with details of stature, limb proportions, articulations and biomechanical aspects. Three weeks were devoted to intensive collecting and screening to ensure the recovery of all bone fragments from the site. Laboratory preparation and analysis has only just begun, and in this report it is possible to mention only a few salient points.

The mandible is not heavily built; it is 30.0 mm deep and 19.0 mm thick in the region of $M_1$. The $M_3$s are fully erupted and occlusal wear facets are just appearing. The symphysis is intact with a slight post-incisive planum. Although the incisor crowns are absent, it is apparent that this region was quite small. The remaining dentition is small and not very worn. The $P_3$s are interesting with a sloping buccal surface and almost no development of a metaconid. The form of the dental arch as well as the body of the mandible is distinctly V-shaped.

The cranium is not sufficiently complete to estimate cranial capacity. The cranial bones are thin, exhibit no sutures (internally or externally) and no marked development of nuchal or temporal musculature is present.

The left innominate is complete, although it is somewhat distorted in the pubic region and particularly in the area of sacral articulation. In size the specimen resembles Sterkfontein (Sts) 14; the ilium, however, gives the appearance of being higher, and the anterior border is relatively straight. A strongly developed anterior inferior spine is apparent. The acetabulum is shallow when compared with modern man and with Sts 14. The sciatic notch is broad, the subpubic angle obtuse and the pubis exhibits a pronounced ventral arc, all of which suggests the skeleton belonged to a female. When viewed from the superior aspect, the base of the sacrum is divided into thirds, with the diameter of the sacral body equal to each of the alae. This again suggests that AL 288 was female.

颈部非常扁平，没有结节外展的迹象，转子间线的痕迹也不明显，螺旋线发达，从前面看不到小转子。这个标本十分大且相当粗壮。

AL 288–1 是股骨骨干的远端部分，是从砂岩中发现并复原的。该标本并不大，但是表现出粗线很发达的迹象。它比 AL 129–1A 要小。

## 不完整的骨架

于 11 月 24 日发现的不完整的骨架（AL 288–1，见图 5）受到过沙的侵蚀，它是 1974 年野外考察工作中所采集到的最不同凡响的人科动物标本。发现该骨架的地层就位于 KHT 之上，其年代尚未确定。该发现的化石保存状况非常好，一些易破碎的化石，例如鳄鱼、乌龟蛋以及蟹螯都有发现。很明显，这一发现给我们提供了一个独一无二的机会，让我们能够比之前更详细地对早期人科动物的解剖学结构进行重建。已经计划对不完整的骨架 AL 288 进行大量的描述性和比较性研究，这些研究将为我们提供关于早期人科动物的身材、肢骨比例、关节和生物力学方面的详细信息。我们用了三个星期对该遗址进行深入的搜索和筛选，以确保可以复原所有的骨骼碎片。实验室的准备和分析工作才刚刚开始，在本次报告中，只能提一下其中几个要点。

其下颌骨不是很结实；在 $M_1$ 处有 30.0 mm 深，19.0 mm 厚。两侧 $M_3$ 完全萌出，咬合处磨损面刚刚出现。联合部完整，门齿后平面单薄。尽管门齿齿冠缺失，但是很明显该区域非常小。其余齿系小且磨损不严重。$P_3$ 很有趣，有一个倾斜的颊面而且下后尖几乎不发育。牙弓以及下颌骨体的形状都呈明显的 V 形。

颅骨不太完整，不足以估计出颅容量。颅骨很薄，没有任何缝线（内部或外部），没有明显的颈肌或颞肌发育的迹象。

尽管左侧髋骨在耻骨区，尤其是骶骨关节区域有点变形，但总体较完整。在尺寸上，该标本与斯泰克方丹（Sts）14 号接近，但是髂骨看起来更高，并且其前缘相对直一些。很明显有一个非常发达的前下棘。与现代人或 Sts 14 相比，其髋臼较浅。其坐骨切迹很宽，耻骨下角呈钝角，耻骨有突出的腹侧弧，所有这些都表明该骨架属于一名女性。从上面看，骶骨基底被分成了三部分，骶骨体的直径与每个骨翼都是相等的。这再次表明 AL 288 是一名女性的骨架。

A complete left femur is associated with the innominate. But the distal portion is badly crushed. Its total length has been estimated at 280 mm but may be slightly revised when the distal end is reconstructed. The femur has minimal trochanteric flare, the neck is anteroposteriorly flattened, an intertrochanteric line is present and the lesser trochanter is not visible from the anterior aspect.

The proximal right tibia is nearly identical in size and morphology to AL 129-1b. The distal tibia is associated, and articulates with a talus and a distal fibula.

The right humerus is complete with some crushing of the proximal end. Its total length is estimated at ~ 235 mm giving a value of 83.9 for the humeral-femoral index. The distal end possesses a marked ridge separating the capitulum and trochlea.

## Significance of the Hadar Hominids

Detailed studies of the Hadar hominids have just recently been initiated and definitive interpretations are not yet possible. Because of the geological antiquity, and in some instances the completeness of the specimens, however, we proffer a number of preliminary impressions concerning their phyletic affinities and resemblances to other specimens.

The partial skeleton exhibits a number of similarities to the Sterkfontein sample. Specifically, the size of the pelvis and to some degree its morphology are reminiscent of Sts 14. The shallow acetabulum and relatively high ilium, however, demonstrate certain divergences from the Sterkfontein specimen and possibly reflect a somewhat more primitive status for the AL 288 specimen. The associated V-shaped mandible is noteworthy. Leakey[10] has drawn attention to mandibular shape and has suggested that KNM-ER 1482 (Kenya National Museum, East Rudolph), and Omo 18 should be considered primitive because of their V-shaped contours. Should this prove to be a diagnostic character, it is possible that AL 288 retains more primitive features than *Australopithecus africanus*, recognized from Sterkfontein.

Previously the 1973 postcranial material has not been assigned to a taxon. It is now clear that it should probably be included in the same category as the AL 288 specimen because of the striking similarity of the proximal tibial fragments in size and morphology as well as the preserved femoral fragments. This is important because: there is now evidence of at least two individuals of a very small hominid in Hadar, and the AL 128 and 129 specimens are situated stratigraphically 80 m below the partial skeleton (Fig. 2).

The presence of another taxon is suggested by two other specimens in the Hadar hominid collection. AL 211-1 resembles very closely Olduvai Hominid (OH) 20 (ref. 11) as well as the two proximal femora from Swartkrans (SK 82 and SK 97). Similarities are not only in size but also in morphological detail; stout shafts, flattened necks, a lack of trochanteric flare and posteriorly facing lesser trochanters not visible in anterior view.

与髋骨相连的一块完整的左股骨，其远端粉碎严重。其总长度估计为 280 mm，但是重建远端时可能对其进行了些微的修正。该股骨具有最小的结节外展，颈部在前后方向上是扁平的，转子间线存在，从前面看不到小转子。

右侧胫骨近端在尺寸和形态上几乎与 AL 129–1b 完全相同。胫骨远端与一块距骨和一块腓骨远端以关节相连。

右肱骨完整，近端有些粉碎。其总长度估计在 235 mm 左右，说明其肱骨－股骨指数值为 83.9。其远端具有明显的嵴，该嵴将肱骨小头和滑车分离开。

## 哈达尔人科动物的重要性

最近刚刚启动了对哈达尔人科动物的详细研究，现在还不可能对其进行确定的解释。然而，由于地质年代古老以及有些标本较完整，对于它们的系统亲缘关系及它们与其他标本的相似性，我们提出了许多初步想法。

该不完整的骨架显示出许多与斯泰克方丹标本的相似性。确切地说，骨盆的尺寸以及在某种程度上的形态与 Sts14 颇为相似。但是，较浅的髋臼和相对高的髂骨表明其与斯泰克方丹标本有一定差异，并且 AL 288 标本可能反映了一种更为原始的状态。属于同一个体的 V 形下颌骨值得我们注意。利基 [10] 引起了我们对下颌骨形状的注意，并且提出 KNM–ER 1482（肯尼亚国家博物馆，鲁道夫湖以东）和 Omo 18 应该被归为原始人类标本，因为他们也具有 V 形的下颌。如果证明这是一种具有判别性的特征，那么 AL 288 有可能保留了比南方古猿非洲种更加原始的特征，这些特征正是从斯泰克方丹的标本中辨认出来的。

在此之前，1973 年得到的颅后材料没有被划入到任何分类单元中。现在很明显，它们很可能被划入与 AL 288 标本相同的分类单元中去，因为他们的胫骨近端的尺寸和形态以及保存下来的股骨残段都具有显著的相似性。这很重要，因为现在有证据证明在哈达尔至少有两个个体非常小的人科动物，AL 128 和 AL 129 标本在地层学上位于发现不完整的骨架的地层之下 80 m 处（图 2）。

哈达尔人科动物中的另外两个标本暗示着另一个分类单元的存在。AL 211–1 与奥杜威人科动物（OH）20（参考文献 11）以及斯瓦特克朗斯的两块股骨近端（SK 82 和 SK 97）非常相似。他们不仅在尺寸上具有相似性，在形态学细节方面也具有相似性；例如，强壮的骨干、扁平的颈部、缺少结节外展、从前面看不到朝后的小转子等等。

The temporal fragment (AL 166-9) resembles material from Swartkrans and East Rudolf which has also been assigned to a large *Australopithecus* pattern, particularly in the large bulbous mastoid process and heavy pneumatisation, as well as the broad temporal shelf. It is, however, less typical of this pattern in the broad, flat mandibular fossa and absence of a strong articular tubercle.

The close association of AL 199-1 and AL 200-1, as well as their stratigraphic equivalence, is important because of the high probability that they sample the same taxon. Except for size differences, these two specimens are remarkably similar, and suggest variation within a single taxon. The complete maxilla has large canines, broad central incisors and large posterior dentition. These characters as well as other details suggest resemblances with some *Homo erectus* material, particularly *Pithecanthropus* IV. This dental pattern is also seen in KNM-ER 1590 from East Rudolf, a specimen with large cranial capacity assigned to the genus Homo[10,12]. It must be recognized that other aspects of the AL 200 maxilla are "primitive", such as the guttered nasal margin and the alveolar prognathism.

The AL 266-1 and AL 277-1 mandibles resemble, in details of the dentition and mandibular morphology, other specimens assigned to *Homo*, such as OH 7 (ref. 13) and KNM-ER 1802 (ref. 10).

On the basis of the present hominid collection from Hadar it is tentatively suggested that some specimens show affinities with *A. robustus*, some with *A. africanus* (*sensu stricto*), and others with fossils previously referred to *Homo*.

The understanding of Plio-Pleistocene hominid remains is undergoing intensive revision and re-evaluaton. With continued collection of specimens from the three million year-old time range in Hadar and elsewhere, and with additional detailed studies and comparisons, our attempts to interpret the earliest hominids should become more clear.

Special gratitude is expressed to Y. Coppens for his assistance in preparation of this manuscript. Owen Lovejoy also provided helpful comments.

(**260**, 293-297; 1976)

D. C. Johanson* and M. Taieb[†]

*Cleveland Museum of Natural History, Department of Anthropology, Case Western Reserve University, Cleveland, Ohio 44106

†Laboratoire de Géologie du Quaternaire, CNRS, Meudon-Bellevue, France

Received September 25, 1975; accepted February 9, 1976.

颞骨破片（AL 166–9）与斯瓦特克朗斯标本和已经被归属到一种大型南方古猿的鲁道夫湖以东标本相像，尤其是大的球状乳突、大量的气腔以及宽阔的颞架。但是，宽阔、平坦的下颌窝不是典型特征，且缺少强壮的关节结节。

AL 199–1 与 AL 200–1 关联密切且地层相当，这一点很重要，因为它们来自同一分类单元的可能性极大。除了尺寸上的差异，这两个标本非常相似，这表明它们的差异属于同一分类单元内的差异。完整的上颌骨具有大的犬齿、宽的中门齿和大的后齿列。这些特征及其他细节都表明它们与一些直立人材料，尤其是与猿人属 IV 具有相像之处。在鲁道夫湖以东的 KNM–ER 1590 中也出现了这种牙齿模式，后者具有大的颅容量，被归属到人属中 [10,12]。不得不承认，上颌骨 AL 200 的其他方面是"原始的"，例如开沟的鼻缘和牙槽前突。

在齿列和下颌骨的形态学细节方面，下颌骨 AL 266–1 和 AL 277–1 与其他归属到人属的标本相像，例如 OH 7（参考文献 13）和 KNM–ER 1802（参考文献 10）。

根据现在已从哈达尔采集到的人科动物标本，暂且可以认为有些标本与南方古猿粗壮种有亲缘关系，有些与南方古猿非洲种有亲缘关系，其余的则与之前称为人属的化石有亲缘关系。

对上新世－更新世时期人科动物遗存的认识正处于进一步修正与重新评定的时期。随着对哈达尔和其他地方的属于三百万年这一时段的标本的持续收集，以及其他详细的研究和比较，我们尝试阐明最早人科动物的前景将会更加明朗。

特别感谢科庞在准备本文原稿时所提供的帮助。欧文·洛夫乔伊也提供了有益的意见。

（刘皓芳 翻译；赵凌霞 审稿）

References:

1. Taieb, M., Coppens, Y., Johanson, D. C., and Kalb, J., *C. r. hebd. Séanc. Acad. Sci., Paris,* **275D**, 819-822 (1972).

2. Taieb, M., Johanson, D. C., Coppens, Y., Bonnefille, R., and Kalb, J., *C. r. hebd. Séanc. Acad. Sci., Paris,* **279D**, 735-738 (1974)

3. Taieb, M., Johanson, D. C., and Coppens. Y., *C. r. hebd. Séanc. Acad. Sci., Paris,* **281D**, 1297-1300 (1975).

4. Taieb, M., thesis, Université de Paris VI (1974).

5. Taieb, M., Johanson, D. C., Coppens, Y., Aronson, J. L., *Nature,* **260**, 289-293 (1976).

6. Johanson, D. C., Taieb, M., and Coppens, Y., in *African Hominidae of the Plio-Pleistocene* (edit. by Jolly, C. L.,) (Duckworth, London, in the press).

7. Clark, J., Beerbower, J. R., and Kietzke, K. K., *Fieldiana, Geol. Mem.,* **5**, 1-158 (1957).

8. Kern, H. M., and Straus, W. L., *Am. J. Phys. Anthrop.,* **7**(1), 53-66 (1949).

9. Heiple, K. C., and Lovejoy, C. O., *Am. J. Phys. Anthrop.,* **35**(1), 75-84 (1971).

10. Leakey, R. E. F., *Nature,* **248**, 653-656 (1974).

11. Day, M. H., *Nature,* **221**, 230-233 (1969).

12. Leakey, R. E. F., *Nature,* **242**, 170-173 (1973).

13. Leakey, L. S. B., Tobias, P. V., and Napier, J. R., *Nature,* **202**, 7-9 (1964).

668

# Single-Channel Currents Recorded from Membrane of Denervated Frog Muscle Fibres

E. Neher and B. Sakmann

## Editor's Note

**The modern view is that nerve cells communicate with the outside world by means of channels on a molecular scale spanning the outer membrane of the cells, using the channels to import or export particular chemicals such as the ions of sodium or potassium. Typically nerve cells have a great variety of channels specific for different chemicals in their exterior membranes. The interest of this paper is that it describes a technique for isolating individual channels by means of exceedingly fine glass pipettes which is now known as the "patch-clamp" technique. The clamp is a means of maintaining a fixed voltage across the membrane of the cells being studied. The authors Bert Sakmann and Erwin Neher were awarded the Nobel Prize for Medicine in 1991.**

THE ionic channel associated with the acetylcholine (ACh) receptor at the neuromuscular junction of skeletal muscle fibres is probably the best described channel in biological membranes. Nevertheless, the properties of individual channels are still unknown, as previous studies were concerned with average population properties. Macroscopic conductance fluctuations occurring in the presence of ACh were analysed to provide estimates for single channel conductance and mean open times[1-3]. The values obtained, however, depended on assumptions about the shape of the elementary conductance contribution—for example, that the elementary contribution is a square pulse-like event[2]. Clearly, it would be of great interest to refine techniques of conductance measurement in order to resolve discrete changes in conductance which are expected to occur when single channels open or close. This has not been possible so far because of excessive extraneous background noise. We report on a more sensitive method of conductance measurement, which, in appropriate conditions, reveals discrete changes in conductance that show many of the features that have been postulated for single ionic channels.

The key to the high resolution in the present experiments lies in limiting the membrane area from which current is measured to a small patch, and thereby decreasing background membrane noise. This is achieved by applying closely the tip of a glass pipette, 3-5 μm in diameter, on to the muscle surface, thus isolating electrically a small patch of membrane (Fig. 1). This method has been applied previously in various modifications and mostly with larger pipette tips to muscle[4], molluscan neurones[5,6], and squid axon[7]. The pipette, which has fire-polished edges, is filled with Ringer's solution and contains the cholinergic agonist at micromolar concentrations. Its interior is connected to the input of a virtual-ground circuit, which clamps the potential inside the pipette to ground and at the same time

# 切除神经的青蛙肌纤维膜上的单通道电流

内尔，萨克曼

## 编者按

现代观点认为，神经细胞可以借助横跨细胞膜的分子通道输入或输出特定的化学物质，如钠离子或钾离子等，来实现与外部世界的通讯联络。典型的神经细胞外膜上有很多针对不同化学物质的特异通道。本文的亮点在于，描述了一种借助玻璃微电极分离单独通道的技术，即现在所知的"膜片钳"技术。膜片钳是维持被研究细胞跨细胞膜固定电压的一种方法。本文作者贝尔特·萨克曼和埃尔温·内尔获得了 1991 年诺贝尔医学奖。

在骨骼肌纤维的神经肌肉连接处，与乙酰胆碱（ACh）受体相关的离子通道是生物膜中研究的最为深入的通道。然而，单离子通道的性质仍然不清楚，以前的研究工作所涉及的都是群体通道的平均性质。通过对 ACh 存在时所发生的宏观电导率的波动进行分析来评估单通道电导率和平均开放时间 [1-3]。但是所得到的数值取决于基础电导产生波的形状，例如是否为矩形脉冲波 [2]。显然，为了区分在单通道开放或关闭时期预计会出现的电导率的不连续变化，提高电导率的测量技术就非常重要。由于大量外来的背景噪音，至今这种精细技术还没有实现。本文将报道一种用于测定电导率更为灵敏的方法。在适合条件下，这种方法中所出现的电导率的不连续变化显示了被假定为单离子通道的许多特征。

本实验中高分辨率技术的关键在于通过将测定电流的膜的面积限制到很小的小块，从而降低膜的背景噪音。为达到该目的，将直径 3~5 微米的玻璃吸管尖端紧靠在肌肉表面上，从而使一小片膜绝缘（图 1）。以前，这种方法经过不同的改进，多采用较大的尖管，用于肌肉 [4]、软体动物神经 [5,6] 和枪乌贼神经轴突 [7] 的记录。将边缘经火抛光的尖管内充满林格溶液，其内含有微摩尔级浓度的类胆碱激动剂。管内部接有有效接地的输入电路，这是通过夹持管内壁使其电势接地来实现的。与此同时，测定流经管内即流经被管口罩住的小片膜的电流。用两个常规的微电极夹将肌细胞

measures current flowing through the pipette, that is, through the patch of membrane covered by the pipette opening. The interior of the muscle fibre is clamped locally to a fixed value by a conventional two-microelectrode clamp[8]. Thus, voltage-clamp conditions are secured across the patch of membrane under investigation. Since current densities involved are very small, a simple virtual ground inside the pipette is preferable to more complicated arrangements for stabilizing potential described previously[6].

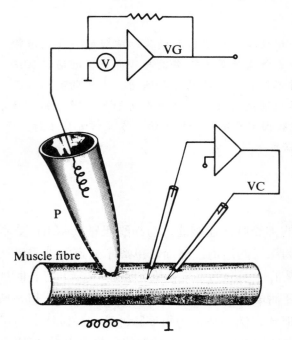

Fig. 1. Schematic circuit diagram for current recoding from a patch of membrane with an extracellular pipette. VC, Standard two-microelectrode voltage clamp circuit to set locally the membrane potential of the fibre to a fixed value. P, Pipette, fire polished, with 3-5 μm diameter opening, containing Ringer's solution and agonist at concentrations between $2 \times 10^{-7}$ and $6 \times 10^{-5}$ M. d. c. resistance of the pipette: 2-5 MΩ. The pipette tip applied closely on to the muscle fibre within 200 μm of the intracellular clamp electrodes. VG, Virtual ground circuit, using a Function Modules Model 380K operational amplifier and a 500 MΩ feedback resistor to measure membrane current. The amplifier is mounted together with a shielded pipette holder on a motor-driven micromanipulator. V, Bucking potential and test signal for balancing of pipette leakage and measuring pipette resistance.

The dominant source of background noise in these measurements was the leakage shunt under the pipette rim between membrane and glass. It was constantly monitored by measuring the electrical conductance between pipette interior and bath. Discrete conductance changes could be resolved only when the conductance between pipette interior and bath decreased by a factor of four or more after contact between pipette and membrane. To minimize the leakage conductance, the muscle was treated with collagenase and protease[9]. This enzyme treatment digested connective tissue and the basement membrane, thereby enabling closer contact between glass and membrane. At the same time, however, it made the membrane fragile and more sensitive to damage by the approaching pipette. It did not, however, change the ACh sensitivity of the fibre or alter

（纤维）局部固定 [8]。这样，研究中玻璃微管口下方的小片膜就被完全绝缘。由于流过的电流量很小，因此将管内进行简单有效的接地要优于以前所描述的用于稳定电压而进行的各种更复杂的方式 [6]。

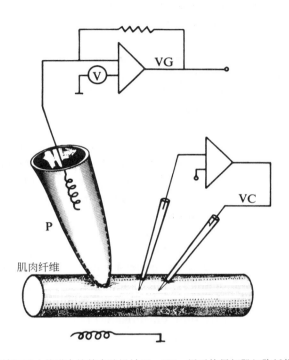

图 1. 用一个胞外玻璃管记录小片膜电流的电路设计图。VC，用于使局部肌细胞纤维膜电势达到一固定值的标准双微电极电压夹钳电路。 P，管口经火抛光的玻璃微管，直径 3~5 μm，装有林格溶液和浓度介于 $2 \times 10^{-7} \sim 6 \times 10^{-5}$ M 之间的激动剂。管的直流电阻为 2~5 MΩ。管尖紧靠肌纤维细胞，距细胞内夹钳电极 200 μm 以内。VG，有效的接地电路，通过功能模块模型 380K 运算放大器和一个 500 MΩ 的反馈电阻器测定膜电流。放大器与电驱动马达推进的显微操纵器和固定肌细胞夹持器装在一起。V，对抗电势和检测用于平衡移液管泄漏和测定移液管电阻的信号。

　　在这些测定中，背景噪音的主要来源是介于膜和玻璃之间的管边缘下出现的泄漏。通过借助于测定管内和浴池之间的电导率而进行不断的监控。只有当管和膜接触后管内和室间的电导率降低到 1/4 或更多时，才能分辨出不连续的电导率变化。为了将泄漏电导率降到最低，肌肉都经过了胶原酶和蛋白酶的处理 [9]，结缔组织和基膜中的胶原得以消化，从而使玻璃和膜之间可以更加紧密的接触。然而，与此同时，这样的处理也使得膜变得易碎，且对插进的管造成的破坏更敏感。但是，这并没有改变纤维对 ACh 的敏感性，也没有改变 ACh 诱导的电导率出现波动的特性（内

the properties of ACh-induced conductance fluctuations (E.N. and B.S., unpublished).

All experiments were carried out on the extrasynaptic region of denervated hypersensitive muscle fibres. The uniform ACh sensitivity found over most of the surface of these fibres greatly enhanced the probability of the occurrence of agonist-induced conductance changes at the membrane patch under investigation. Extrasynaptic ACh channels of denervated muscle fibres have mean open times which are about three to five times longer than those of endplate channels[1,10-12]. The longer duration facilitated the detection of conductance changes. Additional measures were taken which are known to either increase the size of the elementary current pulse or prolong its duration: the membrane was hyperpolarized up to $-120$ mV; suberyldicholine (SubCh) was used as an agonist in most of the experiments; the preparation was cooled to 6-8 °C.

Figure 2 shows a current recording taken in the conditions outlined above. Current can be seen to switch repeatedly between different levels. The discrete changes are interpreted as the result of opening and closing of individual channels. This interpretation is based on the very close similarity to single-channel recordings obtained in artificial membrane systems[13]. The preparation under study is, however, subject to a number of additional sources of artefact. Therefore it is necessary to prove that the recorded events do show the properties which are assigned to ionic channels of the cholinergic system. These are: a correlation with the degree of hypersensitivity of the muscle membrane; an amplitude dependent on membrane potential as predicted by noise analysis; a mean length or channel open time, which should depend on voltage in a characteristic manner[2]; pharmacological specificity with different mean open times for different cholinergic agonists[14,15]. The experiments bore out all of the above-mentioned points as outlined below.

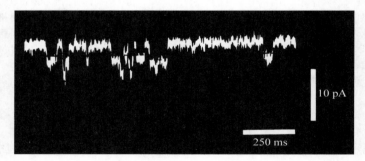

Fig. 2. Oscilloscope recording of current through a patch of membrane of approximately 10 μm². Downward deflection of the trace represents inward current. The pipette contained $2 \times 10^{-7}$ M SubCh in Ringer's solution. The experiment was carried out with a denervated hypersensitive frog cutaneus pectoris (*Rana pipiens*) muscle in normal frog Ringer's solution. The record was filtered at a bandwidth of 200 Hz. Membrane potential: $-120$ mV. Temperature: 8 °C.

The frequency of occurrence of single blips depended on the sensitivity of the patch under investigation. A plot of the number of current pulses per second against the iontophoretically measured sensitivity of the membrane region, determined either

尔和萨克曼未发表数据）。

　　所有实验都在去神经后的超敏肌纤维的突触外区域进行。在这些区域都表现出对 ACh 的一致敏感性，这大大提高了所研究的膜片上能发生激动剂诱导的电导率变化的可能性。突触外的去神经肌肉纤维 ACh 通道的平均开放时间比终板通道的开放时期长约 3~5 倍 [1,10-12]。较长的持续开放时间有助于检测电导率的变化。同时还做了能增加基础电流脉冲大小，或者可以延长电流脉冲时间的实验检测：膜被超极化到 −120 mV；在大多数实验中使用的激动剂是环庚基二胆碱（SubCh）；样本被冷却至 6~8℃。

　　图 2 所示为在上述条件下记录的电流。电流在不同水平间重复转换。由于单通道的开和关，电流出现了不连续的变化。这种解释基于其与在人工膜系统中得到的单通道记录的高度相似性 [13]。然而，本研究的制备物受到许多附加的人工因素的影响。因此，很有必要证实所记录的结果确实说明了类胆碱功能系统的离子通道的性质。这些性质是：与肌肉膜超敏感性程度的相互关系；依赖于噪音分析所预测的膜电势的幅度；以典型方式依赖于电压的通道平均长度或通道平均开放时间 [2]；对不同类胆碱激动剂的不同平均开放时间的药理学特异性 [14,15]。正如下述，实验完全证明了上述所有提到的要点。

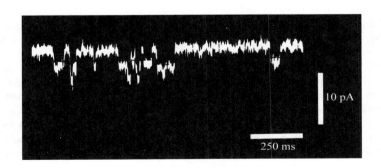

图 2. 示波器对通过约 10 μm² 的小片膜的电流的记录结果。向下的微小偏差代表的是内部电流。　管内的林格溶液含有 $2 \times 10^{-7}$ M 的 SubCh。本实验采用的是切除了神经的超敏感美洲豹蛙（*Rana pipiens*）肌肉细胞，实验在普通的蛙林格溶液中进行。记录经 200 Hz 的带宽过滤。膜电势 −120 mV，温度 8℃。

　　单个信号的发生频率取决于所研究的小片膜的敏感性。将每秒电流脉冲数对所测定的膜区域离子渗透敏感性作图，在玻璃微管夹住前后立即测定。结果显示，两

immediately before or after the pipette experiment, revealed a distinct correlation between both quantities with a correlation coefficient of 0.91 for a linear regression (Fig. 3*b*). Student's *t* test assigned a significance better than 0.1% to the relationship.

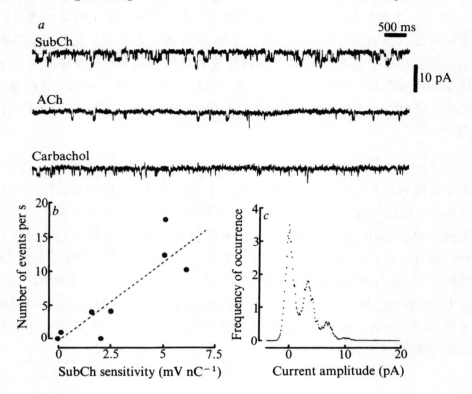

Fig. 3. Characterisation of single-channel currents. *a*, Comparison of current recordings obtained with different cholinergic agonists at concentrations of $2 \times 10^{-7}$ M(SubCh), $2 \times 10^{-6}$ M(ACh), and $6 \times 10^{-5}$ M (carbachol). Downward deflection of the trace represents inward current. Three different experiments. Pen records replayed from analogue tape at a bandwidth of 100 Hz. All experiments at $-120$ mV membrane potential; 8°C. *b*, Number of current blips per second is plotted against iontophoretic sensitivity of the membrane region under investigation. Sensitivity was determined by 100-ms iontophoretic pulses delivered from a pipette filled with 1 M SubCh (40 M$\Omega$ pipette resistance, 10 nA bucking current, sensitivity measured at resting potential). Pooled data from eight experiments. Broken line represents linear regression. *c*, Amplitude histogram of membrane current. Current traces were digitalised and baselines fitted by eye to data records, each 4 s in length. Frequency of occurrence of deviations from the baseline is shown in arbitrary units. Histograms were calculated on a PDP-11 computer; 2-8 histograms were averaged to obtain curves like the one shown. 8°C; $-120$ mV membrane potential.

To estimate the size of the current pulses amplitude histograms were calculated from the current recordings (Fig. 3*c*). The histograms show a prominent peak of gaussian shape around zero deviation, the width of which is a measure of the high frequency background noise of the current trace. Multiple, equally spaced peaks at larger deviations represent the probabilities that either one, two, or three channels are open simultaneously. The peak separation gives the amplitude of the single-channel contribution, which was 3.4 pA for the histogram shown in Fig. 3*c*.

者的数量都呈现出相关系数为 0.91 的线性回归（图 3b），具有明显的相关性。对这种关系来说，$t$ 检验给予的显著性要好于 0.1%。

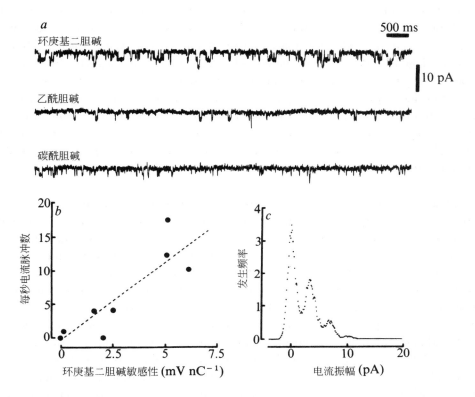

图 3. 单通道电流的特征。$a$，对浓度为 $2 \times 10^{-7}$ M 的环庚基二胆碱、$2 \times 10^{-6}$ M 的 ACh 和 $6 \times 10^{-5}$ M 的碳酰胆碱等所记录的电流进行比较。向下的微量偏差是内部电流。有 3 个不同的实验。记录类似于 100 Hz 的带宽下的重复值。所有实验的膜电势为 −120 mV，实验温度 8℃。$b$，将屏上显示的每秒钟的电流脉冲数对研究膜区的离子电渗敏感性作图。通过充满 1 M SubCh（管电阻 40 ΩM，屏蔽电流 10 nA，在静电势下测定敏感性）的微管中传递过来的 100-ms 的离子电渗脉冲测定敏感性。合并 8 个实验的数据。虚线代表线性回归。$c$，膜电流振幅图。将微量电流数字化，并通过对记录数据的观察设定基线，每次的时间长度为 4 s。由基线发生偏差的频率以任意单位显示。经过 PDP-11 计算机计算并作直方图，如图所示的曲线为对 2~8 张图平均化的结果，温度 8℃，电势 −120 mV。

为了估计电流脉冲的大小，通过计算记录的电流值给出了幅度图（图 3c）。该图显示，在零偏差处有一个高斯形状的显著峰，其宽度是在高频率背景噪音下测定的痕量电流值。其后较大偏差处的多个等距离的峰代表了一个、两个或三个通道同时开放的可能性。分开的峰显示了单通道的幅度，如图 3c 所示，其值大约为 3.4 pA。

This was obtained from an experiment at $-120$ mV membrane potential. A similar histogram from the same muscle fibre obtained at $-80$ mV yields a current pulse amplitude of 2.2 pA. These two values extrapolate to an equilibrium potential of $-7$mV. Channel conductance is estimated as 28 pmhos in this case. It scattered from fibre to fibre with a mean value of $22.4\pm0.3$ pmhos (mean$\pm$s.e.; number of determinations $= 27$). This value is somewhat lower than the one derived from noise analysis at normal endplates, which is 28.6 pmhos for SubCh[15]. Higher order peaks in the histograms are not merely scaled images of the zero order peak. They tend to be smeared out due to non-uniformity of current pulse amplitudes. We cannot decide at present whether this is a real feature of the channels or a measurement artefact. Such an effect could arise if not all of the channels are located ideally in the central region of the pipette opening. Current contributions from peripherally located channels would only partially be picked up by the pipette. This source of error is also likely to lead to an underestimate of channel size if the pipette seal is not optimal.

Temporal analysis of the current records was carried out partly by measurement of individual channel length and averaging 40-50 measurements, and partly by calculation of the power spectrum of the current recordings. In the latter case, the cutoff frequency $f_0$ of the Lorentzian spectrum yielded an estimate of mean channel open time $\tau$ (or pulse duration) through the relationship $\tau = 1/(2\pi f_0)$. Values of mean open times obtained by the two methods were consistent within $\pm30\%$. For SubCh as an agonist and at a temperature of 8°C it was $45\pm3$ ms ($n=11$) at $-120$ mV and $28\pm3$ ms ($n=14$) at $-80$ mV. These values are approximately three times longer than the corresponding mean open times of endplate channels derived from noise analysis[15]. Note, however, that lengthening of channel durations by factors of three to five at extrajunctional sites with respect to endplate values has been measured independently by conventional noise analysis[12]. The voltage dependence of the values given above corresponds to an $e$-fold change per 80 mV, which is within the range of published values[2].

Channel open times were different when different cholinergic agonists were used (Fig. 3a). For $-120$ mV and 8°C, mean channel open time was $45\pm3$ ms ($n=11$) for SubCh, $26\pm5$ ms ($n=4$) for ACh, and $11\pm2$ ms ($n=3$) for carbachol. This sequence reflects the well known relationship between the open times of channels induced by these drugs at normal endplates[14,15] and at extrasynaptic membrane of hypersensitive fibres[12].

The results obtained so far, especially the pharmacological specificity, lead us to conclude that the observed conductance changes are indeed recordings of single-channel currents. They are consistent with the conclusions drawn from statistical analysis of endplate current fluctuations, and show that current contributions of individual channels are of the form of square pulses. In addition, analysis of areas under the peaks of histograms like Fig. 3c indicates that in our experimental conditions opening of individual channels is statistically independent, since the probabilities of zero, one, or two channels being open simultaneously follow—within the limits of experimental resolution—a Poisson distribution.

该图（图 3c）是在 -120 mV 膜电势下的实验中所得。在 -80 mV 下，同样肌肉纤维所得的类似电流脉冲幅度为 2.2 pA。将两个值进行外推，可以得到平衡电势为 -7 mV。在这种情况下，估计通道电导率为 28 pmhos。不同纤维间的电导率平均值为 $22.4 \pm 0.3$ pmhos（平均值 ± 标准误差；测定数 =27）。该值稍微低于通常情况下终板噪音分析所得的数值，对 SubCh 该值是 28.6 pmhos[15]。图中更高级别的峰并不仅仅是零级次峰的比例图。由于电流脉冲振幅的不一致性，此类峰趋于扩散。我们目前并不能确定这种情况是通道的真正特征，还是由于测量的人工因素造成的假象。如果不能将所有的通道都理想地定位在管口的中心区域，就可能会引起这种效应。周边通道对于电流的贡献只可能被记录电极捕获一部分。这种误差也可能源于管的密封性没有达到最优而造成的对通道大小的低估。

对于记录的电流值的时间分析，一部分来自于对单个通道长度的测定，其值为 40~50 次测量结果的平均值，另一部分来源于对记录的电流的能谱分析。在后种情况下，可以通过洛伦兹谱的截止频率 $f_0$ 估算平均开放时间 $\tau$（或脉冲时长），其关系式为 $\tau =1/(2\pi f_0)$。两种方法所得的平均开放时间值在 $\pm 30\%$ 的误差范围以内是一致的。用 SubCh 作为激动剂，温度为 8℃ 时，-120 mV 下，开放时间为 $45 \pm 3$ ms（$n$=11）；-80 mV 下，开放时间是 $28 \pm 3$ ms（$n$=14）。这些值大约是由噪音分析所得到的终板通道平均开放时间的 3 倍[15]。但是值得注意的是，已经通过常规的噪音分析法独立地测定了关于终板值，在额外的连接点处，通道开放期被延长了 3~5 倍[12]。上述所给值的电压依赖性相当于每 80 mV 发生 e 倍的变化，这在已发表数据的范围之内[2]。

当使用不同的类胆碱激动剂时（图 3a），通道的开放时间是不同的。在 -120 mV，8℃ 下，SubCh 作用下的通道平均开放时间为 $45 \pm 3$ ms（$n$=11）；ACh 作用下的通道平均开放时间为 $26 \pm 5$ ms（$n$=4）；而碳酰胆碱作用下的通道开放时间则为 $11 \pm 2$ ms（$n$=3）。这种顺序反映了由这些药物在常规终板[14,15]上诱导产生的通道开放时间与超敏感纤维的突触外膜处[12]之间的典型关系。

目前为止，所得的结果，特别是药物特异性所得的结果，使我们推断所观察到的电导率变化实际上是记录到的单通道电流。它们与终板电流波动的统计分析所得的结论一致，并且显示了个别通道以矩形脉冲的形式形成电流。此外，对图 3c 的峰下区域的分析表明，在我们的实验条件下，个别通道的开放在统计上是独立的。因为在实验分辨率的限制下，零个、一个或两个通道同时开放的概率遵循泊松分布。

Recordings of single-channel currents finally resolves the third level of quantification in the process of neuromuscular transmission after the discovery of endplate currents and miniature endplate currents. It should facilitate discrimination between factors influencing the properties of single channels and agents creating or modifying different populations of channels.

We thank J. H. Steinbach for help with some experiments. Supported by a USPHS grant to Dr. C. F. Stevens, and a stipend of the Max-Planck-Gesellschaft.

(**260**, 799-802; 1976)

**Erwin Neher\* and Bert Sakmann†**
\*Yale University School of Medicine, Department of Physiology, New Haven, Connecticutt 06510
†Max-Planck-Institut für Biophysikalische Chemie, 3400 Göttingen, Am Fassberg, West Germany

Received January 26; accepted March 1, 1976.

References:

1. Katz, B., and Miledi, R., *J. Physiol., Lond.*, **224**, 665-699 (1972).

2. Anderson, C. R., and Stevens, C. F., *J. Physiol., Lond.*, **235**, 655-691 (1973).

3. Ben Haim, D., Dreyer, F., and Peper, K., *Pflügers Arch. ges. Physiol.*, **355**, 19-26 (1975).

4. Strickholm, A., *J. Gen. Physiol.*, **44**, 1073-1087 (1961).

5. Frank, K., and Tauc, L., in *The Cellular Function of Membrane Transport* (edit by Hoffman, J.) (Prentice Hall, Englewood Cliffs, New Jersey, 1963).

6. Neher, E., and Lux, H. D., *Pflügers Arch. ges. Physiol.*, **311**, 272-277 (1969).

7. Fishman, H. M., *Proc. Natl. Acad. Sci. U.S.A.*, **70**, 876-879 (1973).

8. Takeuchi, A., and Takeuchi, N., *J. Neurophysiol.*, **22**, 395-411 (1959).

9. Betz, W., and Sakmann, B., *J. Physiol., Lond.*, **230**, 673-688 (1973).

10. Neher, E., and Sakmann, B., *Pflügers Arch. ges. Physiol.*, **355**, R63 (1975).

11. Dreyer, F., Walther, Ch., and Peper, K., *Pflügers Arch. ges. Physiol.*, **359**, R71 (1975).

12. Neher, E., and Sakmann, B., *J. Physiol., Lond.* (in the press).

13. Hladky, S. B., and Haydon, D. A., *Nature*, **225**, 451-453 (1970).

14. Katz, B., and Miledi, R., *J. Physiol., Lond.*, **230**, 707-717 (1973).

15. Colquhoun, D., Dionne, V. E., Steinbach, J. H., and Stevens, C. F., *Nature*, **253**, 204-206 (1975).

在发现终板电流和微型终板电流之后，单通道电流的记录最终实现了对神经肌肉传导过程中第三层次的定量分析。这应该有利于辨别影响单通道性质的因子和引起或修饰不同通道群体的化学试剂。

我们感谢斯坦巴克对实验的帮助。本研究受到史蒂文斯博士得到的美国公共卫生署基金的支持，并得到了马克斯·普朗克学会的基金资助。

（荆玉祥 翻译；曾少举 审稿）

# Simple Mathematical Models with Very Complicated Dynamics

R. M. May

## Editor's Note

Theories in population biology, economics and physics often involve a relatively simple class of equations called difference equations. Here Robert May, a pioneer in the dynamics of nonlinear systems, reviews recent findings showing that systems described by difference equations can exhibit rich dynamical behaviour. May focuses on a simple model of population dynamics. It exhibits not only "fixed points", reflecting a population that settles into an unchanging equilibrium, but an infinite number of oscillating population states and, beyond a threshold value of one key parameter, chaotic fluctuations. May implores that these lessons be taught in introductory mathematics courses. Over the next two decades this is indeed what happened, as chaos became recognized as a ubiquitous phenomenon in nature.

---

First-order difference equations arise in many contexts in the biological, economic and social sciences. Such equations, even though simple and deterministic, can exhibit a surprising array of dynamical behaviour, from stable points, to a bifurcating hierarchy of stable cycles, to apparently random fluctuations. There are consequently many fascinating problems, some concerned with delicate mathematical aspects of the fine structure of the trajectories, and some concerned with the practical implications and applications. This is an interpretive review of them.

---

THERE are many situations, in many disciplines, which can be described, at least to a crude first approximation, by a simple first-order difference equation. Studies of the dynamical properties of such models usually consist of finding constant equilibrium solutions, and then conducting a linearised analysis to determine their stability with respect to small disturbances: explicitly nonlinear dynamical features are usually not considered.

Recent studies have, however, shown that the very simplest nonlinear difference equations can possess an extraordinarily rich spectrum of dynamical behaviour, from stable points, through cascades of stable cycles, to a regime in which the behaviour (although fully deterministic) is in many respects "chaotic", or indistinguishable from the sample function of a random process.

This review article has several aims.

First, although the main features of these nonlinear phenomena have been discovered

682

# 具有极复杂动力学行为的简单数学模型

梅

## 编者按

种群生物学、经济学和物理学中的理论经常会涉及一类相对简单的方程——差分方程。在本文中，非线性系统动力学的先驱者罗伯特·梅对近期的一些发现进行了整理归纳，这些发现表明由差分方程所描述的系统可以呈现丰富的动力学行为。梅关注种群动力学的一个简单模型。该模型不仅展示了反映种群处在不变平衡态上的"不动点"，还显示了无限多的振荡种群态和超过一个关键参数阈值的混沌波动。梅恳请在数学导论课中讲授这些课程。在之后的20年里，这果然发生了，就如混沌已被公认为是自然界的普遍现象一样。

在生物学、经济学和社会科学的很多情境中，都会出现一阶差分方程。这些方程，即使是简单的和确定的，也能呈现出一系列惊人的动力学行为，从稳定点到稳定循环的分岔谱系，再到明显的随机波动。由此引来了很多有趣的问题，其中一些涉及关于轨道精细结构的精巧的数学内容，而另外一些则涉及实际含义与应用。本文是对于这些内容的解释性综述。

在很多学科中，至少在粗略的一级近似下，有很多情况可以用一个简单的一阶差分方程来描述。对于这些模型的动力学性质的研究，通常包括寻找常数平衡解，继而导出线性化的分析，以确定它们在微小扰动下的稳定性：明显的非线性动力学特征通常是不加以考虑的。

但是，最近的研究表明，最简单的非线性差分方程也能够具有一系列异常丰富的动力学行为，从稳定点经由各级稳定循环到达这样一种状态：其中的行为（尽管是完全确定的）在很多方面是"混沌的"，或无法与一个随机过程的样本函数相区别。

这篇综述性文章有以下几个目的：

第一，尽管这些非线性现象的主要特征已被发现并被其他的多位学者独立地再

and independently rediscovered by several people, I know of no source where all the main results are collected together. I have therefore tried to give such a synoptic account. This is done in a brief and descriptive way, and includes some new material: the detailed mathematical proofs are to be found in the technical literature, to which signposts are given.

Second, I indicate some of the interesting mathematical questions which do not seem to be fully resolved. Some of these problems are of a practical kind, to do with providing a probabilistic description for trajectories which seem random, even though their underlying structure is deterministic. Other problems are of intrinsic mathematical interest, and treat such things as the pathology of the bifurcation structure, or the truly random behaviour, that can arise when the nonlinear function $F(X)$ of equation (1) is not analytical. One aim here is to stimulate research on these questions, particularly on the empirical questions which relate to processing data.

Third, consideration is given to some fields where these notions may find practical application. Such applications range from the abstractly metaphorical (where, for example, the transition from a stable point to "chaos" serves as a metaphor for the onset of turbulence in a fluid), to models for the dynamic behaviour of biological populations (where one can seek to use field or laboratory data to estimate the values of the parameters in the difference equation).

Fourth, there is a very brief review of the literature pertaining to the way this spectrum of behaviour—stable points, stable cycles, chaos—can arise in second or higher order difference equations (that is, two or more dimensions; two or more interacting species), where the onset of chaos usually requires less severe nonlinearities. Differential equations are also surveyed in this light; it seems that a three-dimensional system of first-order ordinary differential equations is required for the manifestation of chaotic behaviour.

The review ends with an evangelical plea for the introduction of these difference equations into elementary mathematics courses, so that students' intuition may be enriched by seeing the wild things that simple nonlinear equations can do.

## First-order Difference Equations

One of the simplest systems an ecologist can study is a seasonally breeding population in which generations do not overlap[1-4]. Many natural populations, particularly among temperate zone insects (including many economically important crop and orchard pests), are of this kind. In this situation, the observational data will usually consist of information about the maximum, or the average, or the total population in each generation. The theoretician seeks to understand how the magnitude of the population in generation $t+1$, $X_{t+1}$, is related to the magnitude of the population in the preceding generation $t$, $X_t$: such a relationship may be expressed in the general form

$$X_{t+1} = F(X_t) \tag{1}$$

发现，但是，就我所知，还没有一份资料将所有的主要成果汇集起来。因此，我试图采取简略的和描述性的方式给出这样一种概要性说明。这一说明中包括一些新材料，详细的数学证明可以在技术性文献中找到（已用记号标注）。

第二，我要指出一些有趣的数学问题，它们似乎还没有得到完全的解决。其中有一些问题属于实际问题，对看似随机的运动轨道提供一个概率性的描述，即使其根本结构是确定性的。另外一些问题则属于固有的数学趣味，因而把它们看作分岔结构的反常状态，或者是真正的随机行为，当方程（1）中的非线性函数 $F(X)$ 不是解析的时候就会出现。本文的一个目的是激发对于上述问题的研究，特别是对于与数据处理有关的经验问题的研究。

第三，我对上述观点可以找到实际应用的某些领域进行了考察。这些应用包括从抽象的隐喻（如用从一个稳定点到"混沌"的转变来类比流体中湍流的出现）到生物学种群的动力学行为模型（人们可以设法利用野外数据或实验数据来估计差分方程中的参数值）。

第四，本文还包括了对上述一系列动力学行为——稳定点、稳定循环、混沌——可以在二阶或更高阶差分方程（也就是说，二维或更高维，两个或者多个相互作用的物种）中出现的文献的一个极为简略的综述。在这些情况下，混沌的出现通常不需要那么严格的非线性性质。为此，我还对微分方程进行了探讨。看起来，处理混沌行为需要的是一个三维的一阶常微分方程组。

这篇综述性文章以一个热忱的呼吁作为结束，即将这些差分方程引入到初等数学课程中，以便让学生看到简单的非线性方程会呈现复杂的问题，这样使他们的直觉变得更丰富。

### 一阶差分方程

生态学者所能研究的最简单的系统之一，就是各世代没有交叠的季节性繁殖种群[1-4]。很多自然种群，特别是那些温带地区的昆虫（包括很多种重要经济农作物和果园的害虫），都属于这一类型。在这种情况下，观测到的数据通常会由以下信息组成：每一世代种群的最大值、平均值或者是总数。理论研究工作者试图理解第 $t+1$ 世代的种群数量 $X_{t+1}$ 与其前一世代，即第 $t$ 世代的种群数量 $X_t$ 之间有怎样的关系。这种关系可以表达为如下一般形式：

$$X_{t+1} = F(X_t) \tag{1}$$

The function $F(X)$ will usually be what a biologist calls "density dependent", and a mathematician calls nonlinear; equation (1) is then a first-order, nonlinear difference equation.

Although I shall henceforth adopt the habit of referring to the variable $X$ as "the population", there are countless situations outside population biology where the basic equation (1), applies. There are other examples in biology, as, for example in genetics[5,6] (where the equation describes the change in gene frequency in time) or in epidemiology[7] (with $X$ the fraction of the population infected at time $t$). Examples in economics include models for the relationship between commodity quantity and price[8], for the theory of business cycles[9], and for the temporal sequences generated by various other economic quantities[10]. The general equation (1) also is germane to the social sciences[11], where it arises, for example, in theories of learning (where $X$ may be the number of bits of information that can be remembered after an interval $t$), or in the propagation of rumours in variously structured societies (where $X$ is the number of people to have heard the rumour after time $t$). The imaginative reader will be able to invent other contexts for equation (1).

In many of these contexts, and for biological populations in particular, there is a tendency for the variable $X$ to increase from one generation to the next when it is small, and for it to decrease when it is large. That is, the nonlinear function $F(X)$ often has the following properties: $F(0) = 0$; $F(X)$ increases monotonically as $X$ increases through the range $0<X<A$ (with $F(X)$ attaining its maximum value at $X=A$); and $F(X)$ decreases monotonically as $X$ increases beyond $X=A$. Moreover, $F(X)$ will usually contain one or more parameters which "tune" the severity of this nonlinear behaviour; parameters which tune the steepness of the hump in the $F(X)$ curve. These parameters will typically have some biological or economic or sociological significance.

A specific example is afforded by the equation[1,4,12-23]

$$N_{t+1} = N_t\,(a - bN_t) \tag{2}$$

This is sometimes called the "logistic" difference equation. In the limit $b=0$, it describes a population growing purely exponentially (for $a>1$); for $b\neq0$, the quadratic nonlinearity produces a growth curve with a hump, the steepness of which is tuned by the parameter $a$. By writing $X=bN/a$, the equation may be brought into canonical form[1,4,12-23]

$$X_{t+1} = aX_t\,(1 - X_t) \tag{3}$$

In this form, which is illustrated in Fig. 1, it is arguably the simplest nonlinear difference equation. I shall use equation (3) for most of the numerical examples and illustrations in this article. Although attractive to mathematicians by virtue of its extreme simplicity, in practical applications equation (3) has the disadvantage that it requires $X$ to remain on the interval $0<X<1$; if $X$ ever exceeds unity, subsequent iterations diverge towards $-\infty$

这里的函数 $F(X)$ 通常被生物学家称为"密度制约的",而数学家则会称之为非线性的；于是方程（1）就是一个一阶非线性差分方程。

尽管此后我将习惯于将变量 $X$ 称为"种群数量"，但在种群生物学之外还是存在不可胜数的可以应用基本方程（1）的情形。生物学中还有其他一些实例，如在遗传学中 [5,6]（这时该方程描述了基因频率随时间的变化），或者是在流行病学中 [7]（其中 $X$ 是 $t$ 时刻被感染群体所占的比例）。经济学中的例子包括商品数量与价格之间的关系模型 [8]，商业周期理论模型 [9] 以及由各种其他经济学量所产生的时间序列的模型 [10]。方程（1）的一般形式也与社会科学 [11] 有着密切的关系，例如，它会出现在学习理论中（其中 $X$ 可以是一个时间间隔 $t$ 之后能够记住的信息量），或者出现于在各种结构化社会团体内流言传播的问题中（此时 $X$ 是在时间 $t$ 之后听到过流言的人数）。富于想象力的读者还可以为方程（1）设计出其他情境。

在上述多种情境中，特别是对于生物学种群问题，变量 $X$ 有这样一种趋势，当种群很小时，从一个世代到下一个世代逐渐增加，而当种群很大时，则减小。换言之，非线性函数 $F(X)$ 具有以下性质：$F(0) = 0$；当 $0<X<A$ 时，$F(X)$ 随着 $X$ 增加而单调增加（$F(X)$ 在 $X = A$ 处取得最大值）；而在超过 $X = A$ 之后，$F(X)$ 随着 $X$ 的增加而单调减小。此外，$F(X)$ 通常还会包含一个或多个参数，这些参数或可"调节"这种非线性行为的强度，或可调节 $F(X)$ 曲线峰的陡度，它们均有其典型的生物学、经济学或社会学意义。

下列方程提供了一个特别的实例 [1,4,12~23]：

$$N_{t+1} = N_t (a-bN_t) \qquad (2)$$

这个方程有时被称为"逻辑斯谛"差分方程。在 $b = 0$ 的极限情况下，它描述了纯指数形式的种群增长（其中 $a > 1$）；当 $b \neq 0$ 时，二次非线性性质产生一条有一个峰的生长曲线，其陡度由参数 $a$ 所调节。记 $X = bN/a$，可以将该方程转化为如下规范形式 [1,4,12~23]：

$$X_{t+1} = aX_t (1-X_t) \qquad (3)$$

如图 1 所示，在这种形式下，可以说明它是最简单的非线性差分方程。在本文的大多数数值实例和说明中，我都会用到方程（3）。尽管对于数学家来说，它那极端简单性的优点很有吸引力，但在实际应用中，方程（3）却存在一点不足，即它要求 $X$ 始终保持在 $0<X<1$ 范围内，如果 $X$ 超过 1，随后的迭代将会发散到 $-\infty$（这意味着种群

(which means the population becomes extinct). Furthermore, $F(X)$ in equation (3) attains a maximum value of $a/4$ (at $X=\frac{1}{2}$); the equation therefore possesses non-trivial dynamical behaviour only if $a<4$. On the other hand, all trajectories are attracted to $X=0$ if $a<1$. Thus for non-trivial dynamical behaviour we require $1<a<4$; failing this, the population becomes extinct.

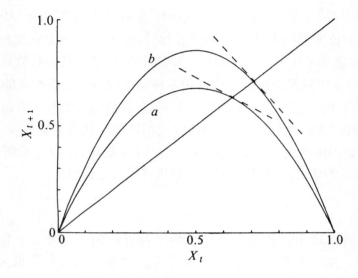

Fig. 1. A typical form for the relationship between $X_{t+1}$ and $X_t$ described by equation (1). The curves are for equation (3), with $a=2.707$ ($a$); and $a=3.414$ ($b$). The dashed lines indicate the slope at the "fixed points" where $F(X)$ intersects the 45° line: for the case $a$ this slope is less steep than −45° and the fixed point is stable; for $b$ the slope is steeper than −45°, and the point is unstable.

Another example, with a more secure provenance in the biological literature[1,23-27], is the equation

$$X_{t+1} = X_t \exp[r(1-X_t)] \tag{4}$$

This again describes a population with a propensity to simple exponential growth at low densities, and a tendency to decrease at high densities. The steepness of this nonlinear behaviour is tuned by the parameter $r$. The model is plausible for a single species population which is regulated by an epidemic disease at high density[28]. The function $F(X)$ of equation (4) is slightly more complicated than that of equation (3), but has the compensating advantage that local stability implies global stability[1] for all $X>0$.

The forms (3) and (4) by no means exhaust the list of single-humped functions $F(X)$ for equation (1) which can be culled from the ecological literature. A fairly full such catalogue is given, complete with references, by May and Oster[1]. Other similar mathematical functions are given by Metropolis et al.[16]. Yet other forms for $F(X)$ are discussed under the heading of "mathematical curiosities" below.

将会灭绝)。此外，方程（3）中的 $F(X)$ 取得最大值为 $a/4$（在 $X = \frac{1}{2}$ 处)，因此，只在 $a<4$ 时，该方程才具有非平凡的动力学行为。另一方面，若 $a<1$，则所有轨道都被吸引到 $X = 0$。于是，为了得到非平凡的动力学行为，我们要求 $1<a<4$，若不满足这一点，种群将会灭绝。

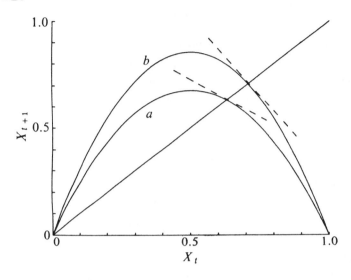

图 1. 方程（1）所描述的 $X_{t+1}$ 与 $X_t$ 之间关系的典型形式。两条曲线对应方程（3），其中（a），$a = 2.707$；（b），$a = 3.414$。虚线所示为 $F(X)$ 与 $45°$ 线的相交处"不动点"的斜率：对于情况 $a$，其倾斜程度不足 $-45°$，因而不动点是稳定的；对于情况 $b$，其倾斜程度超过 $-45°$，因而该点是不稳定的。

另一个在生物学文献中有更可靠出处 [1,23-27] 的实例是方程

$$X_{t+1} = X_t \exp[r(1-X_t)] \tag{4}$$

它所描述的也是这样一个种群，即在低密度时具有简单指数增长的倾向，而在高密度时则具有减小的趋势，其非线性行为的陡度是由参数 $r$ 来调节的。对于单一物种种群在高密度时受一种流行病影响的情况，该模型看起来是合理的 [28]。方程（4）中的函数 $F(X)$ 比方程（3）中的稍微复杂一些，但作为补偿，其优势在于，对于所有 $X > 0$ 的范围内，局域稳定即意味着全局稳定 [1]。

（3）和（4）两种形式绝不是能够从生态学文献中精选出来的形如方程（1）的单峰函数 $F(X)$ 的全部可能。梅和奥斯特 [1] 给出了这样一个相当完整的目录，并且都附有参考文献。梅特罗波利斯等人 [16] 给出了其他类似的数学函数。至于 $F(X)$ 的其他形式，将会在"数学方面的好奇心"这一标题下探讨。

## Dynamic Properties of Equation (1)

Possible constant, equilibrium values (or "fixed points") of $X$ in equation (1) may be found algebraically by putting $X_{t+1} = X_t = X^*$, and solving the resulting equation

$$X^* = F(X^*) \tag{5}$$

An equivalent graphical method is to find the points where the curve $F(X)$ that maps $X_t$ into $X_{t+1}$ intersects the 45° line, $X_{t+1} = X_t$, which corresponds to the ideal nirvana of zero population growth; see Fig. 1. For the single-hump curves discussed above, and exemplified by equations (3) and (4), there are two such points: the trivial solution $X=0$, and a non-trivial solution $X^*$ (which for equation (3) is $X^* = 1 - [1/a]$).

The next question concerns the stability of the equilibrium point $X^*$. This can be seen[24,25,19-21,1,4] to depend on the slope of the $F(X)$ curve at $X^*$. This slope, which is illustrated by the dashed lines in Fig. 1, can be designated

$$\lambda^{(1)}(X^*) = [dF/dX]_{X = X^*} \tag{6}$$

So long as this slope lies between 45° and −45° (that is, $\lambda^{(1)}$ between +1 and −1), making an acute angle with the 45° ZPG line, the equilibrium point $X^*$ will be at least locally stable, attracting all trajectories in its neighbourhood. In equation (3), for example, this slope is $\lambda^{(1)} = 2 - a$: the equilibrium point is therefore stable, and attracts all trajectories originating in the interval $0 < X < 1$, if and only if $1 < a < 3$.

As the relevant parameters are tuned so that the curve $F(X)$ becomes more and more steeply humped, this stability-determining slope at $X^*$ may eventually steepen beyond −45°(that is, $\lambda^{(1)} < -1$), whereupon the equilibrium point $X^*$ is no longer stable.

What happens next? What happens, for example, for $a > 3$ in equation (3)?

To answer this question, it is helpful to look at the map which relates the populations at successive intervals 2 generations apart; that is, to look at the function which relates $X_{t+2}$ to $X_t$. This second iterate of equation (1) can be written

$$X_{t+2} = F[F(X_t)] \tag{7}$$

or, introducing an obvious piece of notation,

$$X_{t+2} = F^{(2)}(X_t) \tag{8}$$

The map so derived from equation (3) is illustrated in Figs 2 and 3.

## 方程（1）的动力学性质

利用代数方法，令 $X_{t+1} = X_t = X^*$，即可求出方程（1）中 $X$ 的可能的常数解，即平衡值（或"不动点"），该解可由下列方程给出：

$$X^* = F(X^*) \tag{5}$$

一种等价的图像解法是寻找将 $X_t$ 映射到 $X_{t+1}$ 的曲线 $F(X)$ 与 45° 线 $X_{t+1} = X_t$ 的交点，它对应于种群零增长的理想情况（图 1）。对于前面所讨论的单峰曲线，以方程（3）和（4）为例，这样的点有两个：平凡解 $X = 0$ 和一个非平凡解 $X^*$（对于方程（3），$X^* = 1-[1/a]$）。

下一个问题与平衡点 $X^*$ 的稳定性有关。可以看到 [24,25,19-21,1,4] 这取决于 $F(X)$ 曲线在 $X^*$ 点处的斜率。如同图 1 中虚线所示，这一斜率可以由下式确定为：

$$\lambda^{(1)}(X^*) = [\mathrm{d}F/\mathrm{d}X]_{X = X^*} \tag{6}$$

只要这个倾斜度位于 45° 到 –45° 之间（也就是说，$\lambda^{(1)}$ 介于 $+1$ 和 $-1$ 之间），与 45° 零增长线构成一个锐角，那么平衡点 $X^*$ 至少是局部稳定的，将吸引邻域内的全部轨道。例如，在方程（3）中，这个斜率是 $\lambda^{(1)} = 2-a$：当且仅当 $1<a<3$ 时，平衡点是稳定的，因而吸引所有源于区间 $0<X<1$ 内的轨道。

由于相关参数的调节使得曲线 $F(X)$ 变得越来越陡峭，决定稳定性的 $X^*$ 点处的倾斜度最终可能超过 $-45°$（也就是说，$\lambda^{(1)} < -1$），于是平衡点 $X^*$ 不再是稳定的。

接下来会发生什么？例如，当方程（3）中的 $a > 3$ 时会发生什么？

要回答这个问题，考察一下相继间隔 2 世代的种群间关系的映射将会是有益的。也就是说，看一看联系 $X_{t+2}$ 与 $X_t$ 的函数。方程（1）的第二次迭代可以写作

$$X_{t+2} = F[F(X_t)] \tag{7}$$

或者引入一个含义明显的记号，

$$X_{t+2} = F^{(2)}(X_t) \tag{8}$$

用这种方式从方程（3）得出的映射如图 2 和图 3 所示。

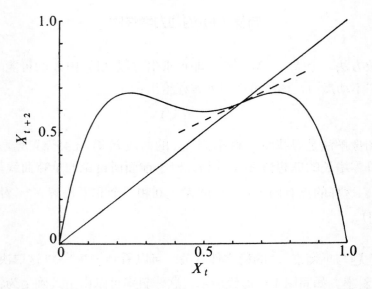

Fig. 2. The map relating $X_{t+2}$ to $X_t$, obtained by two iterations of equation (3). This figure is for the case (a) of Fig. 1, $a=2.707$: the basic fixed point is stable, and it is the only point at which $F^{(2)}(X)$ intersects the 45° line (where its slope, shown by the dashed line, is less steep than 45°).

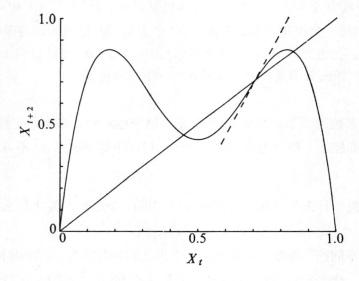

Fig. 3. As for Fig. 2, except that here $a=3.414$, as in Fig. 1b. The basic fixed point is now unstable: the slope of $F^{(2)}(X)$ at this point steepens beyond 45°, leading to the appearance of two new solutions of period 2.

Population values which recur every second generation (that is, fixed points with period 2) may now be written as $X^*_2$, and found either algebraically from

$$X^*_2 = F^{(2)}(X^*_2) \tag{9}$$

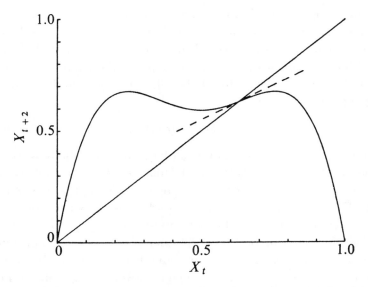

图 2. 联系 $X_{t+2}$ 与 $X_t$ 的映射，通过两次迭代方程（3）而得到。本图对应于图 1 中的情况 ($a$)，$a = 2.707$；基本不动点是稳定的，并且它是 $F^{(2)}(X)$ 与 45° 线的唯一交点（如图中虚线所示，其倾斜度不足 45°）。

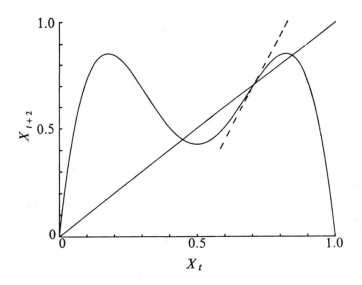

图 3. 与图 2 类似，除了 $a = 3.414$（这与图 1$b$ 中一样）。基本不动点现在是不稳定的：$F^{(2)}(X)$ 在这点处的倾斜度超过了 45°，导致周期为 2 的两个新解出现。

现在可以将在每隔一世代都会重现的种群数值（即周期为 2 的不动点）记为 $X^*_2$，接下来，或者用代数方法从

$$X^*_2 = F^{(2)}(X^*_2) \tag{9}$$

or graphically from the intersection between the map $F^{(2)}(X)$ and the $45°$ line, as shown in Figs 2 and 3. Clearly the equilibrium point $X^*$ of equation (5) is a solution of equation (9); the basic fixed point of period 1 is a degenerate case of a period 2 solution. We now make a simple, but crucial, observation[1]: the slope of the curve $F^{(2)}(X)$ at the point $X^*$, defined as $\lambda^{(2)}(X^*)$ and illustrated by the dashed lines in Figs 2 and 3, is the square of the corresponding slope of $F(X)$

$$\lambda^{(2)}(X^*)=[\lambda^{(1)}(X^*)]^2 \tag{10}$$

This fact can now be used to make plain what happens when the fixed point $X^*$ becomes unstable. If the slope of $F(X)$ is less than $-45°$ (that is, $|\lambda^{(1)}|<1$), as illustrated by curve $a$ in Fig. 1, then $X^*$ is stable. Also, from equation (10), this implies $0<\lambda^{(2)}<1$ corresponding to the slope of $F^{(2)}$ at $X^*$ lying between $0°$ and $45°$, as shown in Fig. 2. As long as the fixed point $X^*$ is stable, it provides the only non-trivial solution to equation (9). On the other hand, when $\lambda^{(1)}$ steepens beyond $-45°$ (that is, $|\lambda^{(1)}|>1$), as illustrated by curve b in Fig 1, $X^*$ becomes unstable. At the same time, from equation (10) this implies $\lambda^{(2)}>1$, corresponding to the slope of $F^{(2)}$ at $X^*$ steepening beyond $45°$, as shown in Fig. 3. As this happens, the curve $F^{(2)}(X)$ must develop a "loop", and two new fixed points of period 2 appear, as illustrated in Fig. 3.

In short, as the nonlinear function $F(X)$ in equation (1) becomes more steeply humped, the basic fixed point $X^*$ may become unstable. At exactly the stage when this occurs, there are born two new and initially stable fixed points of period 2, between which the system alternates in a stable cycle of period 2. The sort of graphical analysis indicated by Figs 1, 2 and 3, along with the equation (10), is all that is needed to establish this generic result[1, 4].

As before, the stability of this period 2 cycle depends on the slope of the curve $F^{(2)}(X)$ at the 2 points. (This slope is easily shown to be the same at both points[1,20], and more generally to be the same at all $k$ points on a period $k$ cycle.) Furthermore, as is clear by imagining the intermediate stages between Figs 2 and 3, this stability-determining slope has the value $\lambda=+1$ at the birth of the 2-point cycle, and then decreases through zero towards $\lambda=-1$ as the hump in $F(X)$ continues to steepen. Beyond this point the period 2 points will in turn become unstable, and bifurcate to give an initially stable cycle of period 4. This in turn gives way to a cycle of period 8, and thence to a hierarchy of bifurcating stable cycles of periods 16, 32, 64,..., $2^n$. In each case, the way in which a stable cycle of period $k$ becomes unstable, simultaneously bifurcating to produce a new and initially stable cycle of period $2k$, is basically similar to the process just adumbrated for $k=1$. A more full and rigorous account of the material covered so far is in ref. 1.

This "very beautiful bifurcation phenomenon"[22] is depicted in Fig. 4, for the example equation (3). It cannot be too strongly emphasised that the process is generic to most functions $F(X)$ with a hump of tunable steepness. Metropolis et al.[16] refer to this hierarchy of cycles of periods $2^n$ as the harmonics of the fixed point $X^*$.

求出，或者用图像方法找出映射 $F^{(2)}(X)$ 与 45° 线的交点，如图 2 和图 3 所示。很明显，方程（5）的平衡点 $X^*$ 是方程（9）的一个解；周期为 1 的基本不动点是周期为 2 的解的一种合并情况。现在我们来做一番简单却极为重要的考察 [1]：曲线 $F^{(2)}(X)$ 在点 $X^*$ 处的斜率定义为 $\lambda^{(2)}(X^*)$，并用虚线表示于图 2 和图 3 中，它是相应的 $F(X)$ 的斜率的平方：

$$\lambda^{(2)}(X^*) = [\lambda^{(1)}(X^*)]^2 \tag{10}$$

现在我们能够用这一事实来解释当不动点 $X^*$ 变得不稳定时所发生的事情。如果 $F(X)$ 的倾斜度小于 $-45°$（即 $|\lambda^{(1)}| < 1$），正如图 1 中曲线 a 所示，那么 $X^*$ 是稳定的。同样，根据方程（10），这就意味着 $0 < \lambda^{(2)} < 1$ 对应于 $F^{(2)}$ 在 $X^*$ 处的倾斜度介于 $0° \sim 45°$，如图 2 所示。只要不动点 $X^*$ 稳定，它就能为方程（9）提供唯一的非平凡解。另一方面，当 $\lambda^{(1)}$ 倾斜度超过 $-45°$（即 $|\lambda^{(1)}| > 1$）时，正如图 1 中曲线 b 所示，$X^*$ 将变得不稳定。同时，根据方程（10）可知，这意味着 $\lambda^{(2)} > 1$，对应的 $F^{(2)}$ 在 $X^*$ 处的倾角超过 45°，如图 3 所示。在这种情况下，曲线 $F^{(2)}(X)$ 必定会形成一个"循环"，并且出现两个周期为 2 的新不动点，如图 3 所示。

　　总而言之，随着方程（1）中的非线性函数 $F(X)$ 逐渐变陡峭，基本不动点 $X^*$ 逐渐变成不稳定的。而在这个阶段中，会产生两个最初稳定且周期为 2 的新不动点，在这两点之间，系统在周期为 2 的稳定循环中振荡。图 1、2 和 3 所表示的图像分析方法，以及方程（10）正是要确定这个一般性结果所需的一切 [1,4]。

　　如前所述，这个周期为 2 的循环的稳定性取决于曲线 $F^{(2)}(X)$ 在两点处的斜率。（两点处的斜率很明显是相同的 [1,20]，更一般地，对于周期为 $k$ 的循环，所有 $k$ 个点处的斜率都是相同的。）不仅如此，通过想象图 2 与图 3 之间的过渡阶段可以知道，这个确定稳定性的斜率在 2 点循环刚产生时的值是 $\lambda = +1$，继而随着 $F(X)$ 的峰逐渐变陡，经由零逐渐减少到 $\lambda = -1$。超过该点之后，周期为 2 的各点将会依次变得不稳定，并且产生分岔而形成周期为 4 的初始稳定循环。照此方式，依次可以产生周期为 8 的循环，进而产生一个周期为 16, 32, 64, …, $2^n$ 的稳定循环的分岔谱系。在各种情况下，周期为 $k$ 的稳定循环逐渐变得不稳定，同时产生分岔而形成周期为 $2k$ 的新初始稳定循环，其方式基本上与对 $k = 1$ 的情况所概括的过程相类似。目前，参考文献 1 包含了更为完整和严格的材料。

　　针对示例方程（3），图 4 给出了这种"极为美丽的分岔现象" [22]。无论怎样着力强调下列事实都不过分：这一过程对于绝大多数具有一个陡度可调的单峰函数 $F(X)$ 来说是普遍适用的。梅特罗波利斯等 [16] 将这种周期为 $2^n$ 的循环谱系称为不动点 $X^*$ 的谐振。

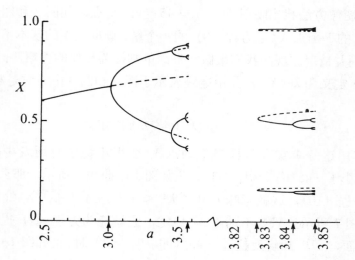

Fig. 4. This figure illustrates some of the stable (———) and unstable (- - - -) fixed points of various periods that can arise by bifurcation processes in equation (1) in general, and equation (3) in particular. To the left, the basic stable fixed point becomes unstable and gives rise by a succession of pitchfork bifurcations to stable harmonics of period $2^n$; none of these cycles is stable beyond $a = 3.5700$. To the right, the two period 3 cycles appear by tangent bifurcation: one is initially unstable; the other is initially stable, but becomes unstable and gives way to stable harmonics of period $3 \times 2^n$, which have a point of accumulation at $a = 3.8495$. Note the change in scale on the $a$ axis, needed to put both examples on the same figure. There are infinitely many other such windows, based on cycles of higher periods.

Although this process produces an infinite sequence of cycles with periods $2^n$ ($n \rightarrow \infty$), the "window" of parameter values wherein any one cycle is stable progressively diminishes, so that the entire process is a convergent one, being bounded above by some critical parameter value. (This is true for most, but not all, functions $F(X)$: see equation (17) below.) This critical parameter value is a point of accumulation of period $2^n$ cycles. For equation (3) it is denoted $a_c$: $a_c = 3.5700...$

Beyond this point of accumulation (for example, for $a > a_c$ in equation (3)) there are an infinite number of fixed points with different periodicities, and an infinite number of different periodic cycles. There are also an uncountable number of initial points $X_0$ which give totally aperiodic (although bounded) trajectories; no matter how long the time series generated by $F(X)$ is run out, the pattern never repeats. These facts may be established by a variety of methods[1,4,20,22,29]. Such a situation, where an infinite number of different orbits can occur, has been christened "chaotic" by Li and Yorke[20].

As the parameter increases beyond the critical value, at first all these cycles have even periods, with $X_t$ alternating up and down between values above, and values below, the fixed point $X^*$. Although these cycles may in fact be very complicated (having a non-degenerate period of, say, 5,726 points before repeating), they will seem to the casual observer to be rather like a somewhat "noisy" cycle of period 2. As the parameter value continues to increase, there comes a stage (at $a = 3.6786..$ for equation (3)) at which the first odd period

696

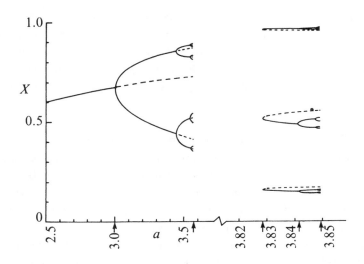

图 4. 此图显示出若干不同周期的稳定的（——）和不稳定的（- - - -）不动点，在一般情况下，它们可以由方程（1）的分岔过程产生，此图是由方程（3）产生。在左边，基本的稳定不动点变得不稳定，从而产生一连串的叉状分岔，形成周期为 $2^n$ 的稳定谐振；超过 $a = 3.5700$ 后，这些循环都不稳定。在右边，通过切分岔出现两个周期为 3 的循环：一个最初就是不稳定的，另一个最初是稳定的，但是逐渐变得不稳定并且让位于周期 $3 \times 2^n$ 的稳定谐振，这些周期以 $a = 3.8495$ 作为累加点。注意 $a$ 轴上有标度的变化，这是为了将两个例子置于同一图中。这样的窗口还有无限多个，它们源于周期更高的其他循环。

　　尽管该过程产生出一个具有周期 $2^n$（$n \to \infty$）的无限循环序列，任一循环的参数范围的"窗口"却是稳定地逐渐减小，致使整个过程是收敛的，其上边界由某个临界参数值所确定（这对形如后面的方程（17）的绝大多数函数 $F(X)$ 都成立，但并非全部）。这一临界参数值是周期为 $2^n$ 的各循环累加点。对于方程（3），将它记为 $a_c$，$a_c = 3.5700\cdots$。

　　超过这个累加点后（如在方程（3）中就是 $a > a_c$），有无限多个具有不同周期性的不动点和无限多个不同的周期性循环。另外还有无数个初始点 $X_0$，它们产生完全非周期性的（尽管是有界的）轨道。无论 $F(X)$ 所产生的时间序列持续多久，其模式都绝不重复。这些事实可以通过若干种方法加以确定 [1,4,20,22,29]。对于这种能够出现无限多个不同轨道的情形，李和约克 [20] 称之为"混沌的"。

　　当参数增加到超过临界值后，开始时全部循环都具有偶数周期，$X_t$ 在不动点 $X^*$ 上方和下方的数值间振荡。尽管这些循环实际上可能是非常复杂的（如每次重复一个 5,726 个点的非简并循环），但对于不认真的观测者来说，它们看起来在某种程度上更像是周期为 2 的"噪声"循环。随着参数值的持续增加，一个新阶段来临（对于方程（3），位于 $a = 3.6786\cdots$ 处），在这里出现了第一个周期为奇数的循环。开

cycle appears. At first these odd cycles have very long periods, but as the parameter value continues to increase cycles with smaller and smaller odd periods are picked up, until at last the three-point cycle appears (at $a=3.8284..$ for equation (3)). Beyond this point, there are cycles with every integer period, as well as an uncountable number of asymptotically aperiodic trajectories: Li and Yorke[20] entitle their original proof of this result "Period Three Implies Chaos".

The term "chaos" evokes an image of dynamical trajectories which are indistinguishable from some stochastic process. Numerical simulations[12,15,21,23,25] of the dynamics of equation (3), (4) and other similar equations tend to confirm this impression. But, for smooth and "sensible" functions $F(X)$ such as in equations (3) and (4), the underlying mathematical fact is that for any specified parameter value there is one unique cycle that is stable, and that attracts essentially all initial points[22,29] (see ref. 4, appendix A, for a simple and lucid exposition). That is, there is one cycle that "owns" almost all initial points; the remaining infinite number of other cycles, along with the asymptotically aperiodic trajectories, own a set of points which, although uncountable, have measure zero.

As is made clear by Tables 3 and 4 below, any one particular stable cycle is likely to occupy an extraordinarily narrow window of parameter values. This fact, coupled with the long time it is likely to take for transients associated with the initial conditions to damp out, means that in practice the unique cycle is unlikely to be unmasked, and that a stochastic description of the dynamics is likely to be appropriate, in spite of the underlying deterministic structure. This point is pursued further under the heading "practical applications", below.

The main messages of this section are summarised in Table 1, which sets out the various domains of dynamical behaviour of the equations (3) and (4) as functions of the parameters, $a$ and $r$ respectively, that determine the severity of the nonlinear response. These properties can be understood qualitatively in a graphical way, and are generic to any well behaved $F(X)$ in equation (1).

We now proceed to a more detailed discussion of the mathematical structure of the chaotic regime for analytical functions, and then to the practical problems alluded to above and to a consideration of the behavioural peculiarities exhibited by non-analytical functions (such as those in the two right hand columns of Table 1).

始时这些奇循环具有极长的周期，但是随着参数值的持续增加，具有越来越小的奇数周期的循环逐渐凸现出来，直到最后出现三点循环（对于方程（3），位于 $a = 3.8284\cdots$ 处）。超过这一点，就会出现具有所有整数周期的循环，以及无数个渐近的非周期性轨道：李和约克 [20] 将他们对这一结果给出的初始证明称为"周期三意味着混沌"。

"混沌"这个词使人们产生了动力学轨道与某些随机过程不可区分的印象。对方程（3）、（4）以及其他类似方程的动力学的数值模拟 [12,16,21,23,25] 也倾向于支持这种印象。但是，对于诸如方程（3）和（4）中那样光滑而"正常的"函数 $F(X)$，根本性的数学事实是对于任意特定的参数值，只存在唯一的一个循环是稳定的，它实际上吸引了所有的初始点 [22,29]（一份简单而清晰的说明参见文献 4，附录 A）。也就是说，有一个循环"拥有"几乎所有的初始点，剩下的其他无限多个循环，以及那些渐近非周期性轨道，拥有一个尽管不可数但却测度为零的点集。

如同表 3 和表 4 所示，任意一个特定的稳定循环都应该占据一个极其狭窄的参数值窗口。这一事实结合与初始条件有关的暂态效果需长时间才能消除，意味着那个唯一循环实际上并不倾向于显露出来，因而对动力学的随机描述看起来是合适的，即使它是基于一个确定性的结构。后文在"实际应用"标题下将对这一点进行进一步说明（译注：实际上后面并没有一个叫作"实际应用"的标题，从具体内容来看，原作者所指的可能是"实际问题"一节）。

表 1 对本节主要信息进行了总结，它将方程（3）和（4）的动力学行为的各种情况分别视为参数 $a$ 和 $r$ 的函数，它们决定了非线性响应的强度。这些性质可以通过图像方法而定性地理解，并且对于方程（1）中任何行为良好的函数 $F(X)$ 都是普遍适用的。

现在我们要对解析函数就混沌区域中的数学结构进行更为详细的探讨，继而对上面涉及的实际问题加以讨论，并对非解析函数（如表 1 右侧两列中的函数）所呈现出的行为特性加以考察。

Table 1. Summary of the way various "single-hump" functions $F(X)$, from equation (1), behave in the chaotic region, distinguishing the dynamical properties which are generic from those which are not

| The function $F(X)$ of equation (1) | $aX(1-X)$ | $X \exp[r\,(1-X)]$ | $aX;$ if $X<\frac{1}{2}$ $a(1-X);$ if $X>\frac{1}{2}$ | $\lambda X;$ if $X<1$ $\lambda X^{1-b};$ if $X>1$ |
|---|---|---|---|---|
| Tunable parameter | $a$ | $r$ | $a$ | $b$ |
| Fixed point becomes unstable | 3.0000 | 2.0000 | 1.0000* | 2.0000 |
| "Chaotic" region begins [point of accumulation of cycles of period $2^n$] | 3.5700 | 2.6924 | 1.0000 | 2.0000 |
| First odd-period cycle appears | 3.6786 | 2.8332 | 1.4142 | 2.6180 |
| Cycle with period 3 appears [and therefore every integer period present] | 3.8284 | 3.1024 | 1.6180 | 3.0000 |
| "Chaotic" region ends | 4.0000† | ∞‡ | 2.000† | ∞‡ |
| Are there stable cycles in the chaotic region? | Yes | Yes | No | No |

* Below this $a$ value, $X=0$ is stable.

† All solutions are attracted to $-\infty$ for $a$ values beyond this.

‡ In practice, as $r$ or $b$ becomes large enough, $X$ will eventually be carried so low as to be effectively zero, thus producing extinction in models of biological populations.

## Fine Structure of the Chaotic Regime

We have seen how the original fixed point $X^*$ bifurcates to give harmonics of period $2^n$. But how do new cycles of period $k$ arise?

The general process is illustrated in Fig. 5, which shows how period 3 cycles originate. By an obvious extension of the notation introduced in equation (8), populations three generations apart are related by

$$X_{t+3} = F^{(3)}(X_t) \tag{11}$$

If the hump in $F(X)$ is sufficiently steep, the threefold iteration will produce a function $F^{(3)}(X)$ with 4 humps, as shown in Fig. 5 for the $F(X)$ of equation (3). At first (for $a<3.8284..$ in equation 3) the 45° line intersects this curve only at the single point $X^*$ (and at $X=0$), as shown by the solid curve in Fig. 5. As the hump in $F(X)$ steepens, the hills and valleys in $F^{(3)}(X)$ become more pronounced, until simultaneously the first two valleys sink and the final hill rises to touch the 45° line, and then to intercept it at 6 new points, as shown by the dashed curve in Fig. 5. These 6 points divide into two distinct three-point cycles. As can be made plausible by imagining the intermediate stages in Fig. 5, it can be shown that the stability-determining slope of $F^{(3)}(X)$ at three of these points has a common value, which is $\lambda^{(3)} = +1$ at their birth, and thereafter steepens beyond $+1$; this period 3 cycle is never stable. The slope of $F^{(3)}(X)$ at the other three points begins at $\lambda^{(3)} = +1$, and

表 1. 对方程（1）中各种"单峰"函数 $F(X)$ 在混沌区域的行为方式的总结，区分出一般性的动力学性质与非一般性的动力学性质

| 方程（1）中的函数 $F(X)$ | $aX(1-X)$ | $X\exp[r(1-X)]$ | 若 $X<\frac{1}{2}$，$aX$<br>若 $X>\frac{1}{2}$，$a(1-X)$ | 若 $X<1$，$\lambda X$<br>若 $X>1$，$\lambda X^{1-b}$ |
|---|---|---|---|---|
| 可调参数 | $a$ | $r$ | $a$ | $b$ |
| 不动点变得不稳定 | 3.0000 | 2.0000 | 1.0000* | 2.0000 |
| "混沌"区域开始 [周期 $2^n$ 循环的累加点] | 3.5700 | 2.6924 | 1.0000 | 2.0000 |
| 第一个奇数周期循环出现 | 3.6786 | 2.8332 | 1.4142 | 2.6180 |
| 周期为 3 的循环出现 [于是任意整数周期存在] | 3.8284 | 3.1024 | 1.6180 | 3.0000 |
| "混沌"区域结束 | 4.0000† | ∞‡ | 2.000† | ∞‡ |
| 混沌区域中是否有稳定循环？ | 是 | 是 | 否 | 否 |

\* 在这个 $a$ 值以下，$X=0$ 是稳定的。

† 当 $a$ 值超过此值后，所有的解都被吸引到 $-\infty$。

‡ 事实上，当 $r$ 或 $b$ 变得足够大时，$X$ 将会变得非常小以致等价于 0，从而导致生物学种群模型中的灭绝。

## 混沌区域的精细结构

我们已经看到初始不动点 $X^*$ 是如何分岔而产生周期为 $2^n$ 的谐振的。但是，周期为 $k$ 的新循环是如何产生的呢？

图 5 中显示了一般性的过程，说明了周期为 3 的循环是如何产生的。通过对方程（8）中所用记号的一个明显推广，相隔三个世代的种群通过下列公式联系起来：

$$X_{t+3} = F^{(3)}(X_t) \tag{11}$$

如果 $F(X)$ 中的峰足够陡峭，三重迭代就会产生一个有 4 个峰的函数 $F^{(3)}(X)$，正如图 5 中所示的方程（3）中 $F(X)$ 所对应的情况。最初（对于方程（3）即为 $a<3.8284\cdots$ 时），45° 线与这条曲线只在唯一的 $X^*$ 处（以及 $X=0$ 处）相交，如同图 5 中用实线所表示的曲线。随着 $F(X)$ 中的峰变陡，$F^{(3)}(X)$ 中的峰和谷变得越来越显著，直到前两个谷下降以及最后一个峰升高至同时触及 45° 线，从而与该线交于 6 个新的点，如图 5 中虚线所示。这 6 个点分成 2 个不同的三点循环。通过想象图 5 中的过渡阶段即可明白，在上述点中的 3 个点处，$F^{(3)}(X)$ 具有相同的决定稳定性的斜率值，即刚产生时的 $\lambda^{(3)}=+1$，之后变得陡峭超过 +1；这个周期为 3 的循环是不稳定的。$F^{(3)}(X)$ 在其他 3 个点处的斜率由 $\lambda^{(3)}=+1$ 开始，随后便向 0 减少，最终结果是一个周期为

then decreases towards zero, resulting in a stable cycle of period 3. As $F(X)$ continues to steepen, the slope $\lambda^{(3)}$ for this initially stable three-point cycle decreases beyond $-1$; the cycle becomes unstable, and gives rise by the bifurcation process discussed in the previous section to stable cycles of period 6, 12, 24, ..., $3{\times}2^n$. This birth of a stable and unstable pair of period 3 cycles, and the subsequent harmonics which arise as the initially stable cycle becomes unstable, are illustrated to the right of Fig. 4.

There are, therefore, two basic kinds of bifurcation processes[1,4] for first order difference equations. Truly new cycles of period $k$ arise in pairs (one stable, one unstable) as the hills and valleys of higher iterates of $F(X)$ move, respectively, up and down to intercept the 45° line, as typified by Fig. 5. Such cycles are born at the moment when the hills and valleys become tangent to the 45° line, and the initial slope of the curve $F^{(k)}$ at the points is thus $\lambda^{(k)} = +1$: this type of bifurcation may be called[1,4] a tangent bifurcation or a $\lambda = +1$ bifurcation. Conversely, an originally stable cycle of period $k$ may become unstable as $F(X)$ steepens. This happens when the slope of $F^{(k)}$ at these period $k$ points steepens beyond $\lambda^{(k)} = -1$, whereupon a new and initially stable cycle of period $2k$ is born in the way typified by Figs 2 and 3. This type of bifurcation may be called a pitchfork bifurcation (borrowing an image from the left hand side of Fig. 4) or a $\lambda = -1$ bifurcation[1,4].

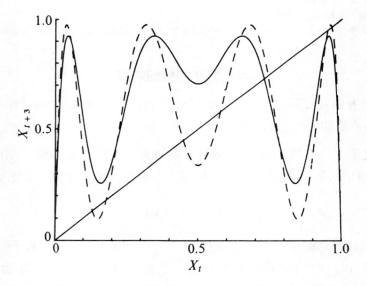

Fig. 5. The relationship between $X_{t+3}$ and $X_t$, obtained by three iterations of equation (3). The solid curve is for $a = 3.7$, and only intersects the 45° line once. As $a$ increases, the hills and valleys become more pronounced. The dashed curve is for $a=3.9$, and six new period 3 points have appeared (arranged as two cycles, each of period 3).

3 的稳定循环。随着 $F(X)$ 持续倾斜，这一初始稳定三点循环的斜率 $\lambda^{(3)}$ 下降至低于 $-1$；循环变得不稳定，并且通过前一节中所讨论的分岔过程而形成具有周期 6，12，24，$\cdots$，$3 \times 2^n$ 的稳定循环。这对周期为 3 的稳定和不稳定循环的产生以及随后由初始稳定循环变得不稳定而导致的谐振的产生，如图 4 的右方所示。

　　因此，对于一阶差分方程而言，存在着两个基本类型的分岔过程 [1,4]。随着 $F(X)$ 较高次迭代的峰和谷分别上下运动而与 45° 线相交，周期为 $k$ 的真正的新循环成对产生（一个稳定，一个不稳定），正如图 5 所代表的。这些循环产生于峰和谷逐渐变成与 45° 线相切的时刻，因而 $F^{(k)}$ 曲线在那些点处的初始斜率就是 $\lambda^{(k)} = +1$：这种类型的分岔可以称为 [1,4] 切分岔或者 $\lambda = +1$ 分岔。反过来，一个周期为 $k$ 的初始稳定循环也可以随着 $F(X)$ 变陡峭而变得不稳定。这发生在周期为 $k$ 的各点处的 $F^{(k)}$ 斜率倾斜到超过 $\lambda^{(k)} = -1$ 时，于是一个新的周期为 $2k$ 的初始稳定循环就产生了，图 2 和图 3 是此方式特征的典型描述。这种类型的分岔可以称为叉形分岔（借用图 4 左边的图像来说明），或称为 $\lambda = -1$ 分岔 [1,4]。

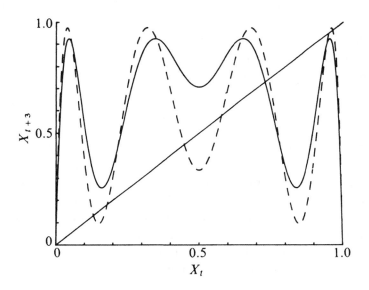

图 5. 通过方程（3）的三次迭代而得到 $X_{t+3}$ 与 $X_t$ 之间的关系。用实线画出的曲线对应于 $a = 3.7$，并且只与 45° 线相交一次。随着 $a$ 增大，峰和谷变得更为显著。用虚线画出的曲线对应于 $a = 3.9$，出现了 6 个新的周期为 3 的点（分布于 2 个周期为 3 的循环）。

Putting all this together, we conclude that as the parameters in $F(X)$ are varied the fundamental, stable dynamical units are cycles of basic period $k$, which arise by tangent bifurcation, along with their associated cascade of harmonics of periods $k2^n$, which arise by pitchfork bifurcation. On this basis, the constant equilibrium solution $X^*$ and the subsequent hierarchy of stable cycles of periods $2^n$ is merely a special case, albeit a conspicuously important one (namely $k = 1$), of a general phenomenon. In addition, remember[1,4,22,29] that for sensible, analytical functions (such as, for example, those in equations (3) and (4)) there is a unique stable cycle for each value of the parameter in $F(X)$. The entire range of parameter values ($1<a<4$ in equation (3), $0<r$ in equation (4)) may thus be regarded as made up of infinitely many windows of parameter values—some large, some unimaginably small—each corresponding to a single one of these basic dynamical units. Tables 3 and 4, below, illustrate this notion. These windows are divided from each other by points (the points of accumulation of the harmonics of period $k2^n$) at which the system is truly chaotic, with no attractive cycle: although there are infinitely many such special parameter values, they have measure zero on the interval of all values.

How are these various cycles arranged along the interval of relevant parameter values? This question has to my knowledge been answered independently by at least 6 groups of people, who have seen the problem in the context of combinatorial theory[18,30], numerical analysis[13,14], population biology[1], and dynamical systems theory[22,31] (broadly defined).

A simple-minded approach (which has the advantage of requiring little technical apparatus, and the disadvantage of being rather clumsy) consists of first answering the question, how many period $k$ points can there be? That is, how many distinct solutions can there be to the equation

$$X^*_k = F^{(k)}(X^*_k)? \tag{12}$$

If the function $F(X)$ is sufficiently steeply humped, as it will be once the parameter values are sufficiently large, each successive iteration doubles the number of humps, so that $F^{(k)}(X)$ has $2^{k-1}$ humps. For large enough parameter values, all these hills and valleys will intersect the $45°$ line, producing $2^k$ fixed points of period $k$. These are listed for $k \leqslant 12$ in the top row of Table 2. Such a list includes degenerate points of period $k$, whose period is a submultiple of $k$; in particular, the two period 1 points ($X=0$ and $X^*$) are degenerate solutions of equation (12) for all $k$. By working from left to right across Table 2, these degenerate points can be subtracted out, to leave the total number of non-degenerate points of basic period $k$, as listed in the second row of Table 2. More sophisticated ways of arriving at this result are given elsewhere[13,14,16,22,30,31].

综上所述，我们得出结论：随着 $F(X)$ 中参数的改变，基本的稳定动力学单元是周期为 $k$ 的循环，由切分岔而产生，以及与其相伴随的周期为 $k2^n$ 的谐振级联，这一谐振由叉形分岔而产生。基于此，恒定的平衡解 $X^*$ 与随之而来的周期 $2^n$ 的稳定循环谱系仅仅是一般现象中的一种特殊情况，当然，很明显，它是一种重要的特殊情况（即 $k = 1$）。此外要记得 [1,4,22,29]，对于合理的、解析的函数（如方程（3）和（4）中的那些函数）来说，对 $F(X)$ 中的每个参数值，存在唯一的稳定循环。因此，可以将参数值可取的整个范围（方程（3）中的 $1 < a < 4$，方程（4）中的 $0 < r$）看作由无限多个参数值窗口组成——一些窗口较大，一些窗口则小到难以想象——每个窗口都恰好对应于一个上述基本动力学单元。下文中的表 3 和表 4 对这一情况进行了说明。这些窗口被各个点（周期为 $k2^n$ 的谐振的累加点）分隔开，在这些点处，系统处于真正的混沌状态，没有任何有吸引能力的循环：尽管有无限多个这样的特殊参数值，它们在全部可取值的区间上的测度却是零。

这些各式各样的循环在相关参数值的区间中是如何分布的呢？就我所知，至少有 6 组人曾经独立地回答过这个问题，他们曾经在组合论 [18,30]、数值分析 [13,14]、种群生物学 [1] 以及（广义的）动力系统理论 [22,31] 等不同背景下审视过这个问题。

一种简单的方法（优点是不需要技术性工具，缺点是过于粗略）是，首先要回答下面的问题：可以有多少个周期为 $k$ 的点？也就是说，方程

$$X^*_k = F^{(k)}(X^*_k)? \tag{12}$$

可以有多少个不同的解？如果函数 $F(X)$ 具有充分陡峭的峰，正如当参数值充分大时它将会呈现出的那样，每次相继的迭代都会使峰的数目加倍，因此，$F^{(k)}(X)$ 有 $2^{k-1}$ 个峰。对于足够大的参数值，所有这些峰和谷都会与 45° 线相交，产生 $2^k$ 个周期为 $k$ 的不动点。它们被列于表 2 首行中 $k \leqslant 12$ 的范围内。表 2 中包含周期为 $k$ 的简并点，其周期是 $k$ 的一个因数；特别地，两个周期为 1 的点（$X = 0$ 和 $X^*$）对于所有的 $k$ 来说都是方程（12）的简并解。从左到右横贯表 2 进行处理，可以将这些简并点全部去掉，保留基本周期为 $k$ 的非简并点的总数，列于表 2 的第二行中。其他一些地方 [13,14,16,22,30,31] 给出了获得这一结果的更为准确的方法。

Table 2. Catalogue of the number of periodic points, and of the various cycles (with periods $k = 1$ up to 12), arising from equation (1) with a single-humped function $F(X)$

| $k$ | 1 | 2 | 3 | 4 | 5 | 6 | 7 | 8 | 9 | 10 | 11 | 12 |
|---|---|---|---|---|---|---|---|---|---|---|---|---|
| Possible total number of points with period $k$ | 2 | 4 | 8 | 16 | 32 | 64 | 128 | 256 | 512 | 1,024 | 2,048 | 4,096 |
| Possible total number of points with non-degenerate period $k$ | 2 | 2 | 6 | 12 | 30 | 54 | 126 | 240 | 504 | 990 | 2,046 | 4,020 |
| Total number of cycles of period $k$, including those which are degenerate and/or harmonics and/or never locally stable | 2 | 3 | 4 | 6 | 8 | 14 | 20 | 36 | 60 | 108 | 188 | 352 |
| Total number of non-degenerate cycles (including harmonics and unstable cycles) | 2 | 1 | 2 | 3 | 6 | 9 | 18 | 30 | 56 | 99 | 186 | 335 |
| Total number of non-degenerate, stable cycles (including harmonics) | 1 | 1 | 1 | 2 | 3 | 5 | 9 | 16 | 28 | 51 | 93 | 170 |
| Total number of non-degenerate, stable cycles whose basic period is $k$ (that is, excluding harmonics) | 1 | – | 1 | 1 | 3 | 4 | 9 | 14 | 28 | 48 | 93 | 165 |

For example, there eventually are $2^6 = 64$ points with period 6. These include the two points of period 1, the period 2 "harmonic" cycle, and the stable and unstable pair of triplets of points with period 3, for a total of 10 points whose basic period is a submultiple of 6; this leaves 54 points whose basic period is 6.

The $2^k$ period $k$ points are arranged into various cycles of period $k$, or submultiples thereof, which appear in succession by either tangent or pitchfork bifurcation as the parameters in $F(X)$ are varied. The third row in Table 2 catalogues the total number of distinct cycles of period $k$ which so appear. In the fourth row[14], the degenerate cycles are subtracted out, to give the total number of non-degenerate cycles of period $k$: these numbers must equal those of the second row divided by $k$. This fourth row includes the (stable) harmonics which arise by pitchfork bifurcation, and the pairs of stable-unstable cycles arising by tangent bifurcation. By subtracting out the cycles which are unstable from birth, the total number of possible stable cycles is given in row five; these figures can also be obtained by less pedestrian methods[13,16,30]. Finally we may subtract out the stable cycles which arise by pitchfork bifurcation, as harmonics of some simpler cycle, to arrive at the final row in Table 2, which lists the number of stable cycles whose basic period is $k$.

Returning to the example of period 6, we have already noted the five degenerate cycles whose periods are submultiples of 6. The remaining 54 points are parcelled out into one cycle of period 6 which arises as the harmonic of the only stable three-point cycle, and four distinct pairs of period 6 cycles (that is, four initially stable ones and four unstable ones) which arise by successive tangent bifurcations. Thus, reading from the foot of the column for period 6 in Table 2, we get the numbers 4, 5, 9, 14.

Using various labelling tricks, or techniques from combinatorial theory, it is also possible to give a generic list of the order in which the various cycles appear[1,13,16,22]. For example, the basic stable cycles of periods 3, 5, 6 (of which there are respectively 1, 3, 4) must appear in

表 2. 周期点数目，以及由具有一个单峰函数 $F(X)$ 的方程（1）所产生的各种循环
（周期 $k$=1，2，…，12）的列表

| $k$ | 1 | 2 | 3 | 4 | 5 | 6 | 7 | 8 | 9 | 10 | 11 | 12 |
|---|---|---|---|---|---|---|---|---|---|---|---|---|
| 具有周期 $k$ 的点的可能总数 | 2 | 4 | 8 | 16 | 32 | 64 | 128 | 256 | 512 | 1,024 | 2,048 | 4,096 |
| 具有非简并周期 $k$ 的点的可能总数 | 2 | 2 | 6 | 12 | 30 | 54 | 126 | 240 | 504 | 990 | 2,046 | 4,020 |
| 周期为 $k$ 的循环的总数，包括简并的和（或）谐振的和（或）没有任何局部是稳定的情况 | 2 | 3 | 4 | 6 | 8 | 14 | 20 | 36 | 60 | 108 | 188 | 352 |
| 非简并循环的总数（包括谐振和不稳定循环） | 2 | 1 | 2 | 3 | 6 | 9 | 18 | 30 | 56 | 99 | 186 | 335 |
| 非简并的稳定循环的总数（包括谐振） | 1 | 1 | 1 | 2 | 3 | 5 | 9 | 16 | 28 | 51 | 93 | 170 |
| 基本周期为 $k$ 的非简并稳定循环的总数（即不包括谐振） | 1 | – | 1 | 1 | 3 | 4 | 9 | 14 | 28 | 48 | 93 | 165 |

例如，最终会有 $2^6 = 64$ 个周期为 6 的点，其中包括两个周期为 1 的点、周期为 2 的"谐振"循环，以及一对周期为 3 的三点组（一个稳定和一个不稳定），总共有 10 个以 6 的一个因数为基本周期的点，还剩下 54 个基本周期为 6 的点。

周期为 $k$ 的 $2^k$ 个点分布于周期为 $k$ 或其因数的各个循环之中，后者随着 $F(X)$ 中参数的变化通过切分岔或者叉形分岔而相继出现。表 2 中的第三行列出了所出现的周期为 $k$ 的不同循环总数。在第四行中 [14]，简并循环被去掉，给出了周期为 $k$ 的非简并循环总数：这些数必然等于第二行中的那些数除以 $k$ 所得的商。第四行中包括由叉形分岔而产生的（稳定）谐振，以及由切分岔所产生的稳定–不稳定循环对。通过除去从一出现就不稳定的那些循环，第五行中给出了可能的稳定循环的总数；利用不太平庸的方法也可以得到这些数字 [13,16,30]。最后，我们可以去除由叉形分岔所产生的那些稳定循环，如某些较简单循环的谐振，而得到表 2 中的最后一行，该行列出了基本周期为 $k$ 的稳定循环的数目。

回到周期为 6 的那个例子，我们已经注意到有以 6 的因数为周期的 5 个简并循环。其余 54 个点被分配到周期为 6 的循环的一个稳定的三点循环谐振及由相继的切分岔所产生 4 个不同的周期为 6 的循环对（即 4 个初始的稳定循环与 4 个不稳定循环）之中。于是从表 2 中周期为 6 的那一列的底部读起，我们得到了数据 4、5、9 和 14。

利用各种标记技巧，或者是来自于组合论的技术，还有可能给出关于各种循环出现顺序的一个一般性列表 [1,13,16,22]。例如，周期 3，5，6 的基本稳定循环（分别有 1 个、3 个和 4 个）必定以 6，5，3，5，6，6，5，6 的顺序出现，对照表 3 和表 4。

the order 6, 5, 3, 5, 6, 6, 5, 6: compare Tables 3 and 4. Metropolis *et al.*[16] give the explicit such generic list for all cycles of period $k \leqslant 11$.

Table 3. A catalogue of the stable cycles (with basic periods up to 6) for the equation

$$X_{t+1} = aX_t(1-X_t)$$

| Period of basic cycle | *a* value at which: | | Subsequent cascade of "harmonics" with period $k2^n$ all become unstable | Width of the range of *a* values over which the basic cycle, or one of its harmonics, is attractive |
| :---: | :---: | :---: | :---: | :---: |
| | Basic cycle first appears | Basic cycle becomes unstable | | |
| 1 | 1.0000 | 3.0000 | 3.5700 | 2.5700 |
| 3 | 3.8284 | 3.8415 | 3.8495 | 0.0211 |
| 4 | 3.9601 | 3.9608 | 3.9612 | 0.0011 |
| 5(*a*) | 3.7382 | 3.7411 | 3.7430 | 0.0048 |
| 5(*b*) | 3.9056 | 3.9061 | 3.9065 | 0.0009 |
| 5(*c*) | 3.99026 | 3.99030 | 3.99032 | 0.00006 |
| 6(*a*) | 3.6265 | 3.6304 | 3.6327 | 0.0062 |
| 6(*b*) | 3.937516 | 3.937596 | 3.937649 | 0.000133 |
| 6(*c*) | 3.977760 | 3.977784 | 3.977800 | 0.000040 |
| 6(*d*) | 3.997583 | 3.997585 | 3.997586 | 0.000003 |

Table 4. Catalogue of the stable cycles (with basic periods up to 6) for the equation

$$X_{t+1} = X_t \exp[r(1-X_t)]$$

| Period of basic cycle | *r* value at which: | | Subsequent cascade of "harmonics" with period $k2^n$ all become unstable | Width of the range of *r* values over with the basic cycle, or one of its harmonics, is attractive |
| :---: | :---: | :---: | :---: | :---: |
| | Basic cycle first appears | Basic cycle becomes unstable | | |
| 1 | 0.0000 | 2.0000 | 2.6924 | 2.6924 |
| 3 | 3.1024 | 3.1596 | 3.1957 | 0.0933 |
| 4 | 3.5855 | 3.6043 | 3.6153 | 0.0298 |
| 5(*a*) | 2.9161 | 2.9222 | 2.9256 | 0.0095 |
| 5(*b*) | 3.3632 | 3.3664 | 3.3682 | 0.0050 |
| 5(*c*) | 3.9206 | 3.9295 | 3.9347 | 0.0141 |
| 6(*a*) | 2.7714 | 2.7761 | 2.7789 | 0.0075 |
| 6(*b*) | 3.4558 | 3.4563 | 3.4567 | 0.0009 |
| 6(*c*) | 3.7736 | 3.7745 | 3.7750 | 0.0014 |
| 6(*d*) | 4.1797 | 4.1848 | 4.1880 | 0.0083 |

梅特罗波利斯等 [16] 对于所有周期 $k \leqslant 11$ 的循环给出了这样一个清晰的一般性列表。

表 3. 对应于方程 $X_{t+1} = aX_t(1-X_t)$ 的稳定循环的目录（基本周期直到 6 为止）

| 基本循环的周期 | 满足下列条件的 $a$ 值 | | 随后出现的具有周期 $k2^n$ 的"谐振"级联全都变得不稳定 | 使基本循环或它的某一个谐振成为吸引子的 $a$ 值范围的宽度 |
| | 基本循环首次出现 | 基本循环变得不稳定 | | |
|---|---|---|---|---|
| 1 | 1.0000 | 3.0000 | 3.5700 | 2.5700 |
| 3 | 3.8284 | 3.8415 | 3.8495 | 0.0211 |
| 4 | 3.9601 | 3.9608 | 3.9612 | 0.0011 |
| 5 (a) | 3.7382 | 3.7411 | 3.7430 | 0.0048 |
| 5 (b) | 3.9056 | 3.9061 | 3.9065 | 0.0009 |
| 5 (c) | 3.99026 | 3.99030 | 3.99032 | 0.00006 |
| 6 (a) | 3.6265 | 3.6304 | 3.6327 | 0.0062 |
| 6 (b) | 3.937516 | 3.937596 | 3.937649 | 0.000133 |
| 6 (c) | 3.977760 | 3.977784 | 3.977800 | 0.000040 |
| 6 (d) | 3.997583 | 3.997585 | 3.997586 | 0.000003 |

表 4. 对应于方程 $X_{t+1} = X_t \exp[r(1-X_t)]$ 的稳定循环的目录（基本周期到 6 为止）

| 基本循环的周期 | 满足下列条件的 $r$ 值 | | 随后出现的具有周期 $k2^n$ 的"谐振"级联全都变得不稳定 | 使基本循环或它的某一个谐振成为吸引子的 $r$ 值范围的宽度 |
| | 基本循环首次出现 | 基本循环变得不稳定 | | |
|---|---|---|---|---|
| 1 | 0.0000 | 2.0000 | 2.6924 | 2.6924 |
| 3 | 3.1024 | 3.1596 | 3.1957 | 0.0933 |
| 4 | 3.5855 | 3.6043 | 3.6153 | 0.0298 |
| 5 (a) | 2.9161 | 2.9222 | 2.9256 | 0.0095 |
| 5 (b) | 3.3632 | 3.3664 | 3.3682 | 0.0050 |
| 5 (c) | 3.9206 | 3.9295 | 3.9347 | 0.0141 |
| 6 (a) | 2.7714 | 2.7761 | 2.7789 | 0.0075 |
| 6 (b) | 3.4558 | 3.4563 | 3.4567 | 0.0009 |
| 6 (c) | 3.7736 | 3.7745 | 3.7750 | 0.0014 |
| 6 (d) | 4.1797 | 4.1848 | 4.1880 | 0.0083 |

As a corollary it follows that, given the most recent cycle to appear, it is possible (at least in principle) to catalogue all the cycles which have appeared up to this point. An especially elegant way of doing this is given by Smale and Williams[22], who show, for example, that when the stable cycle of period 3 first originates, the total number of other points with periods $k$, $N_k$, which have appeared by this stage satisfy the Fibonacci series, $N_k$=2, 4, 5, 8, 12, 19, 30, 48, 77, 124, 200, 323 for $k$=1, 2, …, 12: this is to be contrasted with the total number of points of period $k$ which will eventually appear (the top row of Table 2) as $F(X)$ continues to steepen.

Such catalogues of the total number of fixed points, and of their order of appearance, are relatively easy to construct. For any particular function $F(X)$, the numerical task of finding the windows of parameter values wherein any one cycle or its harmonics is stable is, in contrast, relatively tedious and inelegant. Before giving such results, two critical parameter values of special significance should be mentioned.

Hoppensteadt and Hyman[21] have given a simple graphical method for locating the parameter value in the chaotic regime at which the first odd period cycle appears. Their analytic recipe is as follows. Let $\alpha$ be the parameter which tunes the steepness of $F(X)$ (for example, $\alpha = a$ for equation (3), $\alpha = r$ for equation (4)), $X^*(\alpha)$ be the fixed point of period 1 (the nontrivial solution of equation (5)), and $X_{\max}(\alpha)$ the maximum value attainable from iterations of equation (1) (that is, the value of $F(X)$ at its hump or stationary point). The first odd period cycle appears for that value of $\alpha$ which satisfies[21,31]

$$X^*(\alpha) = F^{(2)}(X_{\max}(\alpha)) \tag{13}$$

As mentioned above, another critical value is that where the period 3 cycle first appears. This parameter value may be found numerically from the solutions of the third iterate of equation (1): for equation (3) it is[14] $a=1+\sqrt{8}$.

Myrberg[13] (for all $k \leqslant 10$) and Metropolis *et al.*[16]. (for all $k \leqslant 7$) have given numerical information about the stable cycles in equation (3). They do not give the windows of parameter values, but only the single value at which a given cycle is maximally stable; that is, the value of $a$ for which the stability-determining slope of $F^{(k)}(X)$ is zero, $\lambda^{(k)} = 0$. Since the slope of the $k$-times iterated map $F^{(k)}$ at any point on a period $k$ cycle is simply equal to the product of the slopes of $F(X)$ at each of the points $X^*_k$ on this cycle[1,8,20], the requirement $\lambda^{(k)} = 0$ implies that $X = A$ (the stationary point of $F(X)$, where $\lambda^{(1)} = 0$) is one of the periodic points in question, which considerably simplifies the numerical calculations.

For each basic cycle of period $k$ (as catalogued in the last row of Table 2), it is more interesting to know the parameter values at which: (1) the cycle first appears (by tangent bifurcation); (2) the basic cycle becomes unstable (giving rise by successive pitchfork bifurcations to a cascade of harmonics of periods $k2^n$); (3) all the harmonics become unstable (the point of accumulation of the period $k2^n$ cycles). Tables 3 and 4 extend the work of May and Oster[1], to give this numerical information for equations (3) and (4), respectively. (The points of accumulation are not ground out mindlessly, but are calculated

作为推论还可以知道，若给定最近出现的循环，就有可能（至少在原则上）列出到这一点为止所有已经出现过的循环。斯梅尔和威廉斯[22]给出了做到这一点的一种特别巧妙的方法。例如，他们指出，当周期为 3 的稳定循环最初产生时，在这一阶段出现的具有周期 $k$ 的其他各点的总数，$N_k$，满足斐波那契序列关系，即当 $k = 1$，2，$\cdots$，12 时，$N_k = 2$，4，5，8，12，19，30，48，77，124，200，323，这与随着 $F(X)$ 持续变陡峭而最终将出现的周期为 $k$ 的点的总数（表 2 的顶行）是不同的。

这种不动点的总数及其出现顺序的目录都是相对容易构造的。与此相反，对于任一特定的函数 $F(X)$，寻找使得任一循环或其谐振在其中稳定的参数值窗口的数值工作则是相对乏味而笨拙的。在给出这些结果之前，应该先谈谈两个具有特殊重要性的临界参数值。

霍彭施泰特和海曼[21]给出了一种简单的图像方法，能够确定第一个奇数周期循环在混沌区域中出现的参数值的位置。他们的分析方法如下：设 $\alpha$ 是调节 $F(X)$ 陡峭程度的参数（如在方程（3）中 $\alpha = a$，在方程（4）中 $\alpha = r$），$X^*(\alpha)$ 是周期为 1 的不动点（方程（5）的非平凡解），而 $X_{\max}(\alpha)$ 是通过方程（1）迭代所得到的最大值（也就是说，$F(X)$ 位于其峰值或平稳点处）。第一个奇数周期的循环当 $\alpha$ 值满足以下方程时出现[21,31]：

$$X^*(\alpha) = F^{(2)}(X_{\max}(\alpha)) \tag{13}$$

如同前面已经提到的，另一个临界值是周期为 3 的循环首次出现的位置。这个参数值可以从方程（1）三次迭代的解中通过数值方法得到。对于方程（3），它就是[14] $a = 1 + \sqrt{8}$。

迈尔伯格[13]（对于全部 $k \leqslant 10$）和梅特罗波利斯等[16]（对于全部 $k \leqslant 7$）给出了关于方程（3）中稳定循环的数值信息。他们没有给出参数值窗口，而是给出了使得一个给定循环最大程度稳定的单独值。也就是说，使得确定稳定性的 $F^{(k)}(X)$ 斜率为 0（$\lambda^{(k)} = 0$）的 $a$ 的值。由于 $k$ 次迭代映射 $F^{(k)}$ 的斜率在周期为 $k$ 的循环上的任意一点处都恰好等于在该循环上每个点 $X^*_k$ 处 $F(X)$ 斜率的乘积[1,8,20]，对 $\lambda^{(k)} = 0$ 的要求意味着 $X = A$（即 $F(X)$ 的平稳点，其中 $\lambda^{(1)} = 0$）是我们所讨论的周期点之一，这就在相当程度上简化了数值计算。

对于每个周期为 $k$ 的基本循环（如同表 2 最后一行中所列出的那样），更为有趣的是了解以下几种情况时的参数值：（1）循环首次出现（通过切分岔）；（2）基本循环变得不稳定（通过相继的叉形分岔导致周期为 $k2^n$ 的谐振级联的出现）；（3）所有的谐振都变得不稳定（周期为 $k2^n$ 的循环的累加点）。表 3 和表 4 中拓展了梅和奥斯特[1]的工作，从而分别给出了对应于方程（3）和（4）的数值信息。（累加点并不是不假思索地算出的，而是通过一种快速收敛迭代过程计算出来的，参见文献 1 中的

by a rapidly convergent iterative procedure, see ref. 1, appendix A.) Some of these results have also been obtained by Gumowski and Mira[32].

## Practical Problems

Referring to the paradigmatic example of equation (3), we can now see that the parameter interval $1<a<4$ is made up of a one-dimensional mosaic of infinitely many windows of $a$-values, in each of which a unique cycle of period $k$, or one of its harmonics, attracts essentially all initial points. Of these windows, that for $1<a<3.5700$ .. corresponding to $k = 1$ and its harmonics is by far the widest and most conspicuous. Beyond the first point of accumulation, it can be seen from Table 3 that these windows are narrow, even for cycles of quite low periods, and the windows rapidly become very tiny as $k$ increases.

As a result, there develops a dichotomy between the underlying mathematical behaviour (which is exactly determinable) and the "commonsense" conclusions that one would draw from numerical simulations. If the parameter $a$ is held constant at one value in the chaotic region, and equation (3) iterated for an arbitrarily large number of generations, a density plot of the observed values of $X_t$ on the interval 0 to 1 will settle into $k$ equal spikes (more precisely, delta functions) corresponding to the $k$ points on the stable cycle appropriate to this $a$-value. But for most $a$-values this cycle will have a fairly large period, and moreover it will typically take many thousands of generations before the transients associated with the initial conditions are damped out: thus the density plot produced by numerical simulations usually looks like a sample of points taken from some continuous distribution.

An especially interesting set of numerical computations are due to Hoppensteadt (personal communication) who has combined many iterations to produce a density plot of $X_t$ for each one of a sequence of $a$-values, gradually increasing from 3.5700 .. to 4. These results are displayed as a movie. As can be expected from Table 3, some of the more conspicuous cycles do show up as sets of delta functions: the 3-cycle and its first few harmonics; the first 5-cycle; the first 6-cycle. But for most values of $a$ the density plot looks like the sample function of a random process. This is particularly true in the neighbourhood of the $a$-value where the first odd cycle appears ($a=3.6786$ ..), and again in the neighbourhood of $a=4$: this is not surprising, because each of these locations is a point of accumulation of points of accumulation. Despite the underlying discontinuous changes in the periodicities of the stable cycles, the observed density pattern tends to vary smoothly. For example, as $a$ increases toward the value at which the 3-cycle appears, the density plot tends to concentrate around three points, and it smoothly diffuses away from these three points after the 3-cycle and all its harmonics become unstable.

I think the most interesting mathematical problem lies in designing a way to construct some approximate and "effectively continuous" density spectrum, despite the fact that the exact density function is determinable and is always a set of delta functions. Perhaps such techniques have already been developed in ergodic theory[33] (which lies at the foundations of statistical mechanics), as for example in the use of "coarse-grained observers". I do not know.

附录 A。)古莫夫斯基和米拉 [32] 也得到了部分上述结果。

## 实 际 问 题

参考方程 (3) 的典型实例，现在我们可以看到，参数区间 $1 < a < 4$ 是由无限多个 $a$ 值窗口的一维马赛克结构所组成的，每个窗口中都有唯一一个周期为 $k$ 的循环，或者是它的一个谐振，实质上吸引了所有的初始点。在这些窗口中，对于 $1 < a < 3.5700\cdots$，即对应于 $k = 1$，其谐振的窗口是目前为止最宽的也是最显著的。超过第一个累加点后，从表 3 中可以看到，这些窗口很狭窄，甚至对于极低周期的循环来说也是如此，并且随着 $k$ 的增加，窗口迅速变得很小。

因此，我们在基础数学行为（它完全是明确的）与人们从数值模拟中得出的"常识"结论之间建立了分界。如果参数 $a$ 在混沌区域中保持为某一恒定值，并且将方程 (3) 对于任意大的代数进行迭代，$X_t$ 在 0 到 1 区间上的观测值的密度图将会有 $k$ 个相同的峰值（更确切地说，是 $\delta$ 函数），对应于适合该 $a$ 值的稳定循环上的 $k$ 个点。但是对于大多数 $a$ 值而言，这个循环会具有一个相当大的周期。不仅如此，它通常还会历经数以千计个迭代才能使与初始条件有关的暂态消除。因此，通过数值模拟而产生的密度图通常看起来像是来自某些连续分布的点的样本。

有一组特别值得关注的数值计算应归功于霍彭施泰特（个人交流），他将很多迭代组合起来，对从 $3.5700\cdots$ 逐渐增加到 4 的一系列 $a$ 值中的每一个值，产生一个 $X_t$ 的密度图，这些结果如同电影般呈现出来。如同从表 3 中可以预期的那样，某些更为显著的循环实际上显示为一系列的 $\delta$ 函数：3– 循环及其前几个谐振；第一个 5– 循环；第一个 6– 循环。但是对于大多数 $a$ 值，密度图看起来就像一个随机过程的样本函数。在第一个奇数循环出现处的 $a$ 值（$a = 3.6786\cdots$）的邻域中，这一点尤为真实，在 $a = 4$ 的邻域中也是如此：这并不令人惊讶，因为在这些位置中，每个都是累加点。尽管稳定循环的周期性质的实质是不连续变化，但是观测到的密度图倾向于光滑变化。例如，随着 $a$ 向出现 3– 循环的数值方向增加，密度图倾向于在三个点附近聚集，并且在 3– 循环之后从这三个点处光滑地扩散开，并且其所有的谐振也变得不稳定。

我认为最有趣的数学问题莫过于设计一种方法来构造某种近似而又"有效连续的"密度谱，尽管精确的密度函数是确定性的，并且总是一系列 $\delta$ 函数。可能在各态历经理论 [33] 中已经有了这样一种技术（建立在统计力学的基础上），如利用"粗粒化观测者"的实例。我并不了解。

Such an effectively stochastic description of the dynamical properties of equation (4) for large $r$ has been provided[28], albeit by tactical tricks peculiar to that equation rather than by any general method. As $r$ increases beyond about 3, the trajectories generated by this equation are, to an increasingly good approximation, almost periodic with period $(1/r) \exp(r-1)$.

The opinion I am airing in this section is that although the exquisite fine structure of the chaotic regime is mathematically fascinating, it is irrelevant for most practical purposes. What seems called for is some effectively stochastic description of the deterministic dynamics. Whereas the various statements about the different cycles and their order of appearance can be made in generic fashion, such stochastic description of the actual dynamics will be quite different for different $F(X)$: witness the difference between the behaviour of equation (4), which for large $r$ is almost periodic "outbreaks" spaced many generations apart, versus the behaviour of equation (3), which for $a \to 4$ is not very different from a series of Bernoulli coin flips.

## Mathematical Curiosities

As discussed above, the essential reason for the existence of a succession of stable cycles throughout the "chaotic" regime is that as each new pair of cycles is born by tangent bifurcation (see Fig. 5), one of them is at first stable, by virtue of the way the smoothly rounded hills and valleys intercept the 45° line. For analytical functions $F(X)$, the only parameter values for which the density plot or "invariant measure" is continuous and truly ergodic are at the points of accumulation of harmonics, which divide one stable cycle from the next. Such exceptional parameter values have found applications, for example, in the use of equation (3) with $a = 4$ as a random number generator[34,35]: it has a continuous density function proportional to $[X(1-X)]^{-\frac{1}{2}}$ in the interval $0<X<1$.

Non-analytical functions $F(X)$ in which the hump is in fact a spike provide an interesting special case. Here we may imagine spikey hills and valleys moving to intercept the 45° line in Fig. 5, and it may be that both the cycles born by tangent bifurcation are unstable from the outset (one having $\lambda^{(k)}>1$, the other $\lambda^{(k)}<-1$), for all $k>1$. There are then no stable cycles in the chaotic regime, which is therefore literally chaotic with a continuous and truly ergodic density distribution function.

One simple example is provided by

$$X_{t+1} = aX_t; \text{ if } X_t < \frac{1}{2}$$
$$X_{t+1} = a(1-X_t); \text{ if } X_t > \frac{1}{2} \tag{14}$$

defined on the interval $0<X<1$. For $0<a<1$, all trajectories are attracted to $X=0$; for $1<a<2$, there are infinitely many periodic orbits, along with an uncountable number of aperiodic trajectories, none of which are locally stable. The first odd period cycle appears at $a=\sqrt{2}$, and all integer periods are represented beyond $a= (1+\sqrt{5})/2$. Kac[36] has given a careful discussion of the case $a=2$. Another example, this time with an extensive biological

当 $r$ 很大时，已经能对方程（4）的动力学性质提供一种有效的随机描述 [28]，不过所使用的处理技巧仅限于这个方程而不是任意的一般方法。随着 $r$ 的增加，大约超过 3 时，由该方程所产生的轨道，在越来越好的近似意义上，几乎是周期性的，其周期为 $(1/r) \exp(r-1)$。

我在本节中要发表的观点是，尽管混沌区域中新颖的精细结构在数学上是令人着迷的，但它与大多数实际用途没有关系。看来下一步要做的是对确定性动力学系统给出一种有效的随机描述。虽然可以用一般性的方式来对不同循环及其出现顺序进行各种叙述，对于不同的 $F(X)$，实际动力学给出的这种随机描述将会大不相同：可以对比方程（4）与方程（3）的行为之间的差异作为证据。前者对于大的 $r$ 几乎是周期性的"爆发"，将很多个代分隔开；后者当 $a \to 4$ 时与伯努利抛币序列没有什么区别。

## 数学方面的好奇心

如同前面已讨论的，贯穿混沌区域的稳定循环序列存在的本质的原因是，当每次通过切分岔而新生成一对循环时（见图 5），其中一个开始时是稳定的，由光滑的峰和谷与 45° 线相交而产生。对于解析函数 $F(X)$，仅有的能够使密度图或"不变测度"为连续并且真正遍历的参数值都位于谐振的累加点处，这些累加点将一个稳定循环与后一个循环分隔开。这些例外的参数值已经找到了用途，如当 $a = 4$ 时，使用方程（3）作为随机数生成器 [34,35]：在区间 $0 < X < 1$ 中，它具有与 $[X(1-X)]^{-\frac{1}{2}}$ 成正比的连续密度函数。

其峰实际上是一个尖峰的非解析函数 $F(X)$，提供了一种有趣的特殊情况。这里我们可以想象，尖锐的峰和谷移向 45° 线而与其相交，如图 5 所示，因而情况有可能是，对于所有的 $k > 1$，通过切分岔而产生的两个循环（一个 $\lambda^{(k)} > 1$，另一个 $\lambda^{(k)} < -1$）从一开始就都是不稳定的。于是在混沌区域中不存在稳定循环，这与混沌的字面意思相符，它具有连续和真正遍历的密度分布函数。

下面提供一个简单的实例：

$$\begin{aligned} 若\ X_t < \frac{1}{2}, \quad X_{t+1} = aX_t \\ 若\ X_t > \frac{1}{2}, \quad X_{t+1} = a(1-X_t) \end{aligned} \tag{14}$$

定义在区间 $0 < X < 1$ 上。当 $0 < a < 1$ 时，所有轨道都被吸引到 $X = 0$；当 $1 < a < 2$ 时，有无限多个周期性轨道，以及无数个非周期轨道，其中没有一个是局部稳定的。第一个奇数周期循环出现在 $a = \sqrt{2}$ 处，而所有的整数周期循环都位于超过 $a = (1 + \sqrt{5})/2$ 的地方。卡克 [36] 曾对于 $a = 2$ 的情况进行了细致的讨论。另一个实

pedigree[1-3], is the equation

$$X_{t+1} = \lambda X_t; \text{ if } X_t < 1 \tag{15}$$
$$X_{t+1} = \lambda X_t^{1-b}; \text{ if } X_t > 1$$

If $\lambda > 1$ this possesses a globally stable equilibrium point for $b < 2$. For $b > 2$ there is again true chaos, with no stable cycles; the first odd cycle appears at $b = (3 + \sqrt{5})/2$, and all integer periods are present beyond $b = 3$. The dynamical properties of equations (14) and (15) are summarised to the right of Table 2.

The absence of analyticity is a necessary, but not a sufficient, condition for truly random behaviour[31]. Consider, for example,

$$X_{t+1} = (a/2)X_t; \text{ if } X_t < \frac{1}{2} \tag{16}$$
$$X_{t+1} = aX_t(1-X_t); \text{ if } X_t > \frac{1}{2}$$

This is the parabola of equation (3) and Fig. 1, but with the left hand half of $F(X)$ flattened into a straight line. This equation does possess windows of $a$ values, each with its own stable cycle, as described generically above. The stability-determining slopes $\lambda^{(k)}$ vary, however, discontinuously with the parameter $a$, and the widths of the simpler stable regions are narrower than for equation (3): the fixed point becomes unstable at $a = 3$; the point of accumulation of the subsequent harmonics is at $a = 3.27..$; the first odd cycle appears at $a = 3.44..$; the 3-point cycle at $a = 3.67..$ (compare the first column in Table 1).

These eccentricities of behaviour manifested by non-analytical functions may be of interest for exploring formal questions in ergodic theory. I think, however, that they have no relevance to models in the biological and social sciences, where functions such as $F(X)$ should be analytical. This view is elaborated elsewhere[37].

As a final curiosity, consider the equation

$$X_{t+1} = \lambda X_t [1+X_t]^{-\beta} \tag{17}$$

This has been used to fit a considerable amount of data on insect populations[38,39]. Its stability behaviour, as a function of the two parameters $\lambda$ and $\beta$, is illustrated in Fig. 6. Notice that for $\lambda < 7.39$ .. there is a globally stable equilibrium point for all $\beta$; for $7.39$ .. $< \lambda < 12.50$ .. this fixed point becomes unstable for sufficiently large $\beta$, bifurcating to a stable 2-point cycle which is the solution for all larger $\beta$; as $\lambda$ increases through the range $12.50$ ..$< \lambda < 14.77$ .. various other harmonics of period $2^n$ appear in turn. The hierarchy of bifurcating cycles of period $2^n$ is thus truncated, and the point of accumulation and subsequent regime of chaos in not achieved (even for arbitrarily large $\beta$) until $\lambda > 14.77...$

例具有广阔的生物学背景 [1-3]，即方程

$$若\ X_t < 1, \quad X_{t+1} = \lambda\, X_t \tag{15}$$
$$若\ X_t > 1, \quad X_{t+1} = \lambda\, X_t^{1-b}$$

若 $\lambda > 1$，则当 $b < 2$ 时，具有全局稳定的平衡点。当 $b > 2$ 时，再次产生没有任何稳定循环的真正的混沌；第一个奇数周期循环出现在 $b = (3 + \sqrt{5})/2$ 处，而所有的整数周期循环则位于超过 $b = 3$ 的地方。表 2 右方对方程（14）和（15）的动力学性质进行了概括。

不具有解析性是一个真正的随机行为的必要非充分条件 [31]。例如，考虑

$$若\ X_t < \frac{1}{2}, \quad X_{t+1} = (a/2)X_t \tag{16}$$
$$若\ X_t > \frac{1}{2}, \quad X_{t+1} = aX_t(1-X_t)$$

这是方程（3）和图 1 中的抛物线，但是 $F(X)$ 的左半段变平而成为一条直线。如同前面的一般性描述，该方程确实具有 $a$ 值的窗口，并且每个窗口都有自己的稳定循环。但是，决定稳定性的斜率 $\lambda^{(k)}$ 随着参数 $a$ 而不连续地变化，因而较简单稳定区域的宽度就变得比方程（3）所对应的更狭窄。在 $a = 3$ 处，不动点变得不稳定；伴随谐振的累加点位于 $a = 3.27\cdots$ 处；第一个奇数周期循环出现在 $a = 3.44\cdots$ 处；3 点循环位于 $a = 3.67\cdots$ 处（对比表 1 的第一列）。

非解析函数表现出的种种行为上的异常，对于探索各态历经理论中的常规问题来说可能是有意义的。不过，我认为，它们与生物学和社会科学中的各种模型没有什么关系，在那些领域中，函数 $F(X)$ 应该是解析的。这一看法在别的地方 [37] 已有详述。

作为最后一个关注点，考虑方程

$$X_{t+1} = \lambda\, X_t\,[1+X_t]^{-\beta} \tag{17}$$

这一方程曾用来拟合相当大量的昆虫种群数据 [38,39]。作为两个参数 $\lambda$ 和 $\beta$ 的函数，它的稳定性行为如图 6 所示。注意到当 $\lambda < 7.39\cdots$ 时，对所有的 $\beta$ 都存在全局稳定的平衡点；当 $7.39\cdots < \lambda < 12.50\cdots$ 时，如果 $\beta$ 足够大，这个不动点将变得不再稳定，而是分岔成为一个稳定的 2 点循环，它是对于所有较大 $\beta$ 的解。随着 $\lambda$ 增大到 $12.50\cdots < \lambda < 14.77\cdots$，各种其他的周期为 $2^n$ 的谐振依次出现。于是周期为 $2^n$ 的分岔循环谱系被截断，而累加点与随后的混沌区域要到 $\lambda > 14.77\cdots$ 时才能得到（即使对于任意大的 $\beta$）。

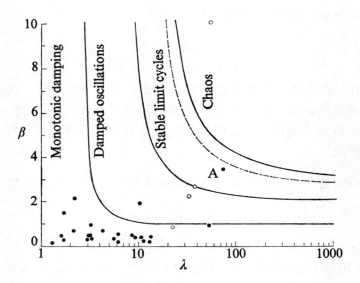

Fig. 6. The solid lines demarcate the stability domains for the density dependence parameter, $\beta$, and the population growth rate, $\lambda$, in equation (17); the dashed line shows where 2-point cycles give way to higher cycles of period $2^n$. The solid circles come from analyses of life table data on field populations, and the open circles from laboratory populations (from ref. 3, after ref. 39).

## Applications

The fact that the simple and deterministic equation (1) can possess dynamical trajectories which look like some sort of random noise has disturbing practical implications. It means, for example, that apparently erratic fluctuations in the census data for an animal population need not necessarily betoken either the vagaries of an unpredictable environment or sampling errors: they may simply derive from a rigidly deterministic population growth relationship such as equation (1). This point is discussed more fully and carefully elsewhere[1].

Alternatively, it may be observed that in the chaotic regime arbitrarily close initial conditions can lead to trajectories which, after a sufficiently long time, diverge widely. This means that, even if we have a simple model in which all the parameters are determined exactly, long term prediction is nevertheless impossible. In a meteorological context, Lorenz[15] has called this general phenomenon the "butterfly effect": even if the atmosphere could be described by a deterministic model in which all parameters were known, the fluttering of a butterfly's wings could alter the initial conditions, and thus (in the chaotic regime) alter the long term prediction.

Fluid turbulence provides a classic example where, as a parameter (the Reynolds number) is tuned in a set of deterministic equations (the Navier-Stokes equations), the motion can undergo an abrupt transition from some stable configuration (for example, laminar flow) into an apparently stochastic, chaotic regime. Various models, based on the Navier-Stokes differential equations, have been proposed as mathematical metaphors for this

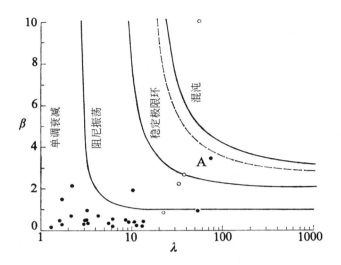

图 6. 实线划分了方程（17）中依赖于密度的参数 β 和种群增长速率 λ 构成的参数平面中的稳定区域；虚线显示了 2 点循环变成周期较高的 $2^n$ 循环的位置所在。实心圆来自于对野外种群生命统计表中数据的分析，而空心圆则来自于实验室中的种群（引自参考文献 3 和参考文献 39）。

## 应　用

　　简单而确定的方程（1）能够具有看起来像某种随机噪声一样的动力学轨道，这一事实具有令人困扰的实际意义。例如，从一个动物种群的普查数据中所具有的看似无规律的波动，不一定能断定它就是不可预测的环境异常或者采样误差造成的：它可能单纯地源于诸如方程（1）那样具有严格确定性的种群增长关系。我在其他地方对这一点进行了更为完整和细致的讨论[1]。

　　换言之，可以看到，混沌区域中任意相近的初始条件经过充分长的时间都能会进入相互偏离很远的轨道。这意味着，即使我们有一个简单模型，其中所有的参数都是精确确定的，但长期预测也是不可能的。在气象学研究背景下，洛伦茨[15]将这种普遍现象称为"蝴蝶效应"：即使可以用一个所有参数均为已知的确定模型来描述大气，一只蝴蝶翅膀的震颤就可能改变初始条件，从而（在混沌区域中）改变长期预测结果。

　　流体的湍流提供了一个经典实例，将一系列确定方程（纳维－斯托克斯方程组）中的一个参数（雷诺数）加以调节，流体运动就能够从某种稳定状态（如层流）发生突变而进入一个显然随机的、混沌的区域。作为对这一过程的数学隐喻，已经提出了很多种基于纳维－斯托克斯微分方程组的模型[15,40,41]。在最近一份关于湍流理论

process[15,40,41]. In a recent review of the theory of turbulence, Martin[42] has observed that the one-dimensional difference equation (1) may be useful in this context. Compared with the earlier models[15,40,41], it has the disadvantage of being even more abstractly metaphorical, and the advantage of having a spectrum of dynamical behaviour which is more richly complicated yet more amenable to analytical investigation.

A more down-to-earth application is possible in the use of equation (1) to fit data[1,2,3,38,39,43] on biological populations with discrete, non-overlapping generations, as is the case for many temperate zone arthropods. Figure 6 shows the parameter values $\lambda$ and $\beta$ that are estimated[39] for 24 natural populations and 4 laboratory populations when equation (17) is fitted to the available data. The figure also shows the theoretical stability domains: a stable point; its stable harmonics (stable cycles of period $2^n$); chaos. The natural populations tend to have stable equilibrium point behaviour. The laboratory populations tend to show oscillatory or chaotic behaviour; their behaviour may be exaggeratedly nonlinear because of the absence, in a laboratory setting, of many natural mortality factors. It is perhaps suggestive that the most oscillatory natural population (labelled $A$ in Fig. 6) is the Colorado potato beetle, whose present relationship with its host plant lacks an evolutionary pedigree. These remarks are only tentative, and must be treated with caution for several reasons. Two of the main caveats are that there are technical difficulties in selecting and reducing the data, and that there are no single species populations in the natural world: to obtain a one-dimensional difference equation by replacing a population's interactions with its biological and physical environment by passive parameters (such as $\lambda$ and $\beta$) may do great violence to the reality.

Some of the many other areas where these ideas have found applications were alluded to in the second section, above[5-11]. One aim of this review article is to provoke applications in yet other fields.

## Related Phenomena in Higher Dimensions

Pairs of coupled, first-order difference equations (equivalent to a single second-order equation) have been investigated in several contexts[4,44-46], particularly in the study of temperate zone arthropod prey—predator systems[2-4,23,47]. In these two-dimensional systems, the complications in the dynamical behaviour are further compounded by such facts as: (1) even for analytical functions, there can be truly chaotic behaviour (as for equations (14) and (15)), corresponding to so-called "strange attractors"; and (2) two or more different stable states (for example, a stable point and a stable cycle of period 3) can occur together for the same parameter values[4]. In addition, the manifestation of these phenomena usually requires less severe nonlinearities (less steeply humped $F(X)$) than for the one-dimensional case.

Similar systems of first-order ordinary differential equations, or two coupled first-order differential equations, have much simpler dynamical behaviour, made up of stable and unstable points and limit cycles[48]. This is basically because in continuous two-dimensional

的综述中，马丁[42]注意到一维差分方程（1）对于这个问题可能是有帮助的。与早先的模型[15,40,41]相比，它的不足在于其数学隐喻意义更为抽象，而其优势则是提供了一份动力学行为谱系，虽然更为复杂，但更适合于分析研究。

一个更为实际的应用是，有可能利用方程（1）来处理具有离散和非重叠世代的生物学种群数据[1,2,3,38,39,43]，如很多种温带节肢动物符合这种情况。图6显示了在用方程（17）处理可获得的数据时，对24个自然种群和4个实验室种群所估计出的参数λ和β[39]的值。图6中还显示了理论稳定性区域：一个稳定点；它的稳定谐振（周期为$2^n$的稳定循环）；混沌。自然种群倾向于具有稳定平衡点行为。实验室种群倾向于显示振荡的或混沌的行为；由于在实验室条件下，很多自然死亡因素的缺失，它们的行为可能会表现为夸张的非线性。这可能暗示了，最具振荡性质的自然种群（图6中标记为 A）是科罗拉多马铃薯甲虫，它与寄主植物的当前关系缺乏进化谱系。这些评述仅仅是假设性的，出于几方面原因的考虑，必须慎重地对待它们。有两个主要的提醒，即在选择和简化数据时存在技术性困难，且自然界不存在单一物种的种群：为了获得一个一维差分方程而将一个种群与其生物学环境和物理学环境之间的相互作用替换为被动参数（例如λ和β），这可能会严重违背现实情况。

上述观念还有很多其他的用武之地，上面第二节中也间接谈到了一些[5-11]。这篇综述文章的一个目的就是促进其在更多其他领域中的应用。

## 高维情况中的相关现象

很多对耦合的一阶差分方程（等价于一个二阶方程）已在若干背景中得到了研究[4,44-46]，特别是在对于温带节肢动物的猎物－捕食者系统的研究中[2-4,23,47]。在这些二维系统中，动力学行为的复杂性中还进一步添加了如下影响因素：(1) 即使对于解析函数，也可能存在真正的混沌行为（如方程（14）和（15）），对应于所谓的"奇异吸引子"；(2) 在同一组参数值下，可以出现两个或更多个不同的稳定状态（如一个稳定点和一个周期为3的稳定循环)[4]。此外，与一维情况相比，这些现象的出现通常只需要不那么显著的非线性性质（峰不是那么陡的 $F(X)$）。

类似的一阶常微分方程组，或者两个耦合的一阶微分方程组成的系统，具有更简单的动力学行为，包括稳定的和不稳定的点以及极限环[48]。这主要是因为在连续二维系统中，内部和外部的闭曲线是可区分的；动力学轨道不可能彼此交叉。当我

systems the inside and outside of closed curves can be distinguished; dynamic trajectories cannot cross each other. The situation becomes qualitatively more complicated, and in many ways analogous to first-order difference equations, when one moves to systems of three or more coupled, first-order ordinary differential equations (that is, three-dimensional systems of ordinary differential equations). Scanlon (personal communication) has argued that chaotic behaviour and "strange attractors", that is solutions which are neither points nor periodic orbits[48], are typical of such systems. Some well studied examples arise in models for reaction–diffusion systems in chemistry and biology[49], and in the models of Lorenz[15] (three dimensions) and Ruelle and Takens[40] (four dimensions) referred to above. The analysis of these systems is, by virtue of their higher dimensionality, much less transparent than for equation (1).

An explicit and rather surprising example of a system which has recently been studied from this viewpoint is the ordinary differential equations used in ecology to describe competing species. For one or two species these systems are very tame: dynamic trajectories will converge on some stable equilibrium point (which may represent coexistence, or one or both species becoming extinct). As Smale[50] has recently shown, however, for 3 or more species these general equations can, in a certain reasonable and well-defined sense, be compatible with any dynamical behaviour. Smale's[50] discussion is generic and abstract: a specific study of the very peculiar dynamics which can be exhibited by the familiar Lotka-Volterra equations once there are 3 competitors is given by May and Leonard[51].

## Conclusion

In spite of the practical problems which remain to be solved, the ideas developed in this review have obvious applications in many areas.

The most important applications, however, may be pedagogical.

The elegant body of mathematical theory pertaining to linear systems (Fourier analysis, orthogonal functions, and so on), and its successful application to many fundamentally linear problems in the physical sciences, tends to dominate even moderately advanced University courses in mathematics and theoretical physics. The mathematical intuition so developed ill equips the student to confront the bizarre behaviour exhibited by the simplest of discrete nonlinear systems, such as equation (3). Yet such nonlinear systems are surely the rule, not the exception, outside the physical sciences.

I would therefore urge that people be introduced to, say, equation (3) early in their mathematical education. This equation can be studied phenomenologically by iterating it on a calculator, or even by hand. Its study does not involve as much conceptual sophistication as does elementary calculus. Such study would greatly enrich the student's intuition about nonlinear systems.

们转向三个或更多个耦合的一阶常微分方程所构成的系统（即三维常微分方程组系统）时，情况在定性的意义上变得更为复杂了，而且在很多方面类似于一阶差分方程。斯坎伦（个人交流）主张，混沌行为和"奇异吸引子"（即既不是点也不是周期轨道的那些解）[48]）对于上述系统是典型的。一些获得充分研究的例子都来自于针对化学和生物学中的反应-扩散系统的模型 [49]，以及前面涉及的洛伦茨 [15] 的模型（三维）、吕埃勒和塔肯斯 [40] 的模型（四维）。这些系统的高维性质使得对于它们的分析比对方程（1）的分析显得更不明确。

最近有一个从这一视角对某一系统进行研究的清晰且相当令人感到吃惊的例子，即生态学中用来描述竞争物种的常微分方程组。对于一个或两个物种，这些系统是极为乏味的：动力学轨道在某些稳定平衡点上收敛（这可以表示为共存，或者是一个或两个物种趋于灭绝）。不过，正如斯梅尔 [50] 最近所指出的那样，从某种合理的并且恰当界定的意义上来讲，对于 3 个或更多个物种，这些一般性的方程能够与任何动力学行为相一致。斯梅尔 [50] 的讨论是一般性的和抽象的：梅和伦纳德 [51] 曾详细研究过在 3 个竞争者的情况下由我们所熟知的洛特卡-沃尔泰拉方程所呈现出来的不寻常的动力学行为。

## 结　论

尽管还有些实际问题有待于去解决，但本综述中所谈到的观念仍可以在很多领域中具有明显的应用。

不过，最重要的应用可能还是在教学方面。

数学理论中与线性系统有关的精巧内容（傅里叶分析、正交函数等）以及它们在物理科学中很多基本线性问题上的成功应用，倾向于使它们在大学高等数学和理论物理学课程中占有相当重要的地位。以这种方式训练而建立数学直觉的学生，对于诸如方程（3）那样最简单的离散、非线性系统所呈现出的奇特行为会感到不理解。但是这些非线性系统在物理科学之外确实是常见的，而不是例外。

因此，我强烈呼吁在数学教育的早期向所有人介绍诸如方程（3）那样的内容。这个方程可以通过计算器，甚至手算的方式，迭代进行唯象研究。对它的研究不像初等微积分那样涉及很多概念意义上的细微精妙。这样的学习将会大大丰富学生对于非线性系统的直觉。

Not only in research, but also in the everyday world of politics and economics, we would all be better off if more people realised that simple nonlinear systems do not necessarily possess simple dynamical properties.

I have received much help from F. C. Hoppensteadt, H. E. Huppert, A. I. Mees, C. J. Preston, S. Smale, J. A. Yorke, and particularly from G. F. Oster. This work was supported in part by the NSF.

(**261**, 459-467; 1976)

**Robert M. May**

King's College Research Centre, Cambridge CB2 1ST; on leave from Biology Department, Princeton University, Princeton 08540

References:

1. May, R. M., and Oster, G. F., *Am. Nat.,* **110** (in the press).

2. Varley, G. C., Gradwell, G. R., and Hassell, M. P., *Insect Population Ecology* (Blackwell, Oxford, 1973).

3. May, R. M. (ed.), *Theoretical Ecology: Principles and Applications* (Blackwell, Oxford, 1976).

4. Guckenheimer, J., Oster, G. F., and Ipaktchi, A., *Theor. Pop. Biol.* (in the press).

5. Oster, G. F., Ipaklchi, A., and Rocklin, I., *Theor, Pop. Biol.* (in the press).

6. Asmussen, M. A., and Feldman, M. W., *J. theor. Biol.* (in the press).

7. Hoppensteadt, F. C., *Mathematical Theories of Populations; Demographics, Genetics and Epidemics* (SIAM, Philadelphia, 1975).

8. Samuelson, P. A., *Foundations of Economic Analysis* (Harvard University Press, Cambridge, Massachusetts, 1947).

9. Goodwin, R. E., *Econometrica*, **19**, 1-17 (1951).

10. Baumol, W. J., *Economic Dynamics*, 3rd ed. (Macmillan, New York, 1970).

11. See, for example, Kemeny, J., and Snell, J. L., *Mathematical Models in the Social Sciences* (MIT Press, Cambridge, Massachusetts, 1972).

12. Chaundy, T. W., and Phillips, E., *Q. J. Math. Oxford*, 7, 74-80 (1936).

13. Myrberg, P. J., *Ann. Akad. Sc. Fennicae, A,* I, No. 336/3 (1963).

14. Myrberg, P. J., *Ann. Akad. Sc. Fennicae, A,* I, No. 259 (1958).

15. Lorenz, E. N., *J. Atmos. Sci.,* **20**, 130-141 (1963); *Tellus,* **16**, 1-11 (1964).

16. Metropolis, N., Stein, M. L., and Stein, P. R., *J. Combinatorial Theory,* **15**(A), 25-44 (1973).

17. Maynard Smith, J., *Mathematical Ideas in Biology* (Cambridge University Press, Cambridge, 1968).

18. Krebs, C. J., *Ecology* (Harper and Row, New York, 1972).

19. May, R. M., *Am. Nat.,* **107**, 46-57 (1972).

20. Li, T-Y., and Yorke, J. A., *Am. Math. Monthly,* **82**, 985-992 (1975).

21. Hoppensteadt, F. C., and Hyman, J. M. (Courant Institute, New York University: preprint, 1975).

22. Smale, S., and Williams, R. (Department of Mathematics, Berkeley: preprint, 1976).

23. May, R. M., *Science,* **186**, 645-647 (1974).

24. Moran, P. A. P., *Biometrics,* **6**,250-258 (1950).

25. Ricker, W. E., *J. Fish. Res. Bd. Can.,* **11**, 559-623 (1954).

26. Cook, L. M., *Nature,* **207**, 316 (1965).

27. Macfadyen, A., *Animal Ecology: Aims and Methods* (Pitman, London, 1963).

28. May, R. M., *J. theor. Biol.,* **51**, 511-524 (1975).

29. Guckenheimer, J., *Proc. AMS Symposia in Pure Math., XIV,* 95-124 (1970).

30. Gilbert, E. N., and Riordan, J., *Illinois J. Math.,* 5, 657-667 (1961).

31. Preston, C. J. (King's College, Cambridge: preprint, 1976).

32. Gumowski, I., and Mira, C., *C. r. hebd, Séanc. Acad. Sci., Paris,* **281a**, 45-48 (1975); **282a**, 219-222 (1976).

33. Layzer, D., *Sci. Am.,* **233**(6), 56-69(1975).

34. Ulam, S. M., *Proc. Int. Congr. Math. 1950, Cambridge, Mass.;Vol. II* . pp.264-273 (AMS, Providence R. I., 1950).

35. Ulam, S. M., and von Neumann, J., *Bull. Am. Math. Soc.* (abstr.), **53**, 1120 (1947).

不仅在研究中，而且在政治和经济领域的日常生活中，如果有更多的人认识到简单的非线性系统并不一定具有简单的动力学性质，那么我们就会生活得更加舒适。

霍彭施泰特、于佩尔、米斯、普雷斯顿、斯梅尔、约克，特别是奥斯特，给了我很大的帮助。本研究部分得到了美国国家科学基金会的支持。

（王耀杨 翻译；李典谟 审稿）

36. Kac, M., *Ann. Math.*, **47**,33-49 (1946).

37. May, R. M., *Science*, **181**, 1074 (1973).

38. Hassell, M. P., *J. Anim. Ecol.*, **44**, 283-296 (1974).

39. Hassell, M. P., Lawton, J. H., and May, R. M., *J. Anim. Ecol.* (in the press).

40. Ruelle, D., and Takens, F., *Comm. math. Phys.*,**20**, 167-192 (1971).

41. Landau, L. D., and Lifshitz, E. M., *Fluid Mechanics* (Pergamon, London, 1959).

42. Martin, P. C., *Proc. Int. Conf. On Statistical Physics, 1975, Budapest* (Hungarian Acad. Sci., Budapest, in the press).

43. Southwood, T. R. E., in *Insects, Science and Society* (edit. by Pimentel, D.), 151-199 (Academic, New York, 1975).

44. Metropolis, N., Stein, M. L., and Stein, P. R., *Numer. Math.,* **10**, 1-19 (1967).

45. Gumowski, I., and Mira, C., *Automatica*, **5**, 303-317 (1969).

46. Stein, P. R., and Ulam, S. M., *Rosprawy Mat.*, **39**, 1-66 (1964).

47. Beddington, J, R., Free, C. A., and Lawton, J, H., *Nature*, **255**, 58-60 (1975).

48. Hirsch, M, W., and Smale, S., *Differential Equations, Dynamical Systems and Linear Algebra* (Academic, New York, 1974).

49. Kolata, G. B., *Science*, **189**, 984-985 (1975).

50. Smale, S. (Department of Mathematics, Berkeley: preprint, 1976).

51. May, R. M., and Leonard, W. J., *SIAMJ. Appl. Math.*, **29**, 243-253 (1975).

# *Australopithecus, Homo erectus* and the Single Species Hypothesis

R. E. F. Leakey and A. C. Walker

## Editor's Note

**Human fossils found in Africa and representing the past three million years or so of human evolution appear to have existed in two distinguishable forms, one of which is heavy boned or "robust" and the other of which has more delicate bones and is called "gracile". This brief paper is a plea by Richard Leakey (Louis Leakey's son) and a Harvard colleague that palaeontologists should acknowledge the coexistence of two species of human beings over the past three million years. The robust species is assumed now to have disappeared.**

AN enormous wealth of early hominid remains has been discovered over the past few years by expeditions within eastern Africa. Evidence has been presented for the existence over a considerable period of time of at least two contemporaneous hominid species[1]. Some of this evidence is compelling, but some less so for a variety of reasons such as the lack of association, fragmentary specimens, geological uncertainties, equivocal anatomical differences and suchlike. Many of these new specimens are of great antiquity and have led to suggestions that an early form of the genus *Homo* was contemporary with at least one species of *Australopithecus*. The evidence presented here deals not with the earlier stages of human evolution, but with the unequivocal occurrence of *H. erectus* from the Koobi Fora Formation, east of Lake Turkana (formerly Lake Rudolf).

Among the variety of hypotheses put forward to accommodate the evidence in an evolutionary framework, the most explicit and directly simple is the single species hypothesis[2]. This hypothesis rests on the assumption that dependence upon tools was the primary hominid adaptation that enabled expansion into open country environments. In the clearest exposition of the hypothesis[3], basic hominid characteristics, including bipedal locomotion, reduced canines and delayed physical maturity are seen to have come about in response to more effective and greater dependence on culture. This assumption of a basic hominid cultural adaptation allied with the principle of competitive exclusion[4,5] leads to the conclusion that two or more hominid species would be extremely unlikely to exist sympatrically. Here we present decisive evidence that shows the existence of two contemporaneous hominid species in the Koobi Fora area.

The adult cranium KNM-ER 3733 (ref. 6) was found *in situ* in the upper member of the Koobi Fora Formation[7]. The sediments lie stratigraphically between the KBS and the Koobi Fora/ BBS tuff complexes. The cranium consists of a complete calvaria and a great deal of the facial skeleton, including the nasal and zygomatic bones. The nearly complete

# 南方古猿、直立人及单物种假说

利基，沃克

## 编者按

非洲发现的人类化石，代表了过去 300 万年左右的人类演化，他们似乎存在着两种显然不同的类型：其中一种的骨头粗壮厚重或称"粗壮型"，另一种的骨头纤细易碎，被称为"纤细型"。在这篇短文中，理查德·利基（路易斯·利基的儿子）与他的一个哈佛的同事认为，古生物学家应该承认过去的 300 万年中同时存在两种人类。其中的粗壮型现在认为已经消失了。

过去几年中，在东非进行的野外调查发现了很多早期人科动物的化石。有证据证明在相当长的一段时间内，在这里同时存在至少两种早期人科动物[1]。这类证据有些让人深信，但有些就不那么令人信服，原因各不相同，比如缺乏相关性，标本不完整，地质年代的不确定性，解剖学上的形态差异模棱两可，等等诸如此类。这些新标本中的很多都很古老，他们暗示人属的早期形式至少与一种南方古猿同时代。这里给出的证据讨论的不是早期人类的演化，而是真正出现在图尔卡纳湖（原名鲁道夫湖）以东库比福勒组的直立人。

在演化框架内针对化石证据提出的各种假说中，单物种假说最为明确和简单[2]。这个假说依赖于如下假设，早期人科动物面对环境作出的第一个适应性的调整就是对工具的依赖，这种调整使得早期人科动物能够向开阔环境扩散。该假说的一个很好的阐释[3]是，对文化更多更有效的依赖促使早期人科动物的一些基本特征发生了改变，包括直立行走、减小的犬齿尺寸以及生理成熟的推迟。这个基本的早期人科动物文化适应的假设与竞争排他原理[4,5]联系在一起，推导出以下结论，两种或更多种人科动物不可能有重叠的生活分布区。而在这里我们将提供确切证据表明在库比福勒地区同时生活着两个人科动物物种。

在库比福勒组上段的地层中就地发现了一个成年颅骨，编号 KNM-ER 3733(参考文献6)[7]。地层位置上，沉积物位于 KBS 与库比福勒/BBS 凝灰岩之间。颅骨包括齐全的头盖骨与大量面部骨骼（包括鼻骨与颧骨）。几乎完整的前部牙齿齿槽，前

alveoli of the anterior teeth and examples of the premolars and molars are preserved. The third molars were lost before fossilisation. Preparation has been limited so far to the external cranial surfaces and part of the brain case. An endocranial capacity is unknown, but by comparison is likely to be of the order of 800-900 ml. In all its features the cranium is strikingly like that of *H. erectus* from Peking[8]. Such orthodox anthropometric comparisons that can be made at present fall well within the range of the Peking specimens.

The cranium is large (glabella to inion/ opisthocranion is 183 mm) with large projecting supraorbital tori and little postorbital constriction (minimum postorbital breadth 91 mm). There is a marked postglabellar sulcus and the frontal squama rises steeply from behind it to reach vertex at bregma. The skull decreases in height from bregma and the occipital bears a pronounced torus where the occipital and nuchal planes are sharply angled. The greatest breadth is low at the angular torus (biauricular breadth 132 mm). There are strong temporal lines that are 60 mm apart at their nearest point. As far as can be judged at present, the vault bones are thick (about 10.0 mm in mid-parietal). The temporal fossae are small. The facial skeleton is partly preserved and shows deep and wide zygomatic portions, longitudinally concave and laterally convex projecting nasals and wide, low piriform aperture. The incisive alveolar plane is short and wide and the large incisive alveoli are set almost in a straight line. There are strong canine juga. The palate is high and roughly square in outline. The facial skeleton is flexed under the calvaria and in the preliminary reconstruction is set at about the same angle as that reconstructed for a female *H. erectus* by Weidenreich[8]. The prosthion to nasion length is 87 mm. This is the best preserved single *H. erectus* cranium known, the facial skeleton being more complete and less distorted than that of "Pithecanthropus VIII" (ref. 9).

Figures 1-3 show KNM-ER 3733 together with KNM-ER 406, another cranium discovered *in situ* in the Upper Member of the Koobi Fora Formation. This latter specimen has been described[10] in some detail and is clearly that of a robust *Australopithecus*. Other specimens of robust *Australopithecus* have been found in deposits of both the Upper and Lower members of the Koobi Fora Formation. Two *in situ* mandibles that must have been associated with this type of cranium are the most massive representatives of this species. KNM-ER 729 (ref. 1) was excavated in 1971 from the base of the Middle Tuff and KNM-ER 3230 (ref. 6) from the upper part of the BBS complex. Other, more incomplete, specimens of robust *Australopithecus* mandibles have come from the higher levels of the Formation between the Karari/ Chari and Koobi Fora/ BBS tuffs. The radioisotopic dating of these tuffs, in spite of a continuing controversy over one of them[11], is not an issue here. The contemporaneity of *Homo erectus* and a robust *Australopithecus* is now clearly established over the period during which the Upper Member of the Koobi Fora Formation was deposited. Using the time scale given by Fitch *et al.*[12], this would be from earlier than about 1.3 to earlier than 1.6 Myr ago.

臼齿和臼齿的样本也都保存了下来。第三臼齿在石化前就失去了。目前的修理准备工作还仅限于颅骨的外表面和部分大脑。颅容量尚属未知，但通过对比推测大概在800~900毫升之间。该颅骨的所有形态特征与周口店直立人[8]表现出惊人的相似。目前能从 KNM-ER 3733 上得到的传统的测量数据正好在周口店直立人标本变化范围之内。

该颅骨很大（从眉间点到枕外隆凸点/颅后点为 183 毫米），其眶上圆枕大而凸出，眶后缩狭不明显（最小眶后宽 91 毫米）。眉脊上沟明显，从其后，额骨倾斜并在前囟点达到最高。头骨的高度从前囟处开始降低，枕外圆枕发育，在此处，枕平面和项平面的过渡部分急剧转折。颅骨最大宽处位于角圆枕处（耳点间宽为 132毫米）。颞线粗重，两侧颞线最近距离 60 毫米。就目前的判断来看，颅顶厚（顶骨中央位置厚大约 10 毫米）。颞窝小。部分被保存下来的面部骨骼显示：颧骨深而宽；突出的鼻鼻骨纵向呈凹形；横向呈凸形；梨状孔宽而低。门齿齿槽平面短而宽，中央门齿齿槽几乎在一条直线上。有明显隆起的犬齿齿槽轭。上颌高，轮廓大体呈方形。颅顶以下面部骨骼变形，初步重构时角度大约与魏登瑞[8]重构的女性直立人的相同。上齿槽中点到鼻根点长 87 毫米。这是已知的保存得最好的单个直立人颅骨，与"爪哇直立猿人Ⅷ"相比，其面部骨骼更齐全，变形更小（参考文献 9）。

图 1~3 显示的是 KNM-ER 3733 与另外一个就地发现在库比福勒组的上段地层中的颅骨（KNM-ER 406）的对比情况。对后一标本进行过较为详细的描述[10]，很清楚它是属于粗壮型南方古猿的。在库比福勒组上下段的沉积物中都发现过其他的粗壮型南方古猿标本。就地出土的两件下颌骨很可能与这类颅骨相关联，组成这个种最有力的代表。KNM-ER 729（参考文献 1）是在 1971 年从中段凝灰岩的底部挖掘出来的，而 KNM-ER 3230（参考文献 6）是从 BBS 层上部挖掘出来的。其他不完整的粗壮型南方古猿下颌骨标本，来自于卡拉里/沙里与库比福勒/BBS 凝灰岩之间的较高层位。对这些凝灰岩的放射性同位素测年结果不再存在问题，尽管对其中一个凝灰岩层的测年结果一直争论不断[11]。现在可以肯定的是，在库比福勒组的上段沉积的这个时期内，直立人与粗壮型南方古猿同时存在。参考菲奇[12]等给出的地质年代表，该时期应该是从大约 130 万年前到 160 万年以前。

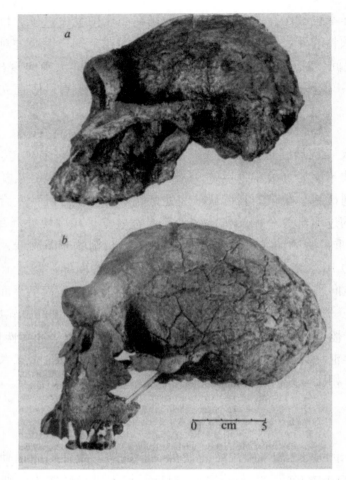

Fig. 1. Lateral aspect of KNM-ER 406 (*a*) and KNM-ER 3733 (*b*).

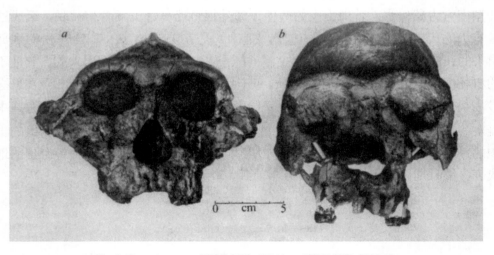

Fig. 2. Frontal aspect of KNM-ER 406 (*a*) and KNM-ER 3733 (*b*).

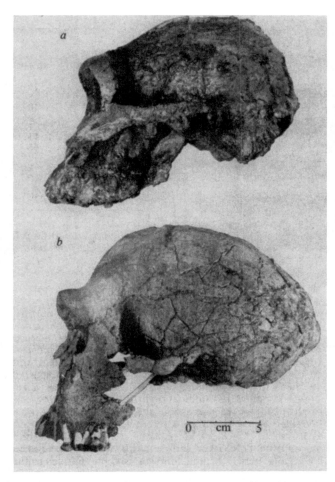

图 1. KNM-ER 406 (*a*) 与 KNM-ER 3733 (*b*) 的侧面观

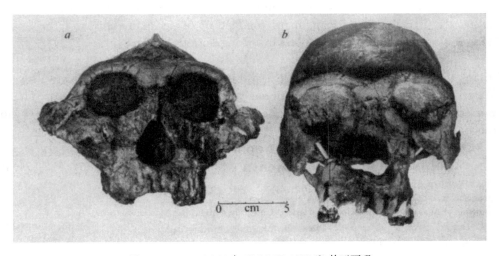

图 2. KNM-ER 406 (*a*) 与 KNM-ER 3733 (*b*) 的正面观

733

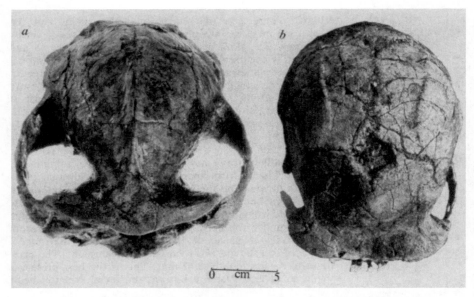

Fig 3. Superior aspect of KNM-ER 406(*a*) and KNM-ER 3733(*b*).

The new data show that the simplest hypothesis concerning early human evolution is incorrect and that more complex models must be devised. The single species hypothesis has served a useful purpose in focusing attention on variability among the early hominids and also on the ecological consequences of hominid adaptations. Alternative concepts, especially those concerning niche divergence and sympatry, should now be formulated. We think that populations antecedent to *H. erectus* ones have been sampled in the Koobi Fora Formation (specimens include KNM-ER 1470, 1590 and 3732). The clear demonstration of at least two hominid species earlier in time should enable us to reconsider our approaches to the problems of earlier hominid evolution. We also think that there is no good evidence for the presence of *Australopithecus* outside Africa, and the finding of an apparently advanced *H. erectus* cranium at Koobi Fora provokes issues such as why *Australopithecus* is only an African form, the nature of its extinction and the apparent stability of some hominid morphologies over long periods of time.

We thank the Museum Trustees of Kenya and the National Museums of Kenya for access to material and facilities and the National Geographic Society for support. The NSF supported A.C.W. We also thank colleagues who helped with suggestions and observations on this paper.

(**261**, 572-574; 1976)

R. E. F. Leakey* and Alan C. Walker†
*National Museums of Kenya, P. O. Box 40658, Nairobi, Kenya
†Departments of Anatomy and Anthropology, Harvard University, Cambridge, Massachusetts 02138

Received February 10; accepted May 4, 1976.

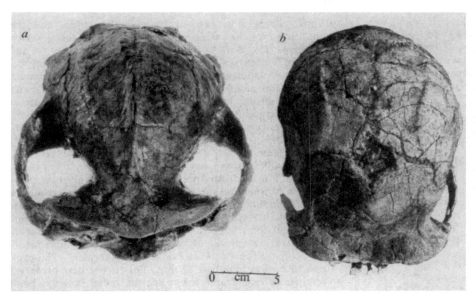

图 3. KNM-ER 406 (*a*) 与 KNM-ER 3733 (*b*) 的顶面

　　新的资料显示关于早期人类演化的最简单假说是不正确的，需设计出更为复杂的模型。单物种假说有益于把注意力集中在早期人科动物的变异以及早期人类适应性的生态影响上。现在应该阐明一些其他的可供选择的概念了，特别是有关小生境分化与分布区重叠。我们认为已经在库比福勒组采到过比直立人更早的样本（标本包括 KNM-ER 1470、1590 与 3732）。对较早时期内同时存在至少两种早期人科动物的证明应使我们能重新考虑对早期人科动物演化问题的解决方法。我们也认为没有好的证据证明非洲之外存在南方古猿，然而在库比福勒发现了明显更进步的直立人的颅骨引出了诸如此类的问题：为什么南方古猿只在非洲存在？为什么南方古猿会灭绝？以及为什么在相当长的时期内某些早期人科动物形态保持稳定不变？

　　我们感谢肯尼亚博物馆理事会与肯尼亚国家博物馆为我们提供研究资料和便利。感谢国家地理学会的支持。沃克获得了国家科学基金会的支持。还要感谢我们的同事，他们为本文提供了观测数据并给出了宝贵的建议。

（田晓阳 翻译；刘武 邢松 审稿）

735

References:

1. Leakey, R. E. F., *Nature,* **231**, 241-245 (1971); **237**, 264-269 (1972); **242**, 447-450 (1973); **248**, 653-656 (1974).

2. Brace, C. L., *The Stages of Human Evolution* (Prentice Hall, Engelwood Cliffs, 1967).

3. Wolpoff, M. H., *Man,* **6**, 601-614 (1971).

4. Gauss, G. F., *The Struggle for Existence* (Williams & Wilkins, Baltimore, 1934).

5. Mayr, E., *Cold Spring Harb. Symp. and Quant. Biol.,* **15**, 108-118 (1950).

6. Leakey, R. E. F., *Nature,* **261**, 574-576 (1976).

7. Bowen, B. E., and Vondra, C. F., *Nature,* **242**, 391-393 (1973).

8. Weidenreich, F., *Palaeont. Sinica,* **10**, 1-291 (1943).

9. Sartono, S., *Koninkl. Ned. Akad. Wet.,* 74, 185-194 (1971).

10. Leakey, R. E. F., Mungai, J. M., and Walker, A. C., *Am. J. Phys. Anthrop.,* **35**, 175-186 (1971).

11. Curtis, G. H., Drake, Cerling, T., and Hampel, *Nature,* **258**, 395-398 (1975).

12. Fitch, F. J., Findlater, I. C., Watkins, R. T., and Miller, J. A., *Nature,* **251**, 213-215 (1974).

# Fossil Hominids from the Laetolil Beds

M. D. Leakey *et al.*

## Editor's Note

The Laetolil Beds are deposits of volcanic rocks and ash-falls 30 miles south of Olduvai. Fossils had been gathered there since the 1930s—the Leakeys had collected there on three occasions—but the absolute ages of the fossils could not be estimated due to a lack of a suitable technique. Mary Leakey and colleagues returned there, and armed with the then-new potassium–argon dating method, dated the fossiliferous deposits to more than three and a half million years old. The latest collection included thirteen hominid fossils, all jaws and teeth, which Leakey and colleagues suggested belonged to the genus *Homo*. It was only later that they were reassigned to *Australopithecus afarensis*, the species to which the Hadar skeleton "Lucy" belonged.

Remains of 13 early hominids have been found in the Laetolil Beds in northern Tanzania, 30 miles south of Olduvai Gorge. Potassium–argon dating of the fossiliferous deposits gives an upper limit averaging 3.59 Myr and a lower limit of 3.77 Myr. An extensive mammalian fauna is associated. The fossils occur in the upper 30 m of ash-fall and aeolian tuffs whose total measured thickness is 130 m.

THE fossil-bearing deposits referred to variously as the Laetolil Beds, Garusi or Vogel River Series lie in the southern Serengeti Plains, in northern Tanzania, 20–30 miles from the camp site at Olduvai Gorge.

Fossils have been collected from the area on several occasions, the largest collection being made by L. Kohl-Larsen in 1938–39, who also found a small fragment of hominid maxilla which was named *Meganthropus africanus* by Weinert[1]. L. S. B. Leakey and M. D. L. visited the area in 1935 and in 1959, while a day trip was made in 1964 in company with R. L. H. The faunal material recovered on these occasions was all collected before the advent of isotopic dating and the age of the fossils remained uncertain until potassium–argon dating was carried out on samples of biotite obtained during the 1975 field season. In 1974, however, lava flows which unconformably overlie the Laetolil Beds had been dated by G. H. C. at 2.4 Myr.

We now report evidence that fossiliferous deposits of several different ages exist in the Laetolil area and that specimens found on the surface are not necessarily derived from the same beds. There are, however, noticeable variations in the colour and physical condition of the surface fossils which provide indications of their origin.

# 在莱托利尔层发现的人科动物化石

## 编者按

莱托利尔层是指在奥杜威南部 30 英里的火山岩和火山灰堆积物。那里的化石采集始于 20 世纪 30 年代——利基夫妇曾在那采集过三次——但由于缺乏合适的技术，一直无法确定化石的绝对年龄。玛丽·利基及其同事重返此地，配备了当时新出现的钾氩断代法，测得该含化石的堆积物的年代已超过距今 350 万年。其最新采集到的标本包括 13 件人科动物化石，全部是颌骨和牙齿，利基及其同事们认为他们均属于人属。不久以后，他们就被重新厘定为南方古猿阿法种，这个种包括哈达尔骨架"露西"。

---

在坦桑尼亚北部的莱托利尔层发现了 13 个早期人科动物的化石，该地在奥杜威峡谷南部 30 英里处。使用钾氩断代法对含化石的堆积物进行测年，得到其上限年代平均值为距今 359 万年，下限年代为距今 377 万年。伴生的哺乳动物群种类很丰富。这些化石出自总厚度为 130 米的火山灰和风积凝灰岩层最上部 30 米。

---

该含有化石的堆积物被不同地称作莱托利尔层、加鲁西或沃格尔河统，它位于坦桑尼亚北部的南塞伦盖蒂平原上，距离奥杜威峡谷营地遗址有 20~30 英里远。

人们已经数次在该处采集到了化石，采集量最大的一次是科尔-拉森在 1938~1939 年间所进行的，他还发现了一小块人科动物上颌骨破片，韦纳特将其命名为非洲魁人[1]。路易斯·利基和玛丽·利基于 1935 年和 1959 年参观了此地，1964 年又与海一起在此逗留了一天。这几次挖掘出的动物化石是在同位素测年法出现之前采集的，所以动物群的年代并不确定。直到用钾氩断代法测得在 1975 年野外季得到的黑云母样品的年代时，这些化石的年代才得以确定。但在 1974 年，柯蒂斯就已经确定了不整合地覆盖在莱托利尔层之上的熔岩流的年代为距今 240 万年。

现在我们报道了莱托利尔地区存在不同年代的含化石的堆积物的证据，而且我们认为地表发现的标本未必源自相同的层位。然而从地表采集到的化石在颜色和物理特征上明显的差异可以暗示它们的来源层位。

Discrepancies in the fauna were noted by Dietrich[2] and Maglio[3] who both postulated faunal assemblages of two different ages. In view of this, it was proposed for a time that the name Laetolil should be abandoned in favour of the more generalised term Vogel River Series, based on the colloquial German name for the Garusi river, which abounds in bird life. As the early fossiliferous deposits here referred to as the Laetolil Beds are not confined to the Garusi valley, this change of name seems unnecessary. Furthermore, the name Laetolil embraces a larger area, because it is the anglicised version of the Masai name (laetoli) for *Haemanthus*, a red lily that is abundant in the locality. The Laetolil Beds, *sensu stricto*, form a discrete unit, distinguishable from later deposits, and M. D. L. considers that the original name proposed by Kent in 1941[4] should be retained for this part of the sequence.

The relationship of the Laetolil to the Olduvai Beds had been under discussion for some years, but in 1969 R. L. H. noted that they underlay bed I at the Kelogi inselberg in the Side Gorge and established that they antedated the Olduvai sequence. This has been further confirmed when tuffs correlatable with bed I as well as an earlier, fossil-bearing series of tuffs were found to lie unconformably on the Laetolil Beds.

Interest in the area was renewed in 1974 after the discovery by George Dove of fossil equid and bovid teeth in the bed of the Gagjingero river, which drains into Lake Masek at the head of Olduvai Gorge. These fossils were found to be eroding from relatively recent deposits, probably the beds named Ngaloba by Kent[4]. Exposures of the Laetolil Beds, not hitherto seen by M. D. L., were found to the east of the Gagjingero river, at the headwaters of the Garusi river and of the Olduvai Side Gorge (referred to as Marambu by Kohl-Larsen[5]). Several fossils, including a hominid premolar, were found at these localities and subsequent visits yielded further hominid remains.

The possibility of establishing the age of the hominid fossils from the Laetolil Beds by radiometric dating and of clarifying the discrepancies in the faunal material led to a 2-month field season during July and August 1975. Samples from the fossiliferous horizons, collected by R. L. H., have now been dated. On the basis of these results the hominid remains and associated fauna can be bracketed in time between 3.59 and 3.77 Myr.

No trace of stone tools or even of utilised bone or stone was observed in the material from the Laetolil Beds, although handaxes and other artefacts occur in conglomerates which are present in certain areas and which are unconformable to the Laetolil Beds.

## Stratigraphy of Laetolil Area

The bulk of the faunal remains and all of the hominid remains were found within an area of about 30 km² at the northern margin of the Eyasie plateau and in the divide between the Olduvai and Eyasie drainage systems (Fig. 1).

迪特里希 [2] 和马利奥 [3] 注意到了动物群的差异，他们都主张存在两种不同年代的动物群。鉴于这一点，曾经有人提议基于加鲁西河的口语化的德语名字，应该弃用莱托利尔这一名称而代之以更广义的名称——沃格尔河统，该河流存在着大量鸟类。由于这里提到的称为莱托利尔层的早期含化石的堆积物并不局限于加鲁西河谷，这种名字的变化似乎并不必要。另外，莱托利尔这个名字涵盖更广泛的区域，因为它是一种在当地很繁盛的红色百合花——网球花属的马赛语名称（莱托里）的英语变体。严格来讲，莱托利尔层形成了一个独立的单元，与后期的堆积物是有区别的，玛丽·利基认为应该保留肯特在 1941 年 [4] 提出的最初的名字作为这部分地层层序的名字。

莱托利尔层和奥杜威层的层序关系已经讨论了数年，但是 1969 年海提出莱托利尔层下伏于侧峡谷的克罗吉岛山的 I 层之下，因此确定了它们早于奥杜威层序。当 I 层与凝灰岩可以对比，以及发现更早的含化石的凝灰岩系不整合地覆盖在莱托利尔层之上时，这一点就得到了进一步的证实。

1974 年，当乔治·达夫在伽津格罗河的河床里发现了马科动物和牛科动物的牙齿后，人们对这一区域的兴趣被再度点燃。伽津格罗河在奥杜威峡谷的源头处流入马赛科湖。这些化石是由于相对更新的堆积物遭遇侵蚀而出露的，这些堆积物很可能是肯特命名的恩加洛巴层 [4]。玛丽·利基迄今还没看到过莱托利尔层的出露，出露地层位于伽津格罗河的东部，在加鲁西河和奥杜威侧峡谷（科尔－拉森称之为马拉姆布 [5]）的源头处。在这些地方发现了好几种化石，其中包括一个人科动物的前臼齿，随后的探查又发现了其他的人科动物化石材料。

为了能够通过放射性测年法确定在莱托利尔层发现的人科动物化石的年代并且澄清动物群的差异，在 1975 年 7~8 月间开展了一次为期两个月的野外工作。海从含化石层采集的样品已经完成了测年。基于这些结果，可以将人科动物化石和伴生动物群的年代圈定在距今 359 万年到 377 万年之间。

尽管在某些区域存在的不整合地覆盖在莱托利尔层之上的砾岩中出现了手斧和其他人工制品，但是在莱托利尔层出土的标本中没有看到石器甚至是被使用过的骨骼或石头的痕迹。

## 莱托利尔地区的地层情况

大部分动物化石和所有人科动物化石都是在埃亚西高原北部边缘以及奥杜威和埃亚西水系的分水岭（图 1）之间的约 30 平方公里的区域内发现的。

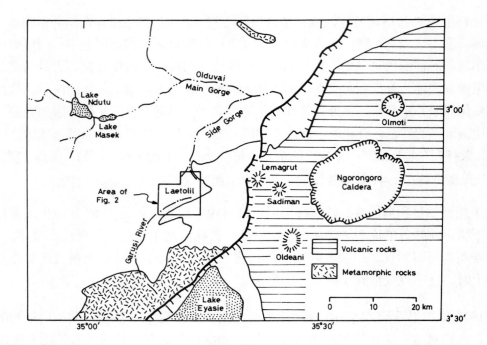

Fig. 1. Map of the southern Serengeti and volcanic highlands.

Kent studied this area as a member of L. S. B. Leakey's 1934–35 expedition, and his short paper is the only published description of the stratigraphy. He recognised three main subdivisions of the stratigraphic sequence, which overlies the metamorphic complex of Precambrian age. The lower unit he named the Laetolil Beds and the upper the Ngaloba Beds. The middle unit consists of olivine-rich lava flows and agglomerate, which are much closer in age to the Laetolil Beds than to the Ngaloba Beds. Kent briefly noted the local occurrence of tuffs younger than the lavas and older than the Ngaloba Beds. He described the Laetolil Beds as subaerially deposited tuffs, and he gave 30 m as an aggregate thickness in the vicinity of Laetolil. The Ngaloba Beds he described as tuffaceous clays, and he gave a thickness of about 5 m at the type locality. Pickering mapped this area as part of a 1:125,000 quarter degree sheet[6] and extended the known occurrence of the Laetolil Beds. He also recognised that at least some of the tuffs are of nephelinite composition.

This picture was modified considerably by stratigraphic work in 1974 and 1975. The Laetolil Beds proved to be far thicker and more extensive than previously recognised. The thickest section, 130 m, was measured in a valley in the northern part of the area (geological localities $A$ to $C$, Fig. 2). The base is not exposed and the full thickness of the Laetolil Beds here is unknown. Sections 100–120 m thick and representing only part of the Laetolil Beds were measured about 10 km south-east of Laetolil. The Laetolil Beds are 15–20 m thick at a distance of 25–30 km to the south-west and 10–15 m thick at Lakes Masek and Ndutu, 30 km to the north-west. The Laetolil Beds are tuffaceous sediments, dominantly of nephelinite composition.

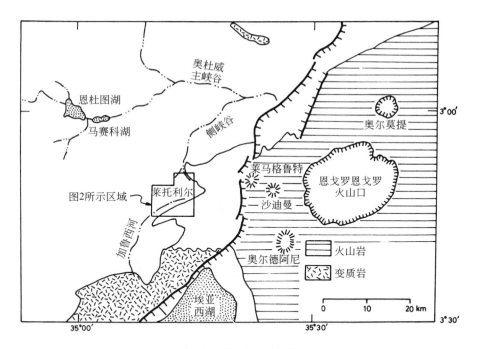

图 1. 南塞伦盖蒂和火山高地的地图。

肯特作为路易斯·利基 1934~1935 年间考察队的成员对该区域进行过研究，他写了一篇简短的文章，是唯一一篇已经发表的有关当地地层情况的描述。他把覆盖在前寒武纪变质杂岩之上的地层按层序划分出三个主要亚层。他将下层命名为莱托利尔层，上层命名为恩加洛巴层。中间的单元包括富含橄榄石的熔岩流和集块岩，它们在年代上更接近于莱托利尔层。肯特简要地说明了出现在局部区域的凝灰岩，它在年代上比熔岩要晚而比恩加洛巴层要早。他将莱托利尔层描述为靠近地面堆积的凝灰岩，并认为它在莱托利尔附近区域的总厚度为 30 米。他将恩加洛巴层描述为凝灰质黏土岩，估计在模式产地的厚度约为 5 米。皮克林将该区域作为 1:125,000 四分之一度表的一部分进行了绘图 [6]，并扩展了已知的莱托利尔层，并且他认为其中至少有些凝灰岩是霞石岩成分的。

1974 年和 1975 年，通过地层学研究工作，这幅图得到了相当大的修改。事实证明莱托利尔层远远比之前认为的要厚，面积也更广。最厚的部分有 130 米，是在该区域北部的一条河谷处测量到的（图 2 中的地质点 A 到 C）。基底没有暴露出来，此处莱托利尔层的全部厚度还是未知的。测量了在莱托利尔东南约 10 千米处的一个仅代表局部莱托利尔层的剖面，其厚度为 100~120 米。莱托利尔层在西南 25~30 千米处的厚度为 15~20 米，在西北 30 千米的马赛科湖和恩杜图湖处的厚度为 10~15 米。莱托利尔层是凝灰质沉积物，主要成分是霞岩。

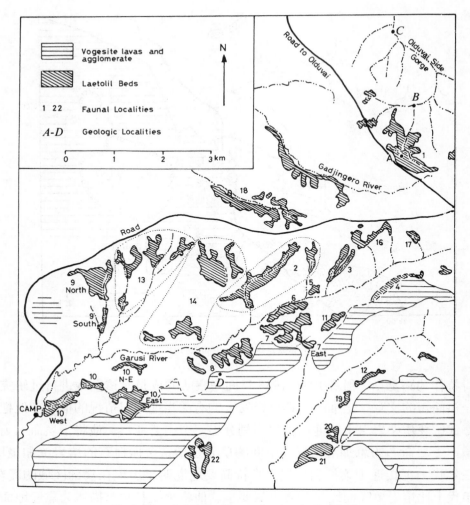

Fig. 2. Map of the Laetolil area showing the fossil beds.

The lavas and agglomerates noted by Kent overlie an irregular surface deeply eroded into the Laetolil Beds. The lavas were erupted from numerous small vents to the south, south-west and west of Lemagrut volcano. Although designated as nephelinite by Kent, the flows proved to be vogesite, a highly mafic lava with interstitial alkali feldspar and phlogopitic biotite. The lavas have reversed polarity as determined by field measurements (personal communication from A. Cox). A sample of lava from geological locality $D$ (Fig. 2) gave K–Ar dates of $2.38\pm0.5$ Myr and $2.43\pm0.7$ Myr (Table 1).

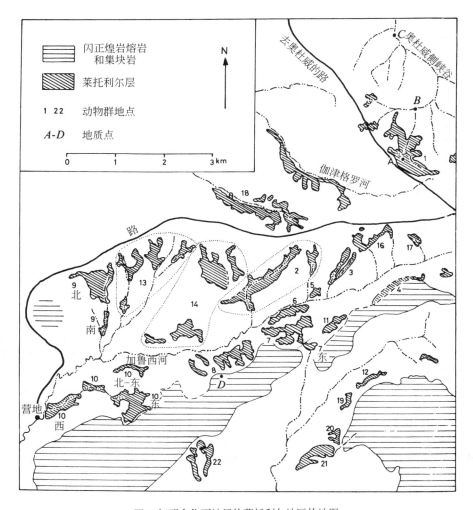

图 2. 标明含化石地层的莱托利尔地区的地图。

　　肯特指出，熔岩和集块岩覆盖在深入侵蚀到莱托利尔层内部的不规则表面之上。熔岩是从莱马格鲁特火山的南侧、西南侧和西侧的许多小出口喷发出来的。尽管肯特将其指定为霞岩，但是事实证明熔岩流成分是闪正煌岩，这是一种夹有碱性长石和金云母质黑云母的高镁铁质的熔岩。现场测量（与考克斯的个人交流）确定，这种熔岩具有反极性。从地质点 D（图 2）取到的一份熔岩样品以钾氩法测定其年代为距今 238 万 ±50 万年和 243 万 ±70 万年（表 1）。

Table 1. K–Ar dates from the Laetolil area

| Sample | KA no. | Dated material | Sample weight (g) | % K | mol g$^{-1}$ $^{40}$Ar radiation×10$^{-11}$ | % $^{40}$Ar atmosphere | Age yr (Myr) | Remarks |
|---|---|---|---|---|---|---|---|---|
| Vogesite lava, Location *D* | 2835 | Whole rock | 10.06588 | 1.013 | 0.419 | 74.0 | 2.38±.05 | Unconformably overlying Laetolil Beds |
| | 2837R | Whole rock | 11.27408 | 1.013 | 0.427 | 84.4 | 2.43±.08 | |
| Tuff *c*, location *A* | 2929 | Whole rock | 1.98629 | 6.96±.03 | 4.118 | 77.5 | 3.41±.08 | Treated with dilute HCl |
| | 2977 | Whole rock | 2.544 | 6.98±.04 | 4.462 | 78.5 | 3.68±.09 | Treated with warm dilute acetic acid |
| | 2979 | Whole rock | 1.94298 | 6.95±.04 | 4.454 | 79.1 | 3.69±.10 | |
| Xenolithic horizon, location *A* | 2930 | Whole rock | 3.07730 | 7.58±.02 | 4.771 | 50.8 | 3.62±.09 | Treated with dilute HCl |
| | 2930R | Whole rock | 1.83909 | 7.58±.02 | 4.733 | 39.7 | 3.59±.05 | |
| Ash-fall tuff, location *B* | 2932 | Whole rock | 1.05978 | 6.00±.1 | 3.996 | 75.0 | 3.82±.16 | Crushed, hand picked, treated with dilute HCl |
| | 2938 | Whole rock | 1.42092 | 6.49±.04 | 4.182 | 78.8 | 3.71±.12 | |

$^{40}$K/K=1.18×10$^{-4}$; $^{40}$K$_\lambda$=5.480×10$^{-10}$ yr$^{-1}$; $^{40}$K$_{\lambda\beta}$=4.905×4.905×10$^{-10}$ yr$^{-1}$; $^{40}$K$_{\lambda e}$=0.575×10$^{-10}$ yr$^{-1}$.

The 130-m section of the Laetolil Beds (Fig. 3) is divisible into an upper half consisting largely of wind-worked, or aeolian, tuff[7] and a lower half consisting of interbedded ash-fall and aeolian tuff with minor conglomerate and breccia. Tephra in the lower half are nephelinite, whereas nephelinite and melilitite are subequal in the upper half. Between these two divisions is a distinctive biotite-bearing coarse lithic-crystal tuff 60 cm thick. Hominid remains and nearly all of the other vertebrate remains are confined to the uppermost 30 m of aeolian tuffs beneath a widespread pale yellow vitric tuff 8 m thick (tuff *d* of Fig. 3). Several other marker tuffs, between 1 m and 30 cm thick, can be used for correlating within the fossiliferous 30-m thickness of sediments. The three prominent marker tuffs, designated *a*, *b*, and *c* (Fig. 3, column 2), can be recognised throughout the area shown in Fig. 2. Widespread horizons of ijolite and lava (mostly nephelinite) xenoliths are at several levels in the fossiliferous part of the section and assist in correlating. Biotite is common in some of the ijolite.

Additional fossiliferous deposits, of mineralogical affinity to the Laetolil Beds and 10–15 m thick, lie between tuff *d* and the bed I (?) tuffs at several places. They are locally separated from tuff *d* and the underlying aeolian tuffs of the Laetolil Beds by an erosional surface with a relief of 8 m. These sediments comprise water-worked tuffs, aeolian tuffs, clay-pellet aggregate of aeolian origin and limestone. The tephra are of phonolite and nephelinite composition. It is not yet clear whether or not these sediments should be regarded as part of the Laetolil Beds.

Beds I and II are represented by sedimentary deposits that lie stratigraphically between the lava and the Ngaloba Beds. The bed II deposits locally contain fossils and artefacts.

表 1. 莱托利尔地区的钾氩年代测定

| 样品 | KA 编号 | 年代测定材料 | 样品质量（克） | % K | 摩尔 / 克 $^{40}$Ar 放射性 $\times 10^{-11}$ | % $^{40}$Ar 大气 | 年代（万年） | 备注 |
|---|---|---|---|---|---|---|---|---|
| 闪正煌岩熔岩，D 地点 | 2835 | 全岩 | 10.06588 | 1.013 | 0.419 | 74.0 | 238±5 | 不整合地覆盖在莱托利层之上 |
| | 2837R | 全岩 | 11.27408 | 1.013 | 0.427 | 84.4 | 243±8 | |
| 凝灰岩 c，A 地点 | 2929 | 全岩 | 1.98629 | 6.96±.03 | 4.118 | 77.5 | 341±8 | 用稀盐酸处理 |
| | 2977 | 全岩 | 2.544 | 6.98±.04 | 4.462 | 78.5 | 368±9 | 用温稀醋酸处理 |
| | 2979 | 全岩 | 1.94298 | 6.95±.04 | 4.454 | 79.1 | 369±10 | |
| 捕虏体岩石地层，A 地点 | 2930 | 全岩 | 3.07730 | 7.58±.02 | 4.771 | 50.8 | 362±9 | 用稀盐酸处理 |
| | 2930R | 全岩 | 1.83909 | 7.58±.02 | 4.733 | 39.7 | 359±5 | |
| 火山灰凝灰岩，B 地点 | 2932 | 全岩 | 1.05978 | 6.00±.1 | 3.996 | 75.0 | 382±16 | 压碎并手工挑选，用稀盐酸处理 |
| | 2938 | 全岩 | 1.42092 | 6.49±.04 | 4.182 | 78.8 | 371±12 | |

$^{40}$K/K=1.18 × 10$^{-4}$；$^{40}$K$_{\lambda}$=5.480 × 10$^{-10}$/ 年；$^{40}$K$_{\lambda\beta}$=4.905 × 4.905 × 10$^{-10}$/ 年；$^{40}$K$_{\lambda\varepsilon}$=0.575 × 10$^{-10}$/ 年。

莱托利尔层 130 米厚的剖面（图 3）可分成上、下两部分，上半部分由大量风加工过的或者说是风成的凝灰岩 [7] 构成，下半部分则由火山灰和含有少量砾岩和火山角砾岩的风成凝灰岩互层而成。在下半部分的火山喷发碎屑是霞岩，而在上半部分霞岩和黄长岩几乎是等量的。这两部分之间是一层独特的含黑云母的粗粒岩屑晶屑凝灰岩，约 60 厘米厚。人科动物化石和几乎所有其他脊椎动物化石都局限在最上面 30 米的风成凝灰岩内，并位于 8 米厚的广泛分布的浅黄色玻屑凝灰岩（图 3 中的凝灰岩 d）之下。其余几种厚度在 1 米至 30 厘米之间的标志性凝灰岩可以作为 30 米厚的含化石沉积物的对比。标为 a、b 和 c 的三种突出的标志性凝灰岩（图 3，第 2 栏），可以通过图 2 所示的整个地区的地图辨认出来。广泛分布的霓霞岩和熔岩（大部分是霞岩）捕虏体层处于该剖面的含化石部分的不同层面上，有利于相互对照。在某些霓霞岩中，黑云母是很常见的。

其他与莱托利尔层具有矿物学相似性的 10~15 米厚的含化石堆积物在好几处地点都存在于凝灰岩 d 和 I 层（？）的凝灰岩之间。它们就地被一个起伏幅度达 8 米的侵蚀面所分隔而与凝灰岩 d 和下伏的莱托利尔层风成凝灰岩分开。这些沉积物由水成凝灰岩、风成凝灰岩、风成来源的黏土颗粒聚集物和石灰岩构成。火山喷发碎屑的成分是响岩和霞岩。目前还没搞清楚这些沉积物是否应该被看作是莱托利尔层的一部分。

I 层和 II 层以在地层上位于熔岩和恩加洛巴层之间的沉积物为代表。II 层堆积物的局部含有化石和人工制品。

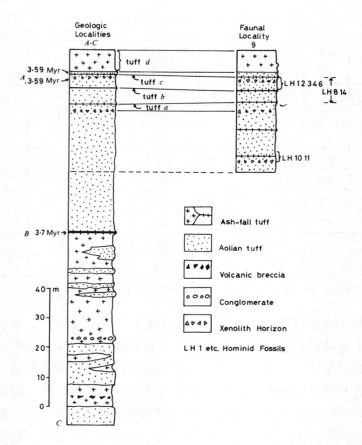

Fig. 3. Stratigraphic column of the Laetolil Beds showing the positions of the dated tuffs and hominid fossils.

Sadiman volcano, about 15 km east of the fossiliferous exposures, seems to have been the eruptive source of the Laetolil Beds. The one K–Ar date, of 3.73 Myr, obtained from Sadiman lava, fits with the K–Ar dates on the Laetolil Beds presented here. This date was published previously as K–Ar 2238 (ref. 8), where it was incorrectly assigned to Ngorongoro because of a mistake in listing the sample numbers.

## Potassium–argon Dating

The vogesite lava is composed of approximately 85–90% olivine and augite. The remainder is principally anorthoclase in the groundmass together with a very small amount of phlogopitic biotite. These two minerals proved too fine-grained and sparse for effective separation, and whole-rock samples were used for dating.

In addition to the vogesite lava unconformably overlying the Laetolil Beds, three of the tuffaceous layers within the Laetolil Beds have been dated by the conventional, total degassing K–Ar method (Table 1), and one of these tuffaceous layers has also been dated by the $^{40}Ar/^{39}Ar$ method, using incremental heating.

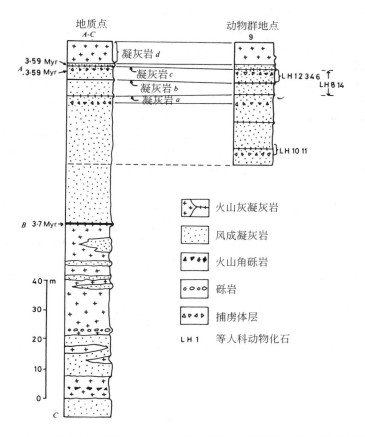

图 3. 显示已确定年代的凝灰岩和人科动物化石位置的莱托利尔层地层柱状剖面。

萨迪曼火山位于含化石的出露地层的东部约 15 千米处，看上去似乎是莱托利尔层的喷发源。其中距今 373 万年这一钾氩年代数据是根据萨迪曼熔岩测出来的，其与本文记述的莱托利尔层的钾氩年代是相符的。这一测年结果曾作为钾氩 2238 发表（参考文献 8），当时由于记录标本编号出现差错而错误地将其归属到了恩戈罗恩戈罗中。

### 钾氩测年

闪正煌岩熔岩的成分有大约 85%~90% 是由橄榄石和辉石构成。其余成分主要是基质中的歪长石和非常少量的金云母质黑云母。由于这两种矿物非常细小而分散，确实难以有效地分离，所以用完整的岩石样品进行年代测定。

除了不整合地覆盖在莱托利尔层之上的闪正煌岩熔岩外，莱托利尔层中的三个凝灰质地层也都使用传统的、全除气钾氩法（表 1）进行了年代测定，其中一个凝灰质层还使用了阶段加热的 $^{40}Ar/^{39}Ar$ 法进行了年代测定。

Tuff $c$ is the uppermost of the dated horizons, lying near the top of the fossiliferous deposits. It is a widespread crystal-lithic air-fall tuff cemented with calcite and generally 10–15 cm thick. Abundant biotite crystals 1–2 cm in diameter occur in the upper part of the tuff, which is composed of nepheline and milelitite. The dated crystals were hand-picked from two outcrops of the tuff at locality $A$ (Figs 2 and 3). The cementing calcite adhering to and interleaving the biotite books was removed by treatment with dilute HCl for a few minutes on one sample and with warm dilute acetic acid on two other samples. This treatment was found to have negligible deleterious effects on biotite standard samples. The three dates obtained for tuff $c$ (3.41±.08 Myr, 3.68±.09 Myr, and 3.69±.10 Myr) have about equal precision so were averaged to give a date of 3.59 Myr.

Two conventional K–Ar dates and one $^{40}Ar/^{39}Ar$ were obtained from a single biotite crystal from a xenolithic horizon at locality $A$ (Figs 2 and 3) approximately 1–2 m below the youngest tuff dated (tuff $c$). This horizon lies within the upper part of the fossiliferous beds and is distinguished by its ejecta of ijolite xenoliths together with nephelinite lava xenoliths. Although the biotite occurs in some of the ijolite clasts, a large single free crystal picked from the tuff was used for dating. The good agreement between the two conventional K–Ar dates for this sample (3.62±0.09 Myr and 3.59±0.05 Myr) and the $^{40}Ar/^{39}Ar$ date which yielded an isochron age of 3.55 Myr (Fig. 4) indicates that initial excess $^{40}Ar$ is not a problem with this sample, and that these dates give an average age for this horizon of 3.59 Myr.

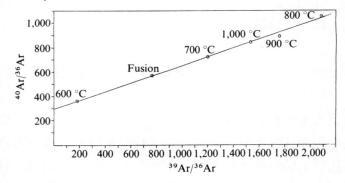

Fig. 4. $^{40}Ar/^{39}Ar$ incremental heating of biotite from xenolithic horizon, locality $C$. Isochron age, 3.55 Myr; $[^{40}Ar/^{39}Ar]_0=294$; $^{40}Ar/^{39}Ar=0.35318$; $J=0.005204$.

Two dates were obtained from a biotite-bearing crystal-lithic tuff 60 cm thick lying approximately 50 m below tuff $c$ near the middle of the thickest section of the Laetolil Beds at location $B$ (Fig. 2). The tuff is of nephelinite composition, containing abundant augite and altered nepheline and 2–3% of biotite, some crystals of which are as much as 1 cm in diameter. Calcite cements the crystals and fragments together. Biotite was separated by crushing, screening and hand picking and was cleaned of calcite with dilute HCl. Two dates, 3.82±0.16 Myr and 3.71±0.12 Myr, average 3.77 and give a lower limit to the age of the hominid remains (which occur below but close to the dated xenolithic horizon higher in the section) in the 30 m section at locality $A$ (Fig. 2) whose base projects approximately 20 m above this tuff at locality $B$ (Fig. 3).

凝灰岩 $c$ 位于已经确定年代的地层的最上层，接近含化石堆积物的顶部。该层是广泛分布的由钙质胶结的晶屑岩屑风成凝灰岩，通常有 10~15 厘米厚。大量直径 1~2 厘米的黑云母晶体出现在该凝灰岩的上部，其由霞岩和黄长岩（编者注：英文原文中为 mileiitite，可能为 melilitite 的错写，应为黄长岩）构成。从 $A$ 地点的两处凝灰岩露头处手工挑选一些晶体用于年代测定（图 2 和图 3）。对于附着在黑云母上并与书页状黑云母交错在一起的钙质胶结物，其中一个样品用稀盐酸处理几分钟后除去，另外两个标本则用温的稀醋酸除去。这种处理方法对于黑云母标准样品具有极小的负面作用。得到的关于凝灰岩 $c$ 的三个年代（距今 341 万 ±8 万年、368 万 ±9 万年和 369 万 ±10 万年）具有几乎一致的精确性，所以可以取其平均值，即年代为距今 359 万年。

从位于年代最年轻的凝灰岩（凝灰岩 $c$）之下大约 1~2 米处的 $A$ 地点（图 2 和图 3）的捕虏体岩石层中得到了一块黑云母晶体，两个通过传统的钾氩法测定的年代和一个 $^{40}Ar/^{39}Ar$ 年代都是根据该黑云母晶体测定的。该地层处于含化石层的上部，以其霓霞岩捕虏体及霞岩熔岩捕虏体喷出物为特征。尽管在某些霓霞岩碎屑中也出现了黑云母，但是研究人员从凝灰岩中挑选了一块大的游离的晶体来进行年代测定。对该样品用传统的钾氩法测定的两个年代（距今 362 万 ±9 万年和 359 万 ±5 万年）和 $^{40}Ar/^{39}Ar$ 年代（该方法得到了距今 355 万年的等时线年龄）（图 4）之间具有很好的一致性，这种一致性表明最初过量的 $^{40}Ar$ 对于这个样品并不构成影响，根据这些年代得出这个地层的平均年龄为距今 359 万年。

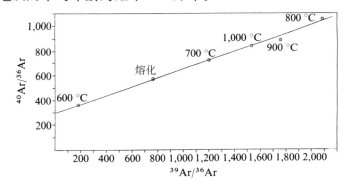

图 4. 从 $C$ 地点的捕虏体岩石层得到的黑云母阶段加热的 $^{40}Ar/^{39}Ar$ 法年代。等时线年龄：距今 355 万年；$[^{40}Ar/^{39}Ar]_0 = 294$；$^{40}Ar/^{39}Ar = 0.35318$；$J = 0.005204$。

从 60 厘米厚的含晶屑岩屑黑云母凝灰岩得到了两个年代，该凝灰岩位于凝灰岩 c 之下约 50 米处，接近 B 地点莱托利尔层最厚剖面的中间（图 2）。该凝灰岩的成分是霞岩，含有丰富的辉石和蚀变的霞石、2%~3% 的黑云母以及直径几乎为 1 厘米的一些晶体。方解石把晶屑和碎屑胶结在一起。通过粉碎、筛选、手工挑选将黑云母分离出来，然后用稀盐酸清洗掉方解石。距今 382 万 ±16 万年和 371 万 ±12 万年这两个年代的平均值是距今 377 万年，给出了在 $A$ 地点的 30 米厚剖面处（图 2）发现的人科动物化石的年代下限（该化石是在下层发现的，但是其与该剖面较高位置的已确定年代的捕虏体岩石地层接近），其基部突出于 $B$ 地点处的这种凝灰岩之上约 20 米处（图 3）。

# Fauna

The fossiliferous deposits in the Laetolil area have been subdivided, for purposes of collecting, into 26 localities. These subdivisions are based on existing topographic features such as grassy ridges, lines of trees, stream channels and so on. This has provided a means of dividing the fossiliferous area into units of restricted size, but does not relate to the former topography.

Eighteen of these localities are in the Garusi valley, one in the valley at the head of the Olduvai Side Gorge, one in the Gadjingero valley, five in a valley to the south of the Garusi river and one in an isolated position to the west (Fig. 2).

Identifiable fossils noted on the exposures were either collected and registered or listed on the sites. Specimens from the Laetolil Beds were distinctively cream coloured or white and sometimes chalky in texture, but the surface material also included brown, grey or black specimens, often rolled. These have been excluded from the material under review, together with fossils which have adhering matrix clearly dissimilar from the tuffs of the Laetolil Beds. Among these are all remains of *Hippopotamus*, *Equus*, *Theropithecus*, *Phacochoerus* and *Tragelaphus*, formerly included in the Laetolil fauna, with the exception of *Hippopotamus*.

The fossil material from the Laetolil Beds is dispersed and fragmentary and it is not possible to assess the number of individuals represented. In this article, "numbers of fossils" refer to individual bones and teeth, except in the case of clear association, confined almost entirely to remains of *Serengetilagus* and *Pedetes*, some of which were associated and even articulated.

Table 2 shows the mean percentage frequency of the more common vertebrate groups at several of the richer localities. A total of 6,288 fossil specimens were identified from the localities considered here.

Table 2. Mean percentage frequency of bones of more common vertebrate groups

| Group | Mean percentage | Range | Nos of localities |
|---|---|---|---|
| Bovidae | 43.0 | 29.5–57.9 | 18 |
| Lagomorpha | 14.4 | 5.6–24.0 | 18 |
| Giraffidae | 11.2 | 6.8–23.2 | 18 |
| Rhinocerotidae | 9.7 | 5.7–17.3 | 18 |
| Equidae | 4.4 | 1.7–7.1 | 18 |
| Suidae | 3.6 | 1.0–7.1 | 18 |
| Proboscidea | 3.4 | 1.0–5.1 | 18 |
| Rodentia | 3.3 | 0.9–7.2 | 17 |
| Carnivora | 3.1 | 0.8–8.2 | 17 |

## 动　物　群

为了采集标本，已将莱托利尔地区的含化石堆积物细分成了 26 个地点。这些分区是基于现存的地形学特征如草嵴、树线、河道等划分的。这提供了一种将含化石区域划分成一定大小单元的方法，但是与先前的地形学研究并无关联。

这些地点中有十八个在加鲁西河河谷，一个位于奥杜威侧峡谷的源头河谷处，一个在伽津格罗河河谷，五个在加鲁西河南部的一个河谷，还有一个在西部的一个孤立的位置（图 2）。

在露头看到的可鉴定化石或者被采集并记录，或者在遗址上标注出来。莱托利尔层的化石都是特殊的乳白色或者白色，并且有时呈白垩的质地，但是从地表采集到的材料也有褐色、灰色或黑色的标本，这些颜色经常是包在标本外面的。本项研究的标本排除了地表采集的标本，同时排除了那些附着有与莱托利尔层凝灰岩明显不同的围岩的化石。这些标本都是河马属、马属、狮尾狒属、疣猪属和林羚属的化石，除了河马属以外，其他原本就包括在莱托利尔动物群中。

莱托利尔层中的化石标本分散而残破不全，因而不可能估计出其代表的个体数量。本文中"化石编号"是指单个的骨骼和牙齿，除非是相互之间关系明确的化石标本，例如塞伦盖蒂兔属和跳兔属化石几乎完全在同一处发现，其中有些骨骼就在一起，甚至是有关节连接的。

表 2 给出了在几处化石较多的地点中较常见的脊椎动物群出现的平均百分频率。在本文研究的地点中总共鉴定出了 6,288 件化石标本。

表 2. 较常见的脊椎动物群的骨骼的平均百分比频率

| 动物群 | 平均百分比 | 范围 | 所在地点的数量 |
| --- | --- | --- | --- |
| 牛科 | 43.0 | 29.5~57.9 | 18 |
| 兔形目 | 14.4 | 5.6~24.0 | 18 |
| 长颈鹿科 | 11.2 | 6.8~23.2 | 18 |
| 犀科 | 9.7 | 5.7~17.3 | 18 |
| 马科 | 4.4 | 1.7~7.1 | 18 |
| 猪科 | 3.6 | 1.0~7.1 | 18 |
| 长鼻目 | 3.4 | 1.0~5.1 | 18 |
| 啮齿目 | 3.3 | 0.9~7.2 | 17 |
| 食肉目 | 3.1 | 0.8~8.2 | 17 |

Reptiles are represented by snake vertebrae at three localities and by tortoises at all localities. The latter have an average frequency of 2.2% and include several giant specimens. Avian remains occur widely and at several localities birds' eggs were completely preserved. There is one example of a shattered clutch of at least eight eggs, rather smaller in size than eggs of domestic fowl. Primates were found at 15 localities, and in one area they constitute 3.8% of the fauna. Both cercopithecines and colobines are present (M. G. Leakey, personal communication).

Rodents are fairly well represented, although not abundant. Of the specimens identified by J. J. Jaeger, the most common are *Pedetes*, *Saccostomus* and *Hystrix*. The carnivore fauna is characterised by a high percentage of viverrids, constituting 32% of all the carnivore specimens. Large carnivores are represented by hyaenids, of which there are several genera, by felids and a machairodont.

Proboscidea include *Deinotherium* and *Loxodonta* sp. (M. Beden, personal communication). There is no evidence that the equid material (other than that derived from later deposits) includes any genus except *Hipparion*. The suids consist only of two genera, *Potamachoerus* and *Notochoerus* (J. Harris, personal communication). The presence of *Ancylotherium* and *Orycteropus*, noted in previous collections, is confirmed and the existence of two rhinocerotids has been established by the discovery of skulls of both *Ceratotherium* and *Diceros*, although only the former was listed previously.

Among the giraffids, *Sivatherium* and a small form of giraffe are equally common. *Giraffe jumae* is also present but is much less well represented. The bovid fauna is chiefly characterised by the very high percentage of *Madoqua* (dikdik). In 18 localities dikdik range from 1.5 to 37.7% of all bovid specimens, with a mean percentage of 15.1%.

The 1975 field season, although mainly confined to surface collection, has established that previous collecting had sampled faunas of several time periods. It is now possible to exclude some genera from the published lists of fauna from the Laetolil Beds[2,9], such as *Theropithecus*, *Tragelaphus*, *Equus* and *Phacochoerus*.

## Fossil Hominids

Thirteen new fossil hominid specimens were recovered from the Laetolil site during 1974 and 1975. The remains include a maxilla, mandibles and teeth. This sample displays a complex of characters seemingly demonstrative of phylogenetic affinity to the genus *Homo*, but also features some primitive traits concordant with its great age.

The hominid specimens are listed in Table 3. Provisional stratigraphic correlation and dating have placed the hominid remains as shown in Fig. 3. With the exception of Laetolil hominids (LH) 7 and 8, all specimens retain the matrix characteristic of the Laetolil Beds from which they have been weathered or excavated. There is no reason to doubt that all the specimens derive from the Laetolil Beds as reported.

在其中三处地点发现的爬行动物主要是蛇椎骨，在所有地点都发现了龟甲。后者出现的平均频率为2.2%，包括几个巨大的标本。鸟类化石出现的范围很广，在几处地点，鸟蛋被完整地保存下来了。有一窝蛋至少包括八个个体，但是都已经破碎了，这些蛋的尺寸都比家禽的蛋要小。在15处地点发现了灵长类；有一个地区，它们占到了整个动物群的3.8%。猕猴亚科和疣猴亚科都存在（米芙·利基，个人交流）。

啮齿类化石广泛存在，但总体数量并不多。在耶格鉴定出的标本中，最常见的是跳兔属、南非囊鼠属和豪猪属。食肉类动物以高比例的灵猫类为特征，它们占所有食肉动物标本的32%。大型食肉动物的主要代表是鬣狗类、猫类和一种剑齿虎，其中鬣狗类有好几个属。

长鼻目包括恐象属和非洲象未定种（贝登，个人交流）。没有证据表明除了三趾马之外还有别的马类化石（除了从较晚的堆积物中发现过外）。猪科动物只包括两个属：河猪属和南方猪属（哈里斯，个人交流）。之前的挖掘中曾发现过爪脚兽属和土豚属的存在，此次再次得到确认。白犀和黑犀头骨的发现证实存在两种犀科动物，但是之前只发现过白犀。

在长颈鹿科动物中，西洼兽属和一种小型的长颈鹿都很常见。朱玛长颈鹿也存在，但是保存状况不太好。牛科动物群以极高比例的犬羚属为特征。在18处地点中，犬羚出现的频率占所有牛科标本出现频率的1.5%~37.7%，平均百分比为15.1%。

在1975年的野外工作中，尽管主要局限在地表标本采集方面，但是确认了之前的采集工作所获得的动物群标本属于几个不同的时期。现在可以将一些属从已发表的莱托利尔层的动物群名单中剔除出去了[2,9]，例如狮尾狒属、林羚属、马属和疣猪属。

## 人科动物化石

1974年到1975年间在莱托利尔遗址挖掘出了13件新的人科动物化石标本。这些化石包括一个上颌骨、一些下颌骨和牙齿。该标本既显示出了一系列似乎证实其在系统发育上与人属具有亲缘关系的特征，但是也具有与其古老年代一致的一些原始特征。

表3列出了这些人科动物标本。根据暂行的地层对比和年代测定确定出的这些人科化石层位如图3所示。除了莱托利尔人科动物（LH）7和8外，所有标本都保留着莱托利尔层特有的围岩，这些标本是从莱托利尔层中被风化出来或挖掘出来的。正如报道的一样，所有这些标本都源自莱托利尔层，这点毫无疑问。

Table 3. Hominid remains recovered in 1974–75

| Laetolil hominid (LH) | Locality | Specimen consists of | Discovered by |
|---|---|---|---|
| 1 | 1 | RP$^4$ fragment | M. Muoka |
| 2 | 3$^{*1}$ | Immature mandibular corpus with deciduous and permanent teeth | M. Muluila |
| 3 (a–t) | 7$^*$ | Isolated deciduous and permanent teeth, upper and lower | M. Muoka |
| 4 | 7 | Adult mandibular corpus with dentition | M. Muluila |
| 5 | 8 | Adult maxillary row: I$^2$ to M$^1$ | M. Muluila |
| 6 (a–e) | 7$^*$† | Isolated deciduous and permanent teeth, upper | M. Muoka |
| 7 | 5 | RM$^1$ or $^2$ fragment | M. Muoka |
| 8 | 11 | RM$^2$, RM$^3$ | E. Kandindi |
| 10 | 10W | Fragment left mandibular corpus with broken roots | E. Kandindi |
| 11 | 10W | LM$^1$ or $^2$ | E. Kandindi |
| 12 | 5 | LM$^2$ or $^3$ fragment | E. Kandindi |
| 13 | 8 | Fragment right mandibular corpus with broken roots | M. Jackes |
| 14 | 19 | Isolated permanent teeth, lower | E. Kandindi |

LH 9 was not valid.

$^*$ *In situ.*

† LH 3 and 6 associated in mixed state.

The Laetolil hominid sample consists of teeth and mandibles. Important features of these specimens are described here, followed by a brief preliminary discussion regarding the phylogenetic status of the fossils.

Remains of deciduous and permanent dentitions have been recovered. The dentitions consist of two maxillary and four mandibular partial tooth rows. Compared with the rest of the East African Pliocene/early Pleistocene hominid sample, the Laetolil anterior teeth are large and the postcanine teeth of small to moderate size.

## Deciduous Dentition

**Canines (LH 2, 3)** Single upper and lower deciduous canines are known. The lower is a slightly projecting, sharp conical tooth in its damaged state. It is smaller but its overall morphology is similar to its permanent counterpart.

**First molars (LH 2, 3)** The upper first deciduous molar displays spatial dominance of the protocone and a well-marked mesiobuccal accessory cusp defined by a strong anterior fovea. The lower first deciduous molar is molarised, with four or five main cusps depending on hypoconulid expression. There is a spatially dominant protoconid with a large flat buccal face, a lingually facing anterior fovea, and an inferiorly projecting mesiobuccal enamel line. Vertical dominance of the protoconid and metaconid is marked in lateral view.

756

表 3. 1974~1975 年间发掘的人科动物化石

| 莱托利尔人科动物（LH） | 地点 | 标本组成 | 发现者 |
|---|---|---|---|
| 1 | 1 | 右 $P^4$ 碎块 | 穆奥卡 |
| 2 | 3*[1] | 保存有乳齿和恒齿的未成年下颌体 | 穆卢伊拉 |
| 3（a~t） | 7* | 单独的上下乳齿和上下恒齿 | 穆奥卡 |
| 4 | 7 | 保存有齿系的成年下颌体 | 穆卢伊拉 |
| 5 | 8 | 成年上颌齿列：$I^2$ 到 $M^1$ | 穆卢伊拉 |
| 6（a~e） | 7*† | 单独的上乳齿和上恒齿 | 穆奥卡 |
| 7 | 5 | 右 $M^1$ 或右 $M^2$ 碎块 | 穆奥卡 |
| 8 | 11 | 右 $M^2$、右 $M^3$ | 坎丁迪 |
| 10 | 10W | 保存有残破齿根的左下颌体碎块 | 坎丁迪 |
| 11 | 10W | 左 $M^1$ 或左 $M^2$ | 坎丁迪 |
| 12 | 5 | 左 $M^2$ 或左 $M^3$ 碎块 | 坎丁迪 |
| 13 | 8 | 保存有残破齿根的右下颌体碎块 | 杰基斯 |
| 14 | 19 | 单独的下恒齿 | 坎丁迪 |

LH 9 无效。

\* 在原地。

† LH 3 和 6 以伴生状态出土。

莱托利尔人科动物化石标本包括牙齿和下颌骨。本文描述了这些标本的重要特征，并且对这些化石的系统发育位置进行了简单的初步探讨。

发掘中也采集到乳齿系和恒齿系标本。齿系包括两个上颌骨和四个下颌骨的部分齿列。与其余的东非上新世 / 早更新世时期的人科动物标本相比，莱托利尔标本的前牙较大，而颊齿则为小到中等尺寸。

## 乳 齿 系

**犬齿**（LH 2、3）：这是已知的唯一的上乳犬齿和下乳犬齿。下乳犬齿稍微有些突出，尖锐的圆锥齿处于受损状态。虽然该牙比恒齿小，但是其总体形态与恒齿很相似。

**第一臼齿**（LH 2、3）：第一上乳臼齿的上原尖很大，一个由发达的前窝限定的近中颊侧附尖明显。第一下乳臼齿臼齿化，依下次小尖的发育状况而有四或五个主尖。下原尖很大，具有大而平的颊面；前窝朝向舌侧；近中颊侧釉质线向下突出。从外侧视下原尖和下后尖明显垂直。

**Second molars (LH 2, 3, 6)** Upper and lower deciduous second molars take the basic form of the analogous permanent first molars but are smaller in overall size. The dM$_2$ of LH 2 is the only lower molar in the Laetolil sample bearing any indication of a tuberculum sextum.

## Permanent Dentition

**Incisors (LH 2, 3, 5, 6, 14)** The single upper central incisor is very large and bears pronounced lingual relief. The upper lateral incisors are smaller, with variable lingual relief. The lower incisors are narrow and very tall, with minimal relief.

**Canines (LH 2, 3, 4, 5, 6, 14)** The incompletely-developed upper canine LH 3 is large, stout and pointed, bearing pronounced lingual relief. LH 6 is slightly smaller, with less lingual relief and a tall, pointed crown. LH 5 bears an elongate dentine exposure on its distal occlusal edge but does not project beyond the occlusal row in its worn state. The lower canines are similar to the uppers in their great size, height and lingual relief.

**Premolars (LH 1, 2, 3, 4, 5, 6, 14)** The upper premolars tend to be buccolingually elongate and bicuspid, with the lingual cusp placed mesially and an indented mesial crown face. The two lower third premolars each have a dominant buccal cusp with mesial and distal occlusal ridges, and a weak lingual cusp placed mesial of the major crown axis. The long axis of the oval crown crosses the dental arcade contour from mesiobuccal to distolingual, donating a "skewed" occlusal profile to the tooth. The lower fourth premolars are fairly square in shape with major buccal and lingual cusps and moderate talonids.

**Molars (LH 2, 3, 4, 5, 6, 7, 8, 11, 12, 14)** The upper molars are of moderate size, their relative proportions unknown. They show a basic four-cusp pattern with spatial dominance of the protocone and typical expression of a pit-like Carabelli feature. The lower molars display progressive size increase from first to third in LH 4. They have a fairly square occlusal outline with hypoconulid apressed anteriorly between hypoconid and entoconid and no trace of a tuberculum sextum. The Y-5 pattern of primary fissuration is constant.

## Mandibles

**Juvenile mandible (LH 2)** This specimen (Figs 5 and 6) is incompletely fused at the midline, and the developing crowns of the permanent canines and premolars are exposed in the broken corpus. The first molars have just reached the occlusal plane. Only the posterior aspect of the symphysis shows fairly intact contours, with a concave post-incisive planum and incipient superior transverse torus. The genioglossal fossa is obscured by midline breakage. Associated distortion has artificially increased the bimolar distances.

**第二臼齿**（LH 2、3、6）：第二上、下乳臼齿与第一恒臼齿具有相似的基本形式，但是总尺寸要小一些。LH 2 的 $dM_2$ 是莱托利尔标本中唯一一枚有第六小尖迹象的下臼齿。

## 恒 齿 系

**门齿**（LH 2、3、5、6、14）：唯一的上中门齿非常大，而且具有明显的舌面突起。上侧门齿较小，舌面突起因不同个体而异。下门齿狭窄而高，突起很小。

**犬齿**（LH 2、3、4、5、6、14）：发育不充分的上犬齿 LH 3 很大、结实而尖锐，具有明显的舌面突起。LH 6 稍微小一点，具有较少的舌面突起和一个高而尖的牙冠。LH 5 在远中侧咬合边缘具有一个延长的牙本质暴露区，但是没有在磨损的状态下突出于咬合列之外。下犬齿与上犬齿在大尺寸、高度和舌面突起方面都很相似。

**前臼齿**（LH 1、2、3、4、5、6、14）：上前臼齿趋于沿颊舌向延伸并呈双尖型，舌侧主尖位于近中侧以及一个锯齿状的近中牙冠面。两枚第三下前臼齿中的每枚都有一个突出的具有近中和远中咬合嵴的颊侧齿尖，还有一个位于主牙冠轴线中间的比较小的舌侧齿尖。椭圆形齿冠的长轴从近中颊侧到远中舌侧穿过齿弓的轮廓，为牙齿提供了一个"斜的"咬合剖面。第四下前臼齿形状上非常接近正方形，具有颊侧主尖和舌侧主尖以及中等大小的下跟座。

**臼齿**（LH 2、3、4、5、6、7、8、11、12、14）：上臼齿的大小适中，它们的相对比例还不清楚。这些牙齿显示出一种基本的四尖型，该模式中原尖很大，表现出坑状卡拉贝利的典型特征。LH 4 的下臼齿表现出从第一颗到第三颗逐渐增大的特点。它们具有方形的咬合轮廓，其下次小尖在下次尖和下内尖之间向前紧贴，没有第六小尖的迹象。嚼面的主凹谷都是 Y-5 型。

## 下 颌 骨

**未成年下颌骨**（LH 2）：该标本（图 5 和图 6）在中线处没有完全融合，发育中的恒犬齿和恒前臼齿牙冠已在断裂的下颌体萌出。第一臼齿刚刚长到咬合面。只有联合部位后面的轮廓是比较完整的，有一个凹进去的后门齿平面和刚开始发育的上横圆枕。颏窝由于中线破裂而模糊不清了。由此引起的扭曲变形不自然地增加了左右臼齿间的距离。

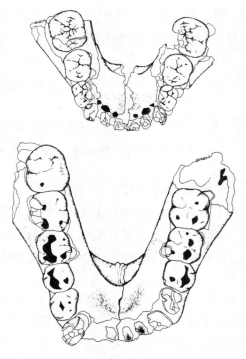

Fig. 5. Occlusal views of juvenile and adult mandibles (LH 2 and 4).

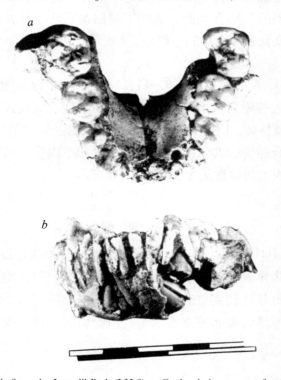

Fig. 6. Juvenile mandible from the Laetolil Beds (LH 2). *a*, Occlusal view; except for the first molars all the teeth are deciduous. *b*, Front view showing the central incisors, canine and P$_3$ in the bone.

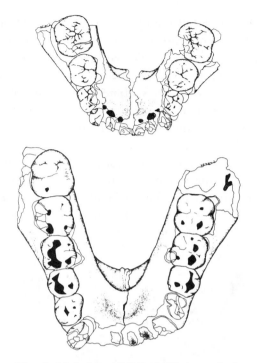

图 5. 未成年和成年下颌骨的嚼面视（LH 2 和 4）。

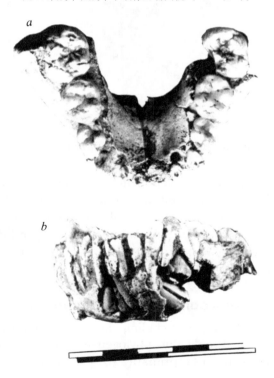

图 6. 莱托利尔层出土的未成年下颌骨(LH 2)。a,嚼面视;除了第一臼齿外,所有牙齿都是乳齿。b,正面视,
展示了骨骼上的中门齿、犬齿和 $P_3$。

**Adult mandible (LH 4)** The adult mandibular corpus is well preserved, with the rami missing (Figs 5 and 7). The dental arcade is essentially undistorted, and presents fairly straight sides which converge anteriorly. The anterior dentition has suffered *post mortem* damage and loss, except for the right lateral incisor which seems to have been lost in life. Largely resorptive alveolar pathology has obliterated its alveolus and has affected the adjacent teeth. There is development of wide interproximal facets for the canine teeth but no C/$P_3$ contact facet. This combines with observation of extensive wear on the buccal $P_3$ face to suggest that C/$P_3$ interlock has prevented mesial drift from eliminating the C/$P_3$ diastema. Judging from the preserved posterior incisor alveoli, these teeth were set in an evenly rounded arcade, projecting moderately anterior to the bicanine axis. The internal mandibular contour is a very narrow parabola in contrast to the wider basal contour which displays great lateral eversion posteriorly. There are weak to moderate superior and inferior transverse tori, the latter bearing strong mental spines.

Fig. 7. Adult mandible from the Laetolil Beds (LH 2), occlusal view.

The anterior root of the ramus is broken at its origin, lateral to $M_2$. Occlusal and basal margins diverge strongly anteriorly, resulting in a deep symphysis. The symphysis is angled sharply posteriorly and the anterior symphyseal contour is rounded and bulbous. The lateral aspects of the corpus have very flat posterior portions and distinctive hollowing in the areas above the mental foramina at the $P_3$ to $P_4$ position. The corpus is tall and fairly narrow, especially in its anterior portion.

## Implications of the Specimens

The Laetolil fossil hominid sample, including the original Garusi maxillary fragment[5], seems to be representative of only one phylogenetic entity or lineage. The variations observed in the material seem to be primarily size-based and stem from individual and sexual factors.

**成年下颌骨**（LH 4）：成年下颌体的保存状况很好，下颌支缺损（图 5 和图 7）。齿弓基本没有变形，两侧的齿列很直并且向前集中。除了似乎在生前就已经丢失了的右侧门齿之外，前齿系都是在死后受损和丢失的。很大程度的再吸收性齿槽病使得其齿槽的痕迹已经不清楚了，并且影响到了相邻的牙齿。犬齿发育了宽的邻接面，但没有 C/P₃ 接触面。这与观察到 P₃ 的颊侧面的较大的磨损共同提示了 C/P₃ 咬合阻止了 P₃ 的近中向迁移使 C/P₃ 间的齿隙消失。从保存下来的后门齿齿槽来判断，这些牙齿是位于曲度均匀的圆形齿弓上的，向前适度突出到左右犬齿间的轴线上。与下颌骨后端显示出明显向外侧外翻的稍宽的基底轮廓相反，下颌骨内轮廓呈现出一条非常窄的抛物线形状。存在从微弱到中度不等的上、下横圆枕，后者具有强壮的颏棘。

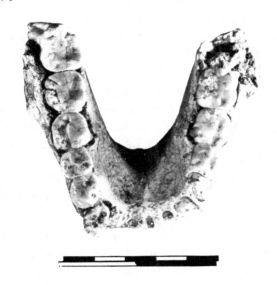

图 7. 莱托利尔层出土的成年下颌骨（LH 2），嚼面视。

下颌支的前根部在前端断裂，侧向延续到 M₂。嚼面和基底缘向前分离很大，使下颌联合部很深。故联合部位后面的角度很尖锐，前面的联合部轮廓圆而呈球根状。下颌体的外侧面具有很平的后部，在 P₃ 到 P₄ 位置处的颏孔之上的区域具有特殊的中空。下颌体高而相当窄，特别是在前部。

## 标本的启示

包括最初的加鲁西上颌骨破块 [5] 在内的莱托利尔人科动物化石标本似乎只代表了一个支系，或者叫一个谱系。观察到的标本上的形态差异似乎主要是大小方面的，并且这些差异是由于个体因素和性别因素引起的。

The deciduous teeth, particularly the lower deciduous first molars, display remarkable similarity to hominid specimens from South Africa (Taung; STS 24)[10] as well as to individuals tentatively assigned to *Homo* in East Africa (KNM ER 820, 1507)[11,12]. They depart strongly from the pattern of molarisation displayed in the South African "robust" specimens (TM 1601; SK 61, 64)[10] as well as from East African specimens generally assigned to the same hominid lineage (KNM ER 1477)[13].

The Laetolil permanent canines and incisors are relatively and absolutely large and bear a great deal of lingual relief. They ally themselves similarly to earlier hominid specimens such as STS 3, 50, 51, 52; MLD 11; OH 7, 16; KNM ER 803, 1590 (refs 10, 15, 18–21), as well as to the younger African and Asian specimens usually assigned to *Homo erectus*. These features set the Laetolil specimens apart from the sample including SK 23, 48, 876 and so on; Peninj; KNM CH 1; OH 5, 38; KNM ER 729, 1171 (refs 10, 15, 18–21). The Laetolil permanent premolars show none of the molarisation seen in the latter specimens and bear particularly strong resemblances to South and East African material (STS 51, 52, 55; OH 7, 16, 24; KNM ER 808, 992) (refs 10–12, 14).

The Laetolil permanent molars are consistent in aligning with the South African "gracile" australopithecus and the East African *Homo* material in both size and morphology. The molars do not display the increased size, extra cusps or bulging, expanded, "puffy" development of the individual cusps seen in high frequency among South and East African "robust" forms (SK 6, 13, 48, 52; TM 1517; Peninj; KNM CH 1; KNM ER 729, 801, 802) (refs 10, 17–20). The adult mandible has resemblances to certain East African specimens such as KNM ER 1802, with similar corpus section and basal eversion.

The Laetolil fossil hominids have several features possibly consistent with their radiometric age. These traits include the large crown size and lingual morphology of the permanent canines; the morphology and wear of the $C/P_3$ complex; the buccolingually elongate upper premolars; the overall square occlusal aspect of the lower permanent molars; the low symphyseal angle; the bulbous anterior symphysis; the relatively straight posterior tooth rows; the low placement of the mental foramina, and the distinctive lateral corpus contours including small, superiorly placed extramolar sulci.

Preliminary assessment indicates strong resemblance between the Laetolil hominids and later radiometrically-dated specimens assigned to the genus *Homo* in East Africa. Such assessment suggests placement of the Laetolil specimens among the earliest firmly dated members of this genus. It should come as no surprise that the earlier members of the genus *Homo* display an increasing frequency of features generally interpreted as "primitive" or "pongid like", which indicate derivation from as yet largely hypothetical ancestors.

Much of the recently discovered comparable fossil hominid material from the Hadar region of Ethiopia shows strong similarity to the Laetolil specimens[23], and further collection combined with detailed comparative analysis of material from both localities

乳齿，尤其是第一下乳臼齿，表现出了与南非的人科动物标本（汤恩；STS 24）[10]以及暂时被归入人属的在东非发现的那些个体（KNM ER 820、1507）[11,12] 具有非常显著的相似性。它们与南非"粗壮型"标本（TM 1601；SK 61、64）[10] 以及被归入同一人科谱系的东非标本（KNM ER 1477）[13] 所表现出来的臼齿化模式非常不同。

莱托利尔的恒犬齿和门齿标本的相对大小和绝对大小都很大，具有大量的舌面突起。它们与早期的人科动物标本在亲缘关系上很相似，例如 STS 3、50、51、52；MLD 11；OH 7、16；KNM ER 803、1590（参考文献 10、15、18~21），与通常被划分为直立人的幼体非洲标本和亚洲标本在亲缘关系上也很相似。这些特征使得莱托利尔标本与如下标本区别开来：SK 23、48、876 等；佩宁伊；KNM CH 1；OH 5、38；KNM ER 729、1171（参考文献 10、15、18~21）。莱托利尔恒前臼齿完全没有在后来的标本中所见到的臼齿化现象，并且与南非和东非标本（STS 51、52、55；OH 7、16、24；KNM ER 808、992）（参考文献 10~12、14）非常相似。

莱托利尔恒臼齿与南非"纤细型"南方古猿和东非人属标本在大小和形态学上都具有一致性。这些臼齿没有表现出在南非和东非"粗壮型"南方古猿（SK 6、13、48、52；TM 1517；佩宁伊；KNM CH 1；KNM ER 729、801、802）（参考文献 10、17~20）中高频出现的尺寸增大、出现额外的牙尖或突起、单个牙尖扩展的、"肿胀的"发育情况等。成年下颌骨与某些东非标本（如 KNM ER 1802）具有相像之处，它们具有相似的下颌体部分和基底外翻。

莱托利尔人科动物化石具有的几个特征可能与它们的放射性年代一致。这些特点包括：恒犬齿的大齿冠尺寸和舌侧形态；C/P3 复合体的形态和磨损情况；颊舌向延长的上前臼齿；下恒臼齿大体呈方形的咬合面；小的联合部角度；球根状的联合部前部；相对直的后齿列；颏孔的低位，以及独特的下颌体外侧面轮廓，包括小型的、位置靠上的外侧臼齿槽。

初期评估暗示莱托利尔人科动物和经放射性测年法确定时代较晚的属于人属的东非标本非常相似。这一估计表明了莱托利尔标本在已确定年代的早期人属成员中的地位。早期的人属成员表现出某些特征的出现频率逐渐增加的趋势，这些特征通常被认为是"原始的"或者"似猩猩科的"，这一现象并不足为奇，这表明了它们很可能是从迄今为止在很大程度上还是假定的祖先进化而来的。

最近在埃塞俄比亚的哈达尔地区发现的很多类似的人科动物化石标本显示出与莱托利尔标本极大的相似性 [23]，对这两处遗址进行进一步的标本采集并对这些标本进行详细的比较分析，这对于进一步理解人类起源是很关键的。莱托利尔标本丰富

is essential for the further understanding of human origins. The Laetolil collection adds to the developing phylogenetic perspective of the early Hominidae and emphasises the need for taxonomic schemes reflective of and consistent with the evolutionary processes involved in the origin and radiation of this family.

We thank the following for facilities, financial support, permission to examine originals and for discussion: the United Republic of Tanzania, the trustees of the National Museums of Kenya, the NSF Graduate Fellowship Program, the Scott Turner Fund, the Rackham Dissertation Fund, the National Geographic Society, G. Brent Dalrymple, C. K. Brain, T. Gray, D. C. Johanson, K. Kimeu, P. Leakey, R. E. F. Leakey, P. V. Tobias, E. Vrba, A. Walker, C. Weiler and B. Wood.

(**262**, 460-466; 1976)

M. D. Leakey[*], R. L. Hay[*], G. H. Curtis[*], R. E. Drake[*], M. K. Jackes[*] and T.D. White[†]
[*]Olduvai Gorge, PO Box 30239, Nairobi, Kenya.
[†]Department of Anthropology, University of Michigan, Ann Arbor, Michigan 48104.

Received March 30; accepted May 26, 1976.

---

References:

1. Weinert, H., *Z. Morph. Anthrop.*, **42**, 138-148 (1950).

2. Dietrich, W. O., *Palaeontographica*, **94A**, 43-133 (1942).

3. Maglio, V. J., *Breviora*, 336 (1969).

4. Kent, P. E., *Geol. Mag., Lond.*, **78**, 173-184 (1941).

5. Kohl-Larsen, L., *Auf des Spuren des Vormenschen*, **2**, 379-381 (1943).

6. Pickering, R., *Endulen, Quarter Degree Sheet 52* (Geological Survey in Tanzania, 1964).

7. Hay, R. L., *Bull. Geol. Soc. Am.*, 1281-1286 (1963).

8. Hay, R. L., *Geology of the Olduvai Gorge* (University of California Press, 1976).

9. Hopwood, A. T., in *Olduvai Gorge* (edit. by Leakey, L. S. B.), (Cambridge University Press, 1951).

10. Robinson, J. T., *Transvaal Museum Mem.*, 9, 1 (1956).

11. Leakey, R. E. F., and Wood, B. A., *Am. J. Phys. Anthrop.*, **39**, 355 (1973).

12. Leakey, R. E. F., and Wood, B. A., *Am. J. Phys. Anthrop.*, **39**, 355 (1974).

13. Leakey, R. E. F., *Nature*, **242**, 170 (1972).

14. Leakey, L. S. B., *Nature*, **188**, 1050 (1960).

15. Leakey, L. S. B., and Leakey, M. D., *Nature*, **202**, 3 (1964).

16. Day, M. H., and Leakey, R. E. F., *Am. J. Phys. Anthrop.*, **41**, 367 (1974).

17. Leakey, R. E. F., *Nature*, **248**, 653 (1974).

18. Carney, J., Hill, A., Miller, J., and Walker, A., *Nature*, **230**, 509 (1971).

19. Leakey, R. E. F., Mungai, J. M., and Walker, A. C., *Am. J. Phys. Anthrop.*, **36**, 235 (1972).

20. Leakey, R. E. F., and Walker, A. C., *Am. J. Phys. Anthrop.*, **39**, 205 (1973).

21. Tobias, P. V., *Olduvai Gorge*, 2 (Cambridge University Press, 1967).

22. Leakey, M. D., Clarke, R. J., and Leakey, L. S. B., *Nature*, **232**, 308 (1971).

23. Johanson, D. C., and Taieb, M., *Nature*, 260, 293-297 (1976).

了对早期人科动物的系统演化的认识，强调了分类学框架需要反映涉及人科动物起源和辐射进化的过程并与此过程保持一致。

我们感谢以下团体和个人为我们提供设备、经济支持，允许我们对原始标本进行研究，以及与我们进行讨论：坦桑尼亚联合共和国、肯尼亚国家博物馆的理事们、国家科学基金会研究生奖学金项目、斯科特·特纳基金、拉克姆论文基金、国家地理学会、布伦特·达尔林普尔、布雷恩、格雷、约翰森、基梅乌、菲利普·利基、理查德·利基、托拜厄斯、弗尔巴、沃克、韦勒和伍德。

（刘皓芳 翻译；董为 审稿）

# Nucleotide Sequence of Bacteriophage ΦX174 DNA

F. Sanger *et al.*

## Editor's Note

By 1977, English biochemist Frederick Sanger had developed the "dideoxy" method for sequencing DNA. Here he applies it to sequence the genome of the ΦX174 bacteriophage, making it the first fully-sequenced DNA-based genome. The single-stranded, circular genome contains just over 5,000 nucleotides. Sanger's group went on to sequence human mitochondrial DNA, and developed the whole-genome shotgun method to decode the genome of bacteriophage lambda, an important virus for molecular biology research. His work laid the foundations for all genome sequencing projects, which continue to shed light on the processes of health, disease, development and evolution. It also earned Sanger his second Nobel Prize in Chemistry. The first, in 1958, was for his work on the structure of proteins.

---

A DNA sequence for the genome of bacteriophage ΦX174 of approximately 5,375 nucleotides has been determined using the rapid and simple "plus and minus" method. The sequence identifies many of the features responsible for the production of the proteins of the nine known genes of the organism, including initiation and termination sites for the proteins and RNAs. Two pairs of genes are coded by the same region of DNA using different reading frames.

---

THE genome of bacteriophage ΦX174 is a single-stranded, circular DNA of approximately 5,400 nucleotides coding for nine known proteins. The order of these genes, as determined by genetic techniques[2-4], is *A-B-C-D-E-J-F-G-H*. Genes *F, G* and *H* code for structural proteins of the virus capsid, and gene *J* (as defined by sequence work) codes for a small basic protein that is also part of the virion. Gene *A* is required for double-stranded DNA replication and single-strand synthesis. Genes *B, C* and *D* are involved in the production of viral single-stranded DNA: however, the exact function of these gene products is not clear as they may either be involved directly in DNA synthesis or be required for DNA packaging, which is coupled with single-strand production. Gene *E* is responsible for lysis of the host.

The first nucleotide sequences established in ΦX were pyrimidine tracts[5-7] obtained by the Burton and Petersen[8] depurination procedure. The longer tracts could be obtained pure and sequences of up to 10 nucleotides were obtained. More recently Chadwell[9] has improved the hydrazinolysis method to obtain the longer purine tracts. These results are included in the sequence given in Fig. 1.

# 噬菌体 ΦX174 的 DNA 核苷酸序列

桑格等

## 编者按

至 1977 年，英国生物化学家弗雷德里克·桑格已经开发出了用于 DNA 测序的"双脱氧"法。本文中，他应用这种方法对 ΦX174 噬菌体的基因组进行了测序，使其成为第一个被完全测序的 DNA 基因组。这个单链环状基因组只包含 5,000 多个核苷酸。紧接着桑格的研究小组对人类线粒体 DNA 进行了测序，还开发了全基因组鸟枪法破译了分子生物学研究中一个重要病毒——λ 噬菌体的基因组。桑格的工作为所有的基因组测序项目奠定了基础，这些项目又进一步为健康、疾病、发育和进化的研究进展提供了线索。这些工作使桑格赢得了他的第二个诺贝尔化学奖，早在 1958 年，在蛋白质结构方面的工作使桑格第一次获得诺贝尔化学奖。

---

应用快速、简便的"加减测序法"，我们确定了大约含有 5,375 个核苷酸的 ΦX174 噬菌体基因组的 DNA 序列。从这一序列发现了这个生物的 9 个已知基因产生蛋白质的许多特征，包括蛋白质和 RNA 的起始位点与终止位点。有两对基因由同一段 DNA 编码，只是具有不同的阅读框。

---

噬菌体 ΦX174 的基因组是一个单链环状 DNA，由将近 5,400 个核苷酸组成，编码 9 种已知蛋白。通过遗传学技术确定的这些基因的排列顺序 [2-4] 为 A–B–C–D–E–J–F–G–H。基因 F、G 和 H 编码病毒衣壳的结构蛋白。基因 J（由测序工作确定）编码一个小的碱性蛋白，这个蛋白也是病毒粒子的一部分。基因 A 负责双链 DNA 的复制和单链 DNA 的合成。基因 B、C 和 D 与病毒单链 DNA 的合成有关；然而，这些基因产物的确切功能还不是很明确，因为它们要么与 DNA 合成直接相关，要么是与单链 DNA 合成相偶联的 DNA 包装所需要的。基因 E 负责宿主的裂解。

在 ΦX 中第一个被测定的序列是嘧啶区域的核苷酸序列 [5-7]，它是通过伯顿和彼得森 [8] 的脱嘌呤方法完成的。我们能够获得长达 10 个核苷酸的纯化片段。最近，查德韦尔 [9] 改进了肼解方法以获得更长的嘌呤区域。在图 1 中给出了上述这些区域的序列。

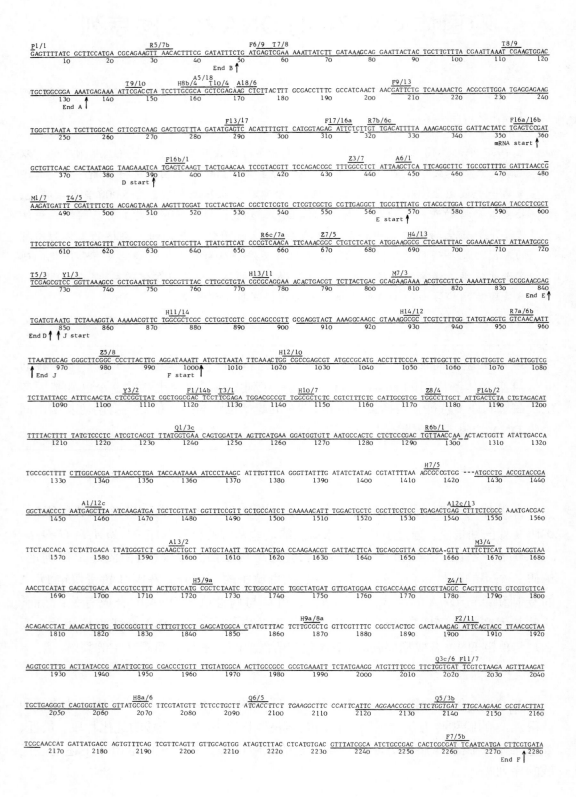

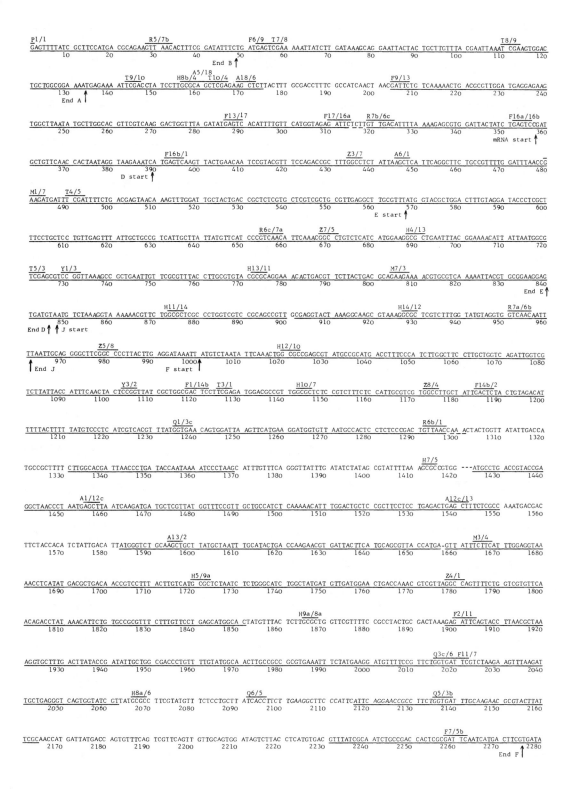

```
                                                      R1/9              H6/3
AAAGATTGAG TGTGAGGTTA TAACCGAAGC GGTAAAAATT TTAATTTTTG CCGCTGAGGG GTTGACCAAG CGAAGCGCGG TAGGTTTTCT GCTTAGGAGT TTAATCATGT TTCAGACTTT
    2290       2300       2310       2320       2330       2340       2350       2360       2370       2380       2390       2400
                                                                                                                    G start ↑

                              A2/16                     A16/15a M4/10                                     A15a/3       R9/10
TATTTCTCGC CACAATTCAA ACTTTTTTTC TGATAAGCTG GTTCTCACTT CTGTTACTCC AGCTTCTTCG GCACCTGTTT TACAGACACC TAAAGCTACA TCGTCAACGT TATATTTTGA
    2410       2420       2430       2440       2450       2460       2470       2480       2490       2500       2510       2520

              M10/9                           R10/2
TAGTTTGACG GTTAATGCTG GTAATGGTGG TTTTCTTCAT TGCATTCAGA TGGATACATC TGTCAACGCC GCTAATCAGG TTGTTTCAGT TGGTGCTGAT ATTGCTTTTG ATGCCGACCC
    2530       2540       2550       2560       2570       2580       2590       2600       2610       2620       2630       2640

              F5b/8 M9/2
TAAATTTTTT GCCTGTTTGG TTCGCTTTGA GTCTTCTTCG GTTCCGACTA CCCTCCCGAC TGCCTATGAT GTTTATCCTT TGGATGGTCG CCATGATGGT GGTTATTATA CCGTCAAGGA
    2650       2660       2670       2680       2690       2700       2710       2720       2730       2740       2750       2760

              Y2/5                                                                                               F8/4
CTGTGTGACT ATTGACGTCC TTCCCCGTAC GCCCCGGCAAT AACGTCTACG TTGGTTTCAT GGTTTGGTCT AACTTTACCG CTACTAAATG CCGCGGATTG GTTTCGCTGA ATCAGGTTAT
    2770       2780       2790       2800       2810       2820       2830       2840       2850       2860       2870       2880

                             Q3b/4
TAAAGAGATT ATTTGTCTCC AGCCACTTAA GTGAGGTGAT TTATGTTTGG TGCTATTGCT GGCGGTATTG CTTCTGCTCT GCCTGGTGGC GCCATGTCTA AATTGTTTGG AGGCGGTCAA
    2890       2900       2910       2920       2930       2940       2950       2960       2970       2980       2990       3000
                      End G ↑    H start ↑                                            H3/2

              Y5/4            Q4/7                                        Q7/2
AAAGCCGCCT CCGGTGGCAT TCAAGGTGAT GTGCTTGCTA CCGATAACAA TACTGTAGGC ATGGGTGATG CTGGTATTAA ATCTGCCATT CAAGGCTCTA ATGTTCCTAA CCCTGATGAG
    3010       3020       3030       3040       3050       3060       3070       3080       3090       3100       3110       3120

Z1/2                                      A3/9
GCCGCCCCTA GTTTTGTTTC GTGTGCTATT GCTAAAGCTG GTAAAGGACT TCTTGAAGGT ACGTTGCAGG CTGGCACTTC TGCCGTTTCT GATAAGTTGC TTGATTTGGT TGGACTTGGT
    3130       3140       3150       3160       3170       3180       3190       3200       3210       3220       3230       3240

                                                                A9/12d                                                   R2/6a
GGCAAGTCTG CCGCTGATAA AGGAAAGGAT ACTCGTGATT ATCTTGCTCC TGCATTTCCT GAGCTTAATG CTTGGGAGCC TGCTGGTGCT GATGCTTCCT CTGCTGGTAT GGTTGACGCC
    3250       3260       3270       3280       3290       3300       3310       3320       3330       3340       3350       3360

Y4/1   F4/14a   A12d/7c                                                       F14a/12
GGATTTGAGA ATCAAAAAGA GCTTACTAAA ATGCAACTGG ACAATCAGAA AGAGATTGCC GAGATGCAAA ATGAGACTCA AAAAGAGATT GCTGGCATTC AGTCGGCGAC TTCACGCCAG
    3370       3380       3390       3400       3410       3420       3430       3440       3450       3460       3470       3480

                                                   F12/10
AATACGAAAG ACCAGGTATA TGCACAAAAT GAGATGCTTG CTTATTC-AC AGAAGGAGTC TACTGCTGCG TTGCGTCTAT TATGGAAAAC ACCAATCTTT CCAAGCAACA GCAGGTTTCC
    3490       3500       3510       3520       3530       3540       3550       3560       3570       3580       3590       3600

    H2/9b                 A7c/8                                            F10/15            R6a/4
GAGATTATGC GCCAAATGCT TACTCAAGCT CAAACGGCTG GTCAGTATTT TACCAATGAC CAAATCAAAG AAATGACTCG CAAGGTTAGT GCTGAGGTTG ACTTAGTTCA TCAGCAAACG
    3610       3620       3630       3640       3650       3660       3670       3680       3690       3700       3710       3720

F15/5c          M2/5         H9b/1                                                                                 A8/14
CAGAATCAGC GGTATGGCTC TTCTCATATT GGCGCTACTG CAAAGGATAT TTCTAATGTC GTCACTGATG CTGCTTCTGG TGTGGTTGAT ATTTTTCATG GTATTGATAA AGCTGTTGCC
    3730       3740       3750       3760       3770       3780       3790       3800       3810       3820       3830       3840

                              A14/7b
GATACTTGGA ACAATTTCTG GAAAGACGGT AAAGCTGATG GTATTGGCTC TAATTTGTCT AGGAAATAAC CGTCAGGATT GACACCCTCC CAATTGTATG TTTTCATGCC TCCAAATCTT
    3850       3860       3870       3880       3890       3900       3910       3920       3930       3940       3950       3960
                                                             End H ↑                                             mRNA start ↑

                                                                       T1/6
GGAGGCTTTT TTATGGTTCG TTCTTATTAC CCTTCTGAAT GTCACGCTGA TTATTTTGAC TTTGAGCGTA TCGAGGCTCT TAAACCTGCT ATTGAGGCTT GTGGCATTTC TACTCTTTCT
    3970       3980       3990       4000       4010       4020       4030       4040       4050       4060       4070       4080
        A start ↑

                                          A7b/7a  M5/8 F5c/3                                      T6/2    Q2/3a         R4/3  Z2/6b
CAATCCCCAA TGCTTGGCTT CCATAAGCAG ATGGATAACC GCATCAAGCT CTTGGAAGAG ATTCTGTCTT TTCGTATGCA GGGCGTTGAG TTCGATAATG GTGATATGTA TGTTGACGGC
    4090       4100       4110       4120       4130       4140       4150       4160       4170       4180       4190       4200

CATAAGGCTG CTTCTGACGT TCGTGATGAG TTTGTATCTG TTACTGAGAA GTTAATGGAT GAATTGGCAC AATGCTACAA TGTGCTCCCC CAACTTGATA TTAATAACAC TATAGACCAC
    4210       4220       4230       4240       4250       4260       4270       4280       4290       4300       4310       4320

                                          M8/6           A7a/4
CGCCCCGAAG GGGACGAAAA ATGGTTTTTA GAGAACGAGA AGACGGTTAC GCAGTTTTGC AAGCTGGCTG CTGAACGCCC TCTTAAGGAT ATTCGCGATG AGTATAATTA CCCCAAAAAG
    4330       4340       4350       4360       4370       4380       4390       4400       4410       4420       4430       4440

                     Z6b/6a
AAAGGTATTA AGGATGAGTG TTCAAGATTG CTGGAGGCCT CCACTAAGAT ATCGCGTAGA GGCTTTGCTA TTCAGCGTTT GATGAATGCA ATGCGACAGG CTCATGCTGA TGGTTGGTTT
    4450       4460       4470       4480       4490       4500       4510       4520       4530       4540       4550       4560

ATCGTTTTTG ACACTCTCAC GTTGGCTGAC GACCGATTAG AGGCGTTTTA TGATAATCCC AATGCTTTGC GTGACTATTT TCGTGATATT GGTCGTATGG TTCTTGCTGC CGAGGGTCGC
    4570       4580       4590       4600       4610       4620       4630       4640       4650       4660       4670       4680
```

```
                                                          R1/9           H6/3
AAAGATTGAG TGTGAGGTTA TAACCGAAGC GGTAAAAATT TTAATTTTTG CCGCTGAGGG GTTGACCAAG CGAAGCGCGG TAGGTTTTCT GCTTAGGAGT TTAATCATGT TTCAGACTTT
      2290       2300       2310       2320       2330       2340       2350       2360       2370       2380       2390       2400
                                                                                                                G start    ↑

                                   A2/16                      A16/15a M4/1o                            A15a/3     R9/1o
TATTTCTCGC CACAATTCAA ACTTTTTTTC TGATAAGCTG GTTCTCACTT CTGTTACTCC AGCTTCTTCG GCACCTGTTT TACAGACACC TAAAGCTACA TCGTCAACGT TATATTTTGA
      2410       2420       2430       2440       2450       2460       2470       2480       2490       2500       2510       2520

                 M1o/9                           R1o/2
TAGTTTGACG GTTAATGCTG GTAATGGTGG TTTTCTTCAT TGCATTCAGA TGGATACATC TGTCAACGCC GCTAATCAGG TTGTTTCAGT TGGTGCTGAT ATTGCTTTTG ATGCCGACCC
      2530       2540       2550       2560       2570       2580       2590       2600       2610       2620       2630       2640

                 F5b/8  M9/2
TAAATTTTTT GCCTGTTTGG TTCGCTTTGA GTCTTCTTCG GTTCCGACTA CCCTCCCGAC TGCCTATGAT GTTTATCCTT TGGATGGTCG CCATGATGGT GGTTATTATA CCGTCAAGGA
      2650       2660       2670       2680       2690       2700       2710       2720       2730       2740       2750       2760

                       Y2/5                                                                                              F8/4
CTGTGTGACT ATTGACGTCC TTCCCCGTAC GCCCGGCAAT AACGTCTACG TTGGTTTCAT GGTTTGGTCT AACTTTACCG CTACTAAATG CCGCGGATTG GTTTCGCTGA ATCAGGTTAT
      2770       2780       2790       2800       2810       2820       2830       2840       2850       2860       2870       2880

                             Q3b/4
TAAAGAGATT ATTTGTCTCC AGCCACTTAA GTGAGGTGAT TTATGTTTGG TGCTATTGCT GGCGGTATTG CTTCTGCTCT TGCTGGTGGC GCCATGTCTA AATTGTTTGG AGGCGGTCAA
      2890       2900       2910       2920       2930       2940       2950       2960       2970       2980       2990       3000
                        ↑         ↑
                   End G    H start  ↑

          Y5/4       Q4/7
AAAGCCGCCT CCGGTGGCAT TCAAGGTGAT GTGCTTGCTA CCGATAACAA TACTGTAGGC ATGGGTGATG CTGGTATTAA ATCTGCCATT CAAGGCTCTA ATGTTCCTAA CCCTGATGAG
      3010       3020       3030       3040       3050       3060       3070       3080       3090       3100       3110       3120

Z1/2                              A3/9
GCCGCCCCTA GTTTTGTTTC TGTGTGCTATT GCTAAAGCTG GTAAAGGACT TCTTGAAGGT ACGTTGCAGG CTGGCACTTC TGCCGGTTTCT GATAAGTTGC TTGATTTGGT TGGACTTGGT
      3130       3140       3150       3160       3170       3180       3190       3200       3210       3220       3230       3240

                                                    A9/12d                                                             R2/6a
GGCAAGTCTG CCGCTGATAA AGGAAAGGAT ACTCGTGATT ATCTTGCTGC TGCATTTCCT GAGCTTAATG CTTGGGACCG TGCTGGTGCT GATGCTTCCT CTGCTGGTGT GGTTGACGCC
      3250       3260       3270       3280       3290       3300       3310       3320       3330       3340       3350       3360

Y4/1     F4/14a   A12d/7c
GGATTTGAGA ATCAAAAAGA GCTTACTAAA ATGCAACTGG ACAATCAGAA AGAGATTGCC GAGATGCAAA ATGAGACTCA AAAAGAGATT GCTGGCATTC AGTCGGCGAC TTCACGCCAG
      3370       3380       3390       3400       3410       3420       3430       3440       3450       3460       3470       3480

                                             F12/1o
AATACGAAAG ACCAGGTATA TGCACAAAAT GAGATGCTTG CTTATTC-AC AGAAGGAGTC TACTGCTGCG TTGCGTCTAT TATGGAAAAC ACCAATCTTT CCAAGCAACA GCAGGTTTCC
      3490       3500       3510       3520       3530       3540       3550       3560       3570       3580       3590       3600

     H2/9b            A7c/8                                          F1o/15         R6a/4
GAGATTATGC GCCAAATGCT TACTCAAGCT CAAACCGCTG GTCAGTATTT TACCAATGAC CAAATCAAAG AAATGACTCG CAAGGTTAGT GCTGAGGTTG ACTTAGTTCA TCAGCAAACG
      3610       3620       3630       3640       3650       3660       3670       3680       3690       3700       3710       3720

F15/5c        M2/5      H9b/1                                                                                          A8/14
CAGAATCAGC GGTATGGCTC TTCTCATATT GGCGCTACTG CAAAGGATAT TTCTAATGTC GTCACTGATG CTGCTTCTGG TGTGGTTGAT ATTTTTCATG GTATTGATAA AGCTGTTGCC
      3730       3740       3750       3760       3770       3780       3790       3800       3810       3820       3830       3840

                         A14/7b
GATACTTGGA ACAATTTCTG GAAAGACGGT AAAGCTGATG GTATTGGCTC TAATTTGTCT AGGAAATAAC CGTCAGGATT GACACCCTCC CAATTGTATG TTTTCATGCC TCCAAATCTT
      3850       3860       3870       3880       3890       3900       3910       3920       3930       3940       3950       3960
                            ↑                                    ↑                                            ↑
                       A start                              End H                                    mRNA start

                                     T1/6
GGAGGCTTTT TTATGGTTCG TTCTTATTAC CCTTCTGAAT GTCACGCTGA TTATTTTGAC TTTGAGCGTA TCGAGGCTCT TAAACCTGCT ATTGAGGCTT GTGGCATTTC TACTCTTTCT
      3970       3980       3990       4000       4010       4020       4030       4040       4050       4060       4070       4080
        ↑
  A start  ↑

                              A7b/7a   M5/8  F5c/3                             T6/2    Q2/3a      R4/3 Z2/6b
CAATCCCCAA TGCTTGGCTT CCATAAGCAG ATGGATAACC GCATCAAGCT CTTGGAAGAG ATTCTGTCTT TTCGTATGCA GGGCGTTGAG TTCGATAATG GTGATATGTA TGTTGACGGC
      4090       4100       4110       4120       4130       4140       4150       4160       4170       4180       4190       4200

CATAAGGCTG CTTCTGACGT TCGTGATGAG TTTGTATCTG TTACTGAGAA GTTAATGGAT GAATTGGCAC AATGCTACAA TGTGCTCCCC CAACTTGATA TTAATAACAC TATAGACCAC
      4210       4220       4230       4240       4250       4260       4270       4280       4290       4300       4310       4320

                            M8/6                      A7a/4
CGCCCCGAAG GGGACGAAAA ATGGTTTTTA GAGAACGAGA AGACGGTTAC GCAGTTTTGC AAGCTGGCTG CTGAACGCCC TCTTAAGGAT ATTCGCGATG AGTATAATTA CCCCAAAAAG
      4330       4340       4350       4360       4370       4380       4390       4400       4410       4420       4430       4440

               Z6b/6a
AAAGGTATTA AGGATGAGTG TTCAAGATTG CTGGAGGCCT CCACTAAGAT ATCGCGTAGA GGCTTTGCTA TTCAGCGTTT GATGAATGCA ATGCGACAGG CTCATGCTGA TGGTTGGTTT
      4450       4460       4470       4480       4490       4500       4510       4520       4530       4540       4550       4560

ATCGTTTTTG ACACTCTCAC GTTGGCTGAC GACCGATTAG AGGCGTTTTA TGATAATCCC AATGCTTTGC GTGACTATTT TCGTGATATT GGTCGTATGG TTCTTGCTGC CGAGGGTCGC
      4570       4580       4590       4600       4610       4620       4630       4640       4650       4660       4670       4680
```

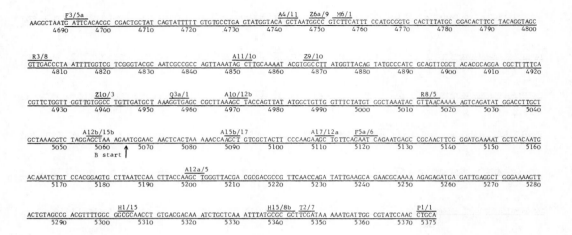

Fig. 1. A provisional nucleotide sequence for the DNA of bacteriophage ΦX174 *am*3 *cs*70. Solid underlining indicates sequences that are fully confirmed; sequences with no underlining probably do not contain more than one mistake per 50 residues. Broken underlining indicates more uncertain sequences. Restriction enzyme recognition sites are indicated (for key to single letter enzyme code see legend to Fig. 2), as are mRNA starts and protein initiation and termination sites. Nucleotides 4,127 to 4,201 have been independently sequenced by van Mansfield *et al.*[58]. The *am*3 codon is at position 587.

More extensive ΦX sequences were obtained using partial degradation techniques, particularly with endonuclease IV (refs 10 and 11). Ziff *et al.*[12,13] used this enzyme in conditions of partial hydrolysis to obtain fragments 50-200 nucleotides long which were purified as [32]P-labelled material by electrophoresis on polyacrylamide gels. The fragments came from the same region of the genome and the sequence of a 48-nucleotide long fragment (band 6, positions 1,047-1,094) was determined using mainly further degradation with endonuclease IV and partial exonuclease digestions.

Another 50-nucleotide long fragment was obtained by Robertson *et al.*[14] as a ribosome binding site. The viral (or plus) strand DNA of ΦX has the same sequence as the mRNA and, in certain conditions, will bind ribosomes so that a protected fragment can be isolated and sequenced. Only one major site was found. By comparison with the amino acid sequence data it was found that this ribosome binding site sequence coded for the initiation of the gene *G* protein[15] (positions 2,362-2,413).

At this stage sequencing techniques using primed synthesis with DNA polymerase were being developed[16] and Schott[17] synthesised a decanucleotide with a sequence complementary to part of the ribosome binding site. This was used to prime into the intercistronic region between the *F* and *G* genes, using DNA polymerase and [32]P-labelled triphosphates[18]. The ribo-substitution technique[16] facilitated the sequence determination of the labelled DNA produced. This decanucleotide-primed system was also used to develop the plus and minus method[1]. Suitable synthetic primers are, however, difficult to prepare and as DNA fragments generated by restriction enzymes are more readily available these have been used for most of the work reported here.

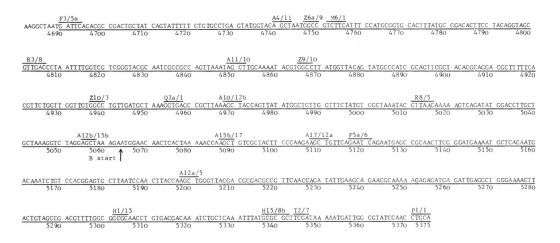

图 1. 噬菌体 ΦX174 *am*3 *cs*70 DNA 的暂定核苷酸序列。下面划实线的序列表示已经被完全确定；下面未划线的序列表示每 50 个核苷酸残基包含不超过 1 个错误碱基。下面划虚线的表示不确定的序列。限制性内切酶识别位点（酶编码的单字母缩写含义见图 2 注），mRNA（信使核糖核酸）转录起始位点，蛋白质翻译起始位点和终止位点均已标明。核苷酸 4,127 到 4,201 已经由范曼斯菲尔德等人[58]独立完成测序。*am*3 密码子在第 587 位。

利用部分降解技术，尤其是利用核酸内切酶 IV（参考文献 10 和 11），人们测定了更多的 ΦX 序列。齐夫等 [12,13] 利用核酸内切酶 IV 对核酸序列进行部分水解，通过聚丙烯酰胺凝胶电泳的方法纯化获得了 $^{32}$P 标记的 50~200 个核苷酸长度的序列。这些片段来自基因组的相同区域，其中片段长度为 48 个核苷酸的序列（条带 6，1,047~1,094 区域）主要是利用核酸内切酶 IV 的进一步降解和外切酶的部分消化来测定的。

罗伯逊等[14] 发现另外一个 50 个核苷酸长度的片段是核糖体结合位点。ΦX 的病毒（正）链 DNA 与其 mRNA 具有相同的序列，并且在某些条件下能与核糖体结合，因此这段受保护的序列才得以分离和测序。用这一方法只发现了一个主要的核糖体结合位点。与氨基酸序列数据比较发现，这段核糖体结合位点的序列（2,362~2,413 区域）编码基因 *G* 蛋白的起始位点 [15]。

在这一时期，利用 DNA 聚合酶进行引物合成的测序技术得到发展 [16]，肖特[17] 合成了一段 10 个核苷酸的序列，该序列与部分核糖体结合位点的序列互补。用这一序列作为引物，利用 DNA 聚合酶和 $^{32}$P 标记的三磷酸盐 [18] 对基因 *F* 和 *G* 之间的顺反子间区进行合成。再用核苷酸置换技术 [16] 对带标记的 DNA 产物进行序列鉴定。这种用 10 个核苷酸作为引物的系统也被用于发展加减测序法 [1]。虽然合成完全相配的引物很不容易，但是利用限制性内切酶产生 DNA 片段却容易，因此这个方法在本文报道的大部分工作中都有应用。

Another approach to DNA sequencing is to make an RNA copy using RNA polymerase with α-[32]P-labelled ribotriphosphates and then to determine the RNA sequence by more established methods. Blackburn[19,20] used this approach on intact single-stranded ΦX and on fragments obtained by digestion with endonuclease IV or with restriction enzymes. Sedat *et al.*[21] were extending their studies on the larger endonuclease IV fragments and their results, taken in conjunction with the transcription of the DNA fragments[20], amino acid sequence of the F protein[22], and the plus and minus method results, made it possible to deduce a sequence of 281 nucleotides (positions 1,016-1,296, Fig. 1) within the *F* gene[23]. Transcription of *Hind*II fragment 10, amino acid sequence data in the *G* gene, and the plus and minus method using *Hind*II fragments 2 and 10 as primers, gave a sequence of 195 nucleotides (positions 2,387-2,582, Fig. 1) at the N terminus of gene *G* (ref. 24).

## The "plus and minus" Method

Further work on the ΦX sequence has been done using chiefly the plus and minus method primed with restriction fragments. Figure 2 shows the various restriction enzymes used and the fragment maps for each (refs 25-30 and C.A.H., submitted for publication, and N.L.B., C.A.H. and M.S., submitted for publication).

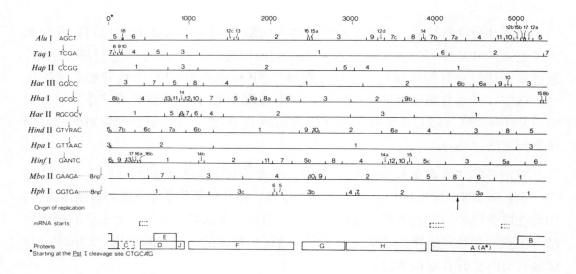

Fig. 2. Fragment maps of restriction enzymes used in the sequence analysis of ΦX174 *am*3 RFI DNA. Fragment maps of ΦX174 have been prepared for *Hind*II (R), *Hae*III (Z) and *Hpa*I+II by Lee and Sinsheimer[25], *Hin*HI and *Hap*II (Y) by Hayashi and Hayashi[26], and for *Alu*I (A) by Vereijken *et al.*[27] and for *Pst*I (P) by Brown and Smith[30]. B.G.B., G.M.A., C.A.H. and D. Jaffe prepared the *Hinf*I (F) map, C.A.H. the *Hph*I (Q) map, and Jeppesen *et al.*[28] the *Hha*I (H), *Alu*I, *Hae*II and *Hap*II maps by using a rapid method depending on priming with DNA polymerase. A rapid two-dimensional hybridisation technique has been developed by C.A.H. (submitted for publication) and recently used for mapping *Mbo*II (M) (N.L.B., C.A.H., and M.S., submitted for publication) and *Taq*I (T)[29]. *Hha*I and *Hinf*I maps have also been prepared by Baas *et al.*[32].

另一种 DNA 测序的方法是利用 RNA 聚合酶和 α–³²P 标记的三磷酸核苷酸合成一段 RNA 拷贝，然后利用更加成熟的方法测定 RNA 序列。布莱克本[19,20] 利用这种方法对完整的 ΦX 单链 DNA 以及用核酸内切酶 IV 或限制性内切酶消化所得的片段进行了测序。赛达特[21] 等将他们的研究拓展到更长的核酸内切酶 IV 酶切片段，他们的研究结果与 DNA 片段的转录[20]、F 蛋白的氨基酸序列[22] 以及加减测序法的结果一起，使得在 F 基因中[23] 推导出一段 281 个核苷酸的序列（1,016~1,269 区域，图 1）成为可能。进而根据 HindII 酶切片段 10 的转录和 G 基因的氨基酸序列数据，以及利用 HindII 片段 2 和 10 作为引物的加减法测序，又推断出 G 基因 N 末端的 195 个核苷酸的序列 （2,387~2,582 区域，图 1）（参考文献 24）。

## "加减法" 测序

我们用限制性酶切片段作为引物，首先主要使用加减法测序对 ΦX 序列进行了进一步的研究。图 2 显示了所用的各种限制性内切酶和每一片段的图谱（参考文献 25~30，哈奇森，已投稿，以及布朗、哈奇森和史密斯，已投稿）。

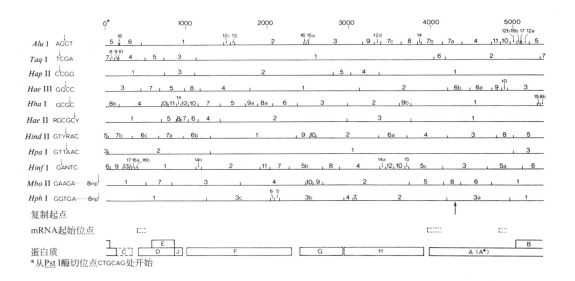

图 2. 在 ΦX174 am3 RFI DNA 序列分析中用到的限制性内切酶的片段图谱。李和辛西默[25] 完成了 HindII (R)、HaeIII (Z)、HpaI+II 的图谱测定，林昌树和林玛丽[26] 完成了 HinHI 和 HapII (Y) 的图谱测定，费赖伊肯等[27] 完成了 AluI (A) 的图谱测定，布朗和史密斯[30] 完成了 PstI (P) 的图谱测定。通过使用基于引物和 DNA 聚合酶的快速扩增方法，巴雷尔、艾尔、哈奇森和贾菲完成了 HinfI (F) 的图谱，哈奇森完成了 HphI (Q) 的图谱，杰普森等[28] 完成了 HhaI (H)、AluI、HaeII 和 HapII 的图谱。哈奇森发展了一种快速的二维杂交技术（已投稿），并于最近用于 MboII (M) （布朗、哈奇森和史密斯，已投稿）和 TaqI (T)[29] 的图谱测定。巴斯等[52] 完成了 HhaI 和 HinfI 的图谱测定。

Figure 1 shows the combined results of the sequence work to date. The sequence is numbered from the single cleavage site of the restriction enzyme *Pst*I. As with other methods of sequencing nucleic acids, the plus and minus technique used by itself cannot be regarded as a completely reliable system and occasional errors may occur. Such errors and uncertainties can only be eliminated by more laborious experiments and, although much of the sequence has been so confirmed, it would probably be a long time before the complete sequence could be established. We are not certain that there is any scientific justification for establishing every detail and, as it is felt that the results may be useful to other workers, it has been decided to publish the sequence in its present form.

As template we have used both the viral (plus) and complementary (minus) strands of ΦX. Usually it is possible to determine a sequence with a single primer starting at about 15-100 nucleotides from the appropriate restriction enzyme site. In a particularly good experiment the sequence can be read out to 150-200 nucleotides but the results may become less reliable. Most sequences have been derived by priming on both strands; this allows more confidence than when only one strand could be used.

A useful method for confirming runs of the same nucleotide is depurination of [32]P-labelled small restriction enzyme fragments or of products of the DNA polymerase priming experiments (ref. 31 and N.L.B. and M.S., in preparation). The most satisfactory way of confirming the DNA sequences is through amino acid sequence data. As the methods used are entirely unrelated, the results of the two approaches complement each other very well and therefore complete sequences can usually be deduced from incomplete data obtained by each method. The complete sequence of genes *G* (ref. 32), *D* (ref. 33), *J* (ref. 33 and Freymeyer, unpublished) and most of *F* have been obtained in this way.

Many of the sequences in Fig. 1 have been amply confirmed and are regarded as established: these are indicated in the figure by underlining. Some sequences are considered to be reasonably accurate and probably contain no more than one mistake in every 50 nucleotides. Sequences that are particularly uncertain—either because of lack of data or conflicting results—are also indicated in Fig. 1.

In considering the sequence of ΦX174 as a functional unit it is convenient to begin in the region between the *H* and *A* genes and to continue around the DNA in the direction of transcription and translation.

## A Promoter and Terminator

Sinsheimer *et al.*[34,35] and Axelrod[36] have determined the sequences of the 5' end of three ΦX *in vitro* mRNA species and have located them on the restriction map. These sequences have been identified on the DNA sequence and one of them (AAATCTTGG) is found only at position 3,954 at which an *in vivo* unstable mRNA start has been located[37]. The sequence to the left of this has some characteristics of typical *E. coli* promoters[38] in that five out of the "ideal" TATPuATPu residues are present. Nearby, to the right of this mRNA initiation,

图1显示了到目前为止序列研究的综合结果。序列自限制性内切酶 *Pst*I 的单一切割位点开始编号。与其他测序方法测定的核苷酸序列相比，加减法测序技术自身不能视为一个可以完全可信的系统，可能偶尔会有错误发生。只有通过更多实验才能消除这些错误和不确定因素。尽管很多序列已经用这样的方法完成测序，但完整序列的全部完成可能还需要很长的时间。我们不很确定继续完成每一个细节的科学理由，但是觉得这些结果会对其他研究人员有所帮助，因此决定以目前的形式公布这个序列。

我们把 ΦX 的病毒（正）链和互补（负）链都用作模板。通常情况下，从合适的限制性内切酶切位点开始大概 15~100 核苷酸处，一个单一引物就可以测定一段序列。在特别好的实验中，能够读出 150~200 个核苷酸，但是这个结果的可信度比较低。这里对大部分序列通过引物进行了双链测定，这比仅仅测定单链具有更高的可信度。

确定一个核苷酸是否正确的一个有效方法是对 [32]P 标记的小的限制性内切酶切片段或者对 DNA 聚合酶扩增的产物进行脱嘌呤（参考文献 31 以及布朗和史密斯准备发表的结果）。验证 DNA 序列最可信的方法是通过氨基酸序列数据分析。由于运用的方法完全不相关，两种方法的结果彼此之间可以很好的互补，因此我们可以通过每种方法得到的不完整核苷酸数据来推断完整的序列。通过这种方法我们已经获得了 G 基因（参考文献 32）、D 基因（参考文献 33）和 J 基因（参考文献 33 以及弗雷迈耶未发表的结果）的全部序列，以及 F 基因的大部分序列。

我们已经充分证实了图1中的许多序列：这些在图中用下划线来标明。有些序列相当准确，可能每 50 个核苷酸中不会多于一个错误。特别不确定的序列是因为缺少数据或者是结果相互冲突，这在图1中也有标明。

考虑到 ΦX174 序列是一个功能单元，为方便起见以下将从基因 H 和基因 A 之间的区域开始，沿 DNA 转录和翻译方向进行介绍。

## A启动子和终止子

辛西默等 [34,35] 和阿克塞尔罗德 [36] 已经在体外确定了 3 种 ΦX mRNA 的 5′ 端序列，并将它们定位在限制性酶切图谱上。这些序列已经在 DNA 序列上得到鉴定，其中一个序列（AAATCTTGG）被发现位于 3,954 位点处，是一个体内不稳定的 mRNA 起始处 [37]。这个序列左侧的序列具有大肠杆菌启动子的一些典型的特征 [38]，

however, is the sequence TTTTTTA which is similar to sequences found at the 3' ends of a number of mRNAs (see ref. 39) and seems a likely signal for mRNA termination. The presence of a rho-independent termination site in this approximate position has been suggested[36,37], but the relative positions of the initiating and putative termination signals is rather surprising since the terminator for one mRNA would be expected to precede the initiator for the next. One possibility is that the $T_6A$ might be acting as an "attenuator" involved in the control of mRNA production in a similar manner to that suggested for the tryptophan operon by Bertrand *et al.*[40]. If indeed it were acting as a transcription terminator one would expect a small RNA of 20 nucleotides to be produced, but no such product has yet been detected. Recent work, however, (Rosenberg, unpublished and ref. 41) indicates that termination may require the presence of a base-paired loop structure before the termination site. From the DNA sequence such a loop is probably present before the $T_6A$ sequence, but in mRNA starting from the initiation site at position 3,954 this loop is not formed (Fig. 3). Therefore mRNA that had started at an earlier promoter and extended through the *H* gene would be expected to terminate here, whereas mRNA newly initiated at position 3,954 would not. This could be a way in which the phage has economised on the use of DNA—by having the ends of the two mRNAs overlapping.

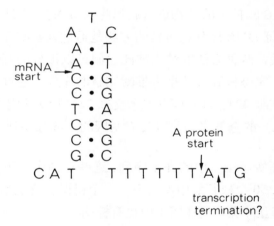

Fig. 3. Potential secondary structure at the *A* mRNA start.

## The A Protein

Where the amino acid sequence is available there is no problem in relating the DNA sequence to its coding properties, but it is more difficult to do so in the absence of such data, as is the case for the A protein. One way of identifying the reading phase of the DNA is from the distribution of nonsense codons. Over a sufficiently long sequence that is known to be coding for a single protein there is usually one phase that contains no nonsense codons, and this is identified as the reading phase. This requires completely accurate determination of the DNA sequences however: omission of a single nucleotide may give completely erroneous results. Another approach is possible in the case of ΦX. The results with the *F* and *G* genes[23,24,32] showed an unexpectedly high frequency of

包含 5 个"理想的"TATPuATPu 残基。然而这个 mRNA 起始处的右侧序列是 TTTTTTA，这与出现在许多 mRNA 的 3′ 端的序列相似（见参考文献 39），似乎是 mRNA 终止的信号。有人提出不依赖于 rho 因子的终止位点就在这个位点附近[36,37]，但起始位点和推测的终止信号的相对位置令人惊讶，因为一般认为一个 mRNA 的终止子应该在下一个启动子之前。一种可能是 T₆A 充当了"衰减子"来控制 mRNA 的生成，其调控模式与伯特兰等人[40] 提出的色氨酸操纵子相似。如果它确实充当转录终止子，我们可以预计将产生一段 20 个核苷酸的小 RNA，但目前为止还没有检测到这样的产物。然而最近的研究（罗森堡，未发表的结果及参考文献 41）表明终止的发生可能需要在终止位点前存在一个碱基配对的环结构。在 DNA 序列中这样一个环可能出现在 T₆A 序列的前面，但在从 3,954 处起始的 mRNA 中并没有形成这个环（图 3）。因此预计由更靠前的一个启动子启动并延伸通过 H 基因的 mRNA 可能终止于此，而新起始于 3,954 位点的 mRNA 并不在此终止。这可能是噬菌体节约使用 DNA 的一种方式——使两个 mRNA 的末端重叠。

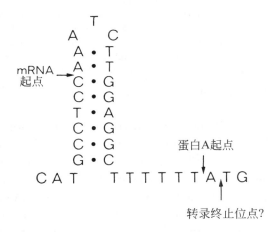

图 3. A基因mRNA起点可能的二级结构

## A 蛋 白

如果已知氨基酸序列就很容易推断出 DNA 序列的编码特性，但是像蛋白 A 这样缺少这些数据时这样做就很困难。鉴别 DNA 阅读框的一个方法是依据无义密码子的分布。对于一段足够长并已知能够编码单一蛋白的序列，通常情况下会有一种读法不含有无义密码子，这就可以断定为是阅读框。这需要对 DNA 序列进行非常精确的测定：缺失一个核苷酸就会导致完全错误的结果。在 ΦX 中还有一种方法也是可行的。F 基因和 G 基因的研究结果[23,24,32] 显示以 T 结尾的密码子的频率出乎意料的高。因此编码区的一个倾向就是每个密码子的第三位核苷酸是 T，这样就可以

codons ending in T. Therefore in a coding region there is a tendency for every third nucleotide to be a T and it is then possible to define the reading phase. Figure 4 illustrates how this characteristic was used to help determine the reading phase for the A protein and to identify its initiation codon at position 3,973. In a similar way the distribution of Ts may be used to identify errors in the DNA sequence, provided that such errors occur only infrequently.

| | | Ts in codon position | | |
|---|---|:---:|:---:|:---:|
| | | (1) | (2) | (3) |
| 3,910 | C C G . T C A . G G A . T T G . A C A . C C C . T C C . C A A . T T G . T A T . | 5 | 2 | 1 |
| | | 3 | 4 | 3* |
| 3,940 | G T T . T T C . A T G . C C T . C C A . A A T . C T T . G G A . G G C . T T T . | 2 | 5 | 5 |
| | | 3 | 5 | 7* |
| 3,970 | T T T . A T G . G T T . C G T . T C T . T A T . T A C . C C T . T C T . G A A . | 5 | 3 | 7 |
| | | 5 | 0 | 7* |
| 4,000 | T G T . C A C . G C T . G A T . T A T . T T T . G A C . T T T . G A G . C G T . | 4 | 2 | 7 |

Fig. 4. Identification of the initiation codon for the A protein. Sequences of 30 nucleotides in the region in which the initiation was expected were written down and arbitrarily marked off in triplets. The number of T residues in the first position in each triplet was then counted and listed, and similarly the number of Ts in the second and third positions. The marked preference for Ts in position 3 in the last two lines, as compared with the first two lines, suggests that they are coding for protein and that the triplets are correctly marked off. The most likely initiation codon for the A protein is the ATG in position 3,973.

*These figures refer to the last five codons of the previous line and the first five of the next line.

A different approach to identifying the initiation site and reading phase in a coding sequence is by looking for a characteristic "initiation sequence". Shine and Dalgarno have shown that a common feature of ribosome binding sites is a number of nucleotides (at least three) preceding the ATG that are capable of forming base pairs with a sequence at the 3′ end of 16S rRNA[42,43]. All of the known initiation sites in ΦX174 that have been identified by direct amino acid sequencing (for the F, G, H, J and D proteins) satisfy this criterion (see Table 2) and the fact that the sequence preceding the ATG in position 3,973 also has this characteristic supports its identification as the initiation site for the A protein.

If, as has been suggested[37], some mRNA from the previous promoter does extend beyond the hairpin structure, initiation of A protein synthesis may be controlled by the inclusion of the region complementary to the 16S rRNA in the hairpin loop. This could explain the presence of two types of mRNA covering the A cistron, as suggested by Hayashi et al.[37]— one unstable and active and the other stable but inactive. The former would be initiated at the A promoter, the latter at an earlier promoter and result from "read-through" at the terminator. The postulated reading frame for the A protein was confirmed by sequencing amber mutants mapping in the N-terminal region of gene A. am86 proved to be a C → T change at position 4,108 and am33 a C → T change at position 4,372. These both result in formation of an amber codon (TAG) in the same reading frame as the proposed

确定阅读框。图 4 阐释了如何利用这个特点来鉴别 A 蛋白的阅读框并确定其起始密码子在 3,973 位点处。与这一方式相似，如果连续是 T 核苷酸的频率非常低的话，多个 T 的连续分布可以用来判定 DNA 序列测定中的错误。

|  |  |  |  | 密码子中T的位置 | | |
|---|---|---|---|---|---|---|
|  |  |  |  | (1) | (2) | (3) |
| 3,910 | C C G . T C A . G G A . T T G . A C A . C C C . T C C . C A A . T T G . T A T . |  |  | 5 | 2 | 1 |
|  |  |  |  | 3 | 4 | 3* |
| 3,940 | G T T . T T C . A T G . C C T . C C A . A A T . C T T . G G A . G G C . T T T . |  |  | 2 | 5 | 5 |
|  |  |  |  | 3 | 5 | 7* |
| 3,970 | T T T . A T G . G T T . C G T . T C T . T A T . T A C . C C T . T C T . G A A . |  |  | 5 | 3 | 7 |
|  |  |  |  | 5 | 0 | 7* |
| 4,000 | T G T . C A C . G C T . G A T . T A T . T T T . G A C . T T T . G A G . C G T . |  |  | 4 | 2 | 7 |

图 4. 蛋白A起始密码子的确定。将预计含有起始位点的30个核苷酸序列按照三联体任意划分。将在每个三联体中第一点为T的数量记录下来，再同样将第二点和第三点出现T的数量也记录下来。将最后两行的第三点优先为T的和前两行比较，表明它们编码蛋白并且三联体划分正确，A蛋白最可能的起始位点是3,973处的ATG。

*这些数字参考前一行后5个密码子和后面一行的前5个密码子。

鉴别编码序列的起始位点和阅读框的另一种方法是寻找"起始序列"的特征。夏因和达尔加诺研究发现核糖体结合位点的一个共同特征就是 ATG 前面存在若干核苷酸(至少有 3 个)可以与 16S rRNA 3′ 端的一段序列形成碱基配对 [42,43]。在ΦX174中，通过直接氨基酸序列分析（如蛋白 F、G、H、J 和 D）确定的所有已知起始位点都满足这一特征（见表 2），事实上在 3,973 位点处的 ATG 之前的序列也具有这一特征，证明了此处正是蛋白 A 的起始位点。

按前面所提及的 [37]，如果来自前一启动子的一些 mRNA 确实延伸并超越了发夹结构，那么发夹环中与 16S rRNA 互补的序列就可以调控蛋白 A 的合成。这样就可以解释林昌树等 [37] 提出的观点：A 顺反子中出现两种 mRNA——一个不稳定但有活性，另一个稳定但没有活性。前者可以在 A 启动子处被激活，后者则在靠前一个启动子处被激活，并把终止子"读过去"了。A 蛋白的推测阅读框通过测定基因 A 的 N 末端区域的琥珀型突变体而获得确认。am86 突变体的 4,108 处 C 变成 T，am33 突变体的 4,372 处 C 变成 T。这两者都导致了在前面提到的起始密码子 ATG 的同一个阅读框中形成了一个琥珀（终止）密码子（TAG），阅读框序列延续到终止密码

initiating ATG and the sequence continues to the termination codon at position 133. The A protein, which is the largest coded by ΦX174, is thus 512 amino acids long with a molecular weight of 56,000, in good agreement with SDS gel estimations (see refs 4 and 44). The A* protein, with a molecular weight of about 35,000, is believed to result from an internal translational start in the *A* gene, in the same reading phase[45]. From consideration of possible ribosome binding sequences[42,43] the ATG in position 4,657 seems to be the most likely initiation site for the A* protein.

## The Origin of Replication

The origin of ΦX viral strand DNA synthesis has been located in gene *A*, in restriction fragment Z6b (ref. 46). This origin, while coding for part of the A protein, probably corresponds to the position of the plus strand nick made by the same protein[44]. Gaps in this region that are found in replicating double-stranded (RF) DNAs are probably related to the position of the nick. Eisenberg *et al.*[47] have investigated such gaps by depurination analysis and identified, in particular, the product $C_6T$. The sequence $CTC_5$ is found in position 4,285 (Fig. 1) and the location of the origin in this region agrees precisely with the results of Baas *et al.*[46]. It is not possible at present to identify the actual position of the origin nick. The region shows no apparent secondary structure or symmetrical sequences, although there is an AT-rich region (4,298-4,307) between two GC-rich regions which might be of significance. Such a region is found near the origin of replication of SV40 DNA (ref. 48).

Table 1. ΦX174 coding capacity

| Gene | Protein molecular weight from SDS gels[*] | Number of nucleotides (Fig. 1) | Protein molecular weight from sequence information |
|------|---------------------------|-------------------------------|----------------------------------------|
| *A* | 55,000-67,000 | 1,536 | 56,000 |
| (*A**) | 35,000 | | |
| *B* | 19,000-25,000 | (360)[†] | 13,845[‡] |
| *C* | 7,000 | | |
| *D* | 14,500 | 456 | 16,811[‡] |
| *E* | 10,000-17,500 | (273)[†] | 9,940 |
| *J* | 5,000 | 114 | 4,097[‡] |
| *F* | 48,000 | 1,275 | 46,400 |
| *G* | 19,000 | 525 | 19,053[‡] |
| *H* | 37,000 | 984 | 35,800 |
| Non-coding and *C* | | 485 | |
| Total | | 5,375 | |

[*] See ref. 4.

[†] Values in parenthesis are overlapping sequences and therefore not included in the addition to obtain the total length of DNA.

[‡] These values are calculated from the amino acid sequence (in the case of B deduced from the nucleotide sequence). The others are derived using the formula

$$\text{Protein molecular weight} = \frac{\text{No. of nucleotides}}{3 \times 0.00915}$$

子所在的 133 处。由此推算 A 蛋白是 ΦX174 编码的最大蛋白，由 512 个氨基酸组成，分子量为 56,000，这通过聚丙烯酰胺凝胶电泳得到了很好的验证（见参考文献 4 和参考文献 44）。我们认为分子量为 35,000 的 A* 蛋白是从基因 $A$ 内部的一个起点所进行的同一阅读框的翻译所致[45]。考虑到可能的核糖体结合位点[42,43]，4,657 处的 ATG 最可能是 A* 蛋白的起始位点。

## 复制起点

ΦX 病毒链 DNA 的复制起点被定位在基因 $A$ 中限制性片段 Z6b 处（参考文献 46）。当编码 A 蛋白时，这个起点可能就是同一蛋白所形成的正链 DNA 的单链切口的位置[44]。在这一区域发现的正在复制的双链 DNA 的缺口可能与单链切口的位置有关。艾森伯格等[47]通过脱嘌呤分析，特别是在 $C_6T$ 产物中鉴定了这个缺口。在 4,285 处发现 $CTC_5$ 序列（图 1），这一区域的起始位点与巴斯等[46]的结果完全一致。目前还不可能确定单链切口起点的实际位置。尽管在两个富含 GC 的区域之间的一段富含 AT 区域 (4,298~4,307 处) 可能有一定意义，但是在这段区域内不存在明显的二级结构或对称序列。这样的区域在 SV40 DNA 复制的起点附近也被发现过（参考文献 48）。

表1. ΦX174编码容量

| 基因 | 根据聚丙烯酰胺凝胶电泳获得的蛋白分子量* | 核苷酸数量（图1） | 从序列信息获得的蛋白分子量 |
| --- | --- | --- | --- |
| $A$ | 55,000~67,000 | 1,536 | 56,000 |
| $(A^*)$ | 35,000 | | |
| $B$ | 19,000~25,000 | (360) † | 13,845‡ |
| $C$ | 7,000 | | |
| $D$ | 14,500 | 456 | 16,811‡ |
| $E$ | 10,000~17,500 | (273) † | 9,940 |
| $J$ | 5,000 | 114 | 4,097‡ |
| $F$ | 48,000 | 1,275 | 46,400 |
| $G$ | 19,000 | 525 | 19,053‡ |
| $H$ | 37,000 | 984 | 35,800 |
| 不编码和$C$ | | 485 | |
| 总计 | | 5,375 | |

\* 见参考文献4。

† 括号中的值是重叠序列，因此计算 DNA 总长的时候没有包含在内。

‡ 这些值从氨基酸序列计算而来（在蛋白 B 中这些值从核苷酸序列推断而来）。其他的用以下公式得出

$$蛋白质分子量 = \frac{核苷酸数量}{3 \times 0.00915}$$

## B Promoter

The second of the mRNA 5′ sequences (AUCGC)[34] has been mapped in restriction fragment R8 (Fig. 2), which starts about 300 nucleotides on from the proposed A* initiation. The sequence ATCGC is found at positions 4,832 and 4,888 in Fig. 1. The only way we can choose between them at the moment is that the second is preceded by the sequence TACAGTA (position 4,877), which is more akin to sequences found in known promoters[38] than are sequences preceding the other possible mRNA start. Irrespective of which of these sequences is used, the mRNA has a long "leader" sequence (232 or 176 nucleotides) before the next proposed initiation codon (gene B).

## The B Protein

From a study of the ribonuclease $T_1$ digestion products of the ribosome binding sites of ΦX mRNAs[49], it was possible to identify an initiating ATG in position 5,064. From the genetic map[2,3], this would be expected to be gene B but, as discussed above, the A protein coding sequence extends right through this region, past the Pst site at residue 1 in Fig. 1, and terminates at residue 133. The initiating codon contained in the ribosome-protected sequence is, however, out of phase with the A protein reading frame. The proposed B protein coding sequence is one nucleotide to the left of the A protein phase, and continues until a termination codon occurs at position 49. Therefore the B protein coding sequence is totally contained within the A gene. These reading frames have been confirmed by sequencing mutants in genes A and B (am16, N.L.B. and M.S., in preparation; am18, am35, ts116 (ref. 50)). Since the B protein has not been purified no protein sequence data is available. The complete amino acid sequence can be predicted from the DNA sequence however. The protein is 120 amino acids long with a molecular weight of 13,845 (including the N-terminal Met). The molecular weight estimates of the B protein obtained by SDS-gel electrophoresis are mostly greater than this (see review, ref. 4), but the electrophoretic mobility varied with gel concentration and cross linker. Such anomalous behaviour suggests that there may be, for instance, carbohydrate attached to the B protein.

## The C Protein

The next known gene product, protein C, maps between genes B and D. Examination of the DNA sequence in this region indicates that the most probable initiating ATG overlaps the termination codon, TGA, of gene A in the sequence ATGA at position 134. A possible termination codon for gene C could then be at position 391, although the sequence and phasing is not yet confirmed through this region. There is another possible protein initiation codon (position 51, overlapping the B protein termination codon) which would result in a slightly shorter gene product terminating at nucleotide 219. For the C protein, however, we favour the "A terminator" start, since only this reading frame contains a CAA sequence, which by a C → T alteration could give the ochre 6 mutant. Ochre 6 is a gene C mutant produced by the decay of ³H-cytosine[51] and has been mapped in fragments A6 and F9 (ref. 52); that is, between nucleotides 170 and 205 (Fig. 1).

## B 启 动 子

第二个 mRNA 5′ 序列（AUCGC）[34]绘制在限制性片段 R8 中（图 2），它起始于之前所提及的 A* 起始位点后约 300 个核苷酸处。序列 ATCGC 在图 1 中的 4,832 位点和 4,888 位点被发现过。目前在它们之间选择的唯一方法是第二种序列位于序列 TACAGTA（4,877 位点）之后，与其他可能的 mRNA 起点之前的序列相比，序列 TACAGTA 与已知启动子中发现的序列更为相似 [38]。不管采用这些序列中的哪一个，在下一个推测的起始密码子（基因 B）之前 mRNA 都有一段长"引导"序列（232 个或 176 个核苷酸）。

## B 蛋 白

通过对 ΦX mRNA[49] 核糖体结合位点的核糖核酸酶 T₁ 消化产物的研究，有可能鉴定出位于 5,064 处的一个起始密码子 ATG。从遗传图谱 [2,3] 可以预测该处是基因 B。但如上讨论，A 蛋白编码序列向右延伸穿过这个区域，经过图 1 中位于残基 1 的 Pst 位点，并终止于第 133 位残基。然而，这个包含核糖体保护序列的起始密码子不在 A 蛋白阅读框内。推算的 B 蛋白编码序列向 A 蛋白序列左侧移动了一个核苷酸，并延伸到位点 49 处出现终止密码子。因此，B 蛋白编码序列完全包含在 A 基因内。这些阅读框通过测定基因 A 和基因 B 内的突变体（am16，布朗和史密斯，准备发表中；am18、am35、ts116（参考文献 50））已经得到确认。因为 B 蛋白还未纯化，所以没有蛋白序列数据。然而可以从 DNA 序列预测完整的氨基酸序列。预计该蛋白长为 120 个氨基酸，分子量为 13,845（包括 N 末端甲硫氨酸）。通过聚丙烯酰胺凝胶电泳得出的 B 蛋白分子量的估计值远大于这个数值（综述见参考文献 4），但电泳迁移率可随凝胶浓度和交联剂变化。这些异常现象说明可能存在与 B 蛋白黏附的物质，例如多糖。

## C 蛋 白

C 蛋白是下一个已知的基因产物，定位于基因 B 和基因 D 之间。这一区域的 DNA 序列分析表明，最可能的起始密码子 ATG 与基因 A 的终止密码子 TGA（位于位点为 134 的 ATGA 序列中）重叠。虽然序列和阅读框在这个区域尚未获得确定，基因 C 的终止密码子位点可能为 391。还有另一个可能的蛋白起始密码子（位点 51，与 B 蛋白终止密码子重叠），它将导致产生稍短的基因产物，终止在核苷酸 219。然而对于 C 蛋白，我们更倾向于"A 终止子"起始，因为只有这个阅读框包含一个 CAA 序列，这个序列通过 C → T 变化可以产生赭石 6 突变体。赭石 6 是基因 C 的一个突变体，通过 ³H– 胞嘧啶 [51] 衰变产生，并已经绘制在片段 A6 和 F9 中（参考文献 52）；也就是说，在核苷酸 170 和 205 之间（图 1）。

## Sequence following the *D* Promoter

The mRNA 5′ sequence which maps before the *D* gene (GAUGC)[34] is found at position 358 in Fig. 1. The sequence preceding the messenger start has only four of the TATPuATPu nucleotides[38]. Thirty-two nucleotides after the mRNA initiation is the ATG (position 390) that initiates D protein synthesis. The amino acid sequence of the D protein has been determined almost completely, and nucleotide and amino acid sequences can be correlated to the termination codon at position 846 (ref. 33). The D protein, which is involved in capsid assembly, is 151 amino acids in length, with a molecular weight of 16,811. The *D* termination codon overlaps the initiation codon for gene *J* in the sequence T<u>AA</u>TG. A similar structure has also been found by Platt and Yanofsky[53] in the tryptophan operon. The DNA sequence following this initiation codon matches the amino acid sequence of the small basic protein (37 amino acids) of the virion determined by D. Freymeyer, P. R. Shank, T. Vanaman, C.A.H. and M. H. Edgell (personal communication). Benbow *et al.*[2,3] suggested that the mutation *am*6 was located in a gene *J*, coding for the small protein of the virion, and mapping immediately before gene *F*. Although marker rescue experiments indicate that *am*6 is not in this region[54], the DNA sequence shows that there is a gene coding for the virion protein and we have defined this as gene *J* (ref. 33). Since the *J* initiation codon overlaps the *D* termination codon we had to look elsewhere for gene *E*, which genetic mapping[2,3] had placed between them. Amber mutants in gene *E* (*am*3, *am*27, *am*34 and *am*N11) were located by the marker rescue technique and sequenced. All were found to be within the *D* coding sequence, with the mutant amber codons one nucleotide to the right of the *D* reading frame[33]. Thus the *E* coding sequence is completely contained within the *D* coding region but in a different reading frame. The proposed initiation and termination codons for the E protein are at nucleotides 568 and 840, respectively[33], giving a protein 91 amino acids in length with a molecular weight of about 9,900 (including the N-terminal methionine).

## The F Protein

Following the *J* gene is an intercistronic region of 39 nucleotides before initiation of the F protein. There is no known function of this apparently untranslated sequence, although the presence of a hairpin structure (positions 969-984) suggests that it could be the site of the *in vivo* messenger termination signal[37] mapped in the region. The F protein is initiated by the ATG at position 1,001. This is the capsid component of the virion, and almost all the amino acid sequence is known[22,24]. There are regions in this gene where the DNA sequence is not completely established, but the protein is about 424 amino acids in length, giving a molecular weight of $\simeq 46,300$.

## The G Protein Region

The termination signal for the F protein (position 2,276) is followed by an unusually long untranslated sequence of 111 nucleotides until the G protein initiation codon[31]. This region contains a looped structure which was postulated to have some functional role, as yet unknown, in the single-stranded DNA or the mRNA.

### D启动子之后的序列

在图 1 的 358 位点处是 *D* 基因（GAUGC）[34] 之前的 mRNA 5′ 序列。该序列位于这个信使起点之前，只有 TATPuATPu 核苷酸 [38] 中的 4 个。mRNA 起始之后第 32 个核苷酸是 ATG（390 位点），它起始 D 蛋白的合成。D 蛋白的氨基酸序列基本已经被完全确定，核苷酸和氨基酸序列都与位于位点 846 处的终止密码子相关（参考文献 33）。D 蛋白参与病毒壳体组装，长度为 151 个氨基酸，分子量为 16,811。*D* 的终止密码子与基因 *J* 的起始密码子在序列 TAATG 内发生重叠。普拉特和亚诺夫斯基 [53] 在色氨酸操纵子中也曾发现过相似结构。这个起始密码子后面的序列与弗雷迈耶、尚克、瓦纳曼、哈奇森和埃杰尔（个人交流）确定的病毒小分子碱性蛋白（37 个氨基酸）的氨基酸序列匹配。本博等人 [2,3] 认为 *am*6 突变位于编码病毒小蛋白的基因 *J* 中，在图上位于基因 *F* 之前并与之紧密相邻。虽然标记获救实验表明 *am*6 并不在此区域内 [54]，但 DNA 序列显示这里存在一个编码病毒蛋白的基因，并且我们确定这就是基因 *J*（参考文献 33）。因为 *J* 的起始密码子与 *D* 的终止密码子重叠，我们不得不在别的区域寻找基因 *E*，遗传图谱显示 *E* 在二者之间。通过标记获救技术和测序，我们对基因 *E* 的琥珀突变体（*am*3、*am*27、*am*34 和 *am*N11）进行了定位。发现它们都位于 *D* 编码序列内，这些突变体的琥珀密码子相对于 *D* 阅读框全部整体右移一个核苷酸 [33]。因此，*E* 编码序列完全包含在 *D* 编码区域内，但是阅读框不同。推测 E 蛋白的起始密码子和终止密码子分别在核苷酸 568 和 840 处 [33]，编码蛋白长度为 91 个氨基酸，分子量为 9,900（包含 N 末端甲硫氨酸）。

### F 蛋 白

*J* 基因之后与 F 蛋白的起始位点之前存在一个 39 个核苷酸构成的顺反子之间的区域。这个看似不翻译的序列的功能未知，但存在一个发夹结构（969~984 区域），提示其可能是图谱上位于此区域内的体内信使终止信号的位点 [37]。F 蛋白起始于 1,001 位点的 ATG 密码子，是病毒衣壳的组分，并且几乎所有氨基酸序列都是已知的 [22,24]。这个基因中有些区域的 DNA 序列尚未完全完成，但其编码的蛋白长度大约为 424 个氨基酸，分子量约为 46,300。

### G蛋白区域

F 蛋白的终止信号（2,276 位点）之后存在一段长达 111 个核苷酸的非翻译序列，直到 G 蛋白起始密码子 [31]。这个区域包含一个环状结构，推测其在单链 DNA 或 mRNA 中有一些未知功能。

Initiation of the G protein at position 2,387 is followed by a sequence of 425 nucleotides until termination at position 2,912, giving a spike protein of molecular weight 19,053. The nucleotide and amino acid sequences of this gene and product are known[24,32].

## The H Protein

The initiation codon for the H protein (position 2,923) was identified first on the basis of the distribution of T nucleotides between the three reading phases, and later confirmed by amino acid sequence analysis. Amino acid sequence data on the H protein is minimal but the five peptide sequences known do correspond to the amino acid sequence, deduced from the DNA sequence by using the high frequency of third position T to help in assigning a reading frame to any given region. The DNA sequence is not entirely confirmed but it is possible to write a reasonably accurate amino acid sequence for the H protein. The protein terminates at nucleotide 3,907, in agreement with carboxypeptidase results, giving a spike protein of molecular weight ≃ 35,600 (326 amino acids). The amino acid sequence at the N terminus seems to be particularly rich in hydrophobic residues, which is consistent with its suggested function as the "pilot" protein that reacts with the bacterial membrane[55,56]. After H protein termination there are 66 nucleotides before initiation of the A protein at position 3,973.

## Coding Capacity of the ΦX174 Genome

The most striking feature of the ΦX DNA sequence is the way in which the various functions of the genome are compressed within the 5,375 nucleotides. Since the identification of ΦX gene products[2,4] it has been clear that proteins of the accepted molecular weights could not be separately coded on the available length of DNA. However, with the presence of two pairs of overlapping genes (*B* within *A* (ref. 50), *E* within *D* (ref. 33)) the genome has more coding capacity than had been originally supposed on the assumption that each gene was physically separate. Table 1 summarises the molecular weights of the known ΦX-coded proteins. There are other potential initiation sites for polypeptide synthesis (for example, in genes *A, F, G* and *H*) and further genetic work may clarify whether there are in fact other ΦX genes as yet unidentified.

## Initiation of Protein Synthesis

Table 2 lists the protein initiation sequences for genes *A, B, D, E, J, F, G* and *H*. It can be noted that there are no extra precursor sequences in proteins D, J, F, G or H at either the N or C terminus. There seems to be no relationship between the degree of complementarity to the 16S rRNA and the amount of protein synthesised, and we see no other features in the sequence that could explain different efficiencies of translation except where genes overlap.

G 蛋白起始位点 2,387 后是一段 425 个核苷酸的序列，直到终止位点 2,912，产生一个分子量为 19,053 的刺突蛋白。这个基因的核苷酸和氨基酸产物的序列是已知的[24,32]。

## H 蛋 白

H 蛋白的起始密码子（位点 2,923）最初是在 3 个阅读框之间 T 核苷酸分布的基础上鉴定出来的，随后通过氨基酸序列分析得到确认。关于 H 蛋白的氨基酸序列数据极少，根据密码子第三位的高频 T 碱基分布有助于鉴定任何给定区域的阅读框，有 5 个已知肽段序列与其氨基酸序列对应。虽然 DNA 序列尚未完全确定，但已可能写出 H 蛋白的比较准确的氨基酸序列。这个蛋白终止于核苷酸 3,907 位点，与羧肽酶结果一致，产生一个分子量约为 35,600（326 个氨基酸）的刺突蛋白。N 末端的氨基酸序列好像特别富含疏水残基，这与其作为"引导"蛋白与细菌膜相互作用的假定功能一致[55,56]。H 蛋白终止之后与 A 蛋白 3,973 起始位点之前之间是一段 66 个核苷酸的序列。

## ΦX174基因组的编码容量

ΦX174 DNA 序列最吸引人的特征是基因组的各种功能压缩在 5,375 个核苷酸中。自从鉴定了 ΦX174 的基因产物[2,4]，就明白在它的 DNA 长度内是不可能分别编码出这些分子量已被确认的蛋白的。然而，由于存在两对重叠基因（B 在 A 内（参考文献 50），E 在 D 内（参考文献 33）），这与最初认为的每个基因在位置上是分离的这一假设相比，这样的基因组具有更大的编码容量。表 1 总结了已知的 ΦX174 编码蛋白的分子量。多肽合成还存在其他的可能起始位点（例如，在基因 A、F、G 和 H 中），进一步的遗传研究可能会阐明是否真的存在尚未鉴定出的其他 ΦX 基因。

## 蛋白合成的起始

表 2 列出了基因 A、B、D、E、J、F、G 和 H 的蛋白起始序列。可以看出在蛋白 D、J、F、G 或 H 的 N 末端或 C 末端都没有额外的前体序列。16S rRNA 的互补程度和该蛋白的合成量之间似乎没有关系，并且除基因重叠区域外，我们在这些序列中没有发现其他特征可以解释翻译效率的不同。

Table 2. Initiation sequences of ΦX174 coded proteins

```
D    C-C-A-C-T-[A-A-T]-A-G-G-T-A-A-G-A-A-A-T-C-A-T-G-A-G-T-C-A-A-G-T-T-A-C-T
                                                              Ser  Gln  Val  Thr

E    C-T-G-C-G-T-T-G-A-G-G-C-T-T-G-C-G-T-T-T-A-T-G-G-T-A-C-G-C-T-G-G-A-C-T

J    C-G-T-G-C-G-G-A-A-G-G-A-G-T-G-A-T-G-T-A-A-T-G-T-C-T-A-A-A-G-G-T-A-A-A
                                                              Ser  Lys  Gly  Lys

F    C-C-C-T-T-A-C-T-T-G-A-G-G-A-T-A-A-A-T-T-A-T-G-T-C-T-A-A-T-A-T-T-C-A-A
                                                              Ser  Asn  Ile  Gln

G    T-T-C-T-G-C-T-T-A-G-G-G-A-G-T-T-T-A-A-T-C-A-T-G-T-T-T-C-A-G-A-C-T-T-T-T
                                                              Met  Phe  Gln  Thr  Phe

H    C-C-A-C-T-[T-T-A-A-G-T]-T-G-A-G-G-T-G-A-T-T-T-A-T-G-T-T-T-G-G-T-G-C-T-A-T-T
                                                              Met  Phe  Gly  Ala  Ile

A    C-A-A-A-T-C-T-T-G-G-A-G-G-C-T-T-T-T-T-T-T-A-T-G-G-T-T-C-G-T-T-C-T-T-A-T

B    A-A-A-G-G-T-C-T-A-G-G-G-A-G-C-T-A-A-A-A-G-A-A-T-G-G-A-A-C-A-A-C-T-C-A-C-T

16S RNA          A-U-U-C-C-U-C-C-A-C-U-A-G
3' end        HO
```

Where the protein start has been independently confirmed by protein sequencing data the amino acid sequences are indicated. The other initiation regions were identified as described in the text. Sequences complementary to the 3' end of 16S rRNA (refs 42, 43) are boxed; broken lines indicate further complementarity if some nucleotides are looped out or not matched. Ribosome binding to mRNA has been demonstrated in these regions for genes J, F, G and B (ref. 49).

## Transcription of ΦX174

The sequences preceding known mRNA starts[34-36] are shown in Table 3. Other studies on promoter sequences[38] have suggested certain features that they may have in common. Although some of these features are present in the sequences preceding the ΦX transcription initiations others are not, and at present it is difficult to suggest what signal on the DNA determines a promoter site or the efficiency with which it initiates RNA synthesis. It is interesting to note that a polymerase binding site found by Chen *et al.*[57], but not associated with any *in vitro* or *in vivo* mRNA starts, mapped near the region where there is the sequence TATGATG characteristic of promoters[38] (positions 2,705-2,711).

表 2. ΦX174编码蛋白质的起始序列

| 基因 | 序列 | 氨基酸序列 |
|---|---|---|
| D | C-C-A-C-T-A-A-T-A-G-G-T-A-A-G-A-A-A-T-C-A-T-G-A-G-T-C-A-A-G-T-T-A-C-T | Ser Gln Val Thr |
| E | C-T-G-C-G-T-T-G-A-G-G-C-T-T-G-C-G-T-T-T-A-T-G-G-T-A-C-G-C-T-G-G-A-C-T | |
| J | C-G-T-G-C-G-G-A-A-G-G-A-G-T-G-A-T-G-T-A-A-T-G-T-C-T-A-A-A-G-G-T-A-A-A | Ser Lys Gly Lys |
| F | C-C-C-T-T-A-C-T-T-G-A-G-G-A-T-A-A-A-T-T-A-T-G-T-C-T-A-A-T-A-T-T-C-A-A | Ser Asn Ile Gln |
| G | T-T-C-T-G-C-T-T-A-G-G-A-G-T-T-T-A-A-T-C-A-T-G-T-T-T-C-A-G-A-C-T-T-T-T | Met Phe Gln Thr Phe |
| H | C-C-A-C-T-T-A-A-G-T-G-A-G-G-T-G-A-T-T-T-A-T-G-T-T-T-G-G-T-G-C-T-A-T-T | Met Phe Gly Ala Ile |
| A | C-A-A-A-T-C-T-T-G-G-A-G-G-C-T-T-T-T-T-T-A-T-G-G-T-T-C-G-T-T-C-T-T-A-T | |
| B | A-A-A-G-G-T-C-T-A-G-G-A-G-C-T-A-A-A-G-A-A-T-G-G-A-A-C-A-A-C-T-C-A-C-T | |
| 16S RNA 3' 末端 | HO A-U-U-C-C-U-C-C-A-C-U-A-G | |

由蛋白质序列数据独立确定出的蛋白质起始位点，表中标明了氨基酸序列。其他起始区域按正文描述的方法鉴定。与16S rRNA 3' 末端互补的序列（参考文献42，参考文献43）加了方框；虚线方框表示如果一些核苷酸成环或未配对而引起的进一步的互补。基因J、F、G和B的mRNA与核糖体结合的区域已经得到阐明（参考文献49）。

## ΦX174的转录

表3中显示了已知mRNA起始位点之前的序列[34-36]。对启动子序列的其他研究[38]表明，这些序列可能具有某些相同的特征。尽管在ΦX转录起始之前的序列中只出现了其中一些特征而其他的没有，并且目前很难确定DNA上哪些信号决定着一个启动子位点或这一位点起始RNA合成的效率。值得注意的是，陈等人[57]发现的一种聚合酶结合位点被定位在启动子TATGATG序列[38]（2,705~2,711区域）附近，而与任何体外或体内mRNA合成起始无关。

Table 3. Promoter sequences in ΦX174

```
                                                                                          3954
A promoter   A-G-G-A-T-T-G-A-C-A-C-C-C-T-C-C-C-A-A-T-T-G-T-A-T-G-T[T-T-T-C-A-T-G-]C-C-T-C-C-A-A-A-T-C-T _ _ _
                                                                                        ↑ 18 nucleotides
                                                                                          to A protein start

             R7b/R6c                                                                      358
D promoter   G-T-T-G-A-C-A-T-T-T-T-A-A-A-A-G-A-G-C-G-T-G-G-A-T-T-A-C[T-A-T-C-T-G-A]G-T-C-C-G-A-T-G-C-T
                                                                                        ↑ 32 nucleotides
                                                                                          to D protein start

                          R3/R8                                                           4832
B promoter?  C-A-G-G-T-A-G-C-G-T-T-G-A-C-C-C-T-A-A-T-T-T-T-G-G-T-C-G[T-C-G-G-G-T-A]C-G-C-A-A-T-C-G-C-C
                                                                                        ↑ 232 nucleotides
                                                                                          to B protein start

                                                                                          4888
B promoter?  A-G-C-T-T-G-C-A-A-A-A-T-A-C-G-T-G-G-C-C-T-T-A-T-G-G-T[T-A-C-A-G-T-A]T-G-C-C-C-A-T-C-G-C-A
                                                                                        ↑ 176 nucleotides
                                                                                          to B protein start
```

mRNA initiation sequences[34-36] are underlined. Boxed regions indicate sequences that may correspond to the TATPuATPu sequence found in other promoters[38], taking into account the distance from the mRNA starts.

## The Use of Codons in ΦX174

Table 4 shows the codons used in regions where the nucleotide sequence is fully confirmed. It is clear that the pattern established by early observations on non-random use of codons[23,24] is continued now that more information is available. In particular, the preference for T at the third position of the codon is marked throughout the genome, as shown in Table 4. In regions of overlapping genes, one of the pair tends to continue the "third T" trend (D and B), thus excluding the other (E and A). This may give some indication of the order in which overlapping genes evolved[33,50]. Another interesting feature is the very low occurrence of codons starting AG, particularly in non-overlapping regions. The base composition of the sequence of ΦX174 DNA shown in Fig. 1 is: A, 23.9%; C, 21.5%; G, 23.3% and T, 31.2%. This is in good agreement with previously determined values (see ref. 4).

Table 4. Codons used in ΦX174

| Phe | TTT | 39 | Ser | TCT | 35 | Tyr | TAT | 36 | Cys | TGT | 12 |
|-----|-----|-----|-----|-----|-----|-----|-----|-----|-----|-----|-----|
|     | TTC | 26 |     | TCC | 9  |     | TAC | 15 |     | TGC | 10 |
| Leu | TTA | 19 |     | TCA | 16 | Ter | TAA | 3  | Ter | TGA | 5  |
|     | TTG | 26 |     | TCG | 14 |     | TAG | 0  | Trp | TGG | 16 |
| Leu | CTT | 36 | Pro | CCT | 34 | His | CAT | 16 | Arg | CGT | 40 |
|     | CTC | 15 |     | CCC | 6  |     | CAC | 7  |     | CGC | 29 |
|     | CTA | 3  |     | CCA | 6  | Gln | CAA | 27 |     | CGA | 4  |
|     | CTG | 24 |     | CCG | 21 |     | CAG | 34 |     | CGG | 8  |
| Ile | ATT | 45 | Thr | ACT | 40 | Asn | AAT | 37 | Ser | AGT | 9  |
|     | ATC | 12 |     | ACC | 18 |     | AAC | 25 |     | AGC | 5  |
|     | ATA | 2  |     | ACA | 13 | Lys | AAA | 47 | Arg | AGA | 6  |
| Met | ATG | 42 |     | ACG | 19 |     | AAG | 31 |     | AGG | 1  |
| Val | GTT | 53 | Ala | GCT | 64 | Asp | GAT | 44 | Gly | GGT | 38 |
|     | GTC | 14 |     | GCC | 17 |     | GAC | 35 |     | GGC | 28 |
|     | GTA | 10 |     | GCA | 12 | Glu | GAA | 27 |     | GGA | 13 |
|     | GTG | 11 |     | GCG | 12 |     | GAG | 34 |     | GGG | 3  |

The totals are derived from sequences in Fig. 1 which are fully confirmed, that is, 377 codons in gene A, 120 in gene B, 152 in gene D,

表 3. ΦX174 的启动子序列

| | | | | 3954 |
|---|---|---|---|---|
| A 启动子 | A-G-G-A-T-T-G-A-C-A-C-C-C-T-C-C-C-A-A-T-T-G-T-A-T-G | ⌐T-T-T-C-A-T-G⌐ | C-C-T-C-C-A-A-A-T-C-T - - - | |

↑ 距离蛋白A起始位点
18个核苷酸

R7b/R6c

| D 启动子 | G-T-T-G-A-C-A-T-T-T-T-A-A-A-A-G-A-G-C-G-T-G-G-A-T-T-A-C | ⌐T-A-T-C-T-G-A⌐ | G-T-C-C-G-A-T-G-C-T | 358 |

↑ 距离蛋白D起始位点
32个核苷酸

R3/R8

| B 启动子 ? | C-A-G-G-T-A-G-C-G-T-T-G-A-C-C-T-A-A-T-T-T-T-G-G-T-C | ⌐T-C-G-G-C-T-A⌐ | C-C-A-C-G-C-C-C | 4832 |

↑ 距离蛋白B起始位点
232个核苷酸

| B 启动子 ? | A-G-C-T-T-G-C-A-A-A-A-T-A-C-G-T-G-G-C-C-T-T-A-T-G-T | ⌐T-A-C-A-G-T-A⌐ | T-G-C-C-A-A-T-C-G-C-A | 4888 |

↑ 距离蛋白B起始位点
176个核苷酸

mRNA 起始序列[34-36] 加了下划线。从 mRNA 起点的距离上考虑，加方框的区域表示可能是与在其他启动子中发现的 TATPuATPu 序列相对应的序列[38]。

## ΦX 174中密码子的使用

表 4 显示了在核苷酸序列已被完全确定的区域中所使用的密码子。很明显，早期对非随机使用密码子的观察结果建立的模式 [23,24] 不断发展而产生了更多可利用信息。特别是，整个基因组密码子第三位碱基都明显地偏好 T，见表 4 所示。在重叠基因区域，一对基因倾向于延续"第三位 T"的趋势（$D$ 和 $B$），因而排除了与另一对的重合（$E$ 和 $A$）。这可能给我们一些关于重叠基因进化顺序的提示 [33,50]。另一个有趣的特征是密码起始于 AG 的发生率很低，特别是在非重叠区域。图 1 显示了 ΦX174 DNA 序列的碱基组成是：A，23.9%；C，21.5%；G，23.3%；T，31.2%。这与以前确定的数值很相符（见参考文献4）。

表 4. ΦX174中使用的密码子

| Phe | TTT | 39 | Ser | TCT | 35 | Tyr | TAT | 36 | Cys | TGT | 12 |
|---|---|---|---|---|---|---|---|---|---|---|---|
| | TTC | 26 | | TCC | 9 | | TAC | 15 | | TGC | 10 |
| Leu | TTA | 19 | | TCA | 16 | Ter | TAA | 3 | Ter | TGA | 5 |
| | TTG | 26 | | TCG | 14 | | TAG | 0 | Trp | TGG | 16 |
| Leu | CTT | 36 | Pro | CCT | 34 | His | CAT | 16 | Arg | CGT | 40 |
| | CTC | 15 | | CCC | 6 | | CAC | 7 | | CGC | 29 |
| | CTA | 3 | | CCA | 6 | Gln | CAA | 27 | | CGA | 4 |
| | CTG | 24 | | CCG | 21 | | CAG | 34 | | CGG | 8 |
| Ile | ATT | 45 | Thr | ACT | 40 | Asn | AAT | 37 | Ser | AGT | 9 |
| | ATC | 12 | | ACC | 18 | | AAC | 25 | | AGC | 5 |
| | ATA | 2 | | ACA | 13 | Lys | AAA | 47 | Arg | AGA | 6 |
| Met | ATG | 42 | | ACG | 19 | | AAG | 31 | | AGG | 1 |
| Val | GTT | 53 | Ala | GCT | 64 | Asp | GAT | 44 | Gly | GGT | 38 |
| | GTC | 14 | | GCC | 17 | | AGC | 35 | | GGC | 28 |
| | GTA | 10 | | GCA | 12 | Glu | GAA | 27 | | GGA | 13 |
| | GTG | 11 | | GCG | 12 | | GAG | 34 | | GGG | 3 |

列出的所有信息都是从图 1 中完全确定的序列中获得，即基因 $A$ 中的 377 个密码子，基因 $B$ 中的 120 个密码子，基因 $D$ 中的 152 个

91 in gene *E*, 38 in gene *J*, 344 in gene *F*, 175 in gene *G* and 49 in gene *H*. Out of a total of 1,346 codons 42.9% terminate in T. The percentages in the different genes are: *A*, 37.1 (non-overlapping region 47.1; overlapping region 15.8); *B*, 34.2; *D*, 42.1; *E*, 14.3; *J*, 47.4; *F*, 52.0; *G*, 54.3; *H*, 49.0. The initiating ATG is included in all cases.

We thank D. McCallum and R. Staden for carrying out the computer data storage and analysis of the sequence.

*Note added in proof:* J. E. Sims and D. Dressler (personal communication) have independently determined the sequence in positions 263-375 and 4,801-4,940. Their results agree with those given in Fig. 1. They have also identified the "B" mRNA start as being at position 4,888.

(**265**, 687-695; 1977)

F. Sanger, G. M. Air*, B. G. Barrell, N. L. Brown†, A. R. Coulson, J. C. Fiddes, C. A. Hutchison III‡, P. M. Slocombe§ & M. Smith¶
MRC Laboratory of Molecular Biology, Hills Road, Cambridge CB2 2QH, UK
Present addresses: *John Curtin School of Medical Research, Microbiology Department, Canberra City ACT 2601, Australia
†Department of Biochemistry, University of Bristol, Bristol BS8 1TD, UK
‡Department of Bacteriology and Immunology, University of North Carolina, Chapel Hill, North Carolina 27514
§Max-Planck-Institut für Molekulare Genetik, 1 Berlin 33, FRG
¶Department of Biochemistry, University of British Columbia, Vancouver BC, Canada V6T 1W5

Received November 30; accepted December 24 1976.

---

References:
1. Sanger, F. & Coulson, A. R. *J. Molec. Biol.* **94**, 441-448 (1975).
2. Benbow, R. M., Hutchison, C. A. III, Fabricant, J. D. & Sinsheimer, R. L. *J. Virol.* **7**, 549-558 (1971).
3. Benbow, R. M., Zuccarelli, A. J., Davis, G. C. & Sinshiemer, R. L. *J. Virol.* **13**, 898-907 (1974).
4. Denhardt, D. T. *CRC Crit. Rev. Microbiol.* **4**, 161-222 (1975).
5. Hall, J. B. & Sinsheimer, R. L. *J. Molec. Biol.* **6**, 115-127 (1963).
6. Ling, V. *Proc. Natl. Acad. Sci. U.S.A.* **69**, 742-746 (1972).
7. Harbers, B., Delaney, A. D., Harbers, K. & Spencer, J. H. *Biochemistry* **15**, 407-414 (1976).
8. Burton, K. & Petersen, G. B. *Biochem. J.* **75**, 17-27 (1960).
9. Chadwell, H. A. Thesis, University of Cambridge (1974).
10. Sadowski, P. D. & Bakyta, I. *J. Biol. Chem.* **247**, 405-412 (1972).
11. Ling, V. *FEBS Lett.* **19**, 50-54 (1971).
12. Ziff, E. B., Sedat, J. W. & Galibert, F. *Nature New Biol.* **241**, 34-37 (1973).
13. Galibert, F., Sedat, J. W. & Ziff, E. B. *J. Molec. Biol.* **87**, 377-407 (1974).
14. Robertson, H. D., Barrell, B. G., Weith, H. L. & Donelson, J. E. *Nature New Biol.* **241**, 38-40 (1973).
15. Air, G. M. & Bridgen, J. *Nature New Biol.* **241**, 40-41 (1973).
16. Sanger, F., Donelson, J. E., Coulson, A. R., Kössel, H. & Fischer, D. *Proc. Natl. Acad. Sci. U.S.A.* **70**, 1209-1213 (1973).
17. Schott, H. *Makromolek. Chem.* **175**, 1683-1693 (1974).
18. Donelson, J. E., Barrell, B. G., Weith, H. L., Kössel, H. & Schott, H. *Eur. J. Biochem.* **58**, 383-395 (1975).
19. Blackburn, E. H. *J. Molec. Biol.* **93**, 367-374 (1975).
20. Blackburn, E. H. *J. Molec. Biol.* **107**, 417-432 (1976).
21. Sedat, J. W., Ziff, E. B. & Galibert, F. *J. Molec. Biol.* **107**, 391-416 (1976).
22. Air, G. M. *J. Molec. Biol.* **107**, 433-444 (1976).
23. Air, G. M. *et al. J. Molec. Biol.* **107**, 445-458 (1976).

密码子，基因 *E* 中的 91 个密码子，基因 *J* 中的 38 个密码子，基因 *F* 中的 344 个密码子，基因 *G* 中的 175 个密码子，基因 *H* 中的 49 个密码子。共 1,346 个密码子，其中有 42.9% 的末位为碱基 T。在不同基因中的百分比为：*A*，37.1（非重叠区域 47.1；重叠区域 15.8）；*B*，34.2；*D*，42.1；*E*，14.3；*J*，47.4；*F*，52.0；*G*，54.3；*H*，49.0。所有例子中都包含起始密码子 ATG。

我们感谢麦卡勒姆和施塔登进行的计算机数据存储和序列分析。

**附加说明**：西姆斯和德雷斯勒（个人交流）已经独立确定了 263~375 区域和 4,801~4,940 区域的序列。他们的结果与图 1 给出的一致。他们也鉴定了"B"mRNA 起始于位点 4,888 处。

（郑建全 李梅 翻译；曾长青 审稿）

797

24. Air, G. M., Blackburn, E. H., Sanger, F. & Coulson, A. R. *J. Molec. Biol.* **96**, 703-719 (1975).

25. Lee, A. S. & Sinsheimer, R. L. *Proc. Natl. Acad. Sci. U.S.A.* **71**, 2882-2886 (1974).

26. Hayashi, M. N. & Hayashi, M. *J. Virol.* **14**, 1142-1152 (1974).

27. Vereijken, J. M., van Mansfeld, A. D. M., Baas, P. D. & Jansz, H. S. *Virology* **68**, 221-233 (1975).

28. Jeppesen, P. G. N., Sanders, L. & Slocombe, P. M. *Nucl. Acids Res.* **3**, 1323-1339 (1976).

29. Sato, S., Hutchison, C. A. III & Harris, J. I. *Proc. Natl. Acad Sci. U.S.A.* (in the press).

30. Brown, N. L. & Smith, M. *FEBS Lett.* **65**, 284-287 (1976).

31. Fiddes, J. C. *J. Molec. Biol.* **107**, 1-24 (1976).

32. Air, G. M., Sanger, F. & Coulson, A. R. *J. Molec. Biol.* **108**, 519-533 (1976).

33. Barrell, B. G., Air, G. M. & Hutchison, C. A. III *Nature* **264**, 34-41 (1976).

34. Smith, L. H. & Sinsheimer, R. L. *J. Molec. Biol.* **103**, 699-735 (1976).

35. Grohmann, K., Smith, L. H. & Sinsheimer, R. L. *Biochemistry* **14**, 1951-1955 (1975).

36. Axelrod, N. *J. Molec. Biol.* **108**, 753-779 (1976).

37. Hayashi, M., Fujimura, F. K. & Hayashi, M. *Proc. Natl. Acad. Sci. U.S.A.* **73**, 3519-3523 (1976).

38. Pribnow, D. *Proc. Natl. Acad. Sci. U.S.A.* **72**, 784-788 (1975).

39. Rosenberg, M., de Crombrugghe, B & Musso, R. *Proc. Natl. Acad. Sci. U.S.A.* **73**, 717-721 (1976).

40. Bertrand, K. *et al. Science* **189**, 22-26 (1975).

41. Sugimoto, K., Sugisaki, H., Okamoto, T. & Takanami, M. *J. Molec. Biol.* (in the press).

42. Shine, J. & Dalgarno, L. *Proc. Natl. Acad. Sci. U.S.A.* **71**, 1342-1346 (1974).

43. Steitz, J. A. & Jakes, K. *Proc. Natl. Acad. Sci. U.S.A.* **72**, 4734-4738 (1975).

44. Henry, T. J. & Knippers, R. *Proc. Natl. Acad. Sci, U.S.A.* **71**, 1549-1553 (1974).

45. Linney, E. & Hayashi, M. *Nature* **249**, 345-348 (1974).

46. Baas, P. D., Jansz, H. S. & Sinsheimer, R. L. *J. Molec. Biol.* **102**, 633-656 (1976).

47. Eisenberg, S., Harbers, B., Hours, C. & Denhardt, D. T. *J. Molec. Biol.* **99**, 107-123 (1975).

48. Subramanian, K. N., Dhar, R. & Weissman, S. M. *J. Biol. Chem.* (in the press).

49. Ravetch, J. V., Model, P. & Robertson, H. D. *Nature* **265**, 698-702 (1977).

50. Smith, M. *et al.* (submitted to Nature).

51. Funk, F. & Sinsheimer, R. L. *J. Virol.* **6**, 12-19 (1970).

52. Baas, P. D., van Heusden, G. P. H., Vereijken, J. M., Weisbeek, P. J. & Jansz, H. S. *Nucl. Acids Res.* **3**, 1947-1960 (1976).

53. Platt, T. & Yanofsky, C. *Proc. Natl. Acad. Sci, U.S.A.* **72**, 2399-2403 (1975).

54. Weisbeek, P. J., Vereijken, J. M., Baas, P. D., Jansz, H. S. & Van Arkel, G. A. *Virology* **72**, 61-71 (1976).

55. Jazwinski, S. M., Lindberg, A. A. & Kornberg, A. *Virology* **66**, 283-293 (1975).

56. Kornberg, A. *DNA Synthesis* (W. H. Freeman, San Francisco, 1974).

57. Chen, C. Y., Hutchison, C. A. III & Edgell, M. H. *Nature New Biol.* **243**, 233-236 (1973).

58. van Mansfeld, A. D. M., Vereijken, J. M. & Jansz, H. S. *Nucl. Acids Res.* **3**, 2827-2843 (1976).

798

# Radio Sources with Superluminal Velocities

M. H. Cohen *et al.*

## Editor's Note

As galaxies and quasars were observed using interferometric methods in the 1970s, it was found that the blobs of material that seemed to be travelling out from their centres were doing so at speeds apparently greater than the speed of light, at face value violating special relativity. This was used to argue by some astronomers that quasars actually were relatively near objects that had been ejected at high speeds from nearby galaxies. Here Michael Cohen and colleagues conclude that the evidence instead favours the genuinely "superluminal" picture. Astronomer Martin Rees had predicted that geometrical effects can account for this motion without violating relativity. However, some of these jets can't be explained this way, but require a more subtle model.

Radio data from four extragalactic sources, three quasars and one galaxy, show evidence for an apparent expansion faster than the speed of light. The data on these "superluminal" sources are reviewed, and their implications briefly discussed.

BRIGHTNESS distributions in four extragalactic radio sources have been seen to vary so rapidly that the apparent transverse velocity of expansion is greater than the velocity of light (assuming a cosmological origin for the redshift). The term superluminal will be used to describe this phenomenon. In this paper we review many of the observations of superluminal expansions, and also add some new material. Blandford, McKee, and Rees[1] have summarised theoretical ideas on the subject.

The observations have all been obtained with very-long-baseline interferometry (VLBI) systems using two to five radio telescopes, spaced over thousands of kilometres, to form multi-element interferometres. Various model-fitting and map-making procedures have been used to estimate parameters of the brightness distribution, such as diameter, separation and flux of components, position angle, and so on. In some cases the data have been sufficiently accurate and extensive to warrant many-parameter models, and detailed contour diagrams have been made. In general, however, the models are not unique. Some have been challenged[2,3]; but there still is general agreement among different workers on the main features of the sources. VLBI map-making is presently in a stage of rapid development; in particular there is a growing use of phase data, and more definitive results are expected in a few years.

# 超光速射电源

科恩等

## 编者按

20 世纪 70 年代，人们利用干涉测量法来观测星系和类星体时，发现从这些星系和类星体中心发出的物质团的运动速度似乎明显高于光速——从表面上看其数值违背了狭义相对论。一些天文学家据此认为类星体实际上更接近于从邻近星系高速喷射出来的物质。本文中迈克尔·科恩及其合作者们的结论是，这些证据反而支持了真正的"超光速"图像。天文学家马丁·瑞斯已经预言，在不违背相对论的情况下，用几何效应就能够解释这种运动。但是，一些这样的喷流不能通过这种方式解释清楚，而需要一种更加巧妙的模型。

---

来自于四个河外源（三个类星体和一个星系）的射电数据表明，它们的视膨胀速度超过光速。本文对这些"超光速"源的数据进行了探讨，并简要讨论了它们的内在意义。

---

我们已经观察到四个河外射电源的亮度分布变化非常快，以至于膨胀的视横向速度超过了光速（假设是宇宙学红移）。以下用"超光速"这一术语来表征该现象。本文，我们探讨了很多例超光速膨胀的观测，同时也增添了一些新的观测资料。布兰福德、麦基和瑞斯 [1] 已经就这个问题总结了一些理论观点。

这些观测数据都是通过甚长基线干涉仪（VLBI）系统得到的。甚长基线干涉仪系统利用二至五个分布范围达几千公里的射电望远镜构成一个多天线干涉仪。我们使用多种模型拟合和成图的步骤来估算亮度分布的各种参数，如直径、位置角、成分源的角分离和流量等。对于一些源，我们已经掌握足够精确广泛的数据，可以去限制多参数模型，而且我们已经得到详细的等光度线图。不过大体上说，这些模型不是唯一的。一些模型已经遭到质疑 [2,3]，但是对于这些源的主要性质，不同研究者的意见总体上还是一致的。VLBI 成图目前正处于一个快速发展时期，特别是越来越多地使用相位数据，在几年内有望得到更加可靠的结果。

Four sources including three quasars (3C345, 3C273, and 3C279) and one radio galaxy (3C120) will be discussed. In each case we give simple angular measures and do not discuss the detailed models of brightness distribution. More complete discussions will be found in the references.

## 3C345 ($z = 0.595$)

Two observing groups[4,5] have independently shown that 3C345 could be accurately described as a simple double source in mid-1974. The two components were approximately Gaussian and contained most or all of the flux density at $\lambda = 2$, 2.8, and 3.8 cm. In these experiments three or four telescopes were used. The simple model was an excellent fit, and there was no requirement for, nor evidence of, a more complex structure. At most other epochs only two or three telescopes were used. The brightness distributions were not as well determined, of course, but a simple double fit the data and the separation, $\theta$, was accurately determined in every case.

Figure 1 shows the separation of the centres of the two components as a function of time. The point at 6 cm is taken from a number of measurements made in 1968 and 1969 (ref. 8). The source was only slightly resolved at that early epoch and $\theta$ was determined from the best-fitting double. The position angle was assumed to be 105°, the value found more recently. The 3.8 cm point at 1971.1 (ref. 7) is similarly model dependent because the source is only partially resolved. The three points in 1976 are provisional because detailed model fitting is yet to be done; however, they are unlikely to change much because $\theta$ is well determined from the sharp minima of the visibility function.

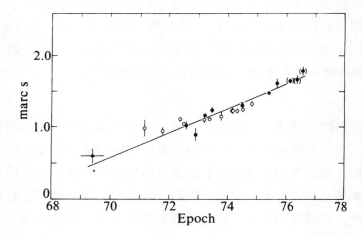

Fig. 1. Apparent separation of the two components of 3C345 as a function of time. The slope of the line is 0.17 marc s yr⁻¹. The observations at 2 cm are taken from ref. 5; the 2.8-cm points are from refs 5 and 6, and the four points in 1972-73 are from private communications with N. Broten and M. Quigley (the points in 1976 are discussed in the text); the 3.8 cm points are from refs 4 and 7; and the 6-cm point is discussed in the text. ×, 2.0 cm; ●, 2.8 cm; ○, 3.8 cm; ▲, 6.0 cm.

我们将对四个源进行讨论，其中包括三个类星体（3C345、3C273 和 3C279）和一个射电星系（3C120）。对每个源我们只给出角度测量值，并不讨论亮度分布的详细模型。更完整的讨论见参考文献。

## 3C345（$z = 0.595$）

两个观测小组[4,5] 根据 1974 年中期的观测分别独立地指出 3C345 可以被准确地描述成简单的双源。两个子源近似高斯型，并包含 $\lambda = 2$ cm、2.8 cm 和 3.8 cm 波段的绝大部分或是全部流量密度。这些观测使用了三至四台望远镜。简单模型就拟合得相当好，没有证据，也没必要去构造更复杂的模型。在其余观测时段只使用了二至三台望远镜。当然，亮度分布并没有被准确测定，但是用简单的双峰模型去拟合数据的话，每次观测都能得到准确的角分离 $\theta$。

两个子源中心的角分离随时间变化如图 1 所示。6 cm 波段的数据点来自 1968 年和 1969 年的多次观测（参考文献 8）。在那样一个较早的时期，3C345 只能被略微分辨开，而角分离 $\theta$ 是通过最佳拟合的双峰模型得到的，其位置角被认定是 105°，这是最近才得到的。类似地，在 1971.1（参考文献 7）的 3.8 cm 波段的数据点也是依赖于模型得到的，因为此源只能部分地分辨开。1976 年的 3 个数据点是暂定的，因为具体的模型拟合还没有做。不过，它们不大可能将参数改变太多，因为根据可见度函数的强极小值可以很好地确定 $\theta$。

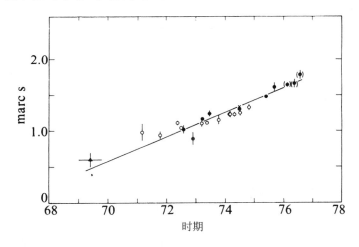

图 1. 3C345 的两个子源视角分离随着时间的变化。拟合直线的斜率是 0.17 marc s · yr⁻¹。2 cm 波段的观测来自参考文献 5；2.8 cm 波段的数据点来自参考文献 5 和 6，1972 年至 1973 年的四个数据点来自和布拉滕和奎格利的私人交流（文中讨论了 1976 年的数据点）；3.8 cm 波段的数据点来自参考文献 4 和 7；6 cm 波段的数据点在文中进行了讨论。×，2.0 cm；●，2.8 cm；○，3.8 cm；▲，6.0 cm。

The points in Fig. 1 show that the brightness distribution expanded by a factor of about 3 in 7 years, at the approximate rate 0.17 marc s per year. The expansion may not be uniform, however, for the slope seems to be flatter in 1972-73, and steeper in 1975-76. The difference in slope explains most of the discrepancy in the rates already reported in the literature[6,9]. The angular rate can be converted into an apparent transverse velocity at the source by multiplying by the cosmological distance and correcting for time dilation with a factor $(1+z)$.

$$\frac{v}{c} = \frac{\theta}{H_0 q_0^2 (1+z)} \left( q_0 z + (q_0-1)[(1+2q_0 z)^{\frac{1}{2}}-1] \right)$$

The line in Fig.1 corresponds to $v/c \approx 7$. ($H_0 = 55$ km s$^{-1}$ Mpc$^{-1}$ and $q_0 = 0.05$.)

The augular separation of the components of the double seems to be independent of wavelength over at least an octave. However, the detailed visibility curves show that the ratio of flux densities varies with wavelength; that is, the components have different spectra.

The position angle (PA) of the double was determined for all cases shown in Fig. 1 for which there were adequate data. There are no substantial differences with wavelength or time; the PA has been constant at $105° \pm 3°$.

Extrapolation of the rate shown in Fig. 1 to zero separation indicates that an "event" occurred in 1966. Figure 2 shows the total flux density of 3C345 at 3.8 cm. A major increase in flux density began in 1966; the flux doubled in two years and has since stayed high. The near coincidence of the times suggests that the outburst and the expansion have a common origin.

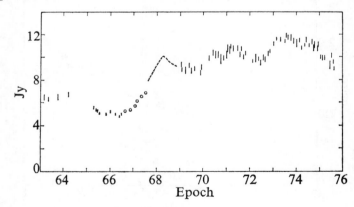

Fig. 2. Total flux density of 3C345 at $\lambda = 3.8$ cm. Points from 1963 to 1966.5 are taken from ref. 10; from 1966.6 to 1967.5, ref. 11; 1969.0 to 1971.6, ref 12; 1971.6 to 1974.4, ref 13; 1974.4 to 1975.6 from private communications with W. A. Dent, and the dashed line is interpolated between observations at 2.8 and 4.5 cm reported in ref. 14.

### 3C273 ($z = 0.158$)

3C273 has a complex elongated structure (refs 3, 15 and 16 and W. D. Cotton *et al.*, in

图 1 中的数据点显示 7 年来亮度分布大约膨胀到了原来的 3 倍，每年近似膨胀 0.17 marc s。不过，膨胀可能不是匀速的，因为从斜率来看似乎 1972 年至 1973 年 要平缓一些，而 1975 年至 1976 年要陡一些。斜率的不同可以解释文献[6,9]中报道过 的大部分速率的差异。通过乘以宇宙学距离以及用因子（1+z）作时间膨胀的修正， 可以将角速率转化为源的表观横向速度。

$$\frac{v}{c} = \frac{\theta}{H_0 q_0^2 (1+z)} \{q_0 z + (q_0 - 1)[(1 + 2q_0 z)^{\frac{1}{2}} - 1]\}$$

图 1 中的直线对应于 $v/c \approx 7$。（$H_0 = 55 \ \text{km} \cdot \text{s}^{-1} \cdot \text{Mpc}^{-1}$，$q_0 = 0.05$。）

在至少一个倍频程内，两个子源的角分离似乎都和波长无关。不过，详细的可见 度曲线显示子源的流量密度比随波长变化；也就是说，两个子源的谱形是不一样的。

我们利用图 1 中所有的观测结果得出双源的位置角（PA），这些观测数据是足 够多的。位置角随着波长或时间没有明显的变化，一直保持在 $105° \pm 3°$。

将图 1 中的速率外推到角分离为零的状况，表明"分裂事件"发生在 1966 年。 图 2 显示了 3C345 在 3.8 cm 波段上的总流量密度。从 1966 年开始，流量密度有了 大幅度的增加；流量在两年内成倍增长，此后一直很高。这些时间上的近乎重合表 明爆发和膨胀的起源相同。

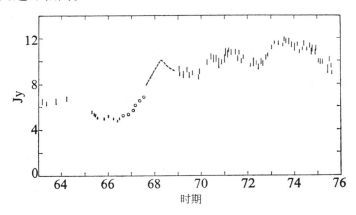

图 2. 3C345 在 λ=3.8 cm 波段的总流量密度。1963 到 1966.5 的数据点来自参考文献 10；1966.6 到 1967.5 的来自参考文献 11；1969.0 到 1971.6 的来自参考文献 12；1971.6 到 1974.4 的来自参考文献 13；1974.4 到 1975.6 的来自和登特的私人交流。虚线是根据参考文献 14 中的 2.8 cm 和 4.5 cm 波段观测得到的插值。

### 3C273（z=0.158）

3C273 具有复杂的伸长结构（参考文献 3、15、16 和科顿等人准备发表的论文）。

preparation). Its low declination (2°) means that the $(u, v)$ coverage is poor and the models are more indeterminate than for high declination sources like 3C345. In consequence, different authors have proposed models of different character, some expanding with time[7,15], and others with stationary components whose intensities are suitably varied[3,17]. All observers agree that the overall size of the brightness distribution increased from 1971 to 1974, but the uniformity and nature of the increase has been argued.

Figure 6 of Schilizzi *et al.* (ref. 15) shows a succession of $(u, v)$ diagrams with the observed lines of maxima and minima of the visibility function. The lines are not equally spaced; therefore, the source cannot be represented by a simple (that is, Gaussian) double. Furthermore, the relative spacings change with time, and successive sets of lines move toward the origin. This means that the shape changes with time, and that, in some measure, it is increasing in size. The visibility data shown by Schilizzi *et al.*, however, do not define the brightness distribution uniquely.

In an attempt to escape difficulties caused by modeling with inadequate data, we have studied one simple measure of the overall size, the distance from the origin to the first minimum of the visibility function. Let $w$ (in wavelengths) be this distance, then $\theta^* \equiv 1/(2w)$ is the angular separation of the components if the source is a simple double. In the more general case where the source consists of several isolated components strung out on a line, $\theta^*$ is a good measure of the overall angular scale. For example, in a wide range of triples which we studied numerically, $\theta^*$ varies from 1.0 to 0.65 times the overall size.

We plot $\theta^*$ at various epochs in Fig. 3. Many of these observations were taken on only one baseline, and the position angles were very poorly determined. So, to provide a consistent basis for calculating $\theta^*$, we assumed PA = 64° in all cases. This is the typical value obtained when multi-baseline data are available, although the source is known to be nonlinear[3,16]. The error bars in Fig. 3 come from the uncertainty in estimating the locations of the minimum, and do not include any errors from an incorrectly assumed position angle. The arrows in mid-1972 signify lower and upper limits.

Further data exist at 2.8 cm for 1975 and 1976, but the character of the visibility function is different then from what it was earlier. The functions do not contain any clearly recognizable extrema (except at the origin), but drop rather smoothly to a "core" value. The brightness distributions may still contain "components", but all (or perhaps all but one) of them must be large enough to be individually resolved at the interferometer spacings which would otherwise produce maxima and minima. In contrast, at 6 cm the structure still had concentrations which could produce the observed minima. These recent results will be discussed separately.

The 2.8-, 3.8-, and 6.0-cm data all fit together very well up to 1975. We conclude that the basic shape was independent of wavelength over this range, although there were spectral differences in component intensities.

它的低赤纬（2°）意味着（u，v）覆盖很差，和 3C345 那样的高赤纬源相比其模型更加难以确定。因此不同作者提出的模型特性各不相同：有些随着时间膨胀 [7,15]，而另一些则子源静止，但流量强度有些变化 [3,17]。所有观测者都认同从 1971 年到 1974 年亮度分布总面积增大了，但是关于这一增大的均匀性和物理本质仍有争论。

斯基利齐等人的文章 ( 参考文献 15) 中的图 6 给出了连续的（u，v）图并表示出可见度函数极大和极小值的观测曲线。曲线不是等距离分布的，所以源不能用简单的双峰（高斯型）来表示。此外，相对间距随着时间改变，连续的线系朝着起点移动。这意味着形状随着时间改变，而且在某种程度上，它的尺度在增大。不过，由斯基利齐等人展示的可见度数据尚不能给出唯一的亮度分度。

为了避开用不充分的数据建立模型所带来的困难，我们研究了对源的整体尺寸的一次简单测量，其距离是从起点到可见度函数的第一个极小值。令 $w$（以波长形式）为距离，如果源为一个简单双峰源，那么 $\theta^* \equiv 1/(2w)$ 是子源的角分离。在更一般的情形下，源包含几个处在一条线上的独立子源，此时 $\theta^*$ 是对整体角尺度的一个很好的量度。例如，在我们进行数值分析的 3 倍范围内，$\theta^*$ 的变化范围在整体尺度的 1.0 倍到 0.65 倍之间。

我们在图 3 上标出了各个时期的 $\theta^*$。大部分观测只建立在一个基线上，因此位置角很难确定。所以，为了给计算 $\theta^*$ 提供统一的基准，我们假定在所有情形下 PA=64°。这是在存在多基线数据时的典型值，尽管我们知道这个源是非线性的 [3,16]。图 3 的误差棒来自估计最小值位置的不确定性，并没有包含由于位置角假设错误带来的误差。1972 年中期的箭头表示数据的下限和上限。

1975 年和 1976 年在 2.8 cm 波段存在更多的数据，但是那时可见度函数的特征与早期的有所不同。该函数不包含任何清晰可识别的极值（除了在起点处），而是略微平稳地下降到一个"核"值。亮度分布可能仍然含有"子源成分"，但是所有这些子源（或者可能有一个例外）必须足够大，以便在干涉仪间距中能够单独分辨出来，否则有可能产生极大和极小值。相反，在 6 cm 波段仍然出现集中点，从中可以得到观测的极小值。我们将对这些最近的观测结果分别进行讨论。

一直到 1975 年，2.8 cm、3.8 cm 和 6.0 cm 波段的数据都彼此符合得很好。我们断定在这期间亮度分布的基本形状与波长无关，尽管子源强度存在频谱差异。

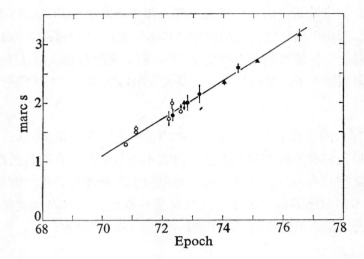

Fig. 3. "Size" of 3C273, where size $\theta^*=(2w)^{-1}$ and $w$ is the distance to the first minimum of the visibility function. The slope of the line is 0.32 marc s yr$^{-1}$. The observations at 2.8 cm are taken from refs 15 and 16 and the points at 3.8 cm are taken from refs 7 and 17-19. The 6-cm points are our previously unpublished data. ● , 2.8 cm; ○ , 3.8 cm; ▲ , 6.0 cm.

The overall size of the brightness distribution increased rather steadily and more than doubled in 6 years. The word "expansion" may properly be used to describe this behavior. The points in Fig. 3 cluster around a line with slope $\theta^* = 0.32$ marc s per year ($v/c = 4.2$). If the line is extrapolated it hits zero in 1966. The total flux density at $\lambda = 3.8$ cm is shown in Fig. 4, and, again, the "expansion" starts, roughly, near the beginning of a large sustained increase in flux density.

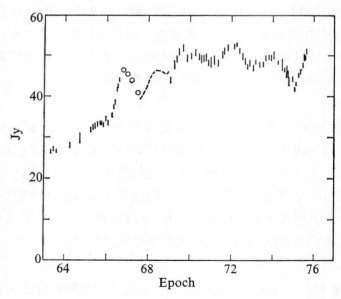

Fig. 4. Total flux density of 3C273 at $\lambda=3.8$ cm. References for the points are as in Fig. 2.

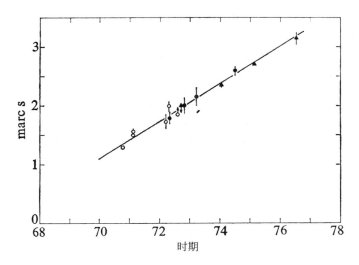

图 3. 3C273 的 "尺度"，其中尺度 $\theta^*=(2w)^{-1}$，$w$ 是可见度函数的首个极小值距离。直线斜率为 0.32 marc s · yr⁻¹。2.8 cm 波段的观测来自参考文献 15 和 16，3.8 cm 波段的数据点来自参考文献 7、17、18 和 19。6 cm 波段的数据点是我们之前未发表的数据。●，2.8 cm；○，3.8 cm；▲，6.0 cm。

亮度分布的整体尺度增加得相当平稳，6 年间增加达两倍多。"膨胀"这个词能够恰当地描述这种现象。图 3 里的数据点聚集在一条斜率 $\theta^*=0.32$ marc s · yr⁻¹ （$v/c=4.2$）的直线周围。如果把线延长，它将在 1966 年到达零点。图 4 显示了在 $\lambda=3.8$ cm 处的总流量密度，而且，"膨胀"再次大致在临近流量密度有持续大量增长的起始处开始。

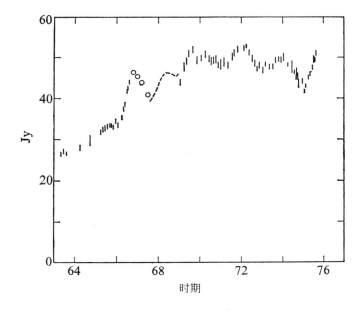

图 4. 3C273 在 $\lambda=3.8$ cm 波段的总流量密度。数据点的参考文献来源和图 2 中的一样。

## 3C120 (z=0.033)

3C120 varies rapidly in flux density and appearance, and has been observed frequently in an attempt to follow its variations[7,15,21-25]. Although many of the observations have been rather incomplete, in several cases very good data were obtained with 3 or 4 telescopes, and simple double models fit very well. The best of these cases comes from our observations at 2.8 cm in 1976.1, when 5 well defined maxima and minima were observed using telescopes at Green Bank, Fort Davis and Owens Valley. As with 3C345, a well-separated Gaussian double accurately fit all the visibility data. However, the compact structure in 3C120 never produced nearly all the total flux, the way it did in 3C345. The compact components of 3C120 are embedded in a larger, undetermined structure.

In all cases with good data the PA was near 65°. To determine a size in the poorer cases, we assumed that a double was always a reasonable representation of the source; and, when necessary, we also assumed PA = 65°.

The separation of the two components of the double is plotted in Fig. 5 for all values in the literature (with exceptions noted below) together with some of our previously unpublished data at 2.8 and 6.0 cm. The parentheses indicate cases where there was ambiguity; typically, the source was only weakly resolved, or the size determination was made from a single minimum on one baseline, or the first minimum was not directly observed.

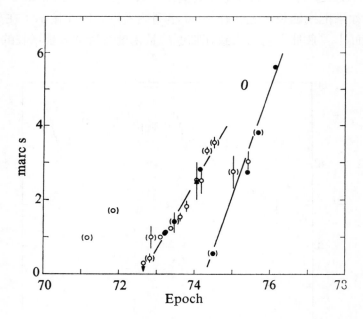

Fig. 5. Separation of the two components of 3C120, assuming a double at PA = 65° when necessary. The slopes of the lines are 1.8 and 2.9 marc s yr⁻¹. The early observations at 2.8 cm are from ref. 15, and the points from 1974.5 on are previously unpublished. The 3.8-cm data are from refs 7, 15, 21-25. The 6-cm point at 1974.5 is previously unpublished. ●, 2.8 cm; ○, 3.8cm; ▲, 6.0 cm.

## 3C120 （$z = 0.033$）

3C120 在流量密度和外形上变化得很快，为了跟踪它的变化，对它的观测较为频繁[7,15,21-25]。尽管许多观测颇为不完整，但是有几个观测项目用三到四台望远镜得到了很好的数据，而且与简单的双峰模型拟合得非常好。这些观测中最好的一次是我们于1976.1 在 2.8 cm 波段进行的观测，我们使用格林班克、戴维斯堡和欧文斯谷的望远镜观测到了 5 个确定得很好的极大和极小值。像 3C345 一样，分离得很好的高斯双峰模型精确拟合了所有的可见度数据。不过，3C120 中的致密结构不像 3C345 中的那样产生几乎全部总流量。3C120 中的致密成分处在一个更大的、未准确测量的结构里。

在所有数据质量良好的情况下，位置角接近于 65°。为了确定在数据质量较差情形下位置角的大小，我们假设双峰结构总是可以作为对这个源的合理描述，然而必要时，我们还是假定位置角为 65°。

文献中所有双峰两个子源的角分离数据（例外的情况在下面做了标注）和我们之前未发表的一些在 2.8 cm 和 6.0 cm 的数据都在图 5 上标出。圆括号代表存在模糊度的情况；通常源只能被微弱地分辨开，或是通过一条基线上的单个极小值来确定尺度，或是第一个极小值没有直接观测到。

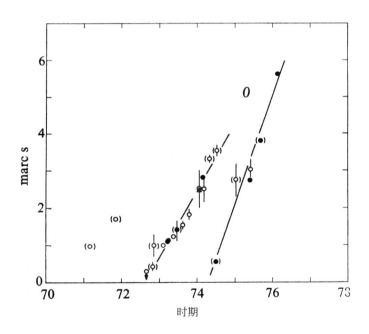

图 5. 3C120 两个子源的角分离，必要时假设其为位置角等于 65° 的双峰结构。两条直线斜率分别为 1.8 marc s·yr⁻¹ 和 2.9 marc s·yr⁻¹。2.8 cm 波段的早期观测来自参考文献 15，1974.5 之后的数据点以前未发表过。3.8 cm 波段的数据来自参考文献 7、15、21~25。1974.5 的 6 cm 波段的数据点以前未发表过。●，2.8 cm；○，3.8 cm；▲，6.0 cm。

We recognize two major epochs of expansion in Fig. 5, and have indicated them with straight lines whose slopes correspond to $v/c = 5$ and $v/c = 8$. At 1974.5 the 3.8 and 2.8 cm observations showed doubles of very different separation. No unique interpretation can be given for this, for the size and strength of the components of the doubles are very poorly determined. The observed double structure did not account for the total flux at either wavelength, so it is possible that both doubles existed at both wavelengths but were not recognized because of the differing resolutions. Thus, the close-spaced double seen at 2.8 cm might not have been recognized at 3.8 cm because its first minimum would have come at $1.9 \times 10^8$ wavelengths, whereas the maximum length of the baseline was only $1.0 \times 10^8$ wavelengths. Similarly, at 2.8 cm where the minimum length of the baseline was $1.6 \times 10^8$ wavelengths, components larger than about 1.5 marc s would have been resolved, and this double would have been missed. Spectral differences of the type apparently seen in 3C273 would increase the size of the outer components at 2.8 cm and accentuate this behaviour.

The points in 1971 were once interpreted as evidence for a superluminal expansion[21], but that result is ambiguous with only two points. Further data exist for early 1972 (refs 22, 23), but they are not plotted. The visibility was changing rapidly then, but remained very low. Therefore, the strong concentrations which must have existed in 1971 had dissipated, and by 1972.3 most of the flux came from regions greater than about 1 marc s in diameter.

During both epochs of expansion the PA was near 65° whenever a good model could be generated.

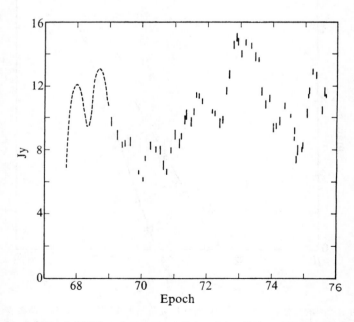

Fig. 6. Total flux density of 3C120 at $\lambda = 3.8$ cm. Points from 1969 to 1971.6 are taken from ref.12; 1971.6 to 1974.4, ref.13; 1974.4 to 1975.6, from private communications with W. A. Dent, and the dashed line is interpolated between observations at 2.8 and 4.5 cm reported in ref.14.

我们在图5中识别出两个主要的膨胀时期，并把它们用斜率对应于 v/c=5 和 v/c=8 的直线表示出来。在 1974.5，3.8 cm 和 2.8 cm 波段的观测显示双峰角分离明显不同。对此不能做出唯一的解释，因为双峰子源的大小、强度都确定得不好。在任一波段观测到的双峰成分都不能解释总流量，所以也可能是两个波段都存在两个双峰结构，但是因为两个波段的分辨率不同，因而没能在某一波段同时分辨出两个双峰结构来。因此，在 2.8 cm 波段看到的近距离间隔的双峰没能在 3.8 cm 波段识别出，可能由于它的第一个极小值在 $1.9 \times 10^8$ 个波长处，而 3.8 cm 的基线最大长度是 $1.0 \times 10^8$ 个波长。类似地，在 2.8 cm 波段基线的最小长度为 $1.6 \times 10^8$ 个波长，只有大于 1.5 marc s 的子源才能被分辨出，因而 3.8 cm 波段的双峰在 2.8 cm 波段却没有观测到。3C273 中明显看到的频谱差别可能在 2.8 cm 波段扩大了外层成分的尺度，因而突出了上面提到的这种情况。

1971 年的数据点一度被解释为是超光速膨胀的证据[21]，不过只依据 2 个数据点，那样的结果是不明确的。1972 年早期有了更多的数据（参考文献 22、23），但还没有标绘。之后可见度变化很大，但仍然很低。所以，在 1971 年密集在一起的成分开始分离开来，到 1972.3，大部分流量就都来自直径大于 1 marc s 的区域。

在两个膨胀时期，只要模型拟合得很好，其位置角都在 65° 附近。

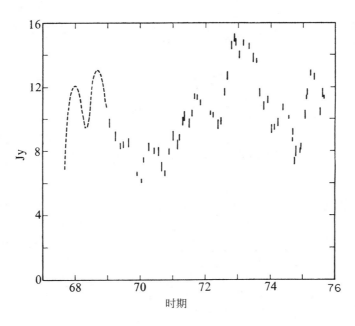

图 6. 3C120 在 λ=3.8 cm 波段的总流量密度。1969 到 1971.6 的数据点来自参考文献 12；1971.6 到 1974.4 的数据来自参考文献 13；1974.4 到 1975.6 的数据来自和登特的私人交流，虚线是根据参考文献 14 中的在 2.8 cm 和 4.5 cm 波段处观测得到的插值。

Figure 6 shows the total flux density of 3C120 at $\lambda = 3.8$ cm. This source varies more rapidly and has a greater fractional variation than 3C345 and 3C273. The largest outburst in Fig. 6 begins in mid-1972 and is coincident with the start of the first expansion shown in Fig. 5. The second expansion starts in early 1974 and does not appear to be correlated with any exceptionally large flux event.

## 3C279 ($z=0.538$)

The available data on 3C279 are mainly at $\lambda = 3.8$ cm. from the period 1970-73 (refs 7, 17-20, 26). Most of this material is from only one baseline, and the interpretations are ambiguous.

The two earliest observations have been interpreted as an expanding double, with separation rate $\theta = 0.27$ marc s yr$^{-1}$ ($v/c =10$) (refs 7, 19). The rate is not well determined with only 2 points, but it is consistent with observations at 6 cm in early 1972 (ref. 17), which give the overall size as about 2 marc s. A minimum in the 13-cm visibility function on baselines from California to Australia[26] near the beginning of 1970 is also consistent with a simple double model based on the 3.8-cm observations, suggesting that the separation of the two components was similar over that range of wavelengths.

A sequence of observations at 3.8 cm in 1972 (ref. 17) can be interpreted as a new expansion event, since an unresolved weak core was seen in March and April 1972, and this became substantially resolved by November 1972. Another possibility is that all the 1972 data came from a triple source whose overall dimensions were constant, but whose component flux densities varied[17]. The published material is consistent with either model, and further data are necessary to discriminate between them.

## Interpretations

It is of interest to ask what fraction of all sources are superluminal, and whether statistical arguments can be made for or against any of the customary interpretations. These are difficult questions because adequate surveys do not exist at the short centimeter wavelengths, and VLBI surveying is particularly incomplete. However, we can make some comments.

At $\lambda = 3.8$ cm, 3C345 is the weakest known superluminal source, with mean flux density $< S_{3.8} \sim 10$ Jy during the expansion. We know of 15 extragalactic sources which have been as strong as 10 Jy at 3.8 cm, at any epoch. Five of these are radio galaxies with most of the flux coming from extended regions. (3C123, 3C353, Vir A, Cen A, Cyg A). The remaining 10 sources are shown in Table 1. The fifth column in Table 1 gives the known range of flux density at $\lambda = 3.8$ cm. The sixth column gives a comment on the structure seen with VLBI, and the seventh column gives references for those sources not discussed in detail above.

图 6 显示了 3C120 在 λ=3.8 cm 的总流量密度。这个源比 3C345 和 3C273 变化更快，局部变化更大。图 6 中最强的爆发开始于 1972 年中期，和图 5 所示的第一次膨胀开始的时间相重合。第二次膨胀开始于 1974 年早期，并且看起来和任何超大流量事件都没有关系。

### 3C279（$z$=0.538）

1970 年到 1973 年期间 3C279 的数据主要集中在 λ=3.8 cm 波段（参考文献 7、17~20、26）。大部分数据是只基于一条基线得到的，而且不能给出明确的解释。

最早的两个观测被解释为是一个膨胀的双峰，分离速率为 θ = 0.27 marc s·yr⁻¹（$v/c$=10）（参考文献 7、19）。由于只有两个数据点，因此这个速率不能很好地确定，但是它和 1972 年早期给出整体尺度约 2 marc s 的 6 cm 波段观测结果（参考文献 17）一致。1970 年初用从加利福尼亚到澳大利亚 [26] 的基线得到的 13 cm 波段可见度函数的最小值也和基于 3.8 cm 波段观测得到的简单双峰模型一致，这表明在这个波长范围内两个子源的分离相似。

1972 年在 3.8 cm 波段的一系列观测（参考文献 17）可以看成 3C279 发生一次新的膨胀事件，因为在 1972 年 3 月和 4 月看到了一个微弱的不可分辨的核，而它到 1972 年 11 月变得可以充分地分辨开来。还一个可能是 1972 年的所有数据都来自一个三源系统，它的整体尺度不变，但是子源的流量密度在变化 [17]。已经发表的数据跟任何一个模型都吻合，因此要区分这些模型就需要更多的数据。

### 结 果 分 析

超光速源在所有源中的比率以及是否存在统计上的论据来支持或者反对通常的解释，这些都是很有意义的问题。但是这些问题也都很难回答，因为在厘米短波上还没有足够多的巡天，并且 VLBI 巡天也特别不完整。不过，我们仍可以做一些评论。

在 λ=3.8 cm 波段，3C345 是已知超光速源中最弱的源，膨胀时的平均流量密度小于 $S_{3.8}$（$S_{3.8}$ 约为 10 Jy）。我们知道 15 个河外源任何时期在 3.8 cm 波段的流量都很大，达到 10 Jy。其中 5 个是射电星系，它们大部分的流量来自延展区域（3C123、3C353、Vir A、Cen A 和 Cyg A）。剩下的 10 个源列在表 1 中。表 1 的第 5 列给出了在 λ = 3.8 cm 波段源的流量密度的已知范围。第 6 列给出了对 VLBI 观测到的结构的意见，第 7 列给出前面没有具体讨论的源的参考文献。

Table 1. Strong compact extragalactic radio sources

| Source | Name | Id | $z$ | $S_{3.8}$(Jy) | VLBI | Refs |
|--------|------|-----|------|--------------|------|------|
| 0316+41 | 3C84 | G | 0.018 | 20-58 | slow variable | 15, 24, 25, 27, 28 |
| 0355+50 | NRAO150 | | | 7.3-15 | stable double(?) | 16, 24, 29 |
| 0430+05 | 3C120 | G | 0.032 | 6.4-15.1 | superluminal | |
| 0923+39 | 4C39.25 | Q | 0.699 | 8.5-11.8 | stable double | 5, 24, 29 |
| 1226+02 | 3C273 | Q | 0.158 | 28-53 | superluminal | |
| 1253-05 | 3C279 | Q | 0.538 | 11.2-17.5 | superluminal | |
| 1641+39 | 3C345 | Q | 0.595 | 8.8-11.9 | superluminal | |
| 2134+00 | | Q | 1.94 | 11.0-13.4 | slow variable | 15, 24 |
| 2200+42 | BLLac | G | 0.07 | 4.8-14.2 | rapid variable | 16, 24, 29, 30 |
| 2251+15 | 3C454.3 | Q | 0.859 | 9.0-20.2 | variable core | 16, 24, 26, 29 |

3C84 has several components which vary in flux density but seem to have little motion. NRAO150 has been observed less than the others and its size is less than 0″.001 so that intercontinental observations are necessary for reasonable resolution.

4C39.25 has a well-defined double structure with constant separation, but the total flux density is variable. 2134+004 apparently is more complex than a simple double, and has slow weak variations in its brightness distribution. BL Lacertae has a double structure which is variable but keeps a constant position angle. The observed changes in BL Lac are not systematic as in the superluminal sources, but it may well be that shorter sampling intervals are required to see them, as this is the most variable source in Table 1. 3C454.3 has a core-halo structure. The variations in total flux density follow those of the unresolved core.

Nearly half the strong compact sources show a superluminal effect. This suggests that mechanisms which require us to be in an especially favorable position are unlikely to be at work. Luminous relativistically moving clouds are one such class, because to see them superluminally we have to be within a small solid angle[1]. However, the blue-shift of the approaching clouds also raises the possibility of a selection effect. Perhaps superluminal sources seem common partly because the blue shift raises their flux density above the minimum level being counted. To study this possibility we need to know the distribution of superluminal sources with flux density, which is unknown at present.

The superluminal sources all show a systematic expansion, and at least one of them shows two epochs of expansion with the same PA. This argues strongly against mechanisms which basically are random and allow both expansions and contractions. Gravitational lenses and some other propagation and opacity effects are of this type. So, too, would be a collection of separated sources which are independent, and flash at random times.

表 1. 河外致密强射电源

| 源 | 名字 | Id | $z$ | $S_{3.8}$ (Jy) | VLBI | 参考文献 |
|---|---|---|---|---|---|---|
| 0316+41 | 3C84 | G | 0.018 | 20~58 | 缓慢变化 | 15、24、25、27、28 |
| 0355+50 | NRAO150 | | | 7.3~15 | 稳定的双峰(？) | 16、24、29 |
| 0430+05 | 3C120 | G | 0.032 | 6.4~15.1 | 超光速 | |
| 0923+39 | 4C39.25 | Q | 0.699 | 8.5~11.8 | 稳定的双峰 | 5、24、29 |
| 1226+02 | 3C273 | Q | 0.158 | 28~53 | 超光速 | |
| 1253−05 | 3C279 | Q | 0.538 | 11.2~17.5 | 超光速 | |
| 1641+39 | 3C345 | Q | 0.595 | 8.8~11.9 | 超光速 | |
| 2134+00 | | Q | 1.94 | 11.0~13.4 | 缓慢变化 | 15、24 |
| 2200+42 | BLLac | G | 0.07 | 4.8~14.2 | 快速变化 | 16、24、29、30 |
| 2251+15 | 3C454.3 | Q | 0.859 | 9.0~20.2 | 变化的核 | 16、24、26、29 |

　　3C84 有几个流量密度变化、但是看起来移动很小的子源成分。NRAO150 比其他源观测的少些，它的尺度小于 0″.001，所以需要通过洲际观测来加以分辨。

　　4C39.25 有非常确定的双峰结构，其分开速率不变但是总流量密度是变化的。2134+004 看起来明显比简单的双峰要复杂，而且它存在缓慢而微弱的亮度分布变化。蝎虎天体有一个变化的双峰结构，但是位置角不变。观测到的蝎虎天体的变化不像超光速源那样有系统性，但可能观测它们需要更短的取样间隔，因为它们是表 1 中变化最快的源。3C454.3 有一个核－晕结构。总流量密度随着不可分辨的核变化。

　　近半的致密强源表现出超光速效应。这意味着那些需要我们处于特别有利位置的机制不太可能再起作用。相对论运动的亮星云是这样的一类天体，为了以超光速观测到它们，我们必须处在一个很小的立体角内 [1]。不过，云逼近时的蓝移也可能导致选择效应。也许超光速源看起来经常出现的部分原因是蓝移导致他们流量密度高于计数的最低水平。为了研究这种可能性，我们需要知道超光速源随流量密度的分布，这个分布目前还是未知的。

　　超光速源都显示出系统性膨胀，并且它们中至少有一个在两个时期内以相同的位置角膨胀。这与那些本质上是随机的，并且膨胀和收缩都可以存在的机制是严重相抵触的，诸如引力透镜和其他一些传播效应以及不透明度效应就是这种类型的机制。这样的话，我们应该收集到很多独立的、随机爆发的源。传播效应和不透明

Propagation and opacity effects also are unlikely because they predict that the separation would be wavelength dependent, contrary to observation.

The fact that the superluminal effect has been seen in a galaxy as well as in three quasars suggests that it cannot be used as evidence against a cosmological origin for the redshifts.

Thus what is now known can be summarized as follows. Nearly half the strong ($S_{3.8} \geq 10$ Jy) compact ($\theta < 0''.01$) sources show a superluminal expansion at centimetre wavelengths, and changes in overall size of up to factor 10 in periods of one to two years have been observed.

No systematic contractions have been seen. The separation of components in a source is basically independent of wavelength from 2 to 6 cm, although the components may have different spectra. In 3C273, and perhaps in 3C120, we may have observed an epoch where component evolution produced different sizes at different wavelengths.

The position angle is substantially constant during an expansion. In at least one case (3C120) there have been two distinct epochs of expansion. The position angle is the same for both.

The brightness distribution does not expand uniformly, but there is an overall trend as shown in the graphs. The epoch of zero separation, determined by extrapolation of the trend, may be close to the start of a major outburst in flux density.

The extensive data for 3C345 at 1974.5 and for 3C120 at 1976.2 strongly suggest a structure which can be represented as a simple double, with the two components being approximately equal. 3C273 is more complex. There are both simple (4C39.25) and complex (3C84) sources which do not show variations in the overall size of the brightness distribution although their total flux densities vary on time scales similar to those for the superluminal sources.

We thank W. A. Dent, and the members of the Canadian-British and the MIT-NASA VLBI groups, for giving us data in advance of its publication, and for useful comments. M. H. C. and J. D. R. are grateful to the Institute of Astronomy, Cambridge, for their hospitality during the period when part of this study was made.

This work was supported in part by grants from the US National Science Foundation. J. D. R. is a US National Science Foundation Graduate Fellow.

(**268**, 405-409; 1977)

度效应也是不可能的机制，因为它们预示着膨胀随波长而变，这与观测结果相反。

在一个星系和三个类星体中观测到超光速效应的事实表明超光速效应不能作为驳斥红移的宇宙学起源的证据。

因此，我们将目前已知的内容总结如下。近半数的强（$S_{3.8} \geq 10$ Jy）致密（$\theta < 0''.01$）源在厘米波段上表现出超光速膨胀，并且在 1 到 2 年的时间内观测到整体尺度增大了 10 倍。

我们没有观察到系统性的收缩。在一个源中，虽然子源会有不相同的谱形，但是子源的分离程度在 2 cm 到 6 cm 的波段范围内基本上与波长无关。在 3C273 中（也可能在 3C120 中）我们也许已经观测到，在一段时间内，子源的演化在不同波长上会导致不同的尺度。

在一个膨胀过程中位置角非常稳定。至少在这样一个源（3C120）中存在明显的两个膨胀时期，而位置角都是一样的。

虽然亮度分布的膨胀并不均匀，但如图所示，存在一个整体的趋势。从外推得出的零角分离时间可能接近于一次流量密度大爆发的起始点。

3C345 在 1974.5 的大量数据和 3C120 在 1976.2 的大量数据有力地表明，这两个源都可用简单的双峰结构来表示，其两个子源近似相同。3C273 要更复杂些。另外还存在一个简单的源（4C39.25）和一个复杂的源（3C84），尽管它们的总流量密度像那些超光速源一样随着时间尺度变化，但它们在亮度分布的整体尺度上都没有显示出变化。

我们感谢登特以及加拿大－大不列颠和麻省理工学院－美国国家航空航天局的甚长基线干涉仪小组的成员将尚未发表的数据提供给我们，并且提出有益的意见。科恩和罗姆尼向剑桥天文研究所在部分研究工作进行期间提供的热情帮助表示感谢。

本项工作得到美国国家科学基金会的部分资助。罗姆尼是美国国家科学基金会研究员。

（肖莉 翻译；何香涛 审稿）

M. H. Cohen*, K. I. Kellermann†, D. B. Shaffer†, R. P. Linfield*, A. T. Moffet*, J. D. Romney*, G. A. Seielstad*, I. I. K. Pauliny-Toth‡, E. Preuss‡, A. Witzel‡, R. T. Schilizzi§ and B. J. Geldzahler‖

*Owens Valley Radio Observatory, California Institute of Technology, Pasadena, California 91125
†National Radio Astronomy Observatory, Green Bank, West Virginia 24944
‡Max-Planck-Institut fur Radioastronomie, Bonn 1, Federal Republic of Germany
§Netherlands Foundation for Radio Astronomy, Radiosterrenwacht, Dwingeloo, The Netherlands
‖University of Pennsylvania, Philadelphia, Pennsylvania 19174

References:

1. Blandford, R. D., McKee, C. F. & Rees, M. J. *Nature* **267**, 211 (1977).

2. Fort, D. N. *Astrophys. J. Lett.* **207**, L155 (1976).

3. Legg, T. H. *et al. Astrophys. J.* **211**, 21 (1977).

4. Wittels, J. J. *et al. Astron. J.* **81**, 933 (1976).

5. Shaffer, D. B. *et al. Astrophys. J.* (in the press).

6. Cohen, M. H. *et al. Astrophys. J. Lett.* **206**, L1 (1976).

7. Cohen, M. H. *et al. Astrophys. J.* **170**, 207 (1971).

8. Kellermann, K. I. *et al. Astrophys. J.* **169**, 1 (1971).

9. Wittels, J. J. *et al. Astrophys. J. Lett.* **206**, L75 (1976).

10. Aller, H. D. & Haddock, F. T. *Astrophys. J.* **147**, 833 (1967).

11. Kellermann, K. I. & Pauliny-Toth, I. I. K. *Ann. Rev. Astron. Astrophys.* **6**, 431 (1968).

12. Dent, W. A. & Kojoian, G. *Astron. J.* **77**, 819 (1972).

13. Dent, W. A. & Kapitsky, J. E. *Astron. J.* **81**, 1053 (1976).

14. Medd, W. J., Andrew, B. H., Harvey, G. A. & Locke, J. L. *Mem. R. astron. Soc.* **77**, 109 (1972).

15. Schilizzi, R. T. *et al. Astrophys. J.* **201**, 263 (1975).

16. Kellermann, K. I. *et al. Astrophys. J.* **211**, 658 (1977).

17. Kellermann, K. I. *et al. Astrophys. J. Lett.* **189**, L19 (1974).

18. Knight, C. A. *et al. Science* **172**, 52 (1971).

19. Whitney, A. R. *et al. Science* **173**, 225 (1971).

20. Niell, A. E., Kellermann, K. I., Clark, B. G. & Shaffer, D. B. *Astrophys. J. Lett.* **197**, L109 (1975).

21. Shaffer, D. B., Cohen, M. H., Jauncey, D. L. & Kellermann, K. I. *Astrophys. J. Lett.* **173**, L147 (1972).

22. Shapiro, I. I. *et al. Astrophys. J. Lett.* **183**, L47 (1973).

23. Kellermann, K. I. *et al. Astrophys. J. Lett.* **183**, L51 (1973).

24. Wittels, J. J. *et al. Astrophys. J.* **196**, 13 (1975).

25. Hutton, L. K. thesis, Univ. Maryland (1976).

26. Gubbay, J. *et al. Astrophys. J.* (in the press).

27. Legg, T. H. *et al. Nature* **244**, 18 (1973).

28. Pauliny-Toth, I. I. K. *et al. Nature* **259**, 17 (1976).

29. Shaffer, D. B. *et al. Astrophys. J.* **201**, 256 (1975).

30. Clark, B. G. *et al. Astrophys. J. Lett.* **182**, L57 (1973).

# New Hominoid Primates from the Siwaliks of Pakistan and their Bearing on Hominoid Evolution

D. Pilbeam *et al.*

## Editor's Note

The Miocene strata of the Siwalik Hills in Pakistan had yielded abundant fossils for decades, but the 1970s were especially rich. Pilbeam *et al.* document 86 new primate specimens from 18 localities, doubling the record then known. Of particular interest were specimens of the ape-like *Ramapithecus*, then thought of as an ancestor of man. Pilbeam and colleagues, however, add words of caution. *Ramapithecus*, along with another form, *Sivapithecus*, belonged to an increasingly appreciated diversity of Miocene apes worldwide, so drawing lines between these and modern forms would have been unwise. We now suspect that *Ramapithecus* and *Sivapithecus* are similar to each other, and closer to the orangutan than to man.

---

Siwalik deposits in the Punjab have yielded a rich collection of hominoid primate remains. Together with other recent finds they indicate the need for some changes in hominoid classification.

---

SINCE 1973 a team from the Geological Survey of Pakistan (GSP) and the Peabody Museum has collected fossils in the Potwar Plateau, Punjab Province, Pakistan (72°30′ E, 33°00′ N) as part of a joint research project aimed at a better understanding of the geological, floral and faunal history of South Asia. Neogene rocks of the Siwalik Group are widely exposed in India and Pakistan as part of the South Asian alpide system. The Soan synclinorium in the Potwar Plateau is the area in which all but one of the type localities for Siwalik formations and South Asian Land Mammal Ages are located (Figs 1 and 2 of preceding article). The lithostratigraphy and biostratigraphy of Siwalik deposits in the Plateau have been discussed in the preceding article[1].

# 巴基斯坦西瓦利克新发现的人猿超科灵长类动物及其在人猿超科进化上的意义

皮尔比姆等

## 编者按

在过去的数十年中，从位于巴基斯坦的西瓦利克山脉的中新世地层中已经出土了大量的化石，但是在 20 世纪 70 年代这里的出土量尤为突出。皮尔比姆等人从来自于 18 个发掘地点的化石中记录了 86 件新的灵长类动物标本，这使得当时已有的记录得以翻番。其中令人特别感兴趣的是似猿的腊玛古猿的标本，随后腊玛古猿被认为是人类祖先。但是皮尔比姆及其同事们提醒人们要谨慎对待这一问题。腊玛古猿和另一种类型的古猿——西瓦古猿，都属于多样性日渐丰富的中新世猿类，因此将它们与现代类型截然区分开是不明智的。现在我们怀疑腊玛古猿和西瓦古猿彼此类似，比起人类，它们更接近于猩猩。

---

旁遮普的西瓦利克沉积物中出土了大量人猿超科灵长类动物化石。结合其他的最新发现表明，有必要对人猿超科的分类做些改动。

---

自 1973 年以来，巴基斯坦地质调查所与皮博迪博物馆组成的考察队已经在巴基斯坦旁遮普省博德瓦尔高原（72°30′E，33°00′N）采集了一些化石，这是一个联合研究项目的一部分，旨在更好地了解南亚的地质、植物群及动物群的历史。作为南亚阿尔卑斯带系统的一部分，西瓦利克群的新近纪岩石在印度与巴基斯坦广泛出露。除了一个例外，其他所有的西瓦利克组及南亚陆地哺乳动物时代所在的典型地点都在博德瓦尔高原的索安复向斜区域（前面文章中的图 1、图 2）。在前面的文章 [1] 中已经对博德瓦尔高原西瓦利克的沉积物进行了岩石地层学与生物地层学方面的讨论。

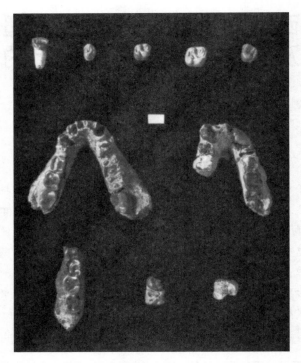

Fig. 1. Top row left to right: GSP 9903, 9906, 5019, 6206, 8702. Middle row: GSP 4622/4857, 9563/9902. Bottom row: GSP 6153, 7619, 7144.

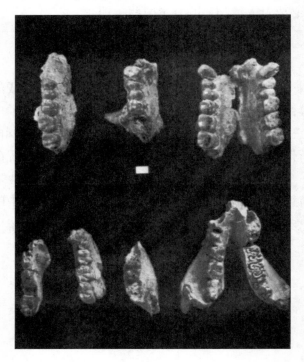

Fig. 2. Top row, left to right: GSP 11708, 11704, 9977/01/05/9564. Bottom row: 11536/7, 13163, 4230, 9977/01/05/9564.

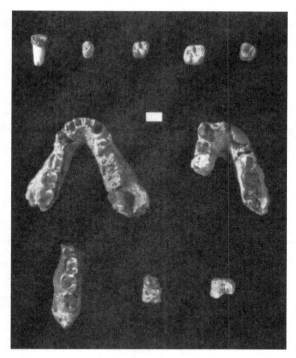

图 1. 上排从左到右：GSP 9903, 9906, 5019, 6206, 8702；中排从左到右：GSP 4622/4857, 9563/9902；下排从左到右：GSP 6153, 7619, 7144。

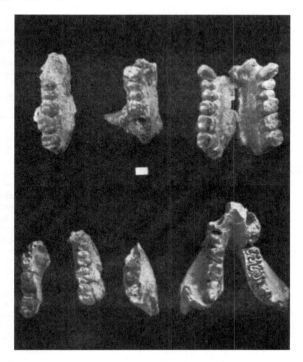

图 2. 上排从左到右：GSP 11708, 11704, 9977/01/05/9564。下排从左到右：11536/7, 13163, 4230, 9977/01/05/9564。

More than 13,000 catalogued fossil specimens representing a diverse vertebrate and invertebrate fauna have been collected from more than 300 localities; 18 localities have yielded 86 new hominoid primate specimens representing a minimum of 43 individuals (Tables 1-3). The hominoids are accurately located stratigraphically with well documented information concerning lithological context and faunal associations. They approximately double the previously known hominoid collections[2]. In addition, new stratigraphic information has facilitated further interpretation of earlier collections. Of particular interest are four localities (Table 2) in which remains of between five and nine hominoid individuals have been found together.

Table 1. Hominoid specimens collected from the Potwar Plateau, Punjab

| Area | Locality | GSP no. | Specimen |
|---|---|---|---|
| Sethi Nagri | 311 | 11536/7 | Infant left mandibular corpus, $dP_{\overline{3}}$, $dP_{\overline{4}}$, associated $M_{\overline{2}}$ |
| | | 10493 | Left $\underline{C}$ |
| | | 11534 | Left $P^4$ fragment |
| | | 11999 | Right $M^1$ |
| | | 13162 | Right $M^1$ fragment |
| | | 12000 | Right $M^1$ fragment |
| | | 9986 | Right $M^1$ |
| | | 10500 | Left $M^2$ fragment |
| | | 11533 | Right $M^2$ fragment |
| | | 7144 | Left $M_{\overline{1}}$ fragment |
| | | 11998 | Right $M_{\overline{2}}$ |
| | | 13164 | Central $\overline{I}$ |
| | | 12648 | Central $\overline{I}$ |
| | | 6663 | Distal humeral epiphyseal fragment |
| | | 6664 | Distal pollicial phalangeal fragment |
| | | 6666 | Distal phalangeal fragment |
| | | 6454 | Intermediate cuneiform |
| | | 12271 | Distal humeral fragment |
| Khaur | 182 | 8928 | Right $I^1$ |
| | | 8925 | Right $\underline{C}$ |
| | | 5019 | Right $M^1$ |
| | | 5018 | Left $M^2$ fragment |
| | | 5067 | Left $M^2$ |
| | | 8702 | Left $M^3$ |

已经从 300 多个地点采集到超过 13,000 个编入目录的化石标本，它们代表了不同的脊椎动物与无脊椎动物的动物群；在 18 个地点共出土了 86 件新的人猿超科灵长类动物标本，它们至少代表了 43 个个体（表 1~3）。利用记载详细的有关岩性背景与动物群的相关信息，准确地定位了人猿超科动物所在的地层。它们几乎是以往已知人猿超科动物标本的两倍[2]。另外，新的地层信息促进了对早期标本的进一步解释。更为有趣的是，在其中 4 个地点（表 2）发现了聚集在一起的人猿超科动物个体，其个体数目介于 5 到 9 个之间。

表 1. 从旁遮普博德瓦尔高原采集到的人猿超科动物的标本

| 地区 | 地点 | GSP编号 | 标本 |
|------|------|---------|------|
| 塞西纳格里 | 311 | 11536/7 | 幼体左下颌共生体，$dP_3$，$dP_4$，共生的 $M_2$ |
| | | 10493 | 左 $\underline{C}$ |
| | | 11534 | 左 $P^4$ 碎片 |
| | | 11999 | 右 $M^1$ |
| | | 13162 | 右 $M^1$ 碎片 |
| | | 12000 | 右 $M^1$ 碎片 |
| | | 9986 | 右 $M^1$ |
| | | 10500 | 左 $M^2$ 碎片 |
| | | 11533 | 右 $M^2$ 碎片 |
| | | 7144 | 左 $M_{\overline{1}}$ 碎片 |
| | | 11998 | 右 $M_2$ |
| | | 13164 | 中 $\overline{I}$ |
| | | 12648 | 中 $\overline{I}$ |
| | | 6663 | 肱骨末端骨骺残片 |
| | | 6664 | 拇指指骨末端残片 |
| | | 6666 | 指骨末端残片 |
| | | 6454 | 中央楔状骨 |
| | | 12271 | 肱骨末端残片 |
| 汉瓦 | 182 | 8928 | 右 $I^1$ |
| | | 8925 | 右 $\underline{C}$ |
| | | 5019 | 右 $M^1$ |
| | | 5018 | 左 $M^2$ 碎片 |
| | | 5067 | 左 $M^2$ |
| | | 8702 | 左 $M^3$ |

*Continued*

| Area | Locality | GSP no. | Specimen |
|---|---|---|---|
| Khaur | 182 | 4622/4857 | Mandible, left $M_{\overline{1}} - M_{\overline{3}}$, right $M_{\overline{3}}$ |
| | | 4230 | Right mandibular fragment with $M_{\overline{2}}$ |
| | | 5464 | Right I- |
| | | 8679 | Right $\overline{C}$ |
| | | 5712 | Left $P_{\overline{3}}$ fragment |
| | | 5020 | Left $P_{\overline{4}}$ |
| | | 4635 | Right $M_{\overline{2}}$ |
| | | 4735 | Right $M_{\overline{3}}$ |
| | | 8926 | Right $M_{\overline{3}}$ |
| | | 8927 | Left $M_{\overline{3}}$ |
| | | 4664 | Left distal calcaneal fragment |
| Khaur | 260 | 9977/01/05/ | Maxilla, left and right $\underline{C}$ $M^{\underline{3}}$ |
| | | 9564 | right $I^{\underline{2}}$; mandible, right $\overline{C}$, left $P_{\overline{4}}$–$M_{\overline{3}}$; right condyle; Cranial and facial fragments |
| | | 9897 | Left maxillary fragment |
| | | 9903 | Right $I^{\underline{1}}$ |
| | | 9898 | Left $I^{\underline{1}}$ |
| | | 13167 | Left $\underline{C}$ |
| | | 9906 | Left $P^{\underline{4}}$ |
| | | 13166 | Left $P^{\underline{4}}$ |
| | | 12647 | Right $M^{\underline{1}}$ |
| | | 9972 | Right $M^{\underline{2}}$ |
| | | 9896 | Left $M^{\underline{2}}$ |
| | | 9969 | Right $M^{\underline{2}}$ |
| | | 9895 | Left $M^{\underline{3}}$ |
| | | 9900 | Right $M^{\underline{3}}$ |
| | | 12709 | Infant mandible, right $\overline{C}$, $dP_{\overline{3}}$ |
| | | 9563/9902 | Mandible, left $P_{\overline{3}}$, $M_{\overline{1}}$, right $M_{\overline{2}}$, $M_{\overline{3}}$ |
| | | 13165 | Right mandibular fragment, $M_{\overline{1}} - M_{\overline{3}}$ |
| | | 9565 | Left $\overline{C}$ fragment |
| | | 9899 | Right $M_{\overline{3}}$ |
| | | 12654 | Femoral fragments |
| | | 9894 | Femoral head fragment |

| 地区 | 地点 | GSP编号 | 标本 |
|------|------|---------|------|
| 汉瓦 | 182 | 4622/4857 | 下颌骨，左 $M_{\overline{1}}$ – $M_{\overline{3}}$，右 $M_{\overline{3}}$ |
| | | 4230 | 有 $M_{\overline{3}}$ 的右颌骨碎片 |
| | | 5464 | 右 I- |
| | | 8679 | 右 $\overline{C}$ |
| | | 5712 | 左 $P_{\overline{3}}$ 碎片 |
| | | 5020 | 左 $P_{\overline{4}}$ |
| | | 4635 | 右 $M_{\overline{3}}$ |
| | | 4735 | 右 $M_{\overline{3}}$ |
| | | 8926 | 右 $M_{\overline{3}}$ |
| | | 8927 | 左 $M_{\overline{3}}$ |
| | | 4664 | 左跟骨末端碎片 |
| 汉瓦 | 260 | 9977/01/05/ | 上颌骨，左右 $\underline{C}$ $M^3$ |
| | | 9564 | 右 $I^2$；下颌骨，右 $\overline{C}$，左 $P_{\overline{4}}$ – $M_{\overline{3}}$ 右骨节；颅骨与面部残片 |
| | | 9897 | 左上颌骨残片 |
| | | 9903 | 右 $I^1$ |
| | | 9898 | 左 $I^1$ |
| | | 13167 | 左 $\underline{C}$ |
| | | 9906 | 左 $P^4$ |
| | | 13166 | 左 $P^4$ |
| | | 12647 | 右 $M^1$ |
| | | 9972 | 右 $M^2$ |
| | | 9896 | 左 $M^2$ |
| | | 9969 | 右 $M^2$ |
| | | 9895 | 左 $M^3$ |
| | | 9900 | 右 $M^3$ |
| | | 12709 | 幼体下颌骨，右 $\overline{C}$，$dP_{\overline{3}}$ |
| | | 9563/9902 | 下颚骨，左 $P_{\overline{3}}$，$M_{\overline{1}}$，右 $M_{\overline{2}}$，$M_{\overline{3}}$ |
| | | 13165 | 右下颌骨残片，$M_{\overline{1}}$ – $M_{\overline{3}}$ |
| | | 9565 | 左 $\overline{C}$ 碎片 |
| | | 9899 | 右 $M_{\overline{3}}$ |
| | | 12654 | 股骨残片 |
| | | 9894 | 股骨头残片 |

*Continued*

| Area | Locality | GSP no. | Specimen |
|---|---|---|---|
| Khaur | 260 | 13168 | Distal phalangeal fragment |
| Khaur | 317 | 11708 | Right maxilla, $P^3$–$M^3$ |
| | | 11786 | Right maxillary fragment, $P^3$–$M^2$ |
| | | 11704 | Right maxillary fragment, $I^2$ root–$M^1$ |
| | | 7618 | Right $M^2$ |
| | | 11706 | Right mandibular fragment |
| | | 11707/85 | Mandible, left $M_{\overline{3}}$ |
| | | 7619 | Left mandibular fragment, $P_{\overline{3}}$ |
| | | 9930 | Left $M_{\overline{3}}$ |
| | | 7611 | Radial diaphysis |
| | | 11867 | Femoral head and neck |
| Khaur | 137 | 3293 | Left $I^1$ |
| | 191 | 12568 | Left $\underline{C}$ |
| | 207 | 5001 | Right $M_{\overline{2}}$ |
| | 211 | 5260 | Right $M^1$ |
| | 221 | 6758 | Left $M^3$ |
| | | 6759 | Right $M_{\overline{3}}$ |
| | 224 | 6153 | Left mandibular fragment, $P_{\overline{4}}$–$M_{\overline{3}}$ |
| | | 7308 | Right $M^1$ fragment |
| | | 6178 | Femoral head fragment |
| | 226 | 6160 | Right mandibular fragment, $P_{\overline{3}}$–$M_{\overline{3}}$ |
| | 227 | 6206 | Right $M^2$ |
| | | 13171 | Left $I^1$ |
| | 230 | 6999 | Right $I^1$ |
| | 251 | 8836 | Right $M^2$ |
| | 261 | 9987 | Right $P^4$ |
| | 309 | 11597 | Left $\underline{C}$ |
| | | 10232 | Left $\underline{C}$ fragment |
| | 310 | 10785 | Talar fragment |
| | 314 | 11003 | Left $\underline{C}$ |
| Chinji | 38 | 780 | Left $\underline{C}$ fragment |

续表

| 地区 | 地点 | GSP编号 | 标本 |
|---|---|---|---|
| 汉瓦 | 260 | 13168 | 指骨末端残片 |
| 汉瓦 | 317 | 11708 | 右上颌骨 $P^3$–$M^3$ |
| | | 11786 | 右上颌骨残片 $P^3$–$M^2$ |
| | | 11704 | 右上颌骨残片 $I^2$ 残根 –$M^1$ |
| | | 7618 | 右 $M^2$ |
| | | 11706 | 右下颌骨残片 |
| | | 11707/85 | 下颌骨，左 $M_{\overline{3}}$ |
| | | 7619 | 左下颌骨残片，$P_{\overline{3}}$ |
| | | 9930 | 左 $M_{\overline{3}}$ |
| | | 7611 | 桡骨骨干 |
| | | 11867 | 股骨头与颈部 |
| 汉瓦 | 137 | 3293 | 左 $I^1$ |
| | 191 | 12568 | 左 $\underline{C}$ |
| | 207 | 5001 | 右 $M_{\overline{3}}$ |
| | 211 | 5260 | 右 $M^1$ |
| | 221 | 6758 | 左 $M^3$ |
| | | 6759 | 右 $M_{\overline{3}}$ |
| | 224 | 6153 | 左下颌骨残片，$P_{\overline{4}}$–$M_{\overline{3}}$ |
| | | 7308 | 右 $M^1$ 残片 |
| | | 6178 | 股骨头残片 |
| | 226 | 6160 | 右下颌骨残片，$P_{\overline{3}}$–$M_{\overline{3}}$ |
| | 227 | 6206 | 右 $M^2$ |
| | | 13171 | 左 $I^1$ |
| | 230 | 6999 | 右 $I^1$ |
| | 251 | 8836 | 右 $M^2$ |
| | 261 | 9987 | 右 $P^4$ |
| | 309 | 11597 | 左 $\underline{C}$ |
| | | 10232 | 左 $\underline{C}$ 残片 |
| | 310 | 10785 | 距骨残片 |
| | 314 | 11003 | 左 $\underline{C}$ |
| 成吉 | 38 | 780 | 左 $\underline{C}$ 残片 |

Table 2. Tentative listing of minimum numbers of hominoid individuals

| Locality | No. of specimens | Minimum nos individuals | | | |
|---|---|---|---|---|---|
| | | G | R | Si | Total |
| 182 | 17 | – | 4 | 2 | 6 |
| 260 | 21 | – | 4 | 5 | 9 |
| 311 | 19 | 1 | 5 | 5 | 6 |
| 317 | 10 | – | 2 | 3 | 5 |
| 137 | 1 | – | – | 1 | 1 |
| 191 | 1 | – | – | 1 | 1 |
| 207 | 1 | – | – | 1 | 1 |
| 211 | 1 | – | – | 1 | 1 |
| 221 | 2 | – | 1 | – | 1 |
| 224 | 3 | – | ?2 | – | 2 |
| 226 | 1 | – | ?1 | – | 1 |
| 227 | 2 | – | ?1 | – | 1 |
| 230 | 1 | – | – | 1 | 1 |
| 251 | 1 | – | 1 | – | 1 |
| 261 | 1 | – | – | 1 | 1 |
| 309 | 2 | – | – | 2 | 2 |
| 310 | 1 | – | ?1 | – | 1 |
| 314 | 1 | – | – | 1 | 1 |
| 38 | 1 | – | – | 1 | 1 |
| 19 | 86 | 1 | 17 | 25 | 43 |

G, *Gigantopithecus*; R, *Ramapithecus*; Si, *Sivapithecus indicus*.

Table 3. Distribution of hominoid parts

| Part preserved | Specimens |
|---|---|
| Cranial | |
| Associated maxillae and mandibles | 1 |
| Adult maxillae | 4 |
| Adult mandibles | 9 |
| Infant mandibles | 2 |
| Isolated teeth | |
| I[1] | 6 |

表 2. 人猿超科动物最小个体数的推测值

| 地点 | 标本编号 | 最小个体数 | | | |
|---|---|---|---|---|---|
| | | G | R | Si | 合计 |
| 182 | 17 | – | 4 | 2 | 6 |
| 260 | 21 | – | 4 | 5 | 9 |
| 311 | 19 | 1 | 5 | 5 | 6 |
| 317 | 10 | – | 2 | 3 | 5 |
| 137 | 1 | – | – | 1 | 1 |
| 191 | 1 | – | – | 1 | 1 |
| 207 | 1 | – | – | 1 | 1 |
| 211 | 1 | – | – | 1 | 1 |
| 221 | 2 | – | 1 | – | 1 |
| 224 | 3 | – | ?2 | – | 2 |
| 226 | 1 | – | ?1 | – | 1 |
| 227 | 2 | – | ?1 | – | 1 |
| 230 | 1 | – | – | 1 | 1 |
| 251 | 1 | – | 1 | – | 1 |
| 261 | 1 | – | – | 1 | 1 |
| 309 | 2 | – | – | 2 | 2 |
| 310 | 1 | – | ?1 | – | 1 |
| 314 | 1 | – | – | 1 | 1 |
| 38 | 1 | – | – | 1 | 1 |
| **19** | **86** | **1** | **17** | **25** | **43** |

G，巨猿；R，腊玛古猿；Si，西瓦古猿印度种。

表 3. 人猿超科动物的部件分布表

| 保存的部件 | 标本 |
|---|---|
| 头颅部分 | |
| 　　共生的上颌骨与下颌骨 | 1 |
| 　　成年上颌骨 | 4 |
| 　　成年下颌骨 | 9 |
| 　　幼体下颌骨 | 2 |
| 单独的牙齿 | |
| 　　$I^1$ | 6 |

*Continued*

| Part preserved | Specimens |
| --- | --- |
| C | 8 |
| P⁴ | 4 |
| M¹ | 6 |
| M² | 11 |
| M³ | 6 |
| I- | 3 |
| C̄ | 2 |
| P₃ | 1 |
| P₄ | 1 |
| M₁ | 1 |
| M₂ | 3 |
| M₃ | 5 |
| Postcranial | 13 |

Detailed descriptions of the geology, revisions of major vertebrate and invertebrate groups, and more extensive descriptions and analyses of the hominoids will be published elsewhere as studies are completed. What follows is a preliminary announcement of the primate finds.

## Geology and Palaeoecology

Most of the new hominoid sites are along the northern rim of the Soan synclinorium between Dhok Mila and Kaulial. One, 311, is at Sethi Nagri, another, 38, south of Chinji; both are along the southern margin of the synclinorium. All the northern sites, with two exceptions (251 and 261), are situated stratigraphically in the upper third of the Nagri Formation; localities 251 and 261 are somewhat lower in the section. Locality 311 at Sethi Nagri is probably situated somewhat below the level of the bulk of the northern sites. Locality 38 is in the Chinji Formation.

Approximate ages can be assigned to the localities on the basis of faunal comparisons to dated sequences elsewhere in the Old World, and these are apparently supported by palaeomagnetic surveys which will be published soon. Locality 38 may be about 12 Myr old; 251 and 261 about 9.5-10 Myr old; and the rest of the sites some 9.0 Myr old.

Abundant vertebrate and invertebrate faunal remains have been recovered from the Potwar Plateau both by us and by previous expeditions, and the biostratigraphic sequence is becoming clear. The upper Nagri levels are particularly well sampled, and new analyses of major taxonomic groups (rodents, carnivores, suids, bovids and equids) suggest close

| 保存的部件 | 标本 |
|---|---|
| C | 8 |
| $P^4$ | 4 |
| $M^1$ | 6 |
| $M^2$ | 11 |
| $M^3$ | 6 |
| I- | 3 |
| $\overline{C}$ | 2 |
| $P_{\overline{3}}$ | 1 |
| $P_{\overline{4}}$ | 1 |
| $M_{\overline{1}}$ | 1 |
| $M_2$ | 3 |
| $M_3$ | 5 |
| 颅后骨骼 | 13 |

　　随着研究的完成，地质学方面的详细描述、对主要的脊椎动物与无脊椎动物的分类的修订，以及对人猿超科动物更为全面的描述与分析将在其他地方公开发表。接下来本文将公开有关灵长类动物的一些初步发现。

## 地质学与古生态学

　　大部分新的人猿超科动物遗址都沿着多克米拉与库里埃之间的索安复向斜的北缘分布。其中，编号为311的遗址位于塞西纳格里；而编号38的遗址则位于成吉之南；两个都是沿着复向斜的南缘分布。除了两个例外（251号与261号），所有北面的遗址都位于纳格里组上部三分之一处；只有251号与261号地点在剖面上稍微低一点。311号地点在塞西纳格里，可能稍微在大部分北面遗址的水平面之下。38号地点则在成吉组内。

　　根据与旧大陆（东半球）的其他地方已测定年代的地层层序的动物群的对比，能够给出每一地点的近似年代值，并且这些数值明显得到了即将公开发表的有关它们的古地磁调查结果的支持。38号地点的年代距今约1,200万年；251号与261号地点的年代则距今约950万到1,000万年；其余的遗址距今约900万年。

　　我们和前人都从博德瓦尔高原的考察中挖掘出了大量属于脊椎动物与无脊椎动物动物群的化石，生物地层序列变得越来越清楚。特别在纳格里上层仔细采样，对于主要的分类组群（啮齿动物、食肉动物、猪科动物、牛科动物及马科动物）的新分析表明，

similarities to European and West Asian sites of late Vallesian and early Turolian age[3].

Earlier studies of Siwalik lithology[4], faunas[5-7] and floras[8,9] generated hypotheses about past habitats. These studies were large scale, involving the analysis of faunas from many localities and broad stratigraphic ranges, or used lithological or floral samples which could not be tied into firm stratigraphic or palaeogeographic frameworks. Only recently have more adequate studies started[10]. Our programme of detailed lithostratigraphical, magnetostratigraphical, sedimentological, taphonomical, faunal and floral analyses is aimed at a better understanding of Siwalik palaeogeography and past plant and animal associations.

Many primate localities are in pellet rock lithologies usually associated with minor grey-green sandstones within a red-bed sequence. In localities where several individuals are preserved, primates are often a relatively abundant component of the fauna. So far collections have been made in a taphonomically adequate way from few sites, nor have faunal analyses involving minimum numbers of individuals been completed. Possible faunal differences between primate and non-primate localities are being investigated. Preliminary faunal analyses from our "best-collected" localities suggest that the overall mammal community lacked a diversity of large mammals and had low numbers of grazing species, herbivores above 100 kg and arboreal species. By comparison with recent and Pleistocene faunas associated with riverine environments, this suggests woodland or bush habitats with open patches of grassland rather than extensive forests. The sedimentary features and lithologies of the upper Nagri indicate a braided fluvial regime of low sinuosity rather than a meandering one, and a rapidly aggrading multiple-channelled river would probably have been characterised by a mosaic of more and less open habitats rather than extensive riparian forest.

There have been too few palynological studies of Siwalik age sediments[8-10] to indicate clearly either the range of habitats at a particular time or habitat changes through time. Available evidence suggests a change during the deposition of the Chinji and Nagri Formations from mainly subtropical, forest habitats to more open, less low-lying habitats. Schaller[11] has summarised views on the modern vegetation of the area: evergreen and semi-evergreen forests have quite restricted distributions, most habitats being deciduous forest or thorn forest. Although South Asian Neogene climates may have been warmer and with more precipitation than Recent climates, it is possible that evergreen forests (including gallery forests) were never very widespread during the time of deposition of Siwalik group rocks. As noted, such limited information as we have suggests non-evergreen forest contexts for at least some of the major primate localities.

## Primates

There is an extensive primary literature on Siwalik primates, and they have been mentioned and discussed many times[2]. Approximately 90 hominoid specimens representing more than 60 individuals are known from previous collections. The Potwar

这里和欧洲及西亚的属于晚瓦里西期与早图洛里安年代的遗址 [3] 非常相似。

对于西瓦利克岩石学 [4]、动物群 [5-7] 及植物群 [8,9] 的早期研究形成关于过去生境的假说。这些研究规模很大，涉及许多地点的动物群分析，且涵盖了广泛的地层范围，或利用并未严格归入到确定的地层学或古地理学格架之中的岩石或者植物群样本。只是最近才开展了更为充分的研究 [10]。我们对岩石地层学、磁性地层学、沉积学、埋藏学、动物群及植物群的详细分析，其目的是更好地理解西瓦利克的古地理学与过去动植物的相互联系。

许多灵长类动物的发掘地点都在球粒岩中，球粒岩通常与红层层序中的微小灰绿砂岩相关。在有几个个体被保存下来的地点上，灵长类动物常常是动物群中相当丰富的组成部分。迄今为止，只在少数几个遗址进行过具有埋藏学意义的充分采集，即使对涉及最小个体数的动物群，也没有完成对它的相关分析。正在对灵长类动物与非灵长类动物地点之间可能存在的动物群的差异性进行研究。我们对"采样采得最好的"地点的动物群的初步分析显示，整个哺乳动物群缺乏多样性的大型哺乳动物，且 100 千克以上的食草动物与树栖种类的数量也少。通过对现代及更新世与河岸环境相关的动物群的对比，显示出的是有着开阔的小块草地的林地或灌木生境而不是广阔的森林。纳格里上部的岩性与沉积特征显示，此处的河流系统是弯曲度低的辫状体系，而不是曲流体系，而且一条迅速淤高的多水道河流将可能以镶嵌状的或多或少的开阔生境为特征，而不是广阔的河滨森林。

对西瓦利克年代沉积物的孢粉学研究很少 [8-10]，不能清楚地显示出一个特定时段的生境，也不能清楚地显示出生境随时间的变化。现有的证据显示，在成吉与纳格里组的沉积期间，从主要是亚热带森林的生境变为更开放、低洼更少的生境。沙勒 [11] 从现代植被的角度概述了这个地区的植被景观：常绿与半常绿林分布非常有限，大多数生境是落叶林或热带旱生林。虽然南亚新近纪气候可能是温暖一点，与全新世的气候相比降水量可能更多，但是在西瓦利克组群岩石沉积期间，可能常绿林（包括长廊林）从没有十分广泛地分布过。正如所述，我们所掌握的有限的信息表明，至少一些主要的灵长类动物地点是非常绿森林环境。

## 灵长类动物

关于西瓦利克灵长类动物的研究有大量的原始文献，它们多次被提及并讨论 [2]。从以前搜集到的标本中分辨出大约 90 个人猿超科动物标本，代表着超过 60 个个体。博德瓦尔高原出土了一些单个的牙齿和少许下颌骨，大多数得自成吉的成吉组；几

Plateau yielded some isolated teeth and a few jaws, the bulk from the Chinji Formation at Chinji; several specimens came from around Hasnot, and a few individual teeth were known from other localities. Ramnagar in Kashmir was the source of a few hominoids, but the best collections came from Haritalyangar in India.

At least four hominoid species are represented in the Siwaliks, thought previously to range in age between about 14 Myr and 6 Myr. The four species are *Ramapithecus punjabicus, Sivapithecus sivalensis, S. indicus* and *Gigantopithecus bilaspurensis*. Until recently species of *Sivapithecus* have been classified in *Dryopithecus,* but it now seems preferable to separate them generically from *D. fontani* and other dryopithecines.

In several recent reviews of Miocene Hominoidea these Siwalik species and others from elsewhere in the Old World have been placed in either the Hominidae or Pongidae. *Ramapithecus* has often been included in Hominidae, while species of the other genera have usually been considered pongids[12]. This arrangement has not been accepted universally.

The new specimens from Pakistan discussed here (Tables 1-3), together with much new material from other Old World localities, facilitate a different view of earlier Neogene hominoid classification and evolution.

The new hominoids are discussed here taxonomically. Assignment of some individuals to species is difficult or impossible, and the scheme outlined is provisional. More comprehensive descriptions and discussions are being prepared. Measurements of the more complete specimens are given in Tables 4 and 5.

Table 4. Tooth measurements on hominoid maxillae

|  |  | 9977/01 |  | 11704 | 11736 | 11708 |
|  |  | L | R | R | R | R |
|---|---|---|---|---|---|---|
| $I^2$ | md | – | 5.5 |  |  |  |
|  | bl | – | 7.5 |  |  |  |
| C | max | 14.2 | 13.4 | 14.6 |  |  |
|  | tr | 10.8 | 10.8 | 10.7 |  |  |
| $P^3$ | md | 9.3 | 9.3 | 9.2 | 9.2 | 9.5 |
|  | bl | 11.8 | 14.3 | 11.2 | – | 11.6 |
| $P^4$ | md | 8.7 | 7.5 | 7.7 | 8.5 | 8.3 |
|  | bl | 12.4 | 12.4 | 11.7 | 12.2 | 12.0 |
| $M^1$ | md | 11.5 | 12.1 | 11.1 | 12.0 | 12.4 |
|  | bl | 13.3 | 13.3 | 12.8 | – | 13.1 |
| $M^2$ | md | 13.5 | 13.6 |  | 12.5 | 13.7 |
|  | bl | 14.6 | 14.2 |  | 13.4 | 14.0 |

个标本来自哈斯诺特附近，在其他地点也识别出来几个单个的牙齿。克什米尔的拉姆讷格尔是几种人猿超科动物的来源地，但是最好的标本来自于印度的哈里塔尔扬加。

西瓦利克至少出现了 4 种人猿超科动物，以往认为它们的生存年代大约在 1,400 万年前到 600 万年前之间。这 4 个种分别是：腊玛古猿旁遮普种、西瓦古猿西瓦种、西瓦古猿印度种及毕拉斯普巨猿。直到最近西瓦古猿的各个种已经被划进森林古猿，但现在看来似乎将它们从种属上与方坦森林古猿及其他的森林古猿亚科分开更合适。

在最近的有关中新世人猿超科动物的几个讨论中，这些西瓦利克种类与其他的来自旧大陆（东半球）其他地方的种类不是被放入人科就是被放入猩猩科。腊玛古猿常常被包括在人科中，而其他属的种类通常被归为猩猩科 [12]。这种分类还未被普遍接受。

此处讨论的来自巴基斯坦的新标本（表 1~3），结合来自旧大陆（东半球）其他地点的许多新标本，都有助于促进关于新近纪早期人猿超科动物分类与进化的不同观点的形成。

在此，从分类学的角度讨论了新的人猿超科动物。要把某些个体指定为某个种类，是困难的或者是不可能的，因此，所概括出的方案也是暂时的。正在准备进行更为全面的描述与讨论。更完整的标本的测量结果列于表 4、表 5。

表 4. 对人猿超科动物上颌牙齿的测量结果

| | | 9977/01 | | 11704 | 11736 | 11708 |
|---|---|---|---|---|---|---|
| | | 左 | 右 | 右 | 右 | 右 |
| $I^2$ | md | – | 5.5 | | | |
| | bl | – | 7.5 | | | |
| $\underline{C}$ | max | 14.2 | 13.4 | 14.6 | | |
| | tr | 10.8 | 10.8 | 10.7 | | |
| $P^3$ | md | 9.3 | 9.3 | 9.2 | 9.2 | 9.5 |
| | bl | 11.8 | 14.3 | 11.2 | – | 11.6 |
| $P^4$ | md | 8.7 | 7.5 | 7.7 | 8.5 | 8.3 |
| | bl | 12.4 | 12.4 | 11.7 | 12.2 | 12.0 |
| $M^1$ | md | 11.5 | 12.1 | 11.1 | 12.0 | 12.4 |
| | bl | 13.3 | 13.3 | 12.8 | – | 13.1 |
| $M^2$ | md | 13.5 | 13.6 | | 12.5 | 13.7 |
| | bl | 14.6 | 14.2 | | 13.4 | 14.0 |

*Continued*

| | | 9977/01 | | 11704 | 11736 | 11708 |
|---|---|---|---|---|---|---|
| | | L | R | R | R | R |
| M³ | md | 12.7 | 12.7 | | | 12.5 |
| | bl | 13.7 | 13.5 | | | 13.8 |

Table 5. Measurements of hominoid mandibles

| | | 9564/9905 | | 13165 | 4622/4857 | 4230 | 9563/9902 | 6153 | 6160 |
|---|---|---|---|---|---|---|---|---|---|
| C̄ | max | 12.3 | (R) | | | | | | |
| | tr | 10.1 | | | | | | | |
| P₃ | max | | | | | | 11.2 | | 11.0 |
| | tr | | | | | | 7.0 | | 7.0 |
| P₄ | md | *9.4 | (L) | | | | | 8.1 | 8.5 |
| | bl | – | | | | | – | 9.5 | 9.8 |
| M₁ | md | *13.0 | (L) | 13.0 | 11.5 | | *10.5 | 10.3 | 11.1 |
| | bl | *12.0 | | *10.9 | 9.5 | | *9.5 | 9.8 | – |
| M₂ | md | 14.5 | (L) | 14.0 | 12.7 | 14.7 | 12.7 | 12.4 | 12.7 |
| | bl | 12.7 | | 11.7 | 10.5 | 12.7 | 10.7 | 10.9 | 10.7 |
| M₃ | md | *15.5 | (L) | *14.5 | 12.9 | – | – | 12.3 | 13.7 |
| | bl | – | | – | 10.5 | – | – | 10.8 | – |
| Breadth at C̄ | | *35 | | | 22.5 | | *25 | | |
| Breadth at M₂ | | *47 | | | 48.0 | | *40 | | |
| Symphysis | | | | | | | | | |
| Depth | | 52.5 | | | *30.0 | | *34 | | |
| Thickness | | 20.0 | | | 15.0 | | *16 | | |
| At P4 | | | | | | | | | |
| Depth | | 43.5 | | 34.0 | 30.5 | | *28 | | |
| Thickness | | 15.5 | | 15.0 | 13.0 | | *14 | | |
| At M3 | | | | | | | | | |
| Depth | | 42.5 | | | 31.0 | 30.5 | | | |
| Thickness | | 24.0 | | | 20.0 | 23.5 | | | |

*Estimated values.

At least one species of *Ramapithecus, R. punjabicus* (Fig. 1), is represented in Siwalik rocks; the genus is found in the Chinji and Nagri Formations, and possibly in rocks equivalent to the Dhok Pathan Formation. The probable age range is 13-8.5 Myr.

| | | 9977/01 | | 11704 | 11736 | 11708 |
|---|---|---|---|---|---|---|
| | | 左 | 右 | 右 | 右 | 右 |
| M³ | md | 12.7 | 12.7 | | | 12.5 |
| | bl | 13.7 | 13.5 | | | 13.8 |

表 5. 人猿超科动物下颌骨的测量结果

| | | 9564/9905 | | 13165 | 4622/4857 | 4230 | 9563/9902 | 6153 | 6160 |
|---|---|---|---|---|---|---|---|---|---|
| $\overline{C}$ | max | 12.3 | （右） | | | | | | |
| | tr | 10.1 | | | | | | | |
| $P_{\overline{3}}$ | max | | | | | | 11.2 | | 11.0 |
| | tr | | | | | | 7.0 | | 7.0 |
| $P_{\overline{4}}$ | md | *9.4 | （左） | | | | | 8.1 | 8.5 |
| | bl | – | | | | | – | 9.5 | 9.8 |
| $M_1$ | md | *13.0 | （左） | 13.0 | 11.5 | | *10.5 | 10.3 | 11.1 |
| | bl | *12.0 | | *10.9 | 9.5 | | *9.5 | 9.8 | – |
| $M_{\overline{2}}$ | md | 14.5 | （左） | 14.0 | 12.7 | 14.7 | 12.7 | 12.4 | 12.7 |
| | bl | 12.7 | | 11.7 | 10.5 | 12.7 | 10.7 | 10.9 | 10.7 |
| $M_{\overline{3}}$ | md | *15.5 | （左） | *14.5 | 12.9 | – | – | 12.3 | 13.7 |
| | bl | – | | – | 10.5 | – | – | 10.8 | – |
| 在$\overline{C}$的宽度 | | *35 | | | 22.5 | | *25 | | |
| 在$M_{\overline{3}}$的宽度 | | *47 | | | 48.0 | | *40 | | |
| 骨联合部 | | | | | | | | | |
| 深度 | | 52.5 | | | *30.0 | | *34 | | |
| 厚度 | | 20.0 | | | 15.0 | | *16 | | |
| 在 $P_4$ | | | | | | | | | |
| 深度 | | 43.5 | | 34.0 | 30.5 | | *28 | | |
| 厚度 | | 15.5 | | 15.0 | 13.0 | | *14 | | |
| 在 $M_3$ | | | | | | | | | |
| 深度 | | 42.5 | | | 31.0 | 30.5 | | | |
| 厚度 | | 24.0 | | | 20.0 | 23.5 | | | |

* 为估计值。

　　至少有一种腊玛古猿——腊玛古猿旁遮普种（图 1）出现在西瓦利克岩石中；在成吉与纳格里组中发现这个属，而且可能在相当于多克帕坦组的岩石中也有发现。其年代范围可能在 1,300 万年前到 850 万年前。

The new material from the Potwar Plateau helps considerably in understanding previous finds as well as adding significant new information. Particularly fine specimens are the adult mandibles GSP 4622/4857 from locality 182 and GSP 9562/9902 from locality 260, and an infant mandible, GSP 12709, also from locality 260. These specimens show that the incisor region was very narrow in *Ramapithecus*, canines small, anterior premolars and canines closely packed together, and postcanine tooth rows and mandibular corpora posteriorly divergent. Most teeth in the upper and lower dentitions are now known. Certain features are worth noting: $P_{\overline{3}}$ has a small but distinct lingual cusp, and its long axis is oriented at some 45° to the mesio-distal line of the tooth row. Unworn cheek teeth resemble thoses of *Australopithecus* and *Homo* quite strongly, particularly the maxillary molars. Occlusal surfaces are constricted and there is marked buccal (mandibular teeth) and lingual (maxillary) flare in unworn specimens (compare ref. 13). Occlusal surfaces broaden with wear and can be almost flat and still show no dentine. This is because occlusal enamel is very thick (between 2.5 and 3.0 mm on mandibular buccal cusps), as shown in a few broken specimens (GSP 8926) and by comparison of unworn and worn homologues of similar size. Mandibular rami are relatively robust; symphyses have marked superior and inferior transverse tori.

*Gigantopithecus bilaspurensis* (Fig. 1) is based on a complete mandible from the Haritalyangar area. It is likely to have an age of around 8.5 Myr[1,2,10], and is not significantly younger than the other hominoid primates from that area.

One partial molar from locality 311, GSP 7144, is tentatively assigned to *Gigantopithecus*, as is a previously described molar, GSI D175 from Alipur near Hasnot[14]. Both are probably 9.0-10 Myr old. Occlusal morphology is rather similar to that of *Ramapithecus*, and occlusal surface enamel is thick (about 3.5 mm on the mandibular buccal cusp of GSP 7144).

Specimens of *Sivapithecus indicus* (Fig. 2) are known from deposits ranging between about 13 and 8 Myr. Several relatively complete new specimens (especially GSP 9977/01/05/9564 from locality 260) facilitate mandibular and lower facial reconstructions. Tooth rows are subparallel with broad incisor regions and postcanine tooth rows that are markedly concave bucally.

Occlusal morphology in *S. indicus* resembles the other genera, although molars are somewhat broader and there are other minor differences. Occlusal surfaces are constricted on cheek teeth with marked buccal and lingual flare; enamel is thick (about 3 mm on mandibular buccal cusps).

Canines are projecting and moderately dimorphic and exhibit mesial, distal and apical wear; $P_{\overline{3}}$s are closely approximated to the canines, their long axes rotated to lie about 45° to the mesio-distal line of the tooth row. Mandibular rami are deep; the symphysis is long with a prominent inferior transverse torus and a relatively small superior transverse torus.

*S. sivalensis* is the most enigmatic of the Siwalik hominoids and it is not absolutely clear that it exists as a separate species.

842

来自博德瓦尔高原的新材料，对理解以前的发现大有帮助，还增加了新的重要信息。来自 182 号地点的 GSP 4622/4857 与来自 260 号地点的 GSP 9562/9902 的成年下颌骨，还有来自 260 号地点的 GSP 12709 的一块幼体下颌骨，都是保存很好的标本。这些标本显示，腊玛古猿的门齿区十分窄，犬齿小，前面的前臼齿与犬齿紧紧地挤在一起，后犬齿齿列与下颌体向后分开。现在已知上下齿列的大部分牙齿。其某些特征值得注意：$P_3$ 的舌侧齿尖虽然小但明显，其长轴与齿列中远端线大约 45°。未受磨损的颊齿，特别是上颌的臼齿，与南方古猿及人属的颊齿极其相似。上下齿咬合面缩小，未受磨损的标本其颊（下颌齿）与舌侧（上颌）倾斜明显（对比参考文献 13）。上下齿咬合面因磨损而变宽，几乎是平的，却仍未露出齿质。正如几个破损的标本（GSP 8926）所表现出来的以及通过对比未受磨损及磨损的程度类似的同源结构所看到的，这是因为上下牙咬合面的釉质非常厚（下颌骨颊侧齿尖，厚度介于 2.5~3.0 毫米之间）。下颌支相当粗壮；骨联合部的上下横向隆凸明显。

毕拉斯普巨猿（图 1）的确认是基于来自于哈里塔尔扬加地区的完整的下颌骨。其可能的年代距今约 850 万年 [1,2,10]，并不比来自于那个地区的人猿超科灵长类动物年轻多少。

一颗来自 311 号地点的 GSP 7144 的部分臼齿被暂时定为是巨猿的，因为这与此前曾被描述的，来自于靠近哈斯诺特的阿里布尔的 GSI D175 的臼齿类似 [14]。两者都可能生存于 1,000 万年前到 900 万年前之间。上下齿咬合面的形态与腊玛古猿上下齿咬合面的形态相当类似，且上下齿咬合面的牙釉质厚（在 GSP 7144 的下颌颊侧齿尖处厚大约 3.5 毫米）。

从大约 1,300 万年前到 800 万年前的沉积物中识别出了西瓦古猿印度种的标本（图 2）。几个相对完整的新标本（特别是来自 260 号地点的 GSP 9977/01/05/9564）使下颌及下面部复原变得容易。齿列近似平行于宽的门牙区而颊齿列在颊侧有明显的凹入。

虽然臼齿稍微有点宽而且也存在其他小的差别，西瓦古猿印度种的上下齿咬合面的形态仍类似于其他属。颊齿的上下咬合面缩小，有明显的颊侧与舌侧倾斜；牙釉质厚（下颌骨颊侧齿尖处厚约 3 毫米）。

犬齿突出，适度二态，中、末端及顶上有磨损；$P_3$ 非常靠近犬齿，其长轴旋转，其与齿列近中—远中线大约 45°。下颌支深；骨联合部长，其下横隆凸突出，上横隆凸相对较小。

西瓦古猿是最令人困惑的西瓦利克人猿超科动物，甚至不能清楚的确定其能作为一个单独的种类而继续存在。

Parts of 13 hominoid postcranial bones (Fig. 3) have been collected so far and fit into three size groups. The largest specimen is a partial distal right humerous, GSP 12271, with the lateral supracondylar ridge, lateral epicondyle, capitulum and radial fossa preserved entire, and the coronoid and olecranon fossae and trochlear surface preserved in part. In its size and morphological features this specimen is similar to the distal humerus of adult female gorillas. Eight specimens are close in size to the corresponding bones of adult pygmy chimpanzees. This group includes a partial distal right humerus, GSP 6663, with parts of the capitular and trochlear surfaces preserved. Hindlimb specimens include a femoral head, GSP 6178, a femoral head plus part of the neck, GSP 11867, the proximal, mid-shaft, and distal non-articular parts of a right femur, GSP 12654, a left intermediate cuneiform, GSP 6454, and the distal end of a proximal hallucial phalanx, GSP 6664. These specimens, together with two distal ends of phalangeal bones, GSP 6666 amd GSP 13168, show some morphological similarities to extant hominoid species, although these are not as marked as in the case of the large specimen. Three fossils are smaller. One of them, a partial left radius, GSP 7611, is clearly juvenile. A partial right talus, GSP 10785, which includes most of the trochlear surface, the lateral process, and most of the posterior calcaneal articular surface, and a partial femoral head, GSP 9894, come from approximately adult macaque-sized animals. It is not certain that they are from adults. A partial calcaneus, GSP 4664, shows a number of equivocal morphological features and is not included in any of the three groups.

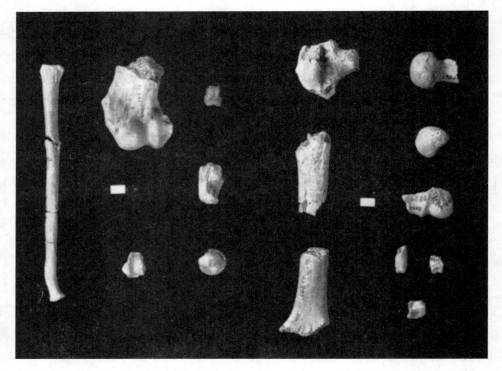

Fig. 3. Left to right, first column: GSP 7611; second column: top, GSP 12271, bottom, GSP 10785; third column: top, GSP 6664, middle, GSP 4664, bottom, GSP 9894; fourth column, GSP 12654; fifth column, top to bottom, GSP 11867, 6178, 6663, 6666 and 13168, 6454.

迄今为止，已经采集到 13 个人猿超科动物的颅后骨（图 3）骼部分，按大小刚好放入 3 组。最大的标本是不完整的右肱骨远端，GSP 12271，带有保存完整的侧髁上脊、侧上髁、肋骨小头与桡骨窝，喙突窝与鹰嘴窝以及滑车面部分保存。在其大小与形态特征上，这个标本类似于成年雌性大猩猩的肱骨远端。8 个标本大小上接近于成年矮小黑猩猩的对应骨头。这一组包括不完整的右肱骨远端，GSP 6663，其小头的部分与滑车面被保存下来。下肢标本包括股骨头，GSP 6178；股骨头加部分股骨颈，GSP 11867；右股骨近端、骨干中部及远端非关节部分，GSP 12654；左中间楔状骨，GSP 6454；以及大拇趾骨的远端，GSP 6664。这些标本及其他两段指骨远端一起，GSP 6666 与 GSP 13168，都在形态上显示出了与现生的人猿超科种类的类似，虽然这些类似并不如在大标本的情形下那样明显。3 块化石较小。其中一块明显是青少年个体的不完整的左桡骨，GSP 7611；GSP 10785 是右距骨的局部，包括大部分滑车面、外侧突、大部分后跟骨关节面；它和一个不完整的股骨头，GSP 9894，都来自于近似于成年猕猴大小的动物。不能肯定它们是来自于成年个体。不完整的跟骨，GSP 4664，表现出大量意义不明确的形态特征，并不包括在上述 3 个组的任一组中。

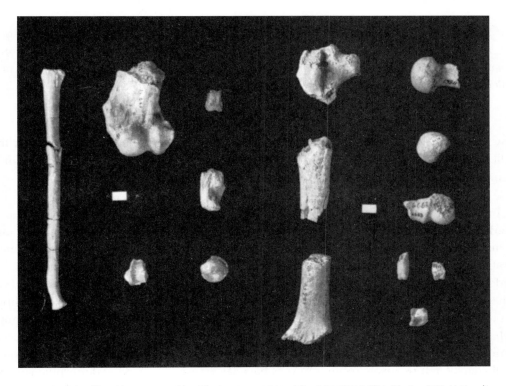

图 3. 从左到右，第 1 列：GSP 7611；第 2 列：上，GSP 12271，下，GSP 10785；第 3 列：上，GSP 6664，中，GSP 4664，下，GSP 9894；第 4 列：GSP 12654；第 5 列：从上到下，GSP 11867、6178、6663、6666 及 13168、6454。

None of these specimens was found in direct association with cranial or dental material. Because only three different sized primate species are definitely represented by cranial and dental specimens, however, the largest postcranial specimen is provisionally assigned to *Gigantopithecus* cf. *bilaspurensis*, the intermediate sized group to *Sivapithecus indicus*, and the smaller specimens to *Ramapithecus punjabicus* (remembering that some of these specimens may represent juveniles of the middle size group). It is significant that the *Gigantopithecus* humeral fragment and many of the *Sivapithecus* specimens come from locality 311; dental remains from that locality include our only *Gigantopithecus* specimen and five *Sivapithecus indicus* (Table 2).

If the postcranial remains are correctly subdivided and if they are associated with the three size groups based on gnathic and dental remains, some interesting conclusions can be drawn.

First, all hominoid species in the Siwaliks apparently have cheek teeth with very thick occlusal enamel. Second, all are truly megadont, in that cheek teeth are very large relative to body size. In these two features, the Siwalik hominoids resemble Plio-Pleistocene hominids and differ from pongines and the Miocene hominoids now assigned to Dryopithecinae (*sensu strictu*, see below). Third, these species share a basically similar occlusal morphology.

The Siwalik hominoids subdivide into two groups, mainly on the basis of anterior tooth size. *S. indicus* has relatively large incisors and, like *S. sivalensis*, large dimorphic canines; *Ramapithecus* and *Gigantopithecus* species have relatively small incisors, (probably) non-projecting and (probably) moderately dimorphic canines.

## Other Hominoid Material

New ideas and new hominoid fossil remains recovered during the past decade suggest that earlier, simpler schemes of hominoid evolution need to be modified. These changes can be summarised briefly as follows.

(1) Important dental differences between later hominids and living pongids lie less in arcade shape and incisor size as often stated in the past, but in relative tooth size and occlusal enamel thickness. Living apes have U-shaped dental arcades, living humans parabolic ones. Such arcade shapes are rarely found in other Neogene hominoids, the predominant form being some variant of a V-shape. Incisor size also seems to have been rather variable at all phases of hominoid evolution. More importhat, the apes, like almost all other non-human higher primates, have relatively small cheek teeth with thin enamel, perhaps an adaptation to predominantly browsing diets. Pliocene and earlier Pleistocene hominids in contrast have large cheek teeth with thick enamel (*Homo sapiens* has evolved small cheek teeth relatively recently). Apes have large tusk-like sexually dimorphic canines; hominids have small, somewhat incisiform canines exhibiting considerably less sexual dimorphism.

846

并没有发现这些标本中的任何一个与颅骨或牙齿材料直接共生。因为仅由颅骨与牙齿标本明确表示出了有 3 种不同大小的灵长类动物。然而，最大的颅后标本被暂时归入毕拉斯普巨猿相似种，中间大小的组被归入西瓦古猿印度种，较小的标本则被归入腊玛古猿旁遮普种（值得提醒的是，这些标本中的某些可能是中等大小组的青少年个体）。巨猿的肱骨残片与许多来自于 311 号地点西瓦古猿的标本意义重大；来自于该地点的牙齿标本包括我们唯一的巨猿标本与 5 个西瓦古猿印度种的标本（表 2）。

如果将颅后骨骼化石再进行恰当的细分，或能将它们与根据颌与牙齿的化石划分出的 3 个大小组别相关联，就可能得出一些有趣的结论。

第一，西瓦利克的所有人猿超科动物有特征明显的颊齿，其上下齿咬合面的牙釉质十分厚。第二，都是真正的巨型牙，相对其身体尺寸，颊齿显得很大。在这两个特征上，西瓦利克人猿超科动物与上新世 – 更新世人科成员类似，而与猩猩科动物以及现在被归入森林古猿亚科（严格意义上的，见下文）的中新世人猿超科动物不同。第三，这些种类的上下齿咬合面在形态上都基本类似。

主要根据前部齿大小，把西瓦利克人猿超科动物再细分为两组。西瓦古猿印度种拥有相对较大的门牙，与西瓦古猿西瓦种相像，犬齿二态性大；腊玛古猿与巨猿种的门齿相对较小，犬齿（可能）不突出并且（可能）适度二态。

## 其他人猿超科动物材料

新的概念以及过去十年间所发现的新人猿超科动物的化石表明，需要对过去关于人猿超科动物进化的较早的、较简单的方案进行修改。这些修改简要概述如下：

（1）在后来的人科动物与现生猩猩科类人猿之间，其牙齿的重要差异，并不像过去常常所说的那样仅仅在于齿弓形状与门牙的大小，而更在于牙齿的相对大小及其上下齿咬合面牙釉质的厚度。现生猿其齿弓呈 U 形，现生人类呈抛物线形。在其他新近纪人猿超科动物上这样的齿弓形状罕见，其主要形状是少许变形了的 V 形。在人猿超科动物进化的所有阶段，门齿的大小也似乎有相当大的变异。更重要的是，与几乎所有其他非人的高等灵长类动物一样，猿的颊齿相当小，其牙釉质薄，可能是为了适应其以草食为主的食性。相反的，上新世与早更新世的人科动物已经具备了大的颊齿和厚的牙釉质（在相对更晚近的时期，智人已经进化出小的颊齿）。猿的犬齿大，像獠牙，性别上二态；人科动物犬齿小，稍稍似门齿的形状，表现出来极少的性别二态现象。

(2) New discoveries in east Africa, and new analyses of earlier finds in Africa and Europe, suggest that early apes were considerably more diverse than previously believed[15]. Classifying them in only one genus, *Dryopithecus*, obscures this diversity. Thus at least three genera (*Proconsul, Rangwapithecus* and *Limnopithecus*) should probably be recognised in east Africa during the early and middle Miocene, separated from *Dryopithecus*, at least two species of which are found in middle Miocene deposits in Europe. These species can all be placed conveniently in the Dryopithecinae (or Dryopithecidae). All have dentitions basically like those of the living African pongids, with thin enamel and, if postcranial remains are correctly allocated, relatively small cheek teeth. Canine-premolar complexes are like those of modern apes.

Postcranial material of this group has proved difficult to interpret in a framework heavily dependent on comparisons with modern primate groups[16]. The fossil species were probably arboreal, and seem to be qualitatively different from living apes, being more "monkey-like" in certain ways; they are probably best viewed as truly primitive relative to modern hominoids.

Where palaeoecological contexts can be inferred plausibly, dryopithecine species seem to have been associated with predominantly forest floras and faunas[15]. Adaptively this rather diverse group was probably more like living ceboids or cercopithecoids than the low-diversity modern hominoids.

(3) Besides dryopithecines, other kinds of hominoids are present in the Old World middle Miocene. New material from Hungary[17], Greece[18], Turkey[19], Kenya[20] and China together with the specimens described here from Pakistan as well as earlier fossils from Europe and Africa show that thick-enamelled and (at least for those with postcranial remains) megadont hominoid species were widely distributed between 14 and 8 Myr ago, probably in predominantly non-forested habitats. During this time cercopithecoid monkeys seem to have been absent from Eurasia, and not particularly diverse in Africa[21].

This thick-enamelled middle Miocene cluster of species can be divided into two groups. One, consisting of species variously described as *Sivapithecus, Bodvapithecus, Ankarapithecus* and *Ouranopithecus* contains forms that are rather more ape-like, with large and sexually dimorphic canines. More than one generic name is probably necessary to reflect adequately the diversity of this group, which would be termed Sivapithecinae (or Sivapithecini). The other group would contain species described as *Gigantopithecus, Ramapithecus* and *Rudapithecus* (at least), forms with canines smaller and less dimorphic than those of pongines, dryopithecines or *Sivapithecus*-group species, although perhaps more so than australopithecines. Canine-premolar complexes resemble those of "primitive" australopithecines[22]. This cluster would be termed Ramapithecinae (or Ramapithecini).

(4) Recent discoveries suggest very strongly that the story of the Plio-Pleistocene hominids was more complex than previously thought. Between about 3.75 and 1 Myr ago several hominid lineages seem to have coexisted, certainly in Africa and possibly in Asia too[23].

（2）在东非的新发现，以及对非洲与欧洲早期发现的最新分析表明，早期猿类的种类多样性要远胜于人们以往所认为的 [15]。把它们仅仅划分为森林古猿这一个属，就使这种多样性变得模糊。因而，在东非中新世早期与中期，至少应该可能识别出 3 个可以从森林古猿属中独立出来的属（原康修尔猿、腊玛古猿及湖猿），其中至少两种发现于欧洲中新世中期的沉积物中。这些种类全都可以被方便地放入森林古猿亚科（或森林古猿科）。所有的齿系基本上都像现生非洲猩猩类的齿系，牙釉质薄且颊齿相对较小（如果对保存的颅后骨骼定位准确的话）。犬齿－前臼齿复合体与现代猿的相像。

已经证明，要在十分依赖于与现代灵长类动物组群对比的框架内 [16] 对这一组的颅后材料进行解释是很困难的。化石种可能是树栖的，而且从性质上而言，似乎不同于现生猿，在某些方面更"像猴"；相对于现代人猿超科动物，它们可能最好被视为是真正原始的。

森林古猿种类似乎一直主要是与森林植物群及动物群相联系 [15]，由此似乎可以推测出古生态环境来。与此相适应的是，这个变化相当大的组群可能更像现生的卷尾猴科或猕猴科动物，而不太像分化程度低的现代人猿超科。

（3）除了森林古猿类之外，其他种类的人猿超科动物出现在中新世中期的旧大陆（东半球）。来自于匈牙利 [17]、希腊 [18]、土耳其 [19]、肯尼亚 [20] 及中国的新标本，跟在此所描述的出自巴基斯坦的标本，还有来自于欧洲与非洲的早期化石一起显示出，在 1,400 万年前到 800 万年前，牙釉质厚的与（至少对那些有颅后化石的）巨型牙的人猿超科动物可能在以非森林占优的生境中是广泛分布的。在此期间，猕猴科的猴子似乎已经不存在于欧亚大陆，而且在非洲种类变化也不是特别多 [21]。

这一牙釉质厚的中新世中期的种类组群，能被分为两个组。其中一组，包括更像猿的形式，拥有大的、具性别二态犬齿的种类，由被描述成为西瓦古猿、波德瓦古猿、安卡拉古猿及乌朗诺古猿的不同种类组成。可能需要不止一个属名才能充分反映这个组的多样性，这个组被称为西瓦古猿亚科（或西瓦古猿族）。另一组将包括被描述为巨猿、腊玛古猿及鲁达古猿（至少）的种类，与猩猩科动物、森林古猿亚科或西瓦古猿组种类相比，这些种类的犬齿较小，性别二态较少，与南方古猿亚科动物相比，更是如此。犬齿－前臼齿复合体类似于"原始"南方古猿的犬齿－前臼齿复合体 [22]。这个组群被称为腊玛古猿亚科（或腊玛古猿族）。

（4）最近的发现强有力地表明上新世—更新世的人科动物的发展历史比以往所认为的要复杂得多。大约在 375 万年前到 100 万年前，几个人科动物的谱系似乎共

These species have been classified in both *Australolithecus* and *Homo*, but are characterised by certain shared features: reduced canines exhibiting moderate size dimorphism, enlarged and thick-enamelled cheek teeth, relatively enlarged brains (compared with dryopithecines and pongines at least), and a postcranial skeleton showing numerous adaptations to habitual bipedalism. At least one of these species, by at least 2 and perhaps 2.5-3 Myr ago, made stone tools.

It has been increasingly realised that these socalled Plio-Pleistocene hominids are not to be regarded merely as "diminutive humans" but as creatures, although recognisably hominid, qualitatively different from middle and late Pleistocene hominids. They are a diverse group of truly primitive species.

The oldest specimens with teeth similar to those of *Australopithecus* or early *Homo* species (and distinguishable from those of the *Sivapithecus* or *Ramapithecus* groups) come from Lukeino and Lothagam in Kenya and are between 5 and 7 Myr old[24,25].

The period after about 7 Myr ago is one during which australopithecines and early hominines diversified; *Sivapithecus*-group and *Ramapithecus*-group species are so far unknown. In both Africa and Eurasia cercopithecoid monkeys, especially the more open-country types, become abundant for the first time.

### Synthesis

Current knowledge of hominoid evolution suggests a tentative taxonomic and phylogenetic scheme that reflects the important advances of the past decade. These are summarised here by D.P.

First, Neogene hominoids were, during most of their evolution, a relatively diverse superfamily. Second, extinct hominoids were not identical with, nor, in some cases, particularly similar to living hominoids, and to interpret extinct hominoids as though they were very "modern" is potentially misleading. Third, it is very difficult to draw exact ancestor-descendant relationships given the complexity of the picture at any given time, the differences between descendants and available ancestral candidates, and the still substantial gaps in the fossil record. Rather, each radiation should be studied for its own sake in order to understand it as an adapted and successful group. Fourth, clearly the two taxonomic categories into which living large hominoids are normally subdivided, Pongidae and Hominidae, cannot be imposed on earlier Neogene species without suppressing important information and obscuring evolutionary concepts.

A minimum of six clusters of species is needed to describe the diversity of Neogene large hominoids, and these can be classified as tribes or subfamilies.

(1) Ponginae: the living great apes. (2) Dryopithecinae: species from Africa and Europe, ranging in age from about 23 to 9 Myr, sharing dental features with pongines but differing

同存在，在非洲肯定是如此，在亚洲也可能是这样 [23]。这些种类已被分类为南方古猿与人属，但是它们仍有某些共同特征：简化的犬齿在尺寸上表现出适度的二态，颊齿增大、其牙釉质厚，脑量相对增大（至少是与森林古猿及猩猩科动物对比），颅后骨骼显示出众多适应两足行走的改变。这些种类中至少有一种，在至少 200 万年前甚至可能是 250 万到 300 万年以前，就可以制造石器。

现在已经越来越多地认识到这些通常所谓的上新世－更新世人科动物，虽然可被识别为人科，但不能仅仅被认为是"小型人类"，而应该从定性的方面上被看作是不同于中、晚更新世的人科动物的生物。它们是和真正原始种类不同的组。

最古老的标本，其牙齿类似于南方古猿或早期人属种类的牙齿（显然不同于西瓦古猿或腊玛古猿组的牙齿），它们出自于肯尼亚的路奇诺与洛萨加姆，年代距今约500 万年至 700 万年 [24, 25]。

南方古猿与早期人亚科是在大约 700 万年前之后的这个时期内发生了分化；而迄今为止尚不明确西瓦古猿组与腊玛古猿组的种类。在非洲与欧亚大陆，猕猴，尤其是生活在更为开阔的空间的类型，第一次变得繁盛。

## 综 合 分 析

依据对人猿超科进化的现有认识，尝试提出了一个反映过去十年在分类和系统上的重要进展的方案。这些由戴维·皮尔比姆在此总结。

第一，新近纪的人猿超科动物，在其大部分进化过程中，是一个种类相对多样的超科。第二，灭绝了的人猿超科与现生人猿超科不会完全相同，也不会在某些情形下特别类似于现生人猿超科，而把灭绝了的人猿超科阐述得仿佛十分"现代"，这可能会产生误导。第三，考虑到情况的复杂性、后代类型与可选择的祖先类型之间的差异以及化石记录上仍然存在的很大的空白，要准确地勾画出祖先与后代的关系，是十分困难的。当然，为了认定它是一个适合的、成功的组，应该研究它的每一支辐射。第四，无疑，猩猩科与人科作为两个分类学单元，其中现生的大人猿超科通常再细分，这样的分类方法是不能强加于新近纪早期种类上的，那就会干扰重要信息，并使进化概念模糊不清。

需要最少 6 个种类集群来描述新近纪人猿超科的多样性，它们能被分为族或亚科。

（1）猩猩亚科：现生大猿。（2）森林古猿亚科：来自非洲与欧洲的种类，年代大约在 2,300 万年前至 900 万年前，其牙齿与猩猩科动物有共同特点，但许多颅后特征不同；（3）西瓦古猿亚科或西瓦古猿族：这是来自欧亚大陆与非洲的种类，年代范

in many postcranial characters; (3) Sivapithecinae or Sivapithecini: species from Eurasia and Africa, ranging in age from around 15 to 8 Myr, sharing dental features with both pongines and dryopithecines on the one hand and with australopithecines and early hominines on the other; (4) Ramapithecinae or Ramapithecini: Eurasian and African species resembling sivapithecines and australopithecines about equally in dental features; (5) Australopithecinae: species from Africa and possibly Asia ranging in age from at least 3.75 (and perhaps as much as 7) to 1 Myr; (6) Homininae: essentially similar to Australopithecinae in dental, cranial and postcranial morphology.

Figure 4 shows these groups distributed along temporal and qualitative morphological axes; the latter axis is shown as unidimensional although it is, of course, multidimensional. Three alternative phylogenies are indicated on the diagram in order of decreasing probability (in my opinion). Although definite relationships between the middle Miocene and Plio-Pleistocene hominoids are unclear because of gaps in the hominid record between 8 and 4 Myr and the pongid record after 9 Myr, I believe that the major groups as defined here represent at least some of the grades through which modern hominoids evolved. Phylogeny A is the most probable; I regard phylogenies B and C as less probable, although plausible.

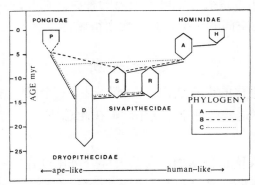

Fig.4. Tentative stratigraphic-morphological distribution of large hominoid groups with possible phylogenies. P, Pongidae; D, Dryopithecidae; S, Sivapithecinae, R, Ramapithecinae; A, Australopithecinae; H, Homininae. (Sivapithecidae should be Ramapithecidae; *note added in proof.*)

I suggest the following classification of large Hominoidea, a compromise of "vertical" and "horizontal" philosophies[26]. (1) Pongidae; (2) Dryopithecidae: including Dryopithecinae and older, more primitive hominoids; (3) Ramapithecidae: Sivapithecinae (or Sivapithecini) and Ramapithecinae (or Ramapithecini); (4) Hominidae: Australopithecinae and Homininae.

The classification is flexible in that it is compatible with any of the three phylogenies suggested in Fig 4. Whether or not the four groups are classified as families, subfamilies or tribes, they should be coordinate. As the fossil record improves I expect that certain (perhaps known) members of Ramapithecidae and Hominidae will prove more conclusively to be ancestors and descendants (that is phylogeny A in Fig. 4 becomes more probable), in

852

围大约在 1,500 万年前到 800 万年前，其牙齿一方面与猩猩科动物及森林古猿亚科有共同特点，另一方面与南方古猿亚科及早期人亚科有共同特点；(4) 腊玛古猿亚科或腊玛古猿族：欧亚大陆与非洲的种类，在牙齿特征上，与西瓦古猿亚科及南方古猿亚科的类似程度相当；(5)南方古猿亚科：这是来自非洲的种类，也可能来自亚洲，年代范围从至少375（可能差不多是 700）万年前至 100 万年前；(6)人亚科：在牙齿、头骨及颅后形态上基本上类似于南方古猿亚科。

图 4 是这些组沿时间轴与定性形态轴的分布图示；虽然定性形态轴毫无疑问是多维的，但这里用一维表示。3 个备选系统发育史在图上依概率降序排列(依我看来)。虽然，由于 800 万年前至 400 万年前人科动物记录的缺失，以及 900 万年前以后猩猩科类人猿记录的缺失，还不清楚中新世中期的人猿超科与上新世－更新世的人猿超科之间的确切关系，但是我相信这里详细说明的主要的组至少代表了现代人猿超科进化的一些阶段。生物系统发育史 A 最为接近；我认为生物系统发育史 B 与 C 可能性小些，虽然它们也似乎有可能。

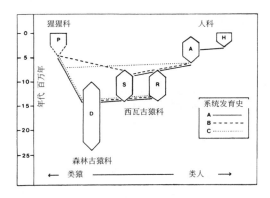

图 4. 反映可能的系统发育史的超大人猿超科群的尝试性地层－形态学分布图。P，猩猩科；D，森林古猿科；S，西瓦古猿亚科；R，腊玛古猿亚科；A，南方古猿亚科；H，人亚科。(附加说明：图中"西瓦古猿科"应为"腊玛古猿科")

对"垂直"与"水平"基本原理进行折中 [26]，我提出如下大的人猿超科分类。(1) 猩猩科；(2) 森林古猿科：包括森林古猿亚科与更古老、更原始的人猿超科；(3) 腊玛古猿科：西瓦古猿亚科（或西瓦古猿族）与腊玛古猿亚科（或腊玛古猿族）；(4) 人科：南方古猿亚科与人亚科。

此分类是很灵活的，它与图4提出的 3 个生物的种系发展史中的任何一个都相容而不矛盾。无论 4 个组是否被分为科、亚科或族，它们都应该是并列的。随着化石记录的改善，我希望某些（可能已知）腊玛古猿科与人科的成员能最后被证明是祖先和后代（即图 4 中的生物种系发展史 A 变得更有可能），这种情形下，一些研

which case some workers might wish to include those (or all) ramapithecids in Hominidae. Finally, two important points should be re-emphasised. A rigidly dichotomous classification of Neogene large hominoids is not only inappropriate but potentially misleading. And the living hominoids are rather aberrant forms when the total array of Neogene large hominoids is considered.

This work was supported by NSF, SFCP, the Government of Pakistan, the Geological Survey of Pakistan, Yale University and NERC. Special thanks go to E. L. Simons and B. Lipschutz.

(**270**, 689-695; 1977)

David Pilbeam*, Grant E. Meyer*, Catherine Badgley*, M. D. Rose[†], M. H. L. Pickford[‡], A. K. Behrensmeyer[§] and S. M. Ibrahim Shah[¶]
* Departments of Anthropology and Geology and Geophysics and Peabody Museum of Natural History, Yale University, New Haven, Connecticut 06520
[†] Section of Gross Anatomy, Department of Surgery, Yale Medical School, New Haven, Connecticut 06520
[‡] Department of Geology, Queen Mary College, London, UK
[§] Division of Earth Sciences, University of California, Santa Cruz, California 95064
[¶] Geological Survey of Pakistan, Quetta, Pakistan

Received 8 August; accepted 11 October 1977.

References:
1. Pilbeam, D. *et al. Nature* **270**, 684-689 (1977).
2. Pilbeam, D. *Les Plus Anciens Hominidés* (eds Tobias, P. V. and Coppens, Y.) 39-59 (Centre National de la Recherche Scientifique, Paris, 1976).
3. Berggren, W. A. & Van Couvering, J. *Palaeogeogr. Palaeoclimatol. Palaeoecol.* **16**, no. 1/2 (1974).
4. Krynine, P. *Am. J. Sci.* **34**, 422-446 (1937).
5. Lewis, G. E. *Am. J. Sci.* **33**, 191-204 (1937).
6. Tattersall, I. *Nature* **221**, 451-452 (1969); **224**, 821-822 (1969).
7. Prasad, K. N. *Nature* **232**, 413-414 (1971).
8. Banerjee, D. *Rev. Palaeobotan. Palynol.* **6**, 171-176 (1968).
9. Nandi, B. *Himalayan Geol.* **5**, 411-424 (1975).
10. Johnson, G. D. *Geol. Rundschau.* **66**, 192-216 (1977).
11. Schaller, G. *The Deer and the Tiger* (Chicago University Press, 1967).
12. Simons, E. L. *J. Hum. Evol.* **5**, 511-528 (1976).
13. Simons, E. L. *Proc. Natl. Acad. Sci. U.S.A.* **51**, 528-535 (1964).
14. Pilgrim, G. E. *Rec. Geol. Surv. India* **45**, 1-74 (1915).
15. Andrews, P. & Van Couvering, J. *Approaches to Primate Paleobiology* (ed. Szalay, F.), 62-103 (Karger, Basel, 1975).
16. McHenry, H. & Corruccini, R. *Folia Primat.* **23**, 227-244 (1975).
17. Kretzoi, M. *Nature* **257**, 578-581 (1975).
18. de Bonis, L. & Melentis, J. *C. r. hebd. Séanc. Acad. Sci.* **284**, 1393-1396 (1977).
19. Tekkaya, I. *Bull. Min. Res. Expl. Inst. Turkey* no. **83**, 148-165 (1974).
20. Andrews, P. & Walker, A. in *Human Origins* (eds Isaac, G. & McCown, E.) 279-304 (Benjamin, New York, 1976).
21. Delson, E. *Approaches to Primate Paleobiology* (ed. Szalay, F.) 167-217 (Karger, Basal, 1975).
22. Johanson, D. & Taieb, M. *Nature* **260**, 293-297 (1976).
23. Leakey, R. & Walker, A. *Nature* **261**, 572-574 (1976).
24. Behrensmeyer, A. *Earliest Man and Environments in the Lake Rudolf Basin* (eds Coppens, Y., Howell, F., Isaac, G. & Leakey, R.) 163-170 (Chicago University Press, 1976).
25. Pickford, M. *Nature* **256**, 279-284 (1975).
26. Simpson, G. G. *Principles of Animal Taxonomy* (Columbia University Press, New York, 1961).

854

究人员可能希望列入人科中的那些（或所有的）腊玛古猿。最后，要再次强调两个重点。把新近纪人猿超科动物严格地分成两类，不仅不合理，还有可能产生误导。如果考虑到新近纪人猿超科动物的总序列，则现生人猿超科是相当的畸形的。

本研究由美国国家科学基金会、史密森外币项目、巴基斯坦政府、巴基斯坦地质调查所、耶鲁大学以及英国自然环境研究理事会资助。特别感谢西蒙斯与利普许茨。

（田晓阳 翻译；林圣龙 审稿）

# Pliocene Footprints in the Laetolil Beds at Laetoli, Northern Tanzania

M. D. Leakey and R. L. Hay

## Editor's Note

Since the 1930s, Louis Leakey and his colleagues had been persuaded that the Olduvai Gorge and the surrounding region would be productive of fossil human remains. This remarkable paper describes the discovery in ancient volcanic tuffs—volcanic ash consolidated by the action of rain—of the footprints of a great variety of animals and even insects and a striking series of imprints of human feet. One set of human prints appears to have been left by two human beings walking northwards alongside each other for more than 100 metres. M. D. Leakey is Mary Leakey, the wife of Louis Leakey.

---

Recent excavation of the tuffs of the Laetolil Beds in Tanzania has revealed the presence of a large variety of footprints from the Pliocene. Many of these prints can be correlated with fossilised remains of Pliocene animals found in the same area.

---

IT was stated previously[1] that the name Laetolil would be used in preference to either Garusi or Vogel River for the area where the Laetolil Beds are exposed. Laetolil, as stated then, is an anglicisation of the Masai word Laetoli and was first used by Kent[2]. The Tanzanian authorities have now asked that the term Laetolil should be dropped in favour of Laetoli. The name Laetoli will be used for the area, but the Pliocene deposits will continue to be known as the Laetolil Beds, as established in 1976[1].

The Laetolil Beds (Figs 1, 2) are dominantly tuffs which have a maximum known thickness of 130 m and are divisible into upper and lower units. Nearly all the fossils have come from the upper unit which is 45-60 m thick.

In 1975 three marker tuffs had been identified in the upper unit of the Laetolil Beds[1]. Since then, more than a dozen widespread air-fall tuffs (Fig. 3) have been recognised, permitting detailed correlations.

# 坦桑尼亚北部莱托利尔层中的上新世足迹

利基，海

## 编者按

从 20 世纪 30 年代开始，路易斯·利基和他的同事们就相信在奥杜威峡谷和周围的区域中保存有大量的人类化石。这篇值得关注的文章记述了在古老火山凝灰岩（在雨水的作用下加固的火山灰）中发现的大量不同种类的动物足迹（甚至是昆虫）和一系列惊人的人类脚印。其中一列人类的脚印有 100 多米长，看起来是由并排向北行走的两个人所留下。文章的第一作者是玛丽·利基，她是路易斯·利基的妻子。

---

最近在坦桑尼亚莱托利尔层的火山凝灰岩中发现了大量上新世时期的足迹。这些足迹中很多能够与在同一区域发现的上新世动物化石进行对比。

---

如前所述[1]，"莱托利尔"原先是用来指加鲁西或沃格尔河的区域，因为这些区域又是莱托利尔层出露的地方。正如之后所表述的，莱托利尔是马赛语莱托里英语化后确定下来的，肯特首次使用了它[2]。现在坦桑尼亚官方已经要求用"莱托里"替代"莱托利尔"。所以"莱托里"这个名称将用来指这个地区，但上新世的沉积物将沿用世人熟知的、于 1976 年确定的"莱托利尔层"[1]。

莱托利尔层（图 1、2）以凝灰岩为主要岩性，目前已知的最大厚度有 130 米，而且被分为上、下两个层位。几乎所有的化石都是从 45~60 米厚的上部层位中发现的。

1975 年在莱托利尔层的上部层位中发现了三个标志凝灰岩层[1]。其后，又辨识出了 12 处以上分布广泛的空落凝灰岩（图 3），它们使不同化石点的地层的详细对比成为可能。

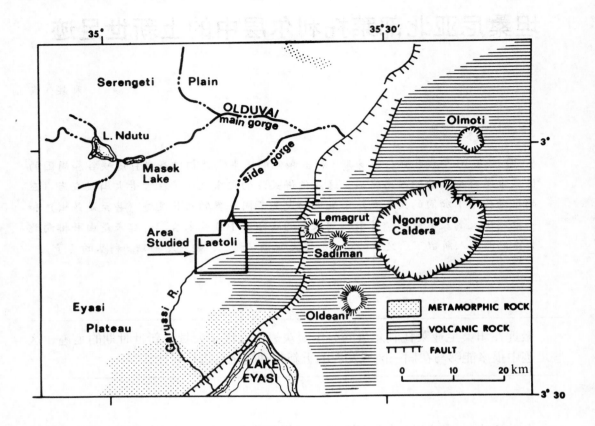

Fig. 1. Map of the southern Serengeti and volcanic highlands showing the position of the Laetoli area.

## Description of the Footprints Tuff

The footprints tuff is divisible into two units of differing lithology and structure. The lower unit, 7-8.6 cm thick, is relatively uniform in thickness and is characterised by widespread ash layers of even thickness, commonly with rainprinted surfaces. The upper unit, generally 5-7 cm thick, thins over the higher areas of the lower unit and thickens in depressions to eliminate the undulations preserved by the mantle bedding of the lower unit.

Several unusual features of these tuffs can be explained by composite ash falls of natrocarbonatite ash and melilitite lava globules. The ash must have been cemented rapidly to have prevented erosion of the sand-sized lava globules by wind in this semi-arid climate in which 80-85% of the sediment was wind-worked. Natrocarbonatite ash would have dissolved incongruently in rainfall to yield soluble carbonates, which would have crystallised under the heat of the Sun to cement the ash layer in a few hours.

Footprints were made on at least six different surfaces but are by far the most common at two levels (Fig. 4). Prints of birds and hares are common to all levels, but prints more than about 10 cm in diameter have been found only in the upper unit. Particularly striking is the number of elephant prints in the higher levels compared to their apparent absence below.

858

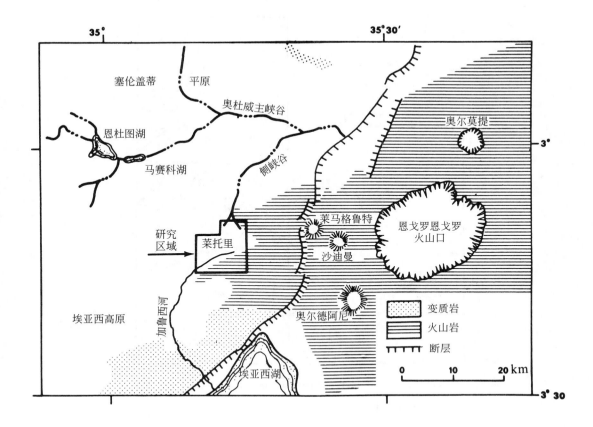

图 1. 莱托里在南塞伦盖蒂和火山高地中的地理位置图

## 足迹凝灰岩描述

足迹凝灰岩可以分为两种不同的岩性和结构。在下部层位中有 7~8.6 厘米厚的凝灰岩，它们厚度相对统一，而且还以广泛分布的相同厚度的火山灰层为特征，这些火山灰层的表面上普遍有雨痕。在上部层位，凝灰岩通常有 5~7 厘米厚，在下部层位较高的区域较薄，同时在低洼处变厚，以抵消下部层位地幔基岩原有的起伏。

这些凝灰岩表现出来的几个不同寻常的特征能够用钠碳酸岩质火山灰和黄长岩熔岩球形成的复成分火山灰降落来解释。在这种有 80%~85% 的沉积是由风成作用形成的半干旱气候下，火山灰必须迅速凝结以防止被砂粒大小的火山熔岩球所风蚀。钠碳酸岩质火山灰会不均匀地溶解在降雨中产生可溶性碳酸盐。可溶性碳酸盐在太阳辐射的加热下会结晶，并在几小时内凝结成火山灰层。

至少在 6 个不同层面发现了足迹，但目前为止只在两个层位中密集分布（图4）。鸟类和野兔的足迹普遍存在于各个层位中，但直径大于 10 厘米的足迹只发现于上部地层中。特别引人注目的是在较高层位中的大象足迹的数量，这与低层位中大象足迹的明显缺失形成鲜明对比。

859

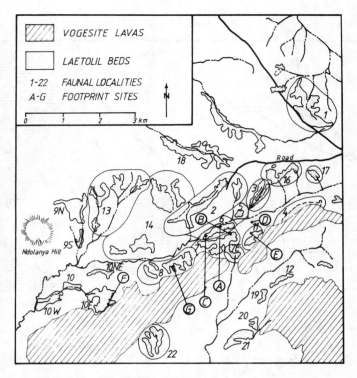

Fig. 2. Map of the fossil localities and footprint sites at Laetoli.

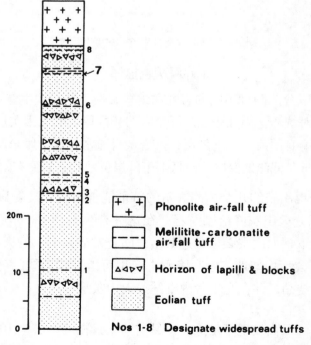

Phonolite air-fall tuff

Melilitite-carbonatite air-fall tuff

Horizon of lapilli & blocks

Eolian tuff

Nos 1-8 Designate widespread tuffs

Fig. 3. Columnar section of the upper unit of the Laetolil Beds at Locality 1 showing air-fall tuffs and horizons of lapilli and blocks. The present report is based on studies of the lower part of Tuff 7, termed the Footprint Tuff. Tuffs 6, 7 and 8 were designated Tuffs a, b and c by Leakey et al.[1]. The pholite tuff was designated Tuff d.

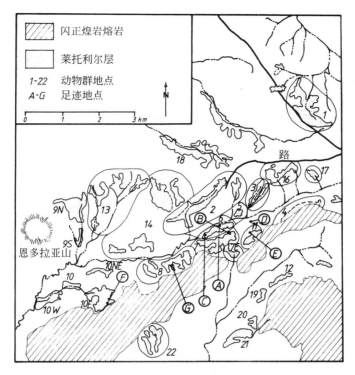

图 2. 莱托里地区的化石产地和足迹地点位置图

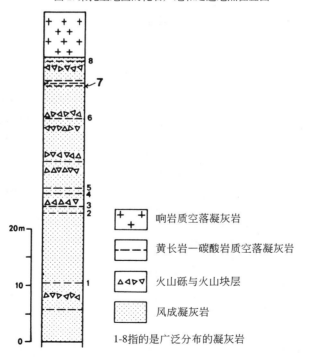

图 3. 地点 1 处的莱托利尔层上部的柱状剖面图，显示空落火山凝灰岩和火山砾、火山块层。本报告针对火山凝灰岩 7（又称为足迹凝灰岩）下部的研究。凝灰岩 6、7 和 8 被利基等人 [1] 称为凝灰岩 a、b 和 c。而响岩质凝灰岩则为凝灰岩 d。

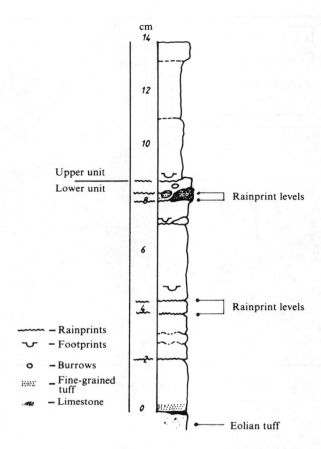

cm
14

12

10

Upper unit
Lower unit

Rainprint levels

6

Rainprint levels

- Rainprints
- Footprints
o - Burrows
- Fine-grained tuff
- Limestone

Eolian tuff

Fig. 4. Generalised columnar section for footprint tuff at site *A*.

On the basis of the available evidence a tentative history of the footprint tuff begins near the end of the dry season and continues into the rainy season. The first showers of ash fell on a relatively bare, nearly flat landscape with scattered *Acacia* trees. The ash layers which constitute the lower unit were cemented by intermittent showers near the beginning of the rainy season. A few times between showers extruded eolian sediments, together with some of the air-fall ash, were redeposited by wind. The sharp contact at the base of the upper unit may mark the onset of the rainy season. Stratification in the upper unit is compatible with sheetwash produced by heavy showers, but is unlike that of the lower unit in which individual ash layers vary little in thickness over a distance of 5 km. The smaller amount of calcite in the upper unit may have resulted from either heavy rains or a smaller original content of carbonatite ash, or both. Thus, the abrupt appearance of footprints of elephants and other large animals in the upper unit may represent, at least in part, their migration which accompanies the rainy season.

The 1975 and 1976 field seasons at Laetoli were devoted to study of the geology of the area and the collection and excavation of fossil vertebrates and molluscs from the Laetolil Beds and later deposits. The age of the upper, fossiliferous part of the Laetolil Beds was

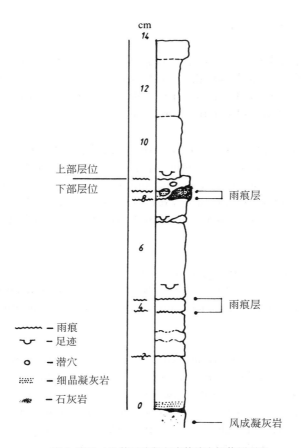

图 4. 遗址 A 处的足迹凝灰岩的综合柱状剖面图

基于现有证据，推想足迹凝灰岩的历史始于干旱季节几近结束时并持续到雨季。首波火山灰洒落在相对裸露、零星分散着金合欢树的近乎平坦的地方。组成下部层位的火山灰被雨季开始时的间歇性阵雨所凝结。在数次阵雨间歇内一些被挤压出的风成沉积物和空落的火山灰一起被风卷起混合后再沉积下来。上部层位底部的锐角不整合的接触可能标志着雨季的开始。上部层位的层理与暴雨产生的片状冲积层相一致，但与下部层位的层理不同，后者在 5 千米范围内，其所包含的单独的火山灰层厚度上几乎没有变化。上部层位中含有的少量方解石，可能是在大雨或者火山灰中原有的少量碳酸盐岩，或二者的共同影响下形成的。因此，在上部层位中突然出现大象和其他大型动物的足迹可能意味着，至少是某种程度上意味着，它们是伴随着雨季迁徙的。

在 1975~1976 年莱托里的野外季中，研究人员致力于该区域地质情况的研究和从莱托利尔层及其上部沉积物中采集和发掘脊椎动物、软体动物化石。莱托利尔层

established at 3.6-3.75 Myr (ref. 1).

While visiting the Laetoli camp during 1976 Dr. Andrew Hill observed a number of depressions in the surface of a fine-grained tuff exposed in a river bed. These proved to be footprints of birds and mammals ranging from elephant and rhinoceros to carnivores and hares, which had been exposed by natural erosion and weathering.

The first site where footprints were observed (site *A* in Fig. 2) lies just south of the Garusi River in fossil Locality 6. An area of ~490 m² has been exposed by natural erosion and by excavation. To the south-west, at a second site (*C*) there are ~156 m² of the footprint-bearing tuff exposed. Both these localities were studied in detail in 1977. Five further areas where the footprint-bearing tuff is well exposed are also known but have not yet been completely studied.

Deeply worn game tracks or pathways can be seen crossing the footprint areas at two sites. These were clearly used repeatedly by animals to reach some objective and on modern behavioural patterns it is likely that they were made by the game going to and from water holes.

Only a proportion of the animals represented in the fossil prints have been identified so far. Investigation of present-day game tracks in National Parks is underway to provide comparative information. In general, however, the fossil record agrees well with the footprints. A Musukuma tracker was employed to assist in identifications. He assisted considerably in identifying to family and generic levels, particularly in the case of Bovidae, which are commonly represented in both the footprint and fossil records.

A partial breakdown of the mammalian specimens recovered from the Laetolil Beds in 1975 was published[1] and may usefully be given here. Additional material was recovered in 1976 and 1977, but the overall proportions of various groups remain close to the first figures (Table 1).

Table 1. Mean percentages of mammalian specimens from various sites

| Bovidae (of which 15.1% are *Madoqua*, dik-dik) | 43% | Equidae | 4.4% |
|---|---|---|---|
| Lagomorpha | 14.4% | Suidae | 3.6% |
| Giraffidae (including both a large and small species, as well as *Sivatherium*) | 11.2% | Proboscidea | 3.4% |
| | | Rodentia | 3.3% |
| Rhinocerotidae | 9.7% | Carnivora | 3.1% |

Avifauna, Cercopithecidae, Hominidae and Pedetinae were omitted from this list.

上部含化石部分的时代已确定为 360 万到 375 万年前（参考文献 1）。

安德鲁·希尔博士在 1976 年访问莱托里营地期间曾观察到出露于河床且具有细晶的凝灰岩表面有很多的凹陷。这些被证明是鸟类及大象、犀牛、食肉动物还有野兔等哺乳动物留下的足迹，它们由于受到自然的侵蚀和风化作用，这些足迹已经暴露出来。

发现足迹的第一处遗址（在图 2 的位置 A）位于加鲁西河的南边的第 6 处化石地点。由于自然侵蚀和挖掘，约 490 平方米的区域已经出露。在位于西南的第二处遗址（C）则有 156 平方米的含足迹凝灰岩出露。1977 年曾对这两个遗址进行过详细研究。还有 5 处已知区域有出露很好的含足迹凝灰岩，但还未得到彻底研究。

在两处遗址的足迹区可以观察到印痕很深的游走足迹或路径。很显然，这些路径被动物屡次使用以到达某个目标，从现代行为学模型来看，它们很可能是动物游走时去水坑和离开水坑时留下的印痕。

在以化石足迹反映出的动物中，迄今只有一部分的分类地位得以确定。用来作为比较信息的现生动物游走足迹正在国家公园中进行研究。然而整体而言，化石记录与足迹十分吻合。我们聘请了一位穆苏库玛追踪者辅助鉴定工作。他在很大程度上辅助了科级与属级的鉴定工作，尤其是在牛科动物的足迹鉴定中，而牛科动物的足迹和化石材料都很常见。

1975 年在莱托利尔层中出土的哺乳动物清单已经部分发表 [1]，在此再复述一下也许有用。1976 年和 1977 年又出土了一些新材料，但不同种类间的总体比例与第一次出土的化石数据相近（表 1）。

表 1. 不同产地哺乳动物种类的平均百分比

| 牛科<br>(15.1% 是犬羚属) | 43% | 马科 | 4.4% |
|---|---|---|---|
| 兔形目 | 14.4% | 猪科 | 3.6% |
| 长颈鹿科<br>（包括大和小物种，以及西洼兽属） | 11.2% | 长鼻目 | 3.4% |
| | | 啮齿目 | 3.3% |
| 犀牛科 | 9.7% | 食肉目 | 3.1% |

该表中省略了鸟类、猴科、人科和跳兔亚科

The footprints that have been recorded are briefly described below, with notes on the fossil material where it seems to be related.

## Diplopoda

A single track approximately 20 cm long is known at site (*A*).

Fossil record: a small fragment of fossilised centipede was found at Locality 4.

## Avifauna

(1) *Struthio* sp. Two isolated prints at site (*A*).

(2) *Phasianidae*, cf. Guinea fowl. Numerous tracks occur at all sites, generally in trails of four or more. They compare closely with tracks of the living helmeted Guinea fowl, common in the Laetoli area today. Average length of eight fossil prints 62 mm, of nine modern prints 60 mm.

(3) Similar but smaller tracks, averaging 45 mm in length, possibly of francolin.

Fossil record: numerous fragments of ostrich eggshell are known but no skeletal remains. Clutches of eggs comparable in size to those of modern Guinea fowl have been found at Locality 10.

## Primates

Cercopithecidae: Tracks are known at three localities.

At site (*C*) there is a single trail comprising six hind foot prints with a digit protruding to one side. Each of these prints is accompanied by a roughly circular impression, always to the left (Fig. 5). When first discovered these prints were interpreted as knuckle impressions, but more thorough cleaning has revealed traces of the palms of the hands and they are undoubtedly prints of the forefeet. In the hind feet the longest digit is central and the prints range in length from 20.1 to 14.7 cm with an average of 17 cm. The width varies from 10.9 to 8.1 cm with an average of 9.9 cm (excluding the great toe). Stride length varies from 34 to 46 cm with an average of 41 cm. (Stride is here interpreted as the distance between the posterior margin of successive heel prints of the same foot.)

The second trail is at site (*D*). It was made by a single animal and is 4 m long. There are prints of both hind and forefeet. All are lightly imprinted on a surface which was clearly wet and slippery when the animal walked over it .The average length of the hind prints is 14.5 cm and of the forefeet prints 11 cm. Stride length averages 27.7 cm. These prints are not only smaller than those at site (*C*) but are relatively broader, with very narrow heel impressions.

下面简要地描述记录下来的足迹化石，同时也标注了这些足迹可能对应的化石材料。

## 倍 足 纲

一条长约 20 厘米的单独的足迹见于遗址（A）。

化石记录：出土于第 4 化石地点的一小段蜈蚣化石。

## 鸟 类 动 物

（1）鸵鸟属未定种。两个单独的脚印见于遗址（A）。

（2）雉科，珍珠鸡相似种。多个足迹见于所有遗址，一般每处有 4 列以上的足迹。它们与莱托里地区常见的现生盔珠鸡足迹非常相似。8 个化石脚印的平均长度为 62 毫米，9 个现生脚印的平均长度为 60 毫米。

（3）相似的但小一点的足迹，脚印平均长度 45 毫米，可能是鹧鸪。

化石记录：有很多鸵鸟蛋壳碎片，但没有骨骼化石。在第 10 化石地点发现了一窝蛋，蛋的大小与现在珍珠鸡蛋的相似。

## 灵 长 目

猴科：其足迹见于 3 处。

在遗址（C）有个单列足迹，由 6 个后脚印组成。脚印中有个趾头向侧面伸出。每个脚印的左侧都伴有一个大致呈圆形的印痕（图 5）。这些脚印在发现的初期被认为是指背行走的印痕，但经深入清理后发现手掌的痕迹，因此无疑是前掌的印痕。后脚的最长脚趾在中间，脚印的长度在 20.1~14.7 厘米之间，平均值为 17 厘米。脚宽在 10.9~8.1 厘米之间，平均值为 9.9 厘米（不包括大拇趾）。步幅长度在 34~46 厘米之间，平均值为 41 厘米（步幅在此的定义为两个相邻的同一只脚的脚印后跟之间的距离）。

第二列足迹在遗址（D）。这是一个个体留下的脚印，长 4 米。前后肢的脚印均有。这些脚印均为较浅的印痕，当动物经过时，地面显然是湿滑的。后脚印平均长 14.5 厘米，前脚印平均长 11 厘米。步幅平均长 27.7 厘米。这些脚印不仅比遗址（C）的要小，而且还相对较宽，后跟的印痕非常窄。

Fig. 5. Print of cercopithecoid fore and hind foot at site C.

At site (F), in fossil Locality 10, there are at least four sets of tracks going in slightly different directions, as do the tracks of present-day baboons when they move in a troop. The average measurements of the hind feet in each of the four trails range from 15.2 to 10 cm and of the forefeet prints from 7.6 to 4 cm (excluding the great toe).

> Fossil record: a number of cercopithecoid mandibles and teeth and a few postcranial fragments have been provisionally attributed to *Papio* sp. and a colobine. Most are as small or even smaller in size than those of a living female baboon, but two mandibular fragments, a calcaneum and the distal ends of a humerus and femur are considerably larger than in any living baboon and compare in size with *Theropithecus oswaldi*. The difference in size between the prints described above is compatible with that of the known fossils, although age and sex differences are factors to be considered.

Hominidae: Three trails believed to be hominid are known at sites (A) (Fig. 6) and (G) (Figs 7, 8), in fossil Localities 6 and 8.

(1) At site (A) there are five prints in a trail 1.5 m long (Fig. 6). Natural erosion has almost entirely exposed two of the prints, but the remaining three are still filled with matrix of the overlying deposits. The exposed prints are short and broad, 15.5 cm long and 10.5 cm wide. The stride is also short with an average length of 31 cm. The gait was somewhat shambling, with one foot crossing in front of the other. Unlike the cercopithecoid prints, the longest digit is the great toe, situated as in the human foot.

图 5. 猴科动物在遗址 C 的前后脚印。

在遗址（F），第 10 化石地点，至少有 4 列去向略有不同的足迹，就如现生狒狒结队行走时会踩出的路径那样。每列后脚印都算出一个平均尺寸，这 4 列足迹平均尺寸在 10~15.2 厘米之间，前脚印的则为 4~7.6 厘米（不包括大拇指）。

化石记录：一些猕猴科动物的下颌骨和牙齿，以及少量颅后骨骼的碎块被暂时归入狒狒属未定种和一种疣猴。在大小方面，大部分与现生雌性狒狒的一样小或比它更小，但是有两件下颌骨破片、1 件跟骨、1 件肱骨远端和 1 件股骨远端显然大于任何现生狒狒，而与奥斯华狮尾狒的个体相近。尽管需要考虑年龄和性别差异的因素，上述脚印大小的差异与所出土的化石材料指示的个头差异是对应的。

人科：在化石地点 6 和 8 中的遗址 A（图 6）和 G（图 7 和图 8）中可见 3 列被认为是人科动物的足迹。

（1）在遗址（A）的一列长 1.5 米的足迹中有 5 个脚印（图 6）。自然侵蚀使其中的两个脚印几乎完全出露，但是其余 3 个仍然被上覆沉积物的围岩填充。出露的脚印又短又宽，长 15.5 厘米，宽 10.5 厘米。步幅也小，平均长度为 31 厘米。步态有点蹒跚，一只脚要绕到另一只脚的前面。与猴类的脚印不同，最长的脚趾是拇趾，位置与人类的脚相同。

Fig. 6. Hominid footprints at site *A*.

Fig. 7. Dual trail of hominid footprints at site *G*.

图 6. 遗址 A 的人科动物足迹。

图 7. 遗址 G 的人科动物的双列足迹。

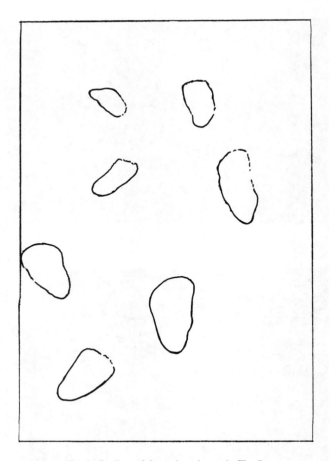

Fig. 8. Outline of footprints shown in Fig. 7.

It has been suggested that these prints might have resulted from the superposition of a hind on forefoot impression, or vice versa, either of a quadrupedal animal or a knuckle-walking primate. Careful examination of the original prints *in situ* reveals no indication of superposition, while the last interpretation invokes the hypothetical existence of an animal which is not present in over 5,000 fossil specimens.

(2) At site (*G*) there are trails left by two individuals travelling north (Figs 7-9). The trails are parallel and ~25 cm apart, too close for the hominids to have walked abreast. They followed the same line or pathway but it is possible that they did not pass by at the same time as there is a noticeable difference in the conditions of the two sets of prints. Those of the smaller individual are sharp and well defined, indicating a firm, compact surface, whilst those of the larger individual, with one notable exception, are blurred at the edges and enlarged, as would be the case if the surface had been dry and dusty. At one point the smaller individual appears to have paused and made a half-turn to the left before continuing in a northerly direction.

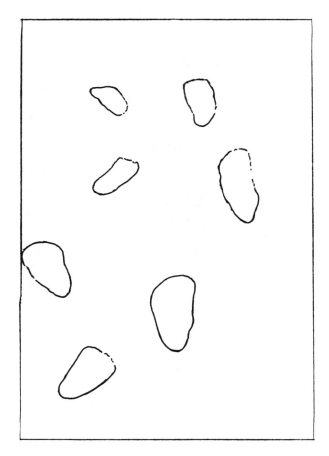

图 8. 图 7 中足迹的轮廓。

　　有人解释这样的脚印是由于后脚踩到前脚印上形成的或者有可能是反过来的，因此这些脚印要么是四足行走的动物要么是指背行走的灵长类的脚印。对原始脚印的现场细致的观察表明没有任何叠覆迹象，然而最后一种解释援引了一种在五千多件化石标本中都未出现的物种的假设性存在。

　　(2) 在遗址（G）有两个个体向北行走留下的足迹（图 7~9）。这两列足迹互相平行，间距为 25 厘米左右；对于并排行走的人科动物来说，这样的间距太小了。这两列脚印沿着相同的路线或路径，但可能是在不同的时间里留下的，因为这两列脚印是在明显不同的情况下留下的。其中个体较小的脚印清晰，轮廓分明，指示一种稳重而紧密的接触状况；而个体较大的脚印，除了其中的一个明显的特例外，其余的都是边缘模糊、印痕扩大，就如在干燥而尘土多的状态下出现的情况一样。较小的个体在行走中似乎还在某处停顿下来向左转弯，然后又继续向北行走。

Fig. 9. Left footprint of larger individual in dual trail at site *G*.

In a number of prints the original surface in which they were made has been eroded, leaving only indentations in the underlying deposits. Thus, the measurements of these prints do not accurately reflect the dimensions of the original impressions and are not included.

The site is now being excavated and the trails have so far been found to extend for a distance of 23.54 m. Trail 1 contains 22 prints and Trail 2 contains 12 prints. The average length/breadth of the prints in Trail 1 is 18.5×8.8 cm and in Trail 2 is 21.5×10 cm. Average stride length in Trail 1 is 38.7 cm and in Trail 2 is 47.2 cm. Note that the longitudinal arch of the foot is well developed and resembles that of modern man, and the great toe is parallel to the other toes (Figs 7, 8 and 9).

Fossil record: two mandibles, parts of 2 maxillae, partial deciduous and permanent dentions as well as a partial infant skeleton and a number of isolated teeth have been recovered from the Laetolil Beds. They bear considerable resemblances to the material collected from the Afar in Ethiopia, although the Ethiopian material is substantially later.

图 9. 遗址 G 的双列足迹中较大个体的左侧足迹。

　　还有一些留下脚印的原始层面受到了侵蚀，仅在层面下的沉积物中留下一些凹痕。因此这些脚印的测量无法准确反映动物原有脚印的大小而没有列入统计中。

　　这处遗址目前还在发掘中，清理出的足迹长度已延续到 23.54 米。第 1 列足迹有 22 个脚印，第 2 列足迹有 12 个。第 1 列足迹的脚印长宽平均值为 18.5 厘米 ×8.8 厘米，而第 2 列足迹的为 21.5 厘米 ×10 厘米。第 1 列足迹的平均步幅长为 38.7 厘米，第 2 列足迹的平均步幅长为 47.2 厘米。请注意其纵向足弓和现代人一样很发育，拇趾和其他脚趾平行（图 7~9）。

　　化石记录：2 件下颌骨，2 件上颌骨残段，若干不完整的乳齿系和恒齿系，1 个不完整的幼体骨架，还有一些单独的牙齿，均出土于莱托利尔层。它们与埃塞俄比亚阿法尔地区出土的材料有很多相似之处，尽管埃塞俄比亚材料要晚得多。

## Leporidae

Innumerable tracks of hares occur at all sites.

Fossil record: mandibles and other remains attributed to *Serengetilagus* sp. are abundant.

## Carnivora

(1) Viverridae, indet. Series of small carnivore prints with non-retractile claws occur at all sites. They are generally lightly imprinted and rather faint. Average length/breadth 34×27 mm. Other small, rounded prints without claw marks, suggest genets. Average length/breadth 28×27 mm.

Fossil record: a variety of Viverridae are known among the fossils, some were described by Dietrich[3], those from the recent collections are being studied by Mme G. Petter.

(3) Hyaenidae. Hyenas have left a series of well-defined and relatively long trails containing large numbers of prints. Eight trails are known and two gaits are represented. Subject to research on living hyaenas, these appear to be a walk and a slow canter or lope. There is uniformity in size, depth and stride within each of the four trails measured, although it is evident that the animals varied in individual size. Average length/breadth/depth measurements:

Trail *C*.22 (19 prints) 122×94×12 mm
Trail *C*.27 (30 prints) 125×102×22 mm
Trail *C*.31 (11 prints) 102×87×13 mm
Trail *C*.39 (18 prints) 111×100×18 mm

Fossil record: in a preliminary report, M. G. Leakey noted the existence of three species of hyena from the Laetolil Beds: (1)*Hyaena bellax* (Ewer 1954); (2)*Hyaenictis* cf. *preforfex* (Hendey 1974); and (3)*Lycyaena* sp.

(3) Felidae. One trail of 12 prints at site (*A*), and several isolated prints appear to correspond in size to those of a serval cat. Average length/breadth/depth 65×52×13 mm. Average length of stride 29 mm.

Fossil record: remains comparable to *F. serval* and *F. caracal* have been noted in the 1974-76 collections.

(4) *Machairodontinae*. Two prints at site (*A*), measuring 134×115 mm and 110×115 mm probably belong to a large sabre-tooth cat, as no other felid of comparable size occurs in the fossil material.

Fossil record: The presence of a large sabre-tooth cat, cf. *Homotherium* is indicated by two teeth.

# 兔 科

所有遗址中都有不计其数的野兔足迹。

化石记录：可以归入塞伦盖蒂兔属未定种的下颌骨和其他部位的化石非常多。

# 食 肉 目

(1) 灵猫科 ( 属种不定 )：带有不可伸缩的爪的一系列小型食肉类的脚印在所有遗址均有发现。它们的脚印较浅，印痕相当模糊，长宽平均值为 34 毫米 × 27 毫米。其他没有爪痕的小圆脚印可能属于麝猫。长宽平均值为 28 毫米 × 27 毫米。

化石记录：化石材料中有多种灵猫科成员，迪特里希曾记述过一些 [3]，彼得夫人正在研究最近采集到的标本。

(2) 鬣狗科：鬣狗留下了一系列清晰的、含有大量脚印的、相对较长的足迹。已知有 8 列足迹，表现出两种步态。据对现生鬣狗的研究，这些足迹像是散步、慢跑或大步慢跑。尽管鬣狗的个体大小显然有差异，但这 4 列足迹的测量显示，它们在大小、深度和步幅上都具有一致性。脚印的长、宽、深平均测量值如下：

列 *C*.22 （19 个脚印） 122 毫米 × 94 毫米 × 12 毫米

列 *C*.27 （30 个脚印） 125 毫米 × 102 毫米 × 22 毫米

列 *C*.31 （11 个脚印） 102 毫米 × 87 毫米 × 13 毫米

列 *C*.39 （18 个脚印） 111 毫米 × 100 毫米 × 18 毫米

化石记录：米芙·利基在一个初步报告中提到莱托利尔层中存在 3 种鬣狗 (1) 好斗鬣狗 （尤尔，1954），(2) 前剪刀鼬鬣狗相似科 （亨戴，1974） 和 (3) 狼鬣狗未定种。

(3) 猫科：1 列 12 个脚印见于遗址 （*A*），并且好几个单独的脚印在大小上似乎符合薮猫的脚印。平均长宽为：65 毫米 × 52 毫米 × 13 毫米。平均步幅长 29 毫米。

化石记录：可以归入薮猫和狞猫的材料见于 1974~1976 年采集到的化石。

(4) 剑齿虎亚科：两个脚印见于遗址 （A），大小为 134 毫米 × 115 毫米和 110 毫米 × 115 毫米，可能属于一种大型剑齿虎，因为化石材料中没有出现其他同样大小的猫科动物。

化石记录：有两枚大型似剑齿虎的牙齿。

## Proboscidea

The proboscidean prints appear to belong to *Loxodonta exoptata* with the exception of one particularly well-preserved print in a trail of four at site (*C*) in which the phalanges and metapodials were more nearly vertical than in other known proboscidean prints and may be of a *Deinotherium*. The *Loxodonta* prints include a number made by juvenile animals as well as some that are usually large by present-day standards. The average for 15 measured prints, mostly adult, is 420×346×34 mm.

> Fossil record: both *Loxodonta exoptata* and *Deinotherium* cf. *bozasi* occur in the Laetolil Beds, but the latter is relatively scarce. A high proportion of the *Loxodonta* teeth are from juvenile animals.

## Equidae

Only two equid trails are known. They have only recently been discovered and have not yet been fully studied. Both are at site (*G*), one on either side of the hominid trails but travelling in an opposite direction, to the south. The best preserved trail is 4.97 m long and contains 15 prints, nine of which can be measured. They range in length from 9.9 to 7.8 cm with an average of 8.6 cm and in width from 10.6 to 8.3 cm with an average of 8.8 cm. The animal appears to have changed gait during this trail.

> Fossil record: numerous teeth, postcranial material and some incomplete mandibles have been found. All can be attributed to *Hipparion* sp.

## Rhinocerotidae

Both *Ceratotherium* and *Diceros* must be represented among the many prints of rhinoceros, but no distinguishing features have been observed to date except on the basis of size. A trail at site (*A*) is one of the longest known, measuring 22 m in length. It contains 31 prints, 23 of which are double, with the hindfoot superimposed on the front. At the western end of the trail, where the animal changed gait, the prints become single and are irregularly spaced. Comparison with modern prints of *Diceros bicornis* at Olduvai show very close similarity. Average length/breadth/depth of double prints in trail: 416×273×31 mm. Single prints, forefoot 246×248×25 mm, hindfoot 256×228×37 mm. Isolated single fore and hind prints in the adjacent game trail are unusually large and may be of *Ceratotherium*. They measure 285×310×42 mm and 400×270×33 mm respectively.

> Fossil record: on the basis of the early collections only *Ceratotherium* was believed to be present in the Laetoli fauna. But a skull of *Diceros* has now been found, as well as numerous teeth and some postcranial material.

## Chalicotheriidae

Two Chalicothere prints were found at site (*C*). They are deeply indented and measure 250×155×63 mm and 243×110×46 mm. The prints comprise impressions of three digits and of the palm. The digits have left symmetrical rounded grooves and the emplacement

## 长 鼻 目

长鼻类的脚印似乎属于古非洲象，只有一个例外是在遗址（C）的一列 4 个脚印中有一个保存得非常好的脚印，与其他已知长鼻目动物脚印相比，其趾骨和掌骨更加近似平直，有可能是恐象。非洲象的脚印包括幼年个体的和以现在标准看的大型个体的。15 个已测脚印（其中大多为成年个体的脚印）的平均值为 420 毫米 ×346 毫米 ×34 毫米。

化石记录：古非洲象和博氏恐象相似种均在莱托利尔层中出现，但后者相对稀少。有很大比例的非洲象牙齿来自幼年个体。

## 马 科

仅发现两列马科动物的足迹。马的脚印是最近才发现的，尚未得到充分研究。两列脚印均发现于遗址（G），有一列在人科动物足迹的一侧，但是行进方向相反，向南方前行。保存最好的足迹有 4.97 米长，包含 15 个脚印，其中 9 个可以测量。其长度在 9.9~7.8 厘米之间，平均值为 8.6 厘米；宽度在 10.6~8.3 厘米之间，平均值为 8.8 厘米。在这列足迹中，这匹马似乎在中途改变了步态。

化石记录：已经发现许多牙齿、颅后骨骼及一些不完整的下颌骨。所有材料可归入三趾马属未定种中。

## 犀 科

在这么多犀牛脚印中肯定有白犀和黑犀，但迄今除了根据大小来区分外还没有发现其他鉴定特征。在遗址（A）发现的一列足迹是目前已知的最长的足迹之一，有 22 米长，包括 31 个脚印，其中有 23 个脚印是重叠的，即后脚踩到前脚的脚印上。在这列足迹的西端，这头犀牛改变了步态，脚印变成单个并呈不规则隔开。它与奥杜威现生的黑犀脚印非常相似。这列足迹中脚印长宽深平均值为：重叠脚印 416 毫米 ×273 毫米 ×31 毫米；单独脚印中前脚印 246 毫米 ×248 毫米 ×25 毫米；后脚印 256 毫米 ×228 毫米 ×37 毫米。在相邻的一个游走足迹中的单独的前后脚印通常较大，并可能是白犀的。前后脚印测量值分别为 285 毫米 ×310 毫米 ×42 毫米和 400 毫米 ×270 毫米 ×33 毫米。

化石记录：根据早期发掘结果，一般认为在莱托利尔动物群中只有白犀，但最近出土了一件黑犀的头骨、许多牙齿和颅后骨骼材料。

## 爪 兽 科

在遗址（C）发现了两个爪兽的脚印。它们的印痕很深，测量值为 250 毫米 ×155 毫米 ×63 毫米和 243 毫米 ×110 毫米 ×46 毫米。脚印由三个脚趾和一个脚掌组成。

for a claw can be seen on one. The prints are 1.30 m apart.

Fossil record: a few specimens which can be referred to *Ancylotherium* cf. *hennigi* have been recovered. They include a calcaneum, astragalus and some phalanges.

## Suidae

Thirteen suid prints at site (*A*) have been measured. They are comparable in size to prints of the living warthog. Average length/breadth/depth measurements are 55×47×11 mm.

Fossil record: only two Suidae are known from the Laetolil Beds, *Potamochoerus* sp. and *Notochoerus euilus*. *Hylochoerus* and *Phacochoerus* were previously believed to be present in the early fauna, but during 1974-77 have only been found in the more recent deposits. On size, the prints are probably of *Potamochoerus*, as *Notochoerus* was a larger animal than the living warthog.

## Giraffidae

(1) Three trails made by single animals are known. They consist of 6, 7 and 11 prints respectively. There are also 19 other prints attributed to giraffe. In one trail, the animal has dragged its feet after each step and left scuffed grooves up to 96 cm long. Average length/breadth/depth measurement for the prints in the trails are 190×151×29 mm, 202×144×10 mm, 211×150×17 mm and 205×150×28 mm. Averages for the isolated prints are 208×155×19 mm.

Fossil record: the prints are of similar size to those of the modern giraffe and can be attributed to *G. jumae* which occurs as a fossil.

(2) Small giraffe cf. *G. stillei*. There are no prints which can positively be allocated to this animal, although its fossil remains are by far the most common giraffid. However, there are many prints, including three trails, which were identified as 'eland' by the tracker. No eland is known in the fossil fauna, nor is there any other bovid in the collection of a size suitable to have made these prints. For the present, it seems justifiable to assign these prints to the small giraffe. They are abundant at site (*A*), where there are three trails consisting of 21, 14 and 5 prints, as well as 72 isolated prints. The average length/breadth/depth measurements for the prints in the three trails are 140×107×14 mm, 139×104×13 mm and 128×94×16 mm.

Fossil record: if the prints are correctly identified, they would belong to the animal originally named *Okapia stillei*, now known as *Giraffa stillei*.

(3) *Sivatherium*. No prints could be identified. The fossils consist mostly of isolated teeth and foot bones.

这些脚趾留下了对称的圆沟，其中一个可以看到脚趾上的爪。脚印的间距为 1.30 米。

化石记录：已经出土了一些可归入钩爪兽相似种的标本，包括 1 个跟骨、距骨和一些趾骨。

## 猪　　科

已经测量了遗址(A)的 13 个猪科动物脚印。它们与现生疣猪的脚印具有可比性。长宽深平均测量值为 55 毫米 ×47 毫米 ×11 毫米。

化石记录：在莱托利尔层中只有两种猪科成员，河猪未定种和南方猪兽。林猪和疣猪曾被认为出现在较早的动物群中，但是在 1974~1977 年的发掘中，只在较晚的沉积物中发现了它们。从大小上判断，脚印很可能是河猪的，因为南方猪是一种比现生的疣猪还要大的动物。

## 长 颈 鹿 科

（1）有 3 列同一个种的动物留下的足迹。它们分别由 6、7、11 个脚印组成。还有其他 19 个脚印被认为是长颈鹿的。在一条足迹中，这头长颈鹿每走一步都拖沓着脚趾，在地面划出一道长达 96 厘米的沟痕。这几列足迹的长宽深平均值分别为 190 毫米 ×151 毫米 ×29 毫米，202 毫米 ×144 毫米 ×10 毫米，211 毫米 ×150 毫米 ×17 毫米，205 毫米 ×150 毫米 ×28 毫米。那些单独脚印的平均值则为 208 毫米 ×155 毫米 ×19 毫米。

化石记录：脚印与现生长颈鹿的大小相似，可以归入朱玛长颈鹿化石。

（2）小型的施氏长颈鹿相似种。没有可以明确归入这种动物的脚印，尽管迄今为止这个种的化石在长颈鹿科动物中最常见。但是有很多脚印，包括 3 列足迹，被跟踪员鉴定为"大羚羊"。而在出土的化石中既没有大羚羊，也没有其他个头合适的牛科动物可以留下那么大的脚印。暂时将这些脚印归入小型长颈鹿无可非议。在遗址（A）有很多脚印，那里有分别由 21、14 和 5 个脚印组成的 3 列足迹，还有 72 个单独的脚印。3 列足迹的长宽深平均值分别为 140 毫米 ×107 毫米 ×14 毫米、139 毫米 ×104 毫米 ×13 毫米和 128 毫米 ×94 毫米 ×16 毫米。

化石记录：如果脚印的鉴定是正确的，那么它们属于施氏长颈鹿，这个种原先被命名为施氏獋狮狓。

（3）西洼兽：没有可鉴定的脚印。化石主要包括一些单独的牙齿和足部骨骼。

## Bovidae

(1) Bovini cf. *Simatherium kohllarseni*. These prints consist of large, rounded and generally deeply indented tracks resembling those of the living African buffalo. They are clearly made by Bovini and can be attributed to *S. kohllarseni,* as this is the only bovine in the fossil record. The prints are represented by four trails containing 16, 12, 10 and 5 tracks, as well as 40 additional prints, either single or in pairs. The average length/breadth/depth measurements for the 43 prints in the trails are 185×149×25 mm.

> Fossil record: a number of horn cores and teeth have been found, including a cranium associated with both horn cores.

(2) *Hippotragus* sp. Seven single prints from sites (*A*) and (*C*) were identified by the tracker as 'roan antelope'. They are characterised by widely splayed, elongate hoof-marks. The average length/breadth/depth measurements are 109×95×16 mm.

> Fossil record: three horn cores and some teeth, collected during 1975 are believed to be a hippotragine and have provisionally been attributed to *Praedamalis deturi*. A horn core and teeth in the earlier collections may also belong to this species which is smaller than the living roan antelope.

(3) Alcelaphini. Eighteen prints at site (*A*) and two at site (*C*) were identified by the tracker as hartebeest. The prints at site (*A*) are both smaller and shallower than those at site (*C*). Average length/breath/depth for the former are 80×60×14 mm and for the latter 103×80×23 mm.

> Fossil record: *Parmularius* sp. has been identified on a frontlet with horn cores, teeth and other fragmentary horn cores. There is also a cranium collected in 1959 which has been attributed to a larger species of alcelaphine. A third species may also be represented.

(4) Small antelopes and gazelles. Prints of dik-dik (*Madoqua*) are rare although dik-dik are the most abundant single species of fossil Bovidae. This anomaly may be explained by the fact that dik-dik are one of the Bovidae who do not require to drink water, subsisting on moisture from vegetation, while tracks of other Bovidae were probably made going to or from water holes.

> Fossil record: *Neotragini?* and *Raphicerus* sp. (Steenbuck) are provisionally identified. *Madoqua* is very abundant. *Antilo-pini*: the gazelle appears to be *G. janenschi*.

## Conclusions

The greater part of the fossil fauna from the Laetolil Beds is recorded in the fossil tracks. In all, over 20 taxa are represented. The preservation of the footprints can be attributed to an unusual and possibly unique combination of climatic, volcanic and mineralogic conditions. The available evidence indicates that the episode took place during a brief

## 牛　科

（1）牛族柯氏司马牛相似种。这些脚印组成大的、圆的、通常印痕很深的足迹，与现生的非洲水牛很像。它们显然是牛亚科动物留下的，可以认为是柯氏司马牛的，因为在化石记录中这是唯一的牛科动物。脚印有4列，分别由16个、12个、10个和5个脚印组成；另外还有40多个单独或成对的脚印。上述足迹中43个脚印的长宽深平均值为185毫米×149毫米×25毫米。

化石记录：已经发现一些牛角角心和牙齿，包括一件带有一对角心的颅骨。

（2）马羚未定种。在遗址（A）和（C）发现了7个单独的脚印，跟踪员把它们鉴定为"马羚"。它们的特点是每个脚印分成两瓣拉长的蹄印。长宽深平均测量值109毫米×95毫米×16毫米。

化石记录：采集于1975年的3件角心和一些牙齿被认为是一种马羚，并被暂时归入狄氏原转角牛羚。早些时候采集到的一件角心和一些牙齿也可以归到这个种，它比现生的马羚要小一些。

（3）狷羚族。遗址（A）的18个脚印和遗址（C）2个脚印被跟踪员鉴定为狷羚的脚印。遗址（A）的脚印比遗址（C）的脚印更小更浅。前者的长宽深平均值80毫米×60毫米×14毫米，后者的为103毫米×80毫米×23毫米。

化石记录：依据一件带有角心的额骨、一些牙齿及角心碎块鉴别出了斗士羚未定种。有一件1959年采集到的颅骨被认为属于一种较大的狷羚类。可能还有第三种狷羚。

（4）小型羚羊和瞪羚。尽管犬羚是牛科化石中最丰富的一个种，但是犬羚的脚印非常少。这一异常现象可以用以下事实来解释，犬羚是牛科中几乎不需要饮水的种类之一，它们依赖植物中的水分生存，而其他牛科动物的足迹路径很可能是在前往水坑或从水坑返回时留下的。

化石记录：暂定的种类有岛羚族（尚未确定）和小岩羚未定种（斯廷巴克）。犬羚非常丰富。羚羊族：该瞪羚似乎为杰南齐瞪羚。

## 结　论

在莱托利尔层中出土的绝大多数化石种类都有化石足迹的记录。总共有超过20个种类。足迹的保留可以归因于气候、火山和矿物条件的异常且独特的组合。现有的证据表明这些足迹是在一个短暂的时期内留下的，大概是在某个雨季开始时恰逢

period, probably during the onset of a single rainy season which happened to coincide with the eruption of light ash showers from the nearby volcano Sadiman.

The locomotor pattern displayed by the trails of hominid footprints is still under examination but it is immediately evident that the Pliocene hominids at Laetoli had achieved a fully upright, bipedal and free-striding gait; a major event in the evolution of man which freed the hands for tool-making and eventually led to more sophisticated human activities. Moreover, evidence supplied by cranial parts of the somewhat later but related hominid fossils from the Afar in Ethiopia (dated between 2.6 and 3 Myr) indicates that bipedalism outstripped enlargement of the brain. To have resolved this issue is an important step in the study of human evolution, as it has long been the subject of speculation and debate.

With the hands free and available for purposes not connected with locomotion it is perhaps surprising that no form of artefact has been found. But the concept of tool-making may well have been beyond the mental ability of these small-brained creatures. Any "tools" or weapons used must have been solely of perishable materials as the Laetolil Beds are devoid not only of artefacts but of all stones other than volcanic ejecta.

Further exploration of sites and analysis of material will continue in 1979, but it is evident that Laetoli will give an unique perspective into hominid environment during Pliocene times.

We thank the United Republic of Tanzania for permission to continue research at Laetoli, the National Geographic Society, Washington, D. C. for financial support, A. A. Mturi, Director of Antiquities, Tanzania and A. J. F. Mgina, Conservator, Ngorongoro Conservation Authority, for their help, Philip Leakey and Peter Jones for organising field seasons, Drs A. W. Gentry, J. Harris and M. G. Leakey for identifying the bovid, giraffid, primate and carnivore fossils and all those who participated in the fieldwork.

(**278**, 317-323; 1979)

**M. D. Leakey\* and R. L. Hay†**
\* P. O. Box 7, Ngorongoro, Tanzania
† Department of Geology and Geophysics, University of California, Berkeley, California 94720

Received 28 September 1978; accepted 2 February 1979.

References:
1. Leakey, M. D. *et al. Nature* **262**, 460-466 (1976).
2. Kent, P. E. *Geol. Mag.* **78**, 173-184 (1941).
3. Dietrich, W. O. *Palaeontographica* **94**, 44-133 (1942).

附近的沙迪曼火山喷发出轻质的火山灰。

人科动物的足迹所表现出的运动模式尚无定论，但显而易见的是，莱托里上新世的人科动物已经具备了完全直立、两足行走并且随意跨步的步态。这在人类进化过程中是一个重大事件，这样就将人类的双手解放出来用以制造工具，并最终导致更加复杂精细的人类活动。此外，由稍晚但相关的来自埃塞俄比亚阿法尔的人科动物化石的部分颅骨（时间在距今 260 万到 300 万年间）提供的证据表明，两足行走的意义胜过人类脑容量的扩增。由于这个问题在很长时间内都是思考和争论的主题，所以解决这个问题是研究人类进化的重要步骤。

尽管解放出的双手可以用于非行走的目的，但或许出乎意料的是还没有发现任何形式的人工制品。制造工具的想法可能已经完全超过了这些小型脑量生物的智力水平。（这些人科动物）使用过的任何"工具"或武器肯定是完全用易腐材料制成的，因为在莱托利尔层中不仅缺乏人工制品，而且除火山喷出物外也没有其他石头。

遗址的进一步勘探和材料的分析将持续到 1979 年，但莱托里显然将为认识上新世人科动物的生存环境提供独特的视角。

感谢坦桑尼亚联合共和国允许我们继续在莱托里地区从事研究，感谢国家地理学会、华盛顿政府的经济支持，感谢坦桑尼亚文物部主管姆图里和管理员姆吉纳，感谢恩戈罗恩戈罗自然保护区管理局的帮助，感谢菲利普·利基和彼得·琼斯组织的野外季，感谢金特里博士、哈里斯和利基帮助鉴定牛科、长颈鹿科、灵长类动物和食肉动物的化石，感谢所有参加野外考察的人员。

（张玉光 翻译；董为 审稿）

# 0957+561 A, B: Twin Quasistellar Objects or Gravitational Lens?

D. Walsh *et al.*

## Editor's Note

Within the framework of general relativity, space is curved by the presence of mass. It was realized in the 1920s and 1930s that this implies that light from distant galaxies may be bent by intervening mass into a ring, or that the distortion could produce several images of the same galaxy—an effect called gravitational lensing. Here Dennis Walsh at Jodrell Bank in England and his coworkers report the first such example. During a spectroscopic study of two blue star-like objects separated by about 6 arcseconds, they realized that the objects were quasars with essentially identical spectra. They concluded that they might be seeing the effect of gravitational lensing by an intervening galaxy. Many such cases are now known.

---

0957+561 A, B are two QSOs of mag 17 with 5.7 arc s separation at redshift 1.405. Their spectra leave little doubt that they are associated. Difficulties arise in describing them as two distinct objects and the possibility that they are two images of the same object formed by a gravitational lens is discussed.

---

SPECTROSCOPIC observations have been in progress for several years on QSO candidates using a survey of radio sources made at 966 MHz with the MkIA telescope at Jodrell Bank. Many of the identifications have been published by Cohen *et al.*[1] with interferometric positions accurate to ~2 arc s and a further list has been prepared by Porcas *et al.*[2]. The latter list consists of sources that were either too extended or too confused for accurate interferometric positions to be measured, and these were observed with the pencil-beam of the 300 ft telescope at NRAO, Green Bank at $\lambda$ 6 cm and $\lambda$ 11 cm. This gave positions with typical accuracy 5-10 arc s and the identifications are estimated as ~80% reliable.

The list of Porcas *et al.* includes the source 0957+561 which has within its field a close pair of blue stellar objects, separated by ~6 arc s, which are suggested as candidate identifications. Their positions and red and blue magnitudes, $m_R$ and $m_B$, estimated from the Palomar Observatory Sky Survey (POSS) are given in Table 1 and a finding chart is given in Fig. 1. Since the images on the POSS overlap, the magnitude estimates may be of lower accuracy than normal, but they are very nearly equal and object A is definitely bluer than object B. The mean position of the two objects is 17 arc s from the radio position, so the identification is necessarily tentative.

# 0957+561A、B：双类星体还是引力透镜？

在广义相对论框架下，空间由于质量的存在而弯曲。在二十世纪二三十年代，人们意识到，这意味着来自遥远星系的光可能会被处于中间的质量扭曲成一个环，或者这种扭曲会使同一个星系产生多个像——这被称为引力透镜效应。本文中英格兰焦德雷尔班克天文台的丹尼斯·沃尔什和他的同事们报告了第一个这样的例子。在对两个相距6角秒的蓝色恒星状天体的光谱研究中，他们意识到这两个天体是具有本质上完全相同光谱的类星体。他们由此得出结论，他们可能看到了由中间星系形成的引力透镜效应。现在我们已经知道了很多这种例子。

---

0957+561A、B 是两颗 17 等、红移 1.405、相距 5.7 arc s 的类星体。从它们的光谱上可以毫无疑问地看出两者是相关联的。将它们描述为两个不同的天体存在一定困难，本文将讨论它们由同一个天体在引力透镜效应下形成两个像的可能性。

---

焦德雷尔班克天文台的 MkIA 望远镜在 966 MHz 对射电源进行过巡天，近年来对类星体候选体的分光观测在不断发展。许多得到证认的天体已经由科恩等人[1]发表，其干涉测量的位置精确到约 2 arc s，波卡斯等人[2]已经准备了进一步的观测列表。后一个列表包括由于本身太过延展或者干涉测量位置不够精确的天体，这些天体是使用格林班克美国国家射电天文台口径 300 英尺的望远镜在波长 λ 为 6 cm 和 11 cm 上用笔型波束探测到的。它给出典型精度 5~10 arc s 的位置，而据估计这些被证认的天体约 80% 是可靠的。

波卡斯等人的列表中包括源 0957+561，在该源的区域内有一对密近的蓝色恒星状天体，两者距离约 6 arc s，它们被认为是类星体认证中的候选天体。它们的位置及红、蓝星等（$m_R$、$m_B$）都是由帕洛玛巡天 POSS 的结果估算给出的，列于表 1；图 1 给出了证认图。由于其图像位于帕洛玛巡天的重叠部分，所以估计所得星等精度可能低于正常情况，但两者仍非常接近，而且天体 A 肯定比天体 B 更蓝。两个天体距射电源的平均距离是 17 arc s，所以这个证认必然是尝试性的。

Table 1. Positions and magnitudes of 0957+561 A, B

| Object | RA | Dec (1950.0) | $M_R$ | $M_B$ |
|---|---|---|---|---|
| 0957+561A | 09 57 57.3 | +56 08 22.9 | 17.0 | 16.7 |
| 0957+561B | 09 57 57.4 | +56 08 16.9 | 17.0 | 17.0 |

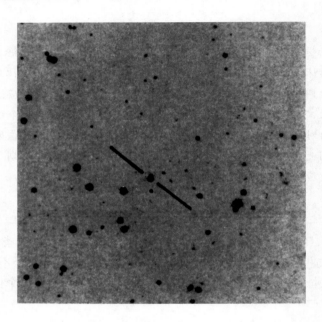

Fig. 1. Finding chart for the QSOs 0957+561 A and B. The chart is 8.5 arc min square with the top right hand corner north preceding and is from the E print of the POSS.

## Observations

The two objects 0957+561 A, B were observed on 29 March 1979 at the 2.1 m telescope of the Kitt Peak National Observatory (KPNO) using the intensified image dissector scanner (IIDS). Sky subtraction was used with circular apertures separated by 99.4 arc s. Some observational parameters are given in Table 2. The spectral range was divided into 1,024 data bins, each bin 3.5 Å wide, and the spectral resolution was 16 Å. After 20-min integration on each object it was clear that both were QSOs with almost identical spectra and redshifts of ~1.40 on the basis of strong emission lines identified as C IV λ1549 and C III] λ1909. Further observations were made on 29 March and on subsequent nights as detailed in Table 2. By offsetting to observe empty sky a few arc seconds from one object on both 29 and 30 March it was confirmed that any contamination of the spectrum of one object by light from the other was negligible. On 1 April the spectral range was altered slightly by tilting the grating to cover the anticipated redshifted wavelength of Mg II λ2798 which was just beyond the limiting wavelength on previous nights.

表 1. 0957+561A、B 的位置及星等

| 天体 | 赤经 | 赤纬（1950.0） | 红星等 | 蓝星等 |
|------|------|------|------|------|
| 0957+561A | 09 57 57.3 | +56 08 22.9 | 17.0 | 16.7 |
| 0957+561B | 09 57 57.4 | +56 08 16.9 | 17.0 | 17.0 |

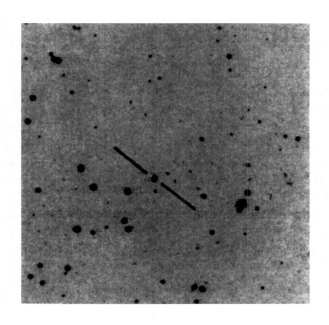

图 1. 类星体 0957+561A 和 B 的证认图。该图为 8.5（arc min）², 右上角方向为北，来自于帕洛玛巡天（POSS）中的 E 色图片。

## 观　测

0957+561A、B 两个天体是在 1979 年 3 月 29 日，由基特峰国家天文台（KPNO）的 2.1 m 望远镜观测的，所用的仪器是加强型析像扫描器（IIDS）。天光去除是用相距 99.4 arc s 的圆形光孔得到的。一些观测参数列于表 2。整个光谱范围被分成了 1024 个数据段，其中每段的宽度为 3.5 Å，光谱分辨率为 16 Å。在对每个天体积分 20 分钟后，可以明显看出两者是有着几乎相同光谱的类星体，基于被认证为 C Ⅳ λ1549 和 C Ⅲ] λ1909 的强发射线，可知红移大概是 1.40。进一步的观测在 3 月 29 日及之后的夜里进行，具体细节列于表 2。在 29 日和 30 日的晚上都对距离天体几角秒的无星天空进行了观测并作为校正，结果证实，一个天体对另外一个天体光谱产生的污染可以忽略不计。4 月 1 日，通过将光栅倾斜，光谱范围出现了细微的改变，以便覆盖预期 Mg Ⅱ λ2798 红移后的波长，这条谱线在之前的夜里刚好在波长极限之外。

Table 2. List of IIDS observations with 2.1 m telescope

| Date (1979) | Aperture (arc s) | Seeing (arc s) | Spectral range (Å) | Integration time, each object (min) |
|---|---|---|---|---|
| 29 March | 3.4 | 4 | 3,200–6,700 | 40 |
| 30 March | 1.8 | 1 | 3,200–6,700 | 20 |
| 1 April | 3.4 | 3 | 3,500–7,000 | 60 |

The spectra obtained on 1 April are shown in Fig. 2. Data on observed spectral lines are given in Table 3. These were taken from the spectra using the interactive picture processing system (IPPS) which makes a linear interpolation between two selected continuum points and calculates the centroid and equivalent width of the emission above the interpolated line. Data from all three nights were used in compiling Table 3; that on 1 April had double the signal-to-noise ratio of the other two nights and was weighted accordingly. The O IV] $\lambda$1402 line is outside the spectral range of Fig. 2 but was present in data taken on the other two nights. Although we believe that Mg II $\lambda$2798 is detected in the data of Fig. 2 for 0957+561B, and He II $\lambda$1640 is also detected taking into account all three nights' data, the low signal-to-noise ratio and poorly defined continuum prevent us deriving useful observed wavelengths or equivalent widths.

Table 3. Wavelengths, equivalent widths (EW) and derived redshifts from IIDS 2.1 m observations

| $\lambda_{em}$ | | O IV] 1402 | C IV 1549 | He II 1640 | C III] 1909 | Mg II 2798 |
|---|---|---|---|---|---|---|
| A | $\lambda_{obs}$(Å) | 3373 | 3729.5 | 3938 | 4584.5 | 6739 |
| | EW(Å) | 24 | 68 | 11 | 54 | 28 |
| | z(vacuum) | 1.407 | 1.4082 | 1.402 | 1.4026 | 1.409 |
| B | $\lambda_{obs}$(Å) | 3376 | 3728.7 | Present | 4582.6 | Present |
| | EW(Å) | 26 | 70 | — | 55 | — |
| | z(vacuum) | 1.409 | 1.4077 | — | 1.4016 | — |

The data on the C IV $\lambda$1549 and C III] $\lambda$1909 lines are much more accurate than those on the other lines and we believe the r.m.s. errors in the observed wavelengths of the centroids of these lines are not greater than 3 Å while the r.m.s. errors in the equivalent widths are estimated to be 7 Å. Within the limits of observational error, the corresponding lines in each object are identical in observed wavelength and equivalent width. For each object there is a difference in the redshift derived from the C IV and C III] lines which is significantly greater than the combined r.m.s. error in each. This may be associated with the problem of giving a precise meaning to the redshift of a broad line of somewhat

表 2. 2.1 m 望远镜的加强型析像扫描器（IIDS）观测结果列表

| 日期<br>（1979） | 孔径<br>（arc s） | 视宁度<br>（arc s） | 光谱范围<br>（Å） | 每个天体的积分时间<br>（min） |
|---|---|---|---|---|
| 3 月 29 日 | 3.4 | 4 | 3,200~6,700 | 40 |
| 3 月 30 日 | 1.8 | 1 | 3,200~6,700 | 20 |
| 4 月 1 日 | 3.4 | 3 | 3,500~7,000 | 60 |

图 2 中给出了 4 月 1 日得到的光谱。观测的谱线数据列于表 3。这些由光谱得到的数据使用交互式图像处理系统（IPPS）进行处理，该系统会对选定的连续两点进行线性插值，并计算该区域的中心及发射线高出插值线的等值宽度。三个夜晚的数据合并组成了表 3；其中 4 月 1 日的信噪比要比另外两天的信噪比高一倍，因此计算中进行了相应的加权。其中 O IV] λ1420 谱线在图 2 的光谱区域外，但却出现在了另外两个晚上得到的数据中。尽管我们相信，在图 2 的 0957+561B 数据中探测到了 Mg II λ2798 谱线，并且也探测到了 He II λ1640 谱线 ( 考虑三个晚上的数据 )，但是较低的信噪比及难以确定的连续谱使我们无法得到有用的观测波长或等值宽度。

表 3. 由 2.1 m 望远镜加强型析像扫描器所得波长、等值宽度 (EW) 及推算出的红移

| $\lambda_{em}$ | | O IV]<br>1402 | C IV<br>1549 | He II<br>1640 | C III]<br>1909 | Mg II<br>2798 |
|---|---|---|---|---|---|---|
| A | $\lambda_{obs}$ (Å) | 3373 | 3729.5 | 3938 | 4584.5 | 6739 |
| | EW (Å) | 24 | 68 | 11 | 54 | 28 |
| | $z$ (真空) | 1.407 | 1.4082 | 1.402 | 1.4026 | 1.409 |
| B | $\lambda_{obs}$ (Å) | 3376 | 3728.7 | 存在 | 4582.6 | 存在 |
| | EW (Å) | 26 | 70 | – | 55 | – |
| | $z$ (真空) | 1.409 | 1.4077 | – | 1.4016 | – |

C IVλ1549 和 C III] λ1909 谱线数据比其它谱线数据精确很多，我们相信这些谱线中心观测波长的均方根误差不会大于 3Å，同时等值宽度的均方根误差估计为 7Å。在观测误差范围内，每个天体相对应谱线的观测波长和等值宽度相同。每个天体由 C IV 和 C III] 谱线得出的红移值有所不同，这种差别比它们各自的综合均方根误差大很多。这可能与精确测量一条不规则宽线的红移会存在问题有关。由 CIV 和 C III] 发射线得到的红移平均值对 A 是 1.4054，对 B 是 1.4047，这个差别在测量误

irregular shape. The mean values of the redshift from the C IV and C III] emission lines are 1.4054 for A and 1.4047 for B, the difference being within the errors of measurement.

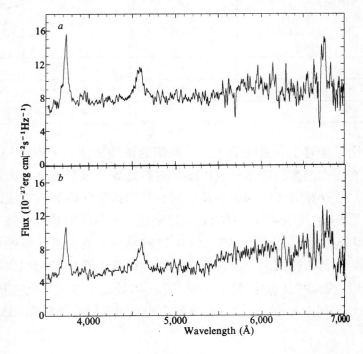

Fig. 2. IIDS scans of 0957+561 A(*a*) and B(*b*). The data are smoothed over 10 Å and the spectral resolution is 16 Å.

Although no attempt was made to carry out accurate spectrophotometry, some characteristics of the continua seem fairly well defined. Below about 5,300 Å they appear to have identical shapes, with QSO A brighter than B by 0.35 mag. Above 5,300 Å, however, the flux from B rises more steeply than that from A and they are equal at ~6,500 Å. These results are consistent with the magnitude estimates of Table 1.

The pair of QSOs provides unusual opportunity to investigate the origin of absorption lines in QSO spectra, a matter which is still in dispute. Accordingly, spectra having a resolution of about 2 Å were obtained of both QSOs on 30 March using the image tube spectrograph attached to the University of Arizona 2.3 m telescope. As in the observations described above, the seeing during the observations was sufficiently good for contamination of the spectrum of one QSO by the light from the other to be negligible. A portion of the tracings of the two plates covering the C IV emission line region is shown in Fig. 3. The absorption lines which have been identified are indicated on the figure, and the measured wavelengths (using a Grant measuring engine) are presented in Table 4, with the corresponding redshifts. The wavelengths of the C IV emission lines given in Table 4 were measured from the tracings by smoothing over the noise and finding the centre of symmetry for each line. Comparison with Table 3 shows that the agreement in wavelength for the C IV emission lines between the two sets of observations is within the errors of measurement.

892

差范围内。

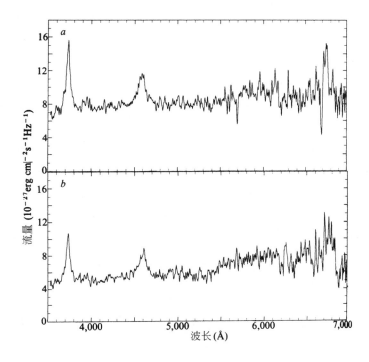

图 2．加强型析像扫描器对类星体 0957+561 A（*a*）、B（*b*）的扫描结果。这些数据以 10 Å 进行平滑，
光谱的分辨率为 16 Å。

尽管没有尝试进行精确的分光光度测量，但是一些连续谱的特征看起来还是相当清楚的。在大约 5,300 Å 之内两者有着相同的形状，类星体 A 比 B 亮 0.35 个星等；然而在 5,300 Å 之外，B 的流量比 A 的流量增加更快，在约 6,500 Å 处二者相等。这些结果与表 1 中的星等估计值相吻合。

这对类星体为研究类星体光谱中吸收线的起源提供了不同寻常的机会，这是个仍有争议的问题。相应地，在 3 月 30 日使用连接在亚利桑那大学 2.3 m 望远镜上的显像管摄谱仪得到了这两个类星体的分辨率大约为 2 Å 的光谱。与以上描述的观测情况一样，观测期间大气视宁度足够好，一个天体的光谱受到另外一个天体的光的污染可以忽略。图 3 中给出了这两个底片中覆盖了 C IV 发射线区域的光谱。已经被认证的吸收线在图中标出，观测所得波长（使用格兰特测量引擎）及相对应的红移值列于表 4。表 4 中列出的 C IV 发射线波长值是根据光谱对噪声进行平滑处理并确定了每条谱线的对称中心后得到的。和表 3 比较可以看出，在测量误差内，两组观测中所得的 C IV 发射线的波长一致。

Table 4. Wavelengths, identifications, and derived redshifts from image-tube spectra, 2.3 m observations

| Object | 0957+561A | | 0957+561B | |
|---|---|---|---|---|
| Identification | $\lambda_{air}$ | $z$ (vacuum) | $\lambda_{air}$ | $z$ (vacuum) |
| — | 3536.4 | — | — | — |
| Si II 1526 | 3648.2 | 1.3903 | (defect) | |
| C IV 1548 | 3699.9 | 1.3905 | 3700.1 | 1.3906 |
| C IV 1550 | 3705.9 | 1.3904 | 3707.4: | 1.3914: |
| C IV 1549(em) | 3728.9: | 1.4078: | 3732.2: | 1.4100: |
| — | 3835.1 | — | — | — |
| Fe II 1608 | 3844.0 | 1.3905 | — | — |
| Al II 1670 | 3992.9 | 1.3905 | 3993.6 | 1.3909 |

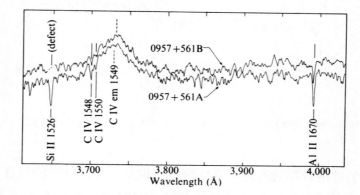

Fig. 3. Microdensitometer tracings of portions of the spectra of 0957+561 A and B. Original dispersion of the plates was 47 Å mm⁻¹. The solid lines mark the position of absorption features in the two QSOs and the dashed lines mark the adopted centres of the C IV emission line.

Low ionisation absorption systems (ones with Si II and Al II strengths > C IV strengths) are clearly present at $z_{abs} = 1.390$ in both QSOs. Even in the low resolution IIDS spectrum of QSO A there is clear evidence for Fe II $\lambda 2383$ and Mg II $\lambda 2798$ absorption. Fe II $\lambda\lambda 2600$ and 2344 are possibly also present. Weak and possibly real absorption lines also appear in the image tube spectrum at $\lambda 3536.1$ and $\lambda 3835.1$ of QSO A. The features at $\lambda 3835.1$ and $\lambda 3844.0$ have a separation close to that of the Mg II doublet (at redshift 0.372). However, $\lambda 3844$ is already identified with Fe II $\lambda 1608$ in the 1.390 system so that the evidence for Mg II at 0.372 is not convincing. In QSO B, the absorption lines seem to be weaker than in QSO A on the basis of both the plate and IIDS data and none are seen in the low resolution spectrum. Unfortunately, a dust speck on the mask used to suppress image tube noise obliterated the Si II line in the spectrum of this object.

表 4. 由 2.3 m 望远镜观测得到的波长、证认结果及由图像管光谱计算得出的红移值

| 天体 | 0957+561A | | 0957+561B | |
| --- | --- | --- | --- | --- |
| 证认结果 | $\lambda_{air}$ | $z$（真空） | $\lambda_{air}$ | $z$（真空） |
| — | 3536.4 | — | — | — |
| Si II 1526 | 3648.2 | 1.3903 | （坏点） | |
| C IV 1548 | 3699.9 | 1.3905 | 3700.1 | 1.3906 |
| C IV 1550 | 3705.9 | 1.3904 | 3707.4: | 1.3914: |
| C IV 1549（发射） | 3728.9: | 1.4078: | 3732.2: | 1.4100: |
| — | 3835.1 | — | — | — |
| Fe II 1608 | 3844.0 | 1.3905 | — | — |
| Al II 1670 | 3992.9 | 1.3905 | 3993.6 | 1.3909 |

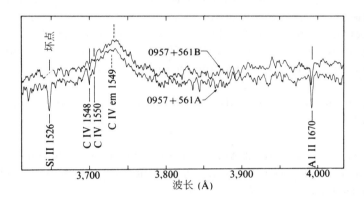

图 3．用显微光密度计对 0957+561A 和 B 测得的光谱中的部分光谱轮廓。各底片原始的色散为 47 Å·mm$^{-1}$。实线标记了两个类星体的吸收线中特征谱线所在位置，虚线标记了所采用的 C IV 发射线的中心位置。

在 $z_{abs}$=1.390 处，两个类星体中都明显地出现了低电离吸收系统（其中 Si II 和 Al II 谱线的强度 > C IV 谱线的强度）。即使在类星体 A 的低分辨率加强型析像扫描器（IIDS）光谱中，也可明显发现 Fe II λ2383 和 Mg II λ2798 吸收线存在的证据。Fe II λλ2600 和 2344 也有可能存在。微弱但可能是真实的吸收线也出现在了从类星体 A 的显像管摄谱仪光谱中 λ3536.1 和 λ3835.1 处。在 λ3835.1 和 λ3844.0 处的谱线间距和 Mg II 双线间距（红移为 0.372）接近。然而在 $z_{abs}$=1.390 的系统中已经将 λ3844 证认为 Fe II λ1608，所以在红移 0.372 处的 Mg II 的证据也变得不可信了。无论是从底片还是从加强型析像扫描器数据都可以看出，类星体 B 中的吸收线都要比类星体 A 的吸收线弱；在较低分辨率的光谱中没有看到这些吸收线。遗憾的是，在遮罩上原本用来限制显像管噪声的灰尘斑点，使该天体光谱中的 Si II 谱线彻底消失了。

The difference between the two absorption redshifts amounts to a velocity difference $\Delta V_{abs} (B - A)$ of only about +45 km s$^{-1}$. However, in addition to the errors in estimating the line centres, somewhat larger errors occur in the zero point of the wavelength scales from plate to plate amounting typically to 100 km s$^{-1}$. As a result the difference between the absorption line redshifts in QSO A and QSO B cannot be considered significant.

The image tube data on the C IV emission lines give a velocity difference $\Delta V_{em}(B - A)$ of +265 km s$^{-1}$. This is also subject to the zero point error, but the major source of error is the uncertainty of ~1.5 Å (=120 km s$^{-1}$) in estimating the position of each line centre. The IIDS data on the C IV and C III] lines permit two independent estimates of the velocity difference leading to a mean $\Delta V_{em}(B - A) = -95$ km s$^{-1}$ with an error slightly larger than for the image tube data. Combining both sets of data, the resulting $\Delta V_{em} (B - A)$ is +120± 150 km s$^{-1}$. Again, the difference between the emission redshifts in the two QSOs cannot be considered significant.

The differences $z_{em}-z_{abs}$ for each QSO based on Table 4 are not affected by the zero point error. They correspond to relative velocities of 2,170 km s$^{-1}$ and 2,400 km s$^{-1}$ for A and B respectively. The relative velocities each have an error of ~120 km s$^{-1}$ due to the uncertainty in the emission line centres. Thus the difference in relative velocities of 230 km s$^{-1}$ seems somewhat larger than the measuring error.

Therefore, either the absorption redshifts, or the emission redshifts may be equal, but possibly not both.

Finally, a plate was obtained on 2 April with the University of Arizona 1.5 m telescope. The seeing was relatively poor (~2.5 arc s), but the two images were well resolved and their measured separation was 5.7 arc s.

## Discussion

The great similarity in the spectral characteristics of these two QSOs which have the same redshift and which are separated by only 6 arc s seems to constitute overwhelming evidence that the two are physically associated, regardless of the nature of their redshifts, and we do not think that a useful *a posteriori* statistical test of this assertion can be carried out. In the rest of the discussion, however, we shall assume the QSO redshifts are cosmological. The same similarities further suggest that we may be dealing with a single source which has been split into two images by a gravitational lens. We shall consider this possibility after examining the more conventional explanation involving two distinct QSOs.

In the conventional interpretation of two adjacent QSOs we must either regard it as a coincidence that the emission spectra are so nearly the same, or assume that the initial conditions, age and environment influencing the development of the QSOs have been so similar that they have evolved nearly identically. For $q_0=0$ and $H_0=50$ km s$^{-1}$ Mpc$^{-1}$

两条吸收线红移值之差对应的速度差 $\Delta V_{abs}(B-A)$ 仅有大约 $+45\ km\cdot s^{-1}$。然而，除了在估计这些谱线中心时的误差外，在某种程度上各底片之间确定波长的零点也会产生更大的误差，其典型量级为 $100\ km\cdot s^{-1}$。因此类星体 A 和 B 中吸收线对应的红移之差并不显著。

C IV 发射线的显像管数据给出的速度差 $\Delta V_{em}(B-A)$ 为 $+265\ km\cdot s^{-1}$。这也与零点确定的误差相关，但误差的主要来源是在估计每条谱线中心位置时的不确定性，大约为 1.5 Å（$=120\ km\cdot s^{-1}$）。根据加强型析像扫描器对 C IV 和 C III] 光谱线给出的数据，可以产生两个独立的速度差估计值，两者给出的平均值为 $\Delta V_{em}(B-A)=-95\ km\cdot s^{-1}$，这个结果的误差要比显像管数据的误差稍微大一些。结合两组观测数据得到，$\Delta V_{em}(B-A)=+120\pm150\ km\cdot s^{-1}$。因此，这两个类星体存在的发射线红移之差也不显著。

基于表 4 的每个类星体的差值 $z_{em}-z_{abs}$ 不受零点误差影响。它们对应于类星体 A 和 B 的相对速度分别为 $2,170\ km\cdot s^{-1}$、$2,400\ km\cdot s^{-1}$。由于在确定发射线中心时的不确定，每个相对速度都存在大约 $120\ km\cdot s^{-1}$ 的误差。因此相对速度 $230\ km\cdot s^{-1}$ 的差值看起来要比测量误差大。

因此，两个天体的吸收线对应的红移值或者发射线对应的红移值有可能会相等，但可能不会都相等。

最后，我们使用亚利桑那大学口径 1.5 m 的望远镜在 4 月 2 日获得了一张底片。其大气视宁度相对较差（约 2.5 arc s），但两个星像很好地被区别开了，测得它们之间的距离为 5.7 arc s。

## 讨　论

这两个有着相同红移值且间距只有 6 arc s 的类星体在光谱上的巨大相似性成了两个天体有物理联系的压倒性证据，不管它们红移的本质是什么。我们认为没有一种归纳性的统计检验能有效地予以解释。然而在接下来的讨论中，我们将假设类星体的红移是宇宙学红移。同样的相似之处进一步表明，我们处理的可能是一个射电源，由于引力透镜而分裂为两个像。在检验更传统的涉及两个分开的类星体的解释之后，我们将考虑这个可能性。

在两个相邻类星体的传统解释中，我们必须把发射线如此近乎相同看作是巧合，或者假设两者的初始条件、年龄及影响演化的环境非常相似，导致两者的演化几乎相同。对于 $q_0=0$、$H_0=50\ km\cdot s^{-1}\cdot Mpc^{-1}$，对应 $\theta=5.7$ arc s 的投影线距离为 68.5 kpc。

the projected linear separation corresponding to $\theta = 5.7$ arc s is 68.5 kpc. The difference between emission line velocities is well within the dispersion in velocities found by Stockton[3] between QSOs and associated galaxies, and the masses implied by orbital motion are of the order of $10^{11} M_\odot$ (because of the errors in $\Delta V$, this is more like an upper limit).

The conventional interpretation of the sources as two QSOs requires additional coincidences to explain the absorption line systems regardless of the mechanism invoked to explain the absorption. Weymann *et al.*[4] have described three classes into which absorption systems found in QSOs in this redshift range may be placed. The first class involves ejection of material from the QSO. If the ejection of the two systems were caused by the two QSOs separately it would be an additional coincidence that the ejection velocities were so similar. If the lines arose from radial ejection by one of the QSOs, then the nearly identical redshift of the two absorption systems (the difference between which we take to be $\leq 150$ km s$^{-1}$) requires a rather small angle between the direction of motion of the ejected cloud and the line of sight to the second QSO against which the cloud is projected. This implies a distance of the ejected material from the ejecting QSO of $\sim 185$ kpc. This in turn implies exceedingly large masses and energies for the ejected material for reasonable covering factors. This argument is very similar to that made by Wolfe *et al.*[5] for the 21 cm absorption in 3C286.

The second class of absorption involves intervening clouds associated with a cluster in which the QSOs are embedded. The velocity differences between the emission and absorption systems of A, B are typical of this class, but we must either ascribe the agreement in redshift of the two absorption systems to chance or assume that the two absorption systems are part of a common halo associated with a galaxy in the same cluster. An unusual feature if this last alternative is true is that the ionisation state is very low for this class. In the survey of Weymann *et al.* only one of about 20 absorption systems was a low ionisation system similar to those in A, B. The third class of absorption involves cosmologically distant intervening material. Neither the agreement in redshift of the systems in A and B nor their low ionization is then especially remarkable, but we must then ascribe to chance the fact that the intervening material happens to be at a redshift so near to the emission redshift.

We now consider the possibility that a gravitational lens is operating. The theory of gravitational imaging in a cosmological context has been considered elsewhere (see ref. 6 and refs therein) and we simply quote the main results of applying this theory. The following are the relevant parameters involved in considering the gravitational lens hypothesis: the angular separation of the images, the shape of the images and their sizes, and the amplification of the two images. There is no evidence on the plate taken on 2 April or on the POSS for any departure of the images from stellar images. The magnitude difference between A and B (Table 1) is $\sim 0.3$. mag and this is confirmed by our observations.

发射线速度差是在斯托克顿[3] 得到的类星体和寄主星系速度弥散的范围之内的，由轨道运动对应得到的质量在 $10^{11} M_\odot$ 的量级上（由于存在 $\Delta V$ 的误差，所以这更像一个上限）。

就算不考虑用于解释吸收的机制，将这些源看作两个类星体的传统解释也要求额外的巧合事件来解释吸收线系统。魏曼等人[4] 对这个红移范围内类星体可能的吸收系统提出了三种情况。第一种情况涉及类星体中的物质喷射。如果这两个系统中的喷射是由这两个类星体分别造成的，那么喷射速度如此相似将是一个额外的巧合。如果这些光谱是由其中的一个类星体的径向喷射产生的，则对于这样两个红移很接近的吸收线系统（这两个系统差值我们设定为 $\leq 150 \ \mathrm{km \cdot s^{-1}}$）需要满足：喷射云的运动方向和第二个类星体的视线方向只存在一个很小的夹角，喷射云对着它运动。这表明被喷射物质和喷出物质的类星体的距离约是 185 kpc。这反过来表明，对于合理的覆盖因子，喷射物质有极大的质量和能量。这个论据和沃尔夫等人[5] 由 3C286 中的 21 cm 吸收线提出的观点很接近。

第二类吸收涉及类星体所在的星系团内的中间云。在这种情况中，类星体 A 和 B 的吸收线和发射线系统存在典型速度差，但我们不得不将两个吸收线系统红移的一致性归因于巧合，或者假设这两个吸收线系统是来自同一个星系团中的同一个星系晕。如果是后一种情况，那么将会有一个非常罕见的特征，即对于这类情况而言电离态非常低。在魏曼等人的巡天中，在大约二十个吸收线系统中只有一个系统是和类星体 A、B 类似的低电离系统。第三类吸收系统的情况涉及了宇宙学距离的中间物质。A 和 B 中红移的一致性以及它们较低的电离度都不是特别值得注意的，但是我们必须将中间物质红移碰巧处于和发射线十分接近的位置归为巧合。

我们现在考虑引力透镜效应发生的可能性。在宇宙学框架内引力透镜成像理论在很多地方被考虑过（见参考文献 6 以及其参考文献），在此我们只是简单引用这个理论的主要结论。以下是在考虑引力透镜假说中涉及的相关参数：像的角分离、像的形状和它们的大小以及这两个像的放大率。在 4 月 2 日得到的底片或者帕洛玛巡天（POSS）得到的观测结果中都没有证据显示图像偏离恒星图像。类星体 A 和 B 的星等差值（表 1）约为 0.3 星等，这已经被我们的观测所证实。

The 0.3 mag difference between the two components requires that the amplification of QSO light is ~4 for the brighter image, and thus implies a normal luminosity for the QSO. (This is also suggested by the absence of a strong narrow component in the C IV emission which might be expected if the source were a strongly amplified Seyfert nucleus.) The maximum angular size of the lens is only ~8 times that of the object, so we should not expect to resolve it on the sky.[6]

If the matter responsible for the gravitational imaging is far from the QSO, then, from simple euclidean space calculations we estimate that at redshift $z_L$ its mass must be ~$10^{13} z_L M_\odot$, and require that it be contained in a radius $\lesssim 30$ kpc. If a galaxy is the cause, then a lower limit of $z_L \sim 0.1$ is likely from its absence on our plate material. However, the centre of such a galaxy must be within ~0.5 arc s of the direct line between the QSO and the observer. The chance of finding such an alignment with a massive elliptical galaxy obtained by folding in our mass requirement with Schechter's[7] luminosity function (with a mass-to-light ratio of 30) is roughly $10^{-5}$, although the precise number depends quite strongly on the magnitude differences and angular separations allowed. Thus, while such coincidences must be very rare, it is not out of the question that we should have one example in the ~1,000 QSOs known.

An apparent objection arises from the difference in the shapes of the continua between the two QSOs. It is possible that differential reddening along the two light paths may be responsible. Note that the observed break at 5,300 Å corresponds to an emitted wavelength of 2,200 Å in the rest system of the QSOs. This is the wavelength of a well known resonance in interstellar extinction by dust in our Galaxy, and a model can be constructed to explain the observed continuum ratio incorporating the 2,200 Å feature at the redshift of the QSOs. This would imply that the intrinsic flux from B exceeds that from A.

Further observations would shed light on the gravitational lens hypothesis. If the flux from the object is variable, the light curves of the two images should be similar but with a relative time delay due to the difference in path lengths. The lag depends on the details of the geometry, but with the parameters discussed above would be expected to be of the order of months to years. Determination of the radio structure would also clearly be of great value.

We thank S. Tapia and Barbara Schaefer for technical assistance, Geoff Burbidge for his comments, and the KPNO staff for their help. R. F. C. thanks the SRC for support and R. J. W. acknowledges support from NSF grant AST 77-23055. D. W. and R. F. C. are visiting astronomers, Kitt Peak National Observatory, which is operated by the Association of Universities for Research in Astronomy, Inc., under contract with the NSF.

Since submission of this article we have heard that on 19, 20, and 21 April the two QSOs were observed by N. Carleton, F. Chaffee and M. Davis (of the Smithsonian Astrophysical Observatory) and R. J. W. using the SAO photon-counting reticon spectrograph attached to the SAO–UA multiple mirror telescope. The observations covered the range 5,900–

对更明亮的像来说，两个部分之间 0.3 个星等的差要求类星体的光增强约 4 倍，这表明该类星体的光度是正常的。（如果这个射电源是一个强烈放大的塞弗特活动星系核，在 CIV 发射谱中可能会出现一个强而窄的发射线。）由于引力透镜的最大角度只有天体分开角度的 8 倍左右，所以我们不能期待天空中会有这种图像 [6]。

由简单的欧氏空间计算，如果造成引力透镜成像的物质远离类星体，那么我们估计在红移 $z_L$ 处其质量必须达到大约 $10^{13} z_L M_\odot$，并且要求其半径 $\lesssim$ 30 kpc。假设存在一个这样的星系，鉴于它在底片上毫无显示，可以得出 $z_L$ 的下限大约是 0.1。然而，这样一个星系的中心必须处于从观测者到类星体之间直线角度的 0.5 arc s 左右以内。既要保证与这样一个大质量椭圆星系排成一线，又要满足我们根据谢克特 [7] 光度函数（其中质光比为 30）给出的质量要求，概率大约是 $10^{-5}$，不过具体数字强烈依赖于容许的星等差和角距。因此，尽管这样的巧合必然非常少见，但我们还是有可能在大约 1,000 个已知的类星体中找到一个例子。

一个明显的反驳来自两个类星体连续谱形状的不同。这有可能是因为两者光线路径有不同的红化。请注意，在波长 5,300 Å 观测到的中断在类星体静止系统中对应于波长 2,200 Å。这是我们银河系中由于尘埃的星际消光形成的一条著名谱线，可以建立一个模型，解释观测到的类星体红移处包括 2,200 Å 特征的连续谱比值。这可能暗示着类星体 B 的内禀流量超过类星体 A。

进一步的观测将辨明引力透镜假设。如果来自天体的流量随时间变化，那么由于路径长度的差异，这两个图像的光变曲线应该相似但是存在一个相对的时间延迟。延迟依赖于几何细节，但是以上文讨论的参数可以预计是几个月到几年的量级。显然射电结构的测定也具有巨大的价值。

我们感谢塔皮亚和芭芭拉·谢弗给予技术支持，杰夫·伯比奇给出了宝贵意见，以及美国基特峰国家天文台全体工作人员的帮助。卡斯韦尔感谢科学研究理事会给予的支持，魏曼感谢国家科学基金会基金 AST 77-23055 的资助。沃尔什和卡斯韦尔是访问天文学家，基特峰国家天文台是与国家科学基金会签约、由大学天文研究协会联合运行的。

自提交本文以来，我们了解到，在 4 月 19 日、20 日和 21 日卡尔顿、查菲和戴维斯（于史密森天体物理台）观测了这两个类星体；魏曼使用了安装在 SAO-UA 的多镜面望远镜上的 SAO 光子计数摄谱仪对它们进行了观测。此次观测覆盖的波长范围从

7,100 Å with a resolution of 4 Å FWHM. Details will be reported elsewhere, but the main results are: (1) to within the measuring errors the Mg II emission lines have the same profiles and observed equivalent widths (85 and 76±12 Å for A and B respectively) and the same redshift (1.4136±0.0015 for both). (2) Absorption lines due to Fe II λλ2586, 2599, Mg II λλ2795, 2802 and Mg I λ2852 are present in both objects but are somewhat stronger in A. The mean heliocentric redshifts of the two absorption systems are 1.3915 for A and 1.3914 for B. A cross-correlation analysis confirms that the difference in the two adsorption redshifts is remarkably small and corresponds to a velocity difference of 7±10 km s$^{-1}$. These observations strengthen the case for a gravitational lens.

(**279**, 381-384;1979)

**D. Walsh**[*], **R. F. Carswell**[†] **and R. J. Weymann**[‡]

[*] University of Manchester, Nuffield Radio Astronomy Laboratories, Jodrell Bank, Macclesfield, Cheshire, UK

[†] Institute of Astronomy, Cambridge, UK

[‡] Steward Observatory, University of Arizona, Tucson, Arizona 85721

Received 25 April; accepted 8 May 1979.

References:

1. Cohen, A. M., Porcas, R. W., Browne, I. W. A., Daintree, E. J. & Walsh, D. *Mem. R. astr. Soc.* **84**, 1 (1977)

2. Porcas, R. W. *et al. Mon. Not. R. astr. Soc.* (submitted).

3. Stockton, A. N. *Astrophys. J.* **223**, 747 (1978).

4. Weymann, R. J., Williams, R. E., Peterson, B. M. & Turnshek, D. A. *Astrophys, J.* (submitted).

5. Wolfe, A. M., Broderick, J. J., Condon, J. J. & Johnston, K. J. *Astrophys. J. Lett.* **208**, L47 (1976).

6. Sanitt, N. *Nature* **234**, 199 (1971).

7. Schechter, P. *Astrophys. J.* **203**, 297 (1976).

5,900 Å 到 7,100 Å，分辨率为半峰全宽 4 Å。细节将在他处报道，但是主要结果如下：（1）在测量误差以内，Mg II 发射线有相同的谱线轮廓和观测等值宽度（类星体 A、B 分别对应为 85 Å 和 76±12 Å）以及相同的红移（两者都是 1.4136±0.0015）。（2）Fe II λλ2586、2599，Mg II λλ2795、2802 和 Mg I λ2852 的吸收线存在于两个天体中，但类星体 A 中更强。两组吸收系统的日心平均红移分别为 1.3915（A）和 1.3914（B）。交叉相关分析确认，这两个吸收线红移之差非常小，对应于速度差 7±10 km · s⁻¹。这些观测结果进一步强化了引力透镜观点。

（冯翀 翻译；何香涛 审稿）

# Single Strands Induce recA Protein to Unwind Duplex DNA for Homologous Pairing

R. P. Cunningham *et al.*

## Editor's Note

Homologous recombination, where genes swap over between DNA strands, plays a key role in generating genetic diversity and repairing DNA damage. Here biochemist Charles M. Radding and colleagues elucidate the function of a key protein in the process, the bacterial enzyme recA. The paper describes how single DNA strands stimulate recA to unwind double-stranded DNA for homologous pairing. The mechanism has since been fine-tuned: it is now known that recA forms a helical filament with single-stranded DNA which then binds to double-stranded DNA and samples for homology. Once found, the filament causes an exchange of strands that yields recombined DNA. Given the ability of short DNA fragment to stimulate unwinding, Radding correctly speculates that recombination may be inducible.

Single-stranded DNA, whether homologous or not, stimulates purified *Escherichia coli* recA protein to unwind duplex DNA. This helps to explain how recA promotes a search for homology in genetic recombination. As oligodeoxynucleotides also stimulate unwinding, a common mechanism may relate the function of recA protein in recombination to other functions (SOS) induced by oligonucleotides.

BECAUSE breakage of DNA by various means stimulates general genetic recombination, some investigators have suggested that recombination begins with the interaction of a single strand with duplex DNA (see ref. 1 for review). As a model for this kind of interaction, Holloman *et al.*[2] and Beattie *et al.*[3] studied the uptake of homologous single strands by superhelical DNA [replicative form I (RFI) or form I], a reaction that produces a D-loop (see Fig. 1). By transfection of *Escherichia coli*, Holloman and C.M.R.[5] implicated the *recA* gene in the homologous interaction of a single-stranded fragment with superhelical DNA. More recently, Shibata *et al.*[4] observed that stoichiometric amounts of highly purified recA protein promoted the rapid formation of D-loops by superhelical DNA and homologous single-stranded fragments (Fig. 1).

The properties of the uncatalysed formation of D-loops, which occurred rapidly only at non-physiological temperatures, suggested that the rate was limited by the initial unstacking of a small number of base pairs in superhelical DNA[3]. As recA protein bypassed this rate-limiting step, we suggested that it acted in part by unstacking base pairs in duplex DNA. We also observed that a preparation of nicked circular DNA (form II) was one-third as active as superhelical DNA in forming complexes with single-stranded fragments[4]. Subsequently, we

904

# 单链DNA诱导recA蛋白解旋DNA以利于同源配对

坎宁安等

## 编者按

同源重组即基因在 DNA 分子之间的交换，在遗传多样性的产生和 DNA 损伤的修复方面具有关键的作用。本文中，生化学家查尔斯·雷丁和他的研究小组阐明了细菌来源的酶 recA 这一关键蛋白在此过程中的功能。本文描述了单链 DNA 是如何触发 recA 将双链 DNA 解旋以进行同源配对的。这一机制是精密可控的：已知 recA 可以和单链 DNA 形成一种螺旋细丝，然后这种单链 DNA 就可以和双链 DNA 结合并进行同源配对。这种结合一旦形成，这段单链就会导致链之间发生交换并产生重组 DNA。如果短的 DNA 片段具有触发解旋的作用，那么雷丁关于重组可能是被诱导的推测就是正确的。

无论是否同源，单链 DNA 都可以触发从大肠杆菌中纯化的 recA 蛋白解旋双链 DNA。这有助于解释 recA 蛋白是如何促进遗传重组中（DNA 的）同源配对的。由于寡脱氧核苷酸也可以触发 DNA 解旋，因此，这种共同的机制可能使 recA 蛋白在遗传重组中的功能与其他由寡核苷酸诱导的功能（如 SOS）建立联系。

由于各种各样的因素所导致的 DNA 链的断裂普遍会触发遗传重组，因此，一些研究人员认为重组起始于单链 DNA 与双链 DNA 的相互作用（见参考文献1）。作为研究此类相互作用的一种模型，霍洛曼等人[2]以及贝蒂等人[3]研究了同源单链 DNA 被超螺旋 DNA [I 复制型（RFI）或 I 型] 结合并形成 D 环（见图1）的过程。通过转染大肠杆菌，霍洛曼和雷丁[5]提出 recA 基因参与单链 DNA 片段与超螺旋 DNA 的同源相互作用。最近，柴田等人[4]观察到化学计量定量的高度纯化的 recA 蛋白可以促进超螺旋 DNA 和同源的单链 DNA 片段迅速形成 D 环（图1）。

非催化的 D 环的形成仅在非生理温度下迅速发生，表明其反应速率受超螺旋 DNA 少量碱基对的起始解离的限制[3]。由于 recA 蛋白不受这一限速步骤的影响，因此我们认为它在某种程度上通过解开双链 DNA 的配对碱基来发挥作用。我们还观察到，带切口的环状 DNA（II 型）在与单链 DNA 片段形成复合物时，其活性只有超螺旋 DNA 的三分之一[4]。接下来，我们证实了 II 型 DNA 是 recA 蛋白形成 D

have confirmed that form II DNA is a substrate for the formation of D-loops by recA protein (see below). The latter observation strengthened the inference that recA protein has an unstacking or unwinding activity, which is the subject of this article.

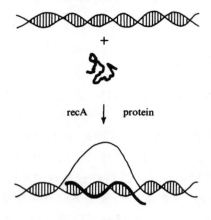

Fig. 1. The formation of a D-loop catalysed by recA protein[4]. The actions of recA protein apparently include (1) unwinding double-stranded DNA, (2) unfolding single-stranded DNA, (3) homologous pairing, and (4) uptake of a single strand rather than rewinding of the original duplex DNA.

## Unwinding of Duplex DNA by recA Protein in the Presence of ATPγS and Single Strands

To obtain direct evidence that recA protein unwinds DNA, we incubated it with fd form II DNA, added DNA ligase, and examined the product by gel electrophoresis and isopycnic centrifugation in CsCl plus propidium diiodide[6,7].

In the absence of recA protein, ligase sealed more than half of the form II DNA as indicated by gel electrophoresis (Fig. 2a, b) and by the assay of Kuhnlein et al.[8] for covalently closed DNA. At the ionic strength of the gel, these covalently closed molecules (form I') migrated as a set of bands of positively superhelical DNA, which overlapped a band due to linear DNA (form III) present in the preparation (Fig. 2b). When recA protein and adenosine 5'-O-(3-thiotriphosphate) (ATPγS) were incubated with form II DNA before ligation, the observed distribution of products was similar; ligase worked well but there was no apparent change in the average linking number of the population of sealed molecules (Fig. 2c). However, when we added fragments of single-stranded ΦX174 DNA during the incubation with recA protein, we observed a very different result. Ligase still closed about one-third to one-half of the fd form II DNA, but all the closed DNA migrated as a single band of more compact DNA, at about the position of form I (Fig. 2d). In three experiments, when recA protein and ATPγS were incubated with form II DNA in the absence of any added single-stranded DNA before ligation, we observed the formation of a small amount of material with the electrophoretic mobility of form I (see Table 1, lines 1 and 2). Controls included the following variations of the mixture represented in Fig. 2d: no recA protein; no form II DNA; no ATPγS; ATP in place of ATPγS; recA protein in the absence of ligase (Fig. 2a). In no case was DNA detected in the position of the rapidly

环时的一个底物（见下文）。这一观察结果进一步加强了关于 recA 蛋白具有解配对或解旋活性的推论，这也是本文的主题。

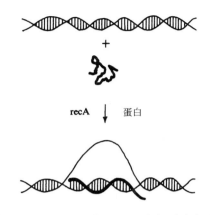

图 1. recA 蛋白催化 D 环的形成 [4]。recA 蛋白的作用显然包括：（1）促进双链 DNA 解旋；（2）促进单链 DNA 的伸展；（3）促进同源配对；（4）促进解旋的 DNA 链与单链结合，而不是促进原始双链 DNA 重新形成螺旋。

## 在 ATPγS 和单链 DNA 存在时 recA 蛋白促使双链 DNA 解旋

为了获得 recA 蛋白能够解旋 DNA 的直接证据，我们将 recA 蛋白与 fd II 型 DNA 共同孵育，并加入 DNA 连接酶进行反应，然后使用凝胶电泳和加入二碘化丙啶的 CsCl 等密度离心的方法来检测反应产物 [6,7]。

正如凝胶电泳的结果（图 2a 和 2b）所示，在没有 recA 蛋白存在时，DNA 连接酶可以将一半以上的 II 型 DNA 封闭。库恩莱因等人[8]关于共价闭合 DNA 的类似的实验进一步证实了这个结果。在凝胶的离子强度下，这些共价闭合的分子（I′型）在凝胶中以一系列正超螺旋 DNA 条带的形式迁移，且与样品中存在的一个线性 DNA（III 型）的条带重叠（图 2b）。如果把 recA 蛋白与硫代三磷酸腺苷（ATPγS）以及 II 型 DNA 在进行连接反应前共同孵育，也可以观察到相似的连接反应产物条带分布。此时连接酶可以正常工作，但是封闭分子的平均链环数似乎没有发生明显的改变（图 2c）。然而，当我们向 recA 蛋白与 DNA 的共同孵育体系中加入单链ΦX174 DNA 片段时，我们观察到了一个非常不同的结果。此时，连接酶仍然可以闭合 1/3~1/2 的 fd II 型 DNA，不过所有这些闭合的 DNA 在电泳实验中以包装更为紧密的 DNA 所对应的单独的一条条带进行迁移，并最终位于 I 型 DNA 大概所处的位置处（图 2d）。在三次实验中，当把 recA 蛋白、ATPγS 和 II 型 DNA 在进行连接反应前共同孵育并且不加入任何单链 DNA 的话，可以观察到形成了少量具有 I 型 DNA 电泳迁移率的物质（见表 1，第 1 和第 2 行）。我们设计了如下各种对照组（混合物成分见图 2d）：不含 recA 蛋白；不含 II 型 DNA；不含 ATPγS；ATP 代替 ATPγS；加入 recA 蛋白但不加连接酶（图 2a）。在这些对照试验中，快速泳动的条带处均检测不

migrating band.

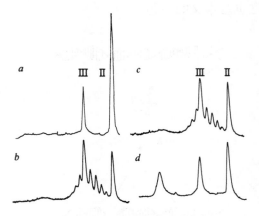

Fig. 2. The linking number of circular DNA sealed in the presence of recA protein and ATPγS (Boehringer-Mannheim). Microdensitometer tracings of electrophoretic gels prepared as described in Fig. 4, legend. *a*, Control, fd form II DNA incubated with recA protein but no ligase. The preparation of DNA contained about 30% form III DNA as indicated. *b*, Ligase only (New England BioLabs). *c*, Ligase plus recA protein. *d*, Ligase, recA protein and 12-μM fragments of heterologous single-stranded DNA from ΦX174. The various forms of circular DNA from phages ΦX174 and fd were prepared as cited previously[4]. Single-stranded fragments were prepared by boiling 840 μM DNA for 15 min in 0.1 mM EDTA and 10 mM Tris-HCl at *p*H7.5. All concentrations of DNA are expressed as mol of nucleotide. The reaction mixture was the same as that described in Table 2 legend, except that heterologous single-stranded fragments were substituted for homologous fragments, the volume was doubled and ATP was replaced by 0.5 mM ATPγS. After incubation at 37°C for 30 min, the mixture was chilled on ice, KCl, $(NH_4)_2SO_4$ and $NAD^+$ added to make their concentrations 25 mM, 10 mM, and 25 μM, respectively, and incubated at 18°C for 5 min. 0.3 units of *E. coli* DNA ligase were then added and the sample, 50 μl total volume, incubated for 90 min. The reaction was stopped by adding EDTA, 28 mM, and SDS, 0.17%. The sample was transferred to a bath at 37°C, proteinase K, 0.2 mg ml$^{-1}$ added and the sample incubated for 15 more minutes.

To determine whether the compact closed DNA had a lower or a higher linking number than the DNA closed by ligase alone (form I′), we centrifuged the products of a similar experiment in an isopycnic gradient of CsCl and propidium diiodide (Fig. 3 and Table 1). In the absence of recA protein, half of the recovered DNA was found in a single peak at the dense end of the gradient, as expected for form I′ DNA derived from the closure of form II by ligase (Fig. 3*b*, Table 1, line 1). Incubation of form II DNA with recA protein and ATPγS before ligation had little effect on the distribution (Fig. 3*a*, Table 1, line 2). However, when recA protein, fd form II DNA, ΦX174 single-stranded fragments and ATPγS were incubated before ligation, the peak of form I′ DNA at the dense end of the gradient disappeared almost entirely and was replaced by DNA with a broad distribution of densities between those of form I′ and linear or form II DNA (Fig. 3*a*, Table 1, line 3), that is, DNA with lower linking numbers than form I′. The peak of material of intermediate density corresponded to the position of negatively superhelical fd DNA (form I DNA). The total recovery of radioactivity was similar in the three parts of this experiment; the fraction of closed circular DNA relative to linear or form II DNA (Fig. 3*a*, Table 1, line 1) was the same as that estimated by the assay of Kuhnlein *et al.*[8], which indicates that the distribution of recovered material was not biased.

到 DNA。

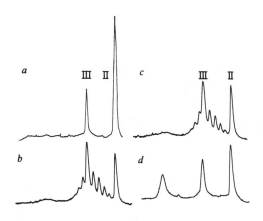

图 2. recA 蛋白和 ATPγS 存在条件下封闭的环状 DNA 的链环数（伯林格－曼海姆）。采用图 4 图注所述的方法制备凝胶电泳的显微密度计测定线。*a*，对照组，将 fdⅡ型 DNA 与 recA 蛋白共同孵育，但不加入连接酶。如图所示，样品中含有约 30% 的 Ⅲ 型 DNA。*b*，只含有连接酶（购自新英格兰生物实验室公司）。*c*，只含有连接酶和 recA 蛋白。*d*，含有连接酶，recA 蛋白以及 12 μM 来自 ΦX174 的异源单链 DNA 片段。采用前文所引用的方法 [4] 制备源于 ΦX174 噬菌体及 fd 噬菌体的各种形式的环状 DNA。将 840 μM 的 DNA 在含有 0.1 mM EDTA 和 10 mM pH 7.5 的 Tris-HCl 缓冲液中煮沸 15 分钟即可得到单链 DNA 片段。所有的 DNA 浓度都使用核苷酸的摩尔数来表示。反应体系与表 2 注中所描述的一致，只不过异源单链 DNA 片段被换成了同源 DNA 片段，溶液的体积也扩大了一倍，另外 ATP 被换成了 0.5 mM 的 ATPγS。在 37℃ 孵育 30 分钟后，将反应体系在冰上冷却，然后向其中加入 KCl、$(NH_4)_2SO_4$ 和 $NAD^+$ 使其终浓度分别为 25 mM、10 mM 和 25 μM。然后，在 18℃ 孵育 5 分钟。向样品中加入 0.3 U 的大肠杆菌连接酶，并将反应液总体积调整到 50 μl，孵育 90 分钟。向反应体系中加入 EDTA 和 SDS，至终浓度分别为 28 mM 和 0.17%，使反应终止。将产物转移到 37℃ 水浴中，加入 0.2 mg/ml 的蛋白酶 K，再孵育 15 分钟。

为了证明紧密闭合 DNA 的链环数比经连接酶闭合的 DNA（Ⅰ′型）低还是高，我们将一个类似实验的反应产物使用 CsCl 和二碘化丙啶进行了等密度梯度离心分离（图 3 和表 1）。当反应体系中没有 recA 蛋白时，约有一半回收的 DNA 在梯度的高密度区形成的一个单峰里，这与预期中的连接酶将 Ⅱ 型 DNA 闭合而形成 Ⅰ′型 DNA 的结果吻合（图 3*b*，表 1，第 1 行）。在连接反应前将 Ⅱ 型 DNA 与 recA 蛋白和 ATPγS 孵育并不会对这种分布产生什么影响（图 3*a*，表 1，第 2 行）。然而，如果在进行连接反应前把 recA 蛋白、fd Ⅱ 型 DNA、ΦX174 单链 DNA 片段以及 ATPγS 一起孵育，则位于梯度中最高密度区的 Ⅰ′型 DNA 的峰几乎完全消失，取而代之的是密度介于 Ⅰ′型 DNA 与线性或 Ⅱ 型 DNA 之间的广泛分布的峰（图 3*a*，表 1，第 3 行），也就是说，这些 DNA 的链环数比 Ⅰ′型 DNA 要低。位于中等密度区域的峰代表负超螺旋 fd DNA（Ⅰ 型 DNA）。在这个实验的三个部分中，放射性的总回收率都很接近。闭合环状 DNA 与线性或 Ⅱ 型 DNA（图 3*a*，表 1，第 1 行）的比值也与库恩莱因等人 [8] 的实验中测得的结果一致，这表明在这些实验中，回收的物质在分布上并不存在偏倚。

Table 1. Unwinding of DNA

|  | Total recovery (%) | Distribution (%) | | |
|---|---|---|---|---|
|  |  | I′ | Intermediate | II + III |
| Ligase only | 22 | 46 | 4 | 50 |
| +recA protein | 29 | 39 | 7 | 54 |
| +recA protein and fragments | 28 | 8 | 21 | 71 |

Data tabulated from Fig. 3. The DNA labelled "Intermediate" has a lower linking number than form I′ DNA, the product of sealing by ligase alone.

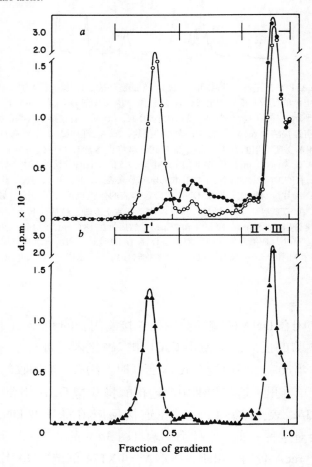

Fig. 3. Decreased linking number of circular DNA sealed in the presence of recA protein and ATPγS; isopycnic centrifugation in CsCl and propidium diiodide[7]. *a*, fd form II DNA sealed in the presence of recA protein only ( ○ ), and in the presence of recA protein plus heterologous fragments of single-stranded DNA from ΦX174 ( ● ). *b*, Control. DNA sealed in the absence of recA protein ( ▲ ). The left end of the figure corresponds to the dense end of the gradient. We summed values as indicated by the brackets (Table 1). All values were corrected for quenching. Solutions, 7.4 ml, contained CsCl to make the density 1.565 g cm$^{-3}$, 500 μg ml$^{-1}$ propidium diiodide, 10 mM Tris-HCl and 1 mM EDTA at *p*H 8.0. These solutions were centrifuged at 44,000 r.p.m. and 20°C for 69 h in a Beckman 75 ti rotor. The resulting gradients were collected from the bottom of the tube and counted in a scintillation fluor containing Triton X-100.

表 1. DNA 的解旋

| | 总回收率（%） | 分布（%） | | |
| --- | --- | --- | --- | --- |
| | | I ′ 型 | 中间体 | II 型 +III 型 |
| 只加连接酶 | 22 | 46 | 4 | 50 |
| 连接酶 +recA 蛋白 | 29 | 39 | 7 | 54 |
| 连接酶 +recA 蛋白 +DNA 片段 | 28 | 8 | 21 | 71 |

根据图 3 制成表的数据。被标记为"中间体"的 DNA 与仅由连接酶封闭的产物 I′ 型 DNA 相比具有更低的链环数。

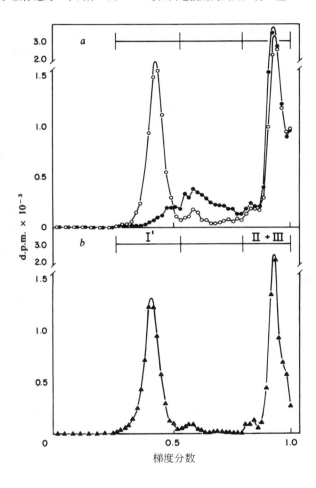

图 3. CsCl 和二碘化丙啶的等密度离心实验 [7] 表明，在 recA 蛋白和 ATPγS 存在时，环状 DNA（由连接酶闭合的，译者注）的链环数减少。a，在只含有 recA 蛋白（○）和同时含有 recA 蛋白及异源 ΦX174 噬菌体单链 DNA 片段（●）时，闭合的 fd II 型 DNA 的量。b，对照组。不含有 recA 蛋白时（▲），闭合的 DNA 的量。图的左端对应着密度梯度的高密度端。我们将各部分的数据相加，如表 1 所示。所有的数据都经过校正。溶液体积 7.4 ml，含有 CsCl，密度为 1.565 g/cm³，二碘化丙啶浓度为 500 μg/ml，另外含有 10 mM pH8.0 的 Tris-HCl 和 1 mM pH 8.0 的 EDTA。这些溶液使用贝克曼 75ti 转子在 20℃和 44,000 转 / 分钟转速下离心 69 小时。从离心管底部逐层收集不同密度梯度的组分，并使用含有 Triton X-100 的荧光闪烁来对 DNA 定量。

## Lack of Topoisomerase Activity of recA Protein

The unwinding observed in the experiments described above could have occurred before or after ligation, but three experiments show that recA protein lacks detectable topoisomerase activity in the presence of either ATPγS or ATP. We incubated recA protein with relaxed closed circular DNA (form I′) in conditions identical to those of the experiments shown in Figs 2 and 3, including a sample which contained heterologous fragments and ATPγS. When we observed the product by gel electrophoresis, we found no DNA in the position of form I DNA, and no perceptible shift in the distribution of form I′ DNA (Fig. 4). With the following additions or omissions, we examined, by gel electrophoresis, the fate of fd RFI incubated for 30 min at 37°C with recA protein and fragments of single-stranded ΦX174 DNA: ATP; ATPγS; ATPγS without single-stranded fragments; ATPγS without recA protein. We observed little or no change in the amount of form I DNA (data not shown).

In further experiments we made D-loops by incubating recA protein with fd form I DNA and fragments of fd single strands in the presence of ATP[4]. Measurement by electron microscopy of 22 D-loops with one or two single-stranded tails showed that the mean length was 416±45 nucleotides. (We were unable to distinguish the double-stranded arm of the D-loop from the single-stranded one. As there was little difference in the lengths of the two arms of any D-loop, we simply measured both and calculated the average of all values.) In the conditions of the reaction, fd form I DNA should contain about 40 superhelical turns which corresponds to a D-loop about 400 nucleotides long. Previous observations have shown a rough equivalence between the length of D-loops measured by electron microscopy and the length predicted from the superhelix density in solution[9]. Observation of the same relationship in these experiments suggests that when recA protein catalysed the formation of D-loops from form I DNA, the linking number of the closed circular DNA was not markedly changed.

Table 2. Homologous pairing of double-stranded DNA and single-stranded fragments

| Fragments | % fd double-stranded [³H] DNA retained | |
| --- | --- | --- |
| | form I | form II |
| None | 1 | 4 |
| fd | 34 | 22 |
| ΦX | 2 | 6 |

The reaction mixture, 20.5 µl in volume, contained 31 mM Tris-HCl at $p$H 7.5, 25 mM MgCl$_2$, 1.8 mM dithiothreitol, 88 µg ml$^{-1}$ bovine serum albumin, 1.3mM ATP, 8.8 µM RF[³H]DNA, 12 µM single-stranded DNA fragments and 98 µg ml$^{-1}$ recA protein[4]. The mixture was incubated at 37°C for 30 min, chilled and 18 µl transferred to 0.5 ml of cold 25 mM EDTA. Aliquots were taken from this mixture to measure total counts, D-loops and closed circular DNA, exactly as described before[4].

## recA 蛋白缺乏拓扑异构酶活性

上述实验中所观察到的解旋现象有可能是在连接反应之前发生的，也可能是在反应完成后才发生的。但是，在这三个实验中，无论是加入 ATP 或是 ATPγS，recA 蛋白都没有可检测到的拓扑异构酶的活性。我们将 recA 蛋白与松弛闭合环状 DNA（Ⅰ′型）在与图 2 和图 3 所示的实验相同的条件下孵育，并在一个样品中加入含有异源单链 DNA 片段和 ATPγS 的样品反应一段时间。当我们使用凝胶电泳实验来分析反应产物时，我们发现在Ⅰ型 DNA 的位置上没有 DNA，而Ⅰ′型 DNA 的分布也没有显著移动（图 4）。于是我们又以下述实验条件的增删继续做了一些实验，把 fd RFI、recA 蛋白和 ΦX174 单链 DNA 片段分别与 ATP、ATPγS、ATPγS 但不含单链 DNA 片段或 ATPγS 但不含 recA 蛋白在 37℃ 孵育 30 分钟，并通过凝胶电泳实验来分析 DNA 迁移率的变化。结果发现Ⅰ型 DNA 的含量几乎没有或仅有微小的改变（数据未展示）。

在进一步的实验中，我们将 recA 蛋白与 fd Ⅰ型 DNA 以及 fd 单链 DNA 一起孵育，并加入 ATP，以产生 D 环 [4]。通过电子显微镜测量 22 个带有一个或两个单链 DNA 尾巴的 D 环，我们发现其平均长度为 416±45 个核苷酸。（我们无法区分 D 环的双链臂与单链臂。由于任一 D 环的这两种臂的长度都差不多，因此我们简单地采取了测量两种环的长度，取平均值的方法。）在这个反应条件下，fd Ⅰ型 DNA 应该含有大约 40 个超螺旋转弯，相当于一个约 400 个核苷酸组成的 D 环。之前的研究表明使用电子显微镜测得的 D 环的长度与通过溶液中超螺旋密度预测的长度大致相等 [9]。这些实验中所观察到的与上述相同的等量关系表明当 recA 蛋白催化Ⅰ型 DNA 形成 D 环时，闭合环状 DNA 的链环数并没有发生显著的改变。

表 2. 双链 DNA 和单链 DNA 片段的同源性配对

| 片段 | 残留的 [³H] 标记的 fd 双链 DNA 的比例（%） | |
|---|---|---|
| | Ⅰ型 | Ⅱ型 |
| 无 | 1 | 4 |
| fd | 34 | 22 |
| ΦX | 2 | 6 |

反应混合物体积 20.5 μl，含有 31 mM pH7.5 的 Tris-HCl，25 mM MgCl₂，1.8 mM 二硫苏糖醇，88 μg/ml 牛血清白蛋白，1.3 mM ATP，8.8 μM RF[³H]DNA，12 μM 单链 DNA 片段以及 98 μg/ml recA 蛋白 [4]。反应混合物在 37℃ 孵育 30 分钟，冷却后取 18 μl 加到 0.5 ml 预冷的 25 mM 的 EDTA 溶液中。将样品等量分装后严格按照文献描述的方法 [4] 分别测量 DNA 总数、D 环数以及闭合环状 DNA 的数量。

## Nature of The Cofactor for Unwinding by recA Protein

Unwinding is supported either by heterologous or homologous single-stranded fragments (Fig. 4*a*, *b*). Circular single-stranded DNA, which does not form D-loops, promoted unwinding (Fig. 4*d*). Double-stranded restriction fragments were inactive, but their boiled products were active (Fig. 4*f*, *g*). This observation indicates that the cofactor was not some fortuitous ingredient of the DNA preparations. A digest, consisting entirely of acid-soluble material produced by treatment with pancreatic DNase and boiling, also supported the unwinding activity very well (Fig. 4*e* ). The following, added singly, promoted little or no unwinding: deoxyadenosine, dAMP, dGMP, dCMP, dTMP, AMP and CMP (data not shown).

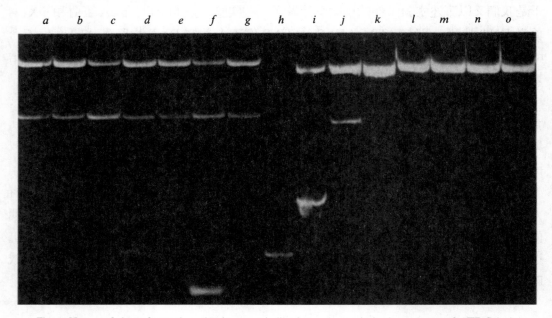

Fig. 4. Nature of the cofactor that stimulates unwinding by recA protein in the presence of ATPγS (*a-g*); absence of topoisomerase activity in recA protein (*l-o*): agarose gel electrophoresis. Lanes *a-g* contained fd form II DNA sealed in the presence of recA protein, ATPγS and 12 μM DNA cofactors: *a*, fragments of single-stranded ΦX174 DNA; *b*, fragments of single-stranded fd DNA; *c*, no addition; *d*, fd phage DNA; *e*, boiled DNase I limit digest of ΦX174 RFI DNA; *f*, restriction endonuclease *Hae*III digest of fd RFI; *g*, the preceding digest boiled. Lanes *h-k* contained markers: *h*, fd phage DNA; *i*, fd RFI DNA; *j*, fd form II DNA (~70%) and fd form III DNA (~30%), *k*, fd form I′ DNA. Lanes *l-o* contained fd form I′ DNA incubated with recA protein and ATPγS: *l*, no addition; *m*, fragments of single-stranded ΦX174 DNA; *n*, preceding sample minus recA protein; *o*, fragments of single-stranded ΦX174 DNA plus ATP instead of ATPγS. To obtain the limit digest indicated above 24 μM ΦX174 RF DNA was treated with 20 μg ml⁻¹ pancreatic DNase (Worthington) for 30 min at 37°C in 5 mM MgCl₂ and 10 mM Tris-HCl at *p*H 7.5, which rendered all the DNA acid soluble. The product was boiled for 4 min to inactivate the pancreatic DNase and denature all the fragments. Nicked circular DNA, sealed by polynucleotide ligase was slightly positively superhelical under the conditions of gel electrophoresis (for example lane *c*) whereas closed circular DNA relaxed by calf thymus topoisomerase had a titrable superhelix density close to zero (for example lane *k*). We used 1% agarose gels, 16 cm×16 cm×0.3 cm in E buffer, which contained 40 mM Tris-acetate, 5 mM sodium acetate and 1 mM EDTA at *p*H 8.0. Current was applied at 35 V for 16-18 h, and the buffer was recirculated between the reservoirs, following which we stained the gels for 2 h in E buffer containing 0.5 μg ml⁻¹ ethidium bromide. We illuminated the gels from below with a short-wavelength UV lamp (Ultra-Violet Products) and photographed them with Polaroid Tyffe 55 Land film. The negatives were scanned with a Joyce-Loebl recording micro-densitometer.

## recA 蛋白解螺旋作用的辅因子的性质

解旋的过程需要异源或同源单链 DNA 片段的协助（图 4a，b）。环状单链 DNA 虽然不能够形成 D 环，但是可以促进双链 DNA 的解旋（图 4d）。双链限制性酶切片段不具有这种活性，但是其煮沸后的产物则可以促进双链 DNA 的解旋（图 4f，g）。这些观察结果表明，解旋的辅因子不是 DNA 样品的某些偶然性成分。使用胰 DNA 酶消化并煮沸处理产生的全部酸溶性产物也具有很好的促进解旋活性（图 4e）。而脱氧腺苷、dAMP、dGMP、dCMP、dTMP、AMP 和 CMP 单独加入反应体系时，不具有或仅具有很低的促进解旋的活性（数据未展示）。

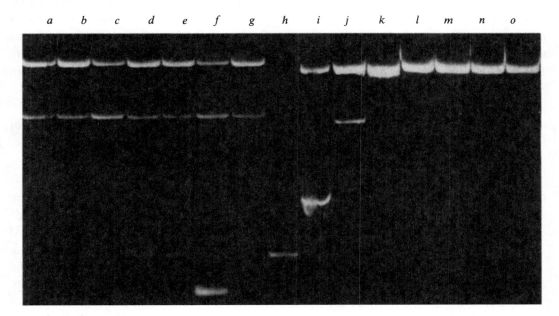

图 4. 琼脂糖凝胶电泳实验结果。当 ATPγS 存在时, 触发 recA 蛋白发挥解旋作用的辅因子的性质（a~g）；recA 蛋白不具有拓扑异构酶的活性（l~o）。a~g 泳道含有在 ATPγS、12 μM DNA 辅因子以及 recA 蛋白作用下闭合的 fd II 型 DNA：(a)，ΦX174 单链 DNA 片段；(b)，fd 单链 DNA 片段；(c)，空白对照；(d)，fd 噬菌体 DNA；(e)，DNA 酶 I 不完全消化 ΦX174 RFI DNA 后经煮沸处理的产物；(f)，fd RFI 的 HaeIII 限制性内切酶酶切产物；(g)，fd RFI 被 HaeIII 限制性内切酶酶切后，经煮沸处理的产物。h~k 泳道为各种分子标记物：(h)，fd 噬菌体 DNA；(i)，fd RFI DNA；(j)，fd II 型 DNA（约 70%）和 fd III 型 DNA（约 30%）；(k)，fd I′型 DNA。l~o 泳道为 fd I′型 DNA 与 recA 蛋白和 ATPγS 共同孵育后的产物：(l)，空白对照；(m)，ΦX174 单链 DNA 片段；(n)，ΦX174 单链 DNA 片段但不加入 recA 蛋白；(o)，ΦX174 单链 DNA 片段，且用 ATP 代替 ATPγS。为了得到上述不完全消化的 DNA，我们用 20 μg/ml 的胰 DNA 酶（购自沃辛顿公司）在含有 5 mM MgCl$_2$、10 mM Tris-HCl 的 pH 7.5 的缓冲液中酶切 24 μM 的 ΦX174 RF DNA，37℃反应 30 分钟，最终所有的核酸都处于酸溶状态。将反应产物煮沸 4 分钟，以灭活其中的胰 DNA 酶，并使所有的 DNA 片段变性。由多核苷酸连接酶闭合的带切口环状 DNA 在凝胶电泳的实验条件下会形成轻微的正超螺旋（例如 c 泳道），而经小牛胸腺拓扑异构酶松弛的闭合环形 DNA 的超螺旋滴定密度则接近于零（例如 k 泳道）。凝胶电泳实验方法如下：1% 琼脂糖凝胶，大小为 16 cm×16 cm×0.3 cm，使用 E 缓冲液（40mM Tris–乙酸，5 mM 乙酸钠，1 mM EDTA，pH 8.0）。恒定电压 35 V，电泳 16~18 小时，其间缓冲溶液在电泳槽之间不断地循环。电泳结束后，使用含有 0.5 μg/ml 溴化乙锭的 E 缓冲液染色 2 小时，然后用短波紫外灯观察凝胶，并使用 Polaroid Tyffe 55 胶片拍照。阴性结果使用 Joyce-Loebl 微量密度计进行扫描。

## Homologous Pairing of Form II DNA and Single-stranded Fragments

Table 2 compares form II and form I DNA as substrates for recA protein in the homologous pairing with single-stranded fragments. In the conditions of these experiments (see Table 2, legend), which differ slightly from previously described conditions[4], the preparation of form II DNA was one-half to two-thirds as active as form I DNA in making complexes that were retained by nitrocellulose filters. As the preparation of form II DNA contained less than a few per cent of form I DNA, these complexes must have been made with DNA that was not superhelical. The synthesis of complexes with form II DNA required homologous single-stranded fragments, and the properties of the product were similar to those of D-loops made from RFI; the complexes were not dissociated by treatment with 0.2% SDS nor by heating at 50°C for 4 min in 1.5 M NaCl and 0.15 M Na citrate at $p$H 7. Preliminary electron microscopic observations suggest that a significant fraction of complexes made with form II DNA contain D-loops (data not shown). Recently, McEntee, Weinstock and Lehman also described the synthesis of D-loops from non-superhelical DNA, in that case, from linear phage P22 DNA[10].

The formation of D-loops by form II DNA suggests that recA protein unwinds DNA in the presence of ATP as well as in the presence of the analogue, ATPγS.

## Discussion

Other experiments have shown that ATPγS competitively inhibits the ATPase activity of recA protein and blocks the formation of D-loops, but promotes the formation of complexes of protein, double-stranded DNA and single-stranded DNA (unpublished observations). The competitive inhibition shows that ATPγS occupies the same binding site as ATP; this, together with the other observations cited, suggests that the accumulation of partially unwound molecules reflects a step in the reaction that normally produces a D-loop. These effects of ATPγS on recA protein are reminiscent of observations on DNA gyrase which also catalyses several partial reactions in the presence of another non-hydrolysable analogue of ATP[11]. From the observed synthesis of D-loops with form II DNA, we infer that recA protein also unwinds DNA in the presence of ATP. The hydrolysis of ATP alters or dissociates the protein–DNA complex and accounts for the failure of partially unwound molecules to accumulate in the presence of ATP and DNA ligase (unpublished observations).

At first glance, the activation of unwinding by heterologous single strands seems incongruous for a mechanism that promotes homologous pairing, but further thought suggests that the opposite is true, that nonspecific stimulation of unwinding by any single strand explains in part how recA protein promotes a search for homology. As recombination in *E. coli* depends strongly on the function of recA[12], the action of recA protein by this mechanism implies that recombination often begins with the interaction of a single strand with duplex DNA.

Mutants of recA are pleiotropic, they affect not only recombination, but also a set of

916

## II 型 DNA 与单链 DNA 片段的同源性配对

表 2 比较了 II 型 DNA 和 I 型 DNA 分别作为 recA 蛋白的底物与单链 DNA 片段进行同源配对的差异。这些实验的反应条件（见表 2，表注）与之前几个实验的条件 [4] 稍有不同，硝酸纤维素过滤器截留到的复合物的量上显示，反应物中 II 型 DNA 在形成复合物方面的活性只有 I 型 DNA 的二分之一到三分之二。由于制备的 II 型 DNA 中仅含有很少量的 I 型 DNA（百分之几），因此这些复合物应该是由非超螺旋的 DNA 形成的。II 型 DNA 在形成复合物时需要同源单链 DNA 片段，其产物的性质与 RFI 形成的 D 环很类似。使用 0.2% 的 SDS 处理，或者在 pH 7 的 1.5 M NaCl、0.15 M 柠檬酸钠混合溶液中 50℃ 加热 4 分钟，都不会引起该复合物的解离。初步的电子显微镜观察结果显示，由 II 型 DNA 形成的复合物中有很显著的一部分含有 D 环（数据未展示）。最近，麦肯蒂、温斯托克和莱曼也报道了非超螺旋 DNA 可以形成 D 环的现象。不过在他们的实验中，使用的是线性 P22 噬菌体 DNA[10]。

II 型 DNA 可以形成 D 环的现象表明，recA 蛋白可以在 ATP 或其类似物 ATPγS 存在的情况下，促进 DNA 解旋。

## 讨　论

其他的实验表明 ATPγS 可以竞争性抑制 recA 蛋白的 ATP 酶活性，从而抑制 D 环结构的形成。但是 ATPγS 会促进由蛋白质、双链 DNA 以及单链 DNA 组成的复合物的形成（未发表的观察结果）。竞争性抑制的现象表明 ATPγS 可以占据 ATP 的结合位点；加上本文引用的其他人的观察结果，我们认为部分解旋的 DNA 分子的积累反映了 recA 蛋白促进双链 DNA 解旋的整个过程中的某个步骤，这个步骤本应该会导致 D 环的形成。ATPγS 对 recA 蛋白的这种作用使我们想到过去关于 DNA 促旋酶的一些实验结果。DNA 促旋酶也可以在另一个不能够被水解的 ATP 类似物存在时催化部分反应的进行[11]。根据 II 型 DNA 可以形成 D 环这一观察结果，我们推断 recA 蛋白在 ATP 存在时也可以促进 DNA 的解螺旋。ATP 的水解会引起蛋白质–DNA 复合物的改变或者解离，并在 ATP 和 DNA 连接酶存在的情况下，抑制部分解旋的 DNA 的积累（未发表的观察结果）。

初看上去，由异源单链 DNA 激活的解旋似乎并不适合作为促进同源配对的机制。但是进一步想来，由任意单链 DNA 非特异性地触发双链 DNA 解旋可以部分地解释 recA 蛋白如何促进对同源配对序列的搜寻，因此这一观点是有道理的。由于在大肠杆菌中，同源重组高度依赖于 recA 蛋白的功能 [12]，因此 recA 蛋白在这种机制下的行为意味着同源重组的过程常常是从单链 DNA 与双链 DNA 的相互作用开始。

recA 蛋白的突变是多效性的，它们不仅会影响同源重组，还会影响一系列由此

inducible functions, the so-called SOS functions[13]; these include error-prone repair, inactivation of phage repressors and the synthesis of recA protein itself (for reviews see refs 14, 15). Damaged DNA or blocked replication are inducing stimuli, and oligonucleotides have been implicated as intermediates in the induction[16,17]. The *tif*-1 mutation, which is located in the *recA* structural gene, makes the synthesis of recA protein thermo-inducible[18-22], indicating that a suitable form of the protein stimulates its own synthesis. The interaction of oligonucleotides with wild-type protein presumably stimulates synthesis by the same mechanism. However, observations on the *tsl* mutation indicate that abundant synthesis of recA protein may not be sufficient to induce fully all of the SOS functions[19,23]. Do oligonucleotides have a direct role in the inducible functions? Roberts *et al.* have studied one of the SOS functions *in vitro*, namely the inactivation of λ repressor by proteolytic cleavage[24,25]. In spite of the difficulty of reconciling proteolysis and unwinding of DNA, there are marked similarities between our observations on the unwinding of DNA by wild-type recA protein and those of Roberts *et al.* on inactivation of λ repressor by *tif* recA protein. Both processes require ATP or ATPγS, and oligonucleotide or single-stranded poly-nucleotide. The experiments described in this article show that both oligonucleotides and single-stranded DNA affect the functional properties of recA protein. The stimulation of unwinding by oligonucleotides, as well as by single strands, suggests that a common mechanism relates the function of recA protein in recombination to the other functions that are induced by oligonucleotides. Accordingly, oligonucleotides or single strands may trigger a conformational change of recA protein that can both unwind DNA and alter the interaction of recA protein with certain other proteins that bind to DNA.

A further inference from the similar effect of single strands and oligonucleotides on recA protein is that recombination may be inducible to some extent. Induction of synthesis of recA protein by single strands would provide the requisite amounts of protein to form D-loops, amounts which are large *in vitro*[4]. On the other hand, the induction of recA protein synthesis by oligonucleotides would not necessarily produce an increase in the number of genetic exchanges if any other factor, such as single strands, were limiting.

T.S. is a visiting fellow from The Institute of Physical and Chemical Research, Saitama, Japan. We acknowledge the technical assistance of Lynn Osber. This research was sponsored by grant no. NP 90E from the American Cancer Society and grant no. PHS CA 16038-05 from the NCI.

(**281**, 191-195; 1979)

Richard P. Cunningham, Takehiko Shibata, Chanchal DasGupta and Charles M. Radding
The Departments of Internal Medicine, and Molecular Biophysics and Biochemistry, Yale University School of Medicine, New Haven, Connecticut 06510

Received 4 May; accepted 18 June 1979.

诱导的功能，比如所谓的 SOS 反应 [13]，其中包括易错修复、噬菌体抑制子的失活以及 recA 蛋白自身的合成（参见参考文献 14 和 15）。DNA 的损伤或复制的阻断会引发 SOS 反应，寡核苷酸也作为媒介参与其中 [16,17]。位于 *recA* 结构基因位点的 *tif*-1 突变会导致 recA 蛋白的合成变成热诱导型 [18-22]，这表明 recA 蛋白的某种合适的形式会促进其自身的合成。寡核苷酸与野生型 recA 蛋白的相互作用很可能也通过相同的机制来触发 recA 蛋白的合成。然而，对 *tsl* 突变体的观察表明，recA 蛋白的大量合成并不一定足以完全诱导所有的 SOS 反应 [19,23]。那么寡核苷酸是否具有直接诱导 SOS 反应的功能呢？罗伯茨等人在体外研究了 SOS 反应的一个功能，即通过水解切割使 λ 抑制子失活 [24,25]。尽管很难使蛋白水解和 DNA 解旋这两个过程相一致，但我们关于野生型 recA 蛋白触发 DNA 解旋的观察结果与罗伯茨等人关于 *tif* 突变的 recA 蛋白导致的 λ 抑制子失活的观察结果有显著的相似之处；以上两个过程均需要 ATP 或 ATPγS 以及寡核苷酸或单链 DNA 片段的参与。本文中所述的实验表明寡核苷酸以及单链 DNA 片段都可以影响 recA 蛋白的功能。寡核苷酸以及单链 DNA 片段可以触发双链 DNA 解旋的现象表明，recA 蛋白在促进同源重组和由寡核苷酸诱导的其他功能之间存在某种共同的作用机制将两者相关联。相应地，寡核苷酸或单链 DNA 片段有可能引起 recA 蛋白发生构象改变，从而既能触发 DNA 解旋，又能改变 recA 蛋白与某些其他可以与 DNA 结合的蛋白的相互作用。

从寡核苷酸与单链 DNA 片段在对 recA 蛋白的作用方面的相似性中得到的进一步推论是，同源重组的过程在某种程度上或许是可诱导的。单链 DNA 片段诱导的 recA 蛋白的合成将产生规定数量的蛋白以形成 D 环，在体外实验中产生的蛋白的产量很高 [4]。另一方面，如果有其他的因素，如单链 DNA 片段的数量有限，那么由寡核苷酸引发的 recA 蛋白的合成未必导致遗传交换数量的增加。

柴田是来自日本崎玉物理与化学研究所的访问学者。我们感谢林恩·奥斯伯在技术方面的协助。本研究受美国癌症协会 NP 90E 项目以及美国国家癌症研究所 PHS CA 16038-05 项目的资助。

（张锦彬 翻译；陈新文 陈继征 审稿）

**References:**

1. Radding, C. M. *Ann., Rev. Biochem.* **47**, 847-880 (1978).

2. Holloman, W. K., Wiegand, R., Hoessli, C. & Radding, C. M. *Proc. Natl. Acad. Sci. U.S.A.* **72**, 2394-2398 (1975).

3. Beattie, K. L., Wiegand, R. C. & Radding, C. M. *J. Molec. Biol.* **116**, 783-803 (1977).

4. Shibata, T., DasGupta, C., Cunningham, R. P. & Radding, C.M. *Proc. Natl. Acad. Sci.U.S.A.* **76**, 1638-1642 (1979).

5. Holloman, W. K. & Radding, C. M. *Proc. Natl. Acad. Sci. U.S.A.* **73**, 3910-3914 (1976).

6. Liu, L. F. & Wang, J. C. *Proc. Natl. Acad. Sci. U.S.A.* **75**, 2098-2102 (1978).

7. Anderson, P. & Bauer, W. *Biochemistry* **17**, 594-601 (1978).

8. Kuhnlein, U., Penhoet, E. E. & Linn, S. *Proc. Natl. Acad. Sci. U.S.A.* **73**, 1169-1173 (1976).

9. Wiegand, R. C., Beattie, K. L., Holloman, W. K. & Radding, C. M., *J. Molec. Biol.* **116**, 805-824 (1977).

10. McEntee, K., Weinstock, G. M. & Lehman, I. R. *Proc. Natl. Acad. Sci. U.S.A.* **76**, 2615-2619 (1979).

11. Sugino, A., Higgins, N. P., Brown, P. O., Peebles, C.L. & Cozzarelli, N. R. *Proc, Natl. Acad. Sci. U.S.A.* **75**, 4838-4842 (1978).

12. Clark, A. J. *A. Rev. Genet.* **7**, 67-86 (1973).

13. Radman, M. in *Molecular Mechanisms for Repair of DNA* Part A (eds Hanawalt, P.C. & Setlow, R. B.) 355-367 (Plenum, New York, 1975).

14. Devoret, R. *Biochimie* **60**, 1135-1140 (1978).

15. Witkin, E. M. *Bact. Rev.* **40**, 869-907 (1976).

16. Oishi, M. & Smith, C. L. *Proc. Natl. Acad. Sci. U.S.A.* **75**, 3569-3573 (1978).

17. Oishi, M., Smith, C. L. & Friefeld, B. *Cold Spring Harb. Symp. Quant. Biol.* **43**, 897-907 (1979).

18. Castellazzi, M., Morand, P., George, J. & Buttin, G. *Molec. gen. Genet.* **153**, 297-310 (1977).

19. McEntee, K. *Proc. Natl. Acad. Sci. U.S.A.* **74**, 5275-5279 (1977).

20. Gudas, L. J. & Mount, D. W. *Proc. Natl. Acad. Sci. U.S.A.* **74**, 5280-5284 (1977).

21. Little, J. W. & Kleid, D. G. *J. Biol. Chem.* **252**, 6251-6252 (1977).

22. Emmerson, P. T. & West, S. C. *Molec. gen. Genet.* **155**, 77-85 (1977).

23. Mount, D.W., Kosel, C.K. & Walker, A. *Molec. gen. Genet.* **146**, 37-41 (1976).

24. Roberts, J. W., Roberts, C. W. & Craig, N. L. *Proc. Natl. Acad. Sci. U.S.A.* **75**, 4714-4718 (1978).

25. Roberts, J., Roberts, C. W., Craig, N. L. & Phizicky, E. *Cold Spring Harb. Symp. Quant. Biol.* **43**, 917-920 (1979).

# Selfish Genes, the Phenotype Paradigm and Genome Evolution

W. F. Doolittle and C. Sapienza

## Editor's Note

In 1976, biologist Richard Dawkins popularized in his book *The Selfish Gene* the growing notion in evolutionary biology that genes are the autonomous agents of Darwinian evolution, which compete for replicative success. In this review article, W. Ford Doolittle and Carmen Sapienza at Dalhousie University in Canada consider the existence of "junk DNA", which proliferates in the genome without an observable effect on an organism's phenotype. They argue that it is this DNA, the only function of which is to replicate itself within the genome, that is truly "selfish". The nature of "junk DNA", and the issue of whether it truly has no role integral to the genome, has become a hot topic of research in the new era of genomics.

---

Natural selection operating within genomes will inevitably result in the appearance of DNAs with no phenotypic expression whose only "function" is survival within genomes. Prokaryotic transposable elements and eukaryotic middle-repetitive sequences can be seen as such DNAs, and thus no phenotypic or evolutionary function need be assigned to them.

---

THE assertion that organisms are simply DNA's way of producing more DNA has been made so often that it is hard to remember who made it first. Certainly, Dawkins has provided the most forceful and uncompromising recent statement of this position, as well as of the position that it is the gene, and not the individual or the population, upon which natural selection acts[1]. Although we may thus view genes and DNA as essentially "selfish", most of us are, nevertheless, wedded to what we will call here the "phenotype paradigm"—the notion that the major and perhaps only way in which a gene can ensure its own perpetuation is by ensuring the perpetuation of the organism it inhabits. Even genes such as the segregation-distorter locus of *Drosophila*[2], "hitch-hiking" mutator genes in *Escherichia coli*[3,4] and genes for parthenogenetic reproduction in many species[4]—which are so "selfish" as to promote their own spread through a population at the ultimate expense of the evolutionary fitness of that population—are seen to operate through phenotype.

The phenotype paradigm underlies attempts to explain genome structure. There is a hierarchy of types of explanations we use in efforts to rationalize, in neo-darwinian terms, DNA sequences which do not code for protein. Untranslated messenger RNA sequences which precede, follow or interrupt protein-coding sequences are often assigned a phenotypic role in regulating messenger RNA maturation, transport or translation[5-7].

# 自私的基因，表型模式和基因组进化

杜利特尔，萨皮恩扎

编者按

1976年，生物学家理查德·道金斯的著作《自私的基因》使得进化生物学中日益兴起这样的观点——基因是达尔文进化论的自主元件，它们为自身的成功复制相互竞争。在这篇综述中，加拿大达尔豪西大学的福特·杜利特尔和卡门·萨皮恩扎认为"垃圾DNA"是存在的，它们在基因组中扩增，并且不会对生物体的表型产生可观测的效应。他们认为，这种DNA唯一的功能是在基因组内自我复制，是十足的"自私"。"垃圾DNA"的性质及其是否真的对基因组没有任何作用这个问题，在基因组的新时代中成为研究热点。

---

基因组内进行的自然选择将不可避免地导致无任何表型表达的DNA的出现，其唯一的"功能"就是存在于基因组内。原核生物的转座元件和真核生物的中度重复序列就可以被看作是这种DNA，它们因此被认为没有表型或者进化的功能。

---

认为生物体只是DNA复制更多DNA的途径的观点是如此普遍，以至于我们都想不起来是谁首先提出了这一观点。毫无疑问，道金斯对这个观点以及自然选择作用于基因本身而不是作用于个体或者种群的观点做出了最强有力和最坚定的最新陈述 [1]。尽管我们可能因此将基因和DNA在本质上看作是"自私的"，但是无论如何，大多数人坚持本文我们称为"表型模式"的观点——基因能够确保长期存在的主要或者可能唯一的方法就是确保其寄存的生物体一直存活。尽管诸如果蝇的分节突变位点 [2]、大肠杆菌的"搭乘"增变基因 [3,4] 以及很多物种的孤雌生殖基因 [4] 等基因都是这样自私，即通过牺牲种群的进化适应性而促进自身的传播，但是它们也是通过表型实现的。

在表型模式的基础上尝试解释基因组结构。从新达尔文主义的角度，我们试图从各个层次给出某些DNA不编码蛋白质的合理解释。这些先于、紧随或者干扰蛋白编码序列的非翻译信使RNA常常在信使RNA的成熟、转运或翻译的调控方面被赋予一些表型作用 [5-7]。转录子的部分去除被认为是处理过程中必需的 [8]。未转

Portions of transcripts discarded in processing are considered to be required for processing[8]. Non-transcribed DNA, and in particular repetitive sequences, are thought of as regulatory or somehow essential to chromosome structure or pairing[9-11]. When all attempts to assign to a given sequence or class of DNA functions of immediate phenotypic benefit to the organism fail, we resort to evolutionary explanations. The DNA is there because it facilitates genetic rearrangements which increase evolutionary versatility (and hence long-term phenotypic benefit)[12-17], or because it is a repository from which new functional sequences can be recruited[18,19] or, at worst, because it is the yet-to-be eliminated by-product of past chromosomal rearrangements of evolutionary significance[9,19].

Such interpretations of DNA structure are very often demonstrably correct; molecular biology would not otherwise be so fruitful. However, the phenotype paradigm is almost tautological; natural selection operates on DNA through organismal phenotype, so DNA structure must be of immediate or long-term (evolutionary) phenotypic benefit, even when we cannot show how. As Gould and Lewontin note, "the rejection of one adaptive story usually leads to its replacement by another, rather than to a suspicion that a different kind of explanation might be required. Since the range of adaptive stories is as wide as our minds are fertile, new stories can always be postulated" (ref. 20).

## Non-phenotypic Selection

What we propose here is that there are classes of DNA for which a "different kind of explanation" may well be required. Natural selection does not operate on DNA only through organismal phenotype. Cells themselves are environments in which DNA sequences can replicate, mutate and so evolve[21]. Although DNA sequences which contribute to organismal phenotypic fitness or evolutionary adaptability indirectly increase their own chances of preservation, and may be maintained by classical phenotypic selection, the only selection pressure which DNAs experience directly is the pressure to survive within cells. If there are ways in which mutation can increase the probability of survival within cells without effect on organismal phenotype, then sequences whose only "function" is self-preservation will inevitably arise and be maintained by what we call "non-phenotypic selection". Furthermore, if it can be shown that a given gene (region of DNA) or class of genes (regions) has evolved a strategy which increases its probability of survival within cells, then no additional (phenotypic) explanation for its origin or continued existence is required.

This proposal is not altogether new; Dawkins[1], Crick[6] and Bodmer[22] have briefly alluded to it.

However, there has been no systematic attempt to describe elements of prokaryotic and eukaryotic genomes as products of non-phenotypic selection whose primary and often only function is self-preservation.

录 DNA 尤其是重复序列被认为具有调节作用或者在某种程度上对染色体的结构或配对是必不可少的 [9-11]。我们将特定的序列或者一类 DNA 的功能认定为有利于生物体的直接表型，当上述所有尝试失败以后，我们只能诉诸进化方面的解释。DNA 的存在是因为它促进了基因重排，有利于增加进化灵活性（因此有利于长期的表型获益）[12-17]，或者因为它可以作为提供新功能性序列的储存库 [18,19]，或者最糟的解释——因为它是过去具有进化意义的染色体重排后即将被清除的副产物 [9,19]。

这种对 DNA 结构的解释常常被证实是正确的；否则分子生物学研究不会如此硕果累累。然而，表型模式几乎总是冗赘的；自然选择通过生物体的表型作用于 DNA，因此，DNA 的结构必定具有即时或者长期（进化）的表型优势，尽管我们无法解释其原因。正如古尔德和列万廷所指出的："抵制一个适应性假说常常导致其被另一个假说替代，而不是怀疑是否需要换种方式来解释。由于适应性假说的范围与我们的思维一样广阔，因此总能推导出新的假说"（文献 20）。

### 非表型选择

本文我们假设有各种各样需要"不同解释"的 DNA。自然选择不仅仅通过生物体的表型作用于 DNA。细胞自身就是 DNA 序列能够复制、突变从而进化的环境 [21]。尽管那些有助于生物体表型适应性或者进化适应性的 DNA 序列间接地增加了其本身被保留的机会，并且可能被经典的表型选择所保留，但是 DNA 直接面对的唯一选择压力是它们在细胞中存活的压力。如果存在某些方式，使 DNA 突变能够增加其在细胞内的存活可能性并且对生物体表型没有影响，那么这种将自我保护作为唯一"功能"的序列必然会增加，并以我们称之为"非表型选择"的方式被保留。此外，如果能够证明一个特定的基因（一个 DNA 片段）或者一组基因（多个片段）以增加其存活于细胞内可能性的策略来进化，那就不再需要针对其起源或持续存在的额外（表型）解释了。

这个提议并不完全新奇；道金斯 [1]，克里克 [6] 和博德默 [22] 都简要地提及过。

但是，并没有系统的尝试将原核生物和真核生物基因组的元件描述为非表型选择的产物，其首要和常规的功能仅是自我保存。

## Transposable Elements in Prokaryotes as Selfish DNA

Insertion sequences and transposons can in general be inserted into a large number of chromosomal (or plasmid) sites, can be excised precisely or imprecisely and can engender deletions or inversions in neighbouring chromosomal (or plasmid) DNAs[12-16]. These behaviours and, at least in some cases, the genetic information for the enzymatic machinery involved, must be inherent in the primary sequences of the transposable elements themselves, which are usually tightly conserved[12-16,23]. Most speculations on the function of transposable elements concentrate on the role these may have, through chromosomal rearrangements and the modular assembly of different functional units, in promoting the evolution of plasmid and bacterial chromosomes, and thus in promoting long-term phenotypic fitness[12-16]. Most assume that it is for just such functions that natural selection has fashioned these unusual nucleic acid sequences.

Although transposable elements may well be beneficially involved in prokaryotic evolution, there are two reasons to doubt that they arose or are maintained by selection pressures for such evolutionary functions.

First, DNAs without immediate phenotypic benefit are of no immediate selective advantage to their possessor. Excess DNA should represent an energetic burden[24,25], and some of the activities of transposable elements are frankly destructive[12-16]. Evolution is not anticipatory; structures do not evolve because they might later prove useful. The selective advantage represented by evolutionary adaptability seems far too remote to ensure the maintenance, let alone to direct the formation, of the DNA sequences and/or enzymatic machinery involved. A formally identical theoretical difficulty plagues our understanding of the origin of sexual reproduction, even though this process may now clearly be evolutionarily advantageous[1,4].

Second, transposability itself ensures the survival of the transposed element, regardless of effects on organismal phenotype or evolutionary adaptability (unless these are sufficiently negative). Thus, no other explanation for the origin and maintenance of transposable elements is necessary. A single copy of a DNA sequence of no phenotypic benefit to the host risks deletion, but a sequence which spawns copies of itself elsewhere in the genome can only be eradicated by simultaneous multiple deletions. Simple translocation (removal from one site and insertion into another) does not provide such insurance against deletion. It is significant that recent models for transposition require retention of the parental sequence copy[26,27], and that bacterial insertion sequences are characteristically present in several copies per genome[16]. The assumption that transposable elements are maintained by selection acting on the cell does not require that they show these characteristics. The evolutionary behaviour of individual copies of transposable elements within the environment represented by a bacterial genome and its descendants can be understood in the same terms as organismal evolution. Replicate copies of a given element may diverge in sequence, but at least those features of sequence required for transposition will be maintained by (non-phenotypic) selection; copies which can no longer be translocated

## 原核生物的转座元件是自私 DNA

插入序列和转座子一般来说都能被插入到大量的染色体（或质粒）位点内，能被精确或者不精确地剪切，并能引起临近染色体（或者质粒）DNA 的缺失或者倒位 [12-16]。至少在某些情况下，这些行为以及涉及这些行为的酶体系的遗传信息必须是转座元件本身的原始序列中固有的，并且通常是高度保守的 [12-16,23]。绝大多数关于转座元件功能的假设均集中于它们可能起到的作用，如通过染色体的重排和不同功能单位的模块化组装促进质粒和细菌染色体的进化，从而促进长期的表型适应性 [12-16]。大部分人认为正是因为这个功能才使得自然选择塑造出了这些不寻常的核酸序列。

尽管转座元件可能在原核生物的进化中有利，但还是有两个理由认为它们未必是在这种进化功能的选择压力下产生或保持的。

首先，没有直接表型优势的 DNA 对于其拥有者没有直接的选择优势。过多的DNA 则代表能量的负担 [24,25]，还有转座元件的一些活动是具有直接破坏性的 [12-16]。进化是不可预期的；结构没有进化是因为它们可能在将来被证明有用。进化适应性所代表的选择优势似乎对于 DNA 序列和（或）涉及的酶体系的保持作用都微乎其微，更别说指导其形成。一个形式上一致的理论难题妨碍了我们对于有性生殖起源的理解，尽管现在很清楚这个过程是具有进化优势的 [1,4]。

其次，可转移性本身确保了已转座元件的存活，无论其对于有机体的表型或者进化适应性是否有作用（除非有充分的负面作用）。因此，没有必要再对转座元件的起源和保留做更多解释。对宿主表型没有益处的单拷贝 DNA 序列存在被删除的风险，但是在基因组内多个位置存在自身拷贝的序列只能通过多个位点同时缺失才能从基因组中彻底删除。单纯的易位（从一个位点移除插入到另一个位点）不能确保序列免于被删除。很显然，近来的转座模型均需要保留亲本的序列拷贝 [26,27]，而且细菌的插入序列特征性地在每个基因组内存在多个拷贝 [16]。假设转座元件通过作用于细胞的选择而得以保留，这个假设的成立并不需要它们具备这些特征。一个细菌基因组及其后代为代表的环境内的单拷贝转座元件的进化行为同样可以用生物体进化的方式来理解。特定元件的复制拷贝可能分散在序列上，但是至少转座所需序列的特征会通过（非表型）选择保留下来；再也不能易位的拷贝最终会被删除。一些分散的拷贝可能更容易转座；它们会以牺牲其他拷贝为代价增加其转座的频率。依靠宿

will eventually suffer elimination. Some divergent copies may be more readily transposed; these will increase in frequency at the expense of others. Transposable elements which depend on host functions run the risk that host mutants will no longer transpose them; it is significant that at least some transposition-specific functions are known to be coded for by the transposable elements themselves[26-29]. It is not to the advantage of a transposable element coding for such functions to promote the transposition of unrelated elements; the fact that given transposable elements generate flanking repeats[16,30] of chromosomal DNAs of sizes characteristic to them (that is, 5, 9 or 11-12 base pairs) may indicate such a specificity in transposition mechanism. It is to the advantage of any transposable element to acquire genes which allow independent replication (to become a plasmid), promote host mating (to become a self-transmissable plasmid) or promote non-conjugational transmission (to become a phage like Mu).

It is certainly not novel to suggest that prokaryotic transposable elements behave in these ways, or to suggest that more frankly autonomous entities like phages have arisen from them[12-16,31]. However, we think it has not been sufficiently emphasized that non-phenotypic selection may inevitably give rise to transposable elements and that no phenotypic rationale for their origin and continued existence is thus required.

## Transposable Elements in Eukaryotes

There has long been genetic evidence for the existence in eukaryotic genomes of transposable elements affecting phenotype[32]. These have been assigned roles in the regulation of eukaryotic gene expression and in evolution, but would have escaped genetic detection had they not had phenotypic effect. More recent evidence for transposable elements whose effects are not readily identified genetically has come fortuitously from studies of cloned eukaryotic DNAs. For instance, the Ty-1 element of yeast (which has no known phenotypic function) is flanked by direct repeats (like some prokaryotic transposons) and is transposable[33]. It is present in some 35 dispersed copies and comprises some 2% of the yeast genome (like a higher-eukaryotic middle-repetitive DNA). The directly repeated δ-sequence elements flanking it are found at still other sites (just as prokaryotic insertion sequences can be found flanking transposons or independently elsewhere in the genome). Cameron *et al.* suggest that "Ty-1 may be a nonviral 'parasitic' DNA" but then go on to suggest, we think unnecessarily, that transposition "allows adaptation of a particular cell to a new environment" (ref. 33). The repetitive elements *412*, *copia* and *297* of *Drosophila* are physically similar to Ty-1 (and to bacterial transposable elements) and are transposable[34-37]. Strobel *et al.* suggest "it is possible that the sole function of these elements is to promote genetic variability, and that their gene products may only be necessary for the maintenance and mobility of the elements themselves, rather than for other cellular processes" (ref. 37). But if maintenance and mobility mechanisms exist, then no cellular function at all need be postulated.

A large fraction of many eukaryotic genomes consists of middle-repetitive DNAs, and the variety and patterns of their interspersion with unique sequence DNA make

主功能的转座子有不再被宿主突变体转座的风险；很显然，至少已知一些转座特异性的功能是由转座元件自身编码的 [26-29]。对于转座元件本身而言，编码这些功能来促进无关元件的转座是无益的；事实上，特定的转座元件产生特异性大小（即 5，9 或者 11~12 个碱基对）的染色体 DNA 两侧的重复序列 [16,30]，这可能说明了转座机制的特异性。对于任何转座子来说，获得一些基因，使其可以独立复制（变成质粒）、促进宿主配对（成为可自我传递的质粒）或者促进非接合传递（成为噬菌体，如 Mu 噬菌体），是非常有利的。

提出原核生物转座元件以这种方式作用或者提出更直接自主的实体（比如噬菌体）就是由上述方式衍生而来的观点并不新颖 [12-16,31]。但是，我们认为还未充分强调的是，非表型选择可能不可避免地产生转座元件，而且我们不需要用表型理论去解释其起源和持续存在。

### 真核生物的转座元件

很早以前就有遗传学证据证明真核生物基因组内存在影响表型的转座元件 [32]。人们认为这些转座元件在真核基因表达的调控以及进化中起作用，但是如果它们没有表型效应，它们可能会被基因检测遗漏。很偶然地，在最近对真核生物 DNA 克隆的研究中，发现了更多不便于从遗传学角度确认功能的转座子的证据。比如，酵母的 Ty-1 元件（没有已知的表型功能）两侧都是正向重复序列（类似某些原核生物转座子），而且可以转座 [33]。这种元件大约以 35 个分散的拷贝存在，构成了约 2% 的酵母基因组（类似高等真核生物的中度重复 DNA）。在其他位点也可以找到两侧正向重复的 δ 序列（就像可以在转座子的侧翼或者基因组中其他独立的位置找到原核生物的插入序列一样）。卡梅伦等指出"Ty-1 可能是一种非病毒的'寄生性'DNA"，他们又进一步指出转座"使得特定细胞适应新环境"（文献 33），但我们认为后续的论述没有必要。果蝇的重复元件 412，copia 和 297 在结构上都类似于 Ty-1（以及细菌的转座元件），并且可以转移 [34-37]。斯特罗贝尔等指出"这些元件的唯一功能可能就是促进遗传变异，它们的基因产物可能仅仅对这些元件本身的保留和移动是必需的，而对其他细胞活动不起作用"（文献 37）。但是如果存在保留和移动的机制，那就无需再假设其他细胞功能了。

很多真核生物基因组含有很大比例的中度重复 DNA，它们与特定的 DNA 序列穿插分布的多样性和形式并没有特别的系统发育或者表型功能的意义。布里滕和戴

no particular phylogenetic or phenotypically functional sense. Britten, Davidson and collaborators have elaborated models which ascribe regulatory functions to middle-repetitive DNAs, and evolutionary advantage (in terms of adaptability) to the quantitative and qualitative changes in middle-repetitive DNA content observed even between closely related species[17,38-40]. Middle-repetitive DNAs are more conserved in sequence during evolution than are unique-sequence DNAs not coding for protein, and Klein *et al.* suggest that "restraint on repetitive sequence divergence, either within the repeat families of a given species, or over evolutionary time spanning the emergence of different species, could be due to [phenotypic] selective pressures which prevent free sequence change in large fraction of the repeat family members. Or perhaps repetitive sequences diverge as rapidly as do other sequences, but the type sequence of the family is preserved by frequent remultiplication of the 'correct' surviving sequences" (ref. 41). The evidence for a phenotypically functional role for middle-repetitive sequences remains dishearteningly weak[40-43], and if the calculations of Kimura[44] and Salser and Isaacson[45] are correct, middle-repetitive DNAs together comprise too large a fraction of most eukaryotic genomes to be kept accurate by darwinian selection operating on organismal phenotype. The most plausible form of "remultiplication of the 'correct' surviving sequences" is transposition. If we assume middle-repetitive DNAs in general to be transposable elements or degenerate (and no longer transposable and ultimately to be eliminated) descendants of such elements, then the observed spectra of sequence divergence within families and changes in middle-repetitive DNA family sequence and abundance can all be explained as the result of non-phenotypic selection within genomes. No cellular function at all is required to explain either the behaviour or the persistence of middle-repetitive sequences as a class.

## The Rest of the Eukaryotic Genome

Middle-repetitive DNA can comprise more than 30% of the genome of a eukaryotic cell[46]. Another 1-40% consists of simple reiterated sequences whose functions remain unclear[10], and Smith has argued that "a pattern of tandem repeats is the natural state of DNA whose sequence is not maintained by selection" (ref. 47). Even unique-sequence eukaryotic DNA consists in large part of elements which do not seem to be constrained by phenotypic selection pressures[45]. Some authors have argued that the intervening sequences which interrupt many eukaryotic structural genes are insertion sequence-like elements[6,48,49]. If they are, they are likely to be the degenerate and no-longer-transposable descendants of transposable sequences whose insertion was rendered non-lethal by pre-existing cellular RNA:RNA splicing mechanisms. Such elements, once inserted, are relatively immune to deletion (since only very precise deletion can be non-lethal), and need retain only those sequence components required for RNA splicing. The rest of the element is free to drift and one expects (and observes) that only the position and number of intervening sequences in a family of homologous genes remain constant during evolution. Although evolutionary and regulatory phenotypic functions have been ascribed to intervening sequences[6,49-51], it is unnecessary to postulate any cellular function at all if these elements are indeed degenerate transposable elements arising initially from non-phenotypic selection. Another explanation for the origin and continued existence of intervening sequences, which also does not require phenotypically or evolutionarily advantageous roles, has been suggested elsewhere[50,51].

930

维森及同事精心构建了一个模型，该模型将调节功能归因于中度重复 DNA，同时将进化优势（在适应性方面）归因于中度重复 DNA 量和质的改变，这些变化甚至在相近物种之间也曾被观察到 [17,38-40]。与单一序列的非编码蛋白质的 DNA 相比，中度重复 DNA 序列在进化过程中更加保守，并且克莱因等指出"对重复序列差异的限制，无论是在特定物种的重复序列家族内还是经过很长的进化时间出现不同的物种，都可归因于 [ 表型 ] 选择压力，这种压力防止了大部分重复家族成员中的自由的序列改变。也可能是因为重复序列和其他序列一样很快发生变化，但是家族的特征性序列通过频繁的'正确'存活序列的再复制而得以保留"（文献 41）。证明中度重复序列具有表型功能的证据仍然不足 [40-43]，而且如果木村 [44] 以及萨尔瑟和艾萨克森 [45] 的计算是正确的，中度重复 DNA 总体在大部分真核生物基因组中所占比例过大，以致作用于生物体表型的达尔文选择不能保持其正确无误。理论上，"正确存活序列的再增殖"最合理的形式就是转座。如果我们假设中度重复 DNA 通常都是转座元件或者这类元件的退化产物（不再具有转座能力并且最终被清除），那么观察到的家族内部序列变异范围以及中度重复 DNA 家族序列和丰度的改变都可以解释为基因组内非表型选择的结果。作为一个群体，中度重复序列的行为或者其持续存在均无需用细胞功能去解释。

## 真核生物基因组的其他组分

中度重复 DNA 可以构成超过真核细胞基因组的 30%[46]。另外 1%~40% 由功能未知的简单重复序列组成 [10]，并且史密斯认为"串联重复的形式是 DNA 的天然状态，其序列并不通过选择来保持"（文献 47）。甚至组成一大部分元件的真核 DNA 的单一序列似乎也不受表型选择压力约束 [45]。一些作者认为那些使很多真核生物结构基因中断的间隔序列都是类似于插入序列的元件 [6,48,49]。如果确实如此，那么它们很可能是转座序列退化并且不再具备转座能力的产物，其插入通过预先存在的细胞 RNA–RNA 剪接机制呈现非致死性。这些元件，一旦插入后，相对难以被删除（因为只有非常精确的删除才是非致命性的），并且仅需保留那些 RNA 剪接所需的序列成分。元件的剩余部分可以自由移动，并且可以预期（并观察到），只有同源基因家族内间隔序列的位置和数目在进化中是保持恒定的。尽管也有人认为间隔序列具有进化和调节表型的功能 [6,49-51]，如果这些元件确实是初始通过非表型选择退化的转座元件产物，那么任何有关细胞功能的假设都没有必要。另外一种有关间隔序列起源和持续存在的解释另有叙述，这种解释同样无需表型上或者进化方面的优势作用 [50,51]。

## Why Do Prokaryotes and Eukaryotes Differ?

It is generally believed that prokaryotic genomes consist almost entirely of unique-sequence DNA maintained by phenotypic selection, whereas the possession of "excess" unique and repetitive DNA sequences whose presence is at least difficult to rationalize in phenotypic terms is characteristic of eukaryotes. However, it is more accurate to say that there is continuum of excess DNA contents; at least 1% of the *E. coli* genome can be made up of copies of six identified insertion sequences alone[16]. Yeast, whose genome is no larger than that of some prokaryotes, has few repeated sequences other than those coding for stable RNAs, and *Aspergillus* may have none[52,53]. There is in general (but with many exceptions) a positive correlation between excess DNA content, genome size and what we anthropocentrically perceive as "evolutionary advancement". Many interpret this as the cause and/or consequence of the increasing phenotypic complexity which characterizes organismal evolution, and attribute to excess DNA a positive role in the evolutionary process[17-19,40]. The interplay of phenotypic and non-phenotypic forces, and the importance of understanding both in attempts to restore the "*C*-value paradox" are discussed more thoroughly by Orgel, and Crick in the following article.[54]

There is another, simpler and perhaps obvious explanation. Non-phenotypic selection produces excess DNA, and excess DNA logically must be an energetic burden; phenotypic selection should favor its elimination[24, 25]. The amount of excess (and hence total) DNA in an organism should be loosely determined by the relative intensities of the two opposing sorts of selection. The intensity of non-phenotypic pressure on DNA to survive even without function should be independent of organismal physiology. The intensity of phenotypic selection pressure to eliminate excess DNA is not, this being greatest in organisms for which DNA replication comprises the greatest fraction of total energy expenditure. Prokaryotes in general are smaller and replicate themselves and their DNA more often than eukaryotes (especially complex multicellular eukaryotes). Phenotypic selection pressure for small "streamlined" prokaryotic genomes with little excess DNA may be very strong.

## Necessary and Unnecessary Explanations

We do not deny that prokaryotic transposable elements or repetitive and unique-sequence DNAs not coding for protein in eukaryotes may have roles of immediate phenotypic benefit to the organism. Nor do we deny roles for these elements in the evolutionary process. We do question the almost automatic invocation of such roles for DNAs whose function is not obvious, when another and perhaps simpler explanation for their origin and maintenance is possible. It is inevitable that natural selection of the special sort we call non-phenotypic will favour the development within genomes of DNAs whose only "function" is survival within genomes. When a given DNA, or class of DNAs, of unproven phenotypic function can be shown to have evolved a strategy (such as transposition) which ensures its genomic survival, then no other explanation for its existence is necessary. The search for other explanations may prove, if not intellectually sterile, ultimately futile.

### 为什么原核生物和真核生物不同？

一般认为原核生物基因组几乎全部由表型选择所保留的单一序列 DNA 组成，而存在难以用表型合理解释的"冗余的"单一和重复 DNA 序列则是真核生物的特征。但是，更加准确地说，冗余 DNA 成分的连续统一体是存在的；至少大肠杆菌 1% 的基因组由六种已被确认的插入序列拷贝单独组成[16]。酵母的基因组不比一些原核生物的大，但是除了那些编码稳定 RNA 的序列之外，几乎没有重复序列，而曲霉菌可能并不含有重复序列[52,53]。一般来说（但是有很多例外），冗余 DNA 成分、基因组大小以及以人类为中心的所谓高级进化产物之间存在正相关性。很多人将这解释为标志生物体进化的表型复杂程度增加的原因和（或）结果，并认为冗余 DNA 在进化过程中具有正面作用[17-19,40]。奥格尔和克里克在后面的文章中更加详细地讨论了表型和非表型影响的相互作用，以及弄清楚二者对试图修复"C 值悖论"的重要性[54]。

有另外一个更简单，可能更显而易见的解释。非表型选择产生了过量的 DNA，理论上过量的 DNA 必然增加了能量负担；表型选择更倾向于清除这些 DNA[24,25]。生物体内冗余 DNA（以及总 DNA）的量应该不严格地由这两种对立选择力量的相对强度决定。非表型压力作用于 DNA，使得即使无功能的 DNA 也得以保存，其强度应该与生物体的生理无关。而清除冗余 DNA 的表型选择压力的强度则不然，该强度在 DNA 复制占据总能量消耗比例最高的生物体内最大。原核生物一般来说更小，并比真核生物更频繁地复制自身及其 DNA（尤其是复杂得多细胞真核生物）。小"流线型"原核生物基因组含有很少冗余 DNA，作用于这种基因组的表型选择压力可能是非常大的。

### 必要和不必要的解释

我们并不否认原核生物转座元件或者真核生物中不编码蛋白质的重复和单一序列 DNA 可能对于生物体具有直接的表型优势。我们也不否认这些元件在进化过程中的作用。如果对上述元件的起源和保留有可能存在其他的或更为简单的解释，那我们就要质疑，将这些作用赋予那些功能并不明显的 DNA，是否合理。不可避免地，我们称之为非表型的自然选择的一种特殊形式帮助 DNA 在基因组中发展，这些 DNA 的唯一"功能"就是在基因组中存活。当一个或者一组未经证实表型功能的特定 DNA 可以被证明进化出一种策略以确保其基因组的存活（比如转座），那么就不再需要其他解释其存在的理由。寻找其他解释的过程，即使不是毫无结果，也是没有意义的。

We thank L. Bonen, R. M. MacKay and M. Schnare for help in development of the ideas presented here, and C. W. Helleiner, M. W. Gray, C. Stuttard, R. Singer, S. D. Wainwright and E. Butz for critical discussions.

We are especially grateful to C. E. Orgel and F. H. C. Crick for discussing with us the ideas presented in the following article before publication and for encouragement and support.

(**284**, 601-603; 1980)

W. Ford Doolittle and Carmen Sapienza

Department of Biochemistry, Dalhousie University, Halifax, Nova Scotia, Canada B3H 4H7

---

References:

1. Dawkins, R. *The Selfish Gene* (Oxford University Press, 1976).

2. Crow, J. F. *Scient. Am.* **240**, 134-146 (1979).

3. Cox, E. C. & Gibson, T. C. *Genetics* 77, 169-184 (1974).

4. Maynard Smith, J. *The Evolution of Sex* (Cambridge University Press, 1978).

5. Darnell, J. E. *Prog. Nucleic Acid Res. Molec. Biol.* **22**, 327-353 (1978).

6. Crick, F. H. C. *Science* **204**, 264-271 (1979).

7. Murray, V. & Holliday, R. *FEBS Lett.* **106**, 5-7 (1979).

8. Sogin, M. L., Pace, B. & Pace, N. R. *J. Biol. Chem.* **252**, 1350-1357 (1977).

9. Fedoroff, N. *Cell* 16, 697-710 (1979).

10. John, B. & Miklos, G. L. G. *Int. Rev. Cytol.* **58**, 1-114 (1979).

11. Zuckerkandl, E. *J. Molec. Evol.* **9**, 73-122 (1976).

12. Cohen, S. N. *Nature* **263**, 731-738 (1976).

13. Starlinger, P. & Saedler, H. *Curr. Topics Microbiol. Immun.* **75**, 111-152 (1976).

14. Nevers, P. & Saedler, H. *Nature* **268**, 109-115 (1977).

15. Kleckner, N. *Cell* 11, 11-23 (1977).

16. Kopecko, D. in *Plasmids and Transposons: Environmental Effects and Maintenance Mechanisms* (eds Stuttard, C. & Rozee, K. R.) (Academic, New York, in the press).

17. Britten, R. J. & Davidson, E. H. *Q. Rev. Biol.* **46**, 111-138 (1971).

18. Ohno, S. *Evolution by Gene Duplication* (Springer, New York, 1970).

19. Hinegardner, R. in *Molecular Evolution* (ed. Ayala, F. J.) 160-199 (Sinauer, Sunderland, 1976).

20. Gould, S. J. & Lewontin, R. C. *Proc. R. Soc.* B205, 581-598 (1979).

21. Orgel, L. *Proc. R. Soc.* B205, 435-442 (1979).

22. Bodmer, W. in *Human Genetics: Possibillities and Realities*, 41-42 (Excerpta Medica, Amsterdam, 1979).

23. Johnsrod, L. *Molec. gen. Genet.* **169**, 213-218 (1979).

24. Zamenhof, S. & Eichorn, H. H. *Nature* **216**, 456-458 (1967).

25. Koch, A. L. *Genetics* 72, 297-316 (1972).

26. Shapiro, J. A. *Proc. Natl. Acad. Sci. U.S.A.* 76, 1933-1937 (1979).

27. Arthur, A. & Sherratt, D. *Molec. gen. Genet.* **175**, 267-274 (1979).

28. Gill, R., Heffron, F., Dougan, G. & Falkow, S. *J. Bact.* **136**, 742-756 (1978).

29. MacHattie, L. A. & Shapiro, J. A. *Proc. Natl. Acad. Sci. U.S.A.* 76, 1490-1494 (1979).

30. Huberman, P., Klaer, R., Kühn, S. & Starlinger, P. *Molec. gen. Genet.* **175**, 369-373 (1979).

31. Campbell, A. in *Biological Regulation and Development* Vol. 1 (ed. Goldberger, R. F.) 19-55 (Plenum, New York, 1979).

32. McClintock, B. *Cold Spring Harb. Symp. Quant. Biol.* 16, 13-47 (1952).

33. Cameron, J. R., Loh, E. Y. & Davis, R. W. *Cell* 16, 739-751 (1979).

34. Finnegan, D. J., Rubin, G. M., Young, M. W. & Hogness, D. S. *Cold Spring Harb. Symp. Quant.Biol.* **42**, 1053-1063 (1977).

感谢博南、麦凯和施纳尔帮助我们形成了文中的观点，并感谢赫莱纳、格雷、斯图塔特、辛格、温赖特和巴茨对此进行的关键讨论。

特别感谢奥格尔和克里克和我们讨论他们未发表的文章观点，以及给予我们的鼓励和支持。

（毛晨晖 翻译；崔巍 审稿）

35. Carlson, M. & Brutlag, D. *Cell* **15**, 733-742 (1978).

36. Potter, S. S., Borein, W. J. Jr, Dunsmuir, P. & Rubin, G. M. *Cell* **17**, 415-427 (1979).

37. Strobel, E., Dunsmuir, P. & Rubin, G. M. *Cell* **17**, 429-439 (1979)

38. Britten, R. J. & Davidson, E. H. *Science* **165**, 349-357 (1969).

39. Davidson, E. H., Klein, W. H. & Britten, R. J. *Devl. Biol.* **55**, 69-84 (1977).

40. Davidson, E. H. & Britten, R. J. *Science* **204**, 1052-1059 (1979).

41. Klein, W. H. *et al. Cell* **14**, 889-900 (1978).

42. Sheller, R. H., Constantini, F. D., Dozlowski, M. R., Britten, R. J. & Davidson, E. H. *Cell* **15**,189-203 (1978).

43. Kuroiwa, A. & Natori, S. *Nucleic Acids Res.* **7**, 751-754 (1979).

44. Kimura, M. *Nature* **217**, 624-626 (1968).

45. Salser, W. & Isaacson, J. S. *Prog. Nucleic Acid Res. Molec. Biol.* **19**, 205-220 (1976).

46. Lewin, B. *Cell* **4**, 77-93 (1975).

47. Smith, G. P. *Science* **191**, 528-534 (1976).

48. Tsujimoto, Y.G. & Suzuki, Y. *Cell* **18**, 591-600 (1979).

49. Gilbert, W. *Nature* **271**, 501 (1978).

50. Doolittle, W. F. *Nature* **272**, 581-582 (1978).

51. Darnell, J. E. *Science* **202**, 1257-1260 (1978).

52. Roberts, T.M., Lauer, G. D. & Klotz, L. *CRC Crit. Rev. Biochem.* **3**, 349-451 (1976).

53. Timberlake, W. F. *Science* **702**, 973-974 (1978).

54. Orgel, G. E. & Crick, F.H.C. *Nature* **284**, 604-607 (1980).

# Selfish DNA: the Ultimate Parasite

L. E. Orgel and F. H. C. Crick

## Editor's Note

In the second of two consecutive review articles on "selfish DNA", Leslie Orgel and Francis Crick at the Salk Institute in California consider how this form of DNA—which proliferates in the genome without significantly affecting an organism's phenotype—might arise during evolution. Such DNA is in effect a kind of relatively harmless parasite, which is insufficiently costly to produce (in metabolic terms) to be efficiently purged from the genome. Orgel and Crick point out that some of this apparently "useless" DNA might occasionally acquire a useful function—but most would not. Not only did these ideas help to dismantle the popular belief that natural selection ensures maximal genomic efficiency, but they also presaged the modern recognition that there is a great deal of DNA in the human genome with unknown function.

---

The DNA of higher organisms usually falls into two classes, one specific and the other comparatively nonspecific. It seems plausible that most of the latter originated by the spreading of sequences which had little or no effect on the phenotype. We examine this idea from the point of view of the natural selection of preferred replicators within the genome.

---

THE object of this short review is to make widely known the idea of selfish DNA. A piece of selfish DNA, in its purest form, has two distinct properties:

(1) It arises when a DNA sequence spreads by forming additional copies of itself within the genome.

(2) It makes no specific contribution to the phenotype.

This idea is not new. We have not attempted to trace it back to its roots. It is sketched briefly but clearly by Dawkins[1] in his book *The Selfish Gene* (page 47). The extended discussion (pages 39-45) after P. M. B. Walker's article[2] in the CIBA volume based on a Symposium on Human Genetics held in June 1978 shows that it was at that time already familiar to Bodmer, Fincham and one of us. That discussion referred specifically to repetitive DNA because that was the topic of Walker's article, but we shall use the term selfish DNA in a wider sense, so that it can refer not only to obviously repetitive DNA but also to certain other DNA sequences which appear to have little or no function, such as much of the DNA in the introns of genes and parts of the DNA sequences between genes. The catch-phrase "selfish DNA" has already been mentioned briefly on two occasions[3,4]. Doolittle and Sapienza[5] (see the previous article) have independently arrived at similar ideas.

# 自私的DNA：最终的寄生物

奥格尔，克里克

编者按

在有关"自私的DNA"的两篇连续综述的第二篇中，加利福尼亚索尔克研究所的莱斯利·奥格尔和弗朗西斯·克里克思考了这种形式的DNA——在基因组中扩增，但不明显影响生物体的表型——是如何在进化中产生的。实际上，这种基因是一种相对无害的寄生物，机体不足以以高代价产生（在代谢方面）将其从基因组中有效清除的机制。奥格尔和克里克指出，这种明显"无用的"DNA有些可能碰巧会获得一种有用的功能——但是大部分不会。这些观点不仅有助于消除人们关于自然选择会保证最大的基因组效率的普遍观念，而且预示人类基因组中有大量未知功能DNA的新认识。

---

高等生物的DNA通常分为两种，特异的和相对非特异的。情况似乎是这样：非特异性序列源于某些序列的扩散，这些序列对表型影响很小或没有影响。我们从基因组中优先复制子的自然选择的观点出发来检验这个想法。

---

这篇简短的综述的目的是普及自私DNA的概念。一段处于最简单形式的自私DNA，具有两种截然不同的特性：

（1）它是一段DNA序列在基因组中复制更多拷贝时产生的。

（2）它对生物的表型没有特定的作用。

这种想法并不新颖，我们还没有尝试追溯它的根源。道金斯[1]曾经在他的著作《自私的基因》（第47页）中简要清楚地叙述过这个观点。基于1978年6月举行的人类遗传学研讨会文集CIBA卷中，在沃克文章[2]后的扩展讨论（第39~45页）中显示，那个时候这种观点已经被博德默、芬彻姆和我们两位作者之一所熟知。这场讨论主要集中于重复DNA，因为这是沃克的文章主题，但是我们应该在更广泛的意义上使用自私的DNA这个概念，它不仅仅指明显的重复DNA，还包括其他的没有或有很少功能的DNA序列，比如内含子内的大多数DNA和基因之间的部分DNA序列。"自私的DNA"这一说法已经在两个场合简要提及[3,4]。杜利特尔和萨皮恩扎[5]（见上篇文章）已经不约而同达成了相似观点。

## The Amount of DNA

The large amounts of DNA in the cells of most higher organisms and, in particular, the exceptionally large amounts in certain animal and plant species—the so-called $C$ value paradox—has been an unsolved puzzle for a considerable period (see reviews in refs 6-8). As is well known, this DNA consists in part of "simple" sequences, an extreme example of which is the very large amounts of fairly pure poly d(AT) in certain crabs. Simple sequences, which are situated in chromosomes largely but not entirely in the heterochromatin, are usually not transcribed. Another class of repetitive sequences, the so-called "intermediate repetitive", have much longer and less regular repeats. Such sequences are interspersed with "unique" DNA at many places in the chromosome, the precise pattern of interspersion being to some extent different in different species. Leaving aside genes which code for structural RNA of one sort or another (such as transfer RNA and ribosomal RNA), which would be expected to occur in multiple copies (since, unlike protein, their final products are the result of only one stage of magnification, not two), the majority of genes coding for proteins appear to exist in "single" copies, meaning here one or a few. A typical example would be the genes for α-globin, which occur in one to three copies and the human $\beta$-like globins, of which there are four main types, all related to each other but used for slightly different purposes. Notable exceptions are the proteins of the immune system, and probably those of the histocompatibility and related systems. Another exception is the genes for the five major types of histone which also occur in multiple copies. Even allowing for all such special case, the estimated number of genes in the human genome appears too few to account for the $3\times10^9$ base pairs found per haploid set of DNA, although it must be admitted that all such arguments are very far from conclusive.

Several authors[8–13] have suggested that the DNA of higher organisms consists of a minority of sequences with highly specific functions plus a majority with little or no specificity. Even some of the so-called single-copy DNA may have no specific function. A striking example comes from the study of two rather similar species of *Xenopus*. These can form viable hybrids, although these hybrids are usually sterile. However, detailed molecular hybridization studies show that there has been a large amount of DNA sequence divergence since the evolutionary separation of their forebears. These authors[13] conclude "only one interpretation seems reasonable, and that is that the specific sequence of much of the single-copy DNA is not functionally required during the life of the animal. This is not to say that this DNA is functionless, only that its specific sequence is not important".

There is also evidence to suggest that the majority of DNA sequences in most higher organisms do not code for protein since they do not occur at all in messenger RNA (for reviews see refs 14, 15). Nor is it very plausible that all this extra DNA is needed for gene control, although some portion of it certainly must be.

We also have to account for the vast amount of DNA found in certain species, such as lilies and salamanders, which may amount to as much as 20 times that found in the human genome. It seems totally implausible that the number of radically different genes needed

## DNA 的数量

大多数高等生物的细胞中存在的大量 DNA，特别是某些动物和植物物种中存在异常大量的 DNA，所谓的 C 值悖论已经在相当长的一段时期内成为一个未解的谜团（见参考文献 6~8 的综述）。众所周知，这种 DNA 存在于部分"简单"的序列中，一个极端的例子就是某种蟹中存在大量非常纯的多聚 d(AT)。大量位于染色体中但不完全位于异染色质中的简单序列通常不被转录。另外一种重复序列即所谓的"中度重复序列"，包含更长但更不规则的重复序列。这些序列与"独特的"DNA 穿插分布到染色体的很多位置，这种分布的精确模式在不同物种中有一定程度的不同。撇开编码各种结构 RNA（例如转运 RNA 和核糖体 RNA）的基因不谈，它们通常存在多个拷贝（与蛋白质的两步合成不同，它们的最终产物是一步合成的结果）。大多数编码蛋白质的基因以"单"拷贝形式存在，这里的"单"拷贝指一个或几个拷贝。一个典型的例子就是 α–球蛋白基因，存在一到三个拷贝；人类 β–样球蛋白有四种主要类型，彼此相互关联但用途稍有不同。值得注意的例外是免疫系统的蛋白质，比如那些组织相容性及其相关系统的蛋白质。另一个例外是编码五种主要类型组蛋白的基因，同样存在多个拷贝。即使算上所有这些特例，相对于每组单倍体 DNA 拥有的 $3×10^9$ 个碱基对，对人类基因组内基因数量的估计还是太少了，虽然不可否认所有这些争议离下结论还为时过早。

几位作者 [8-13] 曾经提出这样的观点：高等生物的 DNA 是由少量具有高度特异性功能的序列和大量特异性程度低或没有特异性的序列组成。甚至一些所谓的单拷贝 DNA 可能也不具有特异性功能。一个突出的例子来自对爪蟾属两种特别相似物种的研究。它们可以繁殖可成活的杂交后代，虽然这些杂交后代通常是不育的。然而精细的分子杂交研究显示，从它们祖先的进化分离开始就出现了大量的 DNA 序列差异。这些作者 [13] 得出结论"只有一种解释较为合理，在动物的生命过程中许多单拷贝 DNA 的特异性序列在功能上并不是必需的。这并不是说这些 DNA 没有功能，只是它的特异序列并不重要。"

同样有证据表明大多数高等生物的大部分 DNA 序列并不编码蛋白质，因为它们根本不出现在信使 RNA 中(综述见参考文献 14,15)。尽管一部分必定会起到作用，但是要说这些多余的 DNA 都是基因调控所必需的，也并不合理。

我们还必须解释的是，在某些物种（例如百合和蝾螈）中发现了惊人数量的 DNA，其数量约为人类基因组的二十倍。蝾螈所需的完全不同基因的数量是人类的二十倍是完全不合理的假设；而且没有证据表明蝾螈的基因大都存在二十个相当类

in a salamander is 20 times that in a man. Nor is there evidence to support the idea that salamander genes are mostly present in about 20 fairly similar copies. The conviction has been growing that much of this extra DNA is "junk", in other words, that it has little specificity and conveys little or no selective advantage to the organism.

Another place where there appears to be more nucleic acid than one might expect is in the primary transcripts of the DNA of higher organisms which are found in the so-called heteronuclear RNA. It has been known for some time that this RNA is typically longer than the messenger RNA molecules found in the corresponding cytoplasm. Heteronuclear RNA contains these messenger RNA sequences but has many other sequences which are never found in the cytoplasm. The phenomenon, has been somewhat clarified by the recent discovery of introns in many genes (for a general introduction see ref. 4). Although the evidence is still very preliminary, it certainly suggests that much of the base sequence in the interior of some introns may be junk, in that these sequences drift rapidly in evolution, both in detail and in size. Moreover, the number of introns may differ even in closely related genes, as in the two genes for rat preproinsulin[16]. Whether there is junk between genes is unclear but it is noteworthy that the four genes for the human $\beta$-like globins, which occur fairly near together in a single stretch of DNA, occupy a region no less than 40 kilobases long[17]. This greatly exceeds the total length of the four primary transcripts (that is the four mRNA precursors), an amount estimated to be considerably less than 10 kilobases. There is little evidence to indicate that there are other coding sequences between these genes (although the question is still quite open) and a tenable hypothesis is that much of this interspersed DNA has little specific function.

In summary, then, there is a large amount of evidence which suggests, but does not prove, that much DNA in higher organisms is little better than junk. We shall assume, for the rest of this article, that this hypothesis is true. We therefore need to explain how such DNA arose in the first place and why it is not speedily eliminated, since, by definition, it contributes little or nothing to the fitness of the organism.

## What is Selfish DNA?

The theory of natural selection, in its more general formulation, deals with the competition between replicating entities. It shows that, in such a competition, the more efficient replicators increase in number at the expense of their less efficient competitors. After a sufficient time, only the most efficient replicators survive. The idea of selfish DNA is firmly based on this general theory of natural selection, but it deals with selection in an unfamiliar context.

The familiar neo-darwinian theory of natural selection is concerned with the competition between organisms in a population. At the level of molecular genetics it provides an explanation of the spread of "useful" genes or DNA sequences within a population. Organisms that carry a gene that contributes positively to fitness tend to increase their representation at the expense of organisms lacking that gene. In time, only those organisms that carry the useful gene survive. Natural selection also predicts the spread of

似的拷贝。所以可以确信，很多这些冗余的 DNA 都是"垃圾"；换句话说，它们几乎没有任何特异性，而且对传递生物的选择优势几乎没有任何贡献。

另一处比预想中有更多核酸的地方在高等生物 DNA 的初级转录物中，这是在所谓的异核 RNA 中发现的。已知这种 RNA 通常比在相应的细胞质中发现的信使 RNA 要长。异核 RNA 包含信使 RNA 的序列，同时还包含许多细胞质中未发现的其他序列。基于近期对基因内含子的一些发现，这种现象在一定程度上得到了解释（简介见参考文献 4）。虽然这些证据还很初步，但是可以肯定一些内含子内部的很多碱基序列可能是垃圾，因为这些序列在进化中会迅速漂变，无论是在内容还是长度方面都是如此。而且在一些非常相似的基因（例如大鼠前胰岛素原的两个基因）中，内含子的数目也有可能不同 [16]。基因之间是否有垃圾序列还不是很清楚，但是值得注意的是人类 β–样球蛋白的四个基因一起紧密地分布在 DNA 的同一条单链上，占据了一段不小于 40kb 的区域 [17]。这大大超过了四个初级转录物（四个 mRNA 前体）的总长度，据估算这些初级转录产物的总长肯定小于 10kb。鲜有证据表明这些基因之间存在其他编码序列（虽然这个问题仍未解决），而一种可靠的假说就是大量分散在其中的 DNA 几乎都没有特异性的功能。

总而言之，大量的证据表明，高等生物中的很多 DNA 和垃圾差不多，但尚未证实。我们可以在下面的叙述中假定这个假设是正确的。那么我们首先需要解释的是这样的 DNA 是怎样产生的，以及既然像所定义的那样，它对生物的适应性几乎不起作用，那它为何最初没有被迅速地淘汰。

### 什么是自私的 DNA？

自然选择学说在其更为广义的阐述中，论述了复制实体间的竞争。该理论认为，在这种竞争中，可以看到能力较强的复制个体以牺牲能力较弱的竞争者为代价增加个体数量。经历了足够长的时间后，只有能力最强的复制子得以存活。自私的 DNA 的理论牢固地建立在自然选择这个普遍学说上，但它解决的是一个不常见的背景中的选择问题。

我们熟知的新达尔文自然选择学说涉及的是种群中生物体间的竞争问题。它在分子遗传学的层面上给出了"有用的"基因或 DNA 序列在种群中扩增的解释。携带一个促进其适应性的基因的生物以牺牲缺乏这种基因的个体为代价提高它们自身的存活率。经过一段时间，只有那些携带这种有用基因的生物才得以存活。自然选

a gene or other DNA sequence within a single genome, provided certain conditions are satisfied. If an organism carrying several copies of the sequence is fitter than an organism carrying a single copy, and if mechanisms exist for the multiplication of the relevant sequence, then natural selection must lead to the emergence of a population in which the sequence is represented several times in every genome.

The idea of selfish DNA is different. It is again concerned with the spread of a given DNA within the genome. However, in the case of selfish DNA, the sequence which spreads makes no contribution to the phenotype of the organism, except insofar as it is a slight burden to the cell that contains it. Selfish DNA sequences may be transcribed in some cases and not in others. The spread of selfish DNA sequences within the genome can be compared to the spread of a not-too-harmful parasite within its host.

## Mechanisms for DNA Spreading

The inheritance of a repeated DNA sequence in a population of eukaryotes clearly requires that the multiplication which produced it occurred in the germ line. Furthermore, any mechanism that can lead to the multiplication of useful DNA will probably lead to the multiplication of selfish DNA (and vice versa). Of course, natural selection subsequently discriminates between multiple sequences of different kinds, but it does not necessarily prevent the multiplication of neutral or harmful sequences.

Multiplication in the germ-line sequence can occur in nondividing cells or during meiosis and mitosis (within lineages that lead to the germ line). In the former case, the mechanisms available resemble those that are well documented for prokaryotes, that is, multiplication may occur in eukaryotes through the integration of viruses or of elements analogous to transposons and insertion sequences. Doolittle and Sapienza[5] have discussed these mechanisms in some detail, particularly for prokaryotes. They are likely to lead to the spreading of DNA sequences to widely separated positions on the chromosomes.

During mitosis and meiosis, multiplication (or deletion) is likely to occur by unequal crossing over. This mechanism will often lead to the formation of tandem repeats. It is well documented for the tRNA "genes" of *Drosophila* and for various other tandemly repeated sequences in higher organisms.

## The Amount and Location of Selfish DNA

Natural selection "within" the genome will favour the indefinite spreading of selfish preferred replicators. Natural selection between genotypes provides a balancing force that attempts to maintain the total amount of selfish DNA at an equilibrium (steady state) level—organisms whose genomes contain an excessive proportion of selfish DNA would be at a metabolic disadvantage relative to organisms with less selfish DNA, and so would be eliminated by the normal mechanism of natural selection. Excessive spreading of functionless replicators may be considered as a "cancer" of the genome—the uncontrolled

择也预言，如果满足所需条件，一个单基因组内的基因或其他DNA序列将在其中得以扩增。如果携带了一段序列的多个拷贝的生物比只携带一个拷贝的生物的适应性要好，并且此机制由于相关序列的增殖而继续存在，那么自然选择将导致一类种群的出现，在这个种群中，该序列在每个基因组中多次重复。

自私的DNA的概念并不相同。它也与基因组中一段给定的DNA的扩增有关。然而，对于自私的DNA来说，扩增的序列对于生物体的表型没有任何贡献，而且在这种情况下对于包含它的细胞来说是个轻微的负担。自私DNA的序列只在某些情况下才可能被转录，其他情况下都不会。自私DNA的序列在基因组中的扩增就像害处不大的寄生虫在宿主中的繁殖。

## DNA扩增的机制

在真核生物种群中，一段重复DNA序列若要遗传下去，必须保证产生该序列的增殖发生在生殖细胞系中。进一步说，任何产生有用DNA的增殖的机制同样可能产生自私DNA的增殖（反之亦然）。当然，自然选择接下来会区别对待不同种类的多种序列，但未必会阻止中性或有害序列的扩增。

生殖细胞系中的序列增殖也会发生在非分裂的细胞中或者减数分裂（在产生生殖细胞系的株系中）和有丝分裂过程中。在前一种情况下，现有的机制类似于已在原核生物中得到很好证明的机制，真核生物中的基因复制可能是通过病毒或与转座子和插入序列类似的元件的整合发生的。杜利特尔和萨皮恩扎[5]已经在某些细节上讨论了这些机制，特别是对于原核生物。它们很可能导致DNA序列扩散到染色体广泛的分散位点上。

在减数分裂和有丝分裂过程中，增殖（或缺失）有可能通过不等交换发生。这种机制经常导致串联重复序列的形成。果蝇的tRNA"基因"和高等生物其他各种串联重复序列就是很好的证明。

## 自私DNA的数量和位点

基因组内的自然选择倾向于自私的优先复制子的无限扩增。基因型间的自然选择提供了一种平衡力使自私DNA的总量保持平衡（稳定状态）——基因组中含过量比例的自私DNA的生物比含较少自私DNA的生物，在新陈代谢方面将处于劣势，因此将在自然选择的正常机制下被淘汰。没有功能的复制子的过度扩增可以看作是基因组的"癌症"——基因组中一个片段不受控制的扩增将最终导致允许这种扩增

expansion of one segment of the genome would ultimately lead to the extinction of the genotype that permits such expansion. Of course, we do not know whether extinction of genotypes in nature even occurs for this reason.

It is hard to get beyond generalities of this kind. To do so we would, at least, need to know how much selective disadvantage results from the presence of a given amount of useless DNA. Even this minimal information is not easily acquired, so we cannot produce other than qualitative arguments.

It seems certain that the metabolic energy cost of replicating a superfluous short DNA sequence in a genome containing $10^9$ base pairs would be very small. If, for example, the selective advantage were equal to the proportion of the genome made up by the extra DNA, a sequence of 1,000 base pairs would produce a selective disadvantage of only $10^{-6}$. If the selective disadvantage were proportional to the extra energy cost divided by the total metabolic energy expended per cell per generation, the disadvantage would be much smaller. The selective disadvantage might be greater in more stringent conditions, but it is still hard to believe that a relatively small proportion of selfish DNA could be selected against strongly.

On the other hand, when the total amount of selfish DNA becomes comparable to or greater than that of useful DNA, it seems likely that the selective disadvantage would be significant. We may expect, therefore, that the mechanisms for the formation and deletion of nonspecific DNA will adjust, in each organism, so that the load of DNA is sufficiently small that it can be accommodated without producing a large selective disadvantage. The proportion of nonspecific DNA in any particular organism will thus depend on the lifestyle of the organism, and particularly on its sensitivity to metabolic stress during the most vulnerable part of the life cycle.

We can make one prediction on the basis of energy costs. Selfish DNA will accumulate to a greater extent in non-transcribed regions of the genome than in those that are transcribed. Of course, selfish DNA will in most cases be excluded from translated sequences, because the insertion of amino acids within a protein will almost always have serious consequences, even in diploid organisms (but see the suggestion by F.H.C.C.[18]).

At first sight it might seem anomalous that natural selection does not eliminate all selfish DNA. Since the suggestion that much eukaryotic DNA is useless distinguishes the selfish DNA hypothesis from many closely related proposals, it may be useful to take up this point in some detail.

First, the elimination of disadvantaged organisms from a population, by their more favoured competitors, takes a number of generations several times larger than the reciprocal of the selective disadvantage. If the selective disadvantage associated with a stretch of useless DNA in higher organisms is only $10^{-6}$, it would take $10^6$-$10^8$ years to

的基因型的消失。当然，我们甚至不知道自然界中基因型的消失是否是出于这个原因。

在这类问题上得到超出一般性的概括是很困难的。如果要研究，我们至少要知道一定数量无用 DNA 的存在将会产生多少选择性的劣势。即使这个最基本的信息都很难得到，所以我们只能进行一些定性的讨论。

似乎可以确定的是，在一个拥有 $10^9$ 个碱基对的基因组中复制一段多余的短 DNA 序列所消耗的代谢能量是很低的。例如，如果选择优势与冗余 DNA 组成的基因组的比例是均等的，那么一段 1,000 个碱基对的序列产生的选择劣势仅仅为百万分之一。如果这种选择劣势与每一代每个细胞消耗的总代谢能量分配的额外能量消耗成比例，这种劣势将会更微不足道。这种选择劣势在较苛刻的条件下可能会变得更加重要，但是仍然很难让人相信相对较小比例的自私 DNA 会面临激烈淘汰。

另一方面，当自私 DNA 的总量与有用 DNA 的量相当或者比其更大的时候，选择性的劣势可能会变得很显著。因此，我们可以预见，非特异性 DNA 形成和消除的机制会在每个生物体中得以调节，使 DNA 的负荷足够小来适应环境，而不至于产生大的选择性劣势。因此任何特定生物中非特异 DNA 的比例将取决于这种生物的生存方式，特别是取决于它在整个生命周期最脆弱时期对代谢压力的敏感性。

我们可以基于能量消耗进行一番假设。自私 DNA 在基因组非转录区域将比转录区域积累的数量多。当然，自私 DNA 在大多数情况下被排除在翻译序列之外，因为蛋白质内氨基酸的插入往往会产生严重后果，即使在二倍体生物中也是如此（见克里克 [18] 的建议）。

自然选择并没有淘汰所有的自私 DNA，最初看起来有些不合常理。由于真核生物的多数 DNA 无用的观点使自私 DNA 假说与许多相近的提议区别开来，那么对这个观点进行一些深入研究可能是有用的。

首先，处于劣势的生物被处于相对优势的竞争者从种群中淘汰，需要经历的代数比选择劣势的倒数大很多倍。在高等生物中如果与一段无用 DNA 相关联的选择劣势只有 $10^{-6}$，那么通过竞争淘汰这段基因大概需要 $10^6\sim10^8$ 年。对一些典型的

eliminate it by competition. For typical higher organisms this is a very long time, so the elimination of a particular stretch of selfish DNA may be a very slow process even on a geological time scale. Second, the mechanisms for the deletion of short sequences of DNA may be inefficient, since there is no strong selective pressure for the development of "corrective" measures when the "fault" carries a relatively small selective penalty. Taken together, these arguments suggest that the elimination of a particular piece of junk from the genome may be a very slow process.

This in turn suggests that the amount of useless DNA in the genome is a consequence of a dynamic balance. The organism "attempts" to limit the spread of selfish DNA by controlling the mechanism for gene duplication, but is constrained by imperfections in genetic processes and/or by the need to permit some duplication of advantageous genes. Selfish DNA sequences "attempt" to subvert these mechanisms and may be able to do so comparatively rapidly because mutation will affect them directly. On the other hand, the defence mechanisms of the host are likely to depend on the action of protein and therefore may evolve more slowly. Once established within the genome, useless sequences probably have a long "life expectancy".

For any particular type of selfish DNA, there is no reason that a steady state should necessarily be reached in evolution. The situation would be continually changing. A particular type of DNA might first spread rather successfully over the chromosomes. The host might then evolve a mechanism which reduced or eliminated further spreading. It might also evolve a method for preferentially deleting it. At the same time, random mutations in the selfish DNA might make it more like ordinary DNA and so, perhaps, less easy to remove. Eventually, these sequences, possibly by now rather remote from those originally introduced, may cease to spread and be slowly eliminated. Meanwhile, other types of selfish DNA may originate, expand and evolve in a similar way.

In short, we may expect a kind of molecular struggle for existence within the DNA of the chromosomes, using the process of natural selection. There is no reason to believe that this is likely to be much simpler or more easy to predict than evolution at any other level. At bottom, the existence of selfish DNA is possible because DNA is a molecule which is replicated very easily and because selfish DNA occurs in an environment in which DNA replication is a necessity. It thus has the opportunity of subverting these essential mechanisms to its own purpose.

## The Inheritance of Selfish DNA

Although the inheritance of selfish DNA will occur mainly within a mendelian framework, it is likely to be different in detail and more complex than simple mendelian inheritance. This is due both to the multiplication mechanisms, which in one way or another will produce repeated copies (see the discussion by Doolittle and Sapienza[5]), and to the fact that these copies are likely to be distributed round the chromosomes rather than being located in a single place in the genome as most normal genes are. For both these reasons,

高等生物来说这是一段很长的时间，所以淘汰一段特定的自私DNA即使在地质年代表中也可能是一段漫长的过程。其次，短序列DNA的消除机制效率很低，因为当这种"错误"带来的选择惩罚相对较小时，对"矫正"措施的发展就没有很大的选择压力。总之，这些争议提示，从基因组中淘汰一段特定的垃圾序列可能是一段很漫长的过程。

这也反过来提示基因组中大量无用DNA的存在可能是一种动态平衡的结果。生物"试图"通过控制基因复制的机制来限制自私DNA的扩增，但是受到一些限制，包括遗传过程的缺陷和（或）一些有利基因复制的需求。自私DNA序列"试图"破坏这些机制，而且由于突变的直接影响而可能相对较快地实现。另一方面，宿主的防御机制很可能是依靠蛋白质的功能，所以进化得更加缓慢。一旦在基因组中形成，无用序列很可能拥有一段很长的"期望寿命"。

对任何一种特定类型的自私DNA而言，它们都没有理由要在进化过程中达到一种稳定状态。情况会一直变化。一种特定类型的DNA会首先在染色体范围成功扩增。宿主会随之进化出相应机制来减少或消除其进一步的扩增，也有可能进化出某种方法优先删除这段序列。与此同时，自私DNA内部的随机突变很可能使它与普通DNA更加类似，从而更加难以去除。最终，这些序列与当初产生时相比已经有了很大差异，而且可能会逐渐停止扩增并慢慢被淘汰。同时，其他类型的自私DNA也以相似的方式产生、扩散和进化。

总之，我们可以认为这是染色体DNA内的分子为了生存，利用自然选择过程而进行的一种战斗。没有理由相信这个过程比其他水平的进化过程更简单或更容易。从根本上说，自私DNA的存在是可能的，因为DNA是一种很容易复制的分子，而且自私的DNA所处的环境中，DNA复制是一种必需。因此它有机会破坏这些基本机制，以达到自己的目的。

## 自私DNA的遗传

虽然自私DNA的遗传方式基本处在孟德尔定律的框架中，但是与单纯的孟德尔定律相比，其在细节上有所不同并且更加复杂。这不仅仅是因为增殖机制会以某种形式产生重复序列（见杜利特尔和萨皮恩扎[5]的讨论），还因为这些拷贝很可能分散到染色体各处，而不会像大多数普通基因那样只定位于基因组某个固定的位置。基于这两个原因，一种特殊类型的自私DNA很可能比低选择优势的普通基因在种

a particular type of selfish DNA is likely to spread more rapidly through a population than would a normal gene with a low selective advantage. It will be even more rapid if selfish DNA can spread horizontally between different individuals in a population, due to viruses or other infectious agents, although it should be remembered that such "infection" must affect the germ line and not merely the soma. If this initial spread takes place when the additional DNA produced is relatively small in amount, it is unlikely to be seriously hindered by the organism selecting against it. The study of these processes will clearly require a new type of population genetics.

## Can Selfish DNA Acquire a Specific Function?

It would be surprising if the host organism did not occasionally find some use for particular selfish DNA sequences, especially if there were many different sequences widely distributed over the chromosomes. One obvious use, as repeatedly stressed by Britten and Davidson[19,20], would be for control purposes at one level or another. This seems more than plausible.

It has often been argued (see, for example, ref. 21) that for the evolution of complex higher organisms, what is required is not so much the evolution of new proteins as the evolution of new control mechanisms and especially mechanisms which control together sets of genes which previously had been regulated separately. To be useful, a new control sequence on the DNA is likely to be needed in a number of distinct places in the genome. It has rarely been considered how this could be brought about expeditiously by the rather random methods available to natural selection.

A mechanism which scattered, more or less at random, many kinds of repeated sequences in many places in the genome would appear to be rather good for this purpose. Most sets of such sequences would be unlikely to find themselves in the right combination of places to be useful but, by chance, the members of one particular set might be located so that they could be used to turn on (or turn off) together a set of genes which had never been controlled before in a coordinated way. A next way of doing this would be to use as control sequences not the many identical copies distributed over the genome, but a small subset of these which had mutated away from the master sequence in the same manner.

On this picture, each set of repeated sequences might be "tested" from time to time in evolution by the production of a control macromolecule (for example, a special protein) to recognize those sequences. If this produced a favourable result, natural selection would confirm and extend the new mechanism. If not, it would be selected against and discarded. Such a process implies that most sets of repeated sequences will never be of use since, on statistical grounds, their members will usually be in unsuitable places.

It thus seems unlikely that all selfish DNA has acquired a special function, especially in those organisms with very high $C$ values. Nor do we feel that if one example of a particular sequence acquires a function, all the copies of that sequence will necessarily do

群中扩增得更快。如果自私 DNA 能通过病毒或其他感染因子在一个种群的不同个体中水平扩散，速度将会更快，应当记住，尽管这种"感染"肯定要影响整个生殖细胞系而不是仅仅影响体细胞。如果这种初始扩增在产生的冗余 DNA 数量相对较小时发生，则不太可能受到生物体选择对其的严重阻碍。对于这些过程的研究显然需要一种新型的种群遗传学。

## 自私 DNA 能获得一种特异性功能吗？

如果宿主生物没能偶然地发现特定自私 DNA 序列的某些功能，这会很令人惊奇，特别是有很多不同序列广泛分布于染色体的时候。如布里滕和戴维森 [19,20] 反复强调的，一个明显的功能就是在一定水平上实现调控的目的。这似乎是非常合理的。

我们经常讨论（例如见参考文献 21），对于复杂的高等生物的进化，与其说需要新蛋白的进化，不如说需要新的调控机制的进化，特别是集中调控几组基因的机制，而这几组基因之前是被分别调控的。更为有用的是，一段 DNA 上新的调控序列可能被基因组中很多不同的位置需求。很少有人思考，非常随机的自然选择是如何使这些事件快速发生的。

将多种重复序列或多或少任意地分散到基因组各处的机制对达成这个目标是很有利的。大多数这样的序列组不太可能位于正确的位置而发挥作用，但是偶尔也有可能某组特定序列的成员正好处在合适的位置可用来共同开启（或关闭）一组以前从未以协同方式调控的基因。接下来发生的是，这些序列被用作调控序列，它们并不是遍布基因组的很多相同的拷贝，而只是这些拷贝中以相同方式从主序列变异而来的一小部分序列。

在这个框架下，每组重复序列在进化过程中都会时常受到一个调控大分子（如一种特殊的蛋白质）的"检测"而得到识别。如果产生了一个有利的结果，自然选择就会认可并推广这种新机制。如果没有，这种机制就会被排斥并被淘汰。这样一个过程表明大多数的重复序列毫无用处，因为从统计学角度来看，它们的成员通常会位于不适当的位置。

因此，所有自私 DNA 都具有特殊功能是不太可能的，特别是对于那些具有高 $C$ 值的生物而言。我们认为，如果一段特殊序列的一个拷贝获得了一种功能，其他

so. As selfish DNA is likely to be distributed over the chromosomes in rather a random manner, it seems unlikely that every copy of a potentially useful sequence will be in the right position to function correctly. For example, if a specific sequence within an intron were used to control the act of splicing that intron, a similar sequence in an untranscribed region between genes would obviously not be able to act in this way.

In some circumstances, the sheer bulk of selfish DNA may be used by the organism for its own purpose. That is, the selfish DNA may acquire a nonspecific function which gives the organism a selective advantage. This is the point of view favoured by Cavalier-Smith in a very detailed and suggestive article[12] which the reader should consult. He proposes that excess DNA may be the mechanism the cell uses to slow up development or to make bigger cells. However, we suspect that both slow growth and large cell size could be evolved just as well by other more direct mechanisms. We prefer to think that the organism has tolerated selfish DNA which has arisen because of the latter's own selective pressure.

Thus, some selfish DNA may acquire a useful function and confer a selective advantage on the organism. Using the analogy of parasitism, slightly harmful infestation may ultimately be transformed into a symbiosis. What we would stress is that not all selfish DNA is likely to become useful. Much of it may have no specific function at all. It would be folly in such cases to hunt obsessively for one. To continue our analogy, it is difficult to accept the idea that all human parasites have been selected by human beings for their own advantage.

## Life Style

The effect of nonspecific DNA on the life style of the organism has been considered by several authors, in particular by Cavalier-Smith[12] and by Hindergardner[8]. We shall not attempt to review all their ideas here but instead will give one example to show the type of argument used.

Bennett[22] has brought together the measurements of DNA content for higher herbaceous plants. There is a striking connection between DNA content per cell and the minimum generation time of the plant. In brief, if such an angiosperm has more than 10 pg of DNA per cell, it is unlikely to be an ephemeral (that is, a plant with a short generation time). If it is a diploid and has more than 30 pg of DNA, it is highly likely to be an obligate perennial, rather than an annual or an ephemeral. The converse, however, is not true, there being a fair number of perennials with a DNA content of less than 30 pg and a few with less than 10 pg. A clear picture emerges that if a herbaceous plant has too much DNA it cannot have a short generation time.

This is explained by assuming that the extra DNA needs a bigger nucleus to hold it and that this increases both the size of the cell and the duration of meiosis and generally slows up the development of the plant. An interesting exception is that the duration of meiosis,

所有的拷贝未必也会获得该功能。由于自私 DNA 可能是以相当随机的方式遍布于染色体中，所以一个潜在有用序列的每一个拷贝不太可能都位于正确的位置发挥正常功能。例如，如果一段位于内含子内部的特异性序列起到调控内含子剪接的作用，那么显然另一段位于基因间非转录区的相似序列并不能发挥这种作用。

在一些情况下，生物体可能会利用自私 DNA 的绝对数量来达到自己的目的。即自私 DNA 可能获得一种非特异性的功能而使生物体具有选择优势。这是卡弗利尔 – 史密斯在一篇详尽且很有启发性的文章 [12] 中所支持的观点，读者可以作为参考。他提出冗余的 DNA 可能是细胞用于减缓发育或者产生更大细胞的机制。然而，值得我们怀疑的是减缓生长与增大细胞尺寸方面的进化都可以通过其他更直接的方式实现。我们更倾向于认为，生物体包容了因为（自私 DNA）自身选择压力而产生的自私 DNA。

因此，一些自私 DNA 可能获得有用的功能而赋予生物体选择优势。与寄生的过程相类似，轻微有害的感染最终可能转化为共生。我们应当强调的是并非所有的自私 DNA 都可能变成有用的。它们中的大多数根本没有任何特异性功能。在这些情况下，执意寻求一个功能是愚蠢的。继续我们的类比，这就好像很难让人接受所有的人类寄生虫都是由人类为自身利益而选择出来的。

## 生命方式

已有多位作者考虑到非特异性 DNA 对生物生命方式的影响，特别是卡弗利尔 – 史密斯 [12] 和欣德加德纳 [8]。在这里我们不再试图复述他们所有的观点而是举例来说明用到的论据的类型。

本内特 [22] 归纳了高等草本植物 DNA 含量的测量方法。每个细胞内的 DNA 含量和植物最短世代时间之间有显著相关性。简而言之，如果一种被子植物每个细胞含有超过 10 pg 的 DNA，它就不可能是一种短生植物（指世代时间很短的植物）。如果它是二倍体并含有超过 30 pg 的 DNA，那它极有可能是专性多年生植物，而不是一年生或短生植物。然而逆命题并不成立，有相当一部分多年生植物的 DNA 含量低于 30 pg，甚至有几种低于 10 pg。可以得到一个清晰的结论是如果一种草本植物含有大量 DNA，那么它的世代时间不会很短。

这种现象可以用一种假设解释，那就是冗余 DNA 需要更大的细胞核来容纳，这就增加了细胞的大小和减数分裂持续的时间，通常也减缓了植物的生长。但有一

is, if anything, shorter for polyploid species than for their diploid ancestors[23]. This suggests that it is the ratio of good DNA to junk DNA rather than the total DNA content which influences the duration of meiosis.

An analogous situation may obtain in certain American species of salamander. These often differ considerably in the rapidity of their development and of their life cycles, the tropical species tending to take longer than the more temperate ones. Drs David Wake and Herbert MacGregor (personal communication) tell us that preliminary evidence suggests that species with the longer developmental times often have the higher $C$ values. This appears to parallel the situation just described for the herbacious plants. It remains to be seen if further evidence will continue to support this generalization. (See the interesting paper by Oeldorfe et al.[25] on 25 species of frogs. They conclude that "genome size sets a limit beyond which development cannot be accelerated".)

## Testing the Theory

The theory of selfish DNA is not so vague that it cannot be tested. We can think of three general ways to do this. In the first place, it is important to know where DNA sequences occur which appear to have little obvious function, whether they are associated with flanking or other sequences of any special sort and how homologous sequences differ in different organisms and in different species, either in sequence or in position on the chromosome. For example, it has recently been shown by Young[24] that certain intermediate repetitive sequences in *Drosophila* are often in different chromosomal positions in different strains of the same species.

Second, if the increase of selfish DNA and its movement around the chromosome are not rare events in evolution, it may be feasible to study, in laboratory experiments, the actual molecular mechanisms involved in these processes.

Third, one would hope that a careful study of all the nonspecific effects of extra DNA would give us a better idea of how it affected different aspects of cellular behaviour. In particular, it is important to discover whether the addition of nonspecific DNA does, in fact, slow down cells metabolically and for what reasons. Such information, together with a careful study of the physiology and life style of related organisms with dissimilar amounts of DNA, should eventually make it possible to explain these differences in a convincing way.

## Conclusion

Although it is an old idea that much DNA in higher organisms has no specific function[8-12], and although it has been suggested before that this nonspecific DNA may rise to levels which are acceptable or even advantageous to an organism[8,12], depending on certain features of its life style, we feel that to regard much of this nonspecific DNA as selfish DNA is genuinely different from most earlier proposals. Such a point of view is especially useful in thinking about the dynamic aspects of nonspecific DNA. It directs attention

个有趣的例外，多倍体物种减数分裂所持续的时间比它们的二倍体祖先更短[23]。这种现象说明，影响减数分裂时间的是有用 DNA 与垃圾 DNA 的比值，而不是全部 DNA 的含量。

在美国的某种蝶蝾中也可以发现类似的情况。它们的发育和生长周期的速率往往相差很大，热带品种通常比温带品种需要更长的生长发育时间。戴维·韦克博士和赫伯特·麦格雷戈博士（个人交流）告诉我们，有初步证据显示发育期较长的物种通常具有较高的 C 值。这个结论与前面描述的草本植物的情况相类似。是否有更进一步的证据来继续支持这个推断，还要拭目以待。（请参阅厄尔德费等[25]关于 25 种蛙类的有趣文章。他们得出结论"基因组的大小为发育设置了上限，导致其不能加速发育。"）

### 检验此学说

自私 DNA 的学说并没有模糊到不可检验。我们可以想到三种普适的检验方法。首先，重要的是弄清楚那些看似没有显著功能的 DNA 序列位于什么位置，它们是否与侧翼或其他任何特殊类型的序列相关，以及同源序列在不同生物不同物种间差别如何，包括序列本身及其在其染色体中所处位置。例如近期扬[24]发现果蝇中某些中度重复序列在同一物种的不同种系中常常位于染色体的不同位置。

第二，如果在进化过程中，自私 DNA 的增加及其在染色体内的移动并不罕见，那么在实验室中研究这个过程中实际的分子机制是可行的。

第三，我们希望对冗余 DNA 所有非特异性作用的深入研究可以帮助我们更好地理解它如何影响细胞活动的不同方面。特别重要的是，去探索这些非特异性 DNA 的加入是否的确减缓了细胞的新陈代谢，以及是什么原因造成了这种现象。这些信息，加上对不同含量 DNA 的相关生物的生理和生命方式的深入研究，最终可能会有力地解释这些差异。

### 结　论

虽然高等生物的大多数 DNA 都没有特异性功能[8-12]这一想法不再新奇，以前也有人认为这种非特异性的 DNA 会升级到一定程度，使其不但被生物体接受，甚至会使生物具有一定优势[8,12]。但是基于它的生命方式的某些特点，我们认为把大量非特异性 DNA 视为自私 DNA 的观点与早期的大多数提议有切实的差异。这个观点在

to the mechanisms involved in the spread and evolution of such DNA and it cautions one against looking for a special function for every piece of DNA which drifts rapidly in sequence or in position on the genome.

While proper care should be exercised both in labelling as selfish DNA every piece of DNA whose function is not immediately apparent and in invoking plausible but unproven hypotheses concerning the details of natural selection, the idea seems a useful one to bear in mind when exploring the complexities of the genomes of higher organisms. It could well make sense of many of the puzzles and paradoxes which have arisen over the last 10 or 15 years. The main facts are, at first sight, so odd that only a somewhat unconventional idea is likely to explain them.

We thank W. Ford Doolittle and C. Sapienza for showing us their article before publication, and Drs D. Wake and H. MacGregor for allowing us to quote some of their unpublished conclusions about salamanders. This work was supported by the Eugene and Estelle Ferhauf Foundation, the J. W. Kieckhefer Foundation, the Ahmanson Foundation and the Samuel Roberts Noble Foundation.

(**284**, 604-607; 1980)

L. E. Orgel and F. H. C. Crick
The Salk Institute, 10010 N. Torrey Pines Road, La Jolla, California 92037

References:

1. Dawkins, R. *The Selfish Gene* (Oxford University Press, 1976).

2. Walker, P. M. B. in *Human Genetics: Possibilities and Realities*, 25-38 (Excepta Medica, Amsterdam, 1979).

3. Crick, F. H. C. in *From Gene to Protein: Information Transfer in Normal and Abnormal Cells* (eds Russell, T. R., Brew, K., Faber, H. & Schultz, J.) 1-13 (Academic, New York, 1979).

4. Crick, F. H. C. *Science* **204**, 264-271 (1979).

5. Doolittle, W. F. & Sapienza, C. *Nature* **284**, 601-603 (1980).

6. Callan, H. G. *J. Cell Sci.* **2**, 1-7 (1967).

7. Thomas, C. A. *A. Rev. Genet.* **5**, 237-256 (1971).

8. Hinegardner, R. in *Molecular Evolution* (ed. Ayata, F. J.) 179-199 (Sinauer, Sunderland, 1976).

9. Commoner, B. *Nature* **202**, 960-968 (1964).

10. Ohno, S. *J. Hum. Evolut.* **1**, 651-662 (1972).

11. Comings, D. E. *Adv. Hum. Genet.* **3**, 237-436 (1972).

12. Cavalier-Smith, T. *J. Cell Sci.* **34**, 274-278 (1978).

13. Galan, G. A., Chamberlin, M. E., Hough, B. R., Britten, R. J. & Davidson, E. H. in *Molecular Evolution* (ed. Ayala, F. J.) 200-224 (Sinauer, Sunderland, 1976).

14. Bishop, J. O. *Cell* **2**, 81-86 (1974).

15. Lewin, B. *Cell* **4**, 11-20 (1975); *Cell* **4**, 77-93 (1975).

16. Lomedico, P. *et al. Cell* **18**, 545-558 (1979).

17. Bernards, R., Little, P. F. R., Annison, G., Williamson, R. & Flavell, R. A. *Proc. Natl. Acad. Sci. U.S.A.* **76**, 4827-4831 (1979).

18. Crick, F. H. C. *Eur. J. Biochem.* **83**, 1-3 (1978).

19. Britten, R. J. & Davidson, E. H. *Science* **165**, 349-358 (1969).

20. Davidson, E. U. & Britten, R. J. *Science* **204**, 1052-1059 (1979).

21. Wilson, A. C. in *Molecular Evolution* (ed. Ayala, F. J.) 225-236 (Sinauer, Sunderland, 1976).

思考非特异 DNA 的动态变化方面特别有帮助。它将人们注意力导向这种 DNA 扩增和进化的机制上，而且告诫我们不要在基因组上的序列或位点中试图寻找每段快速漂变 DNA 的特异功能。

然而在给每段功能还未直接显现的 DNA 贴上自私 DNA 的标签以及在引用看似合理但未经证实的关于自然选择细节的假说的过程中，还应仔细斟酌。在探索高等生物基因组的复杂性时，参考这个想法或许会起到一些作用。它能很好地解释过去 10 到 15 年间提出的很多难题和矛盾。主要的事实起初看来非常奇怪，以至于只有些许非常规的想法才能解释它们。

感谢福特·杜利特尔和萨皮恩扎允许我们拜读他们未发表的文章，以及韦克博士和麦格雷戈博士允许我们引用一些关于蝾螈尚未发表的结论。此项工作受到尤金和埃斯特尔·费尔哈夫基金会，基克希弗基金会，阿曼森基金会以及塞缪尔·罗伯茨荣誉基金会的支持。

（李响 翻译；崔巍 审稿）

22. Bennett, M. D. *Proc. R. Soc.* B**181**, 109-135 (1972).

23. Bennett, M. D. & Smith, J. B. *Proc. R. Soc.* B**181**, 81-107 (1972).

24. Young, M. W. *Proc. Natl. Acad. Sci. U.S.A.* **76**, 6274-6278 (1979).

25. Oeldorfe, E., Nishioka, M. & Bachmann, K. *Sonderdr. Z. F. Zool. System. Evolut.* **16**, 216-24 (1978).

# Selfish DNA

L. E. Orgel *et al.*

## Editor's Note

In April of this year, the authors of this article published reviews examining how "selfish DNA" that has no phenotypic function can "live" within the genomes of organisms. Their views drew much comment, and here they reassess the earlier papers in the light of the ensuing debate. They clarify their terminology and acknowledge that there are several classes of DNA in genomes, including "dead" DNA that has lost its coding function, and DNA that functions much like a symbiotic entity.

---

In two review articles in the 17 April issue Doolittle and Sapienza (p. 601) and Orgel and Crick (p. 604) separately suggested that much of the DNA in the genome of higher organisms could be described as "selfish". They argued that such DNA has no appreciable phenotypic effect and functions only to ensure its own self-preservation within the genome. This view point stimulated a great deal of comment, some of which was published in the issue of 26 June (p. 617). Now the original authors have joined up with one of their critics and reassessed their ideas in the two articles below. A further comment is added by H. K. Jain.

---

DIFFICULTIES have been caused by the words "selfish", "junk", "specific" and "phenotype" that were used in the two reviews of selfish DNA[1,2].

Many people dislike the term "selfish DNA" and a more acceptable alternative might be "parasitic DNA". The word "parasitic" does not imply that the DNA can move between individuals, though certain viral DNAs might do this. It does imply that such DNA can usually move between different chromosomes in the same cell.

The word "junk" also seems to arouse strong feelings. The idea behind it can be clarified by considering what is meant by "specific". We consider a sequence highly specific if the change of any one of its bases almost always has a considerable effect on the organism.

---

The "selfish DNA" design at the top of the page was created by Linda Angeloff-Sapienza of Halifax, Canada and originally appeared on the cover of the issue of 17 April, 1980.

# 自私的DNA

奥格尔等

编者按

当年4月，本文的作者发表了两篇综述，探究了没有表型功能的"自私DNA"是怎样"生活"在生物体的基因组内的。他们的观点引起了众多评论，在此他们根据后续争论重新评价了之前的论文。他们澄清了他们的术语并认可基因组中有多种DNA，包括已经失去编码功能的"死"DNA和那些功能类似于共生实体的DNA。

4月17日那一期刊登了两篇分别由杜利特尔和萨皮恩扎（第601页）及奥格尔和克里克（第604页）发表的综述文章，这两篇文章指出高等生物基因组中的许多DNA可以被描述为"自私的"。他们认为这种DNA没有明显的表型效应和功能，它们仅能保证自身在基因组中的自我保存。这一观点激起了许多争论，其中有部分评论发表在了6月26日版上（第617页）。现在原创作者与其中的一位评论者一起，在下面两篇文章中重新评估他们的观点。贾因做了一些补充评论。

在关于自私DNA的两篇综述里，对"自私的"、"垃圾"、"特异的"、"表型"这些词的使用引起了一些麻烦 [1,2]。

许多人不喜欢"自私DNA"这个术语，而更倾向于接受"寄生DNA"这一替代词语。尽管某些病毒的DNA可以在个体之间移动，但是"寄生"这一词语并不意味着DNA可以在个体之间转移。不过这个词语的确暗示这种DNA可以在同一细胞的不同染色体间发生移动。

"垃圾"一词似乎也具有强烈的感情色彩。其隐藏的含意可以通过考虑"特异"这一含义而得以阐明。如果一条序列任意一个碱基的变化几乎都会对生物产生明显影响的话，我们就将其视为一条高度特异性的序列，例如一个与生理相关的限制性

---

本页最上方的"自私DNA"的设计图案是由加拿大哈利法克斯市的琳达·安杰洛夫－萨皮恩扎创作的，最早出现于1980年4月17日版的封面上。

An example would be the recognition site for a physiologically relevant restriction enzyme. At the other extreme are sequences whose deletion or extensive alteration would produce a negligible effect. Such sequences could reasonably be called junk. However, there is probably a continuum between these two extremes, including fairly specific sequences, where the alteration of most bases will produce some effect (many sequences coding for protein, and the different signals for starting and stopping transcription are likely to be of this type) and sequences whose deletion or extensive alteration will usually produce a small effect, such as a change in the local rate of recombination. In some cases close similarity of two sequences may be important, while the base sequences themselves may matter hardly at all—for example, within the introns of two neighbouring versions of a gene. The word "junk" is perhaps too broad to cover all those cases for which the effect of sequence on the phenotype of an organism is small or zero. We hope a more precise terminology will evolve as the facts become better known.

The word "phenotype" has also caused difficulties in spite of Doolittle and Sapienza's careful use of "organismal phenotype" to make their meaning clear. We obviously need two words: one to refer to the phenotype of the organism and the other to apply solely to the "phenotype" of the parasitic DNA, a distinction we would certainly make in the case of a true parasite. For the former we would suggest "organismal phenotype" and for the latter, following Cavalier-Smith[3], "intragenomic phenotype", but we would allow the word "phenotype" alone to be used when the context makes the meaning clear.

In our original definition we said that selfish DNA had two distinct properties: (1) It arises when a DNA sequence spreads by forming additional copies of itself within the genome. (2) It makes no specific contribution to the phenotype. By "phenotype" we meant organismal phenotype. We intended "specific" to be understood as "highly specific" or "fairly specific" in the discussion above. However it has been pointed out to us by R. Pritchard[4] that "no... contribution" is unnecessarily strict. It would have been more useful to include also DNA which made a small contribution to the organismal phenotype, either positive or negative. An example of the latter might be a viral DNA which became part of the genome.

There is obviously a continuum of possible selective advantages (positive or negative) to the organism. We had excluded from our definition of selfish DNA those cases where the selective advantage is very high. To decide whether a repeated sequence is parasitic or not, one must determine whether the presence of the repeated sequence in the population is mainly due to the efficiency with which the sequence spreads intragenomically or mainly due to the reproductive success of those individuals in the population who possess repeated copies of the sequence. Only in the former case do we consider it useful to use the term selfish or parasitic DNA, as opposed to useful or symbiotic DNA—the borderline between the two may not be sharp.

内切酶的识别位点。另一个极端是有些序列的缺失或广泛变异所产生的影响都微乎其微，这样的序列被称为垃圾 DNA 还是很合理的。然而，这两个极端之间可能存在着一个连续集合，这其中包括那些大部分碱基的变化会产生某种影响的相当特异的序列（许多编码蛋白质及转录起始和终止的不同信号的序列可能就是这种类型的），以及缺失或者广泛变化通常产生微弱效应的那些序列，例如局部重组率的变化。某些情况下，两条序列的密切相似性可能很重要，而碱基序列本身则几乎无关紧要——例如一个基因的两个相邻译本间的内含子。"垃圾"一词可能涵义太宽泛而不能囊括所有对生物表型影响很小或者没有影响的那些序列。我们希望随着事实变得越来越明朗，能够总结出一个更准确的术语。

尽管杜利特尔和萨皮恩扎谨慎地用了"生物表型"一词来让他们表达更明确，但是"表型"这一词语还是引起了一些麻烦。显然我们需要两个词语：一个用来表示生物的表型，另一个则只用来表示寄生 DNA 的"表型"，这样当我们遇到真正的寄生生物时就能有一个明确的区分。对于前者我们建议使用"生物表型"，而对于后者，我们想沿用卡弗利尔－史密斯[3]的"基因组内表型"，但是当上下文意思很明确时，我们也允许单独使用"表型"一词。

在最开始的定义中，我们认为自私 DNA 有两种独有的特征：(1) 当一条 DNA 序列通过形成自身的额外拷贝在基因组内得以传播时，就会产生自私 DNA。(2) 自私 DNA 对表型没有特异性的贡献。我们使用的"表型"是指生物表型。在上述的讨论中，我们认为应该将"特异的"一词理解成"高度特异的"或者"非常特异的"。然而，普理查德[4]给我们指出"没有……贡献"的说法未必严谨。将对生物表型有着很小贡献的 DNA 也包含进去可能更有意义，无论这种贡献是积极的还是消极的。后者的一个例子可能是成为了基因组一部分的病毒 DNA。

很显然，生物存在一个合理的选择优势（积极的或消极的）的连续集合。我们已经从自私 DNA 的定义中排除了那些选择优势非常高的情况。要确定一条重复序列是否是寄生的，就必须确定种群中重复序列的存在主要是序列在基因组间扩散的效率造成的还是主要由于种群中具有重复拷贝序列的那些个体的成功复制产生的。我们认为只有前一种情况使用"自私的"或者"寄生的 DNA"一词才有意义，正如反对使用"有用的"或"共生的 DNA"这种词语的理由一样——二者的界限可能并不明确。

In considering the spread of parasitic DNA one should not underestimate the power of natural selection. For example, if a particular transposon was inserted at random, it would run the risk of inactivating many genes and thus be selected against. A transposon which usually inserted at sites between genes would be at a selective advantage. Sites very near essential genes (as pointed out by Bruce Grant[5]) may be harder to delete than those in the middle of long stretches of junk and so parasitic DNA in the former positions is likely to survive longer. Effects of this type would lead to the selection of selfish DNA sequences that inserted preferentially at special sites in the genome.

Competing theories differ in their analysis of the factors determining the amount of non-specific DNA and of the way in which it comes into existence. Although we cannot at present decide on the quantitative contribution of the different types of non-specific DNA to the genome, it is still helpful to classify the various theories.

We proposed[2] that the amount of non-specific DNA present in a given genome is often determined by the balance between the intragenomic spreading of selfish sequences and phenotypic selection against excess DNA—the weaker the phenotypic selection against non-specific DNA the larger the DNA content of the genome. In another group of theories it is proposed that there is an optimal DNA content for each organism, which may be substantially greater than the amount of specific DNA that is needed to define the phenotype. The amount of non-specific DNA is then principally determined by the difference between the optimal DNA content and the essential content of specific DNA. The theories are not mutually exclusive, but differ substantially in emphasis in their explanation of C-values.

Cavalier-Smith's proposal[3,6] is an interesting example of an "optimal DNA content" theory. One of his ideas, which we misinterpreted in our previous paper[2], is that in large cells, particularly in oocytes, the transport of messenger RNA across the nuclear membrane may become a limiting factor and that the only way to increase the rate of transport is by increasing the number of nuclear pores by extending the surface of the membrane. If the area of nuclear membrane is determined by the DNA content of the nucleus, it follows that selection for a larger cell must lead to an increase in the DNA content of the genome. Thus, rather surprisingly, extra non-specific DNA is selected for because it allows such a cell to grow *faster*. While we do not question the logic of the argument, given the various assumptions, we do not find all the assumptions particularly plausible. It may be that there is sometimes selection for increased cell volume and increased nuclear volume. In cells so selected, non-specific DNA can accumulate. Whether it does so because large cells with large nuclei require such accumulation, or because they simply permit it remains to be seen. We feel that more experimental work is needed to unravel the complexities of the situation. In particular, we should like to know in which stages and in which organisms the surface of the nuclear membrane is saturated with nuclear pores.

Cavalier-Smith[3] also cites the widely different DNA contents of germ cells and somatic cells in some invertebrates as evidence against the selfish DNA hypothesis. However these

当考虑寄生 DNA 的传播时，不应该低估自然选择的力量。例如，如果一个特定的转座子随机插入后，将会经历让许多基因失活的风险，因此它会被选择性地排斥。插入到基因间位点的转座子一般具有选择优势。非常靠近重要基因的位点（布鲁斯·格兰特 [5] 指出的那些位点）可能比那些位于长的垃圾 DNA 中间的那些位点更难发生缺失，所以位于前者中的寄生 DNA 可能存活的更久一些。这种影响会导致对优先插入到基因组特异位点的自私 DNA 序列的选择作用。

与此相对立的学说在分析哪些因素能够决定非特异 DNA 的数量及其产生方式等方面有所不同。尽管目前我们还不能对不同类型的非特异 DNA 对基因组的贡献加以定量，但这仍然有助于对各种不同的学说进行分类。

我们提出 [2] 存在于某一特定基因组中的非特异 DNA 的数量通常由自私序列在基因组内的传播和对冗余 DNA 的表型选择间的平衡来确定——非特异性 DNA 的表型选择越弱，基因组的 DNA 含量越大。另一组学说提出每种生物都有一个最优的 DNA 含量，这一含量可能比用来定义表型所需的特异 DNA 的数量要大得多。非特异 DNA 的数量主要由最优 DNA 含量和特异 DNA 的基本含量之间的差异来确定。这些学说并不是相互排斥的，但是它们在解释 C 值时所强调的重点不同。

卡弗利尔－史密斯的观点 [3,6] 是"最优 DNA 含量"学说中的一个有趣的例子。我们在之前的论文 [2] 中对他的一个观点有些误解，那就是他认为在大细胞中，尤其是在卵母细胞中，信使 RNA 穿过核膜的转运可能变成一个限制因素，唯一可以提高转运速率的方式是通过扩展膜表面来增加核孔的数目。如果核膜面积由细胞核的 DNA 含量决定，那么就会遵循如下原则，即自然选择倾向于大细胞，这必然导致基因组 DNA 含量的增加。因此，令人非常惊讶的是，冗余的非特异 DNA 由于其允许这种细胞生长得**更快**而被选择。尽管我们不会质疑这个论点的逻辑性，但考虑到多方面的假设，我们发现并不是所有的假设都是特别可信的。有时环境可能会选择增大的细胞体积和增大的细胞核体积，在这样选择出来的细胞中，非特异性 DNA 能够积累下来。上述行为的原因，可能是具有大细胞核的大细胞需要这种累积，或者细胞只是简单地允许其能够存在而最终被观察到。我们认为有必要做更多的实验来揭开这一情况的复杂性。尤其我们想知道在哪个阶段以及在何种生物体内核膜表面的核孔能够达到饱和。

卡弗利尔－史密斯 [3] 也引用了某些无脊椎动物的生殖细胞和体细胞的 DNA 含量间的巨大差异作为反对自私 DNA 假说的证据。然而这些结果也可以用自私 DNA

observations can also be explained in terms of the selfish DNA theory. Such DNA "needs" only to remain in the germ line to function parasitically. On the other hand, organismal selection might sometimes be stronger against surplus DNA in the soma than in the germ line. Thus representation in the germ line but not in the soma may sometimes be an optimal strategy for parasitic DNA. As for B chromosomes, in many cases the evidence appears to us to give some support to the idea (originally proposed by Östergren[7] in 1945) that they are largely parasitic, but there is certainly evidence that they sometimes have phenotypic effects which may possibly be useful[8,9].

Smith[10] has pointed out that the DNA of vertebrates usually has about 42 percent GC whereas the GC content of invertebrate and prokaryotic DNA varies over a much wider range. The theory of parasitic DNA has rather little to say on this point. There are many factors which might affect the GC content of an organism's DNA. If much of the parasitic DNA has descended rather recently from insertion elements which themselves originally coded for proteins, then it would not be surprising if their present GC content were similar to that of genes which still code for protein. This may, perhaps, explain the constancy of GC in vertebrates.

As for our own ideas, we now feel that there may perhaps be reasons why too *little* DNA can in some cases produce a selective disadvantage. For example, Zuckerkandel[11] has suggested that there may be a minimum size for a "domain" necessary for stability of the chromatin in the folded state. Thus a domain containing only a few genes might benefit from having some non-specific DNA as "padding". This would mean that there is indeed an optimal amount for total DNA.

In our original paper[2] we feel that we did not put enough emphasis on the distinction between sequences which are repeated, exactly or nearly exactly, in many tandem repetitions and sequences which are more widely dispersed over the chromosomes and which occur in only one or a few copies in any one place. It seems plausible that these two types of sequence evolved different mechanisms. It is possible that the mechanisms generating the tandemly repeated type are usually more "ignorant" (in Dover's sense[12]) than the more dispersed type. If the latter have any specific function it is likely to be that of the control, at one level or another, of gene expression, whereas the tandemly repeated type seem more likely to influence chromosome mechanics.

One possibility to which we feel we should have given more weight is that of "dead genes", also called "pseudogenes"[13,14]; that is, sequences which can no longer code for a protein (or a structural RNA) but which appear to have descended from a sequence that did. Whether these conform to our definition of parasitic DNA remains to be seen, but we suspect this is unlikely, since they usually exist in only a single copy, or as multiple tandem copies in only one place.

In our recent experience most people will agree, after discussion, that ignorant DNA, parasitic DNA, symbiotic DNA (that is, parasitic DNA which has become useful to

学说来解释。自私 DNA 只"需要"待在生殖细胞系中以寄生方式发挥功能。另一方面，有时生物在体细胞中对过剩 DNA 的选择作用可能比其在生殖细胞中的选择作用更强烈。因此对于寄生 DNA 来说，相比存在于体细胞中，存在于生殖细胞系中有时也许是最佳策略。至于 B 染色体，我们看到很多情况下的证据是支持存在大量寄生 DNA 这一观点（最初由奥斯特格伦 [7] 于 1945 年提出），但是也有证据明确表明这些 DNA 有时是有表型效应的，而且这些表型效应可能是有用的 [8, 9]。

史密斯 [10] 指出脊椎动物 DNA 的 GC 含量通常为 42%，而无脊椎动物和原核生物 DNA 的 GC 含量变化范围很大。寄生 DNA 学说对于这一点几乎没做任何解释。影响生物 DNA 中 GC 含量的因素有很多。假设很多寄生 DNA 是近期从插入元件产生而来，而这些插入元件最初是编码蛋白质的，那么它们现在的 GC 含量与那些仍然编码蛋白质的基因的 GC 含量相似一点也不令人感到意外。这也许可以解释脊椎动物的 GC 含量为何具有稳定性。

至于我们自己的观点，目前我们认为，之所以只有极**少**的 DNA 会在个别情况下产生选择劣势是有原因的。例如，楚克尔坎德尔 [11] 提出，为了保证染色质在折叠状态下的稳定性，维持这一稳定性所必要的"结构域"大小可能有一个最低限度的要求。因此只含有几个基因的结构域可能受益于某些作为"填料"的非特异 DNA。这意味着，对于总 DNA 确实具有一个最优数量。

在我们原来的文章 [2] 中，我们认为对于许多串联重复序列中严格重复或接近严格重复的序列与更广泛地分散在染色体上的或者仅在某一位点产生单个或几个拷贝的序列之间的差异，我们强调得还不够。这两种序列有着不同的进化机制，这似乎是有道理的。产生串联重复型序列的机制通常比产生更分散型序列的机制更加"无意识"（在多弗所使用的意义上 [12]）。如果后者有特定功能的话，那么其可能是对基因某一水平的表达进行控制，然而串联重复型序列的作用更有可能是影响了染色体的结构。

我们认为可能更应该侧重的一个方面是"死基因"，也称为"假基因" [13,14]，即不再编码蛋白质（或者结构 RNA），但是似乎这些序列是从某些可以编码蛋白质或者结构 RNA 的序列产生来的。这些与我们对寄生 DNA 的定义是否吻合还有待验证，但是我们推测这种一致性不太可能存在，因为它们通常是以单拷贝存在的，或者只在一个位点作为多串联拷贝存在。

经过讨论，大部分人都同意无意识的 DNA、寄生 DNA、共生 DNA（即对机体有用的寄生 DNA）和"死"DNA 中的任何一种都可能存在于高等生物的染色体中。

the organism) and "dead" DNA of one sort or another are all likely to be present in the chromosomes of higher organisms. Where people differ is in their estimates of the relative amounts. We feel that this can only be decided by experiment. We expect that due to the recent advances in genetic engineering and related techniques much sequence information will accrue in the near future. This should help to decide between the different alternatives.

(**288**, 645-646; 1980)

L. E. Orgel*, F. H. C. Crick* and C. Sapienza†

* The Salk Institute, San Diego, California
† Department of Biochemistry, Dalhousie University, Halifax, Canada

References:

1. Doolittle, W. F. & Sapienza, C. *Nature* **284**, 601 (1980).

2. Orgel, L. E. & Crick, F. H. C. *Nature* **284**, 604 (1980).

3. Cavalier-Smith, T. *Nature* **285**, 617 (1980).

4. Pritchard, R. (personal communication).

5. Grant, B. (personal communication).

6. Cavalier-Smith, T. *J. Cell. Sci.* **34**, 247 (1978).

7. Östergren, G. *Bot. Notiser* **2**, 157 (1945).

8. Jones, R. N. *Int. Rev. Cytol.* **40**, 1 (1975).

9. Ames, A. & Dover, G. *Chromosoma* (in the press).

10. Smith, T. F. *Nature* **285**, 620 (1980).

11. Zuckerkandel, E. (personal communication).

12. Dover, G. *Nature* **285**, 618 (1980).

13. Loomis, W. *Devl. Biol.* **30**, F3-F4 (1973).

14. See, for example, Proudfoot, N. *Nature* **286**, 840 (1980).

人们的分歧之处在于，他们对相对数量的估计不尽相同。我们认为这点只能通过实验来确定。我们希望随着基因工程和相关技术的进步，在不久的将来可以获得并积累更多序列信息。这将有助于我们在不同的学说中做出更科学的选择。

（刘皓芳 翻译；王崴 审稿）

# Modes of Genome Evolution

G. Dover and W. F. Doolittle

## Editor's Note

Following on from the previous addendum to two pieces on "selfish DNA" published in April of this year, here the author of one of those pieces, biochemist Ford Doolittle, collaborates with one of his critics, geneticist Gabriel Dover at Cambridge University, to modify and sharpen his earlier arguments. Doolittle and Dover say that some DNA is better seen as "ignorant" rather than selfish, in that it is prone to generating meaningless rearrangements.

OUR original articles[1,3] presented antagonistic positions and perhaps obscured many areas of agreement. In essence, we are approaching similar phenomena from different perspectives and it might be useful to clarify where our views agree and differ and to indicate the sorts of evidence which would allow one to decide whether the origin of non-coding DNA in eukaryotic cells is more precisely viewed as "ignorant"[3] or "selfish"[1,2].

The eukaryotic genome is constantly in flux, and this plasticity results from a variety of known and as yet mysterious mechanisms which amplify and disperse segments of DNA throughout a set of chromosomes[4-7]. Replication and recombination are complex processes requiring many enzymes that have evolved by natural selection. What we both wish to stress is that, in establishing these processes, evolution has inadvertently endowed the genome with built-in mechanisms for irregular and recurrent random sequence rearrangements and created an environment in which elements capable (to varying extents) of promoting their own amplification and dispersion will inevitably arise[1,2,7]. We acknowledge that there is evidence which suggests that some proportion of genome rearrangements may have effects on the biology of an organism (for instance on chromosome behaviour, on nuclear RNA processing, on cell-cycle times, on recombination frequencies and on gene expression; see refs 1-3, 8). Where this is the case, the change in frequency of a sequence rearrangement and the behaviour of elements which promote their own amplification and dispersion will of course depend on the effects they have on fitness. Hence, the net accumulation of these particular families of sequences reflects a balance between the intrinsic rate of accumulation (intra-genomically) and the effect of natural selection on phenotypic differences.

We agree that the amplification and dispersion of segments may occur either at random (sequence-independent or "ignorant") or with preference for certain sequences (sequence-dependent or "selfish"). Although both "ignorant" and "selfish" are unfortunate terms, they should be understood in the spirit in which they are used and defined: sequence-independent and sequence-dependent processes of amplification and dispersion respectively.

# 基因组的进化模式

上一篇文章是当年四月发表的两篇关于"自私的 DNA"综述的补篇，之后，其中一篇综述的作者——生物化学家福特·杜利特尔，与他的观点批判者——剑桥大学的遗传学家加布里埃尔·多弗进行合作，在本文中修正并深化了他早期的论点。杜利特尔和多弗认为，某些 DNA 更应该被视为"无意识的"，而不是自私的，因为它们更倾向于产生无意义的重排。

我们最初的文献中 [1,3] 介绍了一些对立的观点，这可能使很多存在共识的领域变得模糊。其实，我们正在从不同的角度解释相似的现象，这将有助于阐明我们观点中相同或相异的地方，并有助于指出有关真核细胞中非编码 DNA 起源的各种证据，来判断这种起源该被视为"无意识的"[3]，还是"自私的"[1,2] 才更为精确。

真核基因组一直处于变化状态，这种可塑性是由种种已知的和至今仍未可知的机制导致的，这些机制使 DNA 在一整套染色体中扩增和分散 [4-7]。复制和重组都是复杂的过程，此过程需要许多经由自然选择进化而来的酶。我们想要强调的两点是，在建立这些过程时，进化在无意间赋予了基因组对不规则和重复的随机序列进行重排的内在机制，并且创造出了使元件必然能够（在不同程度上）促进自身扩增和分散的环境 [1,2,7]。我们承认，已有证据表明一定比例的基因组重排可能对生物体产生生物学影响（例如染色体行为、核 RNA 加工、细胞周期时序、重组频率及基因表达等；详情可见参考文献 1~3、8）。在这种情况下，序列重排频率的改变，及那些能促进自身扩增和分散的元件的行为，都必将依赖于它们对适应性的影响。因此，这些特定序列家族的净积累反映了固有累积速率（基因组内部的）与自然选择对表型差异影响之间的一种平衡。

我们赞同以下观点，即片段的扩增和分散可能是随机发生的（序列无关的或"无意识的"），或者也可能更加偏好特定序列（序列相关的或"自私的"）。尽管"无意识的"和"自私的"都是不太贴切的术语，但是应该本着如下应用和定义的初衷对它们进行理解：它们分别用于修饰序列无关和序列相关的扩增和分散过程。

The "selfish process" produces DNAs which are preferentially chosen either by virtue of their nucleotide sequence or by virtue of the fact that they may code for gene products for their own amplification and dispersion. Mobile elements such as bacterial insertion sequences and transposons, the "*Ty-1*-like" elements of yeast, the "*copia*-like" elements of *Drosophila*, and vertebrate retroviruses, which show surprising similarities in structure and (perhaps) dispersal mechanisms[8] are almost certainly the self-perpetuating products of this sort of process. An alternative term "self-selection" might usefully describe the process of accumulation of these sequences. Interestingly, there may be an element of self-selection in the process of accumulation and dispersion of some sequence-independent segments. Extensive sharing of similar sequence patterns of repetitive DNAs between chromosomes (see refs 9 and 10), and occasionally between species[11,12], suggests that an arbitrarily accumulated sequence arrangement preferentially enjoys further rounds of amplification and dispersion[10]. Simulation of unequal recombination by computer appears to show a degree of self-perpetuation of sequences initially chosen at random[13] and also that amplification and dispersion can be part and parcel of the same recombinational irregularity[14].

A process of recurrent amplification can explain the frequent observation of a greater within-species than between-species sequence homogeneity of shared families[6,9,12]. Similarly, polymorphisms and variations in sequence patterns of ribosomal genes[15], histone genes[16] and some non-coding families[17–19] in several diverse organisms can be interpreted as the most recent, and hence localized, amplifications of these sequences.

We wish to emphasize, however, that "ignorant" and "selfish" self-perpetuation are terms that uniquely apply to these particular DNA processes and cannot be used, meaningfully, to describe changes in frequencies of other elements that are totally dependent on the natural selection of phenotypes. "Selfish genes"[20] and "replicator selection"[21] are not synonymous terms and the evolutionary processes to which they allude are unknown. A very limited accumulation of supernumerary B chromosomes is the only other process that can be described as self-accumulation, often the result of meiotic and mitotic non-disjunction. We doubt if this term can be used to describe the mis-named "meiotic drive" mechanisms of regular A chromosomes in the rare instances where this occurs. For example, in the case of segregation distortion (SD) in *Drosophila melanogaster*, the preferential recovery of the SD chromosome is not so much due to its accumulation *per se* but is the outcome of dysgenesis of cells carrying the non-SD homologue[22]. This, and other cases, are analogous to the relative changes in frequency of alleles at a gene locus that are the outcome of natural selection; and "selfish" and "replicator selection" are misleading descriptions of this process of differential accumulation of alleles and chromosomes.

We do not agree upon the relative contributions of randomly accumulated and preferentially accumulated DNAs to the evolution of eukaryote genomes. It is clear that much of the non-coding DNA of yeast could be of the sort one could call "selfish"[4,8] whilst non-coding elements of the *D. melanogaster* genome are made up of varying proportions of essentially "ignorant" repetitive DNA (for example the satellite DNAs[23]) and "selfish"

"自私的过程"会产生由于某些原因被优先选择的 DNA，或者由于这些 DNA 的核苷酸序列，或者由于它们可以编码用于自身扩增和分散所需的基因产物。几乎可以肯定的是，在结构和（可能）分散机制上 [8] 具有惊人相似性的可移动元件（例如细菌的插入序列和转座子，酵母的"*Ty-1* 样"元件，果蝇的"*copia* 样"元件，以及脊椎动物的逆转录病毒），它们多是这类过程自我保存的产物。另一个术语——"自我选择"——可能有助于描述这类序列的积累过程。有意思的是，在某些序列无关片段的积累和分散过程中，可能也存在一个自我选择元件。在染色体之间（见参考文献 9 和 10），偶尔也在不同的物种 [11,12] 之间，大量的 DNA 重复序列具有相似的序列模式，表明一个随意积累的序列排布优先享有下一轮扩增和分散的机会 [10]。计算机对于不对等重组的模拟结果显示，原本通过随机选择产生的序列具有一定程度的自我保存能力 [13]。同时，扩增和分散可能是相同的无规则重组中不可缺少的一部分 [14]。

周期性的扩增过程可以用来说明为什么经常能在种内观察到比种间更高的共有基因家族的序列同质性 [6,9,12]。同样地，可以将各种不同生物体的核糖体基因 [15]、组蛋白基因 [16] 和一些非编码家族 [17-19] 在序列模式上的多态性和多样性解释为这些序列在时间上最近的，也是局部范围内扩增的结果。

然而，我们希望强调的是，所谓的"无意识的"和"自私的"自我保存都是专门用于说明这类特殊 DNA 过程的术语，不能被用作描述其他元件（此类元件完全依赖于对表型的自然选择）的频率变化之用。"自私基因" [20] 和"复制子选择" [21] 并不是同义的术语，至于它们暗指的进化过程，尚不得而知。多余 B 染色体的一种非常有限的积累过程是仅有的另外一个可以被描述为自我积累的过程，它往往是减数分裂和有丝分裂不分离的结果。我们怀疑，这个术语是否可以用于描述极少数情况下，发生在标准 A 染色体上，被误称为"减数分裂驱动"的机制。以黑腹果蝇的偏分离（SD）为例，SD 染色体的优先恢复并不完全取决于它的积累本身，而是携带非 SD 同源物的细胞发育不良的结果 [22]。这种情况及其他情况类似于等位基因在一个基因位点上频率的相对改变，这种改变也是自然选择的结果。"自私的"和"复制子选择"都是对等位基因和染色体的这种差异性积累过程的误导性描述。

我们并不认同随机积累和优先积累的 DNA 对真核基因组进化的相关贡献。很明显，酵母的很多非编码 DNA 都可能是被称为"自私的"的类型 [4,8]；而黑腹果蝇基因组的非编码元件则是由不同比例的本质上"未知的"重复 DNA（例如卫星 DNA [23]）和"无意识的"转座 DNA（例如"*copia* 样"元件 [5]）组成。温辛克和他的同事们 [24]

transposable DNAs (for example the "*copia*-like" elements[5]). The scrambled arrangements of repetitive elements in *D. melanogaster* observed by Wensink and co-workers[24] could reflect either sequence-independent shuffling processes or sequence-dependent insertion of transposable elements, similar to *copia*, at adjacent sites. The available data on repetitive DNA families of species of sea urchins, Graminea, rodents, primates and insects (see ref. 3) do not permit a clear assessment of the mechanisms that gave rise to them, for no direct sequence data are available. The multiple-copy "Alu I" family of mammalian genomes may have a cellular function[25,26], but it is not impossible that these are the descendants of a family of transposable elements[27].

Finally, we suggest that the accumulation of sequences might be affected by constraints on the mechanisms themselves. For example, sequence-dependent amplification and dispersion will favour sequences that accurately contain the required sequence for transposition and that have not drifted too far into unacceptable divergent sequences. Similarly, sequence-independent mechanisms may be constrained to particular lengths of sequences[10]. Such constraints impose a type of selection on sequences, not necessarily as a result of their phenotypic effects but more as a consequence of the molecular mechanisms of replication and recombination.

We do not know what proportions of the repetitive DNAs of "higher" organisms are amplified and dispersed by either sequence-dependent or sequence-independent mechanisms. Similarly, we do not know to what extent each of these mechanisms is constrained nor do we know the extent to which the frequencies of sequence patterns are an outcome of their possible effects on individual fitness. It is clear, however, that there are several modes of sequence rearrangement within rapidly evolving genomes. The problem now, as with most scientific debates, is one of quantification.

(**288**, 646-647; 1980)

Gabriel Dover* and W. Ford Doolittle†
* Department of Genetics, University of Cambridge, UK
† Department of Biochemistry, Dalhousie University, Canada

References:
1. Doolittle, W. F. & Sapienza, C. *Nature* **284**, 601 (1980).
2. Orgel, L. E. & Crick, F. H. C. *Nature* **284**, 604 (1980).
3. Dover, G. A. *Nature* **285**, 618 (1980).
4. Cameron, J. R. *et al. Cell* **16**, 739 (1979).
5. Potter, S. S. *et al. Cell* **17**, 424 (1979).
6. Flavell, R. B. *et al.* in *Genome Organization and Expression in Plants* (Plenum, 1980).
7. Dover, G. A. *Chromosomes Today* **6**, 105 (1977).
8. *Cold Spring Harb. Symp. Quant. Biol.* **45** (1980).
9. Dover, G. A. *Nature* **272**. 123 (1978).
10. Brown, S. D. M. & Dover, G. A. *Nucleic Acids Res.* **8**, 781 (1979)
11. Brown, S. D. M. & Dover, G. A. *Nature* **285**, 47 (1980).
12. Donehower, L. & Gillespie, D. *J. Molec. Biol.* **134**, 805 (1979).

在黑腹果蝇中观察到的重复元件的无序排列可能反映了序列无关的交换过程，也可能反映了在相邻位点上序列相关的转座元件（类似于 *copia*）的插入。由于无法获得直接的序列数据，凭借现有的关于海胆类、禾本科、啮齿目动物、灵长类和昆虫等生物在重复 DNA 家族方面的数据（见参考文献 3），我们还不能对其产生机制进行确切估计。哺乳动物基因组的多拷贝“Alu I”家族可能具备一种细胞功能[25,26]，但要说它们是转座元件家族的后代，也不是不可能[27]。

最后，我们认为序列的积累可能受到它们自身机制约束的影响。例如，序列相关的扩增和分散将更倾向以下两种序列：精确包含了转座必需序列的序列和那些没有过分漂移至不可接受的相异序列的序列。同样地，序列无关的机制可能受制于序列的特定长度[10]。这些约束强加给序列一种选择，这种选择更多的是一种复制和重组的分子机制作用的后果，而没有必要将其视为表型效应的结果。

我们不知道“高等”生物体有多大比例的重复 DNA 是通过序列相关或者序列无关的方式进行扩增和分散的。同样，我们不知道这些机制各自在多大程度上受到约束；我们也不知道，序列模式的频率在多大程度上可能是它们作用在个体适应性上的结果。然而，很明显的是，在快速进化的基因组中，确实存在数个序列重排模式。伴随着大多数科学辩论，如今这只是一个量化的问题。

（阮玉辉 翻译；王嵬 审稿）

13. Smith, G. P. *Science* **191**, 528 (1976).

14. Smith, T., Brown, S. D. M. & Dover, G. A. (unpublished results).

15. Wellauer, P. K. *et al. J. Molec. Biol.* **105**, 487 (1976).

16. Cohn, R. H. & Kedes, L. J. *Cell* **18**, 855 (1979).

17. Cooke, H. J. & Hindley, J. *Nucleic Acids Res.* **6**, 3177 (1979).

18. Christie, N. T. & Skinner, D. M. *Proc. Natl. Acad. Sci. U.S.A.* **77**, 2786 (1980).

19. Donehower, L. *et al. Proc. Natl. Acad. Sci. U.S.A.* **77**, 2129 (1980).

20. Dawkins, R. *The Selfish Gene* (Oxford Univ. Press, 1976).

21. Dawkins, R. A. *Tierpsychology* **47**, 61 (1978).

22. Crow, J. F. *Scientific American* **104**, 1 February (1979).

23. Brutlag, E. E. *et al. Cold Spring Harb. Symp. Quant. Biol.* **42**, 1137 (1979).

24. Wensink, P. C. *et al. Cell* **18**, 1231 (1977).

25. Jelinek, W. R. *et al. Proc. Natl. Acad. Sci. U.S.A.* **77**, 1398 (1980).

26. Rubin, C. M. *et al. Nature* **284**, 372 (1980).

27. Bell, G. L. *et al. Nucleic Acids Res.* **8**, 4091 (1980).

# Mutations Affecting Segment Number and Polarity in *Drosophila*

C. Nüsslein-Volhard and E. Wieschaus

## Editor's Note

How do higher organisms get their shape? It was recognized that they are generally composed of similar repeating units, the segmented body of the fruit fly *Drosophila melanogaster* being a prime example. But the genetics of the patterning process was still obscure. Here Christiane Nüsslein-Volhard and Eric Wieschaus of the European Molecular Biology Laboratory in Heidelberg identify the key genes responsible for *Drosophila* segmental development, mutations of which alter the body plan. It later became clear that body shapes in a wide variety of organisms are controlled by just a few so-called homeobox or *Hox* genes, of which these are examples. This work earned the two researchers the Nobel Prize in Physiology or Medicine in 1995.

---

In systematic searches for embryonic lethal mutants of *Drosophila melanogaster* we have identified 15 loci which when mutated alter the segmental pattern of the larva. These loci probably represent the majority of such genes in *Drosophila*. The phenotypes of the mutant embryos indicate that the process of segmentation involves at least three levels of spatial organization: the entire egg as developmental unit, a repeat unit with the length of two segments, and the individual segment.

---

THE construction of complex form from similar repeating units is a basic feature of spatial organisation in all higher animals. Very little is known for any organism about the genes involved in this process. In *Drosophila*, the metameric nature of the pattern is most obvious in the thoracic and abdominal segments of the larval epidermis and we are attempting to identify all loci required for the establishment of this pattern. The identification of these genes and the description of their phenotypes should lead to a better understanding of the general mechanisms responsible for the formation of metameric patterns.

In *Drosophila*, the anlagen for the individual segments arise as equally sized subdivisions of the blastoderm, each segment represented by a transverse strip of about three or four cell diameters[1]. A cell lineage restriction between neighbouring segments is established at or soon after this stage[2]. Two basic types of mutation have been described which change the segmental pattern of the *Drosophila* larva. Maternal effect mutations like *bicaudal* lead to a global alteration of the embryonic pattern[3]. Bicaudal embryos develop two posterior ends arranged in mirror-image symmetry, and lack head, thorax and anterior abdomen. The *bicaudal* phenotype suggests that the initial spatial organisation of the egg established

# 影响果蝇体节数量和极性的突变

尼斯莱因－福尔哈德，维绍斯

## 编者按

高等生物的形状是如何获得的？公认的是，它们一般由相似的重复单元组成，黑腹果蝇分节的身体就是一个典型的例子。但是，模式形成过程中涉及的遗传学内容仍然模糊不清。在本文中，海德堡欧洲分子生物学实验室的克里斯蒂亚娜·尼斯莱因－福尔哈德和埃里克·维绍斯确定了负责果蝇体节发育的关键基因，这些基因的突变会改变机体规划。后来知道，在很多生物体中，体型仅仅由少数所谓的同源框或者Hox基因控制，这些就是例子。这项工作使得两位研究者在 1995 年获得了诺贝尔生理学或医学奖。

在对黑腹果蝇胚胎致死突变体的系统研究中，我们鉴定出 15 个突变后可以改变幼虫体节模式的基因座。这些基因座可能代表了果蝇中大多数这类基因。突变胚胎的表型表明果蝇分节过程至少涉及空间结构的三个层次：作为发育单位的整个卵、一个具有两体节长度的重复单元以及单个体节。

由相似的重复单位构成的复杂结构是所有高等动物空间结构的基本特征。而参与这一过程的基因在任何生物体中都知之甚少。果蝇中这种类型的体节性质在幼虫表皮胸节和腹节上体现得最明显，并且我们正试图鉴定控制这种模式建成所需的所有基因座。对这些基因的确定和表型的描述可以帮助我们更好地理解分节模式形成的普遍机制。

在果蝇中，发育成单个体节的原基起源于胚盘上同样大小的细化区域，每个体节是一个长约三到四个细胞直径的横向条状区域[1]。在这个时期或稍后会在相邻体节之间形成一个细胞系界线[2]。本文描述了改变果蝇幼虫分节模式的两个基本突变类型。类似"双腹"突变的母体效应突变会导致胚胎形态的完全改变[3]。"双腹"突变的胚胎发育出两个尾部，成镜像对称分布，没有头部、胸部和前腹部。"双腹"突变表型说明在卵子发生时建立起来的最初的空间结构涉及成形素的梯度分布，成形

during oogenesis involves a morphogen gradient that defines antero-posterior coordinates in early embryonic pattern formation[3,4]. The subdivision of the embryo into segments is thought to occur by a differential response of the zygotic genome to the maternal gradient. Homeotic mutations (for example, *bithorax*[5,6]) seem to be involved in a final step of this response process. These mutations change the identity of individual segments; for example, *Ultrabithorax* transforms the metathoracic and first abdominal segments into mesothoracic segments. However, the homeotic loci do not affect the total number, size or polarity of the segments, nor do they point to any other step which might intervene between the maternal gradient and the final pattern of segments.

We have undertaken a systematic search for mutations that affect the segmental pattern depending on the zygotic genome. We describe here mutations at 15 loci which show one of three novel types of pattern alteration: pattern duplication in each segment (segment polarity mutants; six loci), pattern deletion in alternating segments (pair-rule mutants; six loci) and deletion of a group of adjacent segments (gap mutants; three loci) (Table 1, Fig. 1).

Table 1. Loci affecting segmentation in *Drosophila*

| Class | Locus | Map position* | No. of alleles† | Ref. |
|---|---|---|---|---|
| Segment-polarity | *cubitus interruptus*[D] (*ci*[D]) | 4-0 | (2) | 20 |
| | *wingless* (*wg*) | 2-30 | 6 | 9 |
| | *gooseberry* (*gsb*) | 2-104 | 1 | This work |
| | *hedgehog* (*hh*) | 3-90 | 2 | This work |
| | *fused* (*fu*)‡ | 1-59.5 | (9) | 8, 20 |
| | *patch* (*pat*) | 2-55 | 8 | This work |
| Pair-rule | *paired* (*prd*) | 2-45 | 3 | This work |
| | *even-skipped* (*eve*) | 2-55 | 2 | This work |
| | *odd-skipped* (*odd*) | 2-8 | 2 | This work |
| | *barrel* (*brr*) | 3-27 | 2 | This work |
| | *runt* (*run*) | 1-65 | 1 | This work |
| | *engrailed* (*en*) | 2-62 | 6 | 11, 20 |
| Gap | *Krüppel* (*Kr*) | 2-107.6 | 6 | 12, 20 |
| | *knirps* (*kni*) | 3-47 | 5 | This work |
| | *hunchback* (*hb*) | 3-48 | 1 | This work |

* For the new loci (see last column) the map positions are based on recombination between the markers *S, Sp, Bl, cn, bw* for the second chromosome, and *ru, h, th, st, cu, sr, e*[s], *ca* for the third chromosome. For description of markers see ref. 20. The loci *runt*, *Krüppel* and *knirps* were further mapped using the breakpoints of deficiencies and duplications for the respective regions. All mutants were mapped by scoring the embryonic progeny of single recombinant males backcrossed to heterozygous females from the original mutant stocks.

† The numbers in parentheses refer to the alleles listed in Lindsley and Grell[20]. All other alleles, except the *runt* allele,

素浓度梯度在胚胎早期形态建成中决定头部和尾部的分化方向 [3,4]。一般认为胚胎分化成体节是通过合子基因组对母体生理梯度的不同反应所产生的。同源异型突变（如"双胸"突变 [5,6]）似乎参与了这一反应过程的最后一步。这些突变改变了单个体节的特征；比如，"超双胸"基因把后胸和第一腹节转变成了中胸体节。然而，同源异型基因座并不影响体节总数、大小或极性，也无法表明它们具体是哪一步在母体生理梯度和最终体节形态之间起了干扰作用。

我们对依赖合子基因组而影响体节模式的突变展开了系统的研究。本文我们描述的突变体涉及 15 个基因座，每个突变体表现出以下三种新型模式改变中的某一种：每个体节都存在重复模式（体节极性突变体；6 个基因座）、体节交替缺失（成对控制突变体；6 个基因座）和一组邻近体节缺失（间隙突变体；3 个基因座）（表 1，图 1）。

表 1. 影响果蝇体节形成的基因座

| 类型 | 基因座 | 图谱位置 * | 等位基因数目 † | 参考文献 |
|---|---|---|---|---|
| 体节－极性 | 尺骨中断 ($ci^D$) | 4–0 | (2) | 20 |
| | 无翅 (wg) | 2–30 | 6 | 9 |
| | 鹅莓 (gsb) | 2–104 | 1 | 本文 |
| | 刺猬 (hh) | 3–90 | 2 | 本文 |
| | 融合 (fu) ‡ | 1–59.5 | (9) | 8, 20 |
| | 斑点 (pat) | 2–55 | 8 | 本文 |
| 成对控制 | 配对 (prd) | 2–45 | 3 | 本文 |
| | 偶数－遗漏 (eve) | 2–55 | 2 | 本文 |
| | 奇数－遗漏 (odd) | 2–8 | 2 | 本文 |
| | 桶状 (brr) | 3–27 | 2 | 本文 |
| | 侏儒 (run) | 1–65 | 1 | 本文 |
| | 锯齿状 (en) | 2–62 | 6 | 11, 20 |
| 间隙 | 跛子 (Kr) | 2–107.6 | 6 | 12, 20 |
| | 折叠扇 (kni) | 3–47 | 5 | 本文 |
| | 驼背 (hb) | 3–48 | 1 | 本文 |

* 对于新的基因座（见上表），图谱定位基于二号染色体的 $S, Sp, Bl, cn$ 和 $bw$ 标记之间的重组以及三号染色体上 $ru, h,$ $th, st, cu, e^s$ 及 $ca$ 标记之间的重组。对标记的描述见参考文献 20。运用各自区域的缺失和复制断点，对"侏儒"、"跛子"和"折叠扇"基因座进行了进一步定位。所有突变都是通过计算重单重组体雄性与来自最初突变体品系的杂合体雌性回交后产生的胚胎后代数量来定位的。

† 圆括号内的数字参考了林斯利和格雷尔所列的等位基因 [20]。除"侏儒"等位基因，三个"跛子"等位基因和一个

three *Kr* alleles and one *knirps* allele, were isolated in screen for embryonic lethal mutants on the second chromosome. 5,800 balanced stocks were established from individual males heterozygous for an ethyl methane sulphonate-treated *cn bw sp* chromosome using the DTS-procedure suggested by Wright[21]. 4,500 of the stocks had one or more new lethal mutations. Unhatched embryos from 2,600 putative embryonic lethal stocks were inspected for cuticular abnormalities[22]. Third chromosomal mutants discovered in the second chromosomal balanced lines were recovered after selection through individual females by balancing individual third chromosomes over TM3. Complementation tests were carried out between mutants with similar phenotypes whereby the occurrence of mutant embryos among the progeny of the crosses served as the criterion for allelism. Three new *Kr* alleles were isolated in a screen for lethals over the original *Kr* of Gloor[12], and one *knirps* allele of presumably spontaneous origin was discovered on a TM1 chromosome. The *runt* allele was isolated in a screen for X-linked lethals.

‡ *fused* is a male-rescuable maternal-effect locus[8]. Thus, the segment polarity reversal is observed in *fu/fu* embryos from *fu/fu* mothers. The progeny of *fu/+* females show a normal embryonic pattern regardless of embryonic genotype.

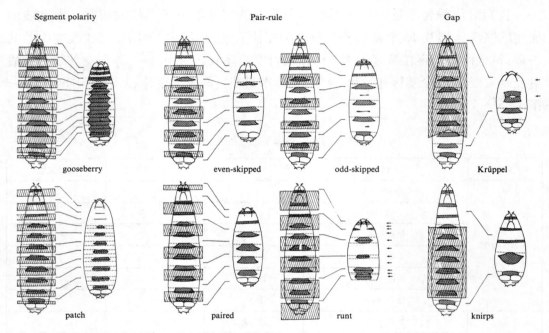

Fig. 1. Semi-schematic drawings indicating the regions deleted from the normal pattern in mutant larvae. Dotted regions indicate denticle bands, dotted lines the segmental boundaries. The regions missing in mutant larvae are indicated by the hatched bars. The transverse lines connect corresponding regions in mutant and normal larvae. Planes of polarity reversal in *runt* and *Krüppel* are indicated by the arrows. The two segment polarity loci *patch* and *gooseberry* are represented at the left. For indication of the polarity of the patterns, see Fig. 3. The patterns of *fused* and *ci*[D] (not shown) look similar to the *gooseberry* pattern, whereas in *hedgehog* and *wingless* the deleted regions are somewhat larger, cutting into the denticle bands at either side. Four pair-rule mutants are shown in the centre. The interpretation of their phenotypes is based on the study of weak as well as strong alleles, combinations with *Ubx* (see text) and, in the case of *runt*, on gynandromorphs (unpublished). They probably represent the extreme mutant condition at the respective loci. The phenotypes of all known *barrel* and *engrailed* alleles (not shown) are somewhat variable and further studies are needed to deduce the typical phenotype. At the right, the two gap loci *Krüppel* and *knirps* are shown. Both patterns represent the amorphic phenotype as observed in embryos homozygous for deficiencies of the respective loci. The only known *hunchback* allele (not shown) deletes the meso- and metathorax.

"折叠扇"等位基因外，所有其他等位基因都是在筛选二号染色体上的胚胎致死突变体时分离到的。用赖特提出的DTS方案 [21]，用甲基磺酸乙酯处理筛选 *cn bw sp* 染色体，用上述方法从单个雄性杂合体中，建立了5,800个平衡品系。其中4,500个品系含有1个或多个新的致死突变。从2,600个假定的胚胎致死品系中取来孵化的胚胎，检查其表皮异常 [22]。在二号染色体的平衡品系中发现了三号染色体突变体，该突变体在通过三号染色体对TM3的雌性平衡个体中筛选后，得到了恢复。对表型相似的突变体进行互补测验，以杂交后代中出现突变胚胎为这些突变的等位性标准。在从格洛尔发现的原始"跛子"突变体中筛选致死胚胎时，分离出了三个新的"跛子"等位基因 [12]，其中，在TM1染色体上发现了一个可能是自然发生的折叠扇等位基因。在筛选X–连锁致死突变体时分离出了"侏儒"等位基因。‡"融合"基因是一个雄性可以补救的母体效应基因座 [8]。因此在"融合"纯合体母代产生的纯合体胚胎中可观察到反转的体节极性。不管胚胎的基因型如何，杂合体母本的后代皆表现正常的胚胎模式。

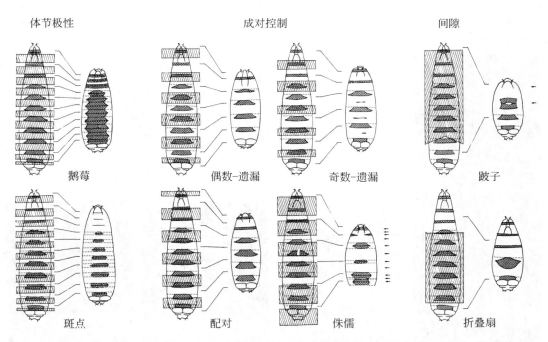

图 1. 半示意图表示突变体幼虫从正常模式中缺失的区域。点状区域表示齿状突起带，点线表示体节边界。阴影框所示为突变体幼虫中的缺失区域。横线连接突变体与正常幼虫中相对应的区域。箭头所示为"侏儒"和"跛子"突变体中极性反转面。图左侧为两个体节极性基因座"斑点"和"鹅莓"的突变体。对这种模式的极性的说明见图3。"融合"和"尺骨中断D"（未显示）的突变体形态与"鹅莓"相似，而"刺猬"和"无翅"突变体的缺失区域略大一些，从每侧切入齿状突起带。图中间所示为四个成对控制突变体。对它们表型的解释基于对弱、强等位基因的研究以及超双胸突变的结合（见正文部分）；至于"侏儒"突变，则基于雌雄嵌合体（未发表）。这或许代表了相应基因座的极端突变情况。所有已知的"桶状"和"锯齿状"等位基因突变的表型（未显示）都有些许多样性，需要深入研究以推断其典型表型。图右侧是两个间隙基因座"跛子"和"折叠扇"的突变体。在缺失相应基因座的纯合胚胎上观察到了这两种基因座所代表的无定形表型。唯一已知的"驼背"等位基因突变（未显示）缺失中胸和后胸。

## The Segmental Pattern of the Normal *Drosophila* Larva

Figure 2 shows the cuticular pattern of a normal *Drosophila* larva shortly after hatching. The larval body is comprised of three thoracic and eight abdominal segments. Although differences are observed in different body regions, all segments have certain morphological features in common. The anterior of each segment is marked with a band of denticles, most of which point posteriorly. The posterior part of each segment is naked. The segment borders run along the anterior margins of the denticle bands[7], they have no special morphological features. The polarity of the pattern is indicated by the orientation of the denticles and, in the abdomen, by the shape of the bands (Fig. 3). In the thoracic segments the bands are narrow with fine denticles whereas those in the abdominal segments are broader and comprised of thick pigmented denticles (for a detailed description of the cuticular pattern see ref. 1).

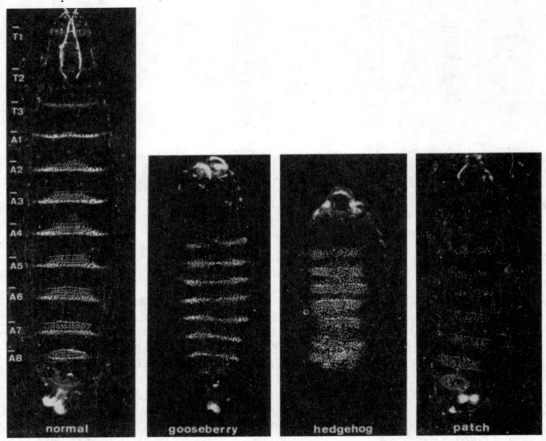

Fig. 2. Ventral cuticular pattern of (from left to right) a normal *Drosophila* larva shortly after hatching, and larvae homozygous for *gooseberry*, *hedgehog* and *patch*. The mutant larvae were taken out of the egg case before fixation. All larvae were fixed, cleared and mounted as described in ref. 22. A, abdominal segment; T, thoracic segment. For further description see text and Fig. 3. ×140.

## 正常果蝇幼虫的分节模式

图 2 显示了一只刚孵化不久的正常果蝇幼虫的表皮模式。幼虫身体由三个胸节和八个腹节组成。虽然可观察到不同身体部位的区别，但所有的体节都有某些共同的形态特征。每个体节的前端都有一条齿状带，它们中的大部分都指向后部。每个体节的后部是裸露的。体节的边界沿着齿状带的前缘延展[7]，它们没有特别的形态特征。小齿的方向及腹部条带的形状都表明了其模式的极性（图 3）。在胸节上条带很窄，且小齿细小，然而在腹节上条带较宽，由具厚重色素的小齿组成（对表皮模式的详细描述见参考文献 1）。

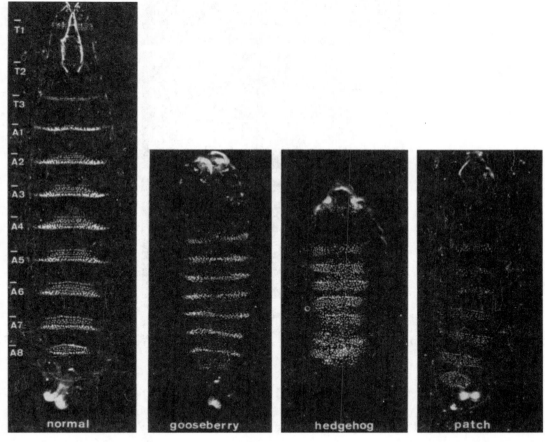

图 2. 从左到右依次是刚孵化不久的正常果蝇幼虫、"鹅莓"、"刺猬"和"斑点"纯合体幼虫的腹侧表皮模式。在固定前将突变幼虫从卵壳中取出。按照参考文献 22 的方法将所有幼虫固定、清洗并制成标本。A，腹节；T，胸节。更多描述见正文及图 3。（×140）。

## Segment Polarity Mutants: Deletions in Each Segment

Mutants in this class have the normal number of segments. However, in each segment a defined fraction of the normal pattern is deleted and the remainder is present as a mirror-image duplication. The duplicated part is posterior to the "normal" part and has reversed polarity (Figs 1–3).

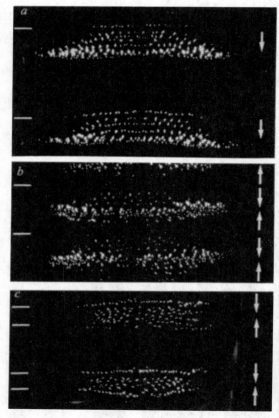

Fig. 3. Details from the ventral abdomen of a normal (*a*), a *gooseberry* (*b*), and a *patch* (*c*) larva. The positions of the segment boundaries are indicated at the left by the transverse lines. The arrows at the right indicate the polarity of the pattern as judged by the orientation of the denticles as well as the shape of the denticle bands.

Six such loci have been identified. Three loci, *fused*[8], *wingless* (ref. 9 and G. Struhl, personal communication) and *cubitus interruptus*[D], were previously known whereas *gooseberry*, *hedgehog* and *patch* are new (Table 1). All the mutations in this class are zygotic lethals and the phenotypes are only produced in homozygous embryos. One of the loci, *fused*, also shows a maternal effect in that a wild-type allele in the mother is sufficient to rescue the mutant phenotype of the homozygous embryos.

In all mutants except *patch* the region deleted includes the naked posterior part of the pattern and the duplication involves a substantial fraction of the anterior denticle band. In

## 体节极性突变：每个体节都有缺失

这个类型的突变体体节数目正常。然而，每个体节都缺失了正常模式中特定的一部分，剩余的部分呈镜像重复。重复的部分位于"正常部分"之后并具有相反的极性（图 1~3）。

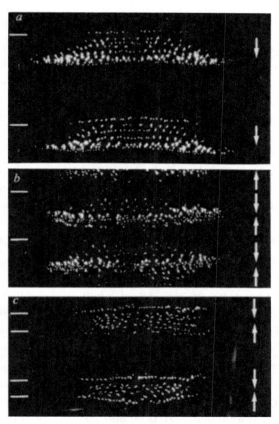

图 3. 幼虫腹节腹侧详图，正常（*a*），"鹅莓"突变体（*b*），"斑点"突变体（*c*）。左侧横线标出了体节边界的位置。右侧箭头指示依据小齿方向和齿状突起带形状所确定的模式的极性。

已经鉴定出了六个这一类型的基因座。其中，"融合"[8]、"无翅"（参考文献 9 以及与斯特鲁尔的个人交流）和"尺骨中断 D"这三个基因座是已知的，而"鹅莓"、"刺猬"和"斑点"是新基因（表 1）。这一类型的所有突变都是纯合致死的，并且突变表型只在纯合胚胎中产生。其中"融合"这个基因座还具有母体效应，因为母体中一个野生型等位基因足以挽救其纯合胚胎的突变体表型。

除"斑点"外，所有突变体的缺失部分都包括体节模式中裸露的后部区域，而其重复部分则都包含前部齿状带的大块区域。突变幼虫每个体节的腹侧都几乎完全

mutant larvae, the ventral side of each segment is almost entirely covered with denticles, the posterior fraction of which point anteriorly. The segment identity seems to be normal, the denticles of the abdominal segments being large and pigmented whereas those of the thorax are short and pale (Figs 1, 2). The anterior margin of the region duplicated in these mutants coincides with the segment boundary in only two cases, *fused* and *gooseberry* (Fig. 3). In *wingless* and *hedgehog* it lies posterior to the boundary, such that these larvae apparently lack all segment boundaries.

The phenotype of embryos homozygous for *patch* contrasts with that produced by the five loci described above in that the duplicated region includes some naked cuticle anterior to each denticle band. The duplicated unit thus involves structures of two adjacent segments. *Patch* larvae, despite the normal number of denticle bands, have twice the normal number of segment boundaries (Figs 1, 3).

Despite these differences, the common feature of all mutants in this class is that a defined fraction of the pattern in each segment is deleted. This deletion is associated with a mirror image duplication of the remaining part of the pattern. We suggest that these loci are involved in the specification of the basic pattern of the segmental units.

## Pair-rule Mutants: Deletions in Alternating Segments

In mutants of this class homologous parts of the pattern are deleted in every other segment. Each of the six loci is characterized by its own specific pattern of deletions (Table 1, Figs 1, 4). For example, in *even-skipped* larvae, the denticle bands and adjacent naked cuticle of the pro- and metathoracic, and the 2nd, 4th, 6th and 8th abdominal segments are lacking. This results in larvae with half the normal number of denticle bands separated by enlarged regions of naked cuticle (Figs 1, 4). In *paired* larvae the apparent reduction in segment number results essentially from the deletion of the naked posterior part of the odd-numbered and the anterior denticle bands of the even-numbered segments (Figs 1, 4). The double segments thus formed are composites of anterior mesothorax and posterior metathorax, anterior first abdominal and posterior second abdominal segment, etc. The identification of the regions present or deleted in mutant larvae is based on the phenotypes produced by alleles with lower expressivity. In such embryos the deletions are in general smaller and variable in size. In a "leaky" allele of *even-skipped*, the denticle bands of the even-numbered segments are frequently incomplete, whereas in *paired²* (*prd²*) the pattern deletions often involve only part of the naked cuticle of the odd-numbered segments, leading to a pairwise fusion of denticle bands (Fig. 4).

被小齿覆盖，小齿后部指向前部。体节特性似乎正常，腹节的小齿大且色素化而胸节的小齿短且颜色淡（图1和2）。只有在"融合"和"鹅莓"这两种突变体中重复部分的前缘才与体节边界一致（图3）。在"无翅"和"刺猬"突变体中，重复部分的前缘位于体节边界之后，以至于这些幼虫明显缺少了所有体节边界。

"斑点"纯合突变胚胎重复区域的每个齿状突起带前部都包含一些裸露表皮，其表型与前面描述的五个基因座突变表型截然不同。所以其重复单位涉及两个相邻体节的结构。因此，尽管"斑点"突变幼虫齿状带的数目正常，但其体节边界数是正常数目的两倍（图1和3）。

虽然有这些区别，但这一类型所有突变体的共同特征是每个体节中都缺失特定的区域，这种缺失与体节模式中剩余部分的镜像重复有关。我们认为这些基因座都参与了对体节单位基本模式的特化。

## 成对控制突变：交替体节的缺失

在这个类型的突变体中，每隔一个体节缺失模式中的同源部分。六个基因座中的每一个都有其独特的缺失方式（表1，图1和4）。例如，在"偶数－遗漏"突变幼虫中，不仅其前、后胸的齿状带和相邻裸露的表皮缺失，同时其第二、四、六、八腹节也缺失了。这导致突变幼虫中半数于正常数目的齿状带被裸露表皮的扩展区域分隔开（图1和4）。在"配对"突变幼虫中，体节数目的明显减少关键是由奇数体节裸露的后部和偶数体节前部的齿状带的缺失造成的（图1和4）。这样就形成了由中胸前部、后胸后部、第一腹节前部和第二腹节后部等组成的双体节。突变幼虫一个区域的存在或缺失是根据低表现度等位基因产生的表型鉴定的。这些胚胎中的基因缺失一般较小且大小变化多样。在"偶数－遗漏"的一个"遗漏"等位基因突变体中，偶数体节的齿状带往往不完整；然而在"配对²"（*prd²*）突变体中，缺失往往只涉及奇数体节裸露表皮的一部分，导致齿状带两两融合（图4）。

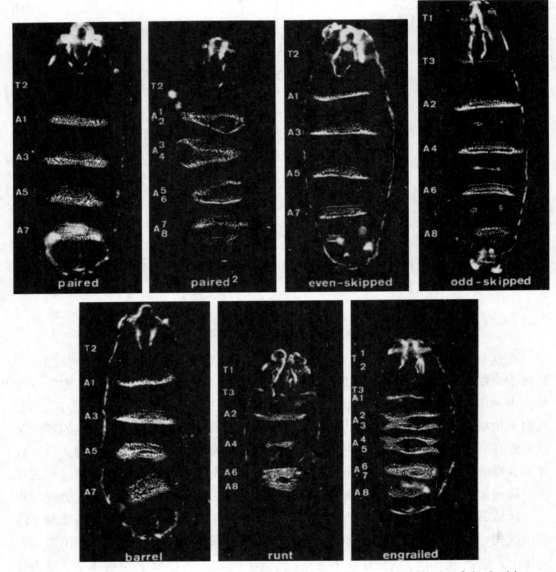

Fig. 4. Larvae homozygous for mutations at the six pair-rule loci. The segmental identity of the denticle bands is indicated at the left of each picture. A, abdominal band; T, thoracic band. For comparison with the normal pattern see Figs 1 and 2.

Further support for the composite nature of the segments in *prd* larvae was obtained in combinations with *Ultrabithorax* (*Ubx*), a homeotic mutation which when homozygous causes the transformation of the first abdominal segment into mesothorax[5]. In such *prd*; *Ubx* larvae, only the *denticle band* of the first double segment in the abdomen is transformed. The posterior margin of this band and the naked cuticle which follows remain abdominal in character and lack, for example, the typical mesothoracic sense organs. The composite nature of the segments in *paired* shows that the establishment of segmental identity does not require the establishment of individual segments as such.

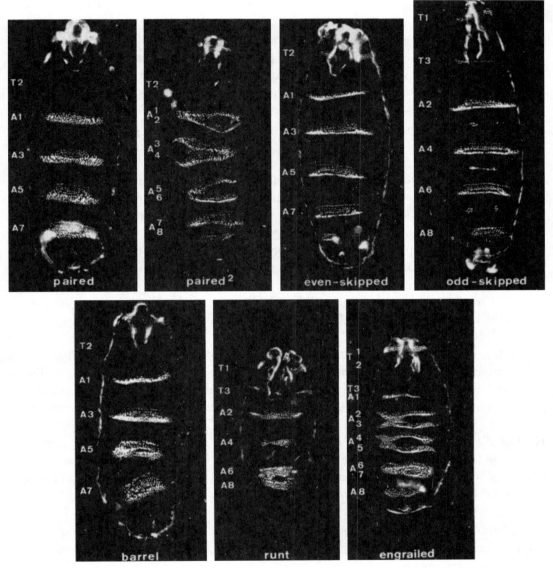

图 4. 六个成对控制基因座纯合突变的幼虫。在每个图的左侧注明了其齿状带的体节特性。A，腹带；T，胸带。其与正常模式的比较见图 1 和图 2。

"超双胸"（Ubx）突变是一种纯合时可以将第一腹节变为中胸的同源异型突变 [5]，它与"配对"突变结合进一步支持了配对突变幼虫中体节的复合性质。在这种"配对 – 超双胸"双突变幼虫中，只有腹部第一个双体节的齿状带转变了。这个条带的后缘和紧接着的裸露表皮保留了腹部的特征并缺失（例如）典型的中胸感觉器官。"配对"突变体中体节的复合性质表明，体节特性的建立并不需要个别体节本身特性的建立。

The segmentation pattern in *prd*; *Ubx* larvae is typical of that of *paired* alone and is not affected by the *Ubx* homeotic transformation. Similarly, in *prd*; *Polycomb* larvae the naked cuticle of alternating segments is deleted just as it is in *paired* alone, even though in *Polycomb* embryos all the thoracic and abdominal segments have an 8th abdominal character[5]. These combinations, and similar ones with *even-skipped*, indicate that the observed grouping of segments in pairs depends on the position of segments within the segmental array rather than the segmental identity. These combinations thus provide evidence that mutations such as *paired* and *even-skipped* affect different processes from those altered in homeotic mutants.

Other mutants in this class show different deletion patterns. The phenotype of *odd-skipped* is similar to that of *even-skipped*. However, in this case it is the odd-numbered denticle bands that are affected. In *odd-skipped*, the deleted region is smaller and is restricted to a more posterior part of the segment than in *even-skipped* (Figs 1, 4). *Barrel* has a phenotype similar to *paired* although the pattern is often less regular (Fig. 4). *Runt*, on the X chromosome, is the only pair-rule mutant showing mirror-image duplications. *Runt* embryos have half the normal number of denticle bands, each a mirror-image duplication of the anterior part of a normal band (similar to the duplications found in *patch*). The bands in *runt* embryos, as well as the region of naked cuticle separating them, are of unequal sizes (Figs 1, 4).

To the list of pair-rule loci we have added the *engrailed*[10] locus. Lethal *engrailed* alleles[11] lead to a substantial deletion of the posterior region of even-numbered segments. In addition, the anterior margin and adjacent cuticle of each segment are affected. Thus, the defect pattern in *engrailed* shows repeats which are spaced at both one- and two-segment intervals.

Each of the six different pair-rule loci affects a different region within a double segmental repeat. In no case does the margin of the deleted region coincide with a segment boundary. When the deleted region corresponds in size up to one entire segment (*paired*, *even-skipped*) it includes parts of two adjacent segments.

The phenotypes of the pair-rule mutants suggest that at some stage during normal development the embryo is organized in repeating units, the length of which corresponds to two segmental anlagen.

## Gap Mutants: One Continuous Stretch of Segments Deleted

One of the striking features of the mutations of the first two classes is that the alteration in the pattern is repeated at specific intervals along the antero-posterior axis of the embryo. No such repeated pattern is found in mutants of the third class and instead a single group of up to eight adjacent segments is deleted from the final pattern. Three loci have been identified which cause such gaps in the pattern (Table 1, Figs 1, 5). *Krüppel* (*Kr*) was originally described by Gloor[12]. Embryos homozygous for *Kr* lack thorax and anterior abdomen. The posterior-terminal region with the abdominal segments 8, 7 and 6 is normal, although probably somewhat enlarged. Anterior to the 6th abdominal segment is a plane of mirror–image symmetry followed by one further segment band with the

"配对－超双胸"双突变幼虫具有"配对"单突变幼虫体节模式的典型特点，且不受"超双胸"同源异型转变的影响。同样地，虽然在"多梳"单突变胚胎中所有胸节和腹节都具第八腹节的特征 [5]，但是，在"配对－多梳"双突变幼虫中，交替体节裸露表皮的缺失和"配对"单突变中的一样。这些组合及相似的"偶数－遗漏"组合表明，实验中观察到的成对体节组的形成是由体节在序列中的位置而不是体节特性决定的。因此，这些组合证明，诸如"配对"和"偶数－遗漏"的这类基因突变影响的过程不同于同源异型突变体中发生变化的过程。

这个类型的其他突变体表现出不同的缺失模式。"奇数－遗漏"突变表型与"偶数－遗漏"相似。然而，这时受影响的是奇数齿状带。与"偶数－遗漏"突变相比，在"奇数－遗漏"突变中缺失区域更小并局限于体节上更靠后的区域(图1,4)。"桶状"突变与"配对"表型相似但其模式往往较不规律（图4）。"侏儒"位于 X 染色体上，是唯一一个具有镜像重复的成对控制突变体。"侏儒"突变体胚胎有半数于正常数目的齿状带，每个带都有正常突起带前部的镜像重复（与"斑点"突变中的重复类似）。"侏儒"突变胚胎中的突起带及分隔它们的裸露表皮的尺寸大小不均一（图 1, 4）。

在成对控制基因座的列表中我们增加了"锯齿"基因座 [10]。致死的"锯齿"等位基因 [11] 能造成偶数体节后部区域的大量缺失。此外，每个体节的前缘和相邻表皮也会受到影响。因此，"锯齿"缺陷模式表现出在一个或两个体节间隔间的重复。

六个不同的成对控制基因座分别影响双体节重复中的一个不同区域。缺失区域的边缘从不与体节边界一致。当缺失区域大小达到一个完整体节时（"配对"，"偶数－遗漏"），它也会包含两个相邻体节的部分区域。

成对控制基因突变体的表型暗示，在正常发育的某个阶段胚胎被划分为重复单位，每个重复单位的长度相当于两个体节原基。

## 间隙突变体：一组连续体节缺失

前两类突变的一个显著特征是，沿着胚胎的前后轴模式的改变以特定的间隔重复出现。在第三类突变中不存在这种重复特性，取而代之的是在最终模式中最多连续八个相邻体节一起缺失。已经鉴定出三个引起这类间隙突变的基因座（表1，图1和5）。"跛子"（*Kr*）突变最早是由格洛尔描述的 [12]。"跛子"纯合胚胎没有胸部和前腹部。尾部末端及第八、七、六腹节正常，但是有些许变大。在第六腹节的前面是一个镜像对称的平面，该平面连着另一个具有第六体节特征但极性相反的体节带。对称平面的精确位置是变化的，通常不与体节边界一致。"跛子"突变的大部分模式

character of a 6th segment oriented in reversed polarity. The exact position of the plane of symmetry varies and does not usually coincide with a segmental boundary. A large part of the *Krüppel* pattern is reminiscent of the pattern observed in embryos produced by the maternal-effect mutant *bicaudal*, although no maternal component is involved in the production of the *Krüppel* phenotype (in preparation).

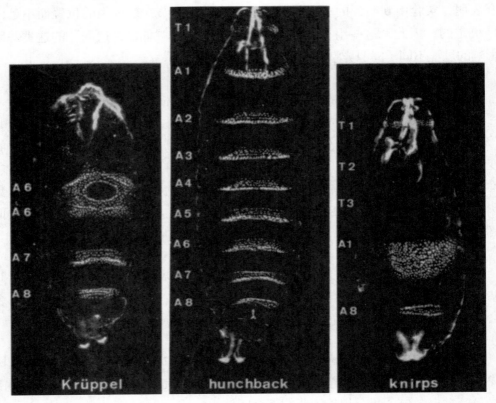

Fig. 5. Larvae homozygous for mutations at the three gap loci. A, abdominal segment; T, thoracic segment.

In the other two loci of this class, the gap in the pattern occurs in specific morphologically defined subregions of the larval pattern, in the thorax and in the abdomen, respectively. In *hunchback*, the meso- and metathoracic segments are deleted. In embryos homozygous for *knirps*, only two rather than eight denticle bands are formed in the abdomen. The posterior-terminal region including the 8th abdominal segment seems normal whereas the anterior abdominal denticle band is considerably enlarged. The anterior margin of the denticle band is morphologically similar to the first abdominal segment but combinations with *Ubx* show that the band is a composite with more than one segmental identity.

All three loci are required for a normal segmental subdivision of one continuous body region. The lack of a repeated pattern of defects suggests that the loci are involved in processes in which position along the antero-posterior axis of the embryo is defined by unique values.

都使人联想到母体效应"双尾"突变体产生的胚胎模式，虽然母体成分并未参与"跛子"表型的产生过程（文章准备发表）。

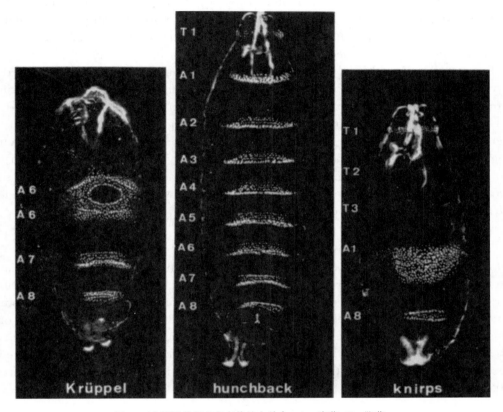

图 5. 三个间隙基因座突变的纯合幼虫。A，腹节；T，胸节。

这一类型的其他两个基因座中，幼虫模式上的间隙分别产生于胸部和腹部的形态特化的亚区域。"驼背"突变幼虫的中胸和后胸体节缺失了。"折叠扇"突变纯合胚胎的腹部只形成了两条而非八条齿状突起带。尾部末端区域包括第八腹节看起来正常，但其前腹部齿状带增大了很多。齿状带的前缘形态上与第一腹节相似，但与"超双胸"突变的组合表现出这条突起带是具有多种体节特性的复合体。

上述三个基因座都是身体上一个连续区域细分成正常体节所必需的。这些缺陷缺少重复性模式，表明这些基因座参与了由固定值划定的胚胎前后轴模式的形成过程。

## When Are Genes Affecting Segment Number Active?

The phenotypes described above are observed only in homozygous embryos, indicating that the loci identified by these mutations are active after fertilization and are crucial for the normal segmental organisation of the embryo. We have described the mutations in terms of their effect on the differentiated pattern. However, in many instances their effect can be observed much earlier in development. In normal embryos segmentation is first visible 1 h after the onset of gastrulation as a repeated pattern of bulges in the ventral ectoderm (unpublished observations). In *paired* and *even-skipped* embryos the number of bulges is reduced and corresponds to the number of segments observed in the differentiated mutant embryos. *Krüppel*, *runt* and *knirps* embryos can be identified 15 min after the onset of gastrulation. All three mutations cause shorter germ bands, a phenomenon clearly related to the strong reduction in segment number observed in the differentiated larvae. Further evidence for an early activity at the *paired* locus was obtained using a temperature-sensitive allele. The extreme phenotype is only obtained when the embryo is kept at the restrictive temperature during the blastoderm stage. All these results indicate that the wild-type genes defined by the mutations are active before the end of gastrulation during normal development.

## Discussion

Segmentation in *Drosophila* proceeds by the transition from a single field into a repeated pattern of homologous smaller subfields. Mutant alleles at the 15 loci we have described interfere with this process at various points. Although each locus has its own distinct phenotype, we were able to distribute the mutations in three classes. In one class only a single large subregion of the embryo is affected, whereas in mutants of the other two classes a reiteration of defects is produced with a repeat length of one or two segments, respectively. This suggests that the process of segmentation involves three different units of spatial organization.

The organization of the egg is thought to be controlled by a monotonic gradient set up during oogenesis under the control of the maternal genome[3,4]. All the mutants we have described depend on the embryonic rather than the maternal genome. None of them alters the overall polarity of the embryo, the head always being at the anterior and the telson at the posterior end of the egg. The most dramatic alterations of the pattern are produced in the gap mutants and involve one large subregion of the egg. *Hunchback* and *knirps* affect the development of thorax and abdomen, respectively, and might be involved in the establishment of these large morphologically unique subregions of the embryo. The large mirror-image duplications found in the posterior pattern of *Krüppel* embryos are similar to those of *bicaudal*. The *bicaudal* phenotype has been interpreted as resulting from an instability in the maternal gradient[3,13], and thus *Krüppel* might be involved in the maintenance of elaboration of this gradient in the posterior egg region after fertilization.

The smallest repeat unit, the individual segment, is affected in mutants at the six segment-polarity loci. The pattern alteration consists of a mirror-image duplication of part of the normal pattern with the remainder deleted. In these mutants the deleted region

## 基因在何时有效地影响体节数目？

上述表型只有在纯合基因突变胚胎中才能得到，说明通过这些突变体鉴定的基因座在受精之后起作用，而且是胚胎形成正常体节所必需的。我们已经描述了这些突变体对分化模式的影响。然而，在许多情况下，它们的影响在更早的发育时期就已出现。正常胚胎中最早观察到体节分化是在最初原肠胚形成后一个小时，表现为外胚层腹侧重复模式的突起（未发表的观察结果）。在"配对"和"偶数－遗漏"突变胚胎中突起数目有减少，并且与已分化的突变体胚胎中观察到的体节数目相同。在最初原肠胚形成后15分钟后就可以鉴定出"跛子"、"侏儒"、"折叠扇"突变体的胚胎。这三种突变都可引起胚带变短，这一现象与在已分化的幼虫中观察到的体节数目大量减少有明显关系。通过温度敏感等位基因得到了关于配对基因座早期活性更深入的证据。只有在囊胚层期将胚胎置于限制温度，才能得到极端突变表型。所有结果表明，在正常发育中，通过突变定义的野生型基因作用于原肠胚形成结束以前。

## 讨　论

果蝇的分节是一个从单域向同源的较小亚区的重复模式的转变过程。我们已经描述的15个基因座的突变体等位基因在不同时间点干扰这个过程。虽然每个基因座都有其独特的表型，但我们还是可以将这些突变体划分为三个类型。在一类中，只有胚胎上一个大的亚区受影响。而在另两类突变体中，分别产生了重复长度为一个体节或两个体节的重复性缺陷。这暗示了分节过程涉及三种不同的空间组织单元。

卵的结构形成被认为是由单一梯度决定的，该梯度是在母体基因组控制下在卵子发生时建立的[3,4]。我们描述的所有突变体都是以胚胎而不是以母体基因组为基础的。它们都未改变胚胎的整体极性，头仍然在卵的前部，尾节仍在卵的后端。间隙突变体产生的模式改变最明显，涉及卵的一个大的亚区。"驼背"和"折叠扇"分别影响胸部和腹部的发育，可能参与胚胎上大的形态独特的亚区的建立。发生在"跛子"突变胚胎后部的大面积镜像重复与"双尾"相似。"双尾"突变表型可以被理解为母体效应不稳定的结果[3,13]，因此，"跛子"可能参与维持了受精后卵的后部区域梯度的细分。

最小的重复单位，即单个体节，在六个体节－极性基因座突变中受到了影响。其模式改变包括部分正常模式的镜像重复及其剩余部分的缺失。在这些突变体中缺

corresponds in size to more than half a segment. Mutations causing smaller deletions in the segmental pattern do not lead to polarity reversals (unpublished observations). The mirror-image duplications produced by the pair-rule mutation *runt* are also associated with a deletion of more than half a repeat unit, that is, more than one segment. The tendency of partial fields containing less than half the positional values to duplicate is well described for imaginal disks in *Drosophila*[14], as well as for the larval epidermis in other insects[15,16]. On the other hand, the same types of pattern duplication are also produced in conditions which do not involve cell death and regeneration, but rather a reorganization of the positional information in the entire field[3,17]. More detailed studies of early development in mutant embryos may reveal which mechanism is responsible for the different mutant phenotypes.

Given the evidence for a homology between segments, the existence of a class of mutants affecting corresponding regions in each individual segment is perhaps not surprising. The discovery of a mutant class affecting corresponding regions in every other segment was not expected and suggests the existence at some time during development of homologous units with the size of two segmental anlagen. It is possible that the double segmental unit corresponds to transitory double segmental fields which are established early during embryogenesis and are later subdivided into individual segments. At the blastoderm stage the epidermal primordium giving rise to thorax and abdomen is only about 40 cells long[1], An initial subdivision into double segments would avoid problems of accuracy encountered in a simultaneous establishment of segment boundaries every three to four cells. A stepwise establishment of segments implies that the borders defining double segments be made before the intervening ones. The mutant phenotypes do not definitely show which, if any, of the segment borders define a primary double segmental division in normal development. The mutant phenotypes which come closest to a pattern one would expect if the transition from the double segment to the individual segment stage were blocked are the patterns of *paired* and *even-skipped*. Both suggest the frame meso- and methathorax, 1st and 2nd, 3rd and 4th abdominal segment, etc.

It is also possible that the double segmental units are never defined by distinct borders in normal development. The existence of a double segmental homology unit may merely reflect a continuous property such as a wave with a double segmental period responsible for correct spacing of segmental boundaries (see, for example, refs 18, 19). We have not found any mutations showing a repeat unit larger than two segments. This may indicate that the subdivision of the blastoderm proceeds directly by the double segmental repeat with no larger intervening homology units. However, the failure to identify such larger units may reflect the incompleteness of our data.

*Drosophila* has been estimated to have about 5,000 genes and only a very small fraction of these when mutated result in a change of the segmental pattern of the larva. Some of the loci described here were known previously but only in the case of *Krüppel* has the embryonic lethal phenotype been recognized as affecting segmentation.[12] The majority of the mutants described here have been isolated in systematic searches for mutations affecting the segmentation pattern of the *Drosophila* larva. These experiments are still incomplete. Most of the alleles on the second chromosome were isolated in one experiment which yielded an average allele frequency of four or five alleles per locus

失区域大于半个体节。引起体节模式中较小缺失的突变并不会导致极性反转（未发表的观察结果）。成对控制突变"侏儒"产生的镜像重复也与大于半个重复单位（也就是大于一个体节）的缺失有关。包含少于一半位置值的部分区域发生重复的趋势已被果蝇成虫盘[14]和其他昆虫幼虫表皮[15,16]为例很好地描述。另一方面，在不涉及细胞死亡和再生的条件下也会产生相同类型的重复模式，但不是完整区域内位置信息的重组[3,17]。对突变胚胎早期发育更细致的研究也许会揭示不同突变表型的形成机制。

鉴于体节之间的同源性，存在一组影响各个体节相应区域的突变体也许并不奇怪。发现一组影响间隔体节相应区域的突变体却出乎意料，这暗示了在某个发育阶段存在大小为两个体节原基的同源单位。很可能双体节单位对应胚胎发生早期形成的短暂存在的双体节区域，这些区域之后再分化成了单个体节。在囊胚期，将要分化为胸部和腹部的上皮原基只有 40 个细胞的长度[1]。最初分化为双体节可避免每三到四个细胞同时形成各体节边界时所遇到的准确性问题。体节的逐步形成意味着双体节边界是在中间边界之前形成的。突变体表型并未确切地显示确立正常发育中的双体节分区的体节边界。如果从双体节到单体节的转变过程被打断，与预期模式最接近的突变表型是"配对"和"偶数–遗漏"突变的表型。两者都提示中胸和后胸，第一、第二、第三和第四腹节等结构。

也可能双体节单位在正常发育中从未被明显的边界所划分。双体节同源单位的存在可能仅仅反映了一种连续性质，就像一种以双体节为周期的波，这种波与体节边界的正确划分有关（举例说明可以见参考文献 18, 19）。我们未发现重复单位大于两个体节的突变体。这可能说明了胚盘直接通过没有更大的中间同源单位的双体节重复进行分化。然而未能确定这种较大的同源单位，可能反映出我们的数据不足。

据估计，果蝇约有 5,000 个基因，其中只有一小部分突变后会引起幼虫体节模式改变。本文描述的基因座中有些是已知的，但只有"跛子"突变体的胚胎致死表型被认为影响分节[12]。本文描述的大多数突变体都已在影响果蝇幼虫分节模式突变的系统研究中分离出来。这些实验仍不完整。二号染色体上绝大多数等位基因是在一个实验中分离出来的，在这个实验中，每个基因座的平均等位基因频率为 4~5 个（基于 42 个胚胎致死基因座）。根据这个结果及三号、一号染色体相似的计算结果，我

(based on 42 embryonic lethal loci). From this yield and similar calculations for the third and first chromosomes, we estimate that we have identified almost all segmentation loci on the second chromosome and about 50% each of those on the third and first chromosome. Our sample of 15 loci should therefore represent the majority of the loci affecting segmentation in the *Drosophila* genome. Thus, in *Drosophila* it would seem feasible to identify all genetic components involved in the complex process of embryonic pattern formation.

We thank Hildegard Kluding for excellent technical assistance, Adelheid Schneider, Maria Weber and Gary Struhl for help during various parts of the mutant screens, Gerd Jürgens for stimulating discussion and our colleagues from the *Drosophila* laboratories in Cambridge, Freiburg, Heidelberg and Zürich for critical comments on the manuscript, and Claus Christensen for the photographic prints. Thomas Kornberg and Gary Struhl provided us with lethal alleles of *engrailed* and *wingless* respectively which facilitated the identification of our alleles. All mutants are available on request.

*Note added in proof*: All known *barrel* alleles fail to complement *hairy*[20], suggesting that the *barrel* mutations are alleles at the *hairy* locus.

(**287**, 795-801; 1980)

**Christiane Nüsslein-Volhard and Eric Wieschaus**
European Molecular Biology Laboratory, PO Box 10.2209, 69 Heidelberg, FRG

Received 26 June; accepted 29 August 1980

References:
1. Lohs-Schardin, M., Cremer, C. & Nüsslein-Volhard, C. *Devl. Biol.* **73**, 239–255 (1979).
2. Wieschaus, E. & Gehring, W. *Devl. Biol.* **50**, 249–263 (1976).
3. Nüsslein-Volhard, C. in *Determinants of Spatial Organisation* (eds Subtelney, S. & Konigs-berg, I. R.) 185–211 (Academic, New York, 1979).
4. Sander, K. *Adv. Insect Physiol.* **12**, 125–238 (1976).
5. Lewis, E. B. *Nature* **276**, 565–570 (1978).
6. Garcia-Bellido, A. *Am. Zool.* **17**, 613–629 (1977).
7. Szabad, J., Schüpbach, T. & Wieschaus, E. *Devl. Biol.* **73**, 256–271 (1979).
8. Counce, S. Z. *Induktive Abstammungs-Vererbungslehre* **87**, 462–81 (1958).
9. Sharma, R. P. & Chopra, V. L. *Devl. Biol.* **48**, 461–465 (1976).
10. Lawrence, P. A. & Morata, G. *Devl. Biol.* **50**, 321–337 (1976).
11. Kornberg, T., in preparation.
12. Gloor, H. *Arch. Julius-Klaus-Stift. VererbForsch*, **25**, 38–44 (1950).
13. Meinhardt, H. *J. Cell Sci.* **23**, 117–139 (1977).
14. Bryant, P. J. *Ciba Fdn Symp.* **29**, 71–93 (1975).
15. Wright, D. & Lawrence, P. A., in preparation.
16. Lawrence, P. A. in *Developmental Systems: Insects* (eds Counce, S. & Waddington, C. H.) 157–209 (Academic, London, 1973).
17. Jürgens, G. & Gateff, E. *Wilhelm Roux Arch.* **186**, 1–25 (1979).
18. Meinhardt, H. & Gierer, A. *J. Cell. Sci.* **15**, 321–346 (1974).
19. Kaufmann, S. A., Shymko, R. M. & Trabert, K. *Science* **199**, 259–270 (1978).
20. Lindsley, D. & Grell, E. H. *Genetic Variations of Drosophila melanogaster* (Carnegie, Washington, 1968).
21. Wright, T. R. F. *Drosoph. Inf. Serv.* **45**, 140 (1970).
22. Vander Meer, J. *Drosoph. Inf. Serv.* **52**, 160 (1977).

们估计我们已经鉴定出了二号染色体上几乎所有的分节基因座，并且完成了对三号、一号染色体上各 50% 的分节基因座的鉴定。所以我们鉴定的 15 个分节基因座可以代表果蝇基因组中影响分节的大部分基因座。因此，鉴定出参与果蝇分节模式形成复杂过程的所有遗传组分是可行的。

我们感谢希尔德加德·克鲁丁出色的技术支持，感谢阿德尔海德·施奈德、玛丽亚·韦伯、加里·斯特鲁尔在突变体筛选各阶段的帮助，感谢格尔德·于尔根斯富有启发性的讨论和来自剑桥、弗赖堡、海德堡、苏黎世等地的果蝇实验室的同事们对手稿的关键性评论，感谢克劳斯·克里斯坦森在图像处理方面的工作。托马斯·科恩伯格和加里·斯特鲁尔分别赠予"锯齿"和"无翅"的致死等位基因便于我们鉴定等位基因。如有需求，所有突变体均可提供。

**附加说明：**所有已知的"桶状"等位基因都不能互补"多毛"突变 [20]，这意味着"桶状"突变体是"多毛"基因座的等位基因。

（李梅 翻译；沈杰 审稿）

# Establishment in Culture of Pluripotential Cells from Mouse Embryos

M. J. Evans and M. H. Kaufman

## Editor's Note

British biologists Martin Evans and Matt Kaufman were the first to isolate and culture stem cells. Here they describe the process, which yielded mouse stem cells capable of self-renewal and differentiation into other cell types. Careful culture conditions and the use of dormant early embryos aided their success, and the study's impact has been enormous. Since researchers demonstrated that the DNA changes in genetically modified stem cells could be passed through the germline of chimaeric animals, thousands of genes have been "knocked out" in mouse models, shedding light on development and disease. Stem cells enabled reproductive cloning to become reality, and are currently being studied for regenerative medicine. In 2007 Evans received a Nobel Prize for his work.

---

Pluripotential cells are present in a mouse embryo until at least an early post-implantation stage, as shown by their ability to take part in the formation of chimaeric animals[1] and to form teratocarcinomas[2]. Until now it has not been possible to establish progressively growing cultures of these cells *in vitro*, and cell lines have only been obtained after teratocarcinoma formation *in vivo*. We report here the establishment in tissue culture of pluripotent cell lines which have been isolated directly from *in vitro* cultures of mouse blastocysts. These cells are able to differentiate either *in vitro* or after inoculation into a mouse as a tumour *in vivo*. They have a normal karyotype.

---

PREVIOUS attempts to obtain cultures of pluripotential cells directly from a mouse embryo have been unsuccessful[3,4] although cells with a similar appearance have been reported to be present transiently[5,6]. We considered that success might depend on three critical factors: (1) the exact stage at which pluripotential cells capable of growth in tissue culture exist in the embryo; (2) explantation of a sufficiently large number of these precursor cells from each embryo; and (3) tissue culture in conditions most conducive to multiplication rather than differentiation of these embryonic cells. These considerations have been discussed at greater length elsewhere[7]. An indication of the optimal stage of embryonic development might be gained by a comparison of the properties of embryonic cells at various stages with established cultures of embryonal carcinoma (EC) cells. Cell-surface antigen expression and the patterns of protein synthesis revealed by two-dimensional electrophoresis have suggested that neither the cells of the $6\frac{1}{2}$-day ectoderm nor those of the $3\frac{1}{2}$-day inner cell mass show homology with EC cells, but that epiblast

# 小鼠胚胎多能细胞培养体系的建立

埃文斯，考夫曼

## 编者按

英国生物学家马丁·埃文斯和马特·考夫曼率先分离并培养干细胞。在本文中，他们描述了这个产生小鼠干细胞的过程，该小鼠干细胞能够进行自我更新并分化成其他细胞类型。严格的培养条件和休眠的早期胚胎的使用促成了他们的成功，而且这项研究非常有影响力。自从研究人员证实在遗传修饰的干细胞中发生的 DNA 改变可以通过嵌合动物的生殖细胞系来遗传，此后数以千计的基因都在小鼠模型中被"敲除"，这些为发育和疾病的研究提供了便利。干细胞使得生殖性克隆成为现实，并且目前人们在再生医学方面正在进行干细胞研究。2007 年，埃文斯凭借他的研究获得了诺贝尔奖。

---

多能细胞在小鼠胚胎中一直存在，至少到着床后阶段的早期才消失，这是因为实验显示它们具有参与形成嵌合动物[1]和畸胎癌[2]的能力。迄今为止还不能在体外建立这些细胞的持续培养体系，而且只有在体内形成畸胎癌后才能获得细胞系。本文中我们报道了直接从体外小鼠囊胚培养物中分离出来的多能细胞系组织培养体系的建立。这些细胞能够在体外分化，或者作为一个肿瘤接种到小鼠体内后发生分化。它们具有正常的核型。

---

尽管已有报道称具有类似多能细胞表型的细胞能够短暂存活于体外[5,6]，但是以前试图直接从小鼠胚胎中获得多能细胞的培养都没有成功[3,4]。我们认为成功培养可能取决于三个关键因素：（1）胚胎中能够在组织培养中生长的多能细胞所处的确切阶段；（2）从每个胚胎中外植足够多的前体细胞；（3）组织培养的条件要最适合于诱导这些胚胎细胞的增殖，而不是分化。这些观点在其他文献中有篇幅更长的讨论[7]。通过比较不同阶段的胚胎细胞与已经建立的胚胎癌（EC）细胞培养物的特性就可以获得胚胎发育最佳阶段的提示。通过二维电泳显示的细胞表面抗原的表达和蛋白合成的模式表明，6.5 天的外胚层细胞与 3.5 天的内细胞团都不与 EC 细胞具有同源性，但是交配后 5.5 天的早期着床后胚胎的上胚层细胞可能与 EC 细胞具有同源性[8]（发现交配栓的时间定义为 0.5 天）。早期着床后胚胎的细胞似乎是用于多能细胞培养的

cells of the early post-implantation embryo at $5\frac{1}{2}$ days post coitum may do so[8] (the day of finding coital plug is termed day $\frac{1}{2}$). Cells from embryos of an early post-implantation stage seem to be the best candidates for direct progenitors of pluripotential cells in culture. As these embryos are difficult to isolate, and as the cell number in the isolated epiblast is small, we chose an alternative route to obtain embryo cells at this stage of development.

Mouse blastocysts may be induced to enter a state of diapause just before implantation. This delay in implantation depends on the maternal hormonal conditions, and may be induced experimentally by ovariectomy at an appropriate stage[9]. Embryos in implantational delay hatch from the zona but remain free-floating in the uterine lumen. A gradual increase in cell number occurs[10], and the primary endoderm may be formed but no further development takes place until implantation occurs, under the control of hormonal stimuli.

129 SvE mice were caged in pairs and examined for mating plugs each morning. They were ovariectomized on the afternoon of day $2\frac{1}{2}$ of pregnancy, injected subcutaneously with 1 mg Depo-Provera (Upjohn), and delayed blastocysts were recovered 4-6 days later. The blastocysts were cultured intact in groups of about six embryos in small drops of tissue culture medium under paraffin oil on tissue culture plastic Petri dishes for 4 days. The blastocysts attached within 48 h and the trophectoderm cells grew out and differentiated into giant trophoblast cells. The inner cell mass cells subsequently developed into large egg cylinder-like structures, with a group of small round cells surrounded by endodermal cells growing attached to the Petri dish. The egg cylinder-like structures were picked off the dish, dispersed by trypsin treatment and passaged on to gelatin-pretreated Petri dishes containing mitomycin C-inactivated STO fibroblasts. All culture was carried out in Dulbecco's modified minimal essential medium supplemented with 10% fetal calf serum and 10% newborn calf serum. The cultures were examined daily and passaged by trypsinization every 2-3 days. Actively proliferating colonies of cells closely resembling EC cells were apparent from an early stage. These colonies were picked out, passaged and mass cultures grown. The cell cultures had the appearance and general growth characteristics of feeder-dependent EC cells (Fig. 1).

直接前体细胞的最佳选择。由于这些胚胎很难分离,而且分离出的上胚层细胞非常少,我们选择了另一种方法来获得这个发育阶段的胚胎细胞。

　　小鼠的囊胚可以在即将着床时被诱导进入休眠状态。这种着床延迟取决于母体激素水平。而且可以在合适的阶段通过卵巢切除,实现着床延迟的实验性诱导[9]。着床延迟的胚胎从透明带中孵出,但是在子宫腔内仍然保持自由漂浮状态。在激素刺激的控制下,细胞的数量逐渐增多[10],原内胚层可能会形成,但是着床之前不会有进一步发育。

　　将 129 SvE 小鼠成对关在笼子里,每天早晨查看是否有交配栓形成。在妊娠 2.5 天的下午切除它们的卵巢,皮下注射 1 毫克狄波－普维拉醋酸甲羟孕酮注射液(普强公司),延迟发育的囊胚在 4~6 天后恢复。以大约 6 个胚胎为一组将囊胚完整地在少量组织培养基中培养 4 天,培养基盛放在组织培养用的塑料培养皿中,上面覆盖石蜡油。囊胚在 48 小时内贴壁,滋养外胚层细胞长出并分化成巨大的滋养层细胞。内细胞团细胞随后发育成大的近似卵筒结构,并伴随一群贴在培养皿上生长的由内胚层细胞包围的小圆形细胞。将近似卵筒结构挑出培养皿,用胰蛋白酶处理使其分散,并在明胶预处理的含有丝裂霉素 C 灭活的 STO 成纤维细胞的培养皿中进行传代。所有的培养都使用杜尔贝科改良的最低必需培养基加上 10% 的胎牛血清和 10% 的新生牛血清。每天检查培养物,每 2~3 天用胰蛋白酶消化进行传代培养。从早期阶段开始,非常类似于 EC 细胞的活跃增殖的细胞集落就很明显了。将这些集落挑出、传代并大规模培养。这些细胞培养物具备饲养层依赖的 EC 细胞的外观和一般生长特征(图 1)。

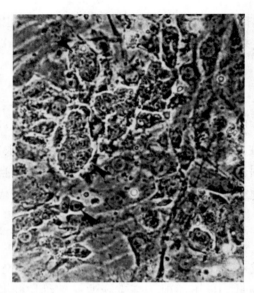

Fig. 1. Groups of pluripotential embryo cells (arrowed) growing in monolayer culture on a background of mitomycin C-inhibited STO cells. The isolation of a definite cell line from a blastocyst takes only ~3 weeks and the pluripotential cell colonies are visible within 5 days of passage. We have had 30% yield of lines from blastocysts in one experiment. Two of the lines have been rigorously cloned by single-cell isolation but most were only colony-picked—this makes no difference.

The embryos used to initiate these cultures are from normal 129 SvE strain mice, that is, from the same strain of mice as many EC cell lines, in particular those grown in this laboratory. Therefore it was important to exclude any possibility of contamination of these cultures with EC cells from established cell lines. Cell cultures were established from different embryos in three separate experimental series, but the best indication of their separate identity came from their karyotype. Cultures were initiated from 6-12 embryos, thus it might be expected that both male and female cells should be present. None of the 129 embryonal carcinoma cell lines in this laboratory have a normal karyotype, and, in particular—in common with most available embryonal carcinoma cell lines—they do not contain a Y chromosome. These embryo-derived cells have a completely normal karyotype. An XY karyotype is shown in Fig. 2. Three additional cell lines have been analysed; two of these are normal 40XX and one is normal 40XY. We have termed these directly embryo-derived cells EK to distinguish them from EC cells. EK cells grow rapidly in culture and have been maintained for over 30 passages *in vitro*.

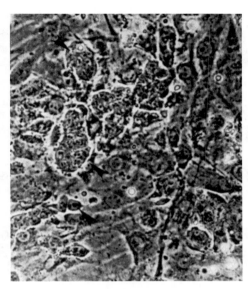

图 1. 在丝裂霉素 C 抑制的 STO 细胞背景中，呈单层生长的多能胚胎细胞群（箭头）。只需要大约 3 周就可从囊胚中分离到一种特定的细胞系，而且在传代 5 天之内就能观察到多能细胞集落。在一次实验中，我们已经从囊胚中获得了 30% 的细胞系。其中两个细胞系已经通过单细胞分离严格地克隆出来，但是多数细胞系仅从集落中挑出——这没有太大的差别。

　　用于起始培养的胚胎均来自正常的 129 SvE 种系小鼠，也就是说，这些胚胎像许多 EC 细胞系尤其是本实验室培养的那些细胞系一样，来源于同一种系的小鼠。因此排除任何来自已建立的细胞系的 EC 细胞污染是非常重要的。在三个单独进行的实验系列中细胞培养物都是从不同的胚胎中建立的，但是核型才是鉴别它们各自特性的最好指标。培养物起始于有 6~12 个胚胎，因此可以预计，雄性和雌性细胞同时存在。本实验室使用的 129 个胚胎癌细胞系都没有正常的核型，而且尤其是，与大部分可获得的胚胎癌细胞系一样，它们都没有 Y 染色体。这些胚胎来源的细胞具有完全正常的核型。图 2 中显示了 XY 核型。我们还分析了另外三个细胞系，其中两个是正常的 40XX，另一个是正常的 40XY。我们将这些直接胚胎来源的细胞称为 EK 细胞，以区别于 EC 细胞。EK 细胞在培养基中生长非常迅速，而且在体外能够维持传代达 30 代以上。

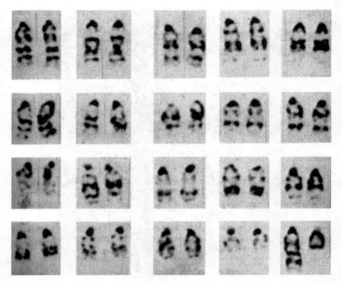

Fig. 2. Karyotype of an embryo-derived pluripotential cell line, 40XY. Over 80% of the spreads of this clonal line possessed 40 chromosomes and had a clearly identifiable Y chromosome.

Cultures of EK cells were collected by trypsinization, and ~$10^6$ cells injected subcutaneously into the flank of syngeneic male mice. Tumours grew in all cases, and histological examination of these revealed that they were teratocarcinomas. When the EK cells were passaged without feeder cells they formed embryoid bodies which, when kept in suspension, became cystic. Embryoid bodies allowed to attach to a Petri dish spread out and differentiated in the usual way into a complex of tissues. Preliminary observations indicate that, like early ectoderm cells of the mouse embryo and EC cells, EK cells carry the cell-surface antigens recognized by M1-22-25 (Forssman)[8,11] and anti-I Ma (lacto-*N*-iso-octaosyl ceramide)[12,13] and also that two dimensional gel electrophoretic separations of their proteins very closely resemble those of the EC cell line PSMB.

We have demonstrated here that it is possible to isolate pluripotential cells directly from early embryos and that they behave in a manner equivalent to EC cells isolated from teratocarcinomas. The network of inter-relationships between the mouse embryo and pluripotential cells derived from it has previously lacked only the direct link between the embryo and cells in culture for completion. We have now demonstrated this (Fig. 3).

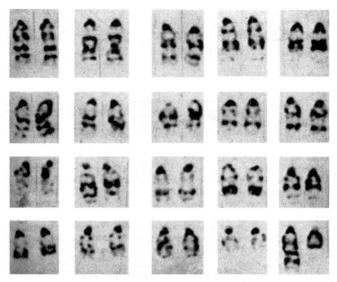

图 2. 胚胎来源的多能细胞系的核型，40XY。这种克隆细胞系超过 80% 的细胞涂片都具有 40 条染色体，并具有清晰可辨的 Y 染色体。

通过胰蛋白酶消化收集培养的 EK 细胞，然后将大约 $10^6$ 个细胞皮下注射到同系雄性小鼠的侧腹部。所有实验小鼠均长出肿瘤，而且组织学检查显示它们都是畸胎癌。如果在没有饲养细胞的情况下对 EK 细胞进行传代，它们就会形成拟胚体，如果保持悬浮培养就会成为囊性胚体。能够黏附到培养皿上的拟胚体就会迅速铺展并按照正常的方式分化成复杂的组织。初步观测结果表明，就像小鼠胚胎的早期外胚层细胞和 EC 细胞一样，EK 细胞携带的细胞表面抗原能够被 M1–22–25（福斯曼）[8,11]和抗 I–Ma（乳酰–N–异 –二十八烷基神经酰胺）[12,13] 识别，而且 EK 细胞蛋白质的二维凝胶电泳分离结果与 EC 细胞系 PSMB 的结果非常接近。

本文中我们已经证明有可能直接从早期胚胎中分离出多能细胞，而且它们的行为方式与从畸胎癌中分离出来的 EC 细胞相同。之前，关于小鼠胚胎和其来源的多能细胞之间完整的相互关系网络仅缺乏胚胎和培养细胞之间的直接联系，我们现在展示这种联系（图 3）。

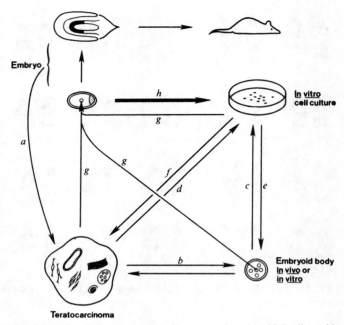

Fig. 3. Inter-relationships of cell lines, teratocarcinomas and embryoid bodies with normal mouse embryos. Arrows indicate routes of cell transfer: *a*, formation of teratocarcinoma by ectopic implantation of embryos; *b*, formation of embryoid bodies from teratocarcinoma and vice versa; *c*, derivation of cell culture from embryoid bodies; *d*, cell culture obtained directly from solid tumours; *e*, differentiation to embryoid bodies from culture; *f*, formation of solid tumours on reinjection of cells from culture; *g*, transfer of embryonal carcinoma cells either from cell culture or from the core of an embryoid body or from a solid tumour back to a blastocyst. All these procedures may result in chimaerism of the resulting mouse; *h*, the missing link supplied here.

Teratocarcinoma cells are now being widely used as a model for the study of developmental processes of early embryonic cell commitment and differentiation. Their use as a vehicle for the transfer into the mouse genome of mutant alleles, either selected in cell culture or inserted into the cells via transformation with specific DNA fragments, has been presented as an attractive proposition. In many of these studies the use of pluripotential cells directly isolated from the embryos under study should have great advantages. We have now shown that these EK cell lines are readily established from cultures of single blastocysts and so far have 15 lines of independent embryonic origin, some of which have been isolated from non-129, outbred mouse stocks. We are now studying the chimaeric mice formed from these cells.

We thank Mrs A. Burling for technical assistance and Dr E. P. Evans for advice regarding karyotype analysis. M.J.E. and M.H.K. were supported by the MRC; M.J.E. also received support from the Cancer Research Campaign.

(**292**, 154-156; 1981)

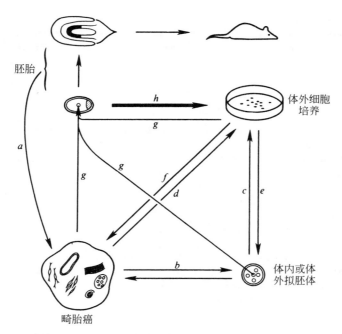

图 3. 细胞系、畸胎癌和拟胚体与正常小鼠胚胎之间的相互关系。箭头表示细胞移植的途径：*a*，胚胎的异位植入形成畸胎癌；*b*，从畸胎癌形成拟胚体，反之亦然；*c*，从拟胚体衍生出细胞培养物；*d*，直接从实体瘤获得细胞培养物；*e*，培养细胞分化成拟胚体；*f*，重新注射培养细胞形成实体瘤；*g*，将细胞培养物、拟胚体核心或者实体瘤来源的胚胎癌细胞移植回囊胚中，所有的这些步骤都可能导致小鼠的嵌合型；*h*，本文获得的先前未发现的联系。

畸胎癌细胞目前作为模型广泛用于研究早期胚胎细胞定向和分化的发育过程。它们的用途是作为载体将突变的等位基因转移到小鼠的基因组中，无论是从细胞培养物中选择突变的等位基因还是通过特定 DNA 片段的转化将其插入细胞，这已经是目前具有吸引力的主题。在这一领域的很多课题中，使用从胚胎中直接分离出来的多能细胞进行研究具有很大的优势。我们已经表明从单个囊胚的培养物中能够容易地建立 EK 细胞系，而且迄今为止已经拥有 15 个独立胚胎来源的细胞系，其中的一些已经从非 129 的远交小鼠品系中分离出来了。我们目前正在研究这些细胞形成的嵌合小鼠。

感谢伯林女士的技术支持和埃文斯博士关于核型分析的建议。埃文斯和考夫曼都得到了医学研究理事会的资助；埃文斯还得到了英国癌症研究运动的支持。

（毛晨晖 翻译；梁前进 审稿）

**M. J. Evans**[*] **and M. H. Kaufman**[†]

[*] Department of Genetics, University of Cambridge, Downing Street, Cambridge CB2 3EH, UK
[†] Department of Anatomy, University of Cambridge, Downing Street, Cambridge CB2 3EH, UK

Received 6 February; accepted 14 April 1981.

---

References:

1. Gardner, R. L. & Papaioannou, V. E. in *The Early Development of Mammals* (eds Balls, M. & Wild, A. E.) 107-132 (Cambridge University Press,1975).

2. Stevens, L. C. *Devl. Biol.*, **21**, 364-382 (1970).

3. Cole, R. J. & Paul, J. in *Preimplantation Stages of Pregnancy* (eds Wolstenholme, G. E. W. & O'Connor, M.) 82-122 (Churchill, London,1965).

4. Sherman, M. I. *Cell* **5**, 343-349 (1975).

5. Atienza-Samols, S. B. & Sherman, M. I. *Devl. Biol.* **66**, 220-231 (1978).

6. Solter, D. & Knowles, B. *Proc. Natl. Acad. Sci. U.S.A.* **72**, 5099-5102 (1975).

7. Evans, M. J. *J. Reprod. Fert.* **62**, 625-631 (1981).

8. Evans, M. J., Lovell-Badge, R. H., Stern, P. L. & Stinnakre, M. -G. INSERM *Symp.* **10**, 115-129 (1979).

9. McLaren, A. *J. Endocr.* **50**, 515-526 (1971).

10. Kaufman, M. H. in *Progress in Anatomy* Vol. 1 (eds Harrison, R. J. & Holmes, R. L.) 1-34 (Cambridge University Press, 1981).

11. Stern, P. L. *et al. Cell* **14**, 775-783 (1978).

12. Feizi, T. *Blood Transfusion Immunohaemat.* **23**, 563-577 (1980).

13. Kapadia, A., Feizi, T. & Evans, M. J. *Expl Cell Res.* **131**, 185-195 (1980).

# Test-tube Babies, 1981

R. G. Edwards

## Editor's Note

Robert Edwards, in collaboration with Patrick Steptoe in England, enabled the first birth of a baby by *in vitro* fertilization (IVF), Louise Brown, in 1978. Their research had been considered controversial, and the birth was met with a mixture of surprise, excitement and dismay. As the title of this article by Edwards indicates, infants born by IVF were almost immediately dubbed "test-tube babies", even though only the fertilization of the egg by sperm and very initial growth of the embryo were conducted "in glass". Edwards implies that by 1981 the technique was already becoming routine, with 15–20 IVF babies born in the UK that year. In that sense, this paper records the "normalization" of this form of assisted conception.

---

Between fifteen and twenty babies will be born this year after the *in vitro* fertilization of human eggs. Many of the essential steps now have high rates of success, including the recovery of preovulatory oocytes, and fertilization and embryo cleavage *in vitro*. Implantation of the embryo following its replacement in the mother remains the major difficulty. Some implications of the work are discussed.

---

THIS year should prove a turning point for the birth of children by the fertilization of human eggs *in vitro*. Between 15 and 20 such babies will be born in approximately equal numbers in the United Kingdom and Australia, and there will be one or two elsewhere. These methods will be introduced in many countries, primarily to alleviate human infertility. Fundamental aspects of human conception will be analysed and increasing debate will presumably be given to genetic engineering. This is, therefore, an appropriate time to assess the relevant clinical and scientific issues raised by this work[1].

## The First Essential: Timing of Ovulation

I will first discuss the methods involved in timing ovulation for the collection of preovulatory oocytes.

Harvesting preovulatory oocytes is the first of several steps essential for obtaining human embryos. They must be collected during their final stages of maturation just before ovulation occurs, when meiosis is advanced and cortical granules have established the defence against polyspermy. Follicular growth and ovulation must be regulated by endocrine therapy, or natural ovulation must be closely predicted during the menstrual cycle.

# 试管婴儿，1981

爱德华兹

编者按

1978 年，在英国科学家罗伯特·爱德华兹及其同事帕特里克·斯特普托的努力下，第一例体外受精（IVF）的婴儿——路易丝·布朗诞生了。他们的研究曾被认为具有争议性，人们对试管婴儿的诞生表现出惊喜、兴奋和惊慌交加的复杂感情。正如爱德华兹的这篇文章标题所示，尽管只有精子和卵细胞的受精作用和非常早期的胚胎的生长是在"玻璃（试管）"中进行，但通过体外受精诞生的婴儿却几乎立即就被称为"试管婴儿"。爱德华兹暗示，截至 1981 年，这项技术已经成为了常规技术，当年在英国有 15~20 例试管婴儿诞生。从这个意义上考虑，本文记录了这种辅助受孕形式的"常态化"。

这一年将有 15 到 20 名婴儿通过人类卵细胞的体外受精方式诞生。很多关键步骤目前都有很高的成功率，包括排卵期前的卵母细胞的收集以及体外的受精及胚胎卵裂。主要的困难仍然在于胚胎移入母体后的着床。本文还对这项研究的一些应用进行了讨论。

这一年应该是通过人类卵细胞体外受精诞生婴儿的转折点。在英国和澳大利亚，将有 15 到 20 名婴儿通过这种方式来到人世，两个国家的数目相近，其他国家也有 1~2 名。很多国家会引入这种技术，主要用于减轻人类不育症。影响人类怀孕的基本因素将得到分析，而且针对基因工程的争论想必也将越来越多。因此，是时候来评价这项技术带来的相关临床和科学问题了 [1]。

## 第一项要素：排卵时间

首先我将讨论计算排卵时间以便收集排卵期前的卵母细胞的方法。

获得人类胚胎的几个关键步骤中首要步骤是收集排卵期前的卵母细胞。卵母细胞必须刚好在排卵前成熟的最后阶段进行收集，这时候减数分裂还在进行，皮质颗粒已经形成了抵御多精入卵的屏障。卵泡生长以及排卵必须通过激素疗法来调节，或者必须准确预测月经周期中的自然排卵。

The regulation of ovulation is undoubtedly easier. Several follicles can be primed using human menopausal gonadotropin (HMG) or clomiphene early in the menstrual cycle. An endogenous surge of luteinizing hormone (LH) will then induce ovulation. Alternatively, a single injection of human chorionic gonadotropin (HCG, 5,000 IU) can be given between days 11 and 14, according to the follicular response of each patient. Levels of urinary oestrogens of 80-100 µg per day (refs 2, 3), or follicular diameters of 1.5-2 cm measured by ultrasound[4-6] are believed to be appropriate indications to inject HCG. Ovulation can be induced at any desired time of day or night, a considerable help in organizing laboratory or surgical teams for oocyte recovery. Two or more preovulatory oocytes can be collected from many patients, another advantage of stimulating the ovary.

There may be problems to offset these advantages. Wide variations exist in the rate of growth of individual follicles in each patient, revealed by the different levels of steroids in follicular fluids[7] and by variations in embryonic growth when superovulation techniques are applied to animals. Some patients fail to respond to clomiphene. Others produce increasingly large amounts of oestrogens as several follicles grow, and their endogenous LH surge stimulates ovulation. A difficult situation occurs in patients with moderate or high levels of oestrogens and no endogenous surge of LH (Fig. 1). As in other tissues[8-11], clomiphene may have depleted cytoplasmic oestrogen receptors in the pituitary gland of such patients over several days, so preventing the LH surge in response to rising levels of oestrogens. HCG must be given at some arbitrary time, before follicles become atretic, yet while it is uncertain if the patient will have her own endogenous LH surge. Ovarian stimulation can also distort the menstrual cycle, inducing a short luteal phase and a disorganized endometrium, both incompatible with establishing pregnancy[12]. An average of eight cycles of treatment with clomiphene is needed for oligomenorrhoeic women to conceive naturally[3]. Such disadvantages may be greater with HMG than with clomiphene.

毫无疑问，调节排卵更容易些。在月经周期早期，使用人绝经期促性腺激素（HMG）或者克罗米芬能够促发多个卵泡。随后内源性黄体生成素（LH）峰就能诱导排卵。另一种方法就是，根据每个患者的卵泡反应，在月经周期的第 11 到 14 天期间单次注射人绒毛膜促性腺激素（HCG，5,000 IU）。尿雌激素水平达到每天 80~100 微克（参考文献 2、3）或者超声波测量卵泡直径达到 1.5~2 厘米时 [4-6]，被认为是注射 HCG 的合适时间。诱导排卵可以安排在白天或者晚上任何理想的时间，这对组织实验室或者手术小组进行卵母细胞收集非常有利。刺激卵巢的另一个优点是，很多患者都可以采集到两个或者更多排卵期前的卵母细胞。

但仍然可能会有一些问题抵消这些优点。个体卵泡液中类固醇水平的不同 [7] 以及对动物使用超排卵技术时胚胎生长的差异显示，每个患者各个卵泡的生长速率差异很大。有一些患者对克罗米芬没有反应；另一些人随着数个卵泡生长产生越来越多的雌激素，并且其内源性 LH 峰刺激了排卵。一种很难处理的情况是患者产生中到高水平的雌激素，但是没有内源性的 LH 峰（图 1）。正如在其他组织中一样 [8-11]，克罗米芬可能在数天内耗尽这些患者脑垂体细胞质中的雌激素受体，从而阻止响应雌激素水平增高的 LH 峰的出现。HCG 必须在卵泡闭锁之前某个任意时间使用，但是很难确定患者是否会有自发产生的内源性 LH 峰。卵巢刺激也会使月经周期紊乱，导致黄体期很短以及子宫内膜紊乱，这两者均对妊娠建立不利 [12]。通常使月经过少的女性自然怀孕平均需要 8 个周期的克罗米芬治疗 [3]。与使用克罗米芬相比，使用 HMG 时这种缺点更为明显。

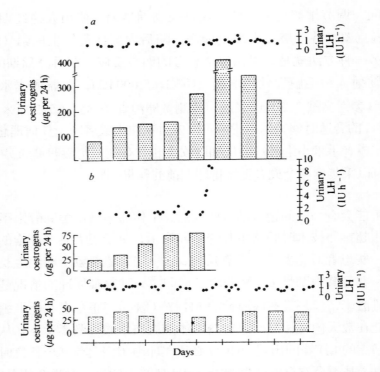

Fig. 1. Response of patients to clomiphene. *a*, Levels of urinary oestrogens rose considerably, and then fell in the absence of an endogenous LH surge. *b*, Rising levels of urinary oestrogens followed by surge of LH in urine. *c*, No response in urinary oestrogens and no surge □, Urinary oestrogens; ●, urinary LH, measured by the Hi-Govanis kit.

The alternative is to monitor the approach of ovulation during the natural menstrual cycle, and then aspirate the single preovulatory oocyte. This method was used for the conception of the first child by fertilization *in vitro*[12], and is widely used in our practice today. Plasma or urinary oestrogens are used to assess follicle growth, and the onset of the LH surge at mid-cycle provides a warning of the approach of ovulation.

The disadvantages are obvious. There is usually only one preovulatory oocyte, and any pathological conditions in the ovary or abdomen will limit the chances of collecting it. The LH surge is less predictable than an injection of HCG, hence more difficulty arises in organizing laboratory and clinical staff to collect the oocyte. Some difficulties have proved less than feared. Repeated blood sampling may provide a reliable guide for assaying LH[6,13–15], but is unnecessary, because urine samples are suitable for rapid assays of LH using the kit Hi-Gonavis (Mochida Pharmaceuticals)[12] and for oestrogens. Fortunately, the LH surge begins in early morning in almost three-quarters of the women (Fig. 2), which is most convenient for the collection of preovulatory oocytes 24-28 h later. This "critical period" in the LH surge in women resembles the situation in rats[16,17], and its distinct diurnal component must modify the feedback effects of ovarian oestrogens and LH releasing hormone on the pituitary gland[18]. If women discharge their LH at other times of day, their oocytes must sometimes be aspirated less than 24 h later and cultured *in vitro* to complete maturation.

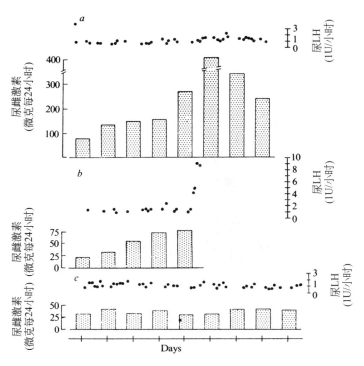

图 1. 患者对克罗米芬的反应。*a*, 尿雌激素水平明显升高, 然后无内源性 LH 峰出现时尿雌激素水平下降。
*b*, 尿雌激素水平逐渐增高, 随后尿中出现 LH 峰。*c*, 尿雌激素对克罗米芬没有响应, 没有 LH 峰。□,
尿雌激素; ●, 尿 LH, 用 Hi-Govanis 试剂盒测量。

    另一种方法是监测自然月经周期中即将排卵的时期, 然后吸取出单个排卵期前
的卵母细胞。第一个体外受精婴儿的孕育就是使用了这种方法 [12], 如今广泛运用于
我们的临床实践。血浆或者尿中的雌激素水平被用于评价卵泡的生长状况, 并且月
经周期中期 LH 峰的出现提供了即将排卵的信号。

    这种方法的缺点是很明显的。通常只有一个排卵期前的卵母细胞, 卵巢或者腹
腔的任何病理情况都将降低其采集的成功率。相对于注射 HCG 来说, LH 峰更难预测,
因此在组织实验室和临床人员收集卵母细胞时将面临更多的困难。实际上, 一些困难
比想象中的要小一些。重复采血能可靠地检测 LH 的水平 [6,13-15], 但这没有必要, 因为
尿液样本很适合使用 Hi-Gonavis 试剂盒（日本持田制药）进行 LH 的快速检测 [12] 以及
雌激素的快速检测。幸运的是, 几乎四分之三的女性 LH 达峰的时间都在清晨（图 2）,
这非常有利于 24~28 小时后收集排卵前的卵母细胞。女性到达 LH 峰的这个 "关键时
期" 与大鼠的情况非常相似 [16,17], 其独特的昼间成分必定改变了卵巢雌激素和促 LH
释放激素对垂体的反馈效应 [18]。如果女性在其他时间释放 LH, 那么必须在 24 小时
内吸取其卵母细胞并体外培养直至完全成熟。

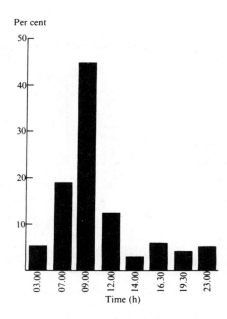

Fig. 2. Diurnal rhythm in the onset of the urinary LH surge in women. The time shows the initial increase in levels of LH which was followed by a sustained rise (see Figs 1*b* and 3).

Fertility may be higher during the natural cycle than after ovarian stimulation, an obvious advantage in establishing pregnancy. Several surveys have revealed a 1 in 4 chance of pregnancy during unprotected intercourse in any menstrual cycle, but even this low rate may be higher than during induced cycles. Clomiphene may be indicated in patients with irregular or prolonged cycles.

## Aspiration of Oocytes

A double aspirating needle or two separate needles are used, one channel being used for aspiration and the other to flush out the follicle if the oocyte is not collected[19,20]. The flushing solution may contain heparin, to prevent clotting within the follicle.

The highest rates of collection are achieved 32 h after the injection of HCG, or 26 h after the rise of LH in urine (Table 1). It is essential to time the onset of ovulation correctly. Should HCG be given after an endogenous surge of LH, ovulation may occur before aspiration begins. Diurnal rhythms in tonic LH release, sometimes reaching low surge levels over a few hours, can confuse the correct timing of the LH surge (Fig. 3). Pelvic adhesions, hydrosalpinx, cystic follicles, endometriosis and other ovarian conditions impair the collection of oocytes, and preliminary laparoscopy may be required to alleviate these conditions. If the ovary is accessible, oocytes can be collected during the natural cycle from almost 90% of patients, laparoscopy being completed within a few minutes (Table 1). None of our patients had ovulated when laparoscopy was performed, and each of them had a large preovulatory follicle.

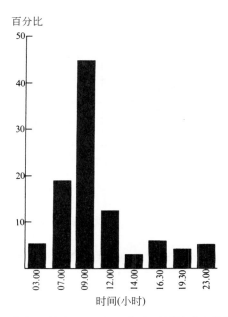

图 2. 女性尿 LH 达峰的昼夜节律。时间轴显示了 LH 水平开始增高并且保持持续增长（见图 1b 和 3）。

自然月经周期下的生殖力要比卵巢刺激后的更高，这在妊娠建立中是一个显著的优势。数个调查显示在月经周期的任何阶段进行无保护性交而怀孕的几率为 1/4，但即便是这个看似很低的几率也要高于诱导周期中的怀孕几率。月经不规律或者周期延长的患者可以使用克罗米芬。

### 卵母细胞的吸取

使用双腔吸引管或者两根单独的针管，一个用于吸取细胞，另一个用于在没有采集到卵母细胞时冲洗掉卵泡 [19, 20]。冲洗液可以含有肝素，可以防止卵泡内凝血。

采集成功率最高的时间是在 HCG 注射后的第 32 小时，或者在尿液中 LH 含量升高后的第 26 小时（表 1）。准确计算排卵起始的时间是非常重要的。如果在内源性 LH 峰后注射 HCG，开始吸取卵母细胞之前排卵就可能发生。紧张性 LH 释放的昼夜节律性有时会在数小时内达到较低的峰值，而混淆了 LH 达峰的准确时间（图 3）。盆腔粘连、输卵管积水、囊状卵泡、子宫内膜异位以及其他卵巢疾病都会影响卵细胞的采集，可能需要用腹腔镜预处理以减轻这些症状。如果卵巢可直接到达的话，几乎 90% 的患者都可以在自然周期中采集到卵母细胞，利用腹腔镜在数分钟内就可以完成这个过程（表 1）。没有一个患者在腹腔镜操作过程中排卵，而且所有患者都有较大的排卵前卵泡。

Table 1. Aspiration of oocytes from preovulatory follicles

|  | Natural cycle* | Natural and clomiphene cycle[20] | Clomiphene cycle[6] |
|---|---|---|---|
| No. of patients | 122 | — | — |
| No. with accessible ovaries | 109 | — | — |
| No. of preovulatory follicles aspirated | 109 | 172 | 107 |
| No. (and %) of oocytes collected | 95 (88%) | 110 (64%) | 96 (89%) |

* Recent series of 122 patients in Bourn Hall, Cambridge. Their average age was 33.9 yr.

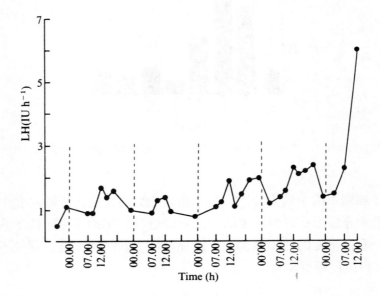

Fig. 3. Diurnal variations in the levels of urinary LH in women. "Tonic" levels rise each morning, then decline. The LH surge began during the morning in this patient.

Preovulatory oocytes can be identified quickly. They are embedded in a viscous follicular fluid, to a diameter of 0.5 cm or more and can be seen by eye[2]. The viscosity of the cumulus mass serves as a guide to the stage of maturity of the oocyte. A few hours in culture in the presence of some follicular fluid helps to complete maturation, especially in those deliberately collected less than 26 h after the LH rise, which appear "unripe".

## Fertilization and Cleavage *In Vitro*

Provided there are no pathological conditions in the husband's spermatozoa, almost 90% of the preovulatory oocytes aspirated during the natural cycle can be fertilized *in vitro* (Table 2). The conditions of culture are rapidly becoming standardized[3,6,7,12]. Simple media are used, including Earle's solution with pyruvate, a medium designed to support mouse embryos *in vitro*[21,22], and Ham's F10, each supplemented with serum albumin or homologous human serum (7.5-8.6%). We prefer Earle's solution containing pyruvate, with

表 1. 从排卵前卵泡内吸取卵母细胞

|  | 自然周期 * | 自然和克罗米芬周期[20] | 克罗米芬周期[6] |
| --- | --- | --- | --- |
| 患者总数 | 122 | – | – |
| 可到达的卵巢数 | 109 | – | – |
| 吸取的排卵前卵泡数 | 109 | 172 | 107 |
| 采集卵母细胞数目（和 %） | 95（88%） | 110（64%） | 96（89%） |

* 剑桥波恩诊所最近的 122 名患者，平均年龄 33.9 岁。

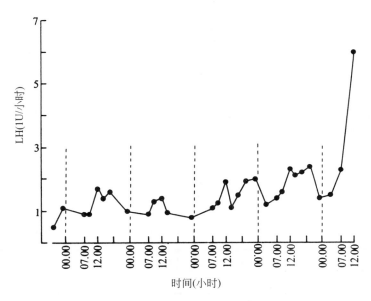

图 3. 女性尿 LH 水平的昼夜变化。"紧张性"LH 水平在每天早上升高，随后又降低。该患者 LH 峰出现在早晨。

排卵前卵母细胞可以被迅速识别。它们包被在黏性卵泡液内，直径达到 0.5 厘米或更大并可用肉眼观察到[2]。周围聚集的卵丘细胞的黏稠度可以指示卵母细胞成熟的阶段。在卵泡液存在的条件下对卵母细胞进行数小时的培养有助于其完全成熟，尤其是那些特意在 LH 升高 26 小时以内时采集的看起来"未成熟"的卵母细胞。

## 体外受精和体外卵裂

假设丈夫的精子没有任何病理状况，在自然周期内吸取的 90% 排卵前卵母细胞都可以在体外完成受精（表 2）。培养条件正在迅速标准化[3,6,7,12]。使用简单的培养液，包括含丙酮酸盐的厄尔氏溶液，一种设计用于体外培养小鼠胚胎的培养液[21,22]，以及汉姆氏 F10，每种培养液中均添加血清白蛋白或者同源的人类血清（7.5%~8.6%）。我们更倾向于采用含丙酮酸钠的厄尔氏溶液，添加各患者自己的血清（表 3）[12]。精

serum from each patient (Table 3)[12]. Sperm numbers vary between $10^5$ and $10^6$ per ml, or between 1 and $5 \times 10^5$ living spermatozoa per ml. Droplets of medium held under paraffin oil or small culture tubes can be used for fertilization. Our present practice is to begin fertilization in droplets of medium under oil, adding $1.5\text{-}2 \times 10^5$ living spermatozoa per ml between 3 and 4 h after aspiration of oocytes; the oocytes are placed in tubes some hours later when most of their cumulus cells have been shed[12].

Table 2. Fertilization of human eggs *in vitro*

| | Patients with occluded oviducts | | Patients with idiopathic infertility[6] |
|---|---|---|---|
| | Bourn Hall* | Melbourne[6] | |
| Total no. patients | 95 | — | — |
| No. with pathological conditions: | | | |
| Spermagglutination cells or debris in semen | 5 | — | — |
| Abnormal movement of spermatozoa | 3 | — | — |
| Viscous seminal plasma | 1 | — | — |
| Remainder | 86 | 40 | — |
| No. (and %) fertilized | 76 (88%) | 37 (92%) | 35% |

\* Recent survey of 122 patients (See Table 1).

Table 3. Composition of the media used for fertilization and cleavage of human eggs *in vitro* $(\text{g l}^{-1})$

| | Modified Earles[12] | Media for mouse eggs[21,22] | Ham's F10* |
|---|---|---|---|
| $CaCl_2 \cdot 2H_2O$ | 0.2649 | — | 0.441 |
| KCl | 0.400 | 0.356 | 0.285 |
| $MgSO_4 \cdot 7H_2O$ | 0.200 | 0.294 | 0.1527 |
| NaCl | 6.800 | 5.140 | 7.400 |
| $NaH_2PO_4 \cdot 2H_2O$ | 0.1583 | — | — |
| $Na_2HPO_4$ | — | — | 0.156 |
| $KH_2PO_4$ | — | 0.162 | — |
| $NaHCO_3$ | 2.1 | 1.9 | 1.2 |
| Ca lactate | — | 0.527 | — |
| Na pyruvate | 0.011 | 0.025 | 0.110 |
| Glucose | 1.000 | 1.000 | 1.100 |
| Na lactate (60% syrup) | — | $3.7 \text{ ml l}^{-1}$ | — |

Embryos growing most rapidly are two-cell by 21 h after insemination, four-cell at 40 h, and eight-cell at 44-54 h (refs 3, 23).

\* Also contains $CuSO_4$, $FeSO_4$, $ZnSO_4$, amino acids, etc.

子的数目波动范围在每毫升 $10^5$ 到 $10^6$ 个，或者每毫升（1~5）× $10^5$ 个活精子。覆盖石蜡油的培养液小滴或者小的培养管都可以用于受精。我们目前采用的是在覆盖石蜡油的培养液小滴中开始受精，在吸取卵母细胞后 3~4 个小时之内，于每毫升培养液中加入（1.5~2）× $10^5$ 个活精子。数小时后当大部分卵丘细胞都脱落时，就把卵母细胞转移到培养管内 [12]。

表 2. 人卵细胞体外受精

| | 输卵管闭塞的患者 | | 原发性不育的患者 [6] |
|---|---|---|---|
| | 波恩诊所 * | 墨尔本 [6] | |
| 患者总数 | 95 | — | — |
| 具有病理状况的患者数 | | | |
| 　精子凝集或精液内有碎片 | 5 | — | — |
| 　精子运动异常 | 3 | — | — |
| 　精浆黏稠 | 1 | — | — |
| 　其他情况 | 86 | 40 | — |
| 受精数目（和百分比） | 76（88%） | 37（92%） | 35% |

\* 最近调查的 122 名患者（见表 1）。

表 3. 人类卵细胞体外受精和卵裂使用的培养液组分（克 / 升）

| | 改良的厄尔氏溶液 [12] | 小鼠受精卵用的培养液 [21, 22] | 汉姆氏 F10* |
|---|---|---|---|
| $CaCl_2 \cdot 2H_2O$ | 0.2649 | — | 0.441 |
| KCl | 0.400 | 0.356 | 0.285 |
| $MgSO_4 \cdot 7H_2O$ | 0.200 | 0.294 | 0.1527 |
| NaCl | 6.800 | 5.140 | 7.400 |
| $NaH_2PO4 \cdot 2H_2O$ | 0.1583 | — | — |
| $Na_2HPO_4$ | — | — | 0.156 |
| $KH_2PO_4$ | — | 0.162 | — |
| $NaHCO_3$ | 2.1 | 1.9 | 1.2 |
| 乳酸钙 | — | 0.527 | — |
| 丙酮酸钠 | 0.011 | 0.025 | 0.110 |
| 葡萄糖 | 1.000 | 1.000 | 1.100 |
| 乳酸钠（60% 糖浆） | — | 3.7 毫升 / 升 | — |

胚胎成长最快的时候是授精后 21 小时的二细胞阶段、40 小时的四细胞阶段以及 44~54 小时的八细胞阶段（参考文献 3、23）。

\* 也含有 $CuSO_4$、$FeSO_4$、$ZnSO_4$、氨基酸等。

The oocytes are fertilized within a few hours. Some have been fertilized following a re-insemination 48 h later and grew normally to the eight-cell stage (J. M. Purdy and R. G. E., unpublished). Conditions such as spermagglutination, viscous seminal plasma and erratic sperm movement reduce the chances of fertilization (Table 2). Almost all eggs are monospermic, indicating that the block to polyspermy is efficient[3,6,23].

Most embryos cleave normally. They tolerate a wide variety of culture media, similar to those used for fertilization. Serum is almost universally added; in our work, we use 15% v/v of homologous serum[12]. Cleavage times are remarkably similar despite the varying concentration of energy sources in different media (Table 3). There have been occasional reports of cell fragments in cleaving eggs, although similar conditions have been found in embryos flushed from the reproductive tract and may not be pathological[24,25]. Many embryos grow to morulae and blastocysts, and escape from the zona pellucida *in vitro*[3,6], although some apparently develop abnormally during these later stages of growth[6]. The fastest-growing embryos are apparently the most successful in establishing pregnancy[6,26]. Cine films of cleavage with IR photography may enable embryos to be examined for their nuclear structure before they are replanted in the mother[27].

## Replanting Embryos

Implantation is the most difficult and unpredictable stage. In animals, rates of implantation are high when embryos are replaced surgically (>70%), but lower if replaced non-surgically via the cervix (~50%)[28,29]. Almost all human embryos have been replaced transcervically, and approximately one-quarter of them have implanted in some series (Table 4). Embryos might be best replaced during the evening[12], because the spontaneous contractility of the human uterus is lower at night[30,31]. Disorders in the luteal phase, including progesterone deficiency and a short luteal phase, could preclude implantation (Table 4). Some implanted embryos live for only a short time after the expected return of menstruation, and are identified by a transitory rise in HCG$\beta$ (ref. 3) (Table 4).

Table 4. Pregnancies after replacing human embryos transcervically (same group of patients as in Tables 1 and 2)

| | Single catheter | Double catheter |
|---|---|---|
| No. of patients | 51 | 23 |
| No. with deficient luteal phases: | | |
| Short luteal phase* | 2* | 0 |
| Progesterone deficiency† | 1 | 3 |
| No. with delayed return to menstruation‡: | | |
| Brief elevated levels of HCG$\beta$ | 2 } (9.8%) | 0 |
| Brief elevated levels of HCG/LH | 3 } (9.8%) | 3 |
| No. pregnant 4 weeks after replacement | 12 (23.1%) | 2 (8.7%) |

* Luteal phase of 12 days or less; these patients had luteal phases of 5 and 12 days, respectively, one also having progesterone deficiency.

† These patients had between 0.4 and 2.7 ng ml$^{-1}$ on days 7 or 8 of the luteal phase.

‡ Some other patients showed a delayed return to menstruation but no evidence was found of elevated HCG$\beta$ or HCG/LH.

卵母细胞在数小时内完成受精。有些卵母细胞会在48小时后再授精时完成受精，并正常成长到八细胞阶段（珀迪和爱德华兹，未发表）。诸如精子凝集、精浆黏稠以及精子运动不稳定等状况都会降低受精的几率（表2）。几乎所有的卵细胞都是单精受精，说明卵细胞可有效地阻止多精受精[3,6,23]。

大多数胚胎都正常分裂。它们能够耐受多种培养液，这些培养液与受精时使用的培养液类似。它们几乎都加入了血清；在我们的工作中，我们使用体积比为15%的同源血清[12]。尽管不同培养液中能源物质的浓度各不相同（表3），但胚胎的分裂次数却非常相似。偶有报道称分裂的受精卵中有细胞碎片，但类似的情况也会发生在从生殖道中排出来的胚胎中，因此可能并非病理性的[24,25]。很多胚胎在体外长到桑椹胚和囊胚阶段，并可在体外培养中从透明带逸出[3,6]，尽管有些胚胎在发育的后期阶段会出现明显的发育异常[6]。很明显，生长最快的胚胎是最容易成功建立妊娠的[6,26]。红外摄影得到的分裂期照片有助于在胚胎重新植入母体之前对其进行核结构的检查[27]。

## 胚 胎 移 植

着床是最困难且无法预测的阶段。在动物中，手术移植胚胎着床的成功率较高（>70%），但是如果用非手术方式经宫颈移植则着床成功率较低（~50%）[28,29]。几乎所有的人类胚胎都是经宫颈移植的，一些研究中报告大约四分之一能够成功着床（表4）。胚胎着床最好在夜间[12]，因为夜间人类子宫的自发收缩较弱[30,31]。黄体期的异常，包括孕酮缺乏以及黄体期缩短都能影响着床（表4）。一些移植的胚胎只能在预期的月经复潮之后存活很短时间，这可以通过HCGβ的暂时升高来判断（参考文献3）（表4）。

表4. 人类胚胎经宫颈移植后的妊娠情况（与表1和2是同一批患者）

| | 单导管 | 双导管 |
|---|---|---|
| 患者总数 | 51 | 23 |
| 黄体期不全的数目 | | |
| 　黄体期短 * | 2* | 0 |
| 　孕酮缺乏 † | 1 | 3 |
| 月经复潮延迟的数目 ‡ | | |
| 　短暂的 HCGβ 水平升高 | 2 ⎫ | 0 |
| 　短暂的 HCG/LH 水平升高 | 3 ⎭ (9.8%) | 3 |
| 着床 4 周后妊娠的数目 | 12 (23.1%) | 2 (8.7%) |

\* 黄体期12天或更短；两位患者的黄体期分别是 5 和 12 天，其中一位还有孕酮缺乏。

† 这些患者在黄体期的第 7 天或者第 8 天体内孕酮的浓度是 0.4 ng/ml 到 2.7 ng/ml 之间。

‡ 一些其他患者表现出了月经复潮的延迟，但是没有发现 HCGβ 或者 HCG/LH 升高的证据。

Why do so few embryos implant? Perhaps 20% or thereabouts is all that can be expected, since it is similar to the incidence of natural human fertility reported in serval surveys. This view seems to be pessimistic. Some embryos may be lost or infected if there are difficulties in passing a catheter through the internal os. An outer metal cannula can be useful in such cases, but pregnancy rates are lower (Table 4). A Teflon catheter with a smooth tip and side aperture evidently passes easily through the internal os[6], but may require the use of a tenaculum on the cervix. Implantations have occurred after replacing all stages between the two-cell and blastocyst, but there are insufficient data as yet on the optimal stage for replacement[26].

Physiological disorders might prevent implantation. Vaginal distension during replacement could invoke discharges of prolactin, and a catheter passed through the uterine cavity may invoke a premature decidualization of the endometrium. Slight myometrial contractions could expel embryos soon after their replacement and might be inhibited using $\beta_2$-mimetics[30,31]. Restricting the volume of medium might encourage implantation (0.03-0.10 ml are used at present). Surgical transfer might circumvent these problems, but a second anaesthesia will be needed soon after that used for oocyte recovery, and the myometrium and endometrium will undoubtedly bleed when a needle is passed through them. In rhesus monkeys, 11 out of 15 embryos replaced surgically in the oviduct, and 2 of 8 replaced in the uterus developed to advanced stages of gestation[32].

## Growth of Human Fetuses after Replacement in the Mother

At least 12 children have been born after fertilization *in vitro*, 3 in the initial series in Oldham[33], 7 in Australia[6,34], and 2 recently in the United Kingdom. Two of these were born prematurely at approximately 20 weeks, soon after amniocentesis. The children have been healthy, although a male twin required corrective surgery, and several current pregnancies appear to be progressing normally[6,26]. Details of all pregnancies are being recorded in an international register to evaluate any risks to the fetuses and the causes of abortion or fetal death.

Between one-quarter and two-fifths of the fetuses arising from fertilization *in vitro* die *in utero*, mostly in the first trimester. Maternal age (late thirties and early forties) may be a disposing factor in some cases. One dead fetus was triploid[33], the others have not been karyotyped. Triploidy may not be serious quantitatively, as the vast majority of fertilized eggs are monospermic. Most triploid fetuses arising during fertilization *in vivo* are caused by dispermy, fewer being due to fertilization by a diploid spermatozoon or cleavage errors in the embryo[35]. Nor should trisomy be more frequent after fertilization *in vitro*. Most human trisomies arise during the first meiotic division of the oocyte[36,37], a stage which is virtually complete before the oocytes are aspirated. Others arise during the second meiotic division, that is, after fertilization, or during cleavage of the embryos, but there is no record of their incidence *in vitro*. Amniocentesis should be performed on all fetuses arising through fertilization *in vitro*, if the parents agree, until the risks of trisomy have been assessed.

为什么只有少数胚胎能着床？或许预期着床成功的几率只有 20% 左右，这个数据类似于数个调查中所报告的人类自然生育率。这个观点似乎有些悲观。如果导管进入宫颈内口遇到困难，那么有些胚胎可能丢失或者被感染。这种情况下使用外层金属套管是有帮助的，但是怀孕率更低（表 4）。带有光滑尖端和侧孔的特氟龙导管明显很容易通过宫颈内口 [6]，但是可能需要在宫颈内使用宫颈钳。从二细胞到囊胚期的各个阶段的胚胎都能够着床，但是没有充足的数据说明哪个阶段是移植的最佳时期 [26]。

生理异常可能妨碍着床。胚胎移植过程中的阴道扩张可能促发催乳素释放，导管通过子宫腔可能促发子宫内膜的过早蜕膜化。子宫肌层的轻度收缩可能将移植后的胚胎排出，但是可以用 $\beta_2$-类似物抑制收缩 [30,31]。限制培养液的体积可能有助于着床（目前使用 0.03~0.10 毫升）。手术移植可能可以避免这些问题，但是卵母细胞采集之后需要马上进行二次麻醉，而且用针穿刺子宫肌层和内膜时无疑会流血。在恒河猴中，通过手术移植到输卵管中的 15 个胚胎中的 11 个以及移植到子宫内的 8 个胚胎中的 2 个都发育到了妊娠后期 [32]。

### 人类胚胎移植后胎儿在母体内的生长

已有至少 12 名体外受精的婴儿诞生，3 名诞生于奥尔德姆的最初实验 [33]，7 名出生在澳大利亚 [6,34]，另外 2 名最近出生在英国。其中 2 名在大约 20 周羊膜穿刺术后不久早产。孩子们都很健康，尽管一对男性双胞胎需要矫正手术，另外几个进行中的妊娠都进展正常 [6,26]。所有的妊娠细节都记录在一个国际登记处，以评价对胎儿产生危险的因素以及流产或者胎儿死亡的原因。

体外受精后四分之一到五分之二的胎儿在子宫内死亡，大部分都死于妊娠早期。在一些案例中母亲的年龄（年近四十或者四十出头）可能是一个决定性因素。一个死亡的胎儿是三倍体 [33]，其他胎儿的染色体组型还没有分型。三倍体不会太多，因为绝大多数受精的卵细胞都是单精受精。体内受精期间大部分三倍体胎儿的形成是因为双精入卵，很少的情况是因为与二倍体精子的受精或者胚胎卵裂异常 [35]。体外受精后三倍体的形成也应该不多。大部分三倍体出现在卵母细胞的第一次减数分裂 [36,37]，事实上在卵母细胞被吸出以前这个阶段已经完成了。另一些出现在第二次减数分裂，也就是受精以后或者卵裂期间，但是没有体外发生这些情况的记录。如果双亲同意，所有体外受精的胎儿都要实施羊膜穿刺术，直到评估了三倍体的风险为止。

Some fetuses may die *in utero* through physiological or embryological factors associated with fertilization *in vitro*. These could include damage to the uterine wall during replacement of the embryos, the introduction of cervical flora into the uterine cavity and the implantation of the embryo low in the uterine canal[3]. Short or deficient luteal phases arising after ovarian stimulation, or through the withdrawal of too many granulosa cells from the preovulatory follicle occur in very few patients (see Table 4)[38]. Abnormal embryonic differentiation *in vitro* might have led to the transitory secretion of HCG in some patients, as the fetus developed into a "blighted ovum" or trophoblastic vesicles, resulting in its early death. Such conditions arise following conception *in vivo*[39,40].

## Genetic Engineering

Arguments sometimes raised against the introduction of fertilization *in vitro* into clinical practice involve the possibility of genetic engineering—chimaeras, hybrids and cloning embryos. These issues are quite distinct from the alleviation of infertility. Three cloned mice have been born, using nuclei from blastocysts[41], and others after the use of nuclei from the embryonic ectoderm and proximal endoderm of 7-day mouse embryos, showing that the developmental potential of nuclei from earlier embryos is retained in these cell types[42].

The thought of cloned human embryos identical to a pre-existing individual is not attractive. Yet, in a sense, uniparental human embryos largely similar to the father already exist. Hydatidiform moles are the remains of diploid androgenetic fetuses, in which the trophoblast proliferates over several weeks to form large grape-like vesicles. Such fetuses evidently arise due to the expulsion of the female pronucleus from the fertilized egg[43-46]. The sperm chromosomes are doubled and the embryo expresses paternal chromosomes only. Rare hydatidiform moles may even retain much of the father's heterozygosity, since they could arise from a diploid spermatozoon. The reason androgenetic embryos undergo hydatidiform changes is not understood. Perhaps the embryonic cells die early, or the mother "rejects" a fetus lacking her own antigens[46]; nevertheless, androgenetic mouse embryos develop normally to full term[47]. Human gynogenones could also arise through similar processes involving expulsion of the male pronucleus from the egg, although no searches have yet been made for them before or after birth. Uniparental embryos could arise through delayed syngamy and an enlarged pronucleus, seen in two human eggs fertilized *in vitro*.

Subtle forms of genetic engineering have been introduced. DNA fragments containing the gene for human insulin were injected into pronucleate mouse eggs, and the gene was identified in tissues of fetuses at the 18th day of pregnancy[42]. The DNA evidently replicated and was inserted into the genome of the fetus, but there is no information as to whether it was transcribed. There is apparently no knowledge of the potential value of such treatments in preventing the expression of inherited conditions such as diabetes.

一些胚胎会因为与体外受精有关的生理或者胚胎因素而胎死宫内。这些因素可能有：胚胎移植过程中损伤了子宫壁，将宫颈菌群带到了子宫腔内以及胚胎低位着床在宫颈管内[3]。在极少部分患者中，由于卵巢的刺激或者从排卵期前卵泡内吸走了太多的粒状细胞而导致黄体期过短或者缺失（见表4）[38]。在一些患者中，体外胚胎的异常分化可能导致暂时性的 HCG 分泌，比如胚胎发育成了"萎缩性胚囊"或者滋养层囊泡，并导致其早期死亡。体内受孕中也会出现这样的情况[39, 40]。

## 基 因 工 程

有时会出现反对将体外受精运用于临床的争论，它们涉及对基因工程——嵌合体、杂交以及克隆胚胎的可能性的担忧。这些问题与治疗不孕症截然不同。用囊胚来源的细胞核已经诞生了 3 只克隆鼠[41]，其他还有使用 7 天小鼠胚胎外胚层细胞核和近端内胚层细胞核而诞生克隆鼠，这说明这些细胞类型中早期胚胎的细胞核保留着发育的潜质[42]。

克隆一个与已经存在的个体完全一样的人胚胎是没有吸引力的。但是，从某种意义上说，非常类似于父本的单性人类胚胎已经存在了。葡萄胎就是雄核发育二倍体胎儿的残余，其中滋养层细胞经过数周的增殖形成了巨大的葡萄样水泡。显然这种胎儿的形成要归因于受精卵中雌原核被排除[43-46]。精子染色体复制成双倍，胚胎仅仅表达了父源性染色体。少数葡萄胎能保留较多父亲的杂合度，因为它们可以来源于二倍体的精子。雄核发育胚胎变成葡萄胎的原因尚不清楚。可能胚胎细胞于早期死亡，或者母亲"拒绝"缺乏其自身抗原的胎儿[46]；不管怎样，雄核发育的小鼠胚胎能够正常发育至临产[47]。人类的雌核生殖可能也通过类似的过程即从受精卵中排除雄原核而形成，尽管还未在产前或者产后的胎儿中进行寻找。通过配子融合的延迟以及原核的扩大就能形成单性生殖的胚胎，这在两个体外受精的人卵细胞中观察到。

基因工程的精细技术已被引入。将含有人类胰岛素基因的 DNA 片段注射到小鼠的原核卵细胞内，这些基因随后可以在妊娠 18 天的胎儿组织中找到[42]。显然 DNA 已经过复制并被插入到了胎儿的基因组中，但是没有信息证明基因是否被转录。显然，有关这种治疗方法在预防遗传性疾病比如糖尿病的基因表达方面的潜在价值还没有相关知识。

## Prospects

Many children will soon be born after the fertilization of human eggs *in vitro*. We have established more than 40 pregnancies since resuming work during the past 9 months, and the majority are surviving. This is most encouraging for those couples who could not be offered any other form of corrective surgery and have so far been without effective treatment (Table 5). The method can be carried out several times on the same patient, and success rates should soon exceed some forms of oviductal surgery. If ovarian stimulation is used, "spare embryos" may be available for embryological studies and one embryo has grown for 9 days *in vitro* until stage 5a (ref. 3). The frozen storage of human embryos still appears to be distant. Some of the fathers were oligospermic, and patients with idiopathic (unexplained) infertility, hostile cervical mucus, incompetent cervix, antibodies against the zona pellucida, might also be helped. Complex disorders leading to the abnormal growth of pronuclei can be investigated[48].

Table 5. Results on a recent series of 122 patients with tubal occlusion

| | |
|---|---|
| No. of patients | 122 |
| Failure to collect oocyte: | |
|     Method failure | 14 ⎫ |
|     Adhesions, endometriosis, etc. | 13 ⎬ 27 |
| (Table 1) | |
| No. with preovulatory oocytes: | 95 |
| Failure of fertilization: | |
|     Method failure | 9+1? ⎫ |
|     Pathological spermatozoa | 9 ⎬ 19 |
| (Table 2) | |
| Embryos not replaced | 2 |
| No. of embryos replaced: | 74 |
| Failure of implantation: | |
|     Short luteal phase/progesterone deficiency | 6 ⎫ |
|     Method failure* | 49 ⎬ 55 |
| Indications of pregnancy: | |
|     Delayed RTM: early abortion? | 5 |
|     Pregnant 4 weeks after replacement | 14 |

The natural menstrual cycle was monitored. RTM, return to menstruation.
* See Table 4.

I thank Jean Purdy and Patrick Steptoe for their help at all stages of this work, and Simon Fishel for his comments on the manuscript.

(**293**, 253-256; 1981)

## 展　望

越来越多的婴儿将会通过人卵细胞体外受精的方式诞生。自恢复体外受精的研究后，在过去的 9 个月内我们已经为 40 多位患者建立妊娠，且绝大多数胎儿仍然存活。对于那些无法获得其他任何形式的矫正手术以及目前为止没有得到有效治疗的夫妇来说，这是非常令人鼓舞的（表 5）。这种方法在同一个患者身上可以进行多次，很快成功率将超过一些其他类型的输卵管手术。如果使用卵巢刺激，"多余的胚胎"还可以用于胚胎学研究，其中一个胚胎在体外一直成长了 9 天直到第 5a 阶段（参考文献 3）。人类胚胎的冷冻储存似乎还很遥远。一些少精父亲、先天性不育患者（尚不能解释原因的）和宫颈黏液不良、宫颈内口松弛、抗透明带抗体的患者也可以得到帮助。同时还可以研究导致原核异常生长的各种复杂疾病[48]。

表 5. 最近 122 名输卵管堵塞患者的研究结果

| 患者总数 | 122 |
|---|---|
| 卵母细胞采集失败： | |
| 　方法失败 | 14 ⎱ 27 |
| 　粘连、子宫内膜异位症等 | 13 ⎰ |
| （表 1） | |
| 排卵期前卵母细胞数目： | 95 |
| 受精失败 | |
| 　方法失败 | 9+1? ⎱ 19 |
| 　病态精子 | 9 ⎰ |
| （表 2） | |
| 未移植的胚胎 | 2 |
| 移植的胚胎数目 | 74 |
| 未着床： | |
| 　黄体期短 / 孕酮缺乏 | 6 ⎱ 55 |
| 　方法失败 * | 49 ⎰ |
| 妊娠的指征： | |
| 　RTM 延迟：早期流产? | 5 |
| 　移植 4 周后的妊娠 | 14 |

监测自然的月经周期。RTM：月经复潮。

* 见表 4。

感谢琼·珀迪和帕特里克·斯特普托在工作的各个阶段给予的帮助，以及西蒙·菲谢尔对手稿的意见。

（毛晨晖 翻译；王敏康 审稿）

**R. G. Edwards**

Physiological Laboratory, Cambridge University, Cambridge CB2 3EG, UK, and Bourn Hall, Cambridge CB3 7TR, UK

References:

1. *3rd World Congress of Human Reproduction,* Berlin (Excerpta Medica, Amsterdam, 1981).
2. Edwards, R. G. & Steptoe, P. C. *J. Reprod. Fert. Suppl.* **22**, 121 (1975); *Lancet* i, 683 (1970).
3. Edwards, R. G. *Conception in the Human Female* (Academic, London, 1980).
4. Kratochwil, A., Urban, G. & Friedrich, F. *Ann. Chir. Gynaec. Fenniae* **61**, 211 (1972).
5. de Crespigny, L. J. Ch., O'Herlihy, C., Hoult, I. J. & Robinson, H. P. *Fert. Steril.* **35**, 25 (1981).
6. Trounson, A. O. *et al. 3rd World Congress of Human Reproduction*, Berlin (Excerpta Medica, Amsterdam, 1981).
7. Fowler, R. E., Edwards, R. G., Walters, D. E., Chan, S. T. H. & Steptoe, P. C. *J. Endocr.* **77**, 161 (1978).
8. Baudendistel, L. J., Ruh, M. F., Nadel, E. M. & Ruh, T. S. *Acta Endocr.* **89**, 599 (1978).
9. Katzellenbogen, B. S. & Ferguson, E. R. *Endocrinology* **97**, 1 (1975).
10. Watson, C. S., Medina, D. & Clark, J. H. *Endocrinology* **108**, 668 (1981).
11. Adashi, E.Y., Hsueh, A. J. W. & Yen, S. S. C. *J. Endocr.* **87**, 383 (1980).
12. Edwards, R. G., Steptoe, P. C. & Purdy, J. M. *Br. J. Obstet. Gynec.* **87**, 737 (1980).
13. Frydman, R., Testart, J. & Feinstein, M. C. *3rd World Congress of Human Reproduction*, Berlin (Excerpta Medica, Amsterdam, 1981).
14. Plashot, M., Mandelbaum, J. & Cohen, J. *3rd World Congress of Human Reproduction*, Berlin (Excerpta Medica, Amsterdam, 1981).
15. Mettler, L. *3rd World Congress of Human Reproduction*, Berlin (Excerpta Medica, Amsterdam, 1981).
16. Everett, J. W. & Sawyer, C. H. *Endocrinology* **47**, 198 (1950).
17. Everett, J. W. *A. Rev. Physiol.* **31**, 383 (1969).
18. Knobil, E. *Recent Prog. Horm. Res.* **36**, 53 (1980).
19. Lopata, A., Johnston, I. W. H., Houalt, I. J. & Speirs, A. L. *Fert. Steril.* **33**, 117 (1980).
20. Renou, P., Trounson, A. O., Wood, C. & Leeton, J. F. *Fert. Steril.* **35**, 409 (1981).
21. Brinster, R. L. in *Reproductive Biology* (eds Balin, H. & Glasser, S.) (Excerpta Medica, Amsterdam, 1972).
22. Hoppe, P. C. & Pitts, J. *Biol. Reprod.* **8**, 420 (1973).
23. Edwards, R. G., Purdy, J. M. & Steptoe, P. C. *Am. J. Obstet. Gynec.* (in the press).
24. Sundström, P., Nilsson, O. & Liedholm, P. *Acta Obstet. Gynec. Scand.* **60**, 109 (1981).
25. Wramsby, H. & Liedholm, P. *3rd World Congress of Human Reproduction,* Berlin (Excerpta Medica, Amsterdam, 1981).
26. Edwards, R. G., Steptoe, P. C. & Purdy, J. M. *3rd World Congress of Human Reproduction*, Berlin (1981).
27. Hamberger, L. *3rd World Congress of Human Reproduction*, Berlin (Excerpta Medica, Amsterdam, 1981).
28. Rowson, L. E. A. (ed.) *Egg Transfer in Cattle* (Commission of European Communities, Brussels, 1976).
29. Sreenan, J. N. *Theriogenology*, **9**, 69 (1978).
30. Lundström, V., Eneroth, P., Granström, E. & Swahn, K.-L. *3rd World Congress of Human Reproduction*, Berlin (Excerpta Medica, Amsterdam, 1981).
31. Akerjund, M., Andersson, K.-E. & Ingermarsson, I. *Br. J. Obstet. Gynec.* **83**, 673 (1976).
32. Marston, J. H., Penn, R. & Sivelle, P. C. *J. Reprod. Fert.* **49**, 175 (1977).
33. Steptoe, P. C., Edwards, R. G. & Purdy, J. M. *Br. J. Obstet. Gynec.* **87**, 757 (1980).
34. Lopata, A. *Nature* **288**, 642 (1980).
35. Jacobs, P. A. *et al. Ann. Hum. Genet.* **42**, 49 (1978).
36. Hassold, T. J. & Matsuyama, A. *Hum. Genet.* **46**, 285 (1978).
37. Niikawa, N., Merotto, E. & Kajii, T. *Hum. Genet.* **40**, 73 (1977).
38. Feichtinger, W., Kemeter, P., Szalay, S., Beck, A. & Janisch, H. *3rd World Congress of Human Reproduction,* Berlin (Excerpta Medica, Amsterdam, 1981).
39. Hertig, A. T. in *Progress in Infertility* (eds Behrman, J. & Kistner, R.W.) (Little Brown, Boston, 1975).
40. Batzer, F. R. Schlaff, S., Goldfarb, A. F. & Carson, S. L. *Fert. Steril.* **35**, 307 (1981).
41. Illmensee, K. & Hoppe, P. C. *Cell* **23**, 9 (1981).
42. Illmensee, K. *3rd World Congress of Human Reproduction*, Berlin (Excerpta Medica, Amsterdam, 1981).
43. Kajii, T. & Ohama, K. *Nature* **268**, 633 (1977).
44. Jacobs, P. A., Wilson, C. M., Sprenkle, J. A., Rosenheim, N. B. & Migeon, B. *Nature* **286**, 714 (1980).
45. Lawler, S. D. *et al. Lancet* ii, 580 (1979).
46. Surti, U., Szulman, A. E. & O'Brien, S. *Hum. Genet,* **51**, 153 (1979).
47. Hoppe, P. C. & Illmensee, K. *Proc. Natl. Acad. Sci. U.S.A.* **74**, 56-57 (1977).
48. Trounson, A. O., Leeton, J. F., Wood, C., Webb, J. & Kovacs, G. *Fert. Steril.* **34**, 431 (1980).

# Enzymatic Replication of *E.coli* Chromosomal Origin is Bidirectional

J. M. Kaguni *et al.*

## Editor's Note

Here molecular biologist Arthur Kornberg and his colleagues at Stanford University in California shed new light on how bacterial genomes are replicated. It was already known that bacterial chromosomes consist of circular double strands of DNA that are replicated in both directions at once, starting from a site denoted *oriC*. Kornberg and colleagues identify an enzyme that will replicate any plasmid (a circular stretch of bacterial DNA) into which the *oriC* segment from *E. coli* has been inserted. This confirmed the supposed replication mechanism, isolated the replicase enzyme, and suggested a way to replicate any arbitrary strand of bacterial DNA for biotechnological purposes.

---

A soluble enzyme system has been discovered which specifically recognizes and replicates plasmids containing the *Escherichia coli* chromosomal origin, *oriC*. Electron microscopy has shown that plasmid replication begins at or near *oriC* from which it progresses bidirectionally to completion. Control of initiation of a cycle of chromosomal replication and mechanisms of priming and fork movement can now be explored using this system.

---

REPLICATION of the *Escherichia coli* K-12 chromosome, as shown by genetic and biochemical analysis *in vivo*, begins at a unique site (*oriC*) and proceeds bidirectionally[1-3]. The DNA fragment containing *oriC* has been isolated by its ability to confer autonomous replication on plasmids or phage whose own replication origin has been inactivated[4-7]. Deletion analysis has localized *oriC* to a sequence of 232-245 base pairs (bp)[8]; insertions, deletions or substitutions in this essential region can inactivate *oriC*.

Initiation of a cycle of chromosomal replication in the cell requires the activities encoded by the genes *dnaA, dnaI* and *dnaP*[9-11]. In addition, *dnaB* and *dnaC* proteins, whose activities are essential for priming the synthesis of nascent chains during replication[12,13], are also required during or shortly after initiation[14,15]. RNA polymerase has also been implicated[16].

A soluble enzyme system has been discovered which specifically recognizes and replicates *oriC* plasmids[17]. The reaction requires *dnaA* protein, RNA polymerase and numerous replication proteins including *dnaB*, single-stranded DNA-binding protein and DNA gyrase. Recently, *dnaC* protein has been shown to be required for *in vitro* replication of *oriC*

# 大肠杆菌染色体起始位点的
# 酶促复制是双向进行的

卡古尼等

**编者按**

在本文中，分子生物学家阿瑟·科恩伯格与其在加州斯坦福大学的同事对细菌基因组的复制方式提出了新的观点。已知，细菌的染色体由环状双链 DNA 构成，其复制可向两个方向同时进行，该复制起始位点是一个被称为 *oriC* 的位点。科恩伯格及其同事发现了一种酶，它可以复制任何一种插入了大肠杆菌 *oriC* 位点的质粒（一段环状细菌 DNA）。这一发现证实了关于复制机制的假设，分离到了复制酶，并且提供了一种出于生物技术目的而复制任何细菌 DNA 链的方法。

我们发现了一个可溶性的酶系统，它可以特异地识别并复制含有大肠杆菌染色体复制起始位点（*oriC*）的质粒。电子显微镜观察结果显示，质粒的复制从 *oriC* 位点或接近 *oriC* 位点的地方起始，双向进行，直至复制完成。通过这个酶系统，可以研究一个染色体复制周期中的起始调控、引发机制以及复制叉移动机制。

体内的遗传学和生物化学分析表明，大肠杆菌 K-12 菌株染色体的复制起始于一个独特的位点（*oriC*），并且是双向进行的 [1-3]。含有 *oriC* 位点的 DNA 片段可以使自身复制失活的质粒或噬菌体 DNA 获得自主复制的能力，人们根据这一特点将其分离出来 [4-7]。通过缺失分析，人们将 *oriC* 位点定位于一段含有 232~245 个碱基对（bp）的序列 [8]，在这段必需序列中发生碱基插入、缺失或替换都会使 *oriC* 位点失活。

细胞中染色体复制周期的起始需要 *dnaA*、*dnaI* 和 *dnaP* 基因编码产物的活性 [9-11]。此外，*dnaB* 和 *dnaC* 蛋白的活性既是复制过程中引发新生 DNA 链合成所必需的 [12,13]，也是复制起始过程中或复制起始后不久所必需的 [14,15]。RNA 聚合酶也在其中发挥作用 [16]。

我们发现了一个可溶性酶系统，它可以特异地识别并复制含有 *oriC* 位点的质粒 [17]。这一反应需要 *dnaA* 蛋白、RNA 聚合酶以及包括 *dnaB* 蛋白、单链 DNA 结合蛋白和 DNA 促旋酶在内的多种复制有关的蛋白质参与。最近，又发现 *dnaC* 蛋白是含有 *oriC* 的质粒在体外复制所必需的（未发表的结果）。对于酶促合成的复制中间体

plasmids (unpublished observations). Biochemical analysis of enzymatically synthesized replicative intermediates showed initiation occurring at or near *oriC* and was consistent with bidirectional progress from that point, but such evidence is essentially a statistical average. Is replication of an individual molecule, once initiated at *oriC,* then extended bidirectionally to completion? We present here the results of an electron microscopic study which indicate that with few exceptions this enzyme system creates an "eye" or replication "bubble" in a plasmid molecule at or near the *oriC* region which is extended in both directions to generate two complete molecules.

## Formation of Replicative Intermediates

Two classes of supercoiled, *oriC* template DNA were examined. One, pSY317, is a 13.5-kilobase (kb) plasmid which contains a 5.6-kb *Eco*RI, *oriC* fragment (from pSY221)[5] and a 7.9-kb *Eco*RI kanamycin-resistance fragment (from pML21)[18]. The *oriC* plasmid contains *oriC* intact, together with extensive flanking sequences. The second template, M13*oriC*26, is a 12.2-kb, chimaeric M13 phage DNA containing *oriC* and its adjacent *asnA* gene[19]. In constructing M13*oriC*26, the *Xho*I site immediately to the right of *oriC* was interrupted. Although interruptions in and around this site do not alter the ability of this and similar *oriC* plasmids to replicate[8,19,20], the directionality of replication was reported to be affected, becoming unidirectional rather than bidirectional[21,22].

The extent of replication was limited to obtain a significant number of replicative intermediates for electron microscopic study. The chain terminator, 2′,3′-dideoxythymidine 5′-triphosphate (ddTTP) was used. This inhibitor, which prevents chain growth when incorporated into DNA, was present at concentrations relative to dTTP that generated replicative intermediates showing different exents of replication[23]. It is assumed that incorporation of a ddTMP residue in the leading or lagging strand at a replication fork stops fork movement. DNAs were purified, spread on parlodion-coated grids by the formamide spreading technique[24], and rotary shadowed at a low angle with platinum-tungsten vapour. Replicative intermediates generated with an enzyme fraction (fraction II)[17] from wild-type cells constituted 10-20% of the molecular forms observed, a value consistent with the fraction of template molecules used in comparable uninhibited reactions. It is possible that the fortuitous arrangement of a DNA fragment overlapping a circular molecule or unit-length linear fragment can give rise to structures that are indistinguishable from true replicative intermediates, but such events are expected to occur only rarely. Circular replicative intermediates of pSY317 and M13*oriC*26 appeared in every case as theta-like structures (see Fig. 2).

的生物化学分析结果显示，复制的起始发生在 *oriC* 位点或 *oriC* 位点附近，并且分析结果与从此位点开始双向进行的复制过程一致，但这些证据是一个平均的统计结果。对于一个单独的分子来说，一旦其复制从 *oriC* 位点开始，是否就双向延伸直到复制完成呢？本文展示了一些电子显微镜的研究结果，这些结果表明，这个酶系统在绝大多数的情况下能够在质粒分子的 *oriC* 位点或其邻近区域形成"眼"或"复制泡"样结构，然后这种结构从两个方向向两端延伸并最终产生两个完整的分子。

## 复制中间体的形成

我们检测了两种类型的含有 *oriC* 位点的超螺旋 DNA 模板。一种模板是 pSY317，它是一个 13.5 kb 的质粒，含有一个大小为 5.6 kb，具有 *Eco*RI 酶切位点的 *oriC* 片段（来自 pSY221）[5] 和一个大小为 7.9 kb，具有 *Eco*RI 酶切位点的卡那霉素抗性片段（来自 pML21）[18]，该 *oriC* 质粒含有完整的 *oriC* 位点以及大量的侧翼序列。另一种模板是 M13*oriC*26，它的大小为 12.2 kb，是含有 *oriC* 位点及其邻近 *asnA* 基因的 M13 噬菌体 DNA 嵌合体 [19]。在构建 M13*oriC*26 质粒的过程中，右侧紧临 *oriC* 位点的 *Xho*I 酶切位点被切断。尽管该位点及其周边区域的破坏并不影响该 *oriC* 质粒及类似质粒的复制 [8,19,20]，但据报道，复制的方向性会受到影响，会从双向复制变成单向复制 [21,22]。

通过控制复制的进程可以得到大量的可供电子显微镜观察的复制中间体。我们使用了可以使 DNA 链延伸过程终止的 2′, 3′–双脱氧胸腺嘧啶–5′–三磷酸（ddTTP）来达到这一目的。ddTTP 进入到 DNA 链后，可以阻止 DNA 链的延伸。通过在反应体系中加入不同比例的 ddTTP 和 dTTP，可以得到各种不同复制程度的复制中间体 [23]。人们据此推断整合到复制叉的前导链或后随链中的 ddTMP 残基可以使复制叉停止移动。使用甲酰胺铺展技术 [24] 将纯化的 DNA 铺展在火棉胶片包被的载网上，然后用铂–钨蒸汽进行小角度旋转投影电镜观察。使用从野生型细胞中分离到的酶组分（组分 II）[17] 所产生的复制中间体在观察到的分子形式中占 10%~20%，这一比例与未受抑制的对照反应中的模板分子含量一致。环状 DNA 分子或单位长度的线性片段与一段 DNA 片段重叠的偶然排列可能形成与真正的复制中间体类似的结构，不过这种情况发生的概率很低。pSY317 和 M13*oriC*26 质粒的环状复制中间体在每个实验中都呈现出 θ 样的结构（见图 2）。

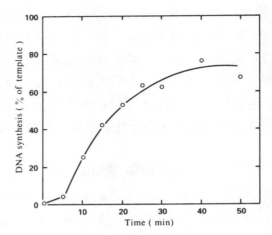

Fig. 1. Time course of *oriC* plasmid in *dnaA*-complementing conditions. Reactions were performed as described previously[17] in a 250 µl volume containing 40 mM HEPES *p*H 7.6, 2 mM ATP, 0.5 mM each of GTP, UTP and CTP, 43 mM creatine phosphate, 100 µM each of dGTP, dATP, dCTP and 5-methyl-[³H]dTPP (85 c.p.m. per pmol of total deoxynucleotide), 6% (w/v) polyvinyl alcohol 24,000, 11 mM magnesium acetate, 100 µg ml⁻¹ creatine kinase (Sigma), 8.6 µg ml⁻¹ supercoiled pSY317 DNA, 2 mg of protein (fraction II, prepared from *E. coli* WM433 *dnaA*204 as described elsewhere[17]) and 230 units of *dnaA*-complementing activity (fraction III). Incubation was at 30°C. Aliquots (25µl) were TCA-precipitated and counted in a liquid scintillation counter. One unit is equal to one pmol of nucleotide incorporated per min.

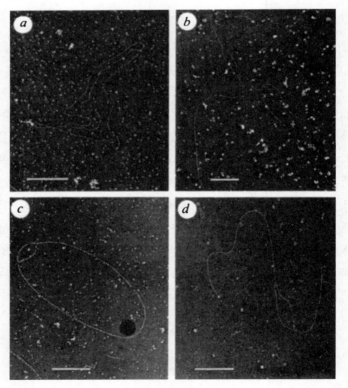

Fig. 2. Replicative intermediates of pSY317 and M13*oriC*26. The reaction with 8.6 µg ml⁻¹ of supercoiled pSY317 was as described in Fig. 1 legend in a 125 µl volume with 50 µM ddTTP, 1,100 µg of *E. coli*

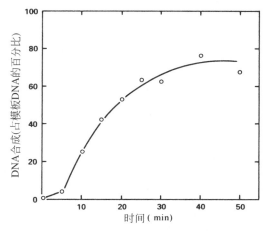

图 1. 在 *dnaA* 互补条件下，含有 *oriC* 位点的质粒复制随时间变化的曲线。反应按照之前文献报道的条件进行[17]。反应体积为 250 µl，含有 40 mM pH 7.6 的 HEPES，2 mM ATP，GTP、UTP 和 CTP 各 0.5 mM，43 mM 磷酸肌酸，dGTP、dATP、dCTP 和 5– 甲基 –[³H]dTPP（总脱氧核苷酸 85 c.p.m./pmol）各 100 µM，6%（w/v）的聚乙烯醇 24,000，11 mM 乙酸镁，100 µg/ml 肌酸激酶（购自西格玛公司），8.6 µg/ml 超螺旋 pSY317 DNA，2 mg 蛋白质（组分 II，采用文献报道的方法[17] 从大肠杆菌 WM433 *dnaA*204 中分离）以及 230 单位的互补活性 *dnaA*（组分 III）。反应在 30℃进行。将反应物分装（25 µl 每管）后使用 TCA 沉淀并用液闪计数器计数。一个活性单位相当于每分钟掺入 1 pmol 核苷酸所需的 *dnaA* 量。

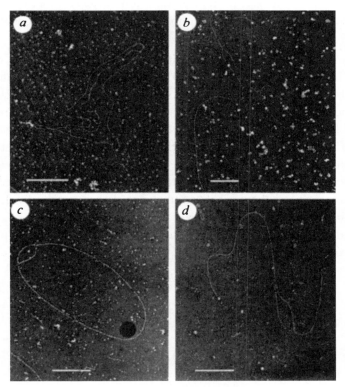

图 2. pSY317 和 M13*oriC*26 的复制中间体。8.6 µg/ml 的 pSY317 超螺旋质粒的反应条件如图 1 注，反应体系为 125 µl，含有 50 µM ddTTP，1,100 µg 提取自大肠杆菌 WM433 菌株的 *dnaA*204 组分 II 以及 275 µg

WM433 *dnaA*204 fraction II and 275 μg of *E. coli* HB101 (pBF101) fraction II, known to be enriched for *dnaA*-complementation activity[17]. Incubation was at 30°C for 10 min after which reactions were terminated by addition of SDS to 1% and EDTA to 50 mM. Following incubation at 65°C for 3 min, aliquots were removed for TCA precipitation and counted in a liquid scintillation counter. The sample was then incubated with 0.5 mg ml$^{-1}$ of proteinase K (Merck) at 37°C for 60 min, phenol-extracted, ether-extracted, and centrifuged in a Beckman airfuge into a CsCl shelf of 1.42 g cm$^{-3}$. The shelf was recovered and DNA was ethanol-precipitated and resuspended in a small volume of 10 mM Tris-HCl *p*H 8.0 and 1mM EDTA. Recovery at this step was 60-70% of the initial reaction product. The sample was then incubated with 5 μg ml$^{-1}$ of pancreatic RNase at 37°C for 60 min to digest contaminating RNA and either relaxed with *Sal*I endonuclease (given by K. Burtis) in the presence of ethidium bromide[31] (*a*), or restricted to completion with *Sal*I endonuclease in 10 mM Tris-HCl *p*H 8.0, 10 mM MgSO$_4$ and 100 mM NaCl at 37°C for 30 min (*b*). DNA was then spread on to parlodion-coated grids by the formamide technique[24], shadowed at a low angle with platinum-tungsten vapour, and viewed in a Philips 300 electron microscope. Replicative intermediates of M13*oriC*26 were prepared for electron microscopy as described above except that the sample was either relaxed with *Eco*RI endonuclease (given by C. Mann) (*c*) or linearized by digestion to completion with *Eco*RI endonuclease in 100 mM Tris-HCl *p*H 7.2, 5 mM MgCl$_2$, 2 mM 2-mercaptoethanol and 50 mM NaCl at 37°C for 60 min (*d*). Scale bars, 0.5 μm.

## Defining the Initiation Site and Direction of Replication

Replication of an *oriC* plasmid (for example pSY317) requires *dnaA* protein[17]. Complementation of a crude enzyme fraction (fraction II)[17] prepared from a *dnaA* mutant provides an assay for purifying *dnaA* protein overproduced in cells bearing a plasmid carrying the *dnaA* gene. In a *dnaA* protein preparation enriched at least 200-fold over wild-type levels, the template molecules were almost completely used in a reaction (Fig. 1).

In conditions which complement *dnaA* activity, replicative intermediates of pSY317 were accumulated by inhibiting the reaction by 60% with 50 μM ddTTP. To determine the site of initiation and direction of replication, molecules were linearized by cleavage with *Sal*I endonuclease and examined by electron microscopy (Figs 2,3). In orienting the molecules in Fig. 3, *oriC* is located at a point 45% of the genome length from the right end of the linearized pSY317. With few exceptions, the replicated segment of the intermediate overlaps *oriC*. Although the slight asymmetry of the *Sal*I restriction cleavage relative to *oriC* introduces some ambiguity in orienting the more extensively replicated intermediates, it is clear that for most of them, replication proceeds bidirectionally. Inspection of the less extensively replicated molecules reveals that initiation occurs at or near *oriC*. Thus, we have shown that in these conditions, replication of the *oriC* plasmid pSY317 proceeds bidirectionally from a start in the *oriC* region.

提取自大肠杆菌 HB101 菌株（pBF101）的组分 II（已知其可以通过 *dnaA* 互补活性被富集[17]）。将反应体系在 30℃ 孵育 10 min，然后加入 SDS 和 EDTA 使其终浓度分别为 1% 和 50 mM 以终止反应。随后，将反应体系在 65℃ 孵育 3 min，分装后用 TCA 沉淀（去除蛋白质）并用液闪计数器计数。将样品加入 0.5 mg/ml 的蛋白酶 K（购自默克公司）在 37℃ 孵育 60 min，然后进行酚抽提和醚抽提，并用贝克曼公司的 airfuge 离心机进行氯化铯密度梯度离心。样品在氯化铯密度梯度中，最终沉降到密度为 1.42 g/cm³ 的一个薄层上。将这一薄层回收，并用乙醇沉淀其中的 DNA，然后用小体积的 10 mM pH 8.0 的 Tris-HCl 和 1 mM EDTA 溶液重悬 DNA。与初始反应产物相比，这一步骤的回收率为 60%~70%。将样品与 5 μg/ml 的胰 RNA 酶 37℃ 孵育 60 min，以消化污染的 RNA，并分别进行如下两种不同的操作来松弛 DNA 超螺旋：(*a*) 在溴化乙啶存在时用 *Sal*I 内切酶（由伯蒂斯馈赠）处理[31]；(*b*) 在含 10 mM pH 8.0 Tris-HCl、10 mM 硫酸镁、100 mM 氯化钠的溶液中用 *Sal*I 内切酶 37℃ 消化 30 min。使用甲酰胺铺展技术[24]将纯化的 DNA 铺展在包覆了火棉胶片的载网上，然后用铂－钨蒸汽进行小角度旋转投影，并使用菲利普斯 300 电子显微镜观察。M13*oriC*26 的复制中间体也用上述方法制备，唯一不同的是样品使用 *Eco*R I 内切酶（由曼馈赠）松弛 (*c*) 或使用 *Eco*RI 内切酶在含 100 mM pH 7.2 Tris-HCl、5 mM 氯化镁、2 mM 2－巯基乙醇、50 mM 氯化钠的溶液中，于 37℃ 下完全消化 60 min 使 DNA 线性化 (*d*)。标尺，0.5 μm。

## 复制起始位点及复制方向的确定

含有 *oriC* 位点的质粒（如 pSY317）的复制需要 *dnaA* 蛋白的参与[17]。从 *dnaA* 突变体中制备的酶粗提物（组分 II）[17]与 *dnaA* 蛋白的功能互补性为纯化 *dnaA* 蛋白提供了方法，该蛋白在含有携带 *dnaA* 基因的质粒的细胞中是过量表达的。当 *dnaA* 蛋白的浓度富集到野生型水平的 200 倍以上时，反应中几乎所有的模板分子都被利用了（图 1）。

在有互补 *dnaA* 活性的条件下，向反应中加入终浓度为 50 μM 的 ddTTP，反应被抑制 60%，并引起 pSY317 复制中间体的积累。为了确定复制的起始位点以及方向，我们用 *Sal* I 限制性内切酶消化切割使之线性化，然后用电子显微镜观察（图 2，3）。在图 3 中，对这些分子进行定向后发现，*oriC* 位点位于距离线性化的 pSY317 质粒右端 45% 基因组长度的位置。除了极少数的例外，绝大部分复制中间体的复制片段都与 *oriC* 位点重叠。尽管相对于 *oriC* 位点，*Sal*I 的限制性内切会造成轻微的不对称性，从而在更长片段的复制中间体的定向中引入了不确定性，但是可以肯定的是对于多数复制中间体来说，复制是双向进行的。对较短的复制分子的观察表明，复制起始于 *oriC* 位点或 *oriC* 位点附近的区域。因此我们已经证明了，在这些条件下，含有 *oriC* 位点的 pSY317 质粒的复制起始于 *oriC* 位点并且是双向进行的。

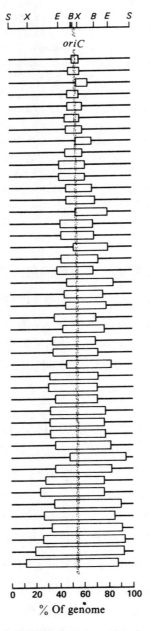

Fig. 3. Replication of the *oriC* plasmid pSY317 initiates at *oriC* and progresses bidirectionally. Replicative intermediates generated with 50 μM ddTTP, then purified and linearized with *Sal*I endonuclease (as described in Fig. 2 legend), were randomly selected and photographed. Molecules were analysed with a Hewlett-Packard 9810A calculator by measuring the non-replicated and both replicated segments of an individual molecule on a Hewlett-Packard 9864A digitizer board, averaging the replicated segments, and expressing each portion as a percentage of the total length. Only molecules in which both replicated segments were identical in length (±5%) and for which the total length was within ±10% of the length expected were included in the analysis. Molecules are aligned so that the longer unreplicated segment is to the left, and they are arranged according to increasing extents of replication. The position of *oriC* is indicated by the stippled area. The open boxes represent the replication "bubble". Restriction endonuclease sites are: S, *Sal*I; X, *Xho*I; E, *Eco*RI; and B, *Bam*HI.

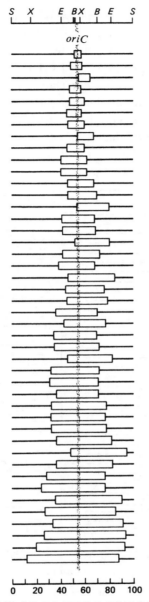

复制片段长度占基因组长度的百分比

图 3. pSY317 质粒的复制从 oriC 位点起始并双向进行。使用 50 µM ddTTP 来制备复制中间体，纯化后使用 SalI 内切酶消化使之线性化（如图 2 注所述）。然后随机选取这些复制中间体进行拍照。通过惠普 9864A 数字转换板测量单个分子未复制的片段和复制后的两个片段的长度，计算复制片段的平均值，将每一部分换算成总长度的百分比，然后，对这些分子进行分析（使用惠普 9810A 计算机）。只有那些两个复制片段的长度相同（±5%），并且分子总长度与预期值的差异不超过 10% 的分子才会列入分析范围。将这些分子排列对齐，使较长的未复制的片段位于左端，并按复制区长度由小到大进行排列。图中点带区域所示为 oriC 的位置。方框所示为"复制泡"。限制性内切酶的位点分别是：S，SalI；X，XhoI；E，EcoRI；B，BamHI。

Replicative intermediates of M13*oriC*26 DNA were generated with an enzyme fraction (fraction II)[17] from wild-type cells at several levels of ddTTP inhibition and analysed after cleavage with *Eco*RI endonuclease (Figs 2,4). In uninhibited reactions, no replication occurred from the M13 origin[17] due to the absence of the M13-encoded gene 2 protein required for replication of supercoiled M13 DNA[25-27]. Inhibition of replication as measured by nucleotide incorporation correlated well with the effect of ddTTP in decreasing the average length of the replicated segment (Fig. 5). These findings and similar results for pSY317 (data not shown) confirm that the "eye" and "Y" forms (molecules with a single fork) are replication intermediates.

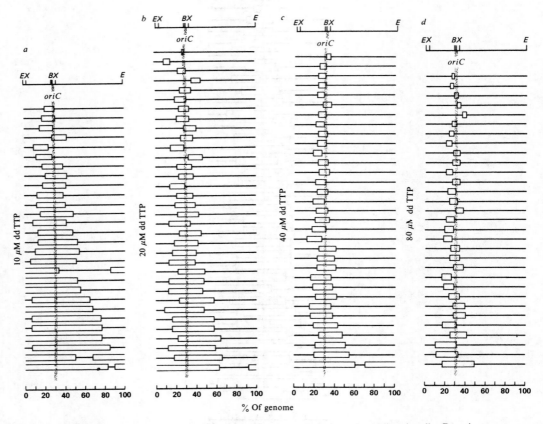

Fig. 4. Replication of M13*oriC*26 DNA initiates at *oriC* and progresses bidirectionally. Reactions were performed as described in Fig. 1 legend in a volume of 125 µl containing ddTTP (as indicated) and 1 mg of enzyme fraction II prepared from *E. coli* C600 as described elsewhere[17]. Incubation was at 30°C for 15 min. Replicative intermediates produced with *a*, 10 µM; *b*, 20 µM; *c*, 40 µM, and *d*, 80 µM ddTTP from samples prepared as described in Fig. 2 were restricted, after treatment with pancreatic RNase, with an excess of *Eco*RI endonuclease, spread on to parlodion-coated grids and examined. Replicative intermediates at each ddTTP concentration were selected randomly, photographed and measured. Only molecules having a correct total length (±10%) in which both replicated segments were the same length (±5%) were included in the analysis. Molecules are aligned so that the longer unreplicated segment is to the right, and they are arranged according to extent of replication. The position of *oriC* is indicated by the stippled area. The open boxes represent the replication "bubble". Restriction endonuclease sites are the same as for Fig. 3.

为了制备 M13*oriC*26 DNA 的复制中间体，我们在反应体系中使用了分离自野生型细胞的酶组分（组分 II）[17]，并且用不同浓度的 ddTTP 终止反应，然后用 *Eco*RI 限制性内切酶进行切割，最后对生成的产物进行分析（图 2，4）。在没有抑制的反应中，由于缺乏 M13 超螺旋 DNA 复制所必需的 M13 编码的基因 2 的蛋白质产物 [25-27]，在 M13 的复制起点 [17] 没有观察到复制的发生。使用掺入核苷酸的方法检测的复制抑制情况与使用 ddTTP 后引起的平均复制片段长度减小的情况非常吻合（图 5）。这些发现以及使用 pSY317 质粒时得到的类似的实验结果（数据未展示）证实"眼睛"样结构和"Y"型结构（只含有一个复制叉的分子）就是复制中间体。

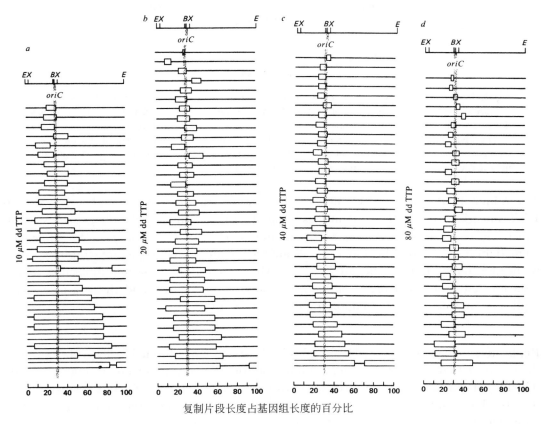

复制片段长度占基因组长度的百分比

图 4. M13*oriC*26 DNA 的复制起始于 *oriC* 位点并且双向进行。反应按照图 1 注中所述的方法进行，反应体积 125 μl，含有 ddTTP（如图中所标注的浓度）以及 1 mg 酶组分 II（按照其他文献所述的方法 [17] 从大肠杆菌 C600 中制备）。30℃ 孵育 15 min。按照图 2 中所述的方法，分别用 (a) 10 μM、(b) 20 μM、(c) 40 μM、(d) 80 μM 的 ddTTP 处理细胞，来制备复制中间体。用胰 RNA 酶消化样品中的 RNA 后，用过量的 *Eco*RI 限制性内切酶消化样品，然后将纯化的 DNA 铺展在包被了火棉胶片的载网上，使用电子显微镜观察。随机挑选在各种浓度的 ddTTP 作用下产生的复制中间体，拍照并测量长度。只有具有正确总长度（±10%）且两条复制片段长度相等（±5%）的分子才会被列入分析范围。将这些分子按照复制片段的长度进行排列，并使较长的未复制的片段位于右端。图中点带区域所示为 *oriC* 的位置。方框所示为"复制泡"。限制性内切酶的位点与图 3 中相同。

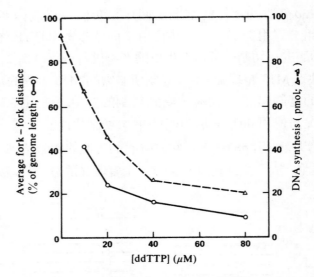

Fig. 5. Inhibition of DNA synthesis by the chain terminator ddTTP correlates with the fork-to-fork distance of replicative intermediates of M13*oriC*26. After incubation, aliquots (25 µl) from the reactions described in Fig. 4 legend were removed for TCA precipitation and counted to determine the amount of DNA synthesis. The replicative intermediates of Fig. 4 were then analysed individually for the extent of replication and averaged. Each point represents the average fork-to-fork distance of 28-34 replicative intermediates generated at the corresponding ddTTP concentration.

The minimal *oriC* sequence is ~30% of the genome length from one end of M13*oriC*26 DNA linearized by *Eco*RI endonuclease (Fig. 4). Recombinant M13 phage DNAs from which *oriC* has been deleted do not replicate from *oriC* either *in vitro* or *in vivo*[17,28]. Molecules aligned in Fig. 4 with the longer replicated segment to the right are consistent with replication initiating from the *oriC* segment. More extensively replicated molecules clearly indicate that replication proceeds bidirectionally in most cases, and the less extensively replicated molecules show initiation to be at or near *oriC*.

Replicative intermediates of M13*oriC*26 (Fig. 4) were analysed individually with respect to the extent of replication to the right and left of *oriC*. These values were averaged for each ddTTP concentration and plotted as the distance rightwards or leftwards relative to *oriC* (Fig. 6). The results indicate that for a population of molecules, replication from *oriC* is bidirectional.

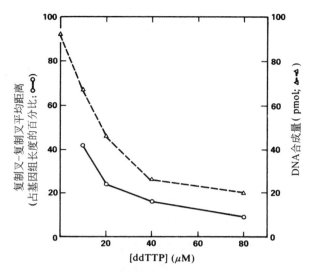

图 5. 链终止子 ddTTP 对 DNA 合成的抑制作用与 M13*oriC*26 复制中间体的复制叉之间的距离相关。反应体系按图 4 注描述的方法配制，孵育后取 25 μl，TCA 沉淀后计数，以确定 DNA 合成量。逐个分析图 4 中所述的复制中间体的复制进行的程度，并计算平均值。图中的每一个点代表在相应浓度的 ddTTP 作用下，28 到 34 个复制中间体的复制叉之间的距离的平均值。

最短的 *oriC* 序列位于距离 *Eco*RI 限制性内切酶消化的线性 M13*oriC*26 DNA 的一端大约 30% 基因组长度的地方（图 4）。敲除掉 *oriC* 位点的重组 M13 噬菌体 DNA 不管是在体外还是体内都无法从 *oriC* 位点起始复制 [17,28]。图 4 中排列对齐的那些在右侧具有较长的复制片段的分子与起始于 *oriC* 片段的复制一致。复制区较长的复制中间体分子表明，在多数情况下复制都是双向进行的，复制区较短的复制中间体分子表明复制起始于 *oriC* 位点或其附近的区域。

为了研究复制向 *oriC* 位点左右两端进行的情况，我们逐一分析了 M13*oriC*26 的复制中间体（图 4）。我们分别计算了各个 ddTTP 浓度下测得的数据的平均值，并用点图标示复制叉距离 *oriC* 位点左侧或右侧的长度（图 6）。结果表明，对于我们研究的这些分子群体来讲，从 *oriC* 位点起始的复制是双向进行的。

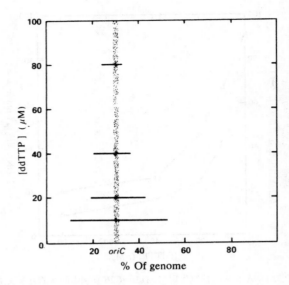

Fig. 6. Replication of M13*oriC*26 DNA is bidirectional for a population of molecules. Replicative intermediates at each ddTTP concentration shown in Fig. 4 were analysed individually for the extent of replication rightwards and leftwards from *oriC*. The values were averaged and plotted relative to the position of *oriC*, indicated by the stippled area, and to the physical map of M13*oriC*26 linearized at the single *Eco*RI site. Molecules (4 of 126) which did not seem to have initiated from *oriC* were excluded from the analysis.

Of 126 M13*oriC*26 replicative intermediates examined, 4 were judged not to have been initiated at *oriC* as the replicated segment did not overlap *oriC* within the error of measurement (5% of the genome length; Fig. 4). These discrepancies may be due to aberrant initiation or improper breakage of the duplex template. For several molecules of both template DNAs, the bidirectional progress of replication appears asymmetric or even unidirectional, which may be due to asynchrony in the initiation of the two replication forks or in chain terminations by ddTTP. In this regard, examination of the replicative intermediates of phage λ and F plasmids, which are known to replicate bidirectionally, also reveals molecules that replicate unidirectionally[29,30].

The bidirectional replication of M13*oriC*26, a template interrupted at the *Xho*I site, contrasts with the analysis of replicative intermediates of the *oriC* plasmids[20], pOC24, produced *in vivo*, in which predominantly unidirectional replication was attributed to an interruption at the same *Xho*I site[21,22]. This discrepancy may be due to differences in either the plasmid sequences or the experimental conditions; in the *in vivo* study, replicative intermediates were detected at a frequency of only 1 in $10^4$ plasmid molecules and thus may not represent the principle mode of replication[21].

This electron microscopic study of individual plasmid molecules replicated in a soluble enzyme system is thus consistent with initiation of replication from *oriC*. Fork movement from that point progresses bidirectionally. The soluble enzymatic system used here and elsewhere[17] should allow a biochemical approach to the events of priming, fork movement,

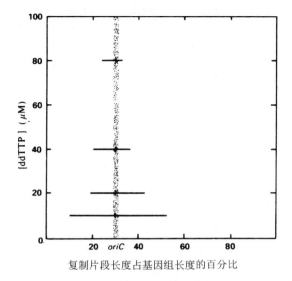

图 6. 对一个质粒分子群体的分析表明，M13*oriC*26 DNA 的复制是双向进行的。我们逐一计算了图 4 中所示的在各个浓度的 ddTTP 作用下产生的复制中间体中，复制从 *oriC* 位点分别向左侧和右侧进行的程度。我们计算了这些数据的平均值，根据与 *oriC* 位点的距离，并对照在 *Eco*RI 单一位点线性化后的 M13*oriC*26 质粒的物理图谱，标注出 *oriC* 的位置，即图中的点带区域。在 126 个分子中有 4 个似乎并不是从 *oriC* 位点起始复制的，我们未分析这些分子。

　　在我们分析的 126 个 M13*oriC*26 复制中间体中，有 4 个分子被判定为不是从 *oriC* 位点起始复制的，因为它们的复制片段在测量误差范围内（基因组长度的 5%，图 4）没有与 *oriC* 位点重合。这一差异可能是由于复制的异常起始或者双链模板的不正常断裂导致的。对于一些分子的两条 DNA 模板链来说，双向复制过程似乎是不对称的甚至可能是单向的，这有可能是由于两个复制叉的启动是不同步的或由于 ddTTP 对链延伸的终止不是同时的。就这一点而言，在对 λ 噬菌体和 F 质粒（已知它们的复制是双向进行的）的复制中间体进行分析时，也发现了一些单向复制的分子 [29,30]。

　　M13*oriC*26 是一种在 *Xho*I 位点被打断的双向复制模板，与体内产生的 *oriC* 质粒 [20] pOC24 复制中间体的分析相反，后者主要为单向复制，这是由于该质粒在同样的 *Xho*I 位点被打断 [21,22] 造成的。这一差异可能是由于质粒的序列不同或实验条件的不同而引起的；在体内实验中，只有万分之一的频率检测到复制中间体，因此无法反映复制的主要模式 [21]。

　　对在可溶性酶系统中复制的单个质粒分子的电子显微镜的研究也表明复制是从 *oriC* 位点起始的。复制叉从这一位点开始的移动是双向的。在本文或其他文献 [17] 中使用的可溶性酶系统，应该能够应用生物化学技术来研究复制的起始、复制叉移动、

regulation of initiation and other events occurring at the *E. coli* origin.

We thank Darrell Dobbertin for assistance in the electron microscopy. This work was supported in part by grants from the NIH and NSF. J.M.K. is a Fellow of the Damon Runyon–Walter Winchell Cancer Fund.

(**296**, 623-627; 1982)

**Jon M. Kaguni, Robert S. Fuller and Arthur Kornberg**
Department of Biochemistry, Stanford University School of Medicine, Stanford, California 94305, USA

Received 21 December 1981; accepted 8 March 1982.

References:

1. Masters, M. & Broda, P. *Nature New Biol.* **232**, 137-140 (1971).

2. Bird, R. E., Louarn, J., Martuscelli, J. & Caro, L. *J. Molec. Biol.* **70**, 549-566 (1972).

3. Prescott, D. M. & Kuempel, P. L. *Proc. Natl. Acad. Sci. U.S.A.* **69**, 2842-2845 (1972).

4. Hiraga, S. *Proc. Natl. Acad. Sci. U.S.A.* **73**, 198-202 (1976).

5. Yasuda, S. & Hirota, Y. *Proc. Natl. Acad. Sci. U.S.A.* **74**, 5458-5462 (1977).

6. von Meyenburg, K., Hansen, F. G., Nielsen, L. D. & Riise, E. *Molec. gen. Genet.* **160**, 287-295 (1978).

7. Miki, T., Hiraga, S., Nagata, T. & Yura, T. *Proc. Natl. Acad. Sci. U.S.A.* **75**, 5099-5103 (1978).

8. Oka, A., Sugimoto, K. & Takanami, M. *Molec. gen. Genet.* **178**, 9-20 (1980).

9. Hirota, Y., Mordon, J. & Jacob, F. *J. Molec. Biol.* **53**, 369-387 (1970).

10. Beyersmann, D., Messer, W. & Schlicht, M. *J. Bact.* **118**, 783-789 (1974).

11. Wada, C. & Yura, T. *Genetics* **77**, 199-220 (1974).

12. Lark, K. G. & Wechsler, J. A. *J. Molec. Biol.* **92**, 145-163 (1975).

13. Wechsler, J. A. *J. Bact.* **121**, 594-599 (1975).

14. Zyskind, J. W. & Smith, D. W. *J. Bact.* **129**, 1476-1486 (1977).

15. Carl, P. *Molec. gen. Genet.* **109**, 107-122 (1970).

16. Lark, K. G. *J. Molec. Biol.* **64**, 47-60 (1972).

17. Fuller, R. S., Kaguni, J. M. & Kornberg, A. *Proc. Natl. Acad. Sci. U.S.A.* **78**, 7370-7374 (1981).

18. Hershfield, V., Boyer, H. W., Yanofsky, C., Lovett, M. A. & Helinski, D. R. *Proc. Natl. Acad. Sci. U.S.A.* **71**, 3455-3459 (1974).

19. Kaguni, J. M., LaVerne, L.S. & Ray, D. S. *Proc. Natl. Acad. Sci. U.S.A.* **76**, 6250-6254 (1979).

20. Messer, W. *et al. Cold Spring Harb. Symp. Quant. Biol.* **43**, 139-145 (1979).

21. Meijer, M. & Messer, W. J. *J. Bact.* **143**, 1049-1053 (1980).

22. Messer, W., Heimann, B., Meijer, M. & Hall, S. *ICN-UCLA Symp. Molec. Cell. Biol.* **19**, 161-169 (1980).

23. Conrad, S. E., Wold, M. & Campbell, J. L. *Proc. Natl. Acad. Sci. U.S.A.* **76**, 736-740 (1979).

24. Davis, R. W., Simon, N. M. & Davidson, N. *Meth. Enzym.* **21**, 413-428 (1971).

25. Lin, N. S.-C. & Pratt, D. *J. Molec. Biol.* **72**, 37-49 (1972).

26. Fidánian, H. M. & Ray, D. *J. Molec. Biol.* **72**, 51-63 (1972).

27. Meyer, T. F. & Geider, K. *Single-stranded DNA Phages* (eds Denhardt, D. T., Dressler, D. & Ray. D. S.) 389-392 (Cold Spring Harbor Laboratory, New York, 1978).

28. Kaguni, L. S., Kaguni, J. M. & Ray, D. S. *J. Bact.* **145**, 974-979 (1981).

29. Eichenlaub, R., Figurski, D. & Helinski, D. R. *Proc. Natl. Acad. Sci. U.S.A.* **74**, 1138-1141 (1977).

30. Schnöss, M. & Inman, R. B. *J. Molec. Biol.* **51**, 61-73 (1970).

31. Shortle, D. & Nathans, D. *Proc. Natl. Acad. Sci. U.S.A.* **75**, 2170-2174 (1978).

复制起始的调控以及在大肠杆菌复制起点发生的其他事件 [31]。

感谢达雷尔·多贝廷在电子显微镜实验中的帮助。本文部分工作受美国国立卫生研究院和美国国家科学基金会的资金的支持。卡古尼是戴蒙·鲁尼恩－沃尔特·温切尔癌症基金会的研究员。

（张锦彬 翻译；梁前进 审稿）

# Temperature Control of Oxygen-Isotope Fractionation of Cultured Planktonic Foraminifera

J. Erez and B. Luz

## Editor's Note

Scientists studying ancient climates had long hoped to use measurements of the ratio of oxygen isotopes ($^{16}O/^{18}O$) in the calcium carbonate shells of planktonic foraminifera in seafloor sediments to deduce the temperature of the oceans in which they were originally formed. But the temperature dependence of the ratio is subject to subtle complications, and in the 1970s doubts were raised about the validity of the approach. Here Jonathan Erez and Boaz Luz in Israel grow foraminifera in the laboratory under temperature-controlled conditions and show that after all there is a clear and linear relationship between oxygen isotope ratio and temperature. The oxygen-isotope method is now central to the reconstruction of past climate change.

The palaeotemperature equation of Epstein et al.[1] relates the oxygen-isotope composition of mollusc carbonate shells to the temperature in which it has been deposited. This equation has been applied extensively to derive palaeotemperatures and other palaeoenvironmental parameters for the Pleistocene epoch, based on the isotopic composition of planktonic foraminifera in deep sea cores[2-11]. Recently, doubt has been expressed as to whether planktonic foraminifera fractionate oxygen isotopes according to the known palaeotemperature equation[12-18], and thus the validity of many palaeoenvironmental studies has been questioned. We present here experimental data demonstrating that planktonic foraminifera of the species *G. sacculifer* deposit calcite skeletons that have an oxygen-isotope composition very close to that predicted by the well-known paleotemperature equation[1].

THE oxygen-isotope composition of planktonic foraminifera in deep sea cores is a major tool in Pleistocene research. It serves to determine palaeotemperatures, palaeosalinities, sea-level changes, continental climatic conditions and provides accurate stratigraphy for the Pleistocene epoch[2-11]. These studies are based on the assumption that oxygen isotopes in planktonic foraminifera shells are fractionated according to the equation of Epstein et al.[1] that was determined experimentally for molluscs. Emiliani[2] tested this assumption by comparing the "isotopic temperature" (the temperature calculated based on the isotopic composition of calcium carbonate), of planktonic foraminifera from superficial sediments, to the actual temperatures of the overlying seawater. He found a good fit between these temperatures and concluded that planktonic foraminifera can be used for palaeotemperature studies. This approach has been repeated on material from

# 培养条件下温度对浮游有孔虫中氧同位素分馏的控制

埃雷兹，卢斯

## 编者按

长久以来，研究古气候学的科学家都希望利用海底沉积物中浮游有孔虫的碳酸钙壳体的氧同位素比值（$^{16}O/^{18}O$）来推测它们最初形成时所处的海洋环境的温度。但是这个比值的温度依赖性易受微小的各种复杂因素的影响，而且在 20 世纪 70 年代这个方法的有效性曾受到质疑。本文中，以色列的乔纳森·埃雷兹和博阿兹·卢斯在实验室温度控制条件下培养了有孔虫，并且表明氧同位素比值和温度之间存在明显的线性关系。目前，该氧同位素方法是重建古气候变化的重要方法。

---

爱泼斯坦等人 [1] 提出的古温度方程指出软体动物碳酸盐外壳中的氧同位素组成与其沉积时所处的环境温度有关。该方程已广泛用于根据深海岩芯中浮游有孔虫的同位素组成来推断更新世古温度及其他古环境参数的研究中 [2-11]。近来，有学者对浮游有孔虫分馏氧同位素是否遵从已知的古温度方程提出了质疑 [12-18]，因此许多古环境研究成果的有效性也受到怀疑。在本文中我们将用实验数据证明浮游有孔虫 *G. sacculifer*（袋拟抱球虫）沉积的方解石壳体中氧同位素组成与著名的古温度方程预测结果 [1] 非常接近。

---

深海岩芯中浮游有孔虫的氧同位素组成是研究更新世的一项主要工具。可以根据它来确定古温度、古盐度、海平面变化、大陆气候状况等；同时，它还可提供精确的更新世的地层学信息 [2-11]。这些研究都是基于一项假设，即浮游有孔虫壳体中氧同位素分馏遵从爱泼斯坦等人 [1] 提出的古温度方程，而该方程是根据软体动物的实验得出的。埃米利亚尼 [2] 通过比较表层沉积物中浮游有孔虫的"同位素温度"（根据碳酸钙的同位素组成计算出的温度）与表层海水的实际温度，对该假设进行了验证。他发现上述温度之间吻合地很好，并由此得出结论认为浮游有孔虫可以用于古温度研究。该方法已经在沉积物质中多次重复验证，并得到了相似的结论 [6,10,19,20]。然而，根据利用拖网采集到的活体浮游有孔

sediments with similar conclusions[6,10,19,20]. However, isotopic temperatures calculated for living planktonic foraminifera that were collected by plankton net tows were almost always significantly higher than those observed in the water in which they were collected[12–18]. It has been proposed that these nonequilibrium isotopic compositions are caused by introduction of metabolic $CO_2$ into the carbonate skeletons, a phenomenon that has been reported in other carbonate depositing organisms, including benthic foraminifera[21,22] and in part was attributed to metabolic activity of symbiotic algae[21]. Attempts to resolve the problems using foraminifera collected in sediment traps did not reach unequivocal conclusions[18,23], and thus palaeoclimatic determinations based on oxygen-isotope compositions of planktonic foraminifera became uncertain.

The ability to culture planktonic foraminifera in the laboratory[24] opened the possibility of resolving this problem experimentally. A detailed account of the entire experiment will be reported elsewhere[25]. Briefly, young (roughly 10-day old) individuals of the planktonic foraminifer *G. sacculifer* were collected from surface water in the Gulf of Eilat using plankton nets. Each individual was cultured in an 100-ml Erlenmeyer flask with 80 ml of filtered seawater and was fed daily by one newly hatched brine shrimp. The Erlenmeyer flasks were kept in temperature controlled baths where the deviations from the desired temperature did not exceed 0.1 °C (based on three daily accurate thermometer readings, and a continuous monitoring of temperature on strip chart recorder). Salinities were monitored every 2 days to ensure that there was no water evaporation. The growth of the foraminifera was monitored daily using an inverted microscope. All individuals considered in this experiment reached maturity and went through reproduction by producing gametes. The average initial weight of these foraminifers was ~5 μg per individual and the final weight was ~45μg per individual. Thus ~90% of the carbonate shells was deposited in controlled conditions. A correction for the original (10% weight) isotopic composition was made using control groups for which the isotopic composition was determined separately. Each experiment lasted roughly 2 weeks; the range of experimental temperatures was between 14 and 30 °C, and in each run there were 2 or 3 different temperatures. Because only individuals that went through gametogenic reproduction were used for the final isotopic analysis, there was no need to clean the protoplasma from the shell. During the process of gametogenesis[24], the entire organic matter has been extruded naturally from the shell and the skeleton that is left behind is white, organic matter free and very similar to material from sediments. Yet before analysis the individuals were crushed in ethanol, dried, vacuum roasted for 30 min at 450 °C. The analysis was carried out according to the method of Shackleton[26] using a VG602 Micromass spectrometer. The water isotopic composition was determined according to the procedure of Epstein and Mayeda[27].

The isotopic temperatures were calculated according to the equation of Epstein *et al.*[1] as modified by Craig[28]

$$pt = 16.9 - 4.2 \left(\delta^{18}O_c - \delta^{18}O_w\right) + 0.13 \left(\delta^{18}O_c - \delta^{18}O_w\right)^2$$

where *pt* is the isotopic temperature and $\delta^{18}O_c$ and $\delta^{18}O_w$ are the isotopic composition of the carbonate and seawater respectively.

1056

虫计算出的同位素温度却几乎总是明显高于在它们所生活的水体中观测到的温度[12-18]。已有学者提出这些不平衡的同位素组成是由碳酸盐壳体中代谢二氧化碳的引入造成的，有报道指出这一现象在包括底栖有孔虫[21,22]在内的其他碳酸盐沉积生物中也存在；此外在某种程度上共生藻类的代谢活动也对此有影响[21]。利用沉积物捕获器采集到的浮游有孔虫尝试来解决上述问题却并未得到明确的结论[18,23]，因此，根据浮游有孔虫的氧同位素组成来确定古气候的方法也变得不确定了。

在实验室内培养浮游有孔虫[24]使得用实验方法解决这一问题成为可能。关于整个实验的详细描述将另文发表[25]。简单来讲就是：利用浮游生物网从埃拉特湾表层水体采集浮游有孔虫 *G. sacculifer* 的幼体（约10天大），将每个个体置于盛有80 ml 过滤海水的100 ml 锥形烧瓶中培养，每天喂食一只刚刚孵化出的卤虫。这些锥形瓶都放在可以进行温度控制的水浴中，该水浴的温度与其所需温度间的偏差不会超过 0.1℃（该结果是根据三个精密温度计每日读数和一个长图记录仪的连续观测温度得出的）。每两天监测一次盐度，以保证没有水分蒸发。用倒置显微镜每天监测有孔虫的长势。该实验中所涉及的个体都发育成熟，并进行配子生殖。这些有孔虫每个平均初始重量约5 µg，每个成年个体最终重量约45 µg。因此，约90%的碳酸盐壳体是在受控环境下沉积的。利用单独测定的对照组对其初始（10%重量）同位素组成进行校正。每次实验大约持续两周，实验温度在14℃到30℃之间，并且每次实验包含2到3个不同的温度组。由于只有通过配子生殖的个体才用于最终的同位素分析，因此没有必要对壳体的原生质进行清除。在配子发育过程中[24]，全部有机质都已从壳体中自然排出，留下的外壳呈白色，不包含有机质，而且与沉积物中的成分非常相似。在分析之前，需先将个体在酒精中压碎、干燥，并在450℃真空条件下烘烤30分钟。根据沙克尔顿[26]的实验方法，采用VG602超微质谱仪进行分析。水的同位素组成是根据爱泼斯坦和梅耶达[27]提出的方法确定的。

根据如下方程计算同位素温度，该方程是经克雷格[28]改进后的爱泼斯坦等人[1]的方程：

$$pt = 16.9 - 4.2\ (\delta^{18}O_c - \delta^{18}O_w) + 0.13\ (\delta^{18}O_c - \delta^{18}O_w)^2$$

其中，$pt$ 为同位素温度，$\delta^{18}O_c$ 和 $\delta^{18}O_w$ 分别为碳酸盐和海水的同位素组成。

The isotopic temperature and the actual culture temperature are compared in Fig. 1. A remarkable fit exists between the isotopic and the actual temperatures. The line of best fit using linear regression has the following parameters:

$$t = -0.07 + 1.01pt$$

where $t$ and $pt$ are the actual and the isotopic temperatures, respectively. The correlation coefficient ($r$) for this linear regression equals 0.95. Ideally, the intercept and the slope should have been 0.0 and 1.0, respectively. The values that we obtained (−0.07 and 1.01) are almost identical to those expected, and would cause only a slight deviation of <1% in palaeotemperature determinations in the range of 14-30 °C.

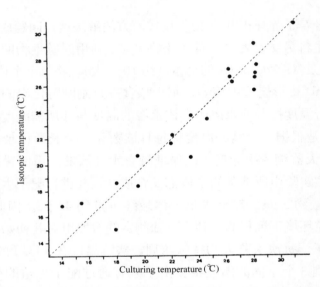

Fig. 1. The isotopic temperature calculated from the oxygen-isotope composition of the shell carbonate of the foraminifer *G. sacculifer* according to the modified equation of Epstein *et al.*[1] plotted against the actual temperature in which the foraminifers were cultured. The dashed line represents the ideal fit between the two temperatures having a slope of 1.0 and an intercept of 0. The best linear fit to the data is a line having slope and intercept of 1.01 and −0.07, respectively, having a correlation coefficient of $r = 0.95$. These experimental data demonstrate the *G. sacculifer* deposits its skeleton close to oxygen isotopic equilibrium, and that the common palaeotemperature equation for molluscs is applicable for this planktonic foraminifer.

We therefore conclude that the planktonic foraminifer *G. sacculifer* fractionate oxygen isotopes with changing temperatures according to the modified equation of Epstein *et al.*[1] that was originally developed for molluscs. Accurate palaeotemperature determinations that are based on *G. sacculifer* isotopic composition should still take into consideration the isotopic composition of seawater and the vertical migration of this species during its ontogeny[12,23]. The nonequilibrium values that have been observed in plankton samples deserve further investigation, but it is not unlikely that they were caused by vacuum roasting of the samples before analysis, which was intended to remove organic contaminants.

同位素温度和实际的培养温度比较见图 1，两者之间存在高度吻合。利用线性回归得到的最佳拟合线具有如下参数：

$$t = -0.07 + 1.01pt$$

其中 $t$ 和 $pt$ 分别为实际温度和同位素温度。该线性回归方程的相关系数（$r$）等于 0.95。理想状态下，截距和斜率应分别为 0.0 和 1.0。这里我们得到的值（−0.07 和 1.01）与理想状态几乎一致，在测定 14~30 ℃的古温度时，其产生的微小偏差小于 1%。

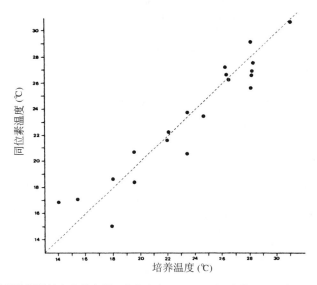

图 1. 根据改进的爱泼斯坦等人[1]的方程，由有孔虫 *G. sacculifer* 壳体碳酸盐中氧同位素组成计算出的同位素温度相对于有孔虫培养环境的实际温度的变化。虚线表示两温度之间的理想拟合线，其斜率为 1.0，截距为 0。测定数据的最佳线性拟合直线的斜率和截距分别为 1.01 和 −0.07，相关系数 $r$ = 0.95。这些实验数据证明 *G. sacculifer* 的壳体沉积接近氧同位素平衡，软体动物的通用古温度方程适用于该浮游有孔虫。

因此，我们认为浮游有孔虫 *G. sacculifer* 随温度的变化对氧同位素的分馏遵从改进后的爱泼斯坦等人[1]的方程，而这一方程最初是针对软体动物提出来的。依据 *G. sacculifer* 同位素组成确定精确的古温度还应考虑海水的同位素组成和个体发育期间该种类的垂直迁移[12,23]。浮游生物样本中观测到的不平衡值有待进一步研究，但这种不平衡也有可能是样品分析前为移除有机污染物而进行的真空烘干造成的。

Our experiment provides more data points to the palaeotemperature equation at the temperature range where it was lacking (14-30 °C) and substantiates the results of earlier palaeoenvironmental studies based on the oxygen-isotope composition of planktonic foraminifera.

We thank A. Szin and A. Shemesh for technical assistance.

(**297**, 220-222; 1982)

Jonathan Erez* and Boaz Luz[†]
* The Hebrew University of Jerusalem, The H. Steinitz Marine Biology Laboratory, Eilat, PO Box 469, Israel
[†] The Hebrew University of Jerusalem, Department of Geology, Jerusalem, Israel

Received 14 December 1981; accepted 15 March 1982.

References:

1. Epstein, S., Buchsbaum, R., Lowenstam, H. A. & Urey, H. C. *Bull. Geol. Soc. Am.* **64**, 1315-1326 (1953).
2. Emiliani, C. *Am. J. Sci.* **252**, 149-158 (1954); *J. Geol.* **63**, 538-578 (1955).
3. Emiliani, C. *J. Geol.* **74**, 102-126 (1966).
4. Shackleton, N. J. & Opdyke, N. D. *Quat. Res.* **3**, 39-55 (1973); *Geol. Soc. Am. Mem.* **145**, 449-464 (1976).
5. Imbrie, J., Van Donk, J. & Kipp, N. G. *Quat. Res.* **3**, 10-38 (1973).
6. Shackleton, N. J. & Vincent, E. *Mar. Micropaleont.* **3**, (1978).
7. Deuser, W. G., Ross, E. H. & Waterman, L. S. *Science* **191**, 1168-1170 (1976).
8. Vergnaud-Grazzini, C., Ryan, W. B. F. & Cita, M. B. *Mar. Micropaleont.* **2**, 353-370 (1977).
9. Williams, D. F., Thunell, R. C. & Kennett, J. P. *Science* **201**, 252-254(1978).
10. Berger, W. H., Killingley, J. S. & Vincent, E. *Oceanol. Acta* **1**, 203-216 (1978).
11. Reiss, Z. *et al. Quat. Res.* **14**, 294-308 (1980).
12. Van Donk, J. thesis, Columbia Univ., New York (1970).
13. Van Donk, J. *Oceanic Micropaleontology* (ed. Ramsay, A. T. S.), 1345-1370 (Academic, New York, 1977).
14. Shackleton, N. J., Wiseman, J. D. & Buckley, H. A. *Nature* **242**, 177-179 (1973).
15. Kahn, M. I. *Oceanol. Acta* **2**, 195-208 (1979).
16. Kahn, M. I. & Williams, D. F. *Paleogeogr. Paleoclimatol. Paleoecol.* **33**, 47-69 (1981).
17. Duplessy, J. C., Be, A. W. H. & Blank, P. L. *Paleogeogr. Paleoclimatol. Paleoecol.* **33**, 9-46 (1981).
18. Deuser, W. G., Ross, E. H., Hemleben, C. & Spindler, M. *Paleogeogr. Paleoclimatol. Paleoecol.* **33**, 103-127 (1981).
19. Lidz, B., Kehm, A. & Miller, H. *Nature* **217**, 245-247 (1968).
20. Savin, S. M. & Douglas, R. G. *Bull. Geol. Soc. Am.* **84**, 2327-2342 (1973).
21. Erez, J. *Nature* **273**, 199-202 (1978).
22. Vinot-Bertuille, A. C. & Duplessy, J. C. *Earth Planet Sci. Lett.* **18**, 247-252 (1973).
23. Erez, J. & Honjo, S. *Paleogeogr. Paleoclimatol. Paleoecol.* **33**, 129-156 (1981).
24. Be, A. W. H. *et al. Micropaleontology* **23**, 155-179 (1977).
25. Erez, J. & Luz, B., *Geochim. Cosmochim. Acta* (submitted).
26. Shackelton, N. J. *Colloqu. Int. Cent. Natn. Rech. Scient.* No. 219, 203-209 (1973).
27. Epstein, S. & Mayeda, T. *Geochim. Cosmochim. Acta* **4**, 213-224 (1953).
28. Craig. H. *Proc. Spoleto Conf. on Stable Isotopes in Oceanographic Studies and Paleotemperatures* Vol. 3 (ed. Tongiorgi, E.) (1965).

我们的实验结果为古环境方程没有涉及的温度范围（14~30℃）提供了更多的数据，并且证实了早期根据浮游有孔虫的氧同位素组成得到的古环境研究结果。

感谢辛和西麦斯提供的技术协助。

（齐红艳 翻译；李三忠 审稿）

# Human EJ Bladder Carcinoma Oncogene is Homologue of Harvey Sarcoma Virus *ras* Gene

L. F. Parada *et al.*

## Editor's Note

Here US cancer researcher Robert Weinberg and colleagues reveal that two seemingly very different types of cancer-causing "oncogene" are in fact very similar at the DNA level. One of the oncogenes, *ras*, was previously identified as the cancer-causing agent in the Harvey sarcoma virus. The other triggers cancerous growth of bladder cells in an entirely non-viral context. Their homology suggested that both types of oncogene might be derived from the same benign, cellular genetic element or "proto-oncogene", and that a single proto-oncogene can be activated by different molecular processes. The concept that proto-oncogenes can become cancer-causing when mutated is now well accepted, and all it takes for the normal *ras* gene to become activated is mutation of a single base.

Examination of homologies between retroviral oncogenes and transforming sequences defined by transfection reveals that the human bladder carcinoma (EJ) oncogene is homologous to the Harvey sarcoma virus oncogene (*ras*). Structural analysis limits the region of homology to a 3.0-kilobase *Sac*I fragment of the EJ oncogene. Both EJ and *ras* DNA probes detect similar transcripts in transfectants derived from bladder carcinoma cell lines.

TWO groups of cellular oncogenes have been discovered during the past decade. The first consists of genes that were characterized by virtue of their association with retroviruses. The prototype of this class is the *src* gene of avian sarcoma virus. Several experiments have indicated that this gene was acquired from the chicken genome by an avian retrovirus, and has been exploited by the chimaeric virus to transform cells[1,2]. Once incorporated into the viral genome, expression of the *src* gene is driven by viral controlling elements and is no longer responsive to control mechanisms that governed its expression while in the cellular chromosome. In addition to the *src* gene, this group includes at least 12 other gene sequences, each associated with a different chimaeric retrovirus[3,4]. These genes are conserved over great evolutionary distances[2,5] implying that they mediate essential cellular or organismic functions.

A second class of cellular transforming genes has been detected by the experimental route of DNA transfection. Recent reports have indicated that the DNAs of some non-virally induced tumour cell lines can induce transformation when applied to mouse

# 人类EJ膀胱癌癌基因是哈维肉瘤病毒*ras*基因的同源基因

帕拉达等

**编者按**

美国癌症研究人员罗伯特·温伯格和他的同事指出，两种看似非常不同的引发癌症的"癌基因"在DNA水平上实际上是非常相似的。*ras*作为一种癌基因，之前就已被鉴定为哈维肉瘤病毒的致癌因子；而另外一种癌基因则在完全无病毒的环境下仍可以触发膀胱细胞的癌变。它们的同源性说明两个类型的癌基因可能起源于同一良性基因，即相同的细胞遗传元件或者"原癌基因"，且单一的原癌基因可以通过不同的分子过程激活。当突变发生时，原癌基因就变为致癌性的，这个观点现已广为接受；且仅仅只是某个单一碱基的突变就足以导致正常*ras*基因被激活。

---

逆转录病毒癌基因和通过转染确定的转化序列的同源性研究显示人类膀胱癌（EJ）癌基因是哈维肉瘤病毒癌基因（*ras*）的同源基因。结构分析将该同源区域限定在EJ癌基因的一个3,000个碱基对的*Sac*I片段上。在膀胱癌细胞系内，用EJ和*ras* DNA探针检测到了相似的转录物。

---

在过去的十年里，人们发现了两组不同的细胞癌基因。第一组由与逆转录病毒关联为特点的基因组成。这一类的原型是禽肉瘤病毒的*src*基因。多个实验表明该基因是通过禽类逆转录病毒从鸡基因组中获得的，并被这个嵌合型病毒利用来转化细胞[1,2]。一旦整合到病毒基因组中，*src*基因的表达就由病毒的控制元件驱动，而不再受细胞染色体中支配其表达的控制机制的影响。除了*src*基因之外，这一组基因还包括至少12个其他基因序列，每一个都与不同的嵌合型逆转录病毒相关[3,4]。这些基因即使在较远的进化距离上也非常保守[2,5]，表明它们介导着非常重要的细胞学或者生物学功能。

通过DNA转染的实验方法检测到了第二类细胞转化基因。最近的报告指出，一些非病毒诱导的肿瘤细胞系的DNA在导入小鼠单层成纤维细胞后能够诱导其转

fibroblast monolayers. These tumour cell lines are derived from chemically induced animal tumours[6-9] and from human tumours of spontaneous origin[7,10-12].

The two classes of oncogenes have many properties in common, the most striking of which is the apparent origin of both types of genes from normally benign, cellular genetic elements. Because of this and other parallels, we undertook a search to determine whether the two groups of genes shared any members in common. Such overlap would have far-reaching consequences for our understanding of the mechanisms of viral and non-viral carcinogenesis.

### Detection of Homologies by Nucleic Acid Hybridization

The search for relatedness between the two groups of genes depended on detection of nucleic acid sequence homologies between individual members of each group. One group consisted of a series of seven retrovirus-associated *onc* genes known to be unrelated or only distantly related to one another[4]. The other group studied was a collection of seven tumour oncogenes that had been defined by transfection[7,10]. Nucleic acid sequence probes have been derived for the retrovirus-associated genes, whereas only a few of the transfection-derived genes have been isolated in the form of molecular clones. We therefore used the virus-derived *onc* probes to survey the DNAs of cells which had acquired, via transfection, copies of the second class of genes. The survey was performed using the Southern gel-filter transfer procedure[13]. Virus-derived *onc* probes were from several sources (see Table 1).

Table 1. Oncogene probes

| Oncogene ‡ | Related virus or tumour | Clone | Sequence complexity | Source | Ref. |
|---|---|---|---|---|---|
| v-*abl* | Murine Abelson leukaemia virus | pAblsub9 | 3.0kbp | J. Y. J. Wang and D. Baltimore | * |
| v-*erb* | Avian erythroblastosis virus | PAE-*Pvu*II | 2.5kbp | T. Gonda and J. M. Bishop | 28 |
| v-ST-*fes* | Snyder-Theilen feline sarcoma virus | PST-3 | 0.6kbp | C. Sherr | 29 |
| c-Ha-*ras*l (rat) | Murine Harvey sarcoma virus | LHXB-3 | 2.3kbp | R. Ellis and E. Scolnick | 30 |
| v-Ha-*ras* | Murine Harvey sarcoma virus | BS9 | 0.45kbp | R. Ellis and E. Scolnick | 21 |
| c-*mos*(Human) | Murine Moloney sarcoma virus | pHM1 | 2.75kbp | G. Vande Woude | † |
| v-*myc* | Avian myelocytomatosis virus | puMyC3-*Pst* | 1.5kbp | T. Gonda and J. M. Bishop | 31 |
| v-*src* | Avian sarcoma virus | SRA-2 | 0.8kbp | T. Gonda and J. M. Bishop | 32 |
| | Human EJ bladder carcinoma | pEJ6.6 | 6.6kbp | C. Shih | 18 |

* J. Y. J. Wang and D. Baltimore, in preparation. † G. Vande Woude, personal communication. ‡ v-indicates viral gene; c-indicates cellular gene.

We used each retrovirus-related *onc* probe to search for novel cross-reacting fragments in each of several transfectants. For example, an analysis using the v-*abl* probe is shown in Fig. 1: lane *a* represents the endogenous mouse sequences detected in the DNA of

化。这些肿瘤细胞系来自化学诱导的动物肿瘤 [6-9] 和人类自发形成的肿瘤 [7,10-12]。

这两类癌基因有许多共同的特性，其中最突出的就是两种基因显然皆起源于正常良性的细胞遗传元件。由于这个以及其他类似的原因，我们试图探究确定这两种基因是否具有共同的组分。这种基因间的重叠可能对我们了解病毒以及非病毒致癌过程的机制具有深远的意义。

## 通过核酸杂交检测同源性

探求两组基因之间的相关性要依靠每组个体成员之间核酸序列同源性的检测。其中一组由七个与逆转录病毒相关的 *onc* 基因组成，并且已知这七个基因之间彼此无关联或者关系甚远 [4]。另一组用于研究的基因经转染已被确定为七个肿瘤癌基因的集合 [7,10]。逆转录病毒相关基因的核酸序列探针已经获得，但是仅有少量转染得到的基因以分子克隆的形式被分离出来。因此，我们使用病毒来源的 *onc* 探针进行DNA印迹分析来检测那些通过转染获得的第二类基因拷贝的细胞的 DNA[13]。病毒 *onc* 探针有多种来源（见表1）。

表 1. 癌基因探针

| 癌基因‡ | 相关病毒或肿瘤 | 克隆 | 序列复杂性 | 来源 | 参考文献 |
|---|---|---|---|---|---|
| v-*abl* | 鼠艾贝尔森白血病病毒 | pAblsub9 | 3.0 kbp | 王和巴尔的摩 | * |
| v-*erb* | 鸟类成红细胞增多症病毒 | PAE-*PvuII* | 2.5 kbp | 贡达和毕晓普 | 28 |
| v-ST-*fes* | 猫科肉瘤病毒 | PST-3 | 0.6 kbp | 谢尔 | 29 |
| c-Ha-*ras*1( 大鼠 ) | 鼠哈维肉瘤病毒 | LHXB-3 | 2.3 kbp | 埃利斯和斯科尼克 | 30 |
| v-Ha-*ras* | 鼠哈维肉瘤病毒 | BS9 | 0.45 kbp | 埃利斯和斯科尼克 | 21 |
| c-*mos*( 人 ) | 鼠莫洛尼肉瘤病毒 | pHM1 | 2.75 kbp | 范德伍德 | † |
| v-*myc* | 鸟类成髓细胞增生症病毒 | puMyC3-*Pst* | 1.5 kbp | 贡达和毕晓普 | 31 |
| v-*src* | 鸟类肉瘤病毒 | SRA-2 | 0.8 kbp | 贡达和毕晓普 | 32 |
|  | 人类 EJ 膀胱癌 | pEJ6.6 | 6.6 kbp | 施 | 18 |

* 王和巴尔的摩，论文撰写中；† 范德伍德，个人交流；‡ v- 表示病毒基因，c- 表示细胞基因。

我们使用每个逆转录病毒相关 *onc* 基因探针在众多转染子中逐个搜索新的交叉反应片段。比如，图 1 显示了用 v-*abl* 探针进行的分析：泳道 *a* 表示用 v-*abl* 探针在未转染的小鼠成纤维细胞 NIH 3T3 细胞 DNA 中检测到的内源性小鼠序列。这些

untransfected NIH 3T3 cells by the v-*abl* sequence probe. These "background" bands of 28, 10 and 6 kilobases (kb) were also found in the DNAs of all transfectants (Fig. 1, lanes *b, d-g* and *i*). Figure 1*c* shows detection of the human homologue of the v-*abl* probe; lanes *d-g* show an analysis of DNAs of mouse cells transfected with four different human oncogenes. None of the DNAs contains any fragments beyond those present in the untransfected mouse control (lane *a*). We concluded that none of these transfected cells acquired the human homologue of the v-*abl* sequence. From a similar analysis in lanes *h* and *i*, we concluded that the rabbit bladder carcinoma oncogene is also not related to the *abl* gene. A more equivocal interpretation came from analysis of the DNA of a mouse cell transfected with a mouse fibroblast oncogene (Fig. 1*a, b*). Due to the lack of species-specific fragment markers, we were unable to rule out the identity of the *abl* and fibroblast oncogene. However, knowledge of their restriction enzyme cleavage sites excludes identity[14,15].

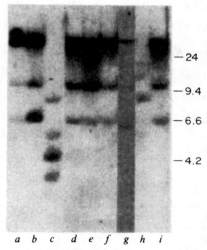

Fig. 1. Southern blot analysis of digested cellular DNAs from various transfectants probed with v-*abl* specific probe (see Table 1). 10 µg of each DNA were digested with endonuclease *Eco*RI, fractionated by electrophoresis through a 1% agarose gel and transferred to nitrocellulose paper[13]. The filters were incubated with $5 \times 10^6$ c.p.m. of nick-translated[39] [32]P-labelled Abelson virus specific probe. The DNAs analysed were from the following cell lines: *a*, NIH 3T3; *b*, Y5-1; *c*, HeLa; *d*, A5-2; *e*, SH-1-1; *f*, SW-2-1; *g*, EJ-6-1; *h*, rabbit embryo fibroblast; *i*, RBC-1. Lanes *a-f* and *h*, *i* are from one filter; *g* is from a different filter. The transfected cell lines are described in Table 2. Migration of *Hind*III-digested λ DNA fragments are shown at the right (in kilobase pairs, kbp).

Figure 2 shows a further Southern blot analysis of DNAs that were prepared from several cell lines derived by transfection of NIH 3T3 cells with DNAs of human tumour cell lines. The probe used was the rat cellular homologue of Harvey sarcoma virus, c-Ha-*ras*1, given by R. Ellis and E. Scolnick[16,17]. A novel fragment of 9.5 kb was found in the DNA of a mouse cell transfected with DNA of the EJ human bladder carcinoma cell line (Fig. 2*c*). In contrast, no novel fragments were present in the transfectants derived from other tumour cell lines (Fig. 2*d-g*).

28kb、10kb、6kb 的背景条带在所有的转染子 DNA 中都能找到（图 1，泳道 *b*、*d~g* 和 *i*）。图 1*c* 为使用 v-*abl* 探针对人类同源基因的检测结果；泳道 *d~g* 为四种不同的人类癌基因转染的小鼠细胞 DNA 的分析结果。结果显示这些 DNA 仅含有未转染的对照小鼠中含有的 DNA 片段（泳道 *a*）。因此我们的结论是：这些转染的细胞都没有获得 v-*abl* 序列的人类同源基因。对泳道 *h* 和 *i* 进行类似的分析，我们得出结论：兔膀胱癌癌基因也与 *abl* 基因无关。但是，对转染了小鼠成纤维细胞癌基因的小鼠细胞的 DNA 进行分析只能得到更为模棱两可的解释（图 1*a*，*b*）。由于缺乏物种特异性的片段标记物，我们不能排除 *abl* 和成纤维细胞癌基因是同一个基因的可能性。但是，对它们限制性内切酶酶切位点的分析结果排除了这种同一性[14,15]。

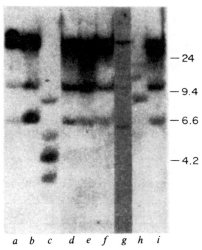

图 1. 用 v-*abl* 特异性探针对被消化的多个转染子来源的细胞 DNA 的 DNA 印迹分析结果（见表 1）。每种 DNA 取 10 μg，用核酸内切酶 *Eco*RI 进行酶切，经 1% 琼脂糖凝胶电泳分离后转移到硝酸纤维素膜上[13]。滤膜与 5×10⁶ c.p.m. 切口平移法[39] 制备的 ³²P 标记的艾贝尔森病毒特异性探针一起温育。所分析的 DNA 来源于以下细胞系：*a*，NIH 3T3；*b*，Y5-1；*c*，HeLa；*d*，A5-2；*e*，SH-1-1；*f*，SW-2-1；*g*，EJ-6-1；*h*，兔胚胎成纤维细胞；*i*，RBC-1。泳道 *a~f* 和 *h*，*i* 来源于同一滤膜，*g* 来源于另一张滤膜。表 2 描述了转染的细胞系，右侧显示了 *Hind*III 消化的 λ DNA 片段的迁移情况（以千碱基对，即 kbp 为单位）。

图 2 显示了用人类肿瘤细胞系的 DNA 转染 NIH 3T3 细胞获得的多个细胞系的 DNA 的进一步 DNA 印迹分析结果。实验使用的探针是埃利斯和斯科尔尼克提供的哈维肉瘤病毒的大鼠细胞同源基因 c-Ha-*ras*1 [16,17]。我们在人类 EJ 膀胱癌细胞系 DNA 转染的小鼠细胞 DNA 中找到了一个长度为 9.5 kb 的新片段（图 2*c*）。与此相反的是，在其他肿瘤细胞系获得的转染子中则没有发现新的片段（图 2*d~g*）。

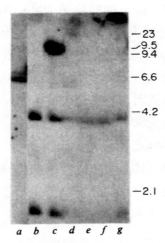

Fig. 2. Southern blot analysis of DNA from transfected cells with rat cellular *ras* probe (c-Ha-*ras*1). [32]P-labelled c-Ha-*ras*1 DNA was prepared as described in Fig. 1 legend and incubated with a filter carrying BamHI-digested DNAs from the following cell lines: *a*, HeLa; *b*, NIH 3T3; *c*, EJ-6-1; *d*, A5-2; *e*, SH-1-1; *f*, SW-2-1; *g*, HL-60-9. Lanes *b-g* are from the same filter. The cell lines are described in Table 2.

Of the seven *onc* probes used in this survey, only one detected the presence of novel DNA fragments in transfection-derived cell lines. The results of this comparative oncogene survey are summarized in Table 2. Below we consider the relationship between the c-Ha-*ras*1 gene and the human bladder carcinoma gene suggested by Fig. 2.

Table 2. Comparison of transfected oncogenes with retrovial *onc* probes

| *onc* Probes | | | | | | Transfected celll lines | | |
|---|---|---|---|---|---|---|---|---|
| | Y5-1-1 | EJ-6-1 | A5-2 | SH-1-1 | SW-2-1 | HL60-1-9 | B104-1-1 | RBC-1 |
| v-*abl* | * | − | − | − | − | − | NT | − |
| v-*erb* | * | − | − | − | − | − | NT | NT |
| v-*fes* | * | − | − | − | − | − | − | NT |
| c-Ha-*ras*1(rat) | * | + | − | − | − | − | − | NT |
| c-*mos* (Human) | * | − | NT | NT | − | − | NT | NT |
| v-*myc* | * | − | − | − | − | − | − | NT |
| v-*src* | * | − | − | NT | − | − | NT | − |

The oncogene probes shown are described in Table 1. The transfected cell lines listed are of the following origins: Y5-1-1 is derived from two serial passages of the oncogenic DNA from a 3-methylcholantherene-induced mouse fibroblast cell line, MCA-16 (refs 6, 33); EJ-6-1 is a secondary transfected cell line derived from DNA of a human bladder carcinoma cell line, EJ[7]; A5-2 is a primary transfected cell line derived from human lung carcinoma cell line, A549 (ref. 34); SH-1-1 is a secondary transfected cell line derived from DNA from human neuroblastoma cell line, SK-N-SH (J. Føgh, personal communication); SW-2-1 is a secondary transfected cell line derived from human colon carcinoma cell line, SW-480 (refs 10, 35); HL60-1-9 is a secondary transfected cell line derived from human leukaemia cell line, HL60 (refs 10, 36); B104-1-1 is a secondary transfected cell line derived from rat neuroblastoma cell line, B104 (refs 7, 37); RBC-1 is a primary transfected cell line derived from rabbit bladder carcinoma cell line, RBC[7,38]. + Indicates hybridization of the probe to novel bands in addition to hybridization with NIH 3T3 cellular sequences; − indicates a well controlled negative correlation. * Apparent negative correlation that is not based on species-specific

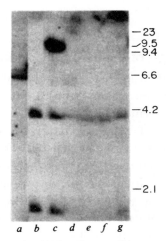

*a b c d e f g*

图 2. 用大鼠细胞 *ras* 探针（c-Ha-*ras*1）对转染细胞 DNA 进行 DNA 印迹分析。将如图 1 注中所述方法制备的 $^{32}$P 标记的 c-Ha-*ras*1 DNA 与含有 *Bam*HI 消化的来源于如下细胞系的 DNA 的滤膜放在一起进行孵育：*a*, HeLa；*b*, NIH 3T3；*c*, EJ-6-1；*d*, A5-2；*e*, SH-1-1；*f*, SW-2-1；*g*, HL-60-9。泳道 *b~g* 来自同一滤膜。表 2 描述了相关细胞系。

这个研究中使用的七个 *onc* 探针中，只有一个在转染细胞系中检测到了新的 DNA 片段。表 2 总结了癌基因检测比较的研究结果。下面我们讨论图 2 揭示的 c-Ha-*ras*1 基因与人膀胱癌基因的关系。

表 2. 逆转录病毒 *onc* 探针对转染癌基因的比较

| *onc* 探针 | | | | | | 转染细胞系 | | |
|---|---|---|---|---|---|---|---|---|
| | Y5-1-1 | EJ-6-1 | A5-2 | SH-1-1 | SW-2-1 | HL60-1-9 | B104-1-1 | RBC-1 |
| v-*abl* | * | – | – | – | – | – | NT | – |
| v-*erb* | * | – | – | – | – | – | NT | NT |
| v-*fes* | * | – | – | – | – | – | – | NT |
| c-Ha-*ras*1（大鼠） | * | + | – | – | – | – | – | NT |
| c-*mos*（人） | * | – | NT | NT | – | – | NT | NT |
| v-*myc* | * | – | – | – | – | – | – | NT |
| v-*src* | * | – | – | NT | – | – | NT | – |

表中显示的癌基因探针在表 1 中描述过。所列出的转染细胞系来源如下：Y5-1-1 是用 3– 甲基胆蒽诱导的小鼠成纤维细胞系 MCA-16（参考文献 6,33）致癌 DNA 两次连续传代得到的细胞系；EJ-6-1 是从人膀胱癌细胞系 EJ[7] DNA 得到的二级转染细胞系；A5-2 是从人肺癌细胞系 A549（参考文献 34）得到的一级转染细胞系；SH-1-1 是从人神经母细胞瘤细胞系 SK-N-SH（福格，个人交流）DNA 得到的二级转染细胞系；SW-2-1 是从人结肠癌细胞系 SW-480（参考文献 10，35）得到的二级转染细胞系；HL60-1-9 是从人白血病细胞系 HL60（参考文献 10,36）得到的二级转染细胞系；B104-1-1 是从大鼠神经母细胞瘤细胞系 B104（参考文献 7，37）得到的二级转染细胞系；RBC-1 是从兔膀胱癌细胞系 RBC[7,38] 得到的一级转染细胞系。+ 表示除了与 NIH 3T3 细胞序列杂交外，探针还能与新的条带杂交；– 表示完全匹配的阴性对照。* 表示不基于可以区分受体细胞中固有染色体 DNA 与供体 DNA 的物种特异性 DNA 片段大小的阴性对照。NT 指未检测。

DNA fragment sizes that distinguish donor DNAs from resident chromosomal DNAs of the recipient cells. NT, not tested.

## Homology of the Two Oncogene DNAs

A series of tests was performed to further substantiate the relationship between the EJ bladder oncogene and the c-*ras* oncogene. Figure 3*A* shows that nine cell lines derived by transfection of EJ bladder carcinoma DNA have all acquired novel DNA fragments reactive with the c-Ha-*ras*1 probe. DNA from untransfected mouse cells (Fig. 3*A*, lane *a*) does not exhibit any of these novel fragments. The *Bam*HI-digested DNAs of the various transfectants exhibit differently sized novel fragments because of rearrangements occurring during the transfection process. Note that the oncogene of the T24 human bladder carcinoma is closely related to that of the EJ bladder carcinoma[18,19]. Figure 3*A*, lane *m*, indicates that a mouse transfectant carrying the T24 oncogene also contains in its DNA a novel acquired fragment reactive with the probe.

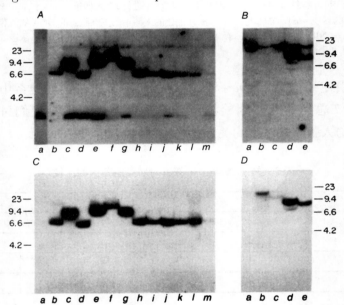

Fig. 3. Analysis of DNAs from EJ and T24 transfectants using the c-Ha-*ras*1 and EJ oncogene probes. DNAs were digested with endonuclease *Bam*HI (*A, C*) or *Eco*RI (*B, D*) and analysed as described in Fig. 1 legend. The filters shown *A* and *B* were incubated with $5 \times 10^6$ c.p.m. of c-Ha-*ras*1 DNA probe ($2 \times 10^8$ c.p.m. $\mu g^{-1}$) and exposed for autoradiography for 16 h. The adsorbed $^{32}$P-labelled probe was removed from the filters by washing in 0.1 M NaOH, 0.5 M NaCl, 1.0 mM EDTA. The washed filters were exposed to film for 48 h to verify that all the radioactive signal had been removed (not shown). The filters were then incubated with $5 \times 10^6$ c.p.m. of nick-translated pEJ6.6 DNA ($6 \times 10^7$ c.p.m. $\mu g^{-1}$). *C* and *D* represent autoradiography after 16 h. The DNAs analysed in panels *A* and *C* were from the following cell lines: *a*, NIH 3T3; *b*, HeLa; *c*, EJ-6-1; *d*, EJ-2-R1; *e*, EJ-2-R5; *f*, E-4-R4-B; *g*, EJ-6-1; *h*, EJ-6-2-R; *i*, EJ-6-3; *j*, EJ-1-2; *k*, EJ-3-2; *l*, T-24 human cells[19]; *m*, T24-8-5. *B* and *D* display DNAs from: *a*, NIH cells; *b*, HeLa cells; *c*, EJ-6-2 (*Bam*)-1 cells; *d*, EJ-6-2(*Bam*)-2 cells; *e*, EJ-4(*Bam*)-1 cells. In *A* and *C*, lanes *c-f* and *h-k* represent DNA from cell lines that were derived from independent serial transfections of the EJ tumour cell oncogene; lanes *g* and *c* are duplicates. Lane *l* contains DNA from human bladder carcinoma cell line T24. Lane *m* contains DNA from a secondary transfectant of T24. Lanes *c-e* of *B* and *D* show an analysis of DNAs from tertiary transfectants induced by exposure to *Bam*HI-cleaved secondary transfectant DNA.

## 两个癌基因 DNA 的同源性

　　人们进行了一系列的检测来进一步证实 EJ 膀胱癌癌基因与 c-ras 癌基因之间的相关性。图 3A 显示了 EJ 膀胱癌 DNA 转染的 9 个细胞系都获得了能与 c-Ha-ras1 探针反应的新 DNA 片段。而未转染的小鼠细胞 DNA（图 3A，泳道 a）不存在任何新片段。由于在转染过程中发生了重排，不同转染子的 DNA 在被 BamHI 消化以后得到了大小不同的新片段。我们注意到 T24 人膀胱癌癌基因与 EJ 膀胱癌癌基因高度相关 [18,19]。图 3A，泳道 m 显示了一个含有 T24 癌基因的小鼠转染子 DNA 中也含有能与探针反应的新片段。

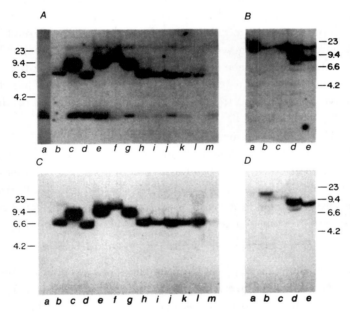

图 3. 用 c-Ha-ras1 和 EJ 癌基因探针分析 EJ 和 T24 转染子的 DNA。DNA 用核酸内切酶 BamHI（A，C）或者 EcoRI（B，D）酶切，并用图 1 注所述的方法进行分析。A 和 B 所示的滤膜与 $5 \times 10^6$ c.p.m. 的 c-Ha-ras1 DNA 探针（$2 \times 10^8$ c.p.m. $\mu g^{-1}$）温育并曝光进行放射自显影 16 小时。用含 0.1 M NaOH，0.5 M NaCl，1.0 mM EDTA 的溶液清洗滤膜以洗脱吸附的 $^{32}$P 标记探针。为确保所有的放射性标记都已被去除，将洗过的滤膜在胶片上曝光 48 小时（图中未显示）。然后将这些滤膜与经切口平移法制备的 $5 \times 10^6$ c.p.m. 的 pEJ6.6 DNA（$6 \times 10^7$ c.p.m. $\mu g^{-1}$）放在一起进行温育。C 和 D 代表 16 小时后的放射自显影成像。图 A 和 C 中分析的 DNA 来自如下细胞系：a, NIH 3T3；b, HeLa；c, EJ-6-1；d, EJ-2-R1；e, EJ-2-R5；f, E-4-R4-B；g, EJ-6-1；h, EJ-6-2-R；i, EJ-6-3；j, Ej-1-2；k, EJ-3-2；l, T-24 人细胞 [19]；m, T24-8-5。B 和 D 显示的 DNA 来自：a, NIH 细胞；b, HeLa 细胞；c, EJ-6-2(Bam)-1 细胞；d, EJ-6-2(Bam)-2 细胞；e, EJ-4(Bam)-1 细胞。在 A 和 C 中，泳道 c~f 和 h~k 代表独立连续转染 EJ 肿瘤细胞癌基因的细胞系的 DNA；泳道 g 和 c 是完全一样的。泳道 l 含有人膀胱癌细胞系 T24 的 DNA。泳道 m 含有 T24 二级转染子的 DNA。B 和 D 的泳道 c~e 为 BamHI 酶切后的二级转染子 DNA 诱导的三级转染子的 DNA 的分析结果。

To further define the linkage between the EJ oncogene and the c-Ha-*ras*1 homologous sequences, we analysed the DNAs of three EJ transfectants derived by transfer of *Bam*HI-cleaved DNA (Fig. 3*B*). The donors of these DNAs were secondary transfectants derived previously by two serial passages of the bladder carcinoma oncogene. As endonuclease *Bam*HI does not inactivate the EJ oncogene[18], the transfection of *Bam*HI-cleaved secondary DNA ensured that almost the only human fragment present in resulting tertiary transfectants was the 6.6-kb *Bam*HI fragment bearing the EJ oncogene. The three DNAs of the tertiary transfectants were analysed after *Eco*RI cleavage as it was thought they might have lost some *Bam*HI sites during the second transfection. The DNAs of the three transfectants (Fig. 3*B*, lanes *a-c*) all showed acquired fragments reactive with the c-Ha-*ras*1 probe. This demonstrated that the linkage between the EJ oncogene and the c-Ha-*ras*1 homologous sequences could not be broken by *Bam*HI cleavage.

A further comparison between the genes depended on the fact that the EJ bladder carcinoma oncogene was one that we have recently isolated as a molecular clone[18]. The EJ human bladder oncogene has been cloned as a biologically active *Eco*RI fragment of 16 kb carried by a Charon 4A λ phage vector and termed Φ631. A biologically active 6.6-kb *Bam*HI fragment subclone has been inserted into plasmid vector pBR322 and termed pEJ6.6. All endonucleases shown to cleave within this 6.6 kb insert (Fig. 4) inactivate the focus-inducing activity of this DNA (ref. 18 and C. Shih, unpublished results).

Using the EJ 6.6-kb *Bam*HI fragment and the c-Ha-*ras*1 oncogene clone as sequence probes, we analysed the DNA fragments homologous to these genes in normal human DNA. Both probes detected a 6.6-kb *Bam*HI fragment (Fig. 3*A*, *C*, lanes *b*) and a 23-kb *Eco*RI fragment (Fig. 3*B*, *D*, lanes *b*) in human DNA (see also ref. 20). Furthermore, the EJ bladder oncogene probe detected the same novel fragments in transfected mouse lines (Fig. 3*C*, lanes *c-k*) that were previously detected using the c-Ha-*ras*1 probe (Fig. 3*A*, lanes *c-k*).

Endonuclease-cleaved Φ631 DNA was immobilized on a cellulose nitrate filter and probed with the c-Ha-*ras*1 sequences. Figure 4*a* indicates that homology between c-Ha-*ras*1 and the EJ clone is limited to the 6.6-kb *Bam*HI fragment of the bladder carcinoma oncogene; lane *b* further reduces the domain of homology between the two oncogenes to a 3.0-kb *Sac*I fragment within the 6.6-kb *Bam*HI fragment. Figure 4*f-i* shows a similar experiment to that of lanes *b-e* but in this case BS-9, a v-Ha-*ras* probe, was used (provided by Drs D. Lowy and E. Scolnick). BS-9 is a *ras* specific subclone of the Harvey sarcoma virus genome[21] and is ~450 base pairs (bp) long. This probe includes the 5′ half of the v-*ras* gene. Comparison of left and right panels of Fig. 4 confirms that the viral probe and c-Ha-*ras*1 crosshybridize with identical fragments of the EJ oncogene DNA. Double digests (Fig. 4*g*, *i*) with *Sac*I + *Kpn*I or *Sac*I + *Xba*I indicate that the v-Ha-*ras* homology straddles the *Kpn*I and *Xba*I cleavage sites indicated at the top of Fig. 4. Most of the reactivity of the c-Ha-*ras*1 probe lies in the larger of the two fragments created by these digests (Fig. 4*c*, *e*). The deduced alignments between the EJ oncogene and the v-Ha-*ras* and c-Ha-*ras*1 probes are shown at the top of Fig. 4. The direction of transcription, deduced from the results of the present study and previous data[16,17], is from right to left on the map.

为了进一步确定 EJ 癌基因和 c-Ha-ras1 同源序列之间的联系，我们分析了 BamHI 酶切后 DNA 转染而来的三个 EJ 转染子的 DNA（图 3B）。这些 DNA 的供体是之前两次连续传代膀胱癌癌基因产生的二级转染子。由于核酸内切酶 BamHI 不会使 EJ 癌基因失活 [18]，因此可以保证，经 BamHI 酶切的二级 DNA 的转染产生的三级转染子中，几乎唯一存在的人类基因片段就是 6.6 kb 的含有 EJ 癌基因的 BamHI 片段。我们分析了经 EcoRI 酶切后三个三级转染子 DNA 的产物，因为我们认为在二次转染的过程中它们可能丢失了一些 BamHI 的位点。三个转染子的 DNA（图 3B，泳道 a~c）都显示产生的片段能与 c-Ha-ras1 探针反应。这表明 BamHI 酶切并不会破坏 EJ 癌基因与 c-Ha-ras1 同源序列之间的关联。

我们最近以分子克隆的形式分离得到了 EJ 膀胱癌癌基因，基因之间的进一步比较正是基于此 [18]。EJ 人类膀胱癌基因已被克隆为 Charon 4A λ 噬菌体载体携带的、具有生物学活性的、16 kb 的 EcoRI 片段，并被命名为 Φ631。一个具有生物学活性的 6.6 kb 的 BamHI 片段亚克隆被插入到质粒载体 pBR322 中，被命名为 pEJ6.6。所有能切开这个 6.6 kb 插入子的核酸内切酶（图 4）都能使该 DNA 失去中心诱导活性（参考文献 18 和施，未发表的结果）。

用 EJ 6.6 kb 的 BamHI 片段和 c-Ha-ras1 癌基因克隆作为序列探针，我们分析了正常人 DNA 中与这些基因同源的 DNA 片段。两个探针都在人类 DNA 中检测到了一个 6.6 kb 的 BamHI 片段（图 3A，C，泳道 b）和一个 23 kb 的 EcoRI 片段（图 3B，D，泳道 b）（见参考文献 20）。此外，EJ 膀胱癌癌基因探针在转染的小鼠细胞系中检测到了与之前用 c-Ha-ras1 探针检测到（图 3C，泳道 c~k）的相同的新片段（图 3A，泳道 c~k）。

经核酸内切酶酶切的 Φ631 DNA 被固定到硝酸纤维素膜上后，用 c-Ha-ras1 探针进行杂交。图 4a 显示了 c-Ha-ras1 和 EJ 克隆之间的同源序列仅限于膀胱癌癌基因上 6.6 kb 的 BamHI 片段；泳道 b 进一步将两种癌基因的同源域缩小到 6.6 kb BamHI 片段内部 3.0 kb 的 SacI 片段上。图 4f~i 显示了与泳道 b~e 类似的实验，只是所使用的探针为一种 v-Ha-ras 探针——BS-9（由洛伊博士和斯科尔尼克博士提供）。BS-9 是哈维肉瘤病毒基因组的 ras 特异性亚克隆 [21]，大约 450 bp。该探针包含了 v-ras 基因的 5′端。图 4 的左右泳道的比较证实了病毒探针及 c-Ha-ras1 与 EJ 癌基因 DNA 的同一片段发生了交叉杂交反应。SacI+KpnI 或 SacI+XbaI 的双酶切结果（图 4g，i）显示，v-Ha-ras 同源片段跨过了图 4 上方所示的 KpnI 和 XbaI 酶切位点。c-Ha-ras1 探针的反应活性主要位于上述酶切反应形成的两个片段中较大的那个（图 4c，e）。推断出的 EJ 癌基因与 v-Ha-ras 及 c-Ha-ras1 探针之间的序列比对结果显示在图 4 的上方。从本研究以及先前的数据 [16,17] 推断出的转录方向在图谱上是从右到左的。

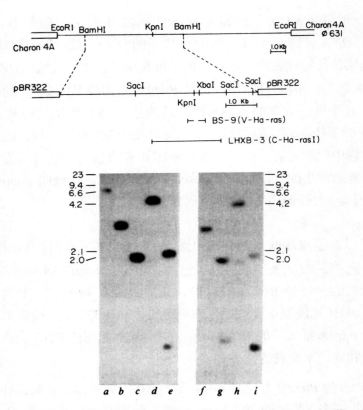

Fig. 4. Alignment of c-Ha-*ras*1 and of v-Ha-*ras* (BS-9) with the physical map of the EJ oncogene. DNA from the EJ-Charon 4A clone Φ631 was digested with several restriction enzymes. DNA (0.5 μg) was loaded onto each lane before electrophoresis and blot transfer. Identical nitrocellulose filters were prepared and incubated with [32]P-labelled DNA of c-Ha-*ras*1 (lanes *a-e*) or with HaSV subclone BS-9 (lanes *f-i*). Φ631 DNA was cleaved with *Bam*HI (*a*); *Bam*HI + *Sac*I (*b, f*); *Sac*I + *Kpn*I (*c, g*); *Bam*HI + *Xba*I (*d, h*); *Sac*I + *Xba*I (*e, i*). The alignment shown is accurate to within 200 nucleotides.

Taken together, these results indicate that the EJ bladder oncogene is closely linked to the human homologue of the rat c-Ha-*ras*1 sequences. Although the limits of the c-Ha-*ras*l structural sequences have been well defined[16,17,20], the corresponding sequences of the EJ gene have not yet been mapped. Thus, the data above cannot exclude the possibility that the two genetic elements were adjacent to one another rather than congruent.

## Analysis of Transcripts Homologous to the Clones

The transcripts encoded by these genes were analysed to further establish their relationship to one another. We examined the RNAs of transfected cells for molecules reactive with the two oncogene probes. As shown in Fig. 5, the two probes each detected transcripts of 1.2 and 5.1 kb in both the parental tumour cell line and in EJ- and T24-transfected mouse cell lines (see also ref. 22). These transcripts were not detected in untransfected NIH 3T3 cells. Thus, introduction of the EJ oncogene into mouse cells results in synthesis of RNAs that are homologous with the rat c-Ha-*ras*1 gene. As discussed below, these data support a congruency between the functionally active region of the EJ gene and that of the c-*ras* gene.

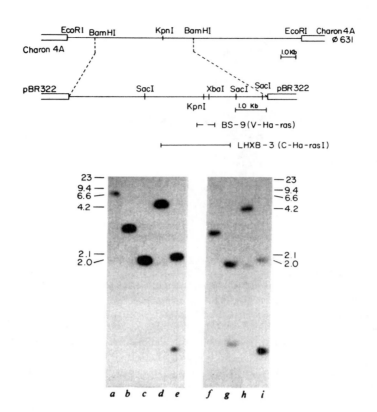

图 4. EJ 癌基因物理图谱及 c-Ha-*ras* 1 和 v-Ha-*ras* (BS-9) 的比对。用多种限制性内切酶对 EJ-Charon 4A 克隆 Φ631 的 DNA 进行酶切。将 DNA （0.5 μg）点到每个泳道上再进行电泳和印迹转移。将准备好的相同的硝化纤维素膜与用 ³²P 标记的 c-Ha-*ras*l （泳道 *a~e*）或者 HaSV 亚克隆 BS-9 （泳道 *f-i*） 的 DNA 放在一起温育。Φ631 DNA 分别用 *Bam*HI (*a*); *Bam*HI+*Sac*I (*b, f*); *Sac*I+*Kpn*I (*c, g*); *Bam*HI+*Xba*I (*d, h*); *Sac*I+*Xba*I (*e, i*) 酶切。图中显示的比对精确到 200 个核苷酸以内。

    总体来讲，这些结果表明 EJ 膀胱癌癌基因与大鼠 c-Ha-*ras*1 序列的人类同源序列关系密切。尽管 c-Ha-*ras*1 结构序列的范围已经明确[16,17,20]，但 EJ 基因中的相应序列图谱却仍未绘出。因此，以上数据并不能排除这两个遗传元件是彼此相邻而非完全相同的可能性。

## 分析与克隆同源的转录物

    为了进一步明确这些基因彼此之间的关系，我们对这些基因编码的转录物进行了分析。我们用两种癌基因探针检验了转染细胞的 RNA 的分子反应。如图 5 所示，这两个探针分别在亲代肿瘤细胞系和 EJ、T24 转染的小鼠细胞系中都检测到了 1.2 kb 和 5.1 kb 的转录物 （见文献 22）。在未转染的 NIH 3T3 细胞中没有检测到这些转录物。因此，转染到小鼠细胞中的 EJ 癌基因导致了与大鼠 c-Ha-*ras*1 基因同源的 RNA 的合成。如下面所讨论的一样，这些数据表明 EJ 基因和 c-*ras* 基因的功能活性区域具有一致性。

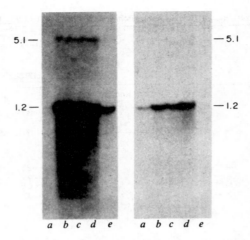

Fig. 5. Cellular polyadenylated RNAs analysed using pEJ6.6 and c-Ha-*ras*l [32]P-labelled probes. In the left-hand panel, nick-translated c-Ha-*ras*l DNA ($2 \times 10^8$ c.p.m. µg$^{-1}$) was used to probe RNA isolated from the following cell lines: *a*, NIH 3T3; *b*, T24-8-1 (a secondary transfectant derived from T24 human cell line); *c*, EJ-4(R1)–2; *d*, EJ-6-2; *e*, EJ human bladder. In the right-hand panel, nick-translated pEJ6.6 ($6.6 \times 10^7$ c.p.m. µg$^{-1}$) was used to probe the following cell lines: *a*, EJ; *b*, EJ-6-2; *c*, EJ-4(R1)-2; *d*, T24-8-1; *e*, NIH 3T3. The polyadenylated RNAs were prepared by the technique of Varmus *et al.*[40]. The RNA was then fractionated by electrophoresis through formaldehyde-containing gels and transferred to nitrocellulose (B. Seed and D. Goldberg, in preparation). [32]P-labelled probes, prepared as described in Fig. 1 legend, were annealed to the immobilized RNAs[41]. Bands which represent sequences homologous to the probes were visualized by autoradiography. Molecular weights were determined by comparison with markers obtained from *in vitro* run-off transcription of the adenovirus late promoter[42] and are shown in kilobases.

## Discussion

The present data strongly suggest an evolutionary homology between the EJ human bladder carcinoma oncogene and the rat c-Ha-*ras*l gene. We now consider the experimental basis for this conclusion and its implications.

The relatedness between the EJ and c-Ha-*ras*l genes was first noted when we demonstrated that a cell acquiring the EJ oncogene also carried a novel DNA fragment reactive with the c-Ha-*ras*l probe. As the linkage between the c-Ha-*ras*l homologous sequence and the EJ oncogene was not broken by endonuclease *Bam*HI, we concluded that the two genetic elements lay within the same 6.6-kb *Bam*HI-generated fragment. These data alone were consistent with the two elements being either physically adjacent or congruent with one another. To resolve this ambiguity, we analysed the transcripts encoded by the two oncogenes. The EJ parental tumour and its derived transfectants, all express 5.1- and 1.2-kb transcripts that react with the oncogene probe. The fact that these transcripts are also present in cells transfected with *Bam*HI-cleaved DNA (data not shown) implies that the entire transcriptional unit of the 5.1-kb RNA is found within the confines of the 6.6-kb *Bam*HI-generated fragment (Fig. 3*B*, *D*).

It could be argued that the transcripts detected in transfected mouse cells are of murine origin. In this case, their synthesis would be induced indirectly in the mouse cells by the

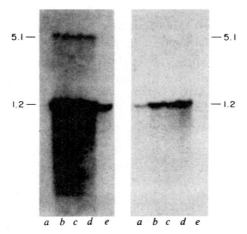

图 5. 用经 $^{32}$P 标记的 pEJ6.6 和 c-Ha-ras1 探针分析细胞多聚腺苷酸 RNA。在左侧图中，用切口平移法制备的 c-Ha-ras1 DNA（$2 \times 10^8$ c.p.m. μg$^{-1}$）作为探针，检测从以下细胞系中分离出的 RNA：a，NIH 3T3；b，T24-8-1（T24 人类细胞系产生的二级转染子）；c，EJ-4(R1)-2；d，EJ-6-2；e，EJ 人类膀胱。在右侧图中，用切口平移法制备的 pEJ6.6（$6.6 \times 10^7$ c.p.m. μg$^{-1}$）作为探针，检测了从以下细胞系中分离出的 RNA：a，EJ；b，EJ-6-2；c，EJ-4(R1)-2；d，T24-8-1；e，NIH 3T3。用瓦默斯等描述的方法 [40] 制备多聚腺苷酸 RNA。使用含有甲醛的凝胶电泳分离这些 RNA 并转移到硝酸纤维素膜上（锡德和戈德堡，论文撰写中）。采用图 1 注所描述的方法制备 $^{32}$P 标记的探针，并退火到已固定的 RNA 上 [41]。通过放射自显影就能看到与探针具有序列同源性的条带。分子量是通过与腺病毒晚期启动子 [42] 体外失控转录所获得的标记物进行比较确定的，以千碱基表示。

## 讨　论

目前的数据有力地表明 EJ 人类膀胱癌癌基因和大鼠 c-Ha-ras1 基因之间的进化同源性。我们接下来讨论这一结论和意义的实验基础。

当证实了获得 EJ 癌基因的细胞同时也携带能与 c-Ha-ras1 探针反应的新的 DNA 片段时，我们才首次注意到了 EJ 和 c-Ha-ras1 基因之间的相关性。由于核酸内切酶 BamHI 并不能破坏 c-Ha-ras1 同源序列与 EJ 癌基因之间的关联，我们认为这两个遗传元件位于同一个由 BamHI 产生的 6.6 kb 的片段内。单就这些数据而言，它们符合两个元件在物理位置上相邻或者是同一个基因的假设。为了明确这一问题，我们分析了由这两个癌基因编码的转录物。EJ 亲代肿瘤及其产生的转染子均表达了与癌基因探针反应的 5.1 kb 和 1.2 kb 的转录物。在 BamHI 酶切过的 DNA 转染的细胞内也存在这些转录子（未显示数据），这个事实表明整个 5.1 kb 的 RNA 转录单元位于由 BamHI 产生的 6.6 kb 的片段内部（图 3B，D）。

可以认为在转染小鼠细胞中检测到的转录物是鼠源性的。假若这样，这些转录物的合成就是在小鼠细胞内由其获得的人类癌基因间接诱发的，而不是由人类基因

acquired human oncogene rather than being encoded directly by the human gene. We consider this unlikely, as the rat c-Ha-*ras*1 probe used had a three-fold higher specific radioactivity than the human EJ probe, but yielded a 3–4-fold lower signal intensity on autoradiography (Fig. 5). This must reflect the relatively lower affinity of the rat probe for human transcripts present in the EJ transfectants. Thus, we conclude that the two probes both detect RNAs transcribed largely, if not entirely, from the human EJ oncogene template.

A similar, if not identical, pair of transcripts has been found by colleagues working with the c-Ha-*ras*1 gene and its RNAs[22]. As both the EJ and c-Ha-*ras*1 homologous 5.1-kb transcriptional units lie within the 6.6-kb *Bam*HI fragment, we conclude that the two genes are congruent with one another rather than adjacent. Consistent with this structural homology is a functional analogy in that both genes are able to induce fibroblast transformation.

The *ras* genes encode proteins of molecular weight 21,000 (ref. 23). Immunoprecipitation of metabolically labelled lysates of transfected cells has detected a protein of this size (R. Finkelstein and R. A. W., unpublished observations). However, the association of this protein with the bladder oncogene will only be well established after its detailed peptide structure has been analysed. Knowledge of the function of this protein may elucidate the important steps in human bladder carcinogenesis.

This p21 polypeptide represents a strong candidate for the protein mediating transformation of a human tumour cell. It is one of the first proteins implicated directly in the oncogenic conversion of a cell following its transformation by non-viral agents, and has been localized at the inner surface of the plasma membrane in Harvey sarcoma virus (HaSV)-transformed cells[24]. If this localization applies also to the EJ bladder carcinoma cells, then the transforming protein of these cells, the p21, should not display extracellular antigenic determinants. In this case, any tumour-specific surface antigens displayed by the bladder carcinoma cell should be encoded by genetic elements other than the oncogene itself.

The present work has several other implications. Perhaps the most apparent is that a single proto-oncogene can be activated by different molecular processes. The c-Ha-*ras*1 oncogene of the rat became activated via its affiliation with retrovirus sequences, forming the chimaeric Harvey sarcoma virus[21,25]. As demonstrated in the accompanying article[26], the human c-Ha-*ras*1 gene is also capable of oncogenic activation after it becomes linked *in vitro* to retrovirus promoter sequences. The mode of activation of the EJ oncogene is different, but not yet understood. Presently evidence suggests that the EJ oncogene and its normal human allelic counterpart sequence are indistinguishable by restriction enzyme site mapping[18]. It is possible that its activation depends on minor structural alterations, such as point mutations.

The relatedness between the EJ oncogene and that of a transforming retrovirus represents

直接编码的。我们认为这不太可能，因为使用的大鼠 c-Ha-*ras*1 探针的放射性比活度比人类 EJ 探针高出三倍，但是在放射自显影图像上其信号强度却低 3~4 倍（图 5）。这可能反映了大鼠探针对 EJ 转染子中存在的人类转录物的亲和力相对较低。因此，我们得出结论：这两个探针都检测到的 RNA 大部分（即便不是全部）是由人类 EJ 癌基因模板转录出来的。

研究 c-Ha-*ras*1 基因及 RNA 的同行们也发现了类似的（即便不是相同的）一对转录物 [22]。因为 EJ 以及 c-Ha-*ras*1 同源的 5.1 kb 的转录单元均位于 6.6 kb 的 *Bam*HI 片段内部，所以我们认为这两个基因就是同一个基因，而不是相邻的两个基因。与这种结构同源性一致的是其功能的相似性，即二者都能诱导成纤维细胞的转化。

*ras* 基因编码了分子量为 21,000 的蛋白质（参考文献 23）。对转染细胞内代谢标记的裂解产物进行的免疫沉淀实验检测到了类似大小的蛋白质（芬克尔斯坦和温伯格的未发表数据）。但是，只有解析了这个蛋白质具体的肽链结构以后，其与膀胱癌癌基因之间的关系才能确定。对这个蛋白质功能的认识可能有助于阐明人膀胱癌发生的关键步骤。

这种 p21 多肽很可能是蛋白介导人类肿瘤细胞转化的参与者。这是首批与通过非病毒元件转化发生癌变过程直接相关的蛋白质之一，并被定位在哈维肉瘤病毒 (HaSV) 转化的细胞质膜内表面上 [24]。如果该定位也适用于 EJ 膀胱癌细胞的话，那么这些细胞的转化蛋白 p21 就不应该是细胞外抗原决定簇。假若这样，膀胱癌细胞所表现的任何肿瘤特异性表面抗原应该是由遗传元件，而不是由癌基因本身编码。

这项工作具有许多其他意义。最显著的也许就是，一个单独的原癌基因能被不同的分子过程激活。大鼠的 c-Ha-*ras*1 癌基因通过逆转录病毒序列的加入而被激活，形成嵌合型哈维肉瘤病毒 [21,25]。正如附录文章所描述的 [26]，人类 c-Ha-*ras*1 基因在体外连接上逆转录病毒启动子序列后其致癌性也会被激活。EJ 癌基因的激活模式是不同的，且是未知的。目前的证据显示 EJ 癌基因及其正常的人类等位基因对应序列用限制性内切酶位点图谱法尚无法区分 [18]。其活化有可能依赖于微小的结构改变，比如点突变。

EJ 癌基因和转化的逆转录病毒基因之间的联系表明我们对人类膀胱癌的分子

an advance in our understanding of the molecular basis of human bladder carcinoma. This stems from the fact that the structure and function of the *ras* genes and their gene products have been extensively studied[16–18,20–23].

We have been unable to demonstrate other homologies between retrovirus *onc* genes and the transfection-derived tumour genes, but this may merely reflect the small repertoire of tumour genes presently available in cloned form. As other genes become available for study, additional connections will probably be found.

Two paradoxes seem to be raised by the unexpected association of a rat sarcoma oncogene with a human bladder oncogene. First, this work implies the ability of the c-Ha-*ras*1 gene to act in unrelated tissue environments. The rat gene, when carried in Harvey sarcoma virus, can induce sarcomas and erythroleukaemias[27] while its human counterpart is now implicated in the genesis of bladder carcinomas[10–12,18,19]. We consider it possible that the *ras* oncogene of either species is capable of transforming a wide range of target tissues, only a small portion of which has been studied experimentally.

Second, we have suggested that the precursor of the EJ oncogene, now identified as c-Ha-*ras*1, represents a preferred target for activation during bladder carcinogenesis[18]. It seems unlikely that the bladder urothelium was the site of acquisition of the *ras* gene during the events that let to the creation of the chimaeric HaSV genome. The two routes of oncogene activation must involve different molecular mechanisms which probably occur at different sites in the organism. Each mode of activation may be favoured by different predisposing factors present in different tissues. For example, in the bladder, the c-Ha-*ras*1 gene may be in a configuration particularly susceptible to mutational activation whereas in certain other tissues it may be expressed in a manner favouring the recombinational events that lead to creation of chimaeric retroviruses.

We thank our colleagues for providing the *onc* probes used in this study. This research was supported by US National Cancer Institute grants CA17537 and CA26717 to R.A.W.

(**297**, 474-478; 1982)

Luis F. Parada, Clifford J. Tabin, Chiaho Shih and Robert A. Weinberg
Center for Cancer Research and Department of Biology, Massachusetts Institute of Technology, Cambridge, Massachusetts 02139, USA

Received 8 April; accepted 17 May 1982.

References:
1. Spector, D.H., Varmus, H.E. & Bishop, J.M., *Proc. Natl. Acad. Sci. U.S.A.* **75**, 4102-4106 (1978).
2. Stehelin, D., Varmus, H.E., Bishop, J.M. & Vogt, P. K. *Nature* **260**, 170-173 (1976).
3. Klein, G. (ed.) *Advances in Viral Oncology: Cell Derived Oncogenes* (Raven, New York, 1981).
4. Coffin, J. M. *et al. J. Virol.* **40**, 953-957 (1981).
5. Shilo, B-Z. & Weinberg, R.A. *Proc. Natl. Acad. Sci. U.S.A.* **78**, 6789-6792 (1981).

基础的认识有了提高。这主要基于对 ras 基因及其基因产物的结构和功能的广泛研究 [16-18, 20-23]。

我们尚不能阐明逆转录病毒 onc 基因和转染产生的肿瘤基因之间的其他同源性，但是这可能仅仅反映了目前以克隆形式获取的肿瘤基因的小部分内容。随着更多基因投入研究，也可能找到更多的联系。

随着大鼠肉瘤癌基因和人膀胱癌癌基因之间意外联系的发现，出现了两个矛盾。第一，这个研究表明 c-Ha-ras1 基因能够在不相关的组织环境中发挥功能。插入到哈维肉瘤病毒上的大鼠基因能够导致肉瘤和红白血病的发生 [27]，而其与人类相应的基因在膀胱癌的发生中起重要作用 [10-12,18,19]。我们认为有可能这两个物种之一的 ras 癌基因能够转化大范围的靶点组织，而正在进行实验研究的只是其中一小部分。

第二，我们已经指出 EJ 癌基因的前体，即现在所认为的 c-Ha-ras1，是膀胱癌致癌作用中偏好激活的靶位 [18]。膀胱上皮细胞似乎不太可能是产生嵌合型 HaSV 基因组过程中获取 ras 基因的位点。两种癌基因的激活途径肯定涉及可能发生在生物不同部位的不同分子机制。不同诱发因素的激活模式可能存在于不同的组织中。例如，在膀胱中，c-Ha-ras1 基因可能处于一种特别容易受到突变激活的构型，而在某些其他组织中，该基因的表达可能在一定程度上促进重组从而产生嵌合型逆转录病毒。

感谢我们的同事提供本研究使用的 onc 探针。美国国家癌症研究所基金 CA17537 和 CA26717 向温伯格赞助了此项研究。

（毛晨晖 翻译；彭小忠 审稿）

6. Shih, C., Shilo, B-Z., Goldfarb, M., Dannenberg, A. & Weinberg, R. A. *Proc. Natl. Acad. Sci. U.S.A.* **76**, 5714-5718 (1979).

7. Shih, C., Padhy, L. C., Murray, M. & Weinberg, R. A. *Nature* **290**, 261-264 (1981).

8. Hopkins, N., Besmer, P., DeLeo, A. B. & Law, L. W. *Proc. Natl. Acad. Sci. U.S.A.* **78**, 7555-7559 (1981).

9. Lane, M. A., Sainten, A. & Cooper, G. M. *Proc. Natl. Acad. Sci. U.S.A.* **78**, 5185-5189 (1981).

10. Murray, M. J. *et al. Cell* **25**, 355-361 (1981).

11. Krontiris, T. G. & Cooper, G. M. *Proc. Natl. Acad. Sci. U.S.A.* **78**, 1181-1184 (1981).

12. Perucho, M. *et al. Cell* **27**, 467-476 (1981).

13. Southern, E. M. *J. Molec. Biol.* **98**, 503-517 (1975).

14. Shilo, B-Z. & Weinberg, R. A. *Nature* **289**, 607-609 (1981).

15. Goff, S. P., Gilboa, E., Witte, O. N. & Baltimore, D. *Cell* **22**, 777-785 (1980).

16. DeFeo, D. *et al. Proc. Natl. Acad. Sci. U.S.A.* **78**, 3328-3332 (1981).

17. Ellis, R. W. *et al. Nature* **292**, 506-511 (1981).

18. Shih, C. & Weinberg, R. A. *Cell* (in the press).

19. Goldfarb, M., Shimizu, K., Perucho, M. & Wigler, M. *Nature* **296**, 404-409 (1982).

20. Chang, E. H., Gonda, M. A., Ellis, R. W., Scolnick, E. M. & Lowy, D. R. *Proc. Natl. Acad. Sci. U.S.A.* (in the press).

21. Ellis, R. W. *et al. J. Virol.* **36**, 408-420 (1980).

22. Ellis, R. W., DeFeo, D., Furth, M. & Scolnick, E. M. *Cell* (in the press).

23. Shih, T. Y., Weeks, M. O., Young, H. A. & Scolnick, E. M. *Virology* **96**, 64-79 (1979).

24. Willingham, M. C., Pastan, I., Shih, T. Y. & Scolnick, E. M. *Cell* **19**, 1005-1014 (1980).

25. Harvey, J. J. *Nature* **204**, 1104-1105 (1964).

26. Chang, E. H., Furth, M. E., Scolnick, E. M. & Lowy, D. R. *Nature* **297**, 479-483 (1982).

27. Chesterman, F. C., Harvey, J. J., Dourmashkin, R. R. & Salaman, M. H. *Cancer Res.* **26**, 1759-1768 (1966).

28. Vennstrom, B., Fanshiev, L., Moscovici, C. & Bishop, J. M. *J. Virol.* **36**, 575-585 (1980).

29. Sherr, C. J., Fedele, L. A., Oskarsson, M., Maizel, J. & Vande Woude, G. *J. Virol.* **34**, 200-212 (1980).

30. Chang, E. H., Gonda, M. A., Ellis, R. A., Scolnick, E. M. & Lowy, D. R., *Proc. Natl. Acad. Sci. U.S.A.* (in the press).

31. Vennstrom, B., Moscovici, C., Goodman, H. & Bishop, J. M. *J. Virol.* **39**, 625-631 (1981).

32. DeLorbe, W. J., Luciw, P. A., Goodman, H. M., Varmus, H. E. & Bishop, J. M. *J. Virol.* **36**, 50-61 (1980).

33. Rapp, V. R., Nowinski, R. C., Reznikoff, C. A. & Heidelberger, C. *Virology* **65**, 329-409 (1975).

34. Giard, D. J. *et al. J. Natl. Cancer Inst.* **51**, 1417-1421 (1973).

35. Leibovitz, A. *et al. Cancer Res.* **36**, 4562-4569 (1976).

36. Collins, E. J., Gallo, R. C. & Gallagher, R. E. *Nature* **270**, 347-349 (1977).

37. Schubert, D. *et al. Nature* **249**, 224-226 (1974).

38. Summerhayes, I. C. & Franks, L. M. *J. Natl. Cancer Inst.* **62**, 1017-1021 (1979).

39. Rigby, P. W., Dieckmann, M., Rhodes, C. & Berg, P. *J. Molec. Biol.* **13**, 237-251 (1977).

40. Varmus, H. E., Quintrell, N. & Ortiz, S. *Cell* **25**, 23-36 (1981).

41. Wahl, G. M., Stern, M. & Stark, G. R. *Proc. Natl. Acad. Sci. U.S.A.* **76**, 3683-3687 (1979).

42. Manley, J. L., Fire, A., Cano, A., Sharp, P. A. & Gefter, M. L., *Proc. Natl. Acad. Sci. U.S.A.* **77**, 3855-3859 (1980).

人类EJ膀胱癌癌基因是哈维肉瘤病毒*ras*基因的同源基因

# Neurone Differentiation in Cell Lineage Mutants of *Caenorhabditis elegans*

J. G. White *et al.*

## Editor's Note

The use of the nematode worm *Caenorhabditis elegans* for studying gene function and development was pioneered by John Sulston. The British biologist developed techniques to study the cell divisions that transform fertilized egg into adult animal, proving that every worm undergoes the same program of cell division and differentiation. Here Sulston and colleagues describe two *C. elegans* mutants that have particular cell divisions blocked. The blocked cells, they show, yield only one of the two daughter cells that would normally be produced, and this is always a neuron. The study shed light on the processes controlling cell fate. Sulston, his coauthor H. Robert Horvitz, and nematode researcher Sydney Brenner later shared a Nobel Prize for their work on *C. elegans*.

---

The nematode *Caenorhabditis elegans* develops by an essentially invariant sequence of cell divisions[1-3] leading to an adult complement of 959 somatic cells. In this organism cell fate is correlated with cell lineage, suggesting that genealogy may be a determining factor for the differentiated state of a cell. The study of mutants with altered cell lineages may help elucidate the precise mechanisms by which cell fate is decided. Several cell lineage mutants have been isolated and characterized[4,5], some having more and some fewer cell divisions than wild type. We have now investigated the cell types produced by two cell lineage mutants; these mutants exhibit blocks in certain terminal or near terminal cell divisions, which in normal animals generally give rise to daughter cells that differentiate into distinctly different cell types. We find that the blocked cells in the mutants generally exhibit the differentiated characteristics of only one of the two daughter cells that normally would be produced. The differentiated state of the blocked precursors may be due to an intrinsic dominance of one cell type over another in what is essentially a fused cell, and/or it may reveal the state of commitment of the precursor in wild-type animals.

---

WE have studied two very similar mutants *unc-59* (*e*1005) and *unc-85* (*e*1414), both of which are variably blocked in some of the later divisions of the lineages that produce the adult complement of motoneurones in the ventral nerve cord[4,5]. These lineages have been characterized in wild-type animals by following the development of living animals in the light microscope[1]. The nuclei of 12 precursor cells (designated P1–P12) migrate into the ventral cord during the first larval stage; each cell then divides

# 秀丽隐杆线虫细胞谱系突变体的神经元分化

怀特等

## 编者按

约翰·萨尔斯顿开创了利用秀丽隐杆线虫来研究基因功能和发育的先河。这位英国生物学家探索出了一套方法来研究动物个体通过细胞分裂实现从受精卵到成体这一转化过程，并得出了每条线虫都经历相同的细胞分裂和分化程序的结论。在本文中，萨尔斯顿和他的同事们描述了两种细胞分裂在特定步骤被阻断的秀丽隐杆线虫的突变体。他们揭示了在这两种突变体中，细胞分裂阻断的细胞仅产生一个子细胞——正常情况下会产生两个子细胞，并且细胞分裂阻断的细胞往往成为神经元。这项研究为阐明细胞命运的调控过程开辟了道路。后来，萨尔斯顿、他的共同作者罗伯特·霍维茨以及线虫研究者西德尼·布伦纳凭借他们在秀丽隐杆线虫方面的工作共享了诺贝尔奖。

秀丽隐杆线虫通过一种基本上程序不变的细胞分裂过程[1-3]，发育形成由959个体细胞组成的成体。在这种生物中，细胞的命运往往与其细胞谱系相对应，这表明了种系可能是细胞分化状态的决定因素。研究细胞谱系发生改变的突变体可能有助于阐明决定细胞命运的确切机制。有数个细胞谱系突变体已经被分离并鉴定[4,5]，与野生型相比，有些突变体的细胞分裂次数增多，而有些减少。目前我们研究了两个细胞谱系突变体的细胞类型；这些突变体在一些细胞分裂的末期或临近末期的时候发生细胞分裂的阻断，而在正常情况下这些细胞能够分裂，并分化成不同的子细胞。我们发现：突变体中分裂阻断的细胞通常表现出正常情况下产生的两个子代细胞之一的分化特征。如果将细胞分裂受阻的细胞理解为两个子细胞融合在一起的状态，那么前体细胞的分化状态可能取决于内在的，其中一种细胞类型相对于另一细胞类型的显性表现，而且（或者）这也可能显示了野生型情况下该前体细胞应该呈现的本来状态。

我们研究了两种非常相似的突变体 *unc-59*(*e*1005) 和 *unc-85*(*e*1414)，这两者都在产生成虫腹神经索运动神经元的细胞分裂的较晚阶段发生了不同程度的细胞分裂阻断[4,5]。在野生型个体中用光学显微镜跟踪活体动物的发育过程，已经明确了这些细胞的分裂谱系[1]。12 个前体细胞（称为 P1~P12）的细胞核在第一龄幼虫期迁移到腹侧索部位，然后每个细胞分裂产生一个神经母细胞和一个上皮细胞。12 个神经母细

1085

to produce a neuroblast and a hypodermal cell. The 12 neuroblasts (together with an additional neuroblast present at hatching) undergo identical sequences of divisions (Fig. 1), each producing 5 cells that intercalate with the pre-existing juvenile motoneurones to form a single row of cells along the ventral cord. All cleavages have longitudinal spindle axes, and descendant cells maintain their relative antero-posterior positions throughout development. Certain cells derived from some of the neuroblasts die soon after their formation; the pattern of cell death is invariant.

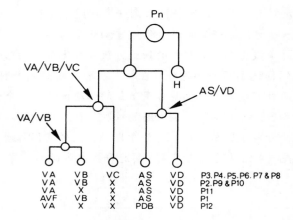

Fig. 1. The ventral cord precursor cells P1–P12 are hypodermal cells (J. G. W., unpublished observations). Their nuclei migrate into the ventral cord and each divides to produce a ventral hypodermal cell (H) (which functionally replaces the mother) and a neuroblast. All 12 neuroblasts then undergo identical series of divisions to produce five descendants[1]. All spindle axes are longitudinal; in the diagram anterior daughters are drawn to the left and posterior daughters to the right. The fates of the descendants from each precursor are shown. Cell types have been assigned on the basis of cell morphology and synaptic connectivity[6]. Precursors P3–P8 produce five classes of ventral cord motoneurone (VA, VB, VC, AS, VD). In the P1–P2 and P9–P12 lineages, cells lineally equivalent to VC neurones undergo programmed cell death (X), as do cells lineally equivalent to VB neurones derived from P11–P12. Alternative fates are seen for some of the cells derived from the two precursors at the ends of the cord (P1,P12): P1 produces an AVF interneurone instead of a VA, and P12 produces a PDB interneurone instead of an AS. (AVF and PDB are two distinct classes of interneurone which are quite dissimilar to the motoneurone classes.) These alternative fates are probably specified by local interactions[1,14]. In the *unc-59* and *unc-85* animals, certain cells which divide in the wild-type fail to do so. Such cells are labelled according to the fate of their normal descendants; for example, an AS/VD cell should have divided to produce an AS and a VD neurone.

The structure of the ventral cord of wild-type animals has been deduced by reconstructions from electron micrographs of serial sections[6]. In neuroblast lineages that do not contain cell deaths the five cells produced differentiate into five distinct classes of motoneurone designated VA, VB, VC, AS and VD (Fig. 1). Classes are defined on the basis of patterns of synaptic connections (see Pn, Table 2) and morphology (Fig. 2). Either criterion is sufficient to assign a cell to a class.

胞将（与孵化时就存在的另一个神经母细胞一起）经历相同顺序的分裂（图1），其中每一个都会产生5个细胞，这5个细胞将并入到已经存在的，未成熟的运动神经元当中，一起形成沿着腹侧索排列的一排细胞。每次分裂都产生纵向的纺锤体轴，并且在整个发育过程中子代细胞都保持相对的前后位置关系。一些来源于神经母细胞的细胞在形成后不久即死亡，这些细胞死亡的模式都是固定不变的。

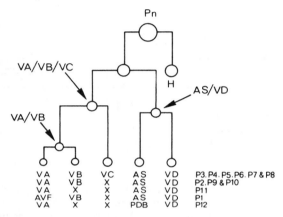

图 1. 腹侧索前体细胞 P1~P12 是上皮细胞（怀特，未发表的结果）。它们的细胞核迁移到腹侧索，而后每个细胞分裂产生一个腹侧上皮细胞（H）（其功能是替代母细胞）和一个神经母细胞。所有的 12 个神经母细胞经过相同的分裂程序，产生 5 个后代 [1]。每次分裂的纺锤体轴都是纵向的。靠前端的子细胞在图中标注于左侧，靠后端的标注于右侧。从每个前体细胞产生的子代细胞的细胞命运标注如图。基于细胞形态和突触的连接性对细胞类型进行了划分 [6]。前体细胞 P3~P8 产生五种腹侧索运动神经元（VA、VB、VC、AS、VD）。在 P1~P2 和 P9~P12 细胞系，相当于 VC 神经元位置的细胞经历程序性细胞死亡（X），而在 P11~P12 细胞谱系中相当于 VB 神经元位置的细胞也发生了程序性死亡。来源于腹侧索末端两个前体细胞（P1，P12）的部分子细胞有不同的命运：P1 产生 AVF 中间神经元，而不是 VA；P12 产生 PDB 中间神经元而不是 AS。（AVF 和 PDB 是两种不同类型的中间神经元，它们都与运动神经元非常不同。）这些另类的分化方式很可能是由局部的相互作用决定的 [1,14]。在 unc-59 和 unc-85 动物中，一些在野生型中能够分裂的细胞失去了分裂能力。根据这些细胞正常子细胞的分化方向对它们进行标记；例如，AS/VD 细胞应该分裂成一个 AS 神经元和一个 VD 神经元。

野生型个体的腹侧索结构已通过连续切片的电子显微图像重建而推断出来了 [6]。在没有发生子细胞死亡的神经母细胞系中，其产生的五个细胞分化成五种不同类型的运动神经元，分别是 VA、VB、VC、AS 和 VD（图1）。分类依据是突触连接的形式（见 Pn，表2）和细胞形态（图2）。二者之中任一标准都足以将一个细胞归到一种类型中。

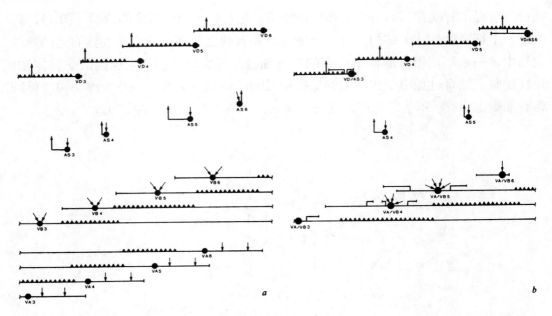

Fig. 2. The morphologies of the motoneurones derived from the precursors P3–P6 are shown for wild type (*a*) and *unc-85* (*b*). The wild-type structures are as described in ref. 6, and the mutant structures were derived, using similar techniques, by reconstruction from 3,000 serial section electron micrographs from an animal of known lineage. Four of the five motoneurone classes derived from the P cells are shown: VA, VB, AS and VD (class VC has been omitted, because it has few distinguishing characteristics). The extent of the processes in the ventral cord and the positions of the cell bodies (—●—), neuromuscular junctions (NMJs) ( ▲▲▲ ), commissures (| → ) and synaptic input (| ← ) are shown. The horizontal axis is equivalent to the longitudinal axis of the animal (anterior is drawn to the left); the vertical axis has been used simply to separate the neurones into their respective classes. VA neurones , which have anteriorly directed axons, form a regular sequence of regions of motor activity with little or no overlap between adjacent members of a class. VB neurones are similar but have posteriorly directed axons. VA neurones receive their synaptic input in a dendritic region near the cell body on a branch opposite the axon; VB neurones receive their synaptic input predomiantly at the cell body. The axons from class AS motoneurones lead to the dorsal cord via commissures and innervate dorsal muscles. They have a short dendritic region in the ventral cord. The axons from VD neurones end abruptly in gap junctions to axons from adjacent VD neurones. The dendritic regions behave in a similar fashion in the dorsal cord (not shown) and connect to the ventral cord via commissures. In the *unc-85* animal, the VA/VB-blocked precursors from P3–P5 had morphologies similar to wild-type VB neurones, forming NMJs from posteriorly directed axons. The blocked VA/VB precursor from P6 had failed to grow an axon. The AS/VD precursors from P4 and P5 had divided normally, and each produced apparently normal AS and VD daughters. The blocked AS/VD cells from P3 and P6 had the characteristic morphologies of VD motoneurones with their processes forming NMJs and ending abruptly in gap junctions with adjacent normal VD motoneurones. The only differences between the morphologies of these blocked precursors and those of their normal posterior daughters is that the former have larger nuclei, a few extra branches and more synaptic inputs.

The post-embryonic development of ventral cord cells was observed in several *unc-59* and *unc-85* animals. In these mutants, P-cell-derived neuroblasts produced fewer progeny cells than normal (Fig. 1), because some cell divisions failed. The set of affected cells varied between animals. Failures resulted in polyploid cells; sometimes the nuclei failed to divide after DNA replication, and sometimes apparently normal nuclei formed but then fused to

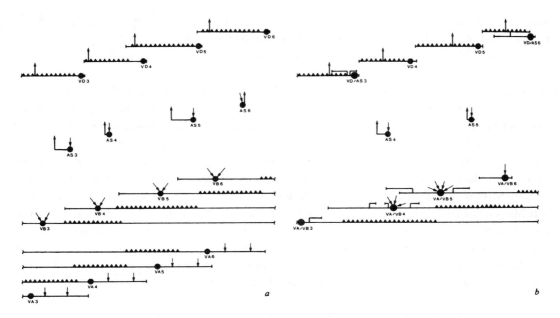

图 2. 图中显示了分别由野生型（a）和 unc-85（b）的前体细胞 P3~P6 来源的运动神经元的形态。野生型的结构见文献 6 中的描述，突变体结构是用类似的技术从一个细胞谱系已知的物种的 3,000 份连续切片电子显微镜图中重建出来的。图中显示了来源于 P 细胞的 5 个运动神经元类型中的 4 种：VA、VB、AS 和 VD（VC 类被略去，因为它的鉴别特征非常少）。图中显示了细胞在腹侧索内延伸的范围和细胞胞体（—●—）、神经肌肉接头（NMJs）（▲▲▲）、神经连合（‖→）和突触传入（‖←）的位置。水平轴相当于动物的纵轴（头端在左侧）；垂直轴用来将神经元划分到它们各自的类型中。VA 神经元向前延伸出轴突，形成常规顺序的运动活性区域，它们在相邻的同类细胞间几乎没有重叠。VB 神经元也是如此，但是轴突延伸方向朝后。VA 神经元通过与轴突相反方向的细胞胞体延伸出来的树突区域接受突触传入信息；VB 神经元主要通过细胞胞体接受突触传入。AS 运动神经元的轴突通过神经连合延伸至背侧索，支配背部的肌肉。它们在腹侧索有短的树突区域。VD 神经元的轴突以间隙连接的方式突然地中止于邻近 VD 神经元的轴突末端。背侧索的树突区域也是如此（数据未显示），并通过接合处与腹侧索相连。在 unc-85 动物中，P3~P5 来源的、细胞分裂受阻的 VA/VB 前体细胞与野生型 VB 神经元的形态类似，通过朝向尾端延伸的轴突形成 NMJs。P6 来源的、细胞分裂受阻的 VA/VB 前体细胞不能长出轴突。P4 和 P5 来源的 AS/VD 前体细胞正常分裂，每一个都产生了正常的 AS 和 VD 子代细胞。P3 和 P6 来源的、细胞分裂受阻的 AS/VD 细胞具有与 VD 运动神经元相似的形态特征，它们形成 NMJs 并以间隙连接的方式突然中止于相邻的正常 VD 运动神经元。细胞分裂受阻的前体细胞与它们正常的子代细胞之间形态的差别仅在于前者具有较大的核、一些额外分叉以及更多的突触传入。

（我们）观察了多个 unc-59 和 unc-85 个体中腹侧索细胞的胚后发育情况。由于一些细胞不能进行分裂，这些突变体的 P 细胞来源的神经母细胞比野生型产生的子代细胞少（图 1）。受影响的细胞系在不同的个体中有差异。细胞分裂失败导致多倍体细胞的产生；有时 DNA 复制后核没有分裂，有时虽然形成了正常的细胞核但随后

form a tetraploid nucleus or remained separated in a binucleate cell[5]. *unc-59* and *unc-85* individuals that displayed several examples of undivided ventral cord nuclei were selected for reconstruction from electron micrographs of serial sections.

In both *unc-59* and *unc-85* animals all blocked cells were found to have differentiated into neurones. Most of these neurones could be unequivocally identified as belonging to one of the motoneurone classes normally produced from these lineages; specifically, the blocked cells acquired the differentiated characteristics of one of the daughter cells that would normally be produced. These results are summarized in Table 1. All blocked VD/AS precursors differentiated into cells that had all the distinguishing characteristics of VD motoneurones (Fig. 2, Tables 1, 2). VA/VB or VA/VB/VC precursors differentiated into VB-like cells in the anterior ventral cord and into VA-like cells in the posterior ventral cord (Tables 1, 2). The choice of VA versus VB for the blocked precursors may be related to the regional preference exhibited by the progeny of these precursors in wild-type development: a VB but no VA is produced by the anterior P1 lineage, whereas a VA but no VB is produced by the posterior P11 and P12 lineages (Fig. 1).

Table 1. Post-embryonic development of P cells from *unc-85* and *unc-59* animals

| Mutant | Blocked precursor | | Cell type |
|---|---|---|---|
| *unc-85* | P3 | VA/VB/* | VB |
| | P3 | AS/VD | VD |
| | P4 | VA/VB/* | VB |
| | P5 | VA/VB | VB |
| | P6 | VA/VB/* | VB‡ |
| | P6 | AS/VD | VD |
| *unc-59* | | | |
| Animal 1 | P3 | VA/VB/VC | VB |
| | P3 | AS/VD | VD |
| Animal 2 | P8 | VA/VB | VA |
| | P8 | AS/VD | VD |
| | P9 | VA/VB/† | VA |
| | P9 | AS/VD | VD |
| | P10 | VA/VB/† | VA |
| | P10 | AS/VD | VD |
| | P11 | VA/†/† | VA‡ |
| | P11 | AS/VD | VD |

* In these lineages a VC nucleus was produced but was not present when the adult was reconstructed. These nuclei probably either fused to make a VA/VB/VC or died.

† The cells lineally equivalent to VC in the P1–P2 and P9–P12 lineages and to VB in the P11–P12 lineages normally undergo programmed cell death[1].

融合成四倍体核或者在双核细胞中仍然保持分离状态[5]。（我们）选取了几个腹侧索细胞核不能分裂的 *unc-59* 和 *unc-85* 突变体进行了连续切片的电子显微镜图像重建分析。

在 *unc-59* 和 *unc-85* 个体中，所有细胞分裂受阻的细胞都分化成了神经元。这些神经元大部分都能够明确地归类到正常情况下由这些细胞系形成的运动神经元类型中去。特别要说明的是，这些细胞分裂受阻的细胞往往获得了其正常情况下产生的某一子代细胞所具有的分化特征。这些结果总结在表 1 中。所有被阻断的 VD/AS 前体细胞都分化成了具有 VD 运动神经元特征的细胞（图 2，表 1 和表 2）。VA/VB 或者 VA/VB/VC 前体细胞在腹侧索前段分化成了类似于 VB 的细胞，在后段分化成了类似于 VA 的细胞（表 1 和表 2）。阻断的前体细胞选择分化成 VA 还是 VB 可能与这些前体细胞在野生型动物的发育中子代细胞所表现出来的区域偏好有关：位于前端的 P1 细胞系产生 VB 而不是 VA，而位于后端的 P11 和 P12 细胞系产生 VA 而不是 VB（图 1）。

表 1. *unc-59* 和 *unc-85* 个体中 P 细胞的胚胎后发育

| 突变体 | | 阻断的前体细胞 | | 细胞类型 |
|---|---|---|---|---|
| *unc-85* | | P3 | VA/VB/* | VB |
| | | P3 | AS/VD | VD |
| | | P4 | VA/VB/* | VB |
| | | P5 | VA/VB | VB |
| | | P6 | VA/VB/* | VB‡ |
| | | P6 | AS/VD | VD |
| *unc-59* | | | | |
| | 个体 1 | P3 | VA/VB/VC | VB |
| | | P3 | AS/VD | VD |
| | 个体 2 | P8 | VA/VB | VA |
| | | P8 | AS/VD | VD |
| | | P9 | VA/VB/† | VA |
| | | P9 | AS/VD | VD |
| | | P10 | VA/VB/† | VA |
| | | P10 | AS/VD | VD |
| | | P11 | VA/†/† | VA‡ |
| | | P11 | AS/VD | VD |

\* 在这些细胞系中，VC 核能够产生，但是在成虫电镜重建时没有出现。这些核很可能融合以形成 VA/VB/VC 或者消亡了。

† 这些细胞在 P1~P2 和 P9~P12 系相当于 VC，在 P11~P12 系相当于 VB，它们正常情况下会经历程序性细胞

‡ Axons failed to grow out of these cells although they had the synaptic contacts characteristic of the cell types indicated.

Table 2. Number of synapses formed by blocked precursors and typical synapses of wild-type ventral cord neurones (Pn)[6]

|  |  | AVA | AVB | VA | VB | VC | AS | VD | NMJ |  |
|---|---|---|---|---|---|---|---|---|---|---|
| *unc-85* | | | | | | | | | | |
| P3 | VA/VB/* | ‡ | ‡ | | | | | | 15 | |
| P3 | AS/VD | | | | § 1 | | | = 1 | 19 | |
| P4 | VA/VB/* | | = 6 | | | | | | 20 | |
| P5 | VA/VB | = 1 | = 9 | | = 5 | | | | 8 | |
| P6 | VA/VB/* | | = 1 | | = 5 | | | | | No axon |
| P6 | AS/VD | | | | § 3 | | | = 1 | 14 | |
| *unc-59* (1) | | | | | | | | | | |
| P3 | VA/VB/VC | | = 15 | | | | | # 1 | 5 | |
| P3 | AS/VD | | | | | | | = 6 | 14 | |
| *unc-59* (2) | | | | | | | | | | |
| P8 | VA/VB | § 6 = 6 | | | | | | | ‡ | |
| P8 | AS/VD | | | § 3 | | | | = 2 | 11 | |
| P9 | VA/VB/† | § 3 = 5 | | | | | | # 3 | 22 | |
| P9 | AS/VD | | | § 3 | | | | = 2 | 13 | |
| P10 | VA/VB/† | § 9 = 5 | | | | | | # 3 | 16 | |
| P10 | AS/VD | | | | | | | =2 | 10 | |
| P11 | VA/†/† | § 7 | | | | | | | | No axon |
| P11 | AS/VD | | | | | | | = 2 | 12 | |
| *Wild type* | | | | | | | | | | |
| Pn | VA | § 4 = 3 | | | | | = 1 | # 1 | 16 | |
| Pn | VB | | = 2 | | = 2 | | | # 2 | 9 | |
| Pn | VC | | | | | § 3 = 5 | | # 7 | 2 | |
| Pn | AS | § 2 = 1 | § 2 | = 1 | | | | | | |
| Pn | VD | | | § 1 | § 2 | § 7 | | = 1 | 26 | |

Values for wild type are the mean values from precursors P3 to P5 obtained from a reconstruction of a wild-type animal. #, Presynaptic; §, postsynaptic; =, gap junctions.

\* In these lineages a VC nucleus was produced but was not present when the adult was reconstructed. These nuclei probably either fused to make a VA/VB/VC or died.

† The cells lineally equivalent to VC in the P1–P2 and P9–P12 lineages and to VB in the P11–P12 lineages normally undergo programmed cell death[1].

‡ Processes in regions that normally would display these synapses were out of the region of reconstruction.

死亡[1]。

‡ 这些细胞不能长出轴突，尽管它们具备这些细胞类型显示出的突触联系特征。

表 2. 阻断的前体细胞形成的突触数目以及野生型腹侧索神经元（Pn）形成的典型突触数目[6]

|  |  | AVA | AVB | VA | VB | VC | AS | VD | NMJ |  |
|---|---|---|---|---|---|---|---|---|---|---|
| *unc-85* |  |  |  |  |  |  |  |  |  |  |
| P3 | VA/VB/* | ‡ | ‡ |  |  |  |  |  | 15 |  |
| P3 | AS/VD |  |  |  | § 1 |  |  | = 1 | 19 |  |
| P4 | VA/VB/* |  | = 6 |  |  |  |  |  | 20 |  |
| P5 | VA/VB | = 1 | = 9 |  | = 5 |  |  |  | 8 |  |
| P6 | VA/VB/* |  | = 1 |  | = 5 |  |  |  |  | 无轴突 |
| P6 | AS/VD |  |  |  | § 3 |  |  | = 1 | 14 |  |
| *unc-59* (1) |  |  |  |  |  |  |  |  |  |  |
| P3 | VA/VB/VC |  | = 15 |  |  |  |  | # 1 | 5 |  |
| P3 | AS/VD |  |  |  |  |  |  | = 6 | 14 |  |
| *unc-59* (2) |  |  |  |  |  |  |  |  |  |  |
| P8 | VA/VB | § 6 = 6 |  |  |  |  |  |  | ‡ |  |
| P8 | AS/VD |  |  | § 3 |  |  |  | = 2 | 11 |  |
| P9 | VA/VB/† | § 3 = 5 |  |  |  |  |  | # 3 | 22 |  |
| P9 | AS/VD |  |  | § 3 |  |  |  | = 2 | 13 |  |
| P10 | VA/VB/† | § 9 = 5 |  |  |  |  |  | # 3 | 16 |  |
| P10 | AS/VD |  |  |  |  |  |  | = 2 | 10 |  |
| P11 | VA/†/† | § 7 |  |  |  |  |  |  |  | 无轴突 |
| P11 | AS/VD |  |  |  |  |  |  | = 2 | 12 |  |
| 野生型 |  |  |  |  |  |  |  |  |  |  |
| Pn | VA | § 4 = 3 |  |  |  |  | = 1 | # 1 | 16 |  |
| Pn | VB |  | = 2 |  | = 2 |  |  | # 2 | 9 |  |
| Pn | VC |  |  |  |  | § 3 = 5 |  | # 7 | 2 |  |
| Pn | AS | § 2 = 1 | § 2 | = 1 |  |  |  |  |  |  |
| Pn | VD |  |  | § 1 | § 2 | § 7 |  | = 1 | 26 |  |

野生型的突触数值是从野生型个体的电镜重建获得的 P3 至 P5 前体细胞突触数值的平均值。#，突触前；§，突触后；=，间隙连接。

* 在这些细胞系中，VC 的细胞核曾经产生，但是在成虫电镜重建时已不存在。这些核可能融合以形成 VA/VB/VC 或者消亡了。

† 这些细胞在 P1~P2 和 P9~P12 系相当于 VC，在 P11~P12 系相当于 VB，正常情况下会经历程序性细胞死亡[1]。

‡ 这些区域内的突起正常时能够显示这些突触，但处于重建区域之外。

Several differences were apparent between the blocked precursors and the corresponding cell types in wild-type animals: the blocked cells had more synaptic inputs (Table 1), larger nuclei and extra branches (Fig. 2). These extra branches were generally devoid of synapses and had none of the characteristics of the other cell type. Even more extensive branching has been seen from precursors that are blocked earlier in ventral cord lineages in the mutant *lin-5* (ref. 7). The supernumerary branches may be a consequence of the polyploid nature of these cells; perhaps the total process length produced from a given neurone is proportional to its ploidy. The embryonically produced neurones in this region (that is, the DA, DB and DD motoneurones[6,8]) were normal in morphology and connectivity.

The observation that characteristics of some cell types were expressed normally in the blocked cells implies that the normal complement of wild-type cell divisions is not a necessary prerequisite for the differentiation of these cell types; however, some other cell cycle event (such as DNA replication[15]) may be required. Blast cells that are blocked earlier in a lineage either by drugs[9,10] or in the mutant *lin*-5 (ref. 7), also exhibit characteristics of their normal descendants, but in these cases characteristics of several cell types may be present in one polyploid cell. This may be a result of either localized differentiation or excessive dilution of regulatory elements within these abnormally large, highly polyploid cells. The isolation and characterization of mutants that are blocked at intermediate levels may shed some light on these differences.

Not all late divisions failed in these mutants, and those that did not fail produced normal cells. This observation indicates that the suppression of the differentiated characteristics of certain cell types seen in the blocked precursors does not simply reflect the inability of the mutants to produce these cell classes but implicates the failure to divide as the cause of their suppression.

The lack of expression of one cell type in the undivided, probably tetraploid precursors of *unc-59* and *unc-85* may be because there is an intrinsic mutual exclusivity in the expression of cell type such as has been described for certain fused cells[11] and cultured sympathetic neurones[12]. An alternative interpretation of these observations is that the differentiated state of the precursors reflects the state of commitment of these cells in wild-type animals; thus, one of the daughters would normally inherit the state of commitment of the mother. Some support for this notion is provided by observations of mutants in the genes *unc-86* and *lin-4*; these mutants undergo extra cell divisions in specific lineages. In these cases one of the daughters reiterates the characteristic divisions of the mother in a stem cell manner[13], indicating that it has the same state of commitment as its mother cell. These two interpretations are not necessarily incompatible if cells may only express one state of commitment at any time because of an intrinsic mutual exclusivity of cell states.

The electron microscopy was done by N. Thomson and Marilyn Anness. We thank S. Brenner and W. Fixsen for helpful discussions. H.R.H. was supported by postdoctoral fellowships from the Muscular Dystrophy Associations of America and the USPHS and by

细胞分裂受阻的前体细胞与野生型中与之相对应的细胞类型之间有几个明显的差别：阻断的细胞具有更多的突触传入（表 1），更大的细胞核和额外的分叉（图 2）。这些额外的分叉通常缺乏突触，而且不具备其他细胞类型的特征。在突变体 *lin-5* 中，腹侧索前体细胞的分裂在更早期被阻断，在这些前体细胞中观察到更大规模的分叉（文献 7）。这些过度的分叉可能是细胞多倍体性的结果；可能一个特定神经元的总突起长度是与其倍性成比例的。在这些区域中胚胎发育时期形成的神经元（即 DA、DB 和 DD 运动神经元 [6,8]）在形态和连接性上都是正常的。

细胞分裂受阻的细胞能够表现出某些细胞类型的特征，这个发现提示野生型中的正常细胞分裂过程并不是细胞分化的必要前提。但是，其他的细胞周期事件（比如 DNA 复制 [15]）可能是必需的。药物处理 [9,10] 或者在 *lin-5* 突变体中（文献 7），细胞分裂在较早时期已经阻断的母细胞是会体现其正常子细胞特征的，但这些情况下往往是多种细胞类型的特征同时出现在同一个多倍体细胞中。这一现象可能是这些超大的，染色体倍数特别多的细胞中的局部分化或者调节元件的过度稀释造成的。细胞分裂被部分阻断的突变体的分离和鉴定可能有助于区分这两种可能性。

（这两种）突变体中并非所有的晚期细胞分裂都不能进行，那些没有被阻断的细胞同样能够产生正常的细胞。这个发现表明：分裂受阻的前体细胞不能出现某些特定细胞类型的分化特性，不仅仅简单地反映了突变体不能产生这些细胞类型，而且暗示分裂失败可能是它们被抑制的原因。

*unc-59* 和 *unc-85* 中未分裂的、可能为四倍体的前体细胞不能显示某种细胞类型特征的原因可能是细胞类型间的内在排他性（这种现象在某些融合细胞 [11] 和培养的交感神经元 [12] 中也曾描述过）。上述现象的另一解释就是前体细胞的分化反映了野生型个体中这些细胞的本来状态；所以子代细胞之一自然就会遗传母细胞本来的分化状态。在突变体 *unc-86* 和 *lin-4* 的研究观察中得到了一些支持这一观点的证据；这些突变体在特定的细胞系中会经历额外的细胞分裂。在这种情况下，子代细胞之一以干细胞的方式反复进行母代特有的细胞分裂 [13]，这表明其具有与母代细胞相同的功能状态。如果由于细胞状态的内在排他性而使得细胞在任何时候都只能表达一种功能状态的话，这两种解释应该是可以共存的。

电子显微镜工作是由汤姆森和玛丽莲·安尼斯完成的。我们感谢布伦纳和菲克森提出的宝贵意见。霍维茨得到了美国肌萎缩协会和美国公共卫生署博士后研究基

USPHS grants GM24663 and GM24943.

(**297**, 584-587; 1982)

J. G. White\*, H. R. Horvitz[†] and J. E. Sulston\*

\* MRC Laboratory of Molecular Biology, Hills Road, Cambridge CB2 2QH, UK

[†] Department of Biology, Massachusetts Institute of Technology, Cambridge, Massachusetts 02139, USA

Received 25 January; accepted 28 April 1982.

---

References:

1. Sulston, J. E. & Horvitz, H. R. *Devl. Biol.* **56**,110-156 (1977).

2. Kimble, J. & Hirsh, D. *Devl. Biol.* **70**, 396-417 (1979).

3. Deppe, U. *et al. Proc. Natl. Acad. Sci. U.S.A.* **75**, 376-380 (1978).

4. Horvitz, R. & Sulston, J. *Genetics* **96**, 435-454 (1980).

5. Sulston, J. & Horvitz, R. *Devl. Biol.* **82**, 41-55 (1981).

6. White, J., Southgate, E., Thomson, N. & Brenner, S. *Phil. Trans. R. Soc.* B**275**, 327-348 (1976).

7. Albertson, D., Sulston, J. & White, J. *Devl. Biol.* **63**, 165-178.

8. White, J., Albertson, D. & Anness, M. *Nature* **271**, 746-766 (1978).

9. Whittaker, J. R. *Proc. Natl. Acad. Sci. U.S.A.* **70**, 2096-2100 (1973).

10. Laufer, J., Bazzicalupo, P. & Wood, W. *Cell* **19**, 569-577 (1980).

11. Davidson, R. L. in *Somatic Cell Hybridization* (eds Davidson, R. L. & de la Cruz, F.) 131-150 (Raven, New York,1974).

12. Reichardt, L. & Patterson, P. *Nature* **270**, 147-151 (1977).

13. Chalfie, M., Horvitz, R. & Sulston, J. *Cell* **24**, 59-69 (1981).

14. Sulston, J. E. & White, J. G. *Devl. Biol.* **78**, 577-598 (1980).

15. Satoh, N. & Susumu, I. *J. Embryol. exp. Morph.* **61**, 1-13 (1981).

金以及美国公共卫生署基金 GM24663 和 GM24943 的支持。

（毛晨晖 翻译；丁梅 审稿）

# A Millisecond Pulsar

D. C. Backer *et al.*

## Editor's Note

Pulsars are rapidly rotating neutron stars that emit regular radio pulses. They generally slow down as they age, as rotational energy is radiated away in the pulses. So it was a surprise when Donald Backer and coworkers discovered that a repeating radio source with no evidence of being "young" was actually a pulsar with a very short period (time between pulses) of about 1.6 milliseconds. More "millisecond pulsars" were discovered subsequently, and it is now believed that they are "recycled" pulsars: old neutron stars that accrete gas from a close companion star. The angular momentum of the gas "spins up" the old star. Millisecond pulsars have been used to test predictions of general relativity, such as gravitational radiation.

The radio properties of 4C21.53 have been an enigma for many years. First, the object displays interplanetary scintillations (IPS) at 81 MHz, indicating structure smaller than 1 arc s, despite its low galactic latitude (−0.3°)[1]. IPS modulation is rare at low latitudes because of interstellar angular broadening. Second, the source has an extremely steep (~$\nu^{-2}$) spectrum at decametric wavelengths[2]. This combination of properties suggested that 4C21.53 was either an undetected pulsar or a member of some new class of objects. This puzzle may be resolved by the discovery and related observations of a fast pulsar, 1937+214, with a period of 1.558 ms in the constellation Vulpecula only a few degrees from the direction to the original pulsar, 1919+21. The existence of such a fast pulsar with no evidence either of a new formation event or of present energy losses raises new questions about the origin and evolution of pulsars.

A literature search in 1979 led to the suggestion that the steep-spectrum, IPS source was superposed on a flat-spectrum ($\nu^{-0.1}$) object with a diameter of ~60 arc s located to the west of the 4C position by one interferometer lobe (−31.6 s). Lobe identification errors in the 4C catalogue can occur in regions of confusion such as the galactic plane.

The superposition of two source components, one very compact with a steep spectrum and the other extended with a flat spectrum, was reminiscent of the radio properties of the Crab nebula and its pulsar in the pre-pulsar era[3]. The conjecture was made that the compact component in 4C21.53W was a pulsar as yet undetected due to pulse broadening of its radiation over one period by interstellar scattering. However, the IPS measurement placed an upper limit on interstellar scattering which, in turn, placed a limit on the pulse broadening. The conclusion was that only a very short period pulsar, $P \leqslant 10$ ms, would have been missed in metre wavelength searches owing to this effect. Searches for such a

# 一颗毫秒脉冲星

巴克尔等

## 编者按

脉冲星是快速旋转的、发出规则射电脉冲的中子星。随着时间推移，转动能被脉冲辐射带走，通常脉冲星旋转会越来越慢。因此，当唐纳德·巴克尔和同事们发现一颗没有"年轻"证据的重复射电源其实就是一颗脉冲星，其自转周期（脉冲之间的间隔）很短，大约只有约 1.6 ms 的时候，人们感到震惊。随着更多的"毫秒脉冲星"被发现，现在它们被认为是"再加速"脉冲星：从其密近伴星吸积气体的年老中子星。这些气体的角动量使得那颗年老中子星自转"加速"。毫秒脉冲星已被用于检验广义相对论的预言，如引力辐射。

---

多年来，4C21.53 的射电性质一直是个谜。首先，尽管这个源的银纬低（$-0.3°$）[1]，但是它在 81MHz 表现出行星际闪烁（IPS），表明它的结构应小于 1 arc s。由于星际角度展宽，在低纬度 IPS 调制很少见。其次，这个源在十米波段的频谱极其陡（$\sim v^{-2}$）[2]。结合这两种性质我们可以看出，如果 4C21.53 不是未被探测到的脉冲星，就是某一类新型天体中的成员。一颗快转脉冲星 1937+214 的发现及相关观测可能解开这个谜。这颗快转脉冲星位于狐狸座，自转周期为 1.558 ms，距离最初发现的脉冲星 1919+21 只有几度。存在如此快速转动的脉冲星，同时又没有与新的形成过程或当前能量损失相关的证据，这引发了关于脉冲星起源和演化的新疑问。

---

通过查找 1979 年的文献得知：这个陡谱的 IPS 源叠加在一个平谱源（$v^{-0.1}$）上。平谱源直径约为 60 arc s，位于其 4C 位置以西一个干涉仪波瓣大小（$-31.6$ arc s）处。4C 源表中的波瓣证认错误会产生于在像银道面这样易混淆的区域。

源的两个成分叠加在一起：一个是具有陡谱的致密源，另一个是具有平谱的延展源。这让人想到在脉冲星发现之前，蟹状星云和其中心脉冲星的射电属性[3]。据推测 4C21.53W 中的致密成分是一颗脉冲星，但星际散射使其在一个周期内的脉冲辐射展宽，从而尚未被探测到。不过，IPS 测量给出的星际散射上限，可以反过来限定脉冲展宽。结论是只有周期非常短的脉冲星（$P \leqslant 10$ ms）才可能由于这种效应在米波段脉冲星搜寻时被遗漏。在厘米波段，脉冲展宽效应将大为减弱。1979 年阿

short period pulsar at centimeter wavelengths, where pulse broadening would be much reduced, were conducted at Arecibo Observatory and at Owens Valley Radio Observatory in 1979 without success.

After the 1979 pulsar searches, Erickson (personal communication) located a steep-spectrum compact source, 4C21.53E, east of the 4C position by one 4C interferometer lobe (+31.6 s). This observation provided evidence against the superposition hypothesis. Furthermore, Very Large Array (VLA) observations at 5 GHz by one of us (D.C.B.) showed that 4C21.53E was a compact double source with separation of 0.8 arc s.

Interest in the extended western object, 4C21.53W, returned when decametric observations at the Clark Lake Radio Observatory showed that both 4C21.53E and 4C21.53W had very steep spectra below 100 MHz (ref. 4). In addition, the Clark Lake observations indicated that the western source showed IPS at 34 MHz. The inferred brightness temperature exceeded $>10^{12}$ K.

Observations of 4C21.53W with the Westerbork Synthesis Radio Telescope (WSRT) at 609 MHz in January 1982 confirmed a suspected position discrepancy based on a Culgoora measurement at 80 MHz (ref. 5) and a Bonn measurement at 5,000 MHz (ref. 6) (Fig. 1). We suspected that the Culgoora position was dominated by the steep-spectrum component and that the Bonn position was dominated by the flat-spectrum, extended component. The division of 4C21.53W into two components, evident in Fig. 1., confirmed our suspicion. The southern and northern components were named 4C21.53W(com) or 1937+214 and 4C21.53W(ext) or 1937+215, respectively. A brief observation at the VLA confirmed the position and steep spectrum of 1937+214. A map of 4C21.53W at 1,415 MHz from a 12-h observation with the WSRT in August 1982 clearly resolved the compact and extended source component (Fig. 2). Recent WSRT observations and 1979 total power observations from Arecibo are summarised in Table 1. The spectra are decomposed into compact and extended object contributions. The Bonn measurement[6] is included for completeness. Erickson's decametric observations of this source are reported elsewhere[7].

雷西博天文台和欧文斯谷射电天文台在厘米波段搜寻过这样的短周期脉冲星，但都没有成功。

在 1979 年的脉冲星搜寻后，埃里克森（个人交流）在 4C 位置以东一个 4C 干涉阵波束（+31.6 s）处发现了一个致密陡谱源 4C21.53E。该观测提供的证据反驳了上述叠加猜想。此外，我们中的一位成员（巴克尔）利用甚大阵（VLA）在 5 GHz 发现 4C21.53E 是一个间隔 0.8 arc s 的致密双源。

当克拉克湖射电天文台在十米波段的观测显示 4C21.53W 和 4C21.53E 的频率在 100 MHz 以下具有非常陡的谱（参考文献 4）时，人们的兴趣回归到西边的延展源 4C21.53W 上。另外，克拉克湖射电天文台的观测显示西边的源在 34 MHz 处有 IPS 并且测算的亮温度超过 $10^{12}$ K。

1982 年 1 月，韦斯特博克综合孔径射电望远镜（WSRT）在 609 MHz 对 4C21.53W 的观测证实了根据 80 MHz 卡尔哥拉的测量（参考文献 5）和 5,000MHz 波恩的测量（参考文献 6）所推测的位置偏差（图 1）。我们怀疑卡尔哥拉测量的位置由陡谱成分主导，波恩测量的位置由延展平谱成分主导。图 1 中 4C21.53W 分裂成为两个源，这证实了我们的想法。南边和北边的成分分别被命名为 4C21.53W（com）或 1937+214 和 4C21.53W（ext）或 1937+215。VLA 的短期观测确认了 1937+214 的位置和陡谱。WSRT 于 1982 年 8 月在 1,415 MHz 对 4C21.53W 进行 12 小时观测后的合成图清晰地分辨出致密和延展源成分（图 2）。表 1 总结了最近的 WSRT 观测和 1979 年阿雷西博总强度观测。频谱被分解成致密源和延展源两种成分的贡献。为了完整起见，我们把波恩的测量 [6] 也包括进来。埃里克森在十米波段对这个源的观测发表在其他文章中 [7]。

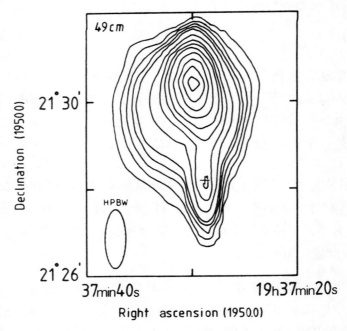

Fig. 1. Image of extended (north) and compact (south, +) components of 4C21.53W from a 12-h synthesis with the WSRT at 608.5 MHz on 15 January 1982. The synthesized beamwidth shown at the lower left is 31.3×80.4 arc s in RA and Dec, respectively.

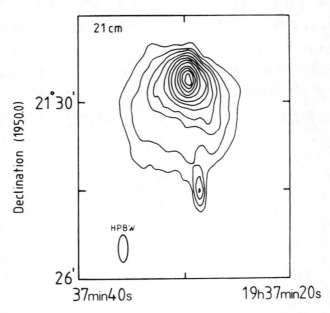

Fig. 2. Image of extended (north) and compact (south) components of 4C21.53W from a 12-h synthesis observation with the WSRT at 1,415 MHz on 8 August 1982. The synthesized beamwidth shown at the lower left is 13.3×37.0 in RA and Dec respectively.

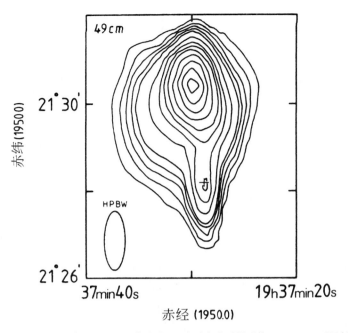

图 1. 1982 年 1 月 15 日 WSRT 在 608.5 MHz 频段上 12 小时合成后得到的 4C21.53W 延展(北)和致密(南，+) 成分图。合成的波束宽度示于左下角，为 31.3 arc s×80.4 arc s（分别在赤经和赤纬方向）。

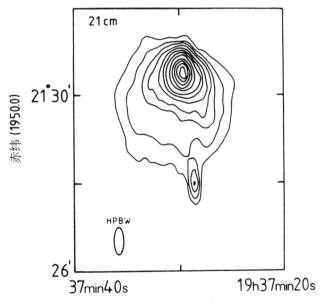

图 2. 1982 年 8 月 8 日 WSRT 在 1,415 MHz 频段上 12 小时观测后合成的 4C21.53W 延展(北)和致密(南) 成分图。合成的波束宽度示于左下角，为 13.3 arc s×37.0 arc s（分别在赤经和赤纬方向）。

Table 1. Flux densities of 4C21.53W

| Frequency (MHz) | Instrument | Total flux density (Jy) | Compact flux density (Jy) | Compact polarization (%) | Extended flux density (Jy) |
|---|---|---|---|---|---|
| 430 | Arecibo | 1.60±0.30 | ~0.3* | — | ~1.3±0.30 |
| 609 | WSRT | 1.15±0.05 | 0.130 | 28±2 | 1.02±0.05 |
| 1,380 | Arecibo | 0.96†±0.05 | ~0.02* | — | 0.94±0.05 |
| 1,415 | WSRT | 0.93±0.02 | 0.017 | 15±2 | 0.91±0.02 |
| 2,380 | Arecibo | 0.90†±0.05 | — | — | 0.90±0.05 |
| 5,000 | Bonn[6] | 0.91† | — | — | 0.92 |

* Estimated from compact source spectral index between 609 and 1,415 MHz
† Corrected for beam sizes.

The spectrum of the extended source is approximately that of an H II region, $\nu^{-0.1}$. The H 166$\alpha$ recombination line was detected at the Arecibo Observatory at the position of the extended source in November 1982. The line temperature is ~1% of the continuum temperature. The velocity of the line is +2 km s$^{-1}$ and its FWHM is ~25 km s$^{-1}$. These properties are comparable with those of an ordinary H II region. The small velocity does not distinguish between kinematic distances of 0 and 8.5 kpc.

The proximity of these two components of 4C21.53W on the sky suggests a possible physical connection. The morphology of the 21-cm continuum maps indicates that the exciting star may be displaced 43 arc s northwards from the centre of the H II region defined by the near-circular, low-level contours. On the other hand, the compact source is displaced 117 arc s southward from the centre. We will return later to the possible connection between these objects.

Interest in further pulsar searches was rekindled following the discovery of a steep-spectrum component in 4C21.53W at decametric wavelengths[4]. Momentum for the search increased when the 609-MHz WSRT map was available. A pulsar search sensitive to periods >4 ms was carried out by Boriakoss (personal communication) at the Arecibo Observatory in March 1982 without success. Detection in September 1982 of strong linear polarization at the compact source position in the WSRT maps made a pulsar detection a near certainty.

A new pulsar search was conducted with the 305-m antenna at the Arecibo Observatory on 25 September 1982 at the position of the compact 15 mJy component detected in the 1,400-MHz synthesis observations. Two harmonics of a millisecond periodicity, 1.558 ms, were discovered at the compact source position. The signal was present for only 3 min of a 7 min sample, and was not seen on a following day at either 1,400 or 2,380 MHz.

表 1 4C21.53W 的流量密度

| 频率（MHz） | 设备 | 总流量密度（Jy） | 致密成分流量密度（Jy） | 致密成分偏振% | 延展成分流量密度（Jy） |
|---|---|---|---|---|---|
| 430 | 阿雷西博射电望远镜 | $1.60 \pm 0.30$ | ~0.3* | — | ~$1.3 \pm 0.30$ |
| 609 | WSRT | $1.15 \pm 0.05$ | 0.130 | $28 \pm 2$ | $1.02 \pm 0.05$ |
| 1,380 | 阿雷西博射电望远镜 | 0.96†$\pm 0.05$ | ~0.02* | — | $0.94 \pm 0.05$ |
| 1,415 | WSRT | $0.93 \pm 0.02$ | 0.017 | $15 \pm 2$ | $0.91 \pm 0.02$ |
| 2,380 | 阿雷西博射电望远镜 | 0.90†$\pm 0.05$ | — | — | $0.90 \pm 0.05$ |
| 5,000 | 波恩射电望远镜 [6] | 0.91† | | | 0.92 |

\* 从致密源 609 MHz 到 1,415 MHz 的谱指数估计得到
† 考虑波束大小后的修正值

延展源的频谱接近于典型的 H II 区的频谱（$v^{-0.1}$）。阿雷西博天文台 1982 年 11 月在延展源位置观测到 H 166α 复合线。谱线温度大约是连续谱温度的 1%。谱线对应的速度为 +2 km·$s^{-1}$，其半高全宽（FWHM）约为 25 km·$s^{-1}$。这些性质和普通 H II 区类似。这样小的速度不能区分开 0 kpc 和 8.5 kpc（译者注：kpc 表示千秒差距，1 秒差距 =$3.08568 \times 10^{16}$ 米）的运动学距离。

4C21.53W 的两个成分在天球上靠得很近，这表明它们之间可能存在物理关联。21 cm 连续谱成像显示，激发星可能向北偏离 H II 区中心 43 arc s，而 H II 区中心由接近圆形、低值等流量线确定。另一方面，致密源的位置在中心以南 117 arc s。我们之后再来讨论这些天体之间可能的联系。

进一步寻找脉冲星的兴趣随着在十米波段上 4C21.53W 陡谱子源的发现被重新激起 [4]。609 MHz WSRT 射电图使得搜寻脉冲星的势头大大增加。博里亚科斯（个人交流）1982 年 3 月在阿雷西博天文台进行了一次对周期 >4 ms 脉冲星敏感的搜寻，但没有成功。1982 年 9 月用 WSRT 射电图上在致密源位置观测到强的线偏振，几乎可以确定这个观测探测到的就是一个脉冲星。

1982 年 9 月 25 日利用阿雷西博天文台 305 m 天线，我们在 1,400 MHz 对在综合孔径天线探测到的 15 mJy 的致密子源位置处，展开了新的脉冲星搜寻。在致密源位置发现了周期为 1.558 ms 的两个谐波。但是信号在 7 min 的测量数据中只出现了 3 min，而且第二天在 1,400 MHz 和 2,380 MHz 频段都没观测到。

In November 1982 the pulsar search was intensified at Arecibo. In addition, we planned a search for interstellar scintillation (ISS) based on the possibility that the compact object was small, but not pulsing. Deep ISS modulation was detected at 1,400 MHz at the position of the compact source (Fig. 3). The amplitude was consistent with the flux density found in synthesis observations. The frequency and time correlation lengths, roughly 2 MHz and 5 min, respectively suggested a relatively small dispersion measure to the object, <100 electrons pc $cm^{-3}$. This observation indicated immediately that the compact source 4C21.53W (com) or 1937+214, was extremely small as only pulsars have shown ISS previously. In addition, the modulation bandwidth and time scale were consistent with the single detection in September. On the following day the millisecond pulsar was confirmed.

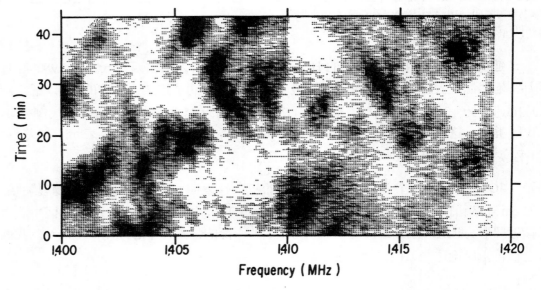

Fig. 3. Interstellar scintillation observation of compact component in 4C21.53W from Arecibo observations on 6 November 1982. Individual spectra were obtained for two polarizations in two 10-MHz bands every 30 s using a 252-channel, 1-bit autocorrelator. Spectra from the two polarization channels were summed and smoothed to a resolution of 100 kHz. The peak intensity in this dynamic spectrum is ~50 mJy.

The waveform of the pulsar contains a main pulse and an interpulse of comparable intensity separated by ~180° (Fig. 4). This morphology repeats precisely the main pulse/interpulse morphology of the Crab pulsar. The Crab pulsar has an additional "precursor" component preceding its main pulse at metre wavelengths. The full widths at half intensity of the pulse components in Fig. 4 are <125 µs, or 8% of the period. The pulses are readily detected with the Arecibo telescope at 1,400 and 430 MHz with a fast signal averager and integrations of a few hundred pulses when positioned on a peak of the ISS modulation pattern (Fig. 3). The waveforms at both frequencies are similar.

1982 年 11 月在阿雷西博天文台我们进一步加强了脉冲星搜寻。另外，基于存在致密源很小又无脉冲的可能，我们计划进行星际闪烁（ISS）搜寻。在 1,400 MHz 频段致密源位置处探测到显度 ISS 调制现象（图 3），其幅度和综合孔径观测到的流量密度一致。频率和时间相关长度分别约为 2 MHz 和 5 min，这表明该天体色散量相对较小，电子柱密度 < 100 pc·cm$^{-3}$。这一观测表明致密源 4C21.53W（com）或 1937+214 的尺度极小，而之前只有脉冲星表现出 ISS 效应。另外，调制带宽和时标与 9 月份的单次观测一致。接下来一天的观测便确认了这颗毫秒脉冲星。

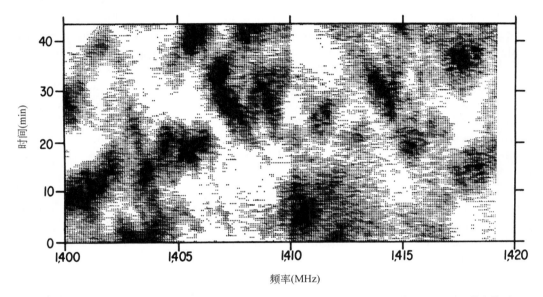

图 3. 1982 年 11 月 6 日阿雷西博观测中对 4C21.53W 致密成分的星际闪烁观测结果。10 MHz 带宽的两路独立偏振信号通过 252 通道，利用 1 比特自相关器每 30 s 采集一次。两个偏振通道的谱加起来，作 100 kHz 分辨率的平均。该动态谱的峰值强度为 ~50 mJy。

这颗脉冲星的波形包含一个主脉冲和一个中间脉冲，两者强度相当，分开约 180°（图 4）。这一形态非常类似蟹状星云脉冲星的主脉冲和中间脉冲的形态。蟹状星云脉冲星在米波波段还有一个早于主脉冲的额外"前导"成分。图 4 中脉冲成分的半高宽均小于 125 μs，或者说是周期的 8%。当阿雷西博望远镜对准 ISS 调制模式（图 3）的峰值处时，在 1,400 MHz 和 430 MHz 利用快速信号平均器对几百个脉冲积分就可以稳定地探测到脉冲。这两个波段的波形是相似的。

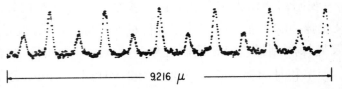

Fig. 4. Waveform of the millisecond pulsar from a signal averager oscilloscope display. Sample spacing is 9 μs. The full trace is roughly six periods, 9,216 μs. The integration lasted ~75 s. The waveform consists of a main pulse and an interpulse separated by nearly 180° of rotational phase. Errors in timing the signal averager and a 20 μs RC time constant are responsible for most of the pulse width.

The first observations have resulted in the following parameters: RA (1950.0) 19 h 37 min 28.72 s, Dec (1950.0) 21° 28' 01.3", Barycentric period 0.001 557 807 (JD 244 5282), Dispersion measure 75 electrons pc cm$^{-3}$. The accuracy of all values is a few parts in the last decimal place. The distance is estimated as 2,500 pc using an average $n_e$ of 0.03 cm$^{-3}$. There is no evidence for binary motion in timing measurements during the second week in November. Timing observations have been initiated to determine the period derivative at the Arecibo Observatory. A previous estimate of the period derivative[8], based on a comparison of measured periods in September and November, has not been substantiated by timing data in November. We suspect that the September measurement was corrupted by sampling errors. Analysis of the November observations results in an upper limit to $P$ of 10$^{-15}$ s per s.

Our original hypothesis that 4C21.53W was a fast pulsar superposed on an extended synchrotron-emitting nebula was only half correct. Now we are faced with a more profound enigma: the existence of a pulsar rotating near the maximum rate possible for a neutron star with a surprising lack of evidence of energetic activity in the vicinity of the pulsar.

The present rotation rate, 642 Hz, is very near the maximum rate of 2,000 Hz where centrifugal forces balance gravitational forces at the surface of a 1 $M_\odot$ neutron star with 10 km radius. Matter on the equator would have a velocity of 0.13$c$. Changes in the equilibrium figure of the pulsar resulting from energy losses to magnetic dipole and gravitational quadrupole radiation (discussed below) may occur as abrupt starquakes if there is such a close balance between gravitational and centrifugal forces. The balance could be tipped in favour of gravity if the pulsar is denser than $\Omega^2/G \sim 2 \times 10^{14}$ g cm$^3$. The amplitude and frequency of starquakes, observable in pulse arrival time measurements, may be able to distinguish between standard (1 $M_\odot$) and high density models for the millisecond pulsar.

The present rotational energy content is $7 \times 10^{51}$ erg for a neutron star moment of inertia 10$^{45}$ g cm$^2$. This energy is comparable to the entire mechanical energy output of a supernova event. A higher density star, as suggested above, could reduce the present energy content if its moment of inertia were smaller than 10$^{45}$ g cm$^2$. Both the rapid spin and the large energy content are indicative of a young object as energy losses to magnetic dipole and gravitational quadrupole radiation are strong functions of the rotation rate, $\Omega^4$ and $\Omega^6$, respectively[9]. The minimum energy loss for this pulsar will be the observed radio emission which amounts to $3 \times 10^{30}$ erg s$^{-1}$ assuming a beam solid angle of 1 sr.

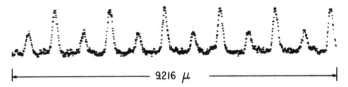

图 4. 信号平均示波器显示的毫秒脉冲星波形。取样间隔是 9 μs。包含约 6 个周期，共 9,216 μs。积分持续约 75 s。波形包含分开接近 180° 旋转相位的一个主脉冲和一个间脉冲。脉冲宽度主要来源于信号平均器的测时误差和 20 μs 的 RC 时间常数。

首次观测得到如下参数：赤经（1950.0）19 时 37 分 28.72 秒，赤纬（1950.0）21° 28′ 01.3″，太阳系质心系周期 0.001 557 807 s（儒略日（JD）244 5282），色散量为 75 个电子秒差距每立方厘米。所有值的精确度达到小数点最后一位。利用 $n_e$ 为 0.03 cm$^{-3}$ 的平均电子密度可以估算出距离为 2,500 pc。11 月第二周的测时观测没有显示此脉冲星存在于双星系统的迹象。为了得到周期变化率，我们在阿雷西博天文台进行了多次测时观测。之前通过比较 9 月和 11 月测得周期给出的周期变化率 [8] 没有被 11 月的测时数据所肯定。我们怀疑 9 月份的观测因取样不当而损坏。通过分析 11 月的观测数据能够得到周期变化率的上限为每秒 10$^{-15}$ s。

我们最初关于 4C21.53W 是快转脉冲星叠加在延展的同步辐射星云的猜想只对了一半。现在我们面临着一个意义更深远的谜团：脉冲星以接近中子星极限的速度旋转，令人吃惊的是周围却没有剧烈活动的证据。

目前 642 Hz 的自转速率非常接近 2,000 Hz 的最大自转速率（离心力和引力在 1 个太阳质量、半径 10 km 的中子星表面达到平衡时中子星的转速）。赤道物质的速度可达到 0.13$c$。假如引力和离心力接近这一平衡，那么因磁偶极和引力四极辐射（下面将讨论到）能量损失所致脉冲星平衡状态的改变可能以突发星震的形式发生。如果脉冲星密度大于 $\Omega^2/G \sim 2 \times 10^{14}$ g·cm$^3$，引力在平衡中将占优势。可由脉冲到达时间测量得到的星震幅度和频率也许能鉴别毫秒脉冲星的标准模型（1 $M_\odot$）和高密度模型。

转动惯量为 10$^{45}$ g·cm$^2$ 的中子星目前总转动能为 7 × 10$^{51}$ erg。这个能量相当于超新星事件的全部机械能输出。对于上面提及的这种更高密度星，如果其转动惯量小于 10$^{45}$ g·cm$^2$，那么星体的转动能将有所减少。因为磁偶极和引力四极辐射均强烈依赖于星体自转频率，分别遵从 $\Omega^4$ 和 $\Omega^6$ [9]，所以快速自转率和高能量都暗示着年轻天体。假设辐射束的立体角为 1 sr，这颗脉冲星的最小能量损失即为观测到的射电辐射，共计 3 × 10$^{30}$ erg·s$^{-1}$。

The age of this pulsar is puzzling. The maximum spin rate for a neutron star is ~2,000 Hz. A model for the Crab pulsar by Ostriker and Gunn[9] predicts a period decay from this rate to 100 Hz in 1 yr due to gravitational quadrupole radiation. We do not observe such a rapid decay. Furthermore, there is a surprising absence of evidence of any debris from a recent neutron star formation event. Our radio maps show no synchrotron-emitting nebula in the vicinity of the pulsar. Einstein observations place a limit of $1.5 \times 10^6$ K for the surface temperature of a neutron star at the pulsar position for the indicated distance of 2 kpc, and exclude the possibility of a synchrotron nebula (D. J. Helfand, personal communication). These X-ray limits do not allow for possible heavy extinction. There is no source at the pulsar position in the COS B catalogue[10]. Lick Observatory observations reveal a 20 mag optical star at the position of the pulsar[11]. In direct analogy to the Crab pulsar, we expect this object will show optical pulsations.

We conclude that despite the large spin and rotational energy, this pulsar is not young. Evidently it has found a way to preserve a large fraction of its original energy. Minimal energy loss requires low values for the perpendicular magnetic dipole moment and the gravitational quadrupole moment. The first binary pulsar, 1913+16, is an example of a rapidly rotating neutron star (17 Hz) with a very low moments based on period derivative measurements. Observations of the spin decay will determine the dominant energy loss mechanism.

Two factors lead us to suggest that the pulsar and the H II region are related: (1) The two objects are in the same area of sky in a region of relatively low radio confusion. (2) The brightest part of the H II region and the pulsar are displaced to opposite sides of the near circular, low-level contours of the H II region.

We propose that the pulsar and the exciting star of the H II region were formerly members of a binary system. One of the components evolved and went through a quiet neutron-star formation stage. Formation of neutron stars in binary systems is also required to explain X-ray and radio pulsar binaries. A large and asymmetric energy and momentum transfer to the neutron star from the other component must have provided the escape velocity necessary to disrupt the binary orbit. This transfer also provides a means for creating a massive, high density object. The present separation of the pulsar from the centre for the HII region suggests an epoch for the disruption event of 7,800 yr ago and a distance of 2 kpc if we assume a typical pulsar transverse velocity of 150 km s$^{-1}$. Proper motion of the pulsar would be southward in declination of 0.015 arc s yr$^{-1}$.

We thank the staff of Arecibo Observatory for support and our colleagues for many exciting discussions. This research is supported by grants from the NSF and the Netherlands Foundation for Radio Astronomy. The Arecibo Observatory is part of the National Astronomy and Ionosphere Centre which is operated by Cornell University under contract with NSF.

(**300**, 615-618; 1982)

这颗脉冲星的年龄还是个谜。对中子星最大的自转率约为 2,000 Hz，奥斯特里克和冈恩[9]的蟹状星云脉冲星模型预言：由于引力四极辐射，将发生周期衰减，在一年内从这个自转率降到 100 Hz。但是我们没有观测到这种快速衰减，更没有发现由近期形成中子星而产生的任何遗迹的证据。我们的射电成图显示脉冲星附近没有同步辐射的星云。在脉冲星的位置、推测距离 2 kpc 处，爱因斯坦卫星的观测给出中子星表面温度上限为 $1.5 \times 10^6$ K，并排除了同步辐射星云的可能性（赫尔方，个人交流）。这些 X 射线方面的限制没有考虑可能的很强的消光。在 COS B 星表[10]里没找到位于这颗脉冲星位置的源。利克天文台在这颗脉冲星位置观测到一颗 20 星等的星[11]。直接类比蟹状星云脉冲星，我们预期这一天体将显示光学脉动。

我们得出结论，尽管这颗脉冲星的自转速率和转动能都很大，但它并不年轻。显然它找到了一种保存大部分原初能量的方式。最小的能量损失要求垂直磁偶极矩和引力四极矩都很小。基于对周期变化率的测量，第一颗脉冲双星 1913+16 就是一颗磁矩和质量矩很低的快转自旋中子星（17 Hz）的例子。自转衰减的观测将确定主导的能量损失机制。

我们基于两个因素认为脉冲星和 H II 区成协：(1)这两个天体位于同一天区，那里的射电混淆度相对较低；(2)H II 区最亮部分和脉冲星反向偏离 H II 区的中心（由近圆形的低值等流量线而定）。

我们认为脉冲星和 H II 区的激发星曾经是一个双星系统。双星成员之一演化并历经了一个并不剧烈的中子星形成阶段。我们也需要中子星在双星系统中的形成来解释 X 射线和射电脉冲双星。从伴星到中子星的巨大而不对称的能量和角动量转移一定能够提供足够的逃逸速度来瓦解双星轨道。这一转移也为产生大质量、高密度天体提供了途径。如果我们取 150 km·s$^{-1}$ 作为脉冲星的典型横向速度，目前脉冲星和 H II 区中心的间距表明：在 7,800 年前，2 kpc 距离处曾发生一起双星轨道瓦解事件。脉冲星应该沿着赤纬向南自行，速度为 0.015 arc s·yr$^{-1}$。

我们对阿雷西博天文台员工的支持以及与我们同事许多令人兴奋的讨论表示感谢。本研究由国家科学基金和荷兰射电天文学基金会资助。阿雷西博天文台隶属于国家科学基金资助、康奈尔大学管理的国家天文与电离层研究中心。

（肖莉 周旻辰 翻译；徐仁新 审稿）

**D. C. Backer\*, Shrinivas R. Kulkarni\*, Carl Heiles\*, M. M. Davis[†] and W. M. Goss[‡]**

\* Radio Astronomy Laboratory and Astronomy Department, University of California, Berkeley, California 94720, USA

[†] National Astronomy and Ionosphere Center, Arecibo, Puerto Rico

[‡] Kapteyn Laboratorium, Groningen, The Netherlands

Received 22 November; accepted 25 November 1982.

---

References:

1. Readhead, A. C. S. & Hewish, A. *Nature* **236**, 440 (1972).
2. Rickard, J. J. & Cronyn, W. *Astrophys. J.* **228**, 755 (1979).
3. Hewish, A. & Okoye, S. E. *Nature* **207**, 55 (1965).
4. Erickson, W. C., *Bull. Am. Astr. Soc.* **12**, 799 (1980).
5. Slee, O. B., *Austr. J. Phys. Suppl.* **36**, 1 (1977).
6. Altenhoff, W. J., Downes, D., Goad, L., Maxwell, A. & Rinehart, R. *Astr. Astrophys. Suppl.* **1**, 419 (1979).
7. Erickson, W. C. *Astrophys. J.* (in the press).
8. Backer, D. C., Kulkarni, S. R., Heiles, C., Davis, M. M. & Goss, W. M. *IAU Circ.* No. 3743 (1982).
9. Ostriker, J. P. & Gunn, J. E. *Astrophys. J.* **157**, 1395 (1969).
10. Swanenberg, B. N. *et al. Astrophys. J. Lett.*, **243**, L69 (1981).
11. Djorgovski, S. *Nature* **300**, 618-619 (1982).

# Evidence on Human Origins from Haemoglobins of African Apes

M. Goodman *et al.*

## Editor's Note

**Fossil evidence for human antiquity was tempered in the 1970s by comparison of protein sequences, which provide a "molecular clock". Rather than supporting the fossil-based idea of a human lineage stretching back more than 10 million years, the molecular data suggested a contradictory story: that humans and chimpanzees diverged around 1.5 million years ago. Here Morris Goodman and colleagues used more refined techniques to show how the rate of change in protein sequences of apes and humans has decelerated over the past few million years, giving more accurate and consistent molecular-clock estimates of this divergence time.**

Molecular data have influenced views concerning human origins, first, by supporting the genealogical classification of *Pan* (chimpanzee) and *Gorilla* with *Homo* rather than with *Pongo* (orangutan)[1,2] and, second, by suggesting that only a few million years separate humans and chimpanzees from their last common ancestor[3,4]. Indeed, the cladistic distances in phylogenetic trees constructed from amino acid sequence data, on detecting many superimposed mutations, yielded a "molecular-clock" divergence date between *Homo* and *Pan* of only 1–1.5 Myr BP[5]. This date, which is even more recent than that (4.2–5.3 Myr BP)[6] calculated using phenetic distances from immunological and DNA-hybridization comparisons (Table 1), is too near the present considering the existence of 3–4 Myr-old fossils of bipedal human ancestors[7] (and a 5.5 Myr-old jaw fragment assigned to *Australopithecus*[8]). Perhaps decelerated sequence evolution occurred; alternatively, hominoid distances could have been underestimated, because chimpanzee and gorilla were represented mostly by sequences inferred from peptide amino acid compositions, as was the case for their haemoglobins[9,10]. To help rectify this situation we report here the rigorously determined $\alpha$- and $\beta$-haemoglobin amino acid sequences not only of chimpanzee (*Pan troglodytes*) and *Gorilla gorilla* but also pygmy chimpanzee (*Pan paniscus*). Our findings favour the explanation of decelerated evolution and point to selection preserving perfected haemoglobin molecules.

THE pygmy chimpanzee sequence is shown in Fig. 1, with supporting data in Fig. 2. There is no difference in this sequence from that of either chimpanzee or man, and only two differences from gorilla. At position $\alpha 23$, gorilla has aspartic acid instead of glutamic acid and at $\beta 104$, lysine instead of arginine. When these sequences are used with other known haemoglobin sequences in phylogenetic reconstructions by the maximum parsimony method, evidence is provided for cladistically joining *Pan* and *Gorilla* to *Homo* in

1114

# 来自非洲猿血红蛋白的人类起源证据

古德曼等

**编者按**

20世纪70年代，通过比较提供"分子钟"的蛋白质序列，古人类的化石证据得到一些修正。基于化石证据，人类谱系可以回溯到一千多万年前；然而分子数据非但不支持这一观点，反而提出了一个与其对立的情形：人类和黑猩猩大约在150万年前分化。本文中莫里斯·古德曼和他的同事们采用更精确的技术，展示了过去几百万年间类人猿和人类的蛋白质序列变化速率是怎样减缓的，并给出了更准确、一致的分离时间的分子钟估计值。

---

分子数据已经影响到了有关人类起源的观点，这种影响体现在两个方面：首先，分子数据支持黑猩猩属和大猩猩属的系统分类与人属相同，而与猩猩属不同[1,2]；其次，分子数据提出，人类和黑猩猩从其最近的共有祖先分离出来只有几百万年的时间[3,4]。实际上，根据检测许多叠加突变的氨基酸序列数据构建的系统演化树的进化支距离，我们可以得到人属和黑猩猩属的"分子钟"分离时间距今仅100万到150万年[5]；比起利用免疫学和DNA杂交比较得到的表型距离计算出的时间（距今420万年到530万年）[6]，这一时间更近（表1）。考虑到存在300万到400万年前的两足行走的人类祖先化石[7]（以及一个被认定为550万年前的南方古猿的下颌骨碎片[8]），这一时间似乎离现在太近了。这有可能是因为序列进化速率减缓了，或者因为黑猩猩和大猩猩的序列主要是以多肽的氨基酸组成推导出来的序列呈现的，就像他们的血红蛋白的情况一样[9,10]，导致了对人科动物进化距离的过低估计。为了帮助修正这一情况，我们在此报道了经过严密方法确定的黑猩猩、大猩猩以及倭黑猩猩的α-血红蛋白和β-血红蛋白的氨基酸序列。我们的发现支持进化减速的解释，并且指出存在某种选择作用，该选择倾向于保留最好的血红蛋白分子。

---

图1所示为倭黑猩猩的序列，其支持数据在图2中列出。倭黑猩猩的这一序列与黑猩猩和人类都没有区别，与大猩猩只在两个位点有所不同。在位点α23，大猩猩是天冬氨酸，而倭黑猩猩是谷氨酸；β104位点处，大猩猩中是赖氨酸，而倭黑猩猩是精氨酸。当采用最大简约法使用这些序列和其他已知血红蛋白序列一起重建系统发育时，就可以得到相关证据证明在进化关系上黑猩猩属和大猩猩属跟人属聚

Homininae rather than to *Pongo* in Ponginae, these two subfamilies being sister groups (Fig. 3*a*). Specifically, substitutions at $\beta$87 (lysine → threonine) and $\beta$125 (glutamine → proline) group *Pan, Homo* and *Gorilla* into Homininae. When all relevant amino acid sequence data are considered, breaking up the African ape–human clade with orang-utan adds at least 10 nucleotide replacements (NRs) over the most parsimonious score (2 NRs apiece for fibrinopeptides A and B, myoglobin and $\beta$-haemoglobin, and 4 NRs for carbonic anhydrase[11]). Further parsimony evidence for a monophyletic chimpanzee–human–gorilla clade has been obtained from mitochondrial DNA nucleotide sequence data, representing close to 900 aligned positions of human[12], chimpanzee[13], gorilla[13], orang-utan[13], gibbon[13], mouse[14] and ox[15]. Taking mouse and ox as outgroups of Hominoidea and calculating NR lengths for each possible dichotomous branching order among the five hominoid lineages, it was found[16] that breaking up the human–chimpanzee–gorilla clade adds at least 19 NRs to the most parsimonious score.

Table 1. Comparison of "clock" dates from different sets of molecular data

| Ancestral node | Immunological | | DNA hybridization (Myr BP) | Amino acid sequence (Myr BP) | |
| --- | --- | --- | --- | --- | --- |
| | Albumin (Myr BP) | Transferrin (Myr BP) | | | |
| Theria | 125 | X | X | 117 | 200 |
| Eutheria | 90–100 | X | X | 90 | 154 |
| Primates | 73.5 | 63 | 91 | 51 | 87.1 |
| Anthropoidea | 35 | 35 | 35 | 20.5 | 35 |
| Catarrhini | 20.3 | 18.6 | 21.4 | 13.4 | 22.9 |
| *Homo-Pan-(Gorilla)* | 4.2(4.2) | 4.6(4.6) | 5.3(5.3) | 1.3(1.8) | 2.2(3.1) |

Times for the Theria (Metatheria–Eutheria) and Eutheria ancestral nodes for albumin immunological distances are from Sarich and Cronin[6] as described in the text of their article; the other divergence times from albumin and transferrin immunological distances and from DNA hybridization distances are calculated from Table 2 of their article using 35 Myr BP[6] for the Anthropoidea (platyrrhine–catarrhine) ancestral node as the setting of the "clock". The divergence clock dates shown in the last two columns are from Table 9 of ref. 5; these dates are based on calculations using phylogenetic trees constructed from amino acid sequence data on up to 10 polypeptide chains ($\alpha$- and $\beta$-haemoglobins, myoglobin, lens $\alpha$-crystallin A, cytochrome *c*, fibrinopeptides A and B, and carbonic anhydrases I, II and III). In the second to last column, the setting of the clock is 90 Myr BP for Eutheria ancestral node. In the last column, 35 Myr BP for Anthropoidea ancestral node is used to set the clock, thus allowing more direct comparison with values from Sarich and Cronin[6]. Note that the so-called molecular clocks are not in markedly good agreement with one another. The value underlined for each set of clock dates is the setting for these calculations. "X" Means that no clock date could be calculated because no corresponding distance value was given in Table 2 of Sarich and Cronin[6].

在人亚科的进化支下，而不是同猩猩属聚在猩猩亚科中。这两个亚科是姊妹群（图3a）。发生在β87（赖氨酸→苏氨酸）和β125（谷氨酸→脯氨酸）两个位点的替换将黑猩猩属、人属和大猩猩属归属到人亚科中。如果考虑到所有相关的氨基酸序列信息，将非洲猿类—人类分支与猩猩所在的分支打断至少会增加超过最大简约度10个NR（血纤肽A和B、肌红蛋白和β–血红蛋白各有两个NR，而碳酸酐酶有四个NR[11]；NR：nucleotide replacement，核苷酸的替代位点）。目前已经由线粒体DNA的核苷酸序列数据得到了更多关于黑猩猩–人类–大猩猩进化谱系是单源进化支系的简约性证据，这里所使用的线粒体DNA核苷酸序列数据代表了人类[12]、黑猩猩[13]、大猩猩[13]、猩猩[13]、长臂猿[13]、小鼠[14]和牛[15]的将近900个位点的比对信息。将小鼠和牛作为人猿超科的外群，在这五种人科家族各种可能的二歧分支次序上计算的核苷酸置换长度，结果发现[16]：打断人类–黑猩猩–大猩猩进化支，最大简约度至少会增加19个NR。

表1. 来自不同分子数据"分子钟"时间的比较

| 祖先节点 | 免疫学 | | DNA 杂交 (Myr BP) | 氨基酸 序列 (Myr BP) | |
| --- | --- | --- | --- | --- | --- |
| | 白蛋白 (Myr BP) | 转铁蛋白 (Myr BP) | | | |
| 兽亚纲 | 125 | X | X | 117 | 200 |
| 真兽次亚纲 | 90~100 | X | X | 90 | 154 |
| 灵长目 | 73.5 | 63 | 91 | 51 | 87.1 |
| 类人猿亚目 | 35 | 35 | 35 | 20.5 | 35 |
| 狭鼻类 | 20.3 | 18.6 | 21.4 | 13.4 | 22.9 |
| 人属–黑猩猩属–（大猩猩属） | 4.2 (4.2) | 4.6 (4.6) | 5.3 (5.3) | 1.3 (1.8) | 2.2 (3.1) |

表1. 兽亚纲（后兽次亚纲–真兽次亚纲）和真兽亚纲的白蛋白免疫距离的祖先节点引用自萨里奇和克罗宁[6]的文章中的描述；其余白蛋白和转铁蛋白的免疫距离的分离时间以及DNA杂交距离的分离时间是由他们文章中表2给出的数据计算出来的，将类人猿亚目（阔鼻次目–狭鼻次目）的祖先节点距今3,500万年[6]作为"分子钟"设定值。最后两栏列出的分子钟日期来自参考文献5的表9；根据多达10条多肽链（包括：α–血红蛋白和β–血红蛋白、肌红蛋白、α–晶状体球蛋白A、细胞色素c、血纤肽A和B、碳酸酐酶I、II和III）的氨基酸序列信息构建系统进化树，利用该进化树计算得出这些日期。从第二栏到最后一栏，真兽次亚纲的祖先节点距今9,000万年作为分子钟设定值。最后一栏中，将类人猿亚目的祖先节点距今3,500万年作为分子钟设定值，因此可以与萨里奇和克罗宁文章中的数值进行更直接的比较[6]。注意：所谓的分子钟彼此并不十分一致。表示每组分子钟日期的数值都用下划线标出，这些数值是为进行这些计算而设定的。"X"表示由于萨里奇和克罗宁文章[6]的表2中没有给出相应的距离值，因而无法计算出其分子钟时间。

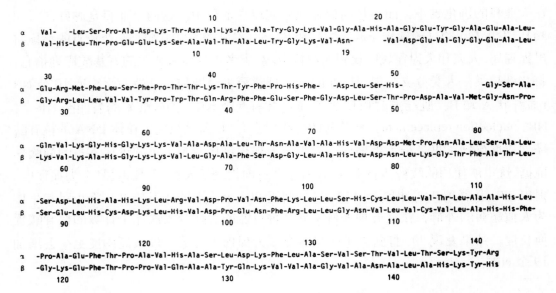

```
              10                                      20
α  Val-    -Leu-Ser-Pro-Ala-Asp-Lys-Thr-Asn-Val-Lys-Ala-Ala-Try-Gly-Lys-Val-Gly-Ala-His-Ala-Gly-Glu-Tyr-Gly-Ala-Glu-Ala-Leu-
β  Val-His-Leu-Thr-Pro-Glu-Glu-Lys-Ser-Ala-Val-Thr-Ala-Leu-Try-Gly-Lys-Val-Asn-     -Val-Asp-Glu-Val-Gly-Gly-Glu-Ala-Leu-
              10                                      19

      30                       40                          50
α  -Glu-Arg-Met-Phe-Leu-Ser-Phe-Pro-Thr-Thr-Lys-Thr-Tyr-Phe-Pro-His-Phe-    -Asp-Leu-Ser-His-          -Gly-Ser-Ala-
β  -Gly-Arg-Leu-Leu-Val-Val-Tyr-Pro-Trp-Thr-Gln-Arg-Phe-Phe-Glu-Ser-Phe-Gly-Asp-Leu-Ser-Thr-Pro-Asp-Ala-Val-Met-Gly-Asn-Pro-
      30                       40                          50

              60                       70                          80
α  -Gln-Val-Lys-Gly-His-Gly-Lys-Lys-Val-Ala-Asp-Ala-Leu-Thr-Asn-Ala-Val-Ala-His-Val-Asp-Asp-Met-Pro-Asn-Ala-Leu-Ser-Ala-Leu-
β  -Lys-Val-Lys-Ala-His-Gly-Lys-Lys-Val-Leu-Gly-Ala-Phe-Ser-Asp-Gly-Leu-Ala-His-Leu-Asp-Asn-Leu-Lys-Gly-Thr-Phe-Ala-Thr-Leu-
      60                       70                          80

              90                      100                         110
α  -Ser-Asp-Leu-His-Ala-His-Lys-Leu-Arg-Val-Asp-Pro-Val-Asn-Phe-Lys-Leu-Leu-Ser-His-Cys-Leu-Leu-Val-Thr-Leu-Ala-Ala-His-Leu-
β  -Ser-Glu-Leu-His-Cys-Asp-Lys-Leu-His-Val-Asp-Pro-Glu-Asn-Phe-Arg-Leu-Leu-Gly-Asn-Val-Leu-Val-Cys-Val-Leu-Ala-His-His-Phe-
              90                      100                         110

              120                      130                         140
α  -Pro-Ala-Glu-Phe-Thr-Pro-Ala-Val-His-Ala-Ser-Leu-Asp-Lys-Phe-Leu-Ala-Ser-Val-Ser-Thr-Val-Leu-Thr-Ser-Lys-Tyr-Arg
β  -Gly-Lys-Glu-Phe-Thr-Pro-Pro-Val-Gln-Ala-Ala-Tyr-Gln-Lys-Val-Val-Ala-Gly-Val-Ala-Asn-Ala-Leu-Ala-His-Lys-Tyr-His
              120                      130                         140
```

Fig. 1. Complete amino acid sequence of pygmy chimpanzee haemoglobin. The sequence is deduced in the liquid phase sequenator using the Quadrol program[26] and the N,N-diethylaminopropyne program[27]. The amino acid analysis of the most important peptides is given in Fig. 2. The amino acid sequences of human haemoglobin A and of the haemoglobins of pygmy chimpanzee and chimpanzee are all identical.

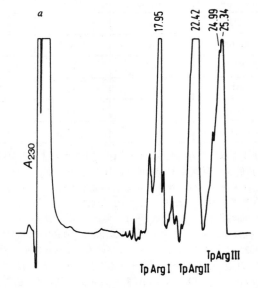

Fig. 2. a, Amino acid analysis of most important peptides for sequencing pygmy chimpanzee haemoglobin. Tp Arg, tryptical peptides after blocking lysine side chains. Pro Pep., C-terminal peptide after hydrophilic splitting of Asp–Pro bond[28]. The separation of most peptides was performed by HPLC chromatography. Separation of the "Arginine" peptides from the α-chains by HPLC (apparatus: Beckman Instruments, RP 2 column acetonitrile gradient; ammonium acetate buffer pH 6.0).

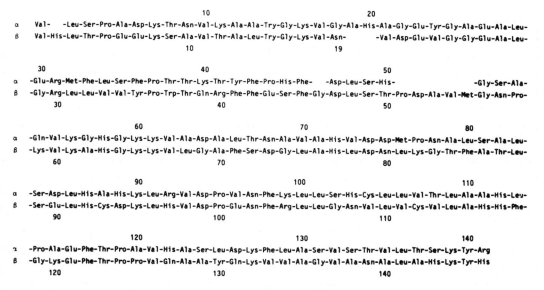

```
                              10                        20
α   Val-   -Leu-Ser-Pro-Ala-Asp-Lys-Thr-Asn-Val-Lys-Ala-Ala-Try-Gly-Lys-Val-Gly-Ala-His-Ala-Gly-Glu-Tyr-Gly-Ala-Glu-Ala-Leu-
β   Val-His-Leu-Thr-Pro-Glu-Glu-Lys-Ser-Ala-Val-Thr-Ala-Leu-Try-Gly-Lys-Val-Asn-        -Val-Asp-Glu-Val-Gly-Gly-Glu-Ala-Leu-
                             10                        19

      30                         40                          50
α   -Glu-Arg-Met-Phe-Leu-Ser-Phe-Pro-Thr-Thr-Lys-Thr-Tyr-Phe-Pro-His-Phe-   -Asp-Leu-Ser-His-              -Gly-Ser-Ala-
β   -Gly-Arg-Leu-Leu-Val-Val-Tyr-Pro-Trp-Thr-Gln-Arg-Phe-Phe-Glu-Ser-Phe-Gly-Asp-Leu-Ser-Thr-Pro-Asp-Ala-Val-Met-Gly-Asn-Pro-
      30                         40                          50

             60                        70                        80
α   -Gln-Val-Lys-Gly-His-Gly-Lys-Lys-Val-Ala-Asp-Ala-Leu-Thr-Asn-Ala-Val-Ala-His-Val-Asp-Asp-Met-Pro-Asn-Ala-Leu-Ser-Ala-Leu-
β   -Lys-Val-Lys-Ala-His-Gly-Lys-Lys-Val-Leu-Gly-Ala-Phe-Ser-Asp-Gly-Leu-Ala-His-Leu-Asp-Asn-Leu-Lys-Gly-Thr-Phe-Ala-Thr-Leu-
      60                        70                        80

             90                        100                       110
α   -Ser-Asp-Leu-His-Ala-His-Lys-Leu-Arg-Val-Asp-Pro-Val-Asn-Phe-Lys-Leu-Leu-Ser-His-Cys-Leu-Leu-Val-Thr-Leu-Ala-Ala-His-Leu-
β   -Ser-Glu-Leu-His-Cys-Asp-Lys-Leu-His-Val-Asp-Pro-Glu-Asn-Phe-Arg-Leu-Leu-Gly-Asn-Val-Leu-Val-Cys-Val-Leu-Ala-His-His-Phe-
      90                        100                       110

             120                       130                       140
α   -Pro-Ala-Glu-Phe-Thr-Pro-Ala-Val-His-Ala-Ser-Leu-Asp-Lys-Phe-Leu-Ala-Ser-Val-Ser-Thr-Val-Leu-Thr-Ser-Lys-Tyr-Arg
β   -Gly-Lys-Glu-Phe-Thr-Pro-Pro-Val-Gln-Ala-Ala-Tyr-Gln-Lys-Val-Val-Ala-Gly-Val-Ala-Asn-Ala-Leu-Ala-His-Lys-Tyr-His
      120                       130                       140
```

图 1. 倭黑猩猩血红蛋白的氨基酸全序列。该序列是使用乙二胺程序 [26] 和 N,N– 二乙基丙炔胺甲酸盐程序 [27] 通过固相序列分析仪推导出来的。图 2 给出了最重要的肽段的氨基酸分析。人类血红蛋白 A 的氨基酸序列与倭黑猩猩和黑猩猩的血红蛋白的氨基酸序列都是一样的。

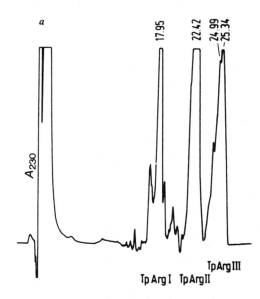

图 2. a，倭黑猩猩血红蛋白测序的重要肽段的氨基酸分析。Tp Arg，阻断赖氨酸侧链之后的胰蛋白酶肽段。Pro Pep.，天冬氨酸–脯氨酸键发生亲水解离后的 C–末端肽 [28]。大部分肽段的分离是通过高效液相色谱法进行的。通过高效液相色谱法将精氨酸肽段从 α–链上分离下来（仪器装置：贝克曼仪器、反向二柱乙腈梯度仪和 pH 6.0 的醋酸铵缓冲液）。

*b*

## Bonobo α–Chains

|  | Tp1 Arg | Tp2 Arg | Tp3 Arg | Pro Pep. | Chain Analysis |
|---|---|---|---|---|---|
| Pos. | 1-31 | 32-92 | 93-141 | 65-141 |  |
| Lys | 3.00 | 5.24 | 3.25 | 3.17 | 11.1 |
| His | 1.21 | 6.27 | 3.20 | 3.13 | 9.80 |
| Arg | 1.11 | 1.08 | 1.08 | 1.05 | 3.00 |
| Asp | 2.16 | 6.80 | 3.07 | 2.40 | 12.32 |
| Thr | 1.08 | 3.83 | 3.70 | 3.80 | 8.74 |
| Ser | 1.08 | 4.92 | 4.80 | 4.80 | 10.80 |
| Glu | 2.98 | 1.15 | 1.08 | 1.27 | 5.30 |
| Pro | 1.01 | 2.94 | 2.86 | 2.86 | 7.05 |
| Gly | 3.84 | 3.19 |  |  | 7.30 |
| Ala | 7.06 | 8.18 | 5.85 | 6.26 | 20.70 |
| Cys |  |  | 0.70 | 0.90 | 0.90 |
| Val | 3.05 | 4.15 | 5.90 | 4.80 | 12.70 |
| Met |  | 1.85 |  |  | 1.70 |
| Leu | 2.20 | 7.12 | 9.10 | 8.86 | 18.20 |
| Tyr | 1.01 | 1.08 | 0.95 | 1.05 | 2.90 |
| Phe |  | 4.22 | 3.12 | 3.13 | 7.05 |
| Try | 0.90 |  |  |  | 0.80 |
| Total | 31 | 61 | 49 | 47 | 141 |

## Bonobo β–Chains

|  | Tp1 Arg | Tp2 Arg | Tp3 Arg | Tp4 Arg | CN1 | CN2 | Pro pep. | Chain Analysis |
|---|---|---|---|---|---|---|---|---|
| Pos. | 1-30 | 31-40 | 41-74 | 75-146 | 1-55 | 56-146 | 70-146 |  |
| Lys | 2.14 |  | 6.29 | 2.92 | 2.26 | 8.84 | 3.14 | 11.40 |
| His | 1.07 |  | 4.36 | 3.62 | 1.21 | 8.10 | 3.97 | 9.10 |
| Arg | 1.07 | 1.07 | 1.01 |  | 2.08 | 1.10 | 0.99 | 3.00 |
| Asp | 2.09 |  | 8.70 | 2.19 | 4.08 | 8.80 | 3.14 | 12.80 |
| Thr | 1.92 | 1.05 | 2.80 | 1.14 | 3.91 | 3.07 | 1.07 | 6.80 |
| Ser | 1.01 |  | 3.80 |  | 2.87 | 2.08 |  | 4.75 |
| Glu | 3.96 | 1.11 | 3.20 | 3.13 | 5.99 | 4.82 | 3.97 | 11.30 |
| Pro | 0.96 | 1.02 | 2.80 | 2.18 | 2.87 | 3.80 | 2.70 | 7.40 |
| Gly | 3.85 |  | 5.90 | 3.18 | 4.78 | 8.11 | 3.30 | 12.80 |
| Ala | 3.00 |  | 5.20 | 7.00 | 4.17 | 10.90 | 6.94 | 14.75 |
| Cys |  |  | 0.80 | 0.90 |  | 1.80 | 1.00 | 1.80 |
| Val | 4.80 | 1.75 | 4.30 | 6.70 | 7.04 | 10.70 | 7.10 | 17.80 |
| Met |  |  | 0.91 |  |  |  |  | 0.81 |
| Leu | 3.05 | 1.98 | 8.20 | 5.06 | 6.20 | 11.90 | 5.29 | 18.30 |
| Tyr |  | 1.03 |  | 1.98 | 1.04 | 1.96 | 1.90 | 3.10 |
| Phe |  |  | 5.89 | 2.14 | 3.21 | 5.10 | 2.97 | 8.10 |
| Try | 1.00 | 0.90 |  |  | 1.80 |  |  | 1.70 |
| N-Ser |  |  |  |  | 1.00 |  |  |  |
| Total | 30 | 10 | 64 | 42 | 55 | 91 | 47 | 146 |

*b*

### 倭黑猩猩 α− 肽链

| | Tp1 Arg | Tp2 Arg | Tp3 Arg | Pro Pep. | 肽链分析 |
|---|---|---|---|---|---|
| Pos. | 1-31 | 32-92 | 93-141 | 65-141 | |
| Lys | 3.00 | 5.24 | 3.25 | 3.17 | 11.1 |
| His | 1.21 | 6.27 | 3.20 | 3.13 | 9.80 |
| Arg | 1.11 | 1.08 | 1.08 | 1.05 | 3.00 |
| Asp | 2.16 | 6.80 | 3.07 | 2.40 | 12.32 |
| Thr | 1.08 | 3.83 | 3.70 | 3.80 | 8.74 |
| Ser | 1.08 | 4.92 | 4.80 | 4.80 | 10.80 |
| Glu | 2.98 | 1.15 | 1.08 | 1.27 | 5.30 |
| Pro | 1.01 | 2.94 | 2.86 | 2.86 | 7.05 |
| Gly | 3.84 | 3.19 | | | 7.30 |
| Ala | 7.06 | 8.18 | 5.85 | 6.26 | 20.70 |
| Cys | | | 0.70 | 0.90 | 0.90 |
| Val | 3.05 | 4.15 | 5.90 | 4.80 | 12.70 |
| Met | | 1.85 | | | 1.70 |
| Leu | 2.20 | 7.12 | 9.10 | 8.86 | 18.20 |
| Tyr | 1.01 | 1.08 | 0.95 | 1.05 | 2.90 |
| Phe | | 4.22 | 3.12 | 3.13 | 7.05 |
| Try | 0.90 | | | | 0.80 |
| Total | 31 | 61 | 49 | 47 | 141 |

### 倭黑猩猩 β− 肽链

| | Tp1 Arg | Tp2 Arg | Tp3 Arg | Tp4 Arg | CN1 | CN2 | Pro pep. | 肽链分析 |
|---|---|---|---|---|---|---|---|---|
| Pos. | 1-30 | 31-40 | 41-74 | 75-146 | 1-55 | 56-146 | 70-146 | |
| Lys | 2.14 | | 6.29 | 2.92 | 2.26 | 8.84 | 3.14 | 11.40 |
| His | 1.07 | | 4.36 | 3.62 | 1.21 | 8.10 | 3.97 | 9.10 |
| Arg | 1.07 | 1.07 | 1.01 | | 2.08 | 1.10 | 0.99 | 3.00 |
| Asp | 2.09 | | 8.70 | 2.19 | 4.08 | 8.80 | 3.14 | 12.80 |
| Thr | 1.92 | 1.05 | 2.80 | 1.14 | 3.91 | 3.07 | 1.07 | 6.80 |
| Ser | 1.01 | | 3.80 | | 2.87 | 2.08 | | 4.75 |
| Glu | 3.96 | 1.11 | 3.20 | 3.13 | 5.99 | 4.82 | 3.97 | 11.30 |
| Pro | 0.96 | 1.02 | 2.80 | 2.18 | 2.87 | 3.80 | 2.70 | 7.40 |
| Gly | 3.85 | | 5.90 | 3.18 | 4.78 | 8.11 | 3.30 | 12.80 |
| Ala | 3.00 | | 5.20 | 7.00 | 4.17 | 10.90 | 6.94 | 14.75 |
| Cys | | | 0.80 | 0.90 | | 1.80 | 1.00 | 1.80 |
| Val | 4.80 | 1.75 | 4.30 | 6.70 | 7.04 | 10.70 | 7.10 | 17.80 |
| Me | | | 0.91 | | | | | 0.81 |
| Leu | 3.05 | 1.98 | 8.20 | 5.06 | 6.20 | 11.90 | 5.29 | 18.30 |
| Tyr | | 1.03 | | 1.98 | 1.04 | 1.96 | 1.90 | 3.10 |
| Phe | | | 5.89 | 2.14 | 3.21 | 5.10 | 2.97 | 8.10 |
| Try | 1.00 | 0.90 | | | 1.80 | | | 1.70 |
| N-Ser | | | | | | 1.00 | | |
| Total | 30 | 10 | 64 | 42 | 55 | 91 | 47 | 146 |

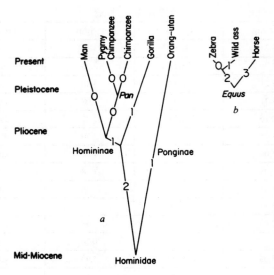

Fig. 3. Hominid (*a*) and equine (*b*) radiations as deduced from maximum parsimony trees of $\alpha$- and $\beta$-haemoglobin sequences. Numbers of NRs are shown on the branches. They result from the following substitutions recorded in the single-letter code for amino acids[21]. *a*, Between Hominidae ancestral node and orangutan: $\alpha$12A → T; between Hominidae and Homininae ancestral nodes: $\beta$87K → T, $\beta$125Q → P; between Homininae ancestral node and gorilla: $\beta$104R → K; between Homininae and *Pan-Homo* ancestral nodes: $\alpha$23D → E. *b*, Between *Equus* ancestral node and horse: $\beta$52A → G, $\beta$87Q → A; between *Equus* and zebra–wild ass ancestral nodes: $\alpha$20H → N, $\alpha$131S → T; between zebra–wild ass ancestral node and wild ass: $\alpha$23E → D. Immunological evidence for cladistically grouping pygmy chimpanzee with chimpanzee in the genus *Pan*[29] is now supported by amino acid sequence results on carbonic anhydrase I (D. Hewett-Emmett, unpublished data). The positioning of the divergence node for pygmy chimpanzee and chimpanzee reflects views[30] based on immunological and electrophoretic distance data.

Aside from supporting inclusion of *Pan* and *Gorilla* in Homininae, the parsimony evidence from amino acid sequence data hints at the possibility that *Pan* is more closely related to *Homo* than to *Gorilla*. One less NR is required with $\alpha$-haemoglobin sequences by grouping *Pan* and *Homo* first before adding gorilla (Fig. 3*a*). This is due to aspartic acid at position $\alpha$23 in New World monkey, gibbon, orang-utan and gorilla chains as compared with glutamic acid at this position in human, chimpanzee and pygmy chimpanzee chains. Amino acid sequences of $\gamma$-haemoglobin chains also point to a *Homo–Pan* clade distinct from gorilla. There are two non-allelic chains in the hominines, $^{G}\gamma$ characterized by glycine at position 136 and $^{A}\gamma$ with alanine at this position. The two sequences in chimpanzee as inferred from amino acid composition data are identical to their human counterparts[17]. In contrast, gorilla $^{A}\gamma$ (as deduced from nucleotide sequence data obtained on gorilla $\gamma$-haemoglobin genes)[18] has arginine at position 104 whereas human and chimpanzee $^{A}\gamma$ chains have lysine. The presence of arginine at position 104 in Old World monkey (*Macaca* and *Papio*) $\gamma$-haemoglobin chains[19] raises the possibility that human and chimpanzee $^{A}\gamma$ have the derived rather than primitive residue.

With mitochondrial DNA sequences there are two trees of lowest NR length grouping *Pan* either with *Gorilla* or with *Homo*[16]; phenetically, however, *Pan* shows more base matches

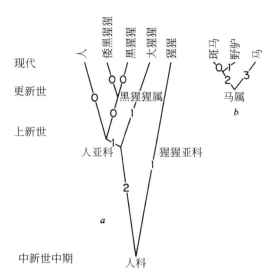

图 3. 基于 α–血红蛋白和 β–血红蛋白序列构建的最大简约进化树，推导出的人科动物（*a*）和马（*b*）的辐射进化关系。NR 数标在每个分支上。它们是由氨基酸密码子的一个字母替换产生的，如下 [21]：*a*，人科的祖先节点与猩猩之间：α12A → T；人科与人亚科的祖先节点之间：β87K → T，β125Q → P；人亚科的祖先节点与大猩猩之间：β104R → K；人亚科与黑猩猩属 – 人属的祖先节点之间：α23D → E。*b*，马属的祖先节点与马之间：β52A → G，β87Q → A；马属与斑马 – 野驴的祖先节点之间：α20H → N，α131S → T；斑马 – 野驴的祖先节点与野驴之间：α23E → D。在进化支上将倭黑猩猩与黑猩猩划分到黑猩猩属 [29] 的免疫学证据现为碳酸酐酶 I 的氨基酸序列结果所支持（休伊特 – 埃米特，数据尚未发表）。倭黑猩猩和黑猩猩的分离节点的定位反映了基于免疫学和电泳距离数据的观点 [30]。

　　除了支持黑猩猩属和大猩猩属属于人亚科之外，由氨基酸序列得到的简约性证据还提示黑猩猩属与人属的亲缘关系可能比它们与大猩猩属的亲缘关系更近。在加上大猩猩之前，如果想通过 α–血红蛋白序列先将黑猩猩和人类进行聚类，那么需要减少一个 NR（图 3*a*）。这是因为处于人类、黑猩猩和倭黑猩猩这一进化链中的 α23 位点都是谷氨酸，与之相比，处于新大陆的猴、长臂猿、猩猩和大猩猩这一进化链中的相应位点却是天冬氨酸。γ–血红蛋白链的氨基酸序列也表明人属 – 黑猩猩属进化支与大猩猩不同。人亚科的 γ–血红蛋白有两条非等位链，这两条链的特征为：Gγ 在位点 136 处为甘氨酸，Aγ 的该位点为丙氨酸。从氨基酸组成数据得出黑猩猩的这两段序列与人类的相一致 [17]。相比之下，大猩猩的 Aγ（从大猩猩的 γ–血红蛋白基因的核苷酸序列推导出来的）[18] 在位点 104 处是精氨酸，而人类和黑猩猩的 Aγ 链的该位点是赖氨酸。旧大陆猴（例如猕猴属和狒狒属）的 γ–血红蛋白链的 104 位点处也是精氨酸 [19]，这提出了一种可能性，即人类和黑猩猩的 Aγ 的残基是派生而来的而不是原本就有的。

　　使用线粒体 DNA 序列得到了两棵具有最低 NR 长度的进化树，分别将黑猩猩属与大猩猩属聚到一类或者将黑猩猩属与人属聚到一类 [16]；然而从表型上看，黑猩猩

with *Homo* than with *Gorilla*[13,16] as it also does with nuclear DNA sequences[20]. Clearly it will be difficult to resolve the *Homo–Pan–Gorilla* trichotomy into two branching events if, as may be suspected, the second branching occurred shortly after the first.

That proteins such as globins show a strong—although uneven—tendency to increasing sequence divergencies with elapsed time is evident in both amino acid difference matrices[21,22] and phylogenetic reconstructions[5]. Accepting empirical observations that this tendency operates in a majority of clades, our finding of almost no sequence differences among hominines in either their $\alpha$- or $\beta$-haemoglobin chains argues for a relatively late ancestral separation of *Homo*, *Pan* and *Gorilla*. Nevertheless, even if common ancestry existed until 5–6 Myr BP (just before the appearance of *Australopithecus* fossils), the rate of hominine haemoglobin evolution was slow, averaging about only 6 NRs per 100 codons per $10^8$ yr (that is, 6 NR%), in contrast to much faster rates averaging about 29 NR% for $\beta$-haemoglobin sequences and 25 NR% for $\alpha$-sequences during eutherian phylogeny[5].

To highlight the slowness of haemoglobin evolution during the hominine radiation, we can compare hominine with equine rates, taking advantage of the fact that $\alpha$- and $\beta$-haemoglobin sequences have been determined for horse (*Equus callabus*), zebra (*Equus zebra*) and wild ass (*Equus hemionus*)[23]. Preceded by *Pliohippus*, the genus *Equus* does not appear in the fossil record until the Pleistocene[24]. Yet, during the short span of time (2 Myr BP to present) of this equine radiation, 2–3 NRs accumulated per equine lineage for the two haemoglobin chain types (Fig. 3*b*), compared with no changes in *Homo* and *Pan*. Even by the conservative assumption that *Homo* and *Pan* had no older separation than zebra and horse, and given a Poisson distribution with a mean of 5 NRs based on *Equus*, the probability of obtaining zero NRs as for *Homo–Pan* is less that 0.007—thus eliminating the hypothesis of homogeneous rates.

The slow rate of globin sequence evolution in hominines indicates prior selection in the pre-hominines of haemoglobin molecules with finely tuned, perfected adaptations. As previously reported[5], we find that between eutherian and hominine ancestral nodes, the fastest evolving positions are $\alpha_1\beta_1$ contact sites, important functional positions which show few normal human variants[25]. Also mutations to proline were fixed at exterior helical positions $\alpha$A2 and at $\beta$A2 and $\alpha_1\beta_1$ contact positions $\beta$D2 and $\beta$H3. These additional prolines, all at the beginning of helices, by producing more stably directed helices, presumably improved subtler functions in the haemoglobin molecule. Furthermore, almost none of the many seemingly normal haemoglobin variants[25] are at polymorphic frequencies, possibly because even these variants harm the finer adaptations of human haemoglobin. The slow rate of haemoglobin evolution in African apes and humans suggests that organismal evolution in our earlier ancestors may have depended on amino acid sequence changes in proteins as well as regulatory changes in gene expression.

We thank Drs A. Spiegel, R. Faust and H. Wiesner for the pygmy chimpanzee,

属与人属之间的碱基匹配比它们与大猩猩属之间匹配得更高 [13,16]，这与核 DNA 序列分析的结果一致 [20]。很明显，如果像我们猜想的那样，第二次分支是在第一次分支后不久发生的，那么要想将人属－黑猩猩属－大猩猩属这种三元关系分解为二分支事件将是很困难的。

诸如球蛋白之类的蛋白质有一个很强但不规则的趋势，即随着时间的流逝序列分支会增大，这一趋势在氨基酸的差异矩阵 [21,22] 及系统进化重建 [5] 中都很明显。如果认同该趋势对大多数进化支都起作用这一经验性观察，那么对于我们的发现——人亚科之间的 α–血红蛋白或 β–血红蛋白链序列几乎没有差异——支持人属、黑猩猩属和大猩猩属的祖先分离相对较晚。然而，即使距今 500 万到 600 万年前（就在南方古猿化石出现之前）共同祖先依旧存在，人亚科的血红蛋白进化速率还是很慢，大概平均每一亿年间每 100 个密码子只有 6 个位点发生核苷酸取代（记作 6 NR%）。与此相比，真兽亚纲的系统发育过程中，其血红蛋白的进化速率要快得多，其中 β–血红蛋白序列的进化速率达到了 29 NR%，而 α–血红蛋白则达到了 25 NR% [5]。

为了强调在人亚科的辐射进化中血红蛋白进化之慢，我们可以利用家马、斑马和野驴的 α–血红蛋白和 β–血红蛋白序列这一已经确定的事实 [23]，将人亚科的血红蛋白进化速率与马的相比较。马属的化石记录最早可追溯至更新世 [24]，首先就是上新马。然而，与人属和黑猩猩属的两条血红蛋白链序列毫无差异相比，马在其辐射进化的很短一段时间内（从距今 200 万年前到现在），这两种血红蛋白链在每种马家族中都积累了 2~3 个 NR（图 3b）。实际上根据最保守的假设——人属和黑猩猩间不比斑马和马分离的时间早，而且考虑到以 5 个 NR 作为马属的平均值而得到的泊松分布，得出人属－黑猩猩属间没有发生核苷酸取代的概率小于 0.007，因此排除了均匀速率的假说。

人亚科的球蛋白序列进化速率之慢暗示：在人亚科形成之前，血红蛋白分子就通过细致调整、完善适应性进行了优先选择。正如之前报道的 [5]，我们发现，在真兽亚纲和人亚科的祖先节点之间，进化最快的是重要的功能性位置，即 $\alpha_1\beta_1$ 接触位点，以上几科未见过正常的人类变异体 [25]。突变成的脯氨酸也被固定在外螺旋位置 $\alpha A2$、$\beta A2$ 以及 $\alpha_1\beta_1$ 接触的位置 $\beta D2$ 和 $\beta H3$ 处。这些额外的脯氨酸都处于螺旋结构的开端，可能通过产生更稳定的定向螺旋结构来提高血红蛋白分子的精细功能。此外，几乎所有的表观正常的血红蛋白变异体 [25] 都不具有多态性频率分布，这可能是因为这些变异体会损害人类血红蛋白完善的适应性。非洲猿和人类血红蛋白进化速度之慢提示：我们祖先的生物进化过程可能依赖于蛋白质的氨基酸序列变化以及基因表达的调控变化。

感谢施皮格尔、福斯特和威斯纳博士为我们提供倭黑猩猩、黑猩猩和大猩猩的

chimpanzee and gorilla blood samples, also Dr Gerard Joswiak and John Czelusniak for valuable discussion of the statistical significance of our findings. Phylogenetic analysis of the sequence data was supported by NSF grant DEB 78-10717.

(**303**, 546-548; 1983)

**Morris Goodman\*, Gerhard Braunitzer[†], Anton Stangl[†] and Barbara Schrank[†]**
\* Department of Anatomy, Wayne State University School of Medicine, Detroit, Michigan 48201, USA
[†] Max-Planck Institut für Biochemie, Abteilung Proteinchemie, D-8033 Martinsried bei Munchen, FRG

Received 30 December 1982; accepted 7 April 1983

---

References:

1. Goodman, M. *Ann. N. Y. Acad. Sci.* **102**, 219-234 (1962).

2. Andrews, P. & Cronin, J.E. *Nature* **297**, 541-546 (1982).

3. Sarich, V. M. & Wilson, A.C. *Science* **158**, 1200-1203 (1967).

4. Goodman, M. *Hum. Biol.* **54**, 247-264 (1982).

5. Goodman, M. *Prog. Biophys. Molec. Biol.* **38**, 105-164 (1981).

6. Sarich, V. M. & Cronin, J. E. in *Molecular Anthropology* (eds Goodman, M.& Tashian, R. E.) 141-170 (Plenum, New York, 1976).

7. Johanson, D. L. & White, T. D. *Science* **203**, 321-330 (1979).

8. Patterson, B., Behrensmeyer, A. K. & Sill, W. *Nature* **226**, 918-921 (1970).

9. Rifkin, D. B. & Konigsberg, W. *Biochim. Biophys. Acta* **104**, 457-461 (1965).

10. Zuckerkandl, E. & Schroeder, W. A. *Nature* **192**, 984-985 (1961).

11. Tashian, R. E., Hewett-Emmett, D. & Goodman, M. in *Isozymes* Vol. 7 (eds Rattozzi, M. C., Scandalias, J. G., Siciliano, M. T.& Whitt, G.S.) 79-100 (Liss, New York, 1983).

12. Anderson, S. *et al. Nature* **290**, 457-465 (1981).

13. Brown, W. M., Prager, E. M., Wong, A. & Wilson, A. C. *J. Molec. Evol.* **18**, 225-239 (1982).

14. Anderson, S. *et al. J. Molec. Biol.* **156**, 683-717 (1982).

15. Bibb, M. H. *et al. Cell* **26**, 167-180 (1981).

16. Goodman, M., Olson, C. B., Beeber, J. E. & Czelusniak, J. *Acta Zool. Fenn.* **169**, 19-35 (1982).

17. DeJong, W. W. *Biochim. Biophys. Acta* **251**, 217-226 (1971).

18. Scott, A. F. *et al. Am. J. Hum. Genet.* **34**, 193A (1982).

19. Mahoney, W. C. & Nute, P. E. *Biochemistry* **19**, 4436-4442 (1980).

20. Hoyer, B. H., Van de Velde, N. W., Goodman, M. & Roberts, R. B. *J. Hum. Evol.* **1**, 645-649 (1972).

21. Dayhoff, M. O. *Atlas of Protein Sequence and Structure* Vol. 5 (National Biochemical Research Foundation, Silver Springs, Maryland, 1972).

22. Dickerson, E. R. & Geis, L. *Hemoglobin: Structure, Function, Evolution, and Pathology* (Benjamin/Cummings, Menlo Park, 1983).

23. Mazur, G. & Braunitzer, G. *Hoppe-Seyler's Z. Physiol. Chem.* **363**, 59-71 (1982).

24. Romer, A. S. *Vertebrate Paleontology* (University of Chicago Press, 1966).

25. Bunn, H.F., Forget, B. G. & Ranney, H. M. *Human Hemogloblins* (Saunders, Philadelphia, 1977).

26. Edman, P. & Begg, G. *Eur. J. Biochem.* **1**, 80-91 (1967).

27. Braunitzer, G. & Schrank, B. *Hoppe-Seyler's Z. Physiol. Chem.* **351**, 417-418 (1970).

28. Jauregui-Adell, J. & Marti, J. *J. Analyt. Biochem.* **69**, 468-473 (1975).

29. Goodman, M. *Hum. Biol.* **35**, 377-436 (1963).

30. Zihlman, A. L., Cronin, J. E., Cramer, D. L. & Sarich, V. M. *Nature* **275**, 744-746 (1978).

血样，同样感谢杰勒德·约斯韦克博士和约翰·泽鲁斯尼亚克对我们的发现的统计学意义进行的有价值的讨论。序列数据的系统进化分析由美国国家科学基金会资助的 DEB 78-10717 项目所支持。

（刘皓芳 翻译；冯兴无 审稿）

# Constraints on Evolution of Earth's Mantle from Rare Gas Systematics

C. J. Allègre *et al.*

## Editor's Note

**The motions of tectonic plates are driven by convective circulation of hot sluggish rock in the Earth's mantle. But geophysicists have long debated whether the circulating cells reach all the way from the bottom to the top of the mantle, or whether convection happens independently in two layers, separated by a boundary at around 660–700 km. Here French geochemist Claude Allègre and colleagues present evidence for two-layer convection (essentially the current consensus). They report relatively high concentrations of rare-gases in some volcanic rocks, showing that these must come from a large mantle reservoir that has not lost such volatile components by "degassing", and which therefore remains largely isolated. Allègre later became a somewhat controversial Minister for Education in France.**

---

Analyses of the isotopic composition of He, Ar and Xe in a suite of glasses from the mid-ocean ridges and from the island of Hawaii show that the Hawaiian samples have systematically lower $^4$He/$^3$He, $^{40}$Ar/$^{36}$Ar and $^{129}$Xe/$^{130}$Xe ratios than the mid-ocean ridge basalts. We interpret this result to imply the existence of an undegassed mantle reservoir. Given the isotopic variations, and the half lives of $^{129}$I and $^{40}$K (parent isotopes of $^{129}$Xe and $^{40}$Ar), the undegassed reservoir must have been separated from the MORB source reservoir at least 4,400 Myr ago. The most reasonable explanation for the data is therefore the existence of a two-layered mantle.

---

THE search for the driving mechanism of plate tectonics has led geophysicists to propose a series of convective mantle models. Morgan[1] proposed the existence of a separate deep mantle, which would generate plumes. McKenzie and Richter[2] proposed a two-layer convection mantle, with a boundary layer at 700 km (maximum depth of earthquakes). On the other hand, several authors[3-5] have argued that geophysical evidence favours whole-mantle convection.

Measurements of isotope ratios in mantle-derived basalts have shown that the mantle is heterogeneous. Based on Sr and Nd isotopic information alone, early studies showed that distinction could be made between a depleted mantle source (that is, the source of mid-ocean ridge basalts (MORB)), and an undepleted mantle, from which oceanic island basalts are derived (see reviews in ref. 6). Assuming that depletion is caused by the extraction of continental crust, and using the geochemical budgets for Sr and Nd, several authors[7-10] calculated that the depleted mantle represents one-third or half of the whole mantle.

# 稀有气体系统对地幔演化的制约

阿莱格尔等

**编者按**

地幔中炽热且运动缓慢的岩石发生对流，从而驱动板块构造运动。关于对流循环单元是否都是从底部直到顶部贯穿整个地幔，还是对流运动只独立发生在以 660~700 km 为边界划分的两个不同层位，即上、下地幔中，地球物理学家们为此争论良久。法国地球化学家克洛德·阿莱格尔和他的同事在此文中为两层对流运动理论（本质上跟现在的理论一致）提供了证据。他们在某些火山岩里发现了浓度相对较高的稀有气体，表明这些稀有气体必定来自于一个大的地幔库，且并未在"去气"过程中丢失这些挥发性组分，从而很大程度上保持了与外界的隔离。其后，阿莱格尔曾成为法国一位颇有争议的教育部部长。

---

对来自洋中脊和夏威夷岛的一组玄武岩玻璃中 He、Ar 和 Xe 的同位素组成分析显示：夏威夷岛样品中 $^4He/^3He$、$^{40}Ar/^{36}Ar$ 和 $^{129}Xe/^{130}Xe$ 的比值系统地低于洋中脊玄武岩中的相应比值。我们认为这一结果意味着存在一个未经去气的地幔库。考虑到同位素的变异以及 $^{129}I$ 和 $^{40}K$（分别为 $^{129}Xe$ 和 $^{40}Ar$ 的母体同位素）的半衰期，这一未去气的地幔库至少在 44 亿年前已经从洋中脊玄武岩（MORB）的源区中分离出来了。因此，对于这些数据最合理的解释是存在着一个双层地幔。

---

对板块构造运动驱动机制的探求，导致地球物理学家们提出了一系列对流地幔的模型。摩根[1]认为，存在另一个分离的、可以产生地幔柱的深地幔。麦肯齐和里克特[2]则提出了一个边界层位于 700 km 处（最大地震深度）的双层对流地幔模型。另一方面，也有学者[3-5]认为，地球物理学证据更有利于一个全地幔对流的系统。

地幔玄武岩中同位素比值的测定结果显示，地幔在化学成分上是不均一的。单纯从 Sr 和 Nd 同位素资料来看，早期的研究表明亏损地幔源（即洋中脊玄武岩（MORB）的源区）和产生大洋岛屿玄武岩的未亏损地幔之间存在明显差异（见参考文献6）。假设这种亏损是由于陆壳的提取所致，有学者[7-10]利用 Sr 和 Nd 的地球化学平衡计算得出，亏损地幔占到了整个地幔的三分之一甚至一半。

Reconciling this conclusion with a two-layered mantle model, these authors assume that the upper 700 km correspond to the depleted mantle. There are several major criticisms of this model. First, it is not clear that depletion is created only by extraction of continental crust, since basaltic extraction on the ridge crest may also have an important role[7,11]. Second, the geochemical budget calculations do not yield the relative geometry of the two assumed mantle reservoirs. Finally, the assumption of only two geochemically homogeneous distinct reservoirs is an oversimplification[10,12,13].

Nd–Sr isotope geochemistry does not allow a unique choice to be made between whole-mantle and layered-mantle convection. For example, proponents of whole-mantle convection have argued that the geochemical heterogeneities can be explained by a lumpy mantle, rather than a layered one (see ref. 14). This would require that the lumps maintain their identity over long periods of time, and are entrained in the overall circulation pattern.

We now report new noble gas measurements on oceanic basalt glasses, and illustrate the importance of these data to the above arguments. Although in recent years several noble gas studies have been carried out on mantle derived rocks (see refs 12, 15–21) this information has not received the attention that it deserves. The noble gases can yield unique constraints on the structure and evolution at the mantle for several reasons.

(1) Due to the volatility of the noble gases, and the involatility of the radioactive parent isotopes ($^{40}K$, $^{238}U$, $^{235}U$, $^{232}Th$, $^{244}Pu$), the isotope evolution is strongly affected by degassing, which is not the case for the Sm–Nd and Rb–Sr systems. Therefore, the variation of mantle noble gas isotope ratios depends on the degassing history of the mantle, and are a function of continental extraction processes only through their parent isotopes.

(2) The radioactive parent isotopes decay with very different half lives which provides unique temporal information. The extinct isotopes $^{129}I$ and $^{244}Pu$ had very fast decay constants ($4.36 \times 10^{-8}$ yr$^{-1}$ and $8.4 \times 10^{-9}$ yr$^{-1}$, respectively) and therefore, xenon isotopic anomalies with respect to their daughter isotopes are very old, having been produced in the first 100 Myr of Earth history. On the other hand, spontaneous fission of $^{238}U$ is much slower ($\lambda_{sf} = 8.47 \times 10^{-17}$ yr$^{-1}$; $\lambda_\alpha = 1.54 \times 10^{-10}$ yr$^{-1}$), has occurred throughout the age of the Earth, and produces a different xenon isotope signature than decay of $^{244}Pu$ (refs 22–24). $^{40}Ar$ is produced by decay of $^{40}K$ ($\lambda = 5.543 \times 10^{-10}$ yr$^{-1}$), and $^{4}He$ is produced by decay of $^{238}U$, $^{235}U$, and $^{232}Th$.

(3) The different rare gases span a large range of atomic number and atomic size, and may have quite different mantle transport properties.

## Rare Gas Isotope Variations in Basalts

A recent study of xenon isotopes in MORB glasses[17] documented a large anomaly in $^{129}Xe/^{130}Xe$ ratio with respect to the atmosphere. Due to the short half life of extinct $^{129}I$,

上述学者将该结论与双层地幔模型相结合，认为上部的 700 km 恰对应着亏损地幔。然而该模型受到了不少质疑：首先，地幔亏损是否仅仅由于大陆地壳的提取所致，目前尚不明确，因为洋中脊玄武岩的提取也可能起到了非常重要的作用 [7,11]；其次，根据地球化学平衡计算结果并不能得出两种假定地幔库的相对几何关系；第三，关于仅存在两类不同地球化学组成的地幔库的假设过于简单化 [10,12,13]。

根据 Nd–Sr 同位素地球化学的相关理论，无法判别到底是存在全地幔对流还是分层地幔对流。例如，支持整个地幔对流的一方认为，地球化学组成的不均一性可用一个团块状而非层状的地幔来解释（见参考文献 14）。这就要求这些团块长时间维持其同一性，并应被卷入进全循环模式中。

本文将报道大洋玄武岩玻璃中稀有气体的最新测定结果，并阐释这些资料对于上述争论观点的重要性。虽然近年来已有多项关于地幔成因岩类中稀有气体的研究（见参考文献 12、15~21），但这类信息并未受到应有的关注。稀有气体可对地幔的结构和演化产生独特的制约作用，原因如下：

（1）鉴于稀有气体的挥发性和其放射性母体同位素（$^{40}K$、$^{238}U$、$^{235}U$、$^{232}Th$ 和 $^{244}Pu$）的不挥发性，稀有气体同位素演化受去气作用的强烈影响，这就不同于 Sm–Nd 和 Rb–Sr 体系。因此，地幔中稀有气体同位素比值的变化取决于地幔去气作用的历史，而大陆提取过程只有经由母体同位素才会产生影响。

（2）放射性母体同位素以不同的半衰期衰变，从而提供了独一无二的时间信息。已经衰变完的灭绝同位素 $^{129}I$ 和 $^{244}Pu$ 衰变速度非常快（衰变常数分别为 $4.36 \times 10^{-8}$ yr$^{-1}$ 和 $8.4 \times 10^{-9}$ yr$^{-1}$），因此，他们的子体同位素氙同位素异常要古老很多，应该产生于地球形成早期的一亿年间。另一方面，$^{238}U$ 的自发裂变则慢得多（$\lambda_{sf} = 8.47 \times 10^{-17}$ yr$^{-1}$；$\lambda_\alpha = 1.54 \times 10^{-10}$ yr$^{-1}$），在地球的整个演化史上都有发生，其形成的氙同位素的特征不同于 $^{244}Pu$ 的衰变产物（参考文献 22~24）。$^{40}Ar$ 是由 $^{40}K$（$\lambda = 5.543 \times 10^{-10}$ yr$^{-1}$）衰变而来的，而 $^{4}He$ 则是由 $^{238}U$、$^{235}U$ 和 $^{232}Th$ 衰变而来。

（3）不同稀有气体的原子序数和原子大小的跨度范围很大，它们在地幔中的运移特性可能也具有非常大的差异。

## 玄武岩中稀有气体同位素的变化

对洋中脊玄武岩玻璃中氙同位素的最新研究 [17] 表明，$^{129}Xe/^{130}Xe$ 的比值相对于大气中的比值存在很大异常。由于灭绝同位素 $^{129}I$ 的半衰期极短，该结果显然说明

this result clearly shows that the separation between the MORB mantle source and the atmosphere occurred 4,400 Myr ago. While this conclusion requires few assumptions, the data did not allow an evaluation of the xenon isotopic signature of the whole mantle, since the MORB mantle is only a fraction of the total. Initially, we interpreted the variations within the suite of MORB glasses to reflect atmospheric contamination[17]. However, there is an alternative explanation, namely, that a significant volume of the mantle contains xenon of atmospheric isotopic composition. The challenge to the experimentalist is to distinguish between these two possibilities.

A similar situation exists for argon isotopes. The literature contains reported $^{40}Ar/^{36}Ar$ ratios for igneous rocks between atmospheric 295.5 and 16,000 (refs 25–27). The importance of the high MORB $^{40}Ar/^{36}Ar$ ratios to degassing models is explained in ref. 18. The controversy regarding interpretation of the low $^{40}Ar/^{36}Ar$ ratios is an old one[28,29]; the present consensus seems to be that most are the result of contamination, either in the laboratory or by interaction with atmosphere during emplacement (see ref. 30).

In contrast, helium isotopic studies of igneous rocks are not subject to equivalent problems of contamination because helium is the least adsorptive of gases and is present only in trace quantities in air. The detection of excess $^3He$ (relative to air) in MORB glasses can only be interpreted as evidence for the existence of "primordial" mantle helium[15,16]. The large variations in $^4He/^3He$ ratios observed for oceanic basalts[12,32] therefore are not the result of atmospheric contamination, but must reflect mantle heterogeneity. The samples with the highest excess of $^3He$ (from Hawaii[12]) can therefore be identified as derived from the most undegassed mantle. Although helium isotope ratios are often reported as $^3He/^4He$, we tabulate them here as $^4He/^3He$ to conform with the convention for other radiogenic isotope systems (that is radiogenic isotope/stable isotope).

The strategy employed in this study was to use the helium isotopes to identify samples from normal MORB type mantle and from undegassed mantle[12,21]. The goal was to document the differences in argon and xenon isotopic compositions between these two different mantle "types". Given the controversy regarding atmospheric contamination, several special precautions were taken. All analyses were performed on fresh vitreous glasses which were hand-picked to avoid alteration, and sonically cleaned in ethanol. To minimize the effective surface area available for adsorption, and gas loss from the vesicles[16], only large chunks of glass (between 3 and 10 mm size) were analysed. To eliminate any further question of atmospheric contamination, stepwise heating was applied to all the samples. Any atmospheric gases not removed during the preanalysis bake-out (200 °C) should be released in the low-temperature step. Finally, blanks were run before and after each sample. As the procedure was identical for all samples, isotopic differences cannot be attributed to atmospheric contamination.

The results for three basaltic glasses from the island of Hawaii and seven MORB glasses are presented in Table 1. Experimental details are given in refs 17, 18. Helium isotopic

洋中脊玄武岩地幔源区和大气的分离发生于 44 亿年前。虽然，这个结论几乎不需要假设，但目前的数据还无法用来评估整个地幔的氙同位素特征，因为洋中脊玄武岩地幔只是整个地幔的一部分。起初我们将洋中脊玄武岩玻璃样品组中的变化解释为大气污染 [17]。不过这也存在另一种解释，即相当部分的地幔中的氙与大气氙具有相同的同位素组成。实验人员所面临的挑战是如何来区分这两种可能性。

氩同位素中也存在类似情况。对于火成岩，本文采用了前人报道的 $^{40}Ar/^{36}Ar$ 同位素比值，大概在 295.5（大气中的比值）和 16,000 之间（参考文献 25~27）。参考文献 18 解释了洋中脊玄武岩中 $^{40}Ar/^{36}Ar$ 比值相对于去气模型的重要性。对低 $^{40}Ar/^{36}Ar$ 比值解释的争论由来已久 [28,29]；现今较为一致的观点是：低比值大部分是污染的结果，而这种污染可能来自实验室，也可能是岩浆侵位过程中与大气的相互作用所致（参考文献 30）。

相反，火成岩中 He 同位素研究则不存在类似的污染问题，因为氦是稀有气体中最不易被吸附的，而且目前在空气中的含量仅为痕量水平。洋中脊玄武岩玻璃中检测到的过量的 $^3He$（相对于空气）只能解释为"原始"地幔氦存在的证据 [15,16]。因此，大洋玄武岩中观察到的 $^4He/^3He$ 的巨大变化 [12,32] 并非大气污染的结果，而是反映了地幔的不均一性。因而，过剩 $^3He$ 最大的样品（来自夏威夷 [12]）可被确定为来自几乎未去气的地幔。虽然氦同位素比值经常被表示为 $^3He/^4He$，但为了与其他放射成因同位素体系一致起见，我们在下面的数据表中将用 $^4He/^3He$ 表示 He 同位素组成（即，放射成因同位素/稳定同位素）。

本文所采用的方法就是利用氦同位素来辨认正常洋中脊玄武岩型地幔（MORB 型地幔）和未去气地幔 [12,21]。目的是要找出这两种地幔"类型"之间氩和氙同位素组成的差异。考虑到关于大气污染的争论，我们专门采取了多项预防措施。所有分析对象都是新鲜的玻璃样品，为了避免蚀变，这些玻璃都经手挑选出，并预先在乙醇中使用超声波清洗。为了使发生吸附作用的有效表面积达到最小，并使气泡中气体损失降到最低 [16]，我们只分析了大块的玻璃样品（尺寸为 3~10 mm）。为了消除任何关于大气污染的进一步质疑，所有样品都采用了阶段加热法。任何在分析前的烘干（200℃）过程中未被去除的大气气体应该在低温阶段被释放。最后，每个样品分析前后都加一个本底样。由于所有样品的处理程序都相同，因而就不能将它们间的同位素差别归因于大气污染。

取自夏威夷群岛的三个玄武岩玻璃样品和七个洋中脊玄武岩玻璃样品的分析结果见表 1。详细的实验流程见参考文献 17 和 18。之前已报道了来自夏威夷地区的样

analyses of the Hawaiian samples have been reported previously[31] as have two of the MORB samples (AII 96 18-1 and ALV 892-2). Although the $^4He/^3He$ ratios presented here were obtained on a glass mass spectrometer optimized for the heavy noble gases, reasonable agreement is obtained (within 15%), considering the larger uncertainty (see refs 16, 31).

Table 1. Helium and argon data for glassy samples from Hawaii and mid-oceanic ridges

| Sample | Temperature (°C) | $^3He$ ($10^{-12}$ cm$^3$ g$^{-1}$) | $^4He/^3He$ | $^{36}Ar$ ($10^{-10}$ cm$^3$ g$^{-1}$) | $^{40}Ar/^{36}Ar$ |
|---|---|---|---|---|---|
| Loihi | | | | | |
| KK-29-10 | 700 | 4.55 | 34,670±8,130 | 3.64±0.03 | 305±5 |
| | 1,000 | 28.77 | 30,810±1,980 | 7.03±0.06 | 425±8 |
| | 1,450 | 5.05 | 32,230±2,460 | 1.56±0.02 | 447±5 |
| | 1,650 | – | – | 0.086±0.006 | 379±5 |
| | Total | 38.37 | 31,460±1,760 | 12.32±0.07 | 392±5 |
| KK-24-7 | 700 | 2.51 | 37,690±2,030 | 3.5±0.1 | 308±16 |
| | 1,000 | 1.98 | 41,180±4,770 | 8.3±0.3 | 385±15 |
| | 1,400 | 0.39 | 101,200±24,160 | 35.1±0.4 | 336±6 |
| | 1,650 | – | – | 112.0±2.0 | 300±5 |
| | Total | 4.88 | 42,880±2,390 | 158.9±2.06 | 313±4 |
| Hualalai | | | | | |
| KK-9-14 | 700 | 0.26 | 251,300±45,400 | 5.11±0.13 | 377±12 |
| | 1,400 | 43.61 | 36,960±203 | 406.2±4.2 | 1,150±19 |
| | 1,650 | – | – | 2.01±1.25 | 2,900±1,830 |
| | Total | 43.87 | 38,210±320 | 413.3±4.38 | 1,149±19 |
| Atlantic | | | | | |
| AII 96-18-1 | 700 | 12.01 | 81,700±1,770 | 0.037±0.006 | 23,810±3,520 |
| | 1,300 | 183.49 | 79,110±260 | 0.420±0.010 | 25,250±690 |
| | 1,650 | – | – | 0.051±0.022 | 18,300±820 |
| | Total | 195.50 | 79,270±240 | 0.508±0.025 | 24,450±1,210 |
| Indian Ocean | | | | | |
| MD23 DR04 | 1,150 | 329.61 | 81,730±330 | 1.33±0.02 | 8,660±80 |
| | 1,400 | 131.26 | 84,750±920 | 1.04±0.03 | 7,040±300 |
| | 1,650 | – | – | – | – |
| | Total | 460.87 | 82,680±350 | 2.37±0.04 | 7,960±150 |

品中氦同位素比值[31]，以及两个洋中脊玄武岩样品（AII 96 18-1 和 ALV 892-2）的氦同位素比值。虽然本文得到的 $^4He/^3He$ 比值是在一个对重稀有气体分析优化了的玻璃质谱仪上得到的，考虑到大的分析误差，结果仍显示了较好的一致性（在15%以内，见参考文献16和31）。

表1. 夏威夷岛和洋中脊玄武岩玻璃样品中氦和氩的测定数据

| 样品 | 温度（℃） | $^3He$ $(10^{-12}cm^3 \cdot g^{-1})$ | $^4He/^3He$ | $^{36}Ar$ $(10^{-10}cm^3 \cdot g^{-1})$ | $^{40}Ar/^{36}Ar$ |
|---|---|---|---|---|---|
| 罗希 | | | | | |
| KK-29-10 | 700 | 4.55 | 34,670±8,130 | 3.64±0.03 | 305±5 |
| | 1,000 | 28.77 | 30,810±1,980 | 7.03±0.06 | 425±8 |
| | 1,450 | 5.05 | 32,230±2,460 | 1.56±0.02 | 447±5 |
| | 1,650 | － | － | 0.086±0.006 | 379±5 |
| | 合计 | 38.37 | 31,460±1,760 | 12.32±0.07 | 392±5 |
| KK-24-7 | 700 | 2.51 | 37,690±2,030 | 3.5±0.1 | 308±16 |
| | 1,000 | 1.98 | 41,180±4,770 | 8.3±0.3 | 385±15 |
| | 1,400 | 0.39 | 101,200±24,160 | 35.1±0.4 | 336±6 |
| | 1,650 | | | 112.0±2.0 | 300±5 |
| | 合计 | 4.88 | 42,880±2,390 | 158.9±2.06 | 313±4 |
| 霍阿拉拉 | | | | | |
| KK-9-14 | 700 | 0.26 | 251,300±45,400 | 5.11±0.13 | 377±12 |
| | 1,400 | 43.61 | 36,960±203 | 406.2±4.2 | 1,150±19 |
| | 1,650 | － | － | 2.01±1.25 | 2,900±1,830 |
| | 合计 | 43.87 | 38,210±320 | 413.3±4.38 | 1,149±19 |
| 大西洋 | | | | | |
| AII96-18-1 | 700 | 12.01 | 81,700±1,770 | 0.037±0.006 | 23,810±3,520 |
| | 1,300 | 183.49 | 79,110±260 | 0.420±0.010 | 25,250±690 |
| | 1,650 | － | － | 0.051±0.022 | 18,300±820 |
| | 合计 | 195.50 | 79,270±240 | 0.508±0.025 | 24,450±1,210 |
| 印度洋 | | | | | |
| MD23 DR04 | 1,150 | 329.61 | 81,730±330 | 1.33±0.02 | 8,660±80 |
| | 1,400 | 131.26 | 84,750±920 | 1.04±0.03 | 7,040±300 |
| | 1,650 | － | － | － | － |
| | 合计 | 460.87 | 82,680±350 | 2.37±0.04 | 7,690±150 |

*Continued*

| Sample | Temperature (°C) | $^3$He ($10^{-12}$ cm$^3$ g$^{-1}$) | $^4$He/$^3$He | $^{36}$Ar ($10^{-10}$ cm$^3$ g$^{-1}$) | $^{40}$Ar/$^{36}$Ar |
|---|---|---|---|---|---|
| Pacific | | | | | |
| ALV 981 R 23 | 600 | 10.13 | 95,200±1,320 | 0.235±0.012 | 295±15 |
| | 850 | 37.53 | 90,890±510 | 0.187±0.102 | 350±175 |
| | 1,000 | 67.94 | 76,950±1,110 | 0.233±0.010 | 5,540±240 |
| | 1,150 | 12.37 | 84,710±610 | 0.128±0.017 | 16,320±2,160 |
| | 1,400 | 19.71 | 90,090±2,100 | 0.210±0.024 | 18,260±2,040 |
| | 1,500 | — | — | 0.130±0.035 | 1,500±500 |
| | Total | 147.68 | 84,150±1,420 | 1.123±0.113 | 6,720±670 |
| ALV 981 R 26 | 1,000 | 81.35 | 80,640±530 | 0.245±0.015 | 3,270±180 |
| | 1,400 | 26.63 | 101,060±2,850 | 0.217±0.020 | 16,600±2,500 |
| | 1,600 | — | — | 0.163±0.048 | 15,300±5,800 |
| | Total | 107.98 | 85,680±1,450 | 0.625±0.054 | 10,890±1,010 |
| ALV 979 R 7 | 950 | 41.96 | 81,520±2,210 | 0.045±0.009 | 930±190 |
| | 1,300 | 95.53 | 83,840±390 | 0.242±0.017 | 21,890±1,530 |
| | 1,650 | — | — | 0.148±0.022 | 14,480±2,150 |
| | Total | 137.49 | 83,130±740 | 0.435±0.029 | 17,190±1,150 |
| CYP 78 09-15 | 950 | 238.86 | 83,130±260 | 0.98±0.012 | 14,500±300 |
| | 1,650 | 120.17 | 82,810±350 | 2.23±0.07 | 3,660±185 |
| | Total | 359.03 | 83,030±210 | 3.21±0.07 | 6,970±190 |
| Galapagos Rise | | | | | |
| ALV 892-2 | 700 | 1.40 | 67,810±4,700 | 0.0155±0.0005 | 329±14 |
| | 900 | 43.14 | 75,220±2,920 | 0.074±0.002 | 14,870±500 |
| | 1,200 | 3.31 | 88,130±3,380 | 0.077±0.002 | 16,680±380 |
| | 1,400 | 15.86 | 74,850±2,410 | 0.082±0.002 | 12,920±290 |
| | 1,650 | 11.21 | 79,020±4,870 | 0.122±0.014 | 14,550±1,640 |
| | Total | 35.26 | 76,150±1,910 | 0.370±0.014 | 14,120±540 |
| Atmosphere | | | 722,540 | | 295.5 |

All samples have been degassed in several temperature steps. Errors are $2\sigma\sqrt{N}$. Absolute concentrations are uncertain to ±10%. The sensitivity for He of $2.7\times10^{-11}$ cm$^3$ mV$^{-1}$ is calculated by comparison with samples ALV 892-2 and AII 96-18-1 measured by Kurz[32] and differs from the value used previously[17].

The results presented in Table 1 reveal important differences between the MORB and Hawaiian samples. The MORB glasses are characterized by typical $^4$He/$^3$He ratios of

| 样品 | 温度（℃） | $^3$He $(10^{-12}cm^3 \cdot g^{-1})$ | $^4$He/$^3$He | $^{36}$Ar $(10^{-10}cm^3 \cdot g^{-1})$ | $^{40}$Ar/$^{36}$Ar |
|---|---|---|---|---|---|
| 太平洋 | | | | | |
| ALV 981 R 23 | 600 | 10.13 | 95,200 ± 1,320 | 0.235 ± 0.012 | 295 ± 15 |
| | 850 | 37.53 | 90,890 ± 510 | 0.187 ± 0.102 | 350 ± 175 |
| | 1,000 | 67.94 | 76,950 ± 1,110 | 0.233 ± 0.010 | 5,540 ± 240 |
| | 1,150 | 12.37 | 84,710 ± 610 | 0.128 ± 0.017 | 16,320 ± 2,160 |
| | 1,400 | 19.71 | 90,090 ± 2,100 | 0.210 ± 0.024 | 18,260 ± 2,040 |
| | 1,500 | – | – | 0.130 ± 0.035 | 1,500 ± 500 |
| | 合计 | 147.68 | 84,150 ± 1,420 | 1.123 ± 0.113 | 6,720 ± 670 |
| ALV 981 R 26 | 1,000 | 81.35 | 80,640 ± 530 | 0.245 ± 0.015 | 3,270 ± 180 |
| | 1,400 | 26.63 | 101,060 ± 2,850 | 0.217 ± 0.020 | 16,600 ± 2,500 |
| | 1,600 | – | – | 0.163 ± 0.048 | 15,300 ± 5,800 |
| | 合计 | 107.98 | 85,680 ± 1,450 | 0.625 ± 0.054 | 10,890 ± 1,010 |
| ALV 979 R 7 | 950 | 41.96 | 81,520 ± 2,210 | 0.045 ± 0.009 | 930 ± 190 |
| | 1,300 | 95.53 | 83,840 ± 390 | 0.242 ± 0.017 | 21,890 ± 1,530 |
| | 1,650 | – | – | 0.148 ± 0.022 | 14,480 ± 2,150 |
| | 合计 | 137.49 | 83,130 ± 740 | 0.435 ± 0.029 | 17,910 ± 1,150 |
| CYP 78 09-15 | 950 | 238.86 | 83,130 ± 260 | 0.98 ± 0.012 | 14,500 ± 300 |
| | 1,650 | 120.17 | 82,810 ± 350 | 2.23 ± 0.07 | 3,660 ± 185 |
| | 合计 | 359.03 | 83,030 ± 210 | 3.21 ± 0.07 | 6,970 ± 190 |
| 加拉帕戈斯海隆 | | | | | |
| ALV 892-2 | 700 | 1.40 | 67,810 ± 4,700 | 0.0155 ± 0.0005 | 329 ± 14 |
| | 900 | 43.14 | 75,220 ± 2,920 | 0.074 ± 0.002 | 14,870 ± 500 |
| | 1,200 | 3.31 | 88,130 ± 3,380 | 0.077 ± 0.002 | 16,680 ± 380 |
| | 1,400 | 15.86 | 74,850 ± 2,410 | 0.082 ± 0.002 | 12,920 ± 290 |
| | 1,650 | 11.21 | 79,020 ± 4,870 | 0.122 ± 0.014 | 14,550 ± 1,640 |
| | 合计 | 35.26 | 76,150 ± 1,910 | 0.370 ± 0.014 | 14,120 ± 540 |
| 大气 | | | 722,540 | | 295.5 |

对所有样品在不同温度阶段进行了去气处理。误差为 $2\sigma\sqrt{N}$。绝对浓度的误差范围为 ±10%。测定的 He 灵敏度 $2.7 \times 10^{-11}cm^3 \cdot mV^{-1}$，是通过与库尔茨 [32] 测定的样品 ALV 892-2 和 AII 96-18-1 值相比较计算得出的，不同于之前所用的值 [17]。

表 1 所列数据揭示了洋中脊玄武岩样品和夏威夷样品之间的重要差异。洋中脊玄武岩玻璃的特征为：$^4$He/$^3$He 比值一般是大气的 1/9，$^{40}$Ar/$^{36}$Ar 和 $^{129}$Xe/$^{130}$Xe 比值相

1/9×atmospheric and quite high $^{40}Ar/^{36}Ar$, and $^{129}Xe/^{130}Xe$ ratios, relative to atmospheric. The sample AII 96-18-1 has the highest $^{129}Xe/^{130}Xe$ and $^{40}Ar/^{36}Ar$ ratios ever reported for a MORB glass (25,250±680 and 7.23±0.4 respectively). In contrast, the Hawaiian samples (from Loihi Seamount and Hualalai) have lower $^4He/^3He$ ratios (see also ref. 31) and lower $^{40}Ar/^{36}Ar$ and $^{129}Xe/^{130}Xe$ ratios. The $^{40}Ar/^{36}Ar$ ratio for the sample with the lowest $^4He/^3He$ ratio (kk 29-10 from Loihi Seamount) is only slightly above atmospheric, and the xenon isotopic composition is indistinguishable from air. The quantities of argon and xenon are both well above the blanks, which were less than 8%, and 10% respectively in all cases.

These isotopic variations are shown on the $^4He/^3He$ versus $^{40}Ar/^{36}Ar$ and $^{129}Xe/^{130}Xe$ versus $^{40}Ar/^{36}Ar$ diagrams in Fig. 1. The correlation between $^{129}Xe/^{130}Xe$ and $^{40}Ar/^{36}Ar$ strongly suggests that atmospheric or seawater contamination cannot be responsible for the variations. Based on the $^{130}Xe/^{36}Ar$ ratios in the glass samples and in air, any mixing line between MORB and atmosphere should be convex on Fig. 1 and is represented by $r = 0.1$ (see refs 33, 34 for a discussion of ratio–ratio plots). Atmospheric contamination also could not explain the striking negative correlation between $^{40}Ar/^{36}Ar$ and $^{87}Sr/^{86}Sr$ (Fig. 2).

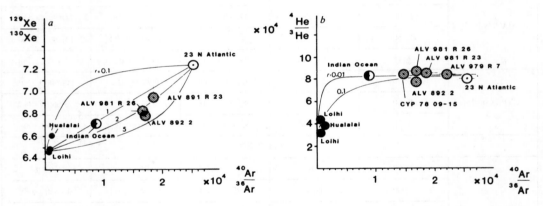

Fig. 1 $a$, $^{129}Xe/^{130}Xe$ versus $^{40}Ar/^{36}Ar$ for the oceanic basalt glass data given in Tables 1 and 2. For sample ALV 979 R7 no xenon data were measured. Sample CYP 78-09-15 is not reported because of possible atmospheric contamination. $b$, $^4He/^3He$ versus $^{40}Ar/^{36}Ar$ for the same samples as in $a$. Note that the points retain the same relative positions on the two diagrams. $r$ stands for the ratio $(^{130}Xe/^{36}Ar)_{LOIHI}/(^{130}Xe/^{36}Ar)_{MORB}$ and $(^3He/^{36}Ar)$ LOIHI$/(^3He/^{36}Ar)$ MORB in $a$ and $b$ respectively. It characterizes the curvature of the hyperbole mixing curves (see ref. 33). Note that contamination of MORB with air in $a$ would result in a curve with $r = 0.1$. For sample description and locations see: A II 96-18-1 in ref. 42 and kk 9-14 in ref. 31; kk-24-7 and kk-29-10 in ref. 39; ALV 892-2 in ref. 16; CYP 78 09-15 in ref. 40; ALV 981 R23 & R26 in ref. 41; ALV 979 R7 is from 105°05′50″ W, 20°50′10″ N; MD23 DR04 from 25°52′ S, 69°19′ E, west indian ridge (R. Schlich, personal communication).

对于空气高出很多。样品 AII 96-18-1 中 $^{129}Xe/^{130}Xe$ 和 $^{40}Ar/^{36}Ar$ 比值是目前已知玄武岩玻璃中最高的（分别为 25,250±680 和 7.23±0.4）。相比之下，夏威夷样品（来自罗希海底山和霍阿拉拉）则具有相对较低的 $^4He/^3He$ 比值（也可参见文献 31）以及 $^{40}Ar/^{36}Ar$ 和 $^{129}Xe/^{130}Xe$ 比值。$^4He/^3He$ 比值最低的样品中（kk 29-10，采自罗希海底山）$^{40}Ar/^{36}Ar$ 的比值仅略高于大气，而氙同位素组成则与空气中组成没有区别。分析所得的氩和氙的量均明显高于本底值，对本次的全部样品而言 Ar 和 Xe 本底均分别小于 8% 和 10%。

这些同位素变化见图 1 中 $^4He/^3He$ 相对于 $^{40}Ar/^{36}Ar$ 的变化以及 $^{129}Xe/^{130}Xe$ 相对于 $^{40}Ar/^{36}Ar$ 的变化图。$^{129}Xe/^{130}Xe$ 和 $^{40}Ar/^{36}Ar$ 之间的相关性强烈表明这种变化并不是由大气或海水污染引起的。根据玻璃样品和空气中 $^{130}Xe/^{36}Ar$ 的比值，图 1 中洋中脊玄武岩和大气之间所有的混合线都应呈凸状，且其 $r=0.1$（见参考文献 33 和 34 中关于比值－比值图的讨论）。而大气污染也无法解释 $^{40}Ar/^{36}Ar$ 和 $^{87}Sr/^{86}Sr$ 之间显著的负相关关系（图 2）。

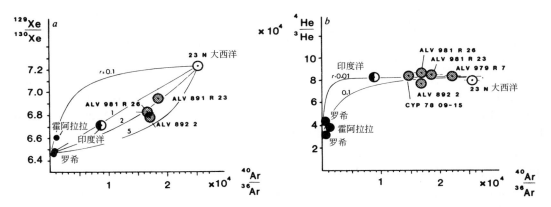

图 1. a，根据表 1 和表 2 中所列大洋玄武岩玻璃相关数据画出的 $^{129}Xe/^{130}Xe$ 相对于 $^{40}Ar/^{36}Ar$ 的变化曲线。样品 ALV 979 R7 的氙同位素数据未予测定。样品 CYP 78-09-15 的数据并未给出，因为其中可能存在大气污染。b，$^4He/^3He$ 相对于 $^{40}Ar/^{36}Ar$ 的变化曲线，所用样品与图 a 相同。特别要注意数据点在两图中相对位置保持不变。r 在图 a 和 b 中分别代表 $(^{130}Xe/^{36}Ar)_{LOIHI}/(^{130}Xe/^{36}Ar)_{MORB}$ 和 $(^3He/^{36}Ar)_{LOIHI}/(^3He/^{36}Ar)_{MORB}$。它表征了该混合双曲线的曲率（见参考文献 33）。可以注意到，图 a 中受到空气污染的洋中脊玄武岩所在曲线的 $r=0.1$。对于样品分布和位置可见如下参考文献：A II 96-18-1 见参考文献 42，kk 9-14 见参考文献 31，kk-24-7 和 kk-29-10 见参考文献 39，ALV 892-2 见参考文献 16，CYP 78 09-15 见参考文献 40，ALV 981 R23 及 R26 见文献 41，ALV 979 R7 采自 105°05'50"W 20°50'10"N，MD23 DR04 采自 25°52'S 69°19'E，位于西印度洋洋中脊（施利希，个人交流）。

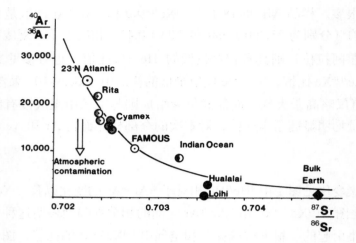

Fig. 2. $^{40}Ar/^{36}Ar$ versus $^{87}Sr/^{86}Sr$ for the oceanic basalt glasses. Sources for values of $^{87}Sr/^{86}Sr$: Loihi seamount from ref. 12, Hualalai, D. Clague in ref. 31; North Atlantic sample AII 96 18-1 from ref. 42. For all other samples only the argon isotopic composition was measured. The strontium values and argon data are given in ref. 18.

## Interpretation

It is generally assumed that mantle gases are residual from atmosphere formation. The noble gas isotopic ratios of the MORB glass samples presented here and elsewhere[17,18] are consistent with this idea, and suggest that the mantle source of MORB was degassed early in Earth's history. The isotopic ratios of the radiogenic or fissiogenic noble gases depend on the $\mu$ value for the isotope system (that is, the radioactive parent/reference isotope ratios: U,Th/$^3$He, $^{40}$K/$^{36}$Ar, $^{129}$I/$^{130}$Xe), and the mantle degassing history. Therefore, the very high radiogenic daughter/reference isotope ratios ($^4$He/$^3$He, $^{40}$Ar/$^{36}$Ar, $^{129}$Xe/$^{130}$Xe) for MORB are the result of early outgassing[17,18].

The results for the Loihi seamount and Hualalai samples require an alternative explanation. Based on the Xe–Ar correlation, the Ar–Sr correlation, the helium isotopic results[12,29], and our experimental precautions, we can immediately eliminate surficial contamination processes. We are therefore left with two hypotheses: the lower $^{40}$Ar/$^{36}$Ar and $^{129}$Xe/$^{130}$Xe ratios (close to atmosphere) are either the result of recycled atmospheric gases in the mantle, or the presence of an undegassed mantle reservoir which has retained its noble gases over the age of the Earth. For these samples, the recycled atmospheric gas hypothesis is not likely because any reasonable recycling mechanism (such as subduction of oceanic crust/sediments) would enrich the mantle in U and K, relative to the rare gases, and produce, after a certain time span, considerable amounts of radiogenic noble gases, leading to higher $^4$He/$^3$He and $^{40}$Ar/$^{36}$Ar ratios; neither of which is observed. Therefore, we conclude that the mantle source for the Loihi and Hualalai samples is less degassed than the MORB source, and contains noble gas isotope ratios similar to the atmosphere (except for helium, due to atmospheric escape).

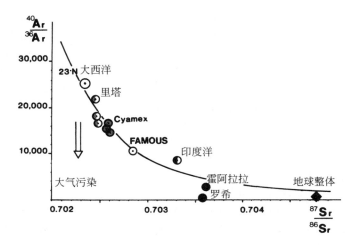

图 2. 大洋玄武岩玻璃 $^{40}Ar/^{36}Ar$ 相对于 $^{87}Sr/^{86}Sr$ 的变化。$^{87}Sr/^{86}Sr$ 比值的来源：罗希海底山地区的值来自文献 12，霍阿拉拉地区，见于克莱格的文献 31；北大西洋样品 AII 96 18-1 引自文献 42。所有其他样品都只测定了氩的同位素组成。锶的值和氩的数据见参考文献 18。[ 编者注：Cyamex 为1978 年法、美、墨联合潜水考察东太平洋海隆的地质研究计划；FAMOUS 为1972~1974 年法美水下联合考察大西洋海隆的计划]

## 解　释

通常认为地幔气体都是大气形成时的残留组分。本文以及其他文献 [17,18] 中所列的洋中脊玄武岩玻璃样品的稀有气体同位素比值均与该观点一致，这说明洋中脊玄武岩地幔源的去气作用发生在地球早期历史时期。放射成因或裂变成因的稀有气体的同位素比值取决于同位素体系的 $\mu$ 值（即，放射性母体同位素与参考同位素的比值：$U,Th/^3He$、$^{40}K/^{36}Ar$ 和 $^{129}I/^{130}Xe$）以及地幔的去气历史。因此，洋中脊玄武岩具有很高的放射成因子体同位素与参考同位素的比值（$^4He/^3He$、$^{40}Ar/^{36}Ar$ 和 $^{129}Xe/^{130}Xe$），这是早期去气作用的结果 [17,18]。

罗希海底山和霍阿拉拉岛样品的分析结果则需要寻找另外的解释。根据 Xe–Ar 相关关系、Ar–Sr 相关关系、氦同位素结果 [12,29] 以及我们实验的预处理方法，可以将表面污染过程马上排除。因此我们只剩两种可能性了：$^{40}Ar/^{36}Ar$ 和 $^{129}Xe/^{130}Xe$ 比值较低（接近大气值）要么是由于地幔中存在再循环大气气体所致，要么是由于未去气地幔库的存在，它在整个地球历史中保存了早期的稀有气体所致。对于这些样品，大气气体再循环的假说不太可能，因为所有可能的再循环机制（如洋壳或沉积物的俯冲）都会使地幔中 U 和 K 产生相对于稀有气体的富集，这样经过一段时间后就会形成大量的放射成因稀有气体，从而导致较高的 $^4He/^3He$ 和 $^{40}Ar/^{36}Ar$ 比值，然而这两种情况都未见到。所以，我们得出结论认为，罗希海底山和霍阿拉拉岛样品的地幔源的去气作用弱于洋中脊玄武岩地幔源，其所包含的稀有气体同位素比值与大气类似（除氦以外，由于大气的逃逸所致）。

Similar conclusions have been reached by other workers based on different information. Kaneoka and Takaoka[21] noted a correlation between $^3He/^4He$ and $^{40}Ar/^{36}Ar$ qualitatively similar to the one displayed in Fig. 1b. However, they observed no correlation with respect to xenon, and analysed phenocrysts and xenocrysts rather than glasses. Based on a literature search, Hart et al.[35] also suggested the existence of undegassed mantle with low $^{40}Ar/^{36}Ar$ ratios. Manuel and Sabu[36] suggested similar conclusions for xenon. The present study offers compelling evidence for an undegassed mantle reservoir, particularly since all the noble gases were measured on the same samples, all of which were fresh glasses.

This has quite important implications for models of mantle structure and evolution. As mentioned earlier, the short half life of extinct $^{129}I$ (parent of $^{129}Xe$) means that any differences in $^{129}Xe/^{130}Xe$ ratio within the mantle must be at least 4,400 Myr old. Using the $^{129}Xe/^{130}Xe$ isotopic differences between MORB and the atmosphere, Staudacher and Allègre[17] calculated that these two systems were separated 10–25 Myr after accretion of the Earth. The calculation is analogous for the separation between the mantle sources of MORB and Hawaiian basalts, since the difference in $^{129}Xe/^{130}Xe$ ratio is similar. Therefore, any mantle model must allow the existence of distinct reservoirs for at least 4,400 Myr. This conclusion is one of the strongest arguments yet offered in favor of a layered mantle. In view of the homogenizing effect of convection (see ref. 37), whole mantle convection over the age of the Earth would have destroyed such heterogeneities in the xenon isotopes, and is therefore untenable. Similar conclusions are reached from the argon isotopes, although the mean ages are slightly higher due to the longer half life of $^{40}K$, and the greater effect of recycling on argon[18].

Note that the relation between degassing and depletion (as used in reference to Rb/Sr, Sm/Nd) is not necessarily simple. Although the noble gasses suggest that the separation between the two mantle layers (MORB and Hawaiian sources) and the atmosphere occurred at least 4,400 Myr ago, Sr and Nd isotopic variations were produced by extraction of the continents, which proceeded later and at a different rate[7,38]. To the extent that isotope ratio variations are generated by present day (recent) mantle mixing, correlations should be observed between the noble gases and the isotopes of Sr and Nd. In fact, Kurz et al. observed correlations between $^3He/^4He$ and $^{87}Sr/^{86}Sr$ on both regional and global scales. The results presented here support the hypothesis that mixing is responsible for the isotopic variations, as is shown by the correlation between $^{40}Ar/^{36}Ar$ and $^{87}Sr/^{86}Sr$ in Fig. 2. The systematics suggest that the mantle source for MORB is both depleted with respect to Rb/Sr and degassed with respect to noble gases, which is also consistent with a layered mantle. Even though degassing and continent formation may not have occurred at the same time, they apparently both acted on the mantle source of MORB, which is presumed to be the upper mantle.

These systematics do not rule out more complex descriptions of the mantle, involving heterogeneities within each of the layers. As mentioned earlier, isotopic evidence suggests that more than two discrete "reservoirs" are required[12], possibly including recycled oceanic crust, and mantle that is affected by core-pumping[7]. The samples analysed for this study

其他学者也根据不同的信息得到了类似的结论。兼冈和高冈 [21] 发现 $^3He/^4He$ 比值和 $^{40}Ar/^{36}Ar$ 比值之间的相关性在性质上与图 1$b$ 所示的相似。不过，他们发现对于氙则无此相关性，而他们分析的是斑晶和捕掳晶而非玻璃。在一项文献研究的基础上，哈特等人 [35] 也表明了 $^{40}Ar/^{36}Ar$ 比值较低的未去气地幔的存在。曼努埃尔和萨布 [36] 也就氙提出了类似的结论。本研究为未去气地幔层的存在提供了强有力的证据，特别是基于同时测定了同一样品的所有稀有气体且所有样品均为新鲜的玻璃。

上述研究结果对于地幔结构和演化模型具有非常重要的启示。如前所述，灭绝同位素 $^{129}I$（$^{129}Xe$ 的母体）的超短半衰期意味着地幔中 $^{129}Xe/^{130}Xe$ 比值的任何差异都已存在至少 44 亿年了。利用洋中脊玄武岩和大气中 $^{129}Xe/^{130}Xe$ 比值的差异，施陶达赫尔和阿莱格尔 [17] 计算得出，这两个体系是在地球吸积增生后 1,000 万到 2,500 万年间分离的。该计算结果与洋中脊玄武岩和夏威夷玄武岩地幔源之间的分离时间类似，因为 $^{129}Xe/^{130}Xe$ 比值的差异很相似。因此，任何地幔模型都应允许有存在至少 44 亿年的独特地幔库。该结论是迄今支持层状地幔最有力的证据之一。考虑到对流的均匀混合效应（见参考文献 37），在地质历史上整个地幔的对流将导致氙同位素中的不均一性被破坏，因而这种说法是站不住脚的。对于氩同位素也可得到类似结论，只是由于 $^{40}K$ 的半衰期较长，且再循环作用对氩的影响更大 [18]，所以其平均年龄要略高些。

值得注意的是，去气作用与亏损之间（应用时通常指 Rb/Sr 和 Sm/Nd）的关系未必是简单的。虽然稀有气体显示两地幔层（洋中脊玄武岩地幔源区和夏威夷玄武岩地幔源区）与大气的分离发生在至少 44 亿年前，但 Sr 和 Nd 同位素的变化是由于大陆的提取所致，该过程是在随后以不同的速率进行的 [7,38]。在现今（近期）地幔混合产生的同位素比值变化范围内，稀有气体与 Sr 和 Nd 同位素之间应该存在相关性。事实上，库尔茨等观测发现 $^3He/^4He$ 及 $^{87}Sr/^{86}Sr$ 在区域和全球尺度上都具有相关性。本文所给出的结果支持混合作用是导致同位素变化的原因这一假说，正如图 2 中 $^{40}Ar/^{36}Ar$ 与 $^{87}Sr/^{86}Sr$ 的相关性所示。该系统显示洋中脊玄武岩地幔源区不仅表现为 Rb/Sr 亏损而且发生过稀有气体去气作用，这也与层状地幔模式一致。虽然去气作用和大陆的形成可能不是同时发生的，但他们显然都对假设位于上地幔的洋中脊玄武岩地幔源区产生过重要影响。

上述研究结果并不能排除地幔中存在更为复杂的情况，包括地幔内每个层的不均一性。如前所述，同位素证据显示，至少存在两个以上的分离的"库" [12]，可能包括再循环的洋壳，以及受地核泵吸效应 [7] 影响的地幔。本研究所分析的样品经过

were chosen specifically to delineate the first-order effects between the best representatives of depleted and undepleted mantle. Note also that the correlations in Figs 1 and 2 do not necessary prove a one-to-one relation between degassed and depleted mantle sources. In fact, it is quite reasonable to assume that the convective structure of the mantle has changed since the degassing took place 4,400 Myr ago. One example of the complexity this may impart to present-day geochemical structure is shown in Fig. 3. If the depth of the top convecting layer decreased after degassing, the continents may then have been extracted from only a part of the degassed mantle, resulting in the existence of a degassed but undepleted reservoir (see Fig. 3). This is only one of the possibilities, which present a challenge both to geophysicists and geochemists.

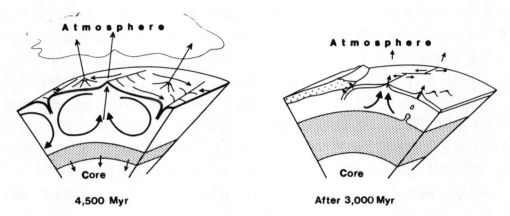

Fig. 3. A simplified mantle profile showing possible differences between depleted and degassed mantle reservoirs. Since the degassing took place 4,400 Myr ago (see text), and continent formation did not occur until much later, this figure illustrates one possible complication that this different timing may imply.

Table 2. Xenon isotopic data normalized to $^{130}\text{Xe}\equiv100$

| Sample | Temperature (°C) | $^{130}\text{Xe}$ $(10^{-14}\ \text{cm}^3\ \text{g}^{-1})$ | $^{124}\text{Xe}$ | $^{126}\text{Xe}$ | $^{128}\text{Xe}$ | $^{129}\text{Xe}$ | $^{130}\text{Xe}$ | $^{131}\text{Xe}$ | $^{132}\text{Xe}$ | $^{134}\text{Xe}$ | $^{136}\text{Xe}$ |
|---|---|---|---|---|---|---|---|---|---|---|---|
| | | | | | Loihi | | | | | | |
| KK-29-10 | 700 | 7.08±0.13 | — | — | 50.3±1.9 | 661±10 | 100 | 522±4 | 664±7 | 262±2 | 212±2 |
| | 1,000 | 16.26±0.11 | 1.9±0.4 | 2.2±0.5 | 46.8±0.9 | 648±5 | 100 | 515±4 | 658±7 | 257±2 | 216±2 |
| | 1,400 | 2.60±0.06 | — | 2.3±3.3 | 46.3±2.1 | 636±7 | 100 | 505±5 | 646±15 | 259±3 | 215±3 |
| | 1,650 | <0.70 | — | — | — | — | — | — | — | — | — |
| KK-24-7 | 700 | <0.40 | — | — | — | — | — | — | — | — | — |
| | 1,000 | 13.3±0.13 | — | — | 47.5±0.6 | 644±7 | 100 | 520±5 | 663±6 | 256±3 | 221±2 |
| | 1,400 | 6.3±0.06 | — | — | 43.9±0.9 | 647±5 | 100 | 517±3 | 664±3 | 261±2 | 221±2 |
| | 1,650 | 8.1±0.12 | — | — | 45.9±0.5 | 644±3 | 100 | 523±2 | 662±4 | 259±2 | 222±1 |

了专门挑选，是为了描述最具代表性的亏损和未亏损地幔之间最近似的一阶效应。还需注意的是，图1和图2中的相关关系并不足以证明去气地幔源和亏损地幔源之间存在一对一的关系。实际上，我们完全有理由假设地幔的对流结构是在44亿年前去气作用发生后开始变化的。图3所示为该结论有可能赋予现今地球化学结构复杂性的一个例子。倘若顶部对流层的深度在去气作用后减小，那么大陆应该只是从去气地幔的一部分中提取出来的，从而导致了一个去气的然而却是未亏损的地幔库的存在（见图3）。这仅是可能性之一，并且这种可能性对地球物理学家和地球化学家都提出了挑战。

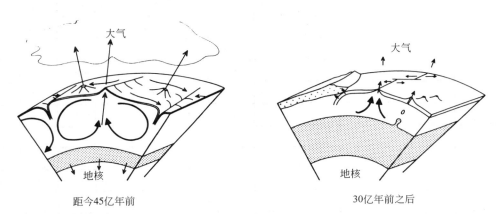

图 3. 一个简化的地幔剖面图，图中给出了亏损地幔库和去气地幔库之间可能存在的区别。由于去气作用发生在44亿年前（见正文），而大陆的形成则晚得多，本图说明了这种不同事件时间的差异所可能产生的众多复杂情形之一。

表 2. 以 $^{130}Xe \equiv 100$ 归一化后的氙同位素数据

| 样品 | 温度 (℃) | $^{130}Xe$ ($10^{-14}cm^3$) | $^{124}Xe$ | $^{126}Xe$ | $^{128}Xe$ | $^{129}Xe$ | $^{130}Xe$ | $^{131}Xe$ | $^{132}Xe$ | $^{134}Xe$ | $^{136}Xe$ |
|---|---|---|---|---|---|---|---|---|---|---|---|
| 罗希 | | | | | | | | | | | |
| KK-29-10 | 700 | $7.08 \pm 0.13$ | – | – | $50.3 \pm 1.9$ | $661 \pm 10$ | 100 | $522 \pm 4$ | $664 \pm 7$ | $262 \pm 2$ | $212 \pm 2$ |
| | 1,000 | $16.26 \pm 0.11$ | $1.9 \pm 0.4$ | $2.2 \pm 0.5$ | $46.8 \pm 0.9$ | $648 \pm 5$ | 100 | $515 \pm 4$ | $658 \pm 7$ | $257 \pm 2$ | $216 \pm 2$ |
| | 1,400 | $2.60 \pm 0.06$ | – | $2.3 \pm 3.3$ | $46.3 \pm 2.1$ | $636 \pm 7$ | 100 | $505 \pm 5$ | $646 \pm 15$ | $259 \pm 3$ | $215 \pm 3$ |
| | 1,650 | <0.70 | – | – | – | – | | – | – | – | – |
| KK-24-7 | 700 | <0.40 | – | – | – | – | | – | – | – | – |
| | 1,000 | $13.3 \pm 0.13$ | – | – | $47.5 \pm 0.6$ | $644 \pm 7$ | 100 | $520 \pm 5$ | $663 \pm 6$ | $256 \pm 3$ | $221 \pm 2$ |
| | 1,400 | $6.3 \pm 0.06$ | – | – | $43.9 \pm 0.9$ | $647 \pm 5$ | 100 | $517 \pm 3$ | $664 \pm 3$ | $261 \pm 2$ | $221 \pm 2$ |
| | 1,650 | $8.1 \pm 0.12$ | – | – | $45.9 \pm 0.5$ | $644 \pm 3$ | 100 | $523 \pm 2$ | $662 \pm 4$ | $259 \pm 2$ | $222 \pm 1$ |

*Continued*

| Sample | Temperature (°C) | $^{130}$Xe ($10^{-14}$ cm$^3$ g$^{-1}$) | $^{124}$Xe | $^{126}$Xe | $^{128}$Xe | $^{129}$Xe | $^{130}$Xe | $^{131}$Xe | $^{132}$Xe | $^{134}$Xe | $^{136}$Xe |
|---|---|---|---|---|---|---|---|---|---|---|---|
| **Hualalai** | | | | | | | | | | | |
| KK-9-14 | 700 | <0.15 | — | — | — | — | — | — | — | — | — |
| | 1,400 | 11.6±0.14 | 2.2±0.8 | 2.7±0.9 | 45.5±1.0 | 660±2 | 100 | 525±2 | 659±3 | 261±1 | 222±1 |
| | 1,650 | <0.2 | — | — | — | — | — | — | — | — | — |
| **Atlantic** | | | | | | | | | | | |
| AII 96-18-1 | 700 | 0.5±0.2 | — | — | — | — | — | — | — | — | — |
| | 1,300 | 4.11±0.06 | 3.0±1.3 | 3.7±1.4 | 45.9±1.5 | 723±4 | 100 | 520±3 | 666±9 | 276±2 | 238±2 |
| | 1,650 | 1.30±0.10 | 6.6±2.8 | — | 39.7±11.9 | 689±21 | 100 | 520±16 | 673±31 | 266±10 | 227±9 |
| **Indian Ocean** | | | | | | | | | | | |
| MD23 DR04 | 1,150 | 10.90±0.03 | — | 2.25±0.07 | 45.6±0.2 | 671±2 | 100 | 519±2 | 659±2 | 263±1 | 224±1 |
| | 1,400 | 14.50±0.04 | — | 2.05±0.09 | 46.9±0.2 | 671±2 | 100 | 482±2 | 662±2 | 260±1 | 223±1 |
| | 1,650 | 4.31±0.06 | — | 2.44±0.43 | 44.4±1.3 | 659±9 | 100 | 524±7 | 664±9 | 260±4 | 223±2 |
| **Pacific** | | | | | | | | | | | |
| ALV981 R 23 | 600–1,150 | — | — | — | — | — | — | — | — | — | — |
| | 1,400 | 2.3±0.3 | — | — | — | 694±11 | 100 | 503±8 | 649±9 | 265±5 | 238±3 |
| | 1,500 | — | — | — | — | — | — | — | — | — | — |
| ALV981 R 26 | 1,000 | 1.02±0.3 | — | — | 59±7 | 633±18 | 100 | 555±19 | 633±17 | 244±9 | 208±7 |
| | 1,400 | 2.60±0.3 | — | — | 47±1 | 681±7 | 100 | 521±6 | 662±7 | 266±3 | 224±2 |
| | 1,600 | 2.44±0.4 | — | — | 49±2 | 680±12 | 100 | 521±9 | 658±11 | 265±5 | 223±4 |
| **Galapagos Rise** | | | | | | | | | | | |
| ALV 892-2 | 700 | <0.2 | — | — | — | — | — | — | — | — | — |
| | 900 | 1.3±0.1 | — | — | 48.4±7.7 | 606±43 | 100 | 484±35 | 607±43 | 240±18 | 228±18 |
| | 1,200 | 8.15±0.17 | — | — | 48.6±2.1 | 679±7 | 100 | 518±5 | 665±6 | 264±3 | 228±3 |
| | 1,400 | 9.22±0.38 | — | — | 50.2±2.7 | 670±11 | 100 | 505±9 | 642±12 | 260±5 | 222±4 |
| | 1,650 | 13.22±0.37 | — | — | 48.0±1.8 | 672±6 | 100 | 519±5 | 654±8 | 262±3 | 222±2 |
| Atmosphere | | | 2.35 | 2.21 | 47.0 | 648 | 100 | 519 | 659 | 256 | 217 |

## Conclusions

The isotopic composition of He, Ar, and Xe in several basalt glasses, from both mid-ocean ridges and the island of Hawaii, require the existence of both a degassed and an undegassed mantle reservoir. The isotopic variations of Ar and Xe, combined with the half lives of $^{40}$K and $^{129}$I, show that these two reservoirs must have been separated for at least 4,400 Myr, a conclusion which argues strongly for a layered mantle.

| 样品 | 温度(℃) | $^{130}Xe$ ($10^{-14}cm^3$) | $^{124}Xe$ | $^{126}Xe$ | $^{128}Xe$ | $^{129}Xe$ | $^{130}Xe$ | $^{131}Xe$ | $^{132}Xe$ | $^{134}Xe$ | $^{136}Xe$ |
|---|---|---|---|---|---|---|---|---|---|---|---|
| 霍阿拉拉 | | | | | | | | | | | |
| KK-9-14 | 700 | <0.15 | – | – | – | – | – | – | – | – | – |
| | 1,400 | 11.6±0.14 | 2.2±0.8 | 2.7±0.9 | 45.5±1.0 | 660±2 | 100 | 525±2 | 659±3 | 261±1 | 222±1 |
| | 1,650 | <0.2 | – | – | – | – | – | – | – | – | – |
| 大西洋 | | | | | | | | | | | |
| AII96-18-1 | 700 | 0.5±0.2 | – | – | – | – | – | – | – | – | – |
| | 1,300 | 4.11±0.06 | 3.0±1.3 | 3.7±1.4 | 45.9±1.5 | 723±4 | 100 | 520±3 | 666±9 | 276±2 | 238±2 |
| | 1,650 | 1.30±0.10 | 6.6±2.8 | – | 39.7±11.9 | 689±21 | 100 | 520±16 | 673±31 | 266±10 | 227±9 |
| 印度洋 | | | | | | | | | | | |
| MD23 DR04 | 1,150 | 10.90±0.03 | – | 2.25±0.07 | 45.6±0.2 | 671±2 | 100 | 519±2 | 659±2 | 263±1 | 224±1 |
| | 1,400 | 14.50±0.04 | – | 2.05±0.09 | 46.9±0.2 | 671±2 | 100 | 482±2 | 662±2 | 260±1 | 223±1 |
| | 1,650 | 4.31±0.06 | – | 2.44±0.43 | 44.4±1.3 | 659±9 | 100 | 524±7 | 664±9 | 260±4 | 223±2 |
| 太平洋 | | | | | | | | | | | |
| ALV981 R23 | 600~1,150 | – | – | – | – | – | – | – | – | – | – |
| | 1,400 | 2.3±0.3 | – | – | – | 694±11 | 100 | 503±8 | 649±9 | 265±5 | 238±3 |
| | 1,500 | – | – | – | – | – | – | – | – | – | – |
| ALV981 R26 | 1,000 | 1.02±0.3 | – | – | 59±7 | 633±18 | 100 | 555±19 | 633±17 | 244±9 | 208±7 |
| | 1,400 | 2.60±0.3 | – | – | 47±1 | 681±7 | 100 | 521±6 | 662±7 | 266±3 | 224±2 |
| | 1,600 | 2.44±0.4 | – | – | 49±2 | 680±12 | 100 | 521±9 | 658±11 | 265±5 | 223±4 |
| 加拉帕戈斯海隆 | | | | | | | | | | | |
| ALV892-2 | 700 | <0.2 | – | – | – | – | – | – | – | – | – |
| | 900 | 1.3±0.1 | – | – | 48.4±7.7 | 606±43 | 100 | 484±35 | 607±43 | 240±18 | 228±18 |
| | 1,200 | 8.15±0.17 | – | – | 48.6±2.1 | 679±7 | 100 | 518±5 | 665±6 | 264±3 | 228±3 |
| | 1,400 | 9.22±0.38 | – | – | 50.2±2.7 | 670±11 | 100 | 505±9 | 642±12 | 260±5 | 222±4 |
| | 1,650 | 13.22±0.37 | – | – | 48.0±1.8 | 672±6 | 100 | 519±5 | 654±8 | 262±3 | 222±2 |
| 大气 | | | 2.35 | 2.21 | 47.0 | 648 | 100 | 519 | 659 | 256 | 217 |

## 结　论

　　来自洋中脊和夏威夷岛的数个玄武岩玻璃中 He、Ar 和 Xe 的同位素组成要求去气和未去气地幔库同时存在。Ar 和 Xe 的同位素变化，结合 $^{40}K$ 和 $^{129}I$ 的半衰期显示，这两个地幔库在至少 44 亿年前就已分离，该结论强烈支持了层状地幔的观点。

We thank Dr. D. Clague for donating the Hawaiian glasses and R. Schlich for several of the MORB examples. M. K. acknowledges support from a NATO–NSF postdoctoral fellowship.

(**303**, 762-766; 1983 )

Claude J. Allègre, Thomas Staudacher, Philippe Sarda and Mark Kurz
Laboratorie de Geochimie et Cosmochimie, Institut de Physique du Globe et Département des Sciences de la Terre, 4 Place Jussieu, 75230 Paris Cedex 05, France

Received 4 February; accepted 26 April 1983.

References:

1. Morgan, J. *Nature* **230**, 42 (1971).

2. McKenzie, D. & Richter, F. *J. Geophys. Res.* **86** (B12), 11667-11680 (1981).

3. Peltier, W. R. & Jarris, G. T. *Phys. Earth Planet. Inter.* **29**, 281-304 (1982).

4. Flasser, W., Olsen, P. & Marsh, B. *J. Geophys. Res.* **84**, 147-155 (1979).

5. O'Connell, R. J. *Tectonophysics* **38**, 119-136 (1977).

6. Allègre, C. J., Brevart, O., Dupré, B. & Minster, J. F. *Phil. Trans. R. Soc.* **A237**, 311 (1980).

7. Allègre, C. J., Ben Othman, D., Polvé. M. & Richard, P. in *Phys. Earth Planet. Inter.* **19**, 293-306 (1979).

8. Jacobsen, S. B. & Wasserburg, G. J. *J. Geophys. Res.* **84**, 7411-7427 (1979).

9. O'Nions, R. K., Evensen, N. M. & Hamilton, P. J. *J. Geophys. Res.* **84**, 6091-6101 (1979).

10. Allègre, C. J. *Tectonophysics* **81**, 109-132 (1982).

11. Anderson, D. L. *Earth Planet. Sci. Lett.* **57**, 1-12 (1982).

12. Kurz, M. D., Jenkins, W. J. & Hart, S. R. *Nature* **297**, 43-47 (1982).

13. Zindler, A., Jagoutz, E. & Goldstein, S. *Nature* **298**, 519-523 (1982).

14. Davies, G. F. *Nature* **290**, 208-13 (1981).

15. Lupton, J. G. & Craig, H. *Earth Planet. Sci. Lett.* **26**, 133 (1975).

16. Kurz, M. D. & Jenkins, W. J. *Earth Planet. Sci. Lett.* **53**, 41-54 (1981).

17. Staudacher, Th. & Allègre, C. J. *Earth Planet. Sci. Lett.* **60**, 389-406 (1982).

18. Sarda, Ph., Staudacher, Th. & Allègre, C. J. *EOS* **63**, 458 (1982).

19. Tolstikhin, I. N. in *Terrestrial Rare Gases* 33-62 (Japan Science Society Press, Tokyo, 1978).

20. Craig, H. & Lupton, J. E. *Earth Planet. Sci. Lett.* **31**, 369-385 (1976).

21. Kaneoka, I. & Takaoka, N. *Science* **208**, 1366-1368 (1980).

22. Alexander, E. C., Lewis, R. S., Reynolds, J. H. & Michel, M. C. *Science* **172**, 837-840 (1971).

23. Shukoljukov, J., Kirsten, T. & Jessberger, F. K. *Earth Planet. Sci. Lett.* **24**, 271 (1974).

24. Teitsma, A., Clarke, W. B. & Allègre, C. J. *Science* **189**, 878 (1975).

25. Ozima, M. *Nature Phys. Sci.* **246**, 41 (1973).

26. Ozima, M. *Geochim. Cosmochim. Acta* **39**, 1127-34 (1975).

27. Fisher, D. E. *Nature* **256**, 113-114 (1975).

28. Brown, J. F., Harper, C. T. & Odom, A. L. *Nature* **250**, 130-133 (1974).

29. Alexander, E. C. & Schwartzman, D. W. *Nature* **259**, 104-109 (1976).

30. Fisher, D. E. *Phys. Earth Planet. Inter.* **29**, 242-251 (1982).

31. Kurz, M. D., Jenkins, W. J., Hart, S. & Clague, D. *Earth Planet. Sci. Lett.* (in the press).

32. Kurz, M. D., thesis MIT/Woods Hole Oceanographic Institution (1982).

33. Clague, M. D., Jenkins, W. J., Schilling, J. G. R. & Hart, S. R. *Earth Planet. Sci. Lett.* **58**, (1982).

34. Langmuir, C. H., Vocke, R. D., Hanson, G. N. & Hart, S. R. *Earth Planet. Sci. Lett.* **37**, 380-392 (1978).

35. Hart, R., Dymond, J. & Hogan, L. *Nature* **278**, 156-159 (1979).

36. Manuel, O. K. & Sabu, D. D. *Geochem. J.* **15**, 245-267 (1981).

37. McKenzie, D. D. *Geophys. J. R. astr. Soc.* **58**, 689-715 (1979).

38. Allègre, C. J. & Rousseau, D. *Earth Planet. Sci. Lett.* (in the press).

39. Moore, J., Clague, D. & Normark, W. *Geology* **10**, 88-92 (1982).

40. Cyamex Scientific Team *Oceanolo. Acta* **3**, 487-503 (1980).

41. Dupré, B., Lambret, R., Rousseau, D. & Allègre, C. J. *Nature* **294**, 552-554 (1981).

42. Machado, N., Ludden, J. & Brooks, C. *Nature* **295**, 226-228 (1982).

感谢克莱格博士提供了夏威夷玄武岩玻璃和施利希提供了一部分洋中脊玄武岩样品。马克感谢北大西洋公约组织－国家科学基金会博士后研究基金提供的支持。

（齐红艳 翻译；周新华 审稿）

# A Conserved DNA Sequence in Homoeotic Genes of the *Drosophila* Antennapedia and Bithorax Complexes

W. McGinnis *et al.*

### Editor's Note

The development of flies and other insects from their fertilized eggs is a complex matter. The successive developmental stages include the appearance of larvae, a period of apparent quiescence (as in chrysalis) and the emergence of an adult insect usually bearing no resemblance to the larval stage. The question for developmental biologists is how the adult stage is specified in the earliest stages of the embryo. The answer, inferred by classical biologists, is that even the larvae contain internal structures that develop into the wings, legs, antennae and other structures embodied in the adult. In 1984 Walter Gehring and his colleagues at the University of Basel in Switzerland found a way of identifying the genes in the fruitfly *Drosophila* that are responsible for the succession of changes. The homoeotic genes, as they are called, are localized on the third chromosome of the fruitfly and have a characteristic structure that makes it possible to recognize genes with similar function in other organisms.

---

A repetitive DNA sequence has been identified in the *Drosophila melanogaster* genome that appears to be localized specifically within genes of the bithorax and Antennapedia complexes that are required for correct segmental development. Initially identified in cloned copies of the genes *Antennapedia*, *Ultrabithorax* and *fushi tarazu*, the sequence is also contained within two other DNA clones that have characteristics strongly suggesting that they derive from other homoeotic genes.

---

MANY of the homoeotic genes of *Drosophila* seem to be involved in the specification of developmental pathways for the body segments of the fly, so that each segment acquires a unique identity. A mutation in such a homoeotic gene often results in a replacement of one body segment (or part of a segment) by another segment that is normally located elsewhere. Many of these homoeotic loci reside in two gene complexes, the bithorax complex and the Antennapedia (Antp) complex, both located on the right arm of chromosome 3 (3R).

The bithorax complex is located in the middle of 3R, and its resident genes impose specific segmental identities on the posterior thoracic and abdominal segments[1]. For example, inactivation of the *bithorax* gene of the complex causes a transformation of the anterior half of the third thoracic segment into the anterior half of the second thoracic segment, resulting in a fly having wing structures in a site normally occupied by haltere.

# 果蝇触角足和双胸基因复合体同源异型基因中的保守DNA序列

麦金尼斯等

**编者按**

苍蝇以及其他昆虫从它们的受精卵开始经历的发育是一个复杂的问题。连续的发育阶段包括幼虫期、一个看似静止的时期（例如：蛹）和通常与幼虫阶段没有相似处的成虫期。发育生物学家的问题是，成虫阶段是如何在胚胎的最早期阶段被特化的？根据经典生物学家的推断，回答是：即使是幼虫也含有可以发育成成虫翅、足、触角和其他结构的内部结构。1984年瑞士巴塞尔大学的沃尔特·格林教授及其同事找到了一种鉴定负责果蝇连续变化的基因的方法。这个被他们称之为同源异型的基因位于果蝇的第3条染色体上，并且具有一个特征性结构，可用于识别其他生物中具有类似功能的基因。

在黑腹果蝇的基因组里发现了一段重复DNA序列，这段序列似乎特异地定位于正常体节发育所需的双胸和触角足基因复合体内部。起初这个序列是在果蝇触角足基因、超级双胸和 *ftz* 基因的克隆拷贝中鉴定出来的，后来在其他两个DNA克隆中也发现了这种序列，它们所具有的特征强有力地说明了这些基因起源于其他的同源异型基因。

果蝇的许多同源异型基因似乎都参与了果蝇体节发育途径的特化，从而每个体节都有其独特的特征。此类同源异型基因中的一个突变常常导致一个体节（或一个体节的一部分）被通常位于其他位置的另一个体节所替代。许多同源异型基因座位于两种基因复合体——双胸基因复合体和触角足基因复合体中，二者都位于3号染色体右臂上。

双胸基因复合体位于3号染色体右臂的中间，其内的基因可以影响后胸部和腹部体节特异性的体节特征[1]。例如，这个基因复合体的双胸基因失活会引起第3胸节的前半部转变成第2胸节的前半部，从而导致果蝇在通常平衡棒所在的位置长出

1151

Other recessive mutations in the complex cause analogous transformations of posterior body structures into structures normally located in a more anterior position. Embryos having a deletion of the entire bithorax complex show a transformation of all the posterior body segments into reiterated segments with structures of the second thoracic segment. Based on the above results and others, Lewis has proposed a model in which segmental identity in the thorax and abdomen is controlled by a stepwise activation of additional bithorax complex genes in more posterior segments[1].

The Antp complex is localized nearer the centromere of 3R than the bithorax complex. The genes of the Antp complex appear to control segmental development in the posterior head and thorax, in a manner analogous to the way in which the bithorax complex operates in the more posterior segments[2–5]. A dominant mutation in the *Antp* locus, for example, can result in the transformation of the antenna of the fly into a second thoracic leg[6,7].

The homoeotic genes of both the bithorax and Antp complexes can be thought of as selector genes, using the nomenclature of Garcia-Bellido[8], that act by interpreting gradients of positional information. Based on their location in the gradient, a specific combination of selector genes are expressed, and thus different regions of the developing fly become selected to proceed down specific developmental pathways. Although the available evidence supports this model[1,9,10], the real situation appears to be more complex as there is also evidence that regulatory interactions between different homoeotic selector genes have a role in limiting their region of expression[10–12].

The physical proximity and similar but distinct functions of the bithorax complex genes led Lewis to propose that the genes of this cluster evolved by mutational diversification of tandemly repeated genes[1]. In the primitive millipede-like ancestors of *Drosophila*, an ancestral gene or genes would direct the development of repetitive segments having similar identities. The evolutionary transition to the Dipterans, with highly diverse segmental structures, might be achieved by duplication and divergence of ancestral genes. According to this model, null mutations in the present set of bithorax complex genes could result in a fly having a more primitive segmental array, that is, with legs on the abdominal segments, or with wings on the third thoracic segment, in addition to those on the second thoracic segment; both types of phenotype are known to result from reduction or loss of function of bithorax complex genes.

Although the bithorax and Antp complexes are widely separated on the third chromosome, their similar functions in specifying segmental identity suggests that both complexes might have evolved from a common ancestral gene or gene complex. A critical test for this hypothesis involves a test for conserved sequences in the genes of the two complexes. These conserved sequences could be relics of ancient gene duplications or regions specifically preserved by selection against mutational change. Here we show that there is DNA sequence homology between some genes of the bithorax complex and the Antp complex. We use this homology, which is imperfect and limited to small regions, to

翅的结构。该基因复合体的其他隐性突变可以引起类似的变化，导致后部身体结构变成通常位于更前部位的结构。整个双胸基因复合体缺失的胚胎，其所有后部体节转变成为具有第二胸节结构的重复体节。基于以上结果和其他信息，刘易斯提出了一个模型，即胸部和腹部的体节特征受控于位于更后部体节中其他双胸复合体基因的逐步激活[1]。

触角足基因复合体位于第 3 号染色体右臂上，它比双胸基因复合体更接近着丝粒。这些触角足复合体中的基因对头后部和胸部的体节发育的控制，似乎是通过一种类似于双胸基因复合体操纵更后部体节发育的方式实现的[2-5]。例如，触角足基因座的显性突变会导致果蝇的触角转变为第二个胸足[6,7]。

根据加西亚－贝利多命名法[8]，可以将双胸基因复合体和触角足基因复合体两者的同源异型基因命名为选择者基因，它们通过解读位置信息的梯度起作用。基于其梯度定位，表达一组特定组合的选择者基因，从而使正在发育的果蝇的不同区域选择进行特定的发育途径。虽然现有的证据支持这个模型[1,9,10]，但真正的情况似乎更为复杂，因为也有证据表明，不同的同源异型选择者基因之间的相互调节作用也有限制它们自身表达区域的作用[10-12]。

双胸复合体中的基因，它们在基因组上的位置邻近，功能相似但又有不同，这使得刘易斯提出，这个基因簇中的基因是通过串联重复基因的突变多样化进化而来[1]。果蝇有一种原始的祖先，类似千足虫，其一个或多个祖先基因可指导具有相似特性的重复体节的发育。膜翅目昆虫具有高度多样的体节结构，其进化转换可能是通过祖先基因的复制和分化而实现的。根据这个模型，在现今的双胸基因复合体中的无效突变可能使果蝇具有一种更原始的体节排列，也就是，除了第二胸节上的足外，在腹或第三胸节上也长有足。这两种表型都被认为由双胸复合体基因功能的下降或缺失所致。

虽然双胸基因复合体和触角足基因复合体在第 3 号染色体上相隔很远，但它们在决定体节特性时的相似功能表明，这两种复合物可能从一个共同的祖先基因，或基因复合物进化而来。对这种假说的一个关键性检验涉及对这两个复合物基因中保守序列的检测。这些保守序列可能是远古基因复制的遗迹，或是通过自然选择作用于突变变化而特异性地保留下来的区域。在此，我们指出双胸基因复合体和触角足基因复合体中的一些基因之间的 DNA 序列具有同源性。我们利用这种不严格的且

isolate other cross-hybridizing clones from the *Drosophila* genome. The cytogenetic map locations and spatial and temporal patterns of expression for the genes homologous to two of the clones suggest that they represent other homoeotic genes.

## Repeated Sequences

Genomic and cDNA clones from the *Antp* locus have been isolated and characterized by Garber *et al.*[13]. To test whether the *Antp* gene might be a member of a multigene family, we hybridized the 903 cDNA probe derived from the *Antp* locus to Southern blots of *Drosophila* genomic DNA. The 903 cDNA (see Fig. 1) is complementary to four non-contiguous chromosomal DNA regions spanning 100 kilobases (kb) at the *Antp* locus. Both normal- and reduced-stringency hybridization conditions were used with the 903 probe; in both types of hybridization conditions we detected many genomic fragments homologous to 903 that gave very strong signals, and many (>50) that were relatively weak. The weak signals were more prominent on the blot hybridized in reduced-stringency conditions (data not shown). A stringent wash of both blots (see Fig. 1 legend) removed the weak signals whereas the strong signals remained. The strongly hybridizing genomic fragments had the expected size for those portions of the genome represented in the 903 cDNA. The weakly hybridizing genomic fragments presumably possessed mismatched homology to one or more repeated sequences within the 903 cDNA.

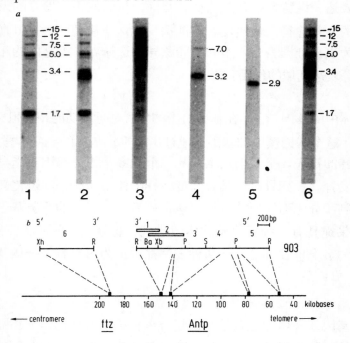

Fig. 1. Repeated sequences in the *Antp* and *ftz* genes. *a*, Individual lanes from *Drosophila* whole genomic Southern blots. The genomic DNA in each case was digested with *Eco*RI. The number below the lanes designates the fragment number used as a probe. The fragment number designations are shown above the respective fragments in *b*. The numbers alongside the lanes indicate the sizes in kilobases (kb) of the hybridizing genomic fragments. All the blots were hybridized and washed in the reduced-stringency conditions described below. Note that the two bands in lane 4 are due to the number 4 probe containing

只限于小区域的同源性，从果蝇基因组里分离出了其他的交叉杂交克隆。与这两个克隆同源的基因的细胞遗传学图谱定位以及时空表达模式表明，它们代表了其他的同源异型基因。

## 重 复 序 列

加伯等人从触角足基因座分离出了基因组和 cDNA 的克隆，并描述了其特征 [13]。为了检测触角足基因是否是多基因家族的成员，我们将来源于触角足基因座的 903 cDNA 探针与果蝇基因组 DNA 进行了 DNA 印迹法杂交。903 cDNA（见图 1）与触角足基因的 4 个非邻接的有 100 千碱基(kb)的染色体 DNA 区域互补。针对 903 探针，采用了正常型和低严紧型两种杂交条件；两种杂交条件下，我们检测到了许多与 903 探针具有同源性的基因组片段，它们有很多给出了非常强烈的信号，同时也有很多（>50）信号相对较弱。在低严紧型条件下的印迹杂交中，弱信号在数据中占优势（数据未列出）。对两种杂交印迹的严紧型洗涤（见图 1 注）可以去除弱信号而保留强信号。强杂交基因组片段显示了所预期的，由 903 cDNA 代表的基因组中部分序列的大小。弱杂交基因组片段大概具有与 903 cDNA 内的一个或多个重复序列错配的同源性。

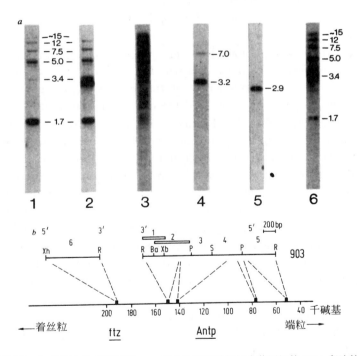

图 1. 触角足基因和 *ftz* 基因中的重复序列。*a*，每个泳道都是果蝇全基因组的 DNA 印迹法杂交片段。每个泳道的基因组 DNA 都用 *Eco*RI 消化。泳道下面的数字是用作探针的片段编号。片段编号列在 *b* 中各自片段的上面。靠泳道旁的数字是以千碱基对表示的杂交基因组片段的大小。所有的印迹都是在下述低严紧条件下进行杂交和洗涤的。注意：泳道 4 中的两个条带是由于 4 号探针含有两个触角足基因外显子。*b*，

a sequence from each of two *Antp* exons. *b*, Map of the portions of the *Antp* and *ftz* genes used as hybridization probes for the genomic blots. *Antp* 903 is a cDNA clone described by Garber *et al.*[13] which contains the regions from the *Antp* locus marked by solid blocks. The broken lines indicate the approximate extent of the cDNA in each genomic location. The bottom line is a representation of the *Antp* region of chromosome 3, as taken from Garber *et al.*[13]; the numbers reflect the distance (in kb) from the *Humeral* chromosomal breakpoint. The 5' and 3' labels show the direction of transcription for the two loci (ref. 17 and A.K., unpublished results). Xh, *Xho*I; R, *Eco*RI; Ba, *Bam*HI; Xb, *Xba*I; P, *Pvu*II; S, *Sph*I.

**Methods:** Reduced-stringency hybridizations were done as follows. Southern blots[31] were prehybridized in 5×SSC, 0.1% bovine serum albumin, 0.1% Ficoll, 0.1% polyvinylpyrrollidone, 250 μg ml⁻¹ sonicated, boiled herring sperm DNA, 50 mM NaPO₄ *p*H 7, 0.1% SDS, 43% deionized formamide at 37 °C for 2-3 h. The prehybridization buffer was removed from the bag and replaced with the same buffer containing $10^6$ c.p.m. ml⁻¹ of hybridization probe. Blots were hybridized at 37 °C for 25-48 h, then washed twice in 2×SSC, 0.1% SDS for 5 min at room temperature, followed by two washes for 15 min each at 45-50 °C. Stringent hybridization and wash conditions differed only in the hybridization buffer, which contained 50% instead of 43% formamide, and in the final wash which was done in 0.2×SSC, 0.1% SDS at 65-70 °C.

To determine which region(s) within the 903 cDNA sequence were repetitive, the cDNA was subdivided into five restriction fragments of ~500 base pairs (bp) each, and these were individually hybridized to replica genomic Southern blots in reduced-stringency conditions (Fig. 1). The two left-most fragments, which overlap in the 3' half of the 903 cDNA, detect the expected genomic fragments at *Antp*, and also cross-hybridize with seven other genomic fragments with less intensity. The next 903 fragment to the right (fragment 3) hybridizes to more than 50 genomic fragments. Finally, the two right-most 903 fragments (4 and 5) detect only their genomic homologues at the *Antp* locus.

Garber *et al.*[13] found weak homology between the 903 cDNA and a site to the left of the *Antp* locus, at position 190 on the map in Fig. 1. This site has subsequently been shown to be part of the transcription unit of the *fushi tarazu* (*ftz*) gene (A.K. and E.H., in preparation). The *ftz* gene is required for the determination of the correct number of segments in the *Drosophila* embryo[4,14]. Embryos that are homozygous for certain mutant alleles of *ftz* die early in development, and show deletions of alternate segment primordial. A 0.9-kb *Xho*I/*Eco*RI fragment (probe 6), containing a 3' portion of the *ftz* transcription unit (A.K., unpublished results), was used as a probe of another Southern blot identical to those used for the five 903 fragments (Fig. 1). In addition to the strong signal contributed by the homologous genomic fragment from the *ftz* locus, eight other genomic fragments weakly cross-hybridized. Five of these weakly hybridizing genomic DNA fragments are identical in size to those detected by the two probes from the 3' region of the 903 cDNA. Thus, the 3' regions of the transcription units of the *Antp* and *ftz* genes share a common sequence, one that appears to be present at five or more locations in the *Drosophila* genome.

Subsequently, we will refer to this low-level repeat as the H repeat, and the high-level repeat in the middle of the 903 cDNA (fragment 3) as the M repeat. The M repeat is not detectable in the DNA of the *ftz* locus.

## Presence of H Repeat in Bithorax Complex

Next, we performed experiments to test for the presence of the H repeat in other homoeotic genes. We hybridized fragments 2 and 6 (from *Antp* and *ftz* respectively; see

用作基因组印迹杂交探针的触角足基因和 *ftz* 基因片段的图谱。触角足基因 903 就是加伯等人 [13] 所述的一个 cDNA 克隆，其所含的基因片段来自图谱中以实心块标记的触角足基因座。虚线表示在每个基因组位点的 cDNA 的大致范围。底线代表加伯等人所取的第 3 号染色体上的触角足基因区域 [13]。数字代表与肱骨染色体断点的距离（以 kb 为单位）。5′ 和 3′ 标记两个基因座的转录方向（参考文献 17 和库若瓦未发表的结果）。Xh，*XhoI*；R，*EcoRI*；Ba，*BamH1*；Xb，*XbaI*；P，*PvuII*；S，*SphI*。

**方法**：低严紧型杂交操作如下：用 5× 柠檬酸钠缓冲液、0.1% 牛血清蛋白、0.1% 聚蔗糖、0.1% 聚乙烯吡咯烷酮、250 µg·ml⁻¹ 超声并煮沸的鲱精 DNA、50 mM NaPO₄，pH7、0.1% 十二烷基硫酸钠、43% 去离子甲酰胺，在 37℃ 下进行 DNA 印迹法 [31] 预杂交 2~3 小时。从杂交袋中去除预杂交缓冲液，加入含有 10⁶ c.p.m. ml⁻¹ 杂交探针的同样的缓冲液，在 37℃ 下印迹杂交 25~48 小时，然后在室温下用 2× 柠檬酸钠缓冲液、0.1% 十二烷基磺酸钠洗涤 2 次，每次 5 分钟。接着在 45~50℃ 下洗涤 2 次，每次 15 分钟。低严紧型杂交和洗涤与严紧型杂交和洗涤条件的差别仅在于所用的杂交缓冲液，后者用 50% 的甲酰胺代替 43% 的甲酰胺；另外，最后一次洗涤时，在 65~70℃ 下用 0.2× 柠檬酸钠缓冲液、0.1% 十二烷基硫酸钠进行。

为了确定 903 cDNA 序列内哪个（或哪些）区域存在重复，该 cDNA 被再分成 5 个各有约 500 碱基对（bp）的限制性酶切片段；在低严紧性条件下，将每个片段与复制基因组进行 DNA 印迹法杂交（图 1）。903 cDNA 两个最左端的片段在 903 cDNA 3′ 端相互重叠，以这两个序列为探针，检测到了所预期的触角足基因上的基因组片段，并且这两个片段也可以与另外 7 个基因组片段进行低强度地交叉杂交。向右数的下一个 903 片段（片段 3）可与超过 50 个基因组片段杂交。最后，两个最右端的 903 片段（4 和 5）只在触角足基因座检测到它们的基因组同源物。

加伯等人发现 903 cDNA 和触角足基因座左端某位点（在图 1 图谱的 190 位置）之间有弱的同源性 [13]。随后，这个位点被证明是 *ftz* 基因的转录单位的一部分（库若瓦和哈芬，文章准备中）。*ftz* 基因是确保果蝇胚胎体节具有正常数目所必需的 [4,14]。该等位基因的突变纯合子胚胎在发育的早期就会死亡，并且显示交替的体节原基的缺失。与其他 5 个 903 片段所用的探针相同，采用含有 *ftz* 转录单位 3′ 端部分（库若瓦，未发表的结果）的一段 0.9-kb 的 *XhoI/EcoRI* 片段（探针 6）作为另一个 DNA 印迹法杂交的探针（图 1）。除了 *ftz* 基因座的同源基因组片段有强杂交信号外，其他 8 个基因组片段有微弱的交叉杂交。其中 5 个微弱杂交的基因组 DNA 片段的大小与 903 cDNA 3′ 端区的 2 个探针检测到的片段相同。因此，触角足基因和 *ftz* 基因转录单位的 3′ 端区拥有一个共同的序列，在果蝇基因组中这样的序列存在 5 个以上。

随后，我们将这种低度重复称为 H 重复，将 903 cDNA 中间位置的高度重复片段（片段 3）称为 M 重复。在 *ftz* 基因座 DNA 中无法检测到 M 重复。

## 双胸基因复合体中存在的 H 重复

接下来，我们的实验是检验其他同源异型基因中 H 重复的存在。在低严紧条件下，我们用片段 2 和 6（分别来自触角足基因和 *ftz* 基因，见图 1）对双胸基因复合

Fig. 1) in reduced-stringency conditions to Southern blots of recombinant clones from the *Ultrabithorax (Ubx)* unit of the bithorax complex, specifically λ2229, λ2269, λ2288 and 2296 (ref. 15) (given by P. Spierer). A 3.2-kb *Bam*HI fragment common to λ2288 and λ2296 hybridized to both H repeat-containing probes (Fig. 2). This *Bam*HI fragment contains most or all of the 3′ exon of the *Ubx* transcription unit (refs 15, 16 and M. Goldschmidt-Clermont, personal communication). Cross-hybridization between the *Antp, ftz* and *Ubx* loci has been independently detected by M. Scott (personal communication). None of the *Ubx* region clones that we tested contained the M repeat.

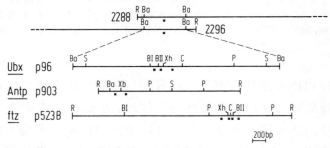

Fig. 2. Localization of the H repeat in clones from the *Ultrabithorax (Ubx), Antennapedia (Antp)* and *fushi tarazu (ftz)* genes. The overlapping region from the *Ubx* locus between λ clones 2288 and 2296 (gifts from. P. Spierer) is shown at the top, as well as the *Bam*HI fragment common to both which hybridizes to fragments 2 and 6 (Fig. 1). Both these clones are described elsewhere[15], although λ2296 is incorrectly labelled as 2269. The indicated *Bam*HI fragment was subcloned into pAT153 and the resulting plasmid designated p96. A map of the p96 insert is shown. Restriction fragments containing the H repeat are marked by asterisks. *Antp* p903 is the same cDNA clone shown in Fig. 1. Restriction fragments to both sides of the *Xba*I site (Xb) show homology to the H repeat. *ftz* p523B is a *Drosophila* genomic clone from region 190 on the map in Fig. 1, an *Eco*RI fragment in pAT153. This fragment contains most of the *ftz* transcription unit (A.K., unpublished results). Again, the restriction fragments containing the H repeat are marked by asterisks.

Figure 2 shows more detailed restriction maps of the regions at each locus that contain the H repeat. The location of the H repeat within each of the *Antp, Ubx* and *ftz* clones was determined by *inter se* hybridizations to Southern blots of each clone digested with various restriction enzymes. The H repeat is the only detectable region of cross-homology between the three clones, and based on the intensity of signal the cross-homology is either very short (<100 bp), or larger but poorly matched. As the region of cross-homology overlaps both ends of the 90-bp *Xho*I/*Bgl*II fragments found in both *Ubx* and *ftz,* the latter possibility is more likely. The intensity of signal obtained from homologous hybridization compared with cross-hybridization due to the H repeat is shown in lane 1 of Fig. 1. Probe fragment 1, from the 3′ end of the *Antp* cDNA 903, hybridizes very strongly to its genomic homologue on a 1.7-kb *Eco*RI fragment, but with at least 10 times less intensity to the 3.4-kb and 7.5-kb genomic fragments in the same lane, which carry the *ftz* and *Ubx* H repeats respectively.

The cloned regions in Fig. 2 are shown with the same 3R chromosomal orientation: the centromere is to the left, and the telomere to the right. The transcriptional direction of the *Ubx* and *Antp* clones is from right to left, and for the *ftz* clone from left to right (refs

体的超双胸（*Ubx*）单位的重组克隆（具体即λ2229、λ2269、λ2288和λ2296克隆（文献15）（施皮雷尔提供））进行DNA印迹杂交。将λ2288和λ2296共有的3.2-kb的 *Bam*HI片段与两个含有H重复的探针杂交（图2）。该 *Bam*HI片段含有 *Ubx* 转录单位的大部分或全部的 3′ 端外显子（文献15、16和戈尔德施密特－克莱蒙，个人交流）。斯科特独立地进行了触角足、*ftz* 和超双胸基因座之间的交叉杂交（个人交流）。我们检测的 *Ubx* 区克隆都没有M重复。

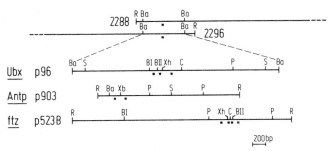

图 2. 超双胸、触角足和 *ftz* 基因克隆中的H重复的定位。λ2288克隆和λ2296克隆（施皮雷尔赠送）之间的超双胸基因的重叠区以及可以与片段2和6杂交的两个基因共有的 *Bam*HI片段都显示在图的顶端（图1）。这两个克隆在其他文献中有描述 [15]，尽管这些描述错误地将λ2296克隆标记为2269。将图中标明的 *Bam*HI 片段亚克隆到pAT153质粒上，并将此质粒命名为p96质粒，其插入图谱如图所示。用星号标记有H重复的限制性酶切片段。触角足 p903 是与图1所示相同的cDNA克隆。限制性酶切片段上 *Xba*I 位点两侧序列显示与H重复有同源性。*ftz* 基因的 p523B 片段是图1图谱中190区的果蝇基因组克隆，是pAT153中的 *Eco*RI 片段，含有 *ftz* 转录单位的大部分（库若瓦，未发表的结果）。同样，其具有H重复的限制性酶切片段用星号标出。

图2标示了含有H重复的每个基因座区域内更详细的限制性酶切图谱。用多种限制性内切酶消化触角足、超双胸、*ftz* 基因克隆，每个克隆彼此之间进行DNA印迹法杂交，从而确定每个克隆的H重复位点。H重复是这3个克隆之间唯一可检测的交叉同源区，而且基于信号强度，交叉同源物要么太短（<100 bp），要么较长但匹配很差。由于交叉同源区与超双胸和 *ftz* 都具有的两个90-bp长的 *Xho*I/*Bgl*II 片的末端重叠，所以后一种情况更有可能。图1的泳道1显示了基于H重复的交叉杂交和同源杂交信号强度间的对比。来自触角足基因 cDNA 903 的 3′ 末端的探针片段1与其基因组同源物在1.7-kb长的 *Eco*RI 片段上有非常强的杂交，但是与同一泳道的3.4-kb和7.5-kb（分别携带着 *ftz* 和 *Ubx* 的H重复）的基因组片段杂交的强度相比，其强度至少弱10倍。

图2中的克隆区域显示的方向与3R染色体相同：左端是着丝粒，右端是端粒。超双胸和触角足基因克隆的转录方向从右到左，*ftz* 基因克隆的转录方向从左到右

16, 17 and A.K., unpublished results). The relative orientation of the *Xho*I and *Bgl*II sites within the cross-homologous regions of *Ubx* and *ftz*, is consistent with the polarity of the H repeat being the same with respect to the direction of transcription. Preliminary DNA sequencing results from these two regions (W.McG., unpublished results) and of the *Antp* 903 cDNA (R. Garber, unpublished results) also indicate that the H repeat is in the same orientation with respect to transcription at each locus.

## Isolation of Clones Containing H Repeat

The observation that the H repeat was associated with three loci known to be crucial for proper segmental development in the fly suggested that it might be a common feature of many homoeotic loci in *Drosophila*. To test this, we first isolated *Drosophila* genomic clones that possessed homology to cloned H repeat sequences. Such clones were then subjected to the following three tests to implicate them as potential new homoeotic loci.

(1) Hybridization of the clones to *Drosophila* polytene chromosomes to determine whether their cytogenetic map locations corresponded to those of genetically characterized homoeotic loci.

(2) Hybridization of subclones containing the H repeat to Northern blots of RNA extracted from successive developmental stages to determine whether the regions were transcribed, and whether their transcription was developmentally regulated in a manner that might be expected for a homoeotic locus.

(3) Hybridization of subclones containing the H repeat to *Drosophila* embryonic tissue sections, to determine whether the transcripts homologous to the subcloned regions were distributed in a segmentally restricted manner, as has been shown for transcripts derived from the homoeotic loci *Antp* and *Ubx*[16,18,19].

## Genomic Library Screen

Approximately 30,000 recombinant bacteriophages (three genome equivalents) from the Charon 4/*Drosophlia* library of Maniatis *et al.*[20] were screened using H repeat probes from *Antp* and *ftz* (fragments 2 and 6 in Fig. 1) as probes of duplicate filters. The hybridizations and washes were done in the reduced-stringency conditions described in Fig. 1 legend. A total of 74 plaques from the original plates hybridized to both probes, with a wide range of signal intensity. All were picked and re-screened with the same probes, and 24 were plaque-purified. DNA was extracted from each recombinant and digested with *Eco*RI, *Bam*HI and both enzymes together, then separated on an agarose gel, and transferred to nitrocellulose.

These blots were hybridized with probes 2 and 6 to determine which region of the insert contained the H repeat. In this way, we found that three of the clones were re-isolates of *ftz*, and two were re-isolates of *Antp*. The remaining 19 clones were divided into two classes on the basis of their extent of homology (as determined by signal intensity) with

（文献 16、17 和库若瓦未发表的结果）。超双胸和 *ftz* 基因的交叉同源区内的 *Xho*I 和 *Bgl*II 位点的相对方向及转录方向与 H 重复的极性是一致的。对这两个区域（麦金尼斯，未发表的结果）和触角足基因 903 cDNA（加伯，未发表的结果）的初步 DNA 测序结果也表明：H 重复的方向与每个基因座的转录方向是相同的。

### 含有 H 重复的克隆的分离

H 重复与已知对果蝇体节正常发育至关重要的 3 个基因座相关，这一观察结果说明，这种重复可能是果蝇中同源异型基因座的一个共同特征。为了检验这一点，我们首先分离了与克隆的 H 重复序列具有同源性的果蝇基因组克隆。然后将这些克隆进行下列 3 项试验，说明它们是潜在的新的同源异型基因座。

（1）将这些克隆与果蝇多线染色体杂交，以确定其细胞遗传学图谱位点是否与通过遗传学手段表征的同源异型基因座相对应。

（2）将含有 H 重复的亚克隆与从连续发育阶段提取的 RNA 进行印迹法杂交，确定这些区域是否被转录，以及其转录作用是否以预计的同源异型基因座的方式受到发育调控。

（3）将含有 H 重复的亚克隆与果蝇胚胎组织切片进行杂交，以确定与亚克隆区同源的转录物是否像同源异型基因座触角足和超双胸基因的转录物所显示的那样，以体节限定的方式分布 [16,18,19]。

### 基因组文库筛选

用触角足和 *ftz* 基因的 H 重复序列（图 1 中的片段 2 和 6）作为印影滤膜的探针，从曼尼阿蒂斯等人 [20] 的 Charon4/ 果蝇库中筛选到大约 30,000 重组噬菌体（三个基因组当量）。在图 1 注中所述的低严紧型条件下进行杂交和洗涤。原来的平板上总共有 74 个噬菌斑能与上述 2 个探针杂交，并表现出广范围的信号强度。挑出所有杂交的噬菌斑，用同样的探针进行再筛选，纯化出 24 株噬菌体。从每个重组子中提取 DNA，分别用 *Eco*RI、*Bam*HI 以及上述两种酶一起进行酶切，然后在琼脂糖凝胶上进行分离，并转移到硝酸纤维素膜上。

为确定哪个插入区域有 H 重复，我们用探针 2 和 6 进行了印迹杂交。通过这种方法发现，其中 3 个克隆是 *ftz* 基因的再分离物，2 个克隆是触角足基因的再分离物。基于与触角足和 *ftz* 基因的 H 重复序列的同源程度（由信号强度决定），将其余的 19 个克隆分成两类。有 7 个克隆交叉杂交相对较强，并且通过相互间杂交

the H repeats from *Antp* and *ftz*. Seven clones cross-hybridized relatively strongly and by *inter se* hybridizations we found that these were derived from two different genomic regions. Representative clones from each of the two regions were designated 93 and 99.

The H repeat lies on a 4.5-kb *Bam*HI/*Eco*RI fragment for clone 93; this fragment was subcloned into plasmid vector pAT153 and is designated p93. The p93 insert is a single-copy sequence in the *Drosophila* genome, when tested by genomic Southern blot analysis in stringent hybridization and wash criteria, and derives from the 15-kb genomic *Eco*RI fragment previously identified by genomic blotting (Fig. 1, lane 1). The clone 99 H repeat lies on a 5-kb *Eco*RI fragment which was cloned into pAT153 and designated p99. The p99 insert is also a single-copy *Drosophila* sequence (in stringent conditions), and corresponds to the 5-kb *Eco*RI genomic fragment detected in Fig. 1, lane 1. Although p99 and p93 were selected by hybridization with the H repeat they also hybridize with the probe 3 shown in Fig. 1, and therefore probably contain the M repeat also.

## *In situ* Localization of p93 and p99

DNA from p93 and from p99 was labelled with biotinylated dUTP by nick-translation, and hybridized to squashes of salivary gland polytene chromosomes. The sites of hybridization were revealed by an immunoperoxidase detection protocol[21]. The stringency of hybridization was sufficient to allow only the detection of the genomic isologues of p93 and p99.

Clone p93 hybridizes to the 89E region on the right arm of chromosome 3 (Fig. 3), the cytogenetic location of the bithorax complex[1]. Bender *et al.*[15,22] have recently reported the isolation of the left half of the bithorax complex DNA, and Karch and Bender have subsequently isolated overlapping cloned genomic DNAs that include much of the right part of the complex (F. Karch and W. Bender, unpublished results); they provided us with a Southern blot containing cloned DNA from the entire cloned bithorax region. We find that the p93 insert is located within their cloned region, to the right of the *bithoraxoid/postbithorax* unit of the bithorax complex, near the *infra-abdominal*-2 locus (data not shown). The same result has been obtained by S. Sakonju (personal communication) and M.S.L.

测试发现，它们来自两个不同的基因组区域。我们将这两个区域的代表性克隆定名为 93 和 99。

H 重复序列位于 93 号克隆的 4.5-kb 长的 BamHI/EcoRI 片段上。将其亚克隆到质粒载体 pAT153 上，命名为 p93。经过在严紧的杂交和洗涤条件下进行的基因组 DNA 印迹法分析发现，p93 插入序列是果蝇基因组上的单拷贝序列，而且是由以前用基因组印迹鉴定（图 1 泳道 1）的 15-kb 长的基因组 EcoRI 片段衍生而来。99 号克隆的 H 重复序列位于克隆的载体质粒 pAT153 上的一段 5-kb 长的 EcoRI 片段上，该片段被克隆至 pTA153 质粒中并被命名为 p99。p99 插入序列也是单拷贝的果蝇序列（在严紧型条件下），与图 1 泳道 1 的 5-kb 长的 EcoRI 基因组片段相对应。虽然 p99 和 p93 是通过与 H 重复序列杂交选择出来的，但它们也能与图 1 所示的探针 3 杂交，因此，它们也可能有 M 重复。

### p93 和 p99 的原位定位

通过切口平移，用生物素脱氧三磷酸尿苷标记 p93 和 p99 的 DNA，再将其与唾液腺多线染色体压片进行杂交。用免疫过氧化物酶检测方法显示杂交位点[21]。杂交的严紧性足以保证只能检测到 p93 和 p99 基因组的同构体。

克隆 p93 与 3 号染色体右臂上的 89E 区（双胸基因复合体的细胞遗传位点[1]）杂交(图 3)。本德尔等人[15,22]最近报道了双胸基因复合体 DNA 左半部的分离。随后，卡奇和本德尔又分离出了包括该复合物右端大部分的重叠克隆基因组 DNA（卡奇与本德尔，未发表的结果）。他们为我们提供的 DNA 印迹包含来自整个双胸克隆区的 DNA 克隆。我们发现 p93 插入序列定位于其克隆区内，在双胸复合体的双胸状的 / 后双胸基因单位的右面，靠近下腹 2 基因座（数据未出示）。左近允（个人交流）和莱文得到了同样的结果。

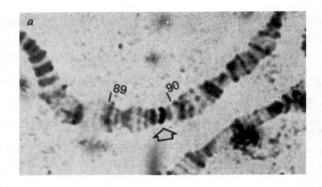

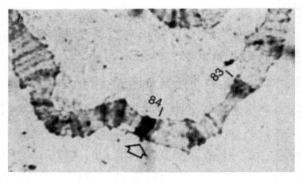

Fig. 3. *In situ* hybridization of H repeat clones p93 and p99 to polytene chromosomes. Clones p93 and p99 were nick-translated with biotinylated nucleotide, and hybridized to squashes of Ore-R chromosomes: p93 to *a*, and p99 to *b*. The hybridized probes were detected by an immunoperoxidase method[21] and the chromosomes stained with Giemsa and photographed. The chromosome 3 divisions are indicated and the sites of hybridization marked by arrowheads.

Clone p99 hybridizes to the 84A region on the right arm of chromosome 3; this is close to the cytogenetic locations of the *ftz* and *Antp* loci, both of which are in 84B1-2 (refs 2, 4, 5). The 84A region contains the Antp complex genes *proboscipedia*, *zerknüllt* and *Deformed*, all of which have been shown to affect the proper development of the posterior head segments of *Drosophila*[4,5,23].

## Transcription

Genetic and developmental studies on the time of expression of homoeotic selector genes show that early to mid-embryo-genesis (0-12 h after oviposition) and pre- and early metamorphosis (late third instar larval and early pupal stages) are possible periods of high levels of expression[24–26]. *Antp* transcripts exhibit their highest levels during both these periods, and *ftz* transcripts are most abundant in early embryogenesis (A.K., unpublished results).

To test whether the regions homologous to p93 and p99 were transcribed, the two clones were hybridized to Northern blots containing *Drosophila* poly (A)⁺ RNA from successive stages of development. The blots were hybridized and washed using the stringent conditions described in Fig. 1 legend.

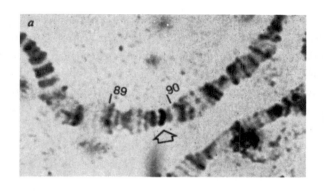

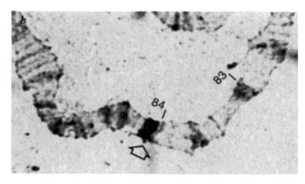

图 3. H 重复克隆 p93 和 p99 与多线染色体的原位杂交。p93 和 p99 克隆用生物素化的核苷酸作切口平移，并与 Ore-R 染色体压片杂交：p93 杂交示于 a，p99 杂交示于 b。用免疫过氧化物酶方法 [21] 检测杂交的探针，用吉姆萨染液给染色体染色并照相。图中显示染色体 3 分区，其中，箭头所示为杂交位点。

p99 克隆与 3 号染色体右臂上的 84A 区域进行杂交，该区域靠近位于 84B1-2 上的 *ftz* 和触角足基因座的细胞遗传学位点（文献 2，4，5）。84A 区有触角足复合体基因中的吻足基因、皱褶基因和变形基因，已知这些基因都能影响果蝇后头部体节的正常发育 [4,5,23]。

转 录

对同源异型选择者基因表达时序的遗传和发育研究显示，早期到中期的胚胎发生（产卵后 0~12 小时）、前期和早期的变态（三龄幼虫晚期和蛹期的早期）都是高表达的可能时期 [24-26]。触角足基因在这两个时期显示了最高的转录量，*ftz* 转录物在胚胎发生的早期最丰富（库若瓦，未发表的结果）。

为了检测与 p93 和 p99 同源的区域是否被转录，将这两个克隆与来自果蝇连续发育阶段的多聚腺嘌呤 RNA 进行印迹法杂交。用图 1 注所述的严紧型条件进行印迹杂交和洗涤。

Clone 93 is homologous to multiple RNA species during embryonic stages, especially in embryos 6-12 h old (Fig. 4). The largest RNA (5.4 kb) homologous to p93 at the 6-12-h stage is also abundant in late third instar larvae, just before pupation. Clone p99 is homologous to an RNA species of 2.8 kb which is most abundant at early embryogenesis (0-6 h) and in the early pupal stage (Fig. 4). The RNA species homologous to p93 and p99 are both present at approximately the same levels as transcripts from the *Antp* locus (A.K., unpublished results).

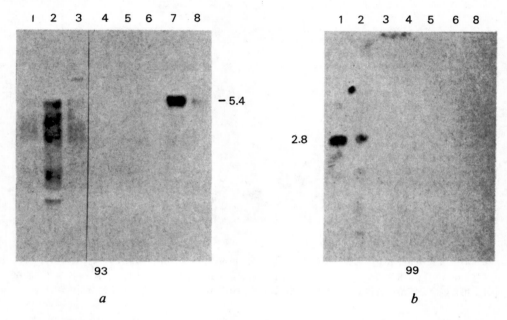

Fig. 4. Transcription from p93 and p99 during *Drosophila* development. Lanes 1, 2 and 3 in each panel contain embryonic RNA from 0-6, 6-12 and 12-18-h stages, respectively. Lanes 4 and 5 in each panel contain RNA from first and second instar larvae. Lanes 6 and 7 in each panel contain RNA from early and late third instar larvae, respectively. Lane 8 in each panel contains RNA from 1-day-old pupae. The numbers alongside the panels indicate the approximate size (in kb) of the largest hybridizing RNAs. On longer exposures a faint band of 2.8 kb was detected in the pupal lane (8) of the blot hybridized with p99 (not shown). Poly(A)+ (10 µg) from successive stages of *Drosophila* development was run on formaldehyde agarose gels and blotted[32]. The blots were hybridized with nick-translated p93 and p99 in the stringent buffer described in Fig. 1 legend. After a stringent wash (also described in Fig. 1) the blots were used to expose X-ray film.

## Localization of Transcripts

The most important experiment that we performed with the p93 and p99 clones was to test whether the transcripts homologous to these clones were spatially restricted during development. It has recently been shown that *Antp* and *Ubx* transcripts are restricted in a segmentally specific manner during embryonic development[16,18,19]. To a rough approximation, the embryonic segments and segmental anlagen that accumulate *Antp* and *Ubx* transcripts are those in which the function of these genes is believed to be required for proper development. Therefore, if the 93 and 99 clones represent other homoeotic selector loci, their transcripts should be restricted during embryonic stages to segments where 93 or 99 expression is required for proper development.

在胚胎时期，特别是 6~12 小时胚龄期间，克隆 93 与多种 RNA 同源（图 4）。在 6~12 小时的阶段，与 p93 同源的最大的 RNA（5.4 kb）在幼虫蛹化前的 3 龄期后期也很丰富。p99 克隆与 2.8 kb 长的 RNA 同源，这一 RNA 在早期的胚胎发生（0~6 小时）和早期蛹的阶段最丰富（图 4）。与 p93 和 p99 同源的 RNA 都与触角足基因座的转录物以大约相同的量存在（库若瓦，未发表的结果）。

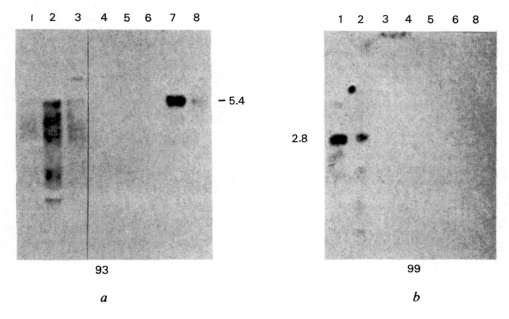

图 4. 果蝇发育期间 p93 和 p99 的转录情况。在每块胶板上，泳道 1、2 和 3 分别加 0~6、6~12、12~18 小时的胚胎 RNA，泳道 4 和 5 分别加 1 龄和 2 龄幼虫的 RNA，泳道 6 和 7 分别加早期和晚期 3 龄幼虫的 RNA，泳道 8 加 1 天龄蛹的 RNA。胶板侧面的数字为最大杂交 RNA 的近似大小（以 kb 为单位）。对 p99 板进行比较长时间的曝光，可检测到泳道（8）有一条 2.8 kb 的模糊条带（未显示）。将果蝇发育的连续阶段的多聚腺嘌呤（10 µg）进行甲醛琼脂糖凝胶电泳 [32]。在图 1 注所述的严紧型缓冲液中与切口平移的 p93 和 p99 进行印迹杂交。严紧型洗涤后（如图 1 所述），印迹在 X 光片上曝光。

## 转录物的定位

我们用 p93 和 p99 克隆进行的最重要的实验是检测与这些克隆同源的转录物在发育期间是否受空间的限定。近来有研究表明，在胚胎发育期间，触角足基因和超双胸基因的转录产物在胚胎发育阶段以体节特异的方式受到限定 [16,18,19]。据粗略估计，胚胎体节和体节原基中积累触角足基因和超双胸基因的转录物，在这些体节中，上述基因的功能是体节正常发育所必需的。因此，如果 93 和 99 号克隆代表其他同源异型选择者基因座，其转录物在胚胎阶段应该被限定在这些基因表达为正常发育所需的体节中。

Figure 5 shows that the transcripts homologous to both p93 and p99 show spatial restrictions during development. We have shown only one developmental stage, when transcript localization is striking, for each clone. More detailed studies on the expression of these cloned regions will be reported elsewhere.

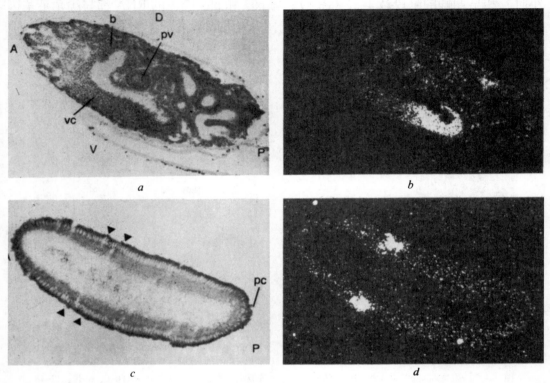

Fig. 5. Localization of transcripts homologous to p93 (*a*, *b*) and p99 (*c*, *d*) in embryonic tissue sections. The embryonic tissue sections were prepared and hybridized to ³H-labelled probes as described by Hafen *et al.*[18]. Labelling of p93 is shown on a sagittal section of an 18–20-h embryo. Both brightfield (*a*) and darkfield (*b*) photographs of a 4-week autoradiographic exposure are shown. The p99 labelling is shown for an embryo 3 h old, just after the stage during which cell membranes envelop the nuclei at the periphery of the embryo. Both bright- and darkfield photomicrographs of a 4-week autoradiographic exposure are shown. The extent of hybridization of the brightfield view (*a*) is marked by arrowheads. A, anterior; P, posterior; vc, ventral nerve cord; b, brain; pv, proventriculus; pc, pole cells; D, dorsal; V, ventral.

The localization of transcripts homologous to p93 is shown on a sagittal section of an 18–20-h embryo. At this advanced stage of embryogenesis, the central nervous system includes the two brain hemispheres and the condensed ventral nerve cord (Fig. 5). Before condensation the ventral cord consists of 12 paired ganglia, the sub-oesophageal ganglion, three thoracic ganglia and eight abdominal ganglia. Each ganglion of the ventral cord innervates its corresponding body segment[27]. The entire central nervous system of the embryo section hybridized with p93 appeared to be labelled above background levels, but a striking and reproducible concentration of label was observed over the posterior region of the ventral nerve cord, encompassing at least posterior-most five or six abdominal neuromeres.

图 5 说明与 p93 和 p99 同源的转录产物在发育期间受到空间限定。在转录物的定位显著时，我们对每个克隆只展示出一个发育阶段。有关这些克隆区域表达更为详细的研究将另行发表。

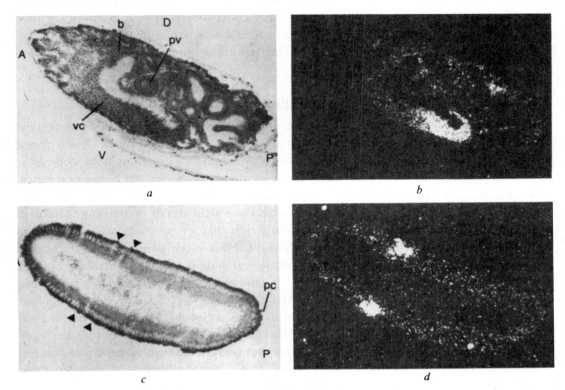

图 5. 胚胎组织切片中与 p93 (*a, b*) 和 p99 (*c, d*) 同源的转录产物的定位。胚胎组织切片的制备和与 ³H 标记的探针杂交按哈芬等人的方法进行 [18]。p93 的标记显示在一个 18~20 小时的胚胎矢状切面上。亮视野(*a*)和暗视野 (*b*) 照片是自动曝光四星期后所得。3 小时胚龄期的切片显示标记的 p99，这一时期正好在细胞膜包裹着胚边缘的细胞核的阶段之后。图中显示了自动曝光四星期的亮视野和暗视野的显微照片。亮视野 (*a*) 的杂交程度用箭头表示。A，前部；P，后部；vc，腹神经索；b，脑；pv，前胃；pc，极性细胞；D，背部；V，腹部。

18~20 小时的胚胎的矢状切面上显示了与 p93 同源的转录物的位置。在此胚胎发生的晚期阶段，中枢神经系统包括两个脑半球和凝缩的腹神经索（图5）。在凝缩前，腹神经索由 12 对神经节组成，即食管下神经节、3 个胸神经节和 8 个腹神经节。腹神经索的每个神经节都支配着相应的体节 [27]。与 p93 杂交的胚胎切面的整个中枢神经系统都显示了高于本底量的标记结果，但是在腹神经索的后区可观察到显著及可重现浓度的标记，环绕着至少最后部的 5 个或 6 个腹部神经管节。

The labelling pattern of p99 is shown at the cellular blastoderm stage, ~3 h after oviposition. The cellular blastoderm consists of a monolayer of morphologically identical cells. It is at this stage that cells first become restricted in their developmental potential, with different regions of the blastoderm acquiring separate determinative fates[28,29]. Transcripts homologous to p99 were found to be concentrated in cells in about 60-65% of the embryo length from the posterior pole. Cell ablation experiments in this region of the cellular blastoderm result in embryos having defects in the first thoracic and posterior head segments[30].

## Conclusions

Our analyses of the 93 and 99 clones, both isolated with the H repeat cross-homology, strongly suggest that they represent other homoeotic loci of *Drosophila*. Both clones fulfilled all three criteria that we applied for representing clones from homoeotic loci. First, both hybridize to cytogenetic locations of previously characterized homoeotic genes; 93 to the right half of the bithorax complex in the chromosome region 89E, and 99 to chromosome region 84A, which contains genes in the proximal half of the Antp complex. Second, both 93 and 99 are homologous to transcripts that are relatively abundant during embryogenesis and just prior to metamorphosis. These are the periods when transcripts homologous to the homoeotic locus *Antp* are most abundant (A.K., unpublished results). Third, and most importantly, the transcripts homologous to 93 and 99 show a striking spatial restriction during development. Transcripts homologous to p93 are most abundant in the posterior abdominal neuromeres of the embryo, as would be expected from a gene in the right half of the bithorax complex. The transcripts homologous to p99 are most abundant in a region of the cellular blastoderm that corresponds to the segmental anlagen of the posterior head or first thoracic segments. This is also consistent with its cytogenetic location in 84A, which contains genes that affect the development of these segments.

The basis for the cross-homology is of great interest. The position of the H repeat in the 3′ region of the transcription units of *Antp*, *Ubx* and *ftz* is consistent with a conserved protein-coding sequence. The DNA sequence of the H repeats of *Antp*, *ftz* and *Ubx* leaves no doubt that the sequence conservation is due to a conserved protein-coding domain (W. McG. and R. Garber, unpublished results). Since faithful copies of the H repeat are strictly delimited and found only in homoeotic genes, we now call the H repeat the "homoeotic sequence". However, it seems clear that not all homoeotic genes carry the homoeobox, for example, we have been unable to detect it in the *bithoraxoid/postbithorax* unit of the bithorax complex (W.McG., F. Karch and W. Bender, unpublished results). It is possible, of course, that another subset of homoeotic genes contains another repeat.

On the basis of these results, we propose that a subset of the homoeotic genes are members of a multigene family, highly diverged but nonetheless detectable by DNA cross-homology. This suggests a common evolutionary origin for some genes of both the Antp and bithorax complexes, as proposed by Lewis[1] for the genes of the bithorax complex. The conspicuous evolutionary conservation of the homoeobox sequence in some homoeotic genes of *Drosophila* suggests that it might also be conserved in other animal

在产卵 3 小时后的细胞囊胚期就可显示 p99 标记模式。细胞囊胚由具有相同形态的单层细胞组成。正是在这个时期，细胞首次被限定了发育潜能，囊胚的不同区域获得了各自限定的命运 [28,29]。与 p99 同源的转录物集中在后极胚胎长度 60%~65% 处的细胞内。该区域囊胚层的细胞消融实验，将导致胚胎在第一胸节和后部的头部体节方面有缺陷 [30]。

## 结　论

我们对 H 重复交叉同源物分离到的两个克隆 (93 和 99) 的分析结果有力地表明，它们代表了果蝇的其他同源异型基因座。两个克隆都符合我们应用的同源基因位点代表性克隆的所有 3 项标准：首先，两个克隆都能与以前表现出同源异型基因特征的细胞遗传学位点杂交。93 号克隆与位于染色体 89E 区的双胸基因复合体的右半部杂交，99 号克隆与有触角足基因复合体近侧一半基因的染色体 84A 区杂交。其次，93 和 99 号克隆两者都与那些胚胎发生期间，正好在变态前含量相当多的转录物同源。这个时期正是与同源异型基因座触角足基因同源的转录产物最丰富的时期（库若瓦，未发表的结果）。最后，也是最重要的，与 93 和 99 同源的转录物在发育期间显示出了明显的空间限定。正如根据双胸基因复合体右半部的一个基因所预期的那样，在胚胎后腹部神经管节中与 p93 同源的转录物最丰富。在与后头部的体节原基或第一胸节对应的细胞囊胚层中，与 p99 同源的转录物最丰富。这与其在 84A 上的细胞遗传学位点一致，该处含有影响这些体节发育的基因。

交叉同源物的基底很有趣。触角足、超双胸和 *ftz* 基因转录单位 3′ 末端区的 H 重复的位置符合保守的蛋白质编码序列。毫无疑问，触角足、超双胸和 *ftz* 基因的 H 重复的 DNA 序列保守性归因于一个保守的蛋白质编码域（麦金尼斯和加伯，未发表的结果）。由于精确的 H 重复拷贝是有严格界限的，而且只在同源异型基因中发现，所以现在我们称 H 重复为"同源异型基因序列"。但是，很显然，并不是所有同源异型基因都携有同源异型框，例如，我们还没有在双胸基因复合体的双胸状的 / 后双胸基因单位中检测到这种框架（麦金尼斯、卡奇和本德尔，未发表的结果）。当然，有可能同源异型基因的另一个亚群具有另一种重复。

基于这些结果，我们提出，同源异型基因的亚群是多基因家族的成员，它们高度分化，但是可用 DNA 交叉同源进行检测。这表明，正如刘易斯 [1] 就双胸基因复合提出的那样，触角足和双胸基因复合体两者的某些基因有共同的进化起源。果蝇的某些同源异型基因的同源框序列显著的进化保守性表明，其他动物种类中同源

species; preliminary experiments strongly support this view (W.McG., unpublished results). It is possible that a fundamental principle in development is to duplicate a gene specifying a segment identity, allowing one of the copies to diverge and acquire new functions, or new spatial restrictions in expression, or both; this might allow, within the limits of natural selection, a striking polymorphism in the different segments of an animal, and the acquisition of highly specialized functions in different segments.

We thank Nadine McGinnis for experimental assistance; Rick Garber for helpful comments during the early phases of this work; Pierre Spierer for the gifts of cloned DNA; and Welcome Bender and Francois Karch for the bithorax complex blot. We also thank Erika Wenger-Marquardt for preparation of the manuscript. M.S.L. and W.McG. were supported by Jane Coffin Childs fellowships. The work was made possible by a grant from the Swiss NSF and the Kanton Basel-Stadt.

(**308**, 428-433; 1984)

W. McGinnis, M. S. Levine, E. Hafen, A. Kuroiwa and W. J. Gehring
Department of Cell Biology, Biocenter, University of Basel, Klingelbergstrasse 70, CH-4056 Basel, Switzerland

Received 12 January; accepted 5 March 1984.

References:

1. Lewis, E. B. *Nature* **276**, 565-570 (1978).

2. Kaufman, T. C., Lewis, R. & Wakimoto, B. *Genetics* **94**, 115-133 (1980).

3. Lewis, R. A., Wakimoto, B. T., Denell, R. E. & Kaufman, T. C. *Genetics* **95**, 383-397 (1980).

4. Wakimoto, B. T. & Kaufman, T. C. *Devl. Biol.* **81**, 51-64 (1981).

5. Hazelrigg, T. & Kaufman, T. C. *Genetics* **105**, 581-600 (1983).

6. Le Calvez, J. *Bull. biol. Fr. Belg.* **82**, 97-113 (1948).

7. Hannah, A. & Strömnaes, O. *Drosoph. Inf. Serv.* **29**, 121-123 (1955).

8. Garcia-Bellido, A. *Am. Zool.* **17**, 613-629 (1977).

9. Duncan, I. & Lewis, E. B. *Developmental Order: Its Origin and Regulation,* 533-554 (Alan R. Liss, New York, 1982).

10. Struhl, G. *Proc. Natl. Acad. Sci. U.S.A.* **79**, 7380-7384 (1982).

11. Struhl, G. *J. Embryol. exp. Morph.* **76**, 297-331 (1983).

12. Hafen, E., Levine, M. & Gehring, W. J. *Nature* **307**, 287-289 (1984).

13. Garber, R. L., Kuroiwa, A. & Gehring, W. J. *EMBO. J.* **2**, 2027-2036 (1983).

14. Nüsslein-Volhard, C., Wieschaus, E. & Jurgens, G. *Verh. dt zool. Ges.* 91-104 (1982).

15. Bender, W. *et al. Science* **221**, 23-29 (1983).

16. Akam, M. *EMBO J.* **2**, 2075-2084 (1983).

17. Scott, M. P. *et al. Cell* (in the press).

18. Hafen, E., Levine, M., Garber, R. L. & Gehring, W. J. *EMBO J.* **2**, 617-623 (1983).

19. Levine, M., Hafen, E., Garber, R. L. & Gehring, W. J. *EMBO J.* **2**, 2037-2046 (1983).

20. Maniatis, T. *et al. Cell* **15**, 687-701 (1978).

21. Langer-Sofer, P. R., Levine, M. & Ward, D. C. *Proc. Natl. Acad. Sci. U.S.A.* **79**, 4381-4385 (1982).

22. Bender, W., Spierer, P. & Hogness, D. S. *J. Molec. Biol.* **168**, 17-33 (1983).

23. Kaufman, T. C. *Genetics* **90**, 579-596 (1978).

24. Morata, G. & Garcia-Bellido, A. *Wilhelm Roux's Arch. Dev. Biol.* **179**, 125-143 (1976).

25. Sanchez-Herrero, E. & Morata, G. *J. Embryol. exp. Morph.* **76**, 251-264 (1983).

26. Morata, G. & Kerridge, S. *Nature* **290**, 778-781 (1981).

序列进化也可能是保守的。初步的实验有力地支持这种观点（麦金尼斯，未发表的结果）。因此，发育的基本原理可能是复制一个指定体节同一性的基因，允许在拷贝中的某个拷贝出现分化从而获得新的功能或表达出新的空间限定，或者两者都有。这样，在自然选择的限度内，一个动物的不同体节就可以出现显著的多态性，以及不同体节可以获得高度特化的功能。

我们对娜丁·麦金尼斯进行的实验协助，里克·加伯对本工作早期的有益评论，皮埃尔·施皮雷尔赠给的克隆 DNA 以及韦尔科姆·本德尔与弗朗索瓦·卡奇做的双胸基因复合体印迹实验表示感谢。我们还要对埃丽卡·文格尔－马夸特准备的初稿表示感谢。莱文和麦金尼斯受到了简·科芬·蔡尔兹研究基金支持。本研究获得瑞士国家科学基金会及坎顿·贝泽尔－施塔特的资助。

（荆玉祥 翻译；沈杰 审稿）

27. Poulson, D. F. *Biology of Drosophila,* 168-274 (ed. Demereo, M.) (Wiley, New York, 1950).
28. Chan, L. N. & Gehring, W. J. *Proc. Natl. Acad. Sci. U.S.A.* **68**, 2217-2221 (1971).
29. Wieschaus, E. & Gehring, W. J. *Devl. Biol.* **50**, 249-263 (1976).
30. Underwood, E. M., Turner, F. R. & Mahowald, A. P. *Devl. Biol.* **74**, 286-301 (1980).
31. Southern, E. *J. Molec. Biol.* **98**, 503-517 (1975).
32. Goldberg, D. A. *Proc. Natl. Acad. Sci. U.S.A.* 77, 5794-5799 (1980).

# Evidence from Crater Ages for Periodic Impacts on the Earth

W. Alvarez and R. A. Muller

## Editor's Note

After it was suggested in 1980 that the impact of a comet or asteroid killed off the dinosaurs, some wondered whether other episodes of mass extinction also coincided with impacts, and whether they happened periodically. A putative distant faint companion of the Sun, dubbed Nemesis, was at one point suggested to periodically propel comets from the Oort cloud into the inner Solar System. Here Walter Alvarez and Richard Muller claim from the cratering record that large impacts recur with a 28.4-million-year cycle. Although other attempts have been made both before and since to identify such periodicities, none has been accepted. Moreover, no other convincing cases have yet been made for impact-related extinctions, though several have been suggested.

Recent evidence has indicated that the impact of a comet or asteroid may have been responsible for mass extinction at the ends of both the Cretaceous[1] and the Eocene[2-4]. Quantitative analysis by Raup and Sepkoski[5] showed that mass extinctions occur with a 26-Myr period, similar to the period seen in qualitative pelagic records by Fischer and Arthur[6]. To account for the possibility of periodic comet showers, Davis *et al.*[7] proposed that such showers could be triggered by an unseen solar companion star as it passes through perihelion on a moderately eccentric orbit. To test a prediction implicit in this model we examined records of large impact craters on the Earth. We report here that most of the craters occur in a 28.4-Myr cycle. Within measurement errors, this period and its phase are the same as those found in the fossil mass extinctions. The probability that such agreement is accidental is 1 in $10^3$.

A recent compilation by Grieve[8] lists 88 dated craters for which signs of shock metamorphism suggest probable impact origin. The known craters are located primarily in stable, well-studied regions in North America, Europe, Australia and the USSR. There are no known impact craters on the sea floor. The list shows a strong bias towards recent craters, most of which will probably be removed by erosion in the near future; 12 of the 88 dated craters have ages within the past 5 Myr.

We restricted ourselves to impact craters in roughly the range of ages in which Raup and Sepkoski saw the periodicity: 5–250 Myr BP. The lower limit of 5 Myr was chosen to reduce the bias from the large number of craters surviving from the recent past. In

# 来自陨石坑年龄的地球周期性受碰撞的证据

阿尔瓦雷斯，穆勒

**编者按**

在 1980 年有人提出一颗彗星或者小行星的撞击灭绝了恐龙之后，一些人对其他大规模灭绝事件是否也和撞击同时发生，以及它们是否周期性发生产生了好奇。一颗假想的遥远而暗弱的太阳伴星，称为复仇女神星，一度被认为周期性地从奥尔特云中将彗星推入内太阳系。本文中，沃尔特·阿尔瓦雷斯和理查德·穆勒根据陨石坑记录指出大的碰撞以 2,840 万年的周期重复发生。尽管在他之前和之后也有其他证认这个周期性的尝试，但没有一个被接受。此外，和撞击相关的灭绝到目前还没有其他有说服力的例子，尽管已经提议了若干。

最近的证据表明一颗彗星或者小行星的撞击可能是导致白垩纪 [1] 和始新世 [2-4] 末期发生大规模生物灭绝的原因。劳普和塞普科斯基 [5] 的定量分析显示大规模灭绝以 2,600 万年的周期发生，与费希尔和阿瑟 [6] 在定性的远洋记录中看到的周期相似。为了说明周期性彗星雨的可能性，戴维斯等人 [7] 提出这种彗星雨可能是由一颗未发现的太阳伴星以适当偏心的轨道经过近日点时触发的。为了检验这个模型中暗含的一个预言，我们检查了地球上大撞击坑的记录。在这里我们指出，大部分陨石坑以 2,840 万年的周期产生。在测量误差范围内，这个周期及其相位与在化石记录的大规模灭绝中发现的一致。这个吻合属于巧合的概率是 $1/10^3$。

格里夫最近整理列出 88 个古老的陨石坑 [8]，冲击变质作用的特征表明了它们可能源于撞击。已知的陨石坑大多分布在北美、欧洲、澳大利亚和苏联稳定且被详细研究过的地区。已知的撞击坑没有分布在海床上。这个列表显示了新生成的陨石坑的明显偏差，它们中的大部分可能在不久的将来被侵蚀掉；88 个古老陨石坑中有 12 个年龄在 500 万年内。

我们将研究限于劳普和塞普科斯基考虑的周期性年龄范围：距今 500 万年到 2.5 亿年的撞击坑。选择 500 万年的下限是为了减小大量在不久前幸存的陨石坑导致的偏差。为了看到短达 2,600 万年的周期，我们只选用年龄不确定度

order to be able to see periods as short as 26 Myr, we included only craters whose age uncertainty is ⩽ 20 Myr. Table 1 lists 13 craters that meet this criterion. There have been some improved measurements since Grieve's compilation, and some older ages need to be revised on the basis of new standardized decay constants. After a search of the literature we developed our own revised values for the crater ages and their uncertainties; these are listed in Table 1. To avoid any possibility of bias, however, we confined the bulk of our present analysis to the values given by Grieve rather than our own. We discuss later the effect on our analysis of using the revised numbers instead of Grieve's values.

Table 1. Impact craters of ⩾5 km diameter having ages between 5 and 250 Myr with 1 s.d. age uncertainties of ⩽20 Myr

| Crater no. | Diameter (km) | Age (Myr) | Revised age† | Ref. | Location |
|---|---|---|---|---|---|
| 43 | 10 | | 7±4 | 15 | Karla, USSR |
| 35 | 20 | | 13±11 | 10 | Haughtom, Canada |
| 73(88*) | 24 | 14.8±0.7 | | | Ries, Germany |
| 60 | 28 | 38±4 | | | Mistastin, Labrador |
| 99 | 8.5 | 37±2 | | | Wanapitei, Ontario |
| 69 | 100 | 39±9 | | | Popigai, Siberia |
| 50 | 14 | 77±4 | 78±2 | 11 | Lappajarvi, Finland |
| 87 | 25 | 95±7 | | | Steen River, Alberta |
| 18 | 25 | 100±5 | | | Boltysh, Ukraine |
| 52 | 17 | 100±20 | | | Logoisk, USSR |
| 56 | 5 | 118±2 | 119±2 | 14 | Mien Lake, Sweden |
| 33 | 22 | 130±6 | 133±6 | | Gosses Bluff, Australia |
| 74 | 23 | 160±5 | | | Rochechouart, France |
| 65 | 15 | | 185±10 | 12 | Obolon, Ukraine |
| 70 | 80 | 183±3 | | | Puchezh-Katunki, USSR |
| 54 | 70 | 210±4 | 214±3 | 13 | Manicouagan, Quebec |

The first age given is taken from Grieve[8], and it is the primary one used in the present analysis. An age value was only included if there was an error estimate available. Only those craters in this list that have a diameter of ⩾10 km are used in Fig 1–3.

*As these two craters are probably from the same event, we included only the larger one.

†Our own estimates based on current values for decay constants, and on radiometric and palaeontological data in the references cited.

In Fig. 1a a rectangle of unit area has been used to represent each crater having a diameter >10 km. (We will discuss the sensitivity of our analysis to the choice of diameter cutoff later.) The width of the rectangle represents twice the standard deviation error for the age, and overlapping rectangles have been stacked. In Fig. 1b the rectangles have been replaced by gaussian distributions, with the r.m.s. for each crater set by the age

≤ 2,000 万年的陨石坑。表 1 列出了符合这个标准的 13 个陨石坑。自格里夫的整理之后，有一些改进的测量方法，一些较老的年龄需要根据新的标准化的衰变常数进行修正。经过对文献的搜索，我们得出自己的关于陨石坑年龄及其不确定度的修订值，列在表 1 中。不过，为了避免任何可能的偏差，我们将目前的大部分分析限制于采用格里夫给出的数据，而不是我们自己的数据。我们随后讨论使用我们的修订值而不是格里夫的值对分析的影响。

表 1. 直径 ≥ 5 km、年龄在 500 万年到 2.5 亿年之间、1 倍年龄标准差（s.d.）≤ 2,000 万年的陨石坑

| 陨石坑号 | 直径（km） | 年龄（百万年） | 修订年龄† | 参考文献 | 位置 |
|---|---|---|---|---|---|
| 43 | 10 | | 7±4 | 15 | 卡尔，苏联 |
| 35 | 20 | | 13±11 | 10 | 霍顿，加拿大 |
| 73（88*） | 24 | 14.8±0.7 | | | 里斯，德国 |
| 60 | 28 | 38±4 | | | 米斯塔汀，拉布拉多 |
| 99 | 8.5 | 37±2 | | | 瓦纳皮蒂，安大略 |
| 69 | 100 | 39±9 | | | 波皮盖，西伯利亚 |
| 50 | 14 | 77±4 | 78±2 | 11 | 拉帕湖，芬兰 |
| 87 | 25 | 95±7 | | | 斯廷河，艾伯塔 |
| 18 | 25 | 100±5 | | | 波泰士，乌克兰 |
| 52 | 17 | 100±20 | | | 洛戈伊斯克，苏联 |
| 56 | 5 | 118±2 | 119±2 | 14 | 米恩湖，瑞典 |
| 33 | 22 | 130±6 | 133±6 | | 戈斯峭壁，澳大利亚 |
| 74 | 23 | 160±5 | | | 罗什舒阿尔，法国 |
| 65 | 15 | | 185±10 | 12 | 奥博隆，乌克兰 |
| 70 | 80 | 183±3 | | | 普切日－卡通基，苏联 |
| 54 | 70 | 210±4 | 214±3 | 13 | 马尼夸根，魁北克 |

第一组年龄来自格里夫[8]，是目前分析中主要在使用的。只包括存在误差估计的年龄数据。图 1~3 只使用了这个表中直径 ≥10 km 的陨石坑。
* 这两个陨石坑可能来自同一个事件，我们只列出较大的陨石坑。
† 我们的估算建立在目前的衰变常数和引用的参考文献中的放射性测量和古生物学数据基础上。

　　图 1a 中单位面积的矩形被用来代表每个直径 >10 km 的陨石坑。（后面将讨论我们的分析对截止直径选择的敏感程度。）矩形宽度代表年龄标准差的两倍，重叠的矩形被堆叠起来。图 1b 中矩形用高斯分布代替，每个陨石坑的方均根值由年龄不确定度决定；这幅图代表了我们对过去 2.5 亿年内地球撞击历史的最佳统计。与劳普和

uncertainty; this plot represents our best statistical representation of the history of impacts on the Earth during the past 250 Myr. A periodicity of about the same frequency and phase as that found in the Raup and Sepkoski analysis is evident, as indicated by the arrows placed at ~28-Myr intervals.

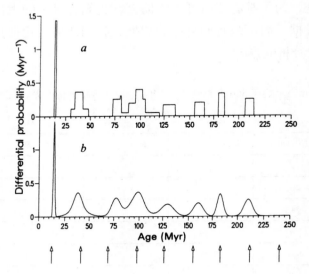

Fig. 1. Impact craters on the Earth having a diameter >10 km and age between 5 and 250 Myr. Only craters having age uncertainties of ≤20 Myr as listed by Grieve[8] have been used. In *a*, each crater is represented by a rectangle of unit area and width equal to twice the age error. In *b*, each crater is represented by the equivalent gaussian curve. The arrows indicate the frequency and phase found from the best fit to the data.

Figure 2 shows the Fourier power spectrum of Fig. 1*b*. (We found no essential difference between the Fourier transforms of Fig. 1*a* and *b*.) In this plot the peak near the frequency 0.035 Myr$^{-1}$ corresponds to a period of 28.4 Myr, with the first maximum at 13 Myr. The arrows in Fig. 1 actually correspond to the frequency and phase found in this Fourier transform. Below we will reconcile our 28.4-Myr period with the 26-Myr period in the palaeontological extinctions.

塞普科斯基的分析中发现的周期性频率和相位明显一致，如箭头所示的约 2,800 万年的时间间隔。

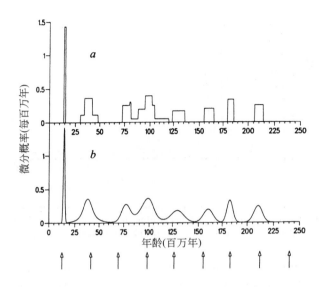

图 1. 地球上直径 > 10 千米、年龄在500万年到2.5亿年之间的撞击陨石坑。图中只使用格里夫[18]列出的年龄不确定度≤2,000万年的陨石坑。*a* 图中每个陨石坑用单位面积的矩形表示，宽度为年龄误差的两倍。*b* 图中每个陨石坑用等值的高斯曲线表示。箭头表示最佳拟合数据得到的频率和相位。

　　图 2 显示了图 1*b* 的傅里叶功率谱。(我们发现图 1*a* 和 1*b* 的傅里叶变换没有本质差别) 图中频率 0.035 (每百万年) 处的峰值对应 2,840 万年的周期，首个极大值在 1,300 万年。图 1 中的箭头实际对应于傅里叶变换中发现的频率和相位。接下来将协调我们的 2,840 万年周期和古生物学灭绝的 2,600 万年周期。

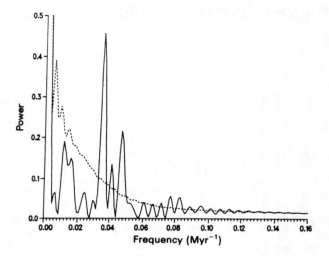

Fig. 2. Fourier power spectrum of Fig. 1*b*. The large peak at 0.035 Myr$^{-1}$ corresponds to a period of 28.4 Myr. The dotted line is a background estimate, taken from the average of 1,000 Monte Carlo-generated data sets, each with a random distribution of crater ages but having the same age uncertainties as the real data.

To understand the statistical significance of the peak in the Fourier power spectrum, we generated Monte Carlo simulations of craters having random ages; 1,000 sets were generated, each containing 11 craters with random ages between 5 and 250 Myr, but with age errors (that is, gaussian widths) identical to and of the same order as those from the real craters. The Fourier transform was calculated for each of the simulated sets; the average of the 1,000 power spectra is indicated by a dotted line in Fig. 2. In each of the 1,000 Fourier power spectra we searched for peaks as high as that seen in the real data; such peaks occurred for frequencies equal to or above 0.035 Myr$^{-1}$ in 8 of the 1,000 randomly generated sets. From this analysis we conclude that the confidence level for the existence of the periodicity is ~99%. Other analyses (for example, finding the number of large peaks in the 1,000 Monte Carlo sets having periods within 2 Myr of the 26-Myr period of Raup and Sepkoski; analysis of the statistics of the peaks; $\chi^2$ calculations; simulations with craters weighted according to diameter) gave confidence levels in the range 97–99.5%. If we take into account the agreement of our periodicity not only in frequency but also in phase with the extinction events of Raup and Sepkoski, we calculate that our confidence level is closer to 99.9%; that is , the probability of random craters giving a signal as large as the one we see, agreeing within 2 Myr in period and 2 Myr in phase.

Figure 3 shows another way of displaying the periodicity (suggested by S. Perlmutter): for every pair of craters in our list of 11 large craters, the difference in their ages was plotted as a gaussian with the two errors combined in quadrature; these gaussians were then superimposed. Peaks are evident in this plot for differences of 28.4 Myr and all multiples thereof.

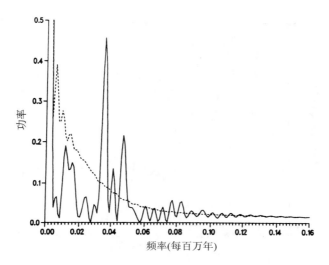

图 2. 图 1*b* 的傅里叶功率谱。0.035（每百万年）处的峰值对应于 2,840 万年的周期。虚线是根据蒙特卡罗模拟产生的 1,000 组数据平均得到的背景估计值，每组的陨石坑年龄随机分布，但是年龄不确定度和真实数据一致。

为了理解傅里叶功率谱中峰值的统计意义，我们对随机年龄的陨石坑进行了蒙特卡罗模拟，生成 1,000 组数据，每组包含 11 个年龄在 500 万年到 2.5 亿年内随机分布的陨石坑，但是年龄误差（即高斯宽度）和真实的陨石坑一致或量级相同。对每组模拟数据进行傅里叶变换计算，1,000 个功率谱的平均在图 2 中用虚线表示。在 1,000 个傅里叶功率谱中，我们寻找与真实数据大小相同的峰值；1,000 组随机生成的数据中有 8 组在频率等于或高于 0.035（每百万年）处发现这样的峰值。从这个分析中我们得出结论，该周期性存在的置信度水平约为 99%。其他的分析（例如，周期在劳普和塞普科斯基的 2,600 万年周期的 200 万年之内的 1,000 组蒙特卡罗模拟数据中寻找大的峰值数目；峰值的统计分析；$\chi^2$ 计算；陨石坑直径加权模拟）置信度水平在 97%~99.5% 之间。如果考虑到我们的周期性不仅在频率，而且在相位上也与劳普和塞普科斯基的灭绝事件一致，那么我们的置信度水平接近 99.9%；这个置信度的意思是，随机分布的陨石坑要产生和我们看到的一样强的信号，周期和相位都要符合在 200 万年以内。

图 3 显示了展示周期性的另一种方式（珀尔马特建议）：对我们 11 个大陨石坑列表中的每一对陨石坑，将他们的年龄差异以两个年龄误差的平方均值的高斯曲线表示；然后将这些高斯曲线叠加。在这幅图中可以明显看到相差 2,840 万年和所有倍数的峰值。

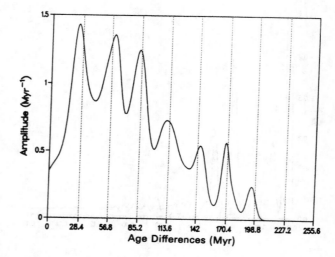

Fig. 3. Distribution of age differences in the crater data. For every possible pair chosen from the 11 craters used in the analysis, the difference in ages was plotted as a gaussian with width equal to the quadratically combined errors for the two ages. The gaussians for all the pairs were then added. The vertical lines are plotted at nominal age differences of 28.4 Myr and multiples thereof.

To estimate the accuracy of our frequency and phase determination, we performed a Monte Carlo generation of 20 sets of craters in each of which the 11 craters were initially forced to occur at precisely 28-Myr intervals, and then randomly "jittered" (using gaussian statistics) according to the uncertainties in the real crater data. The Fourier transform was then taken, and a best-fit frequency and phase determined. From these simulations we estimate the uncertainty in our period to be ~±1 Myr, and the uncertainty in the time of the first maximum to be ±2 Myr.

The age of the first crater maximum, 13±2 Myr, is identical with the age of the first "extinction event" of Raup and Sepkoski. One might worry that our slightly different period (28.4±1 Myr as opposed to 26 Myr) would cause our cycles and theirs to be out of phase after 100 Myr. However, there are uncertainties in the age determination of the palaeontological boundaries that increase significantly for ages >100 Myr. Figure 4 plots a band representing our 28.4±1 Myr period together with the best estimates for the palaeontological ages and errors, as evaluated by Harland et al.[9]. With the possible exception of the Tithonian event, a 28.4-Myr periodicity is a good fit to the extinction events of Raup and Sepkoski. Note that there is a slippage of one cycle between the crater events and the extinction events, so that the Permian–Triassic event is cycle 10 in the extinction sequence and cycle 9 in the crater sequence. The cycle slippage occurs in the 150–200 Myr interval, when there are three minor extinction events (7–15% of the families dying out) but only two predicted. We conclude that the record is not well defined in the region of slippage. This is supported by the fact that when Raup and Sepkoski divided the extinction sequence into two halves, they found that 27–29-Myr periodicities were significant to better than 95% confidence levels in both halves. Fischer and Arthur's qualitative cyclicity record[6] shows one less cycle than ours, with the Permian–Triassic event

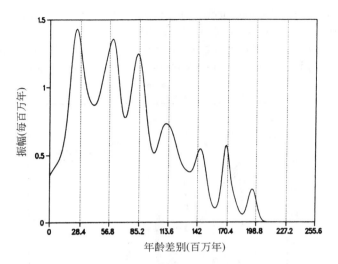

图 3. 陨石坑数据中年龄差别的分布。对分析中使用的 11 个陨石坑的每个可能数据对，年龄的差值用高斯表示，其宽度等于两个年龄误差的平方均值。然后叠加上所有对的高斯曲线。垂直线表示 2,840 万年的标准年龄差值以及倍数值。

为了估计我们频率和相位测定的精确度，我们用蒙特卡罗模拟产生了 20 组陨石坑数据，每组中 11 个陨石坑开始时被强制产生 2,800 万年的间隔，然后再根据真实陨石坑数据的不确定度随机"抖动"（使用高斯统计）。然后进行傅里叶变换，确定最佳拟合的频率和相位。从这些模拟中，我们估计周期不确定度约为 ±100 万年，首个最大值的时间不确定度为 ±200 万年。

首个陨石坑最大的年龄为 1,300 万 ±200 万年，与劳普和塞普科斯基的首个"灭绝事件"时间一致。有人可能担心我们稍微不同的周期（2,840 万 ±100 万年相对于 2,600 万年）可能导致 1 亿年后的严重相位差。不过，古生物学边界年龄测定也存在不确定性，导致对于年龄 >1 亿年的不确定度显著增加。图 4 画了一条带以表示我们的 2,840 万 ±100 万年周期和哈兰等 [9] 作出的古生物学年龄和误差的最佳估计。除了提塘事件可能导致的例外，2,840 万年的周期性是对劳普和塞普科斯基灭绝事件的很好拟合。注意陨石坑事件和灭绝事件滑移了一个周期，所以二叠纪－三叠纪事件在灭绝序列中是周期 10，在陨石坑序列中是周期 9。周期滑移在 1.5 亿到 2 亿年区间内发生，这区间内有 3 个较小的灭绝事件（7%~15% 科灭绝），但是仅预测了两个。我们得出结论，在滑移区域记录不够好。这是有事实支持的，劳普和塞普科斯基把灭绝序列分成两半，他们发现在每一半中 2,700 万到 2,900 万年周期性更加明显，置信度水平好于 95%。费希尔和阿瑟的定性周期性记录 [6] 比我们的少一个周期，二叠纪－三叠纪事件处于周期 8；周期滑移也发生在 1.5 亿到 2 亿年区间，这个区间明显是

at cycle 8; again the cycle slippage occurs in the 150–200-Myr region, which is clearly the weakest part of the palaeontological–stratigraphical record. The ages of the extinction events are best determined in the most recent four cycles; this is the period for which we test the agreement in phase between the extinction events and the crater ages.

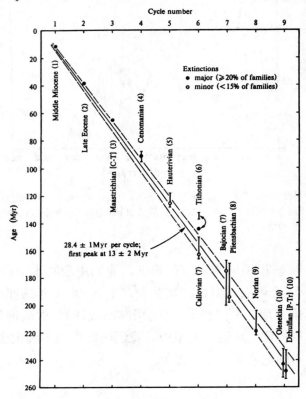

Fig. 4. Comparison of the periodicity found in the crater data with the extinction events from the fossil record. The band represents the periodicity found in the Fourier analysis of the crater data. The data points and confidence limits refer to the "extinction events" of Raup and Sepkoski[5]. The two largest extinctions occur at the Cretaceous–Tertiary (C–T) and Permian–Triassic (P–Tr) boundaries. The error bars assigned to these events are derived from the review of the time scale by Harland *et al.*[9]. Cycle numbers for extinction events are given in parentheses; slippage of one cycle between the two data sets is discussed in the text. Because of the constraint that palaeontological stages must occur in the proper sequence, model ages[9] sometimes fall outside the range of relevant radiometric data, as in the case of the Tithonian.

To test the sensitivity to our chosen cutoffs in age and crater size, we have repeated much of the above analysis for different values of these parameters. We varied the crater diameter cutoff continuously from 0 to 20 km; the 28.4-Myr peak was significant at all these values, and reached its maximum intensity for a 5 km cutoff (20% higher than the peak in Fig. 2). Inclusion of the data below 5 Myr or above 250 Myr did not significantly affect the peak height, but it did increase the background level. We also tried removing craters from our list to test the sensitivity of our analysis to the presence or absence of particular craters. The only crater in our nominal list of 11 which does not contribute to the 28.4-Myr periodicity is Lappajarvi, 77±4 Myr old. When we lowered the diameter

古生物学－地层学记录最薄弱的部分。灭绝事件的年龄在最近的 4 个周期内确定得最好；我们正是在这个周期内检验灭绝事件和陨石坑年龄相位的一致性。

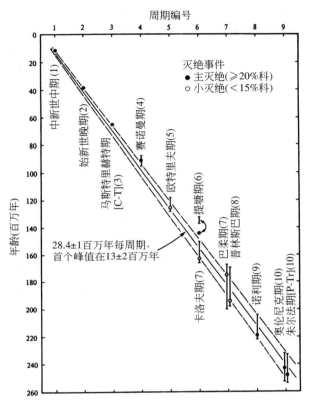

图 4. 陨石坑数据中发现的周期性和从化石记录中发现的灭绝事件的比较。条带代表从陨石坑数据傅里叶变换得到的周期。数据点和置信限表示劳普和塞普科斯基[5] 的"灭绝事件"。两个最大的灭绝事件发生在白垩纪－第三纪（C-T）和二叠纪－三叠纪（P-Tr）边界。这些事件的误差线来自哈兰等人[9] 关于时间尺度的综述。灭绝事件的周期号用圆括号表示；两组数据在一个周期内的滑移在文中讨论。由于古生物学时期必须限制在正确的顺序中，模型年龄[9] 有时落在相关的放射性测量数据范围之外，例如提塘事件的情形。

为了检验我们所选截止年龄和陨石坑尺度的敏感程度，我们对这些参数的不同值重复了以上大部分分析。我们从 0~20 km 连续改变陨石坑的截止直径；在所有这些值中 2,840 万年的峰值都很明显，在 5 km 截止直径处达到最大值（高出图 2 的峰值 20%）。把 500 万年以下或 2.5 亿年以上的数据包括进来不会显著影响峰值高度，但是增加了背景。我们还尝试把陨石坑从列表中移除，来检验我们的分析对某个特定陨石坑存在或消失的灵敏程度。在我们 11 个陨石坑列表中唯一的对 2,840 万年周期性没有贡献的是拉帕湖的陨石坑，年龄为 7,700 万 ±400 万年。当我们降低直径

threshold, adding craters, we found a second peak in the power spectrum at 0.047 Myr$^{-1}$ (period of 21 Myr). A peak at this frequency is also present in Fig. 2 but with less apparent significance. As our noise estimates had been made for random distributions of craters, to investigate the meaning of this peak we generated Monte-Carlo data sets which had a sequence of craters with a real 21-Myr or 28-Myr periodicity, jittered by the age errors, in addition to a few craters with random ages. We found that in the presence of a real 28-Myr period, a spurious second peak often appeared at 21 Myr, but that in the presence of a real 21-Myr period there was no false 28-Myr peak. Based on these simulations, we believe that there is no significant evidence for a real 21-Myr periodicity. The 21-Myr peak was strongly suppressed when we either increased the crater diameter threshold above 2 km, or weighted the contribution of the craters to the Fourier transform by a factor proportional to their diameters.

As mentioned above, to avoid any possibility of bias in crater selection, we deliberately chose not to reevaluate any of the data in performing our initial analysis, but accepted the compilation of Grieve at face value. We now turn our attention to the revised ages[10-15] in Table 1, which are based on our own extensive search of the literature. Palaeontological dates on lake beds within craters have allowed us to add three new craters to the list: Grieve 43 (10 km diameter, age 7±4 Myr), 35 (20 km diameter, age 13±11 Myr) and 65 (15 km diameter, age 185±10 Myr). The latter two agree reasonably well with our periodicity, which includes 13 Myr and 183 Myr among its cycles. We also list four craters for which there are minor adjustments in the age values or their uncertainties; Grieve 50, 56, 33 and 54. These adjustments make no significant difference to our analysis, except for Grieve 50; this is the 14 km crater at Lappajarvi which, as we noted, does not contribute to the spectrum at 28.4 Myr. With the age estimate tightened from 77±4 to 78±2 Myr, we can definitely exclude it from any cyclic process that has a narrow phase of activity, such as that proposed in the solar companion model[7]. It is vital to obtain smaller errors for the crater ages.

The period and phase of the crater data show strong agreement with those of the palaeontological extinctions, in support of the hypothesis that the extinctions were caused by periodic impact showers. The fact that we find typically one or more craters to associate with each cycle, despite the fact that Grieve's compilation covers less than 10% of the Earth's surface, implies that many impacts occur during each shower. This is corroborated by the discovery of at least two different levels of microtektites near the Eocene–Oligocene boundary[16]. However, given the relatively large crater-age uncertainties, we have, as yet, no indication that the showers have a duration as short as 1–2 Myr. The fact that the periodicity is found primarily among the larger craters suggests that there may be a random background of low-energy impacts in addition to the showers. This is plausible if the shower craters come from comets and the background craters from asteroids. Such background impacts, including an occasional very large one, are inevitable in view of the statistics of modern Apollo asteroids. The long-term cratering rate is considered to be compatible with the current flux of Apollo objects and comets[17-20]. The periodicity of the crater ages may require a revision of this view. Comet velocities are higher than those of

阈值，增加陨石坑时，在功率谱 0.047（每百万年）处发现第二个峰值（周期为 2,100万年）。图 2 中在这个频率也存在一个峰值，但是没有这么明显。像我们对随机分布的陨石坑的噪音估计一样，为了研究这个峰值的意义，我们用蒙特卡罗方法生成一系列具有真实 2,100 万年或 2,800 万年周期的陨石坑数据，加入年龄误差，再加上几个随机年龄的陨石坑。我们发现在真实的 2,800 万年周期存在的同时，经常在 2,100万年发现虚假的第二峰值，但是在存在真实的 2,100 万年周期时没有发现虚假的 2,800 万年峰值。基于这些模拟，我们相信没有足够证据显示存在真实的 2,100 万年周期。当我们增加陨石坑直径阈值到 2 km 以上，或者以一个正比于他们直径的因子对陨石坑进行傅里叶变换的贡献加权时，2,100 万年的周期就被强烈抑制了。

如上所述，为了避免陨石坑选择的任何可能性偏差，我们故意在开始的分析中没有使用任何重估的数据，而是使用格里夫整编的数据。我们现在考虑表 1 中基于我们广泛文献搜寻后的修订年龄 [10-15]。古生物学陨石坑中湖床的数据让我们增加了 3 个新的陨石坑到列表中：格里夫 43（直径 10 km，年龄 700 万 ±400 万年）、35（直径 20 km，年龄 1,300 万 ±1,100 万年）和 65（直径 15 km，年龄 18,500 万 ±1,000 万年）。后面两个和我们周期性符合得相当的好，包括 1,300 万年和 1.83 亿年周期。我们也列出 4 个在年龄或不确定度上有小调整的陨石坑；格里夫 50、56、33 和 54。这些调整对我们的分析没有太大的影响，除了格里夫 50；这个陨石坑直径 14 km，位于拉帕湖，如我们所指出的，它在 2,840 万年对傅里叶功率谱没有贡献。随着年龄估计从 7,700 万 ±400 万年紧缩到 7,800 万 ±200 万年，我们能够明确将它从任何有窄相活动的周期过程中排除，例如太阳伴星模型 [7] 中提出的那种。对于陨石坑年龄，获得较小的误差是关键。

陨石坑数据的周期和相位与古生物学灭绝事件的周期和相位非常一致，这支持了周期性撞击雨引起灭绝的假设。尽管格里夫整编后的列表只覆盖了不到 10% 的地球表面，我们发现每个周期通常与一个或多个陨石坑相关，这意味着每次撞击雨中都发生许多碰撞。在始新统 – 渐新统边界发现的微玻璃陨石的至少两个不同的测量值证实了这一点 [16]。不过，考虑相对大的陨石坑年龄不确定度，我们仍然没有证据显示撞击雨持续时间能短到 100 万到 200 万年。周期性主要在较大的陨石坑中发现的这一事实表明：除了撞击雨之外，还有随机背景下的低能撞击。这个结论看起来是合理的，如果撞击雨陨石坑来自彗星而背景陨石坑来自小行星。考虑到现代阿波罗小行星的统计，这种背景撞击，包括偶尔非常大的撞击，是不可避免的。长期的陨石坑形成率被认为和目前的阿波罗小行星及彗星流量符合 [17-20]。陨石坑年龄的周期性可能要求对这个看法进行修正。彗星速度比那些小行星要大，而且一半的彗星（但

the asteroids, and half of the comets (but none of the asteroids) enter the Solar System with retrograde motion leading to head-on impacts. These two factors can increase the impact energies of comets over those of asteroids (assuming equal masses) by an order of magnitude. A modest improvement in the ages measured for a few craters should clarify the nature of the showers.

After this manuscript was submitted, we learned that a solar-companion hypothesis generally similar to that of Davis *et al.*[7] had been independently proposed by Whitmire and Jackson (accompanying paper)[21].

We thank Saul Perlmutter for his help with the analysis. We have benefited greatly from the critical analysis and suggestions of many of our colleagues, particularly L. W. Alvarez, F. Crawford and T. Mast. During this research, W.A. was supported by a fellowship from the John Simon Guggenheim Memorial Foundation, and R.A.M. by a fellowship from the John D. and Catherine T. MacArthur Foundation. The work was partially funded by the NSF Alan T. Waterman Award, by NSF grant EAR-81-15858, and by the Department of Energy under contract DE-AC0376SF00098.

(**308**, 718-720; 1984)

Walter Alvarez* and Richard A. Muller†
\* Department of Geology and Geophysics
† Department of Physics and Lawrence Berkeley Laboratory, University of California, Berkeley, California 94720, USA

Received 30 January, accepted 8 March 1984.

---

References:
1. Alvarez, L. W., Alvarez, W., Asaro, F. & Michel. H. V. *Science* **208**, 1095-1108 (1980).
2. Asaro, F., Alvarez, L. W., Alvarez, W. & Michel, H. V. *Snowbird Conf. Abstr., Lunar Planet. Inst. Contr.* **449**, 2 (1981).
3. Ganapathy, R. *Science* **216**, 885-886 (1982).
4. Alvarez, W., Asaro. F., Michel, H. V. & Alvarez, L. W. *Science* **126**, 886-888 (1982).
5. Raup, D. M. & Sepkoski, J. J. *Proc. Natl. Acad. Sci. U.S.A.* **81**, 801-805 (1984).
6. Fischer, A. G. & Arthur, M. A. *Soc. Econ. Paleont. Miner. Spec. Publ.* **25**, 19-50 (1977).
7. Davis, M., Hut, P. & Muller, R. A. *Lawrence Berkeley Lab. Preprint* LBL-17298 (December 1983); *Nature* **308**, 715-717 (1984).
8. Grieve, R. A. F. *Geol. Soc. Am. Spec. Pap.* **190**, 25-37 (1982).
9. Harland, W. B. *et al. A Geologic Time Scale*, 131 (Cambridge University Press, 1982).
10. Frisch, T. & Thorsteinsson, R. *Arctic* **31**, 108-124 (1978).
11. Jessberger, E. K. & Reimold. W. U. *J. Geophys.* **48**, 57-59 (1980).
12. Val'ter, A. A., Gurov, Ye. P. & Ryabenko, V. A. *Dokl. Akad. Nauk SSSR Earth Sci. Sect.* (transl.) **232**, 37-40 (1977).
13. Jahn, B. M., Floran, R. J. & Simonds, C. H. *J. Geophys. Res.* **83**, 2799-2803 (1978).
14. Bottomley, R. J., York, D. & Grieve, R. A. F. *Contr. Miner. Petrol.* **68**, 79-84 (1978).
15. Masaitis, V. L., Danilin, A. N., Darpov, G. M. & Raykhlin, A. I. *Dokl. Akad. Nauk. SSSR Earth Sci. Sect.* (transl.) **230**, 48-51 (1976).
16. Keller, G., D'Hondt, S. & Vallier, T. *Science* **221**, 150-152 (1983).
17. Wetherill, G. W. & Shoemaker, E. M. *Geol. Soc. Am. Spec. Pap.* **190**, 1-13 (1982).
18. Weissman, P. R. *Geol. Soc. Am. Spec. Pap.* **190**, 15-24 (1982).
19. Shoemaker, E. M. *A. Rev. Earth Planet. Sci.* **11**, 461-494 (1983).
20. Shoemaker, E. M. *Proc. Dahlem Workshop, Berlin*, May 1983 (Springer, Berlin, in the press).
21. Whitmire, D. & Jackson, A. *Nature* **308**, 713-715 (1984).

是没有小行星）逆行进入太阳系后会导致对头碰撞。这两个因素能使彗星的碰撞能量比那些小行星高出一个量级（假设质量相同）。对一些陨石坑的年龄测量适度改进将能阐明撞击雨的特征。

这份手稿提交后，我们得知惠特迈尔和杰克逊独立提出了和戴维斯等 [7] 相似的太阳伴星的猜想（同期文章）[21]。

我们感谢索尔·珀尔马特帮助分析。我们从许多同事批判的分析和建议中受益良多，尤其阿尔瓦雷斯、克劳福德和马斯特。在本研究期间，阿尔瓦雷斯得到约翰·西蒙·古根海姆纪念基金会资助，穆勒得到约翰和凯瑟琳·麦克阿瑟基金会资助。本文得到美国国家科学基金会艾伦·沃特曼奖，美国国家科学基金会 EAR-81-15858 和能源部合同号 DE-AC0376SF00098 的部分资助。

（肖莉 翻译；肖伟科 审稿）

# "Melting Ice" I at 77 K and 10 kbar: a New Method of Making Amorphous Solids

O. Mishima *et al.*

## Editor's Note

When water freezes, the molecules become arranged into an orderly pattern linked together by weak chemical bonds called hydrogen bonds. In 1936 researchers in Canada discovered that ice can also have a disorderly (amorphous) molecular structure, lacking any regular crystal lattice. Here Osamu Mishima and coworkers at the Canadian National Research Council describe a new way to make amorphous ice by using high pressure to melt crystalline ice. The new form of amorphous ice later proved pivotal to an understanding of liquid water: at high pressures and well below water's normal freezing point, there may be two different types of (supercooled) liquid water with different densities, of which the amorphous ices are "arrested" forms.

---

Amorphous solids are made mainly by cooling the liquid below the glass transition without crystallizing it, a method used since before recorded history[1], and by depositing the vapour onto a cold plate[2], as well as by several other methods[3,4]. We report here a new way—by "melting" a solid by pressure below the glass transition of the liquid—and apply it to making a new kind of amorphous ice. Thus, ice I has been transformed to an amorphous phase, as determined by X-ray diffraction, by pressurizing it at 77 K to its extrapolated melting point of 10 kbar. At the melting point, the fluid is well below its glass transition. On heating at a rate of $\sim 2.6$ K min$^{-1}$ at zero pressure it transforms at $\sim 117$ K to a second amorphous phase with a heat evolution of $42 \pm \sim 8$ J g$^{-1}$, and at $\sim 152$ K further transforms to ice I with a heat evolution of $92 \pm \sim 15$ J g$^{-1}$. In one sample, ice Ic was formed and in another, existing crystals of ice Ih grew from the amorphous phase. Heating below the 117 K transition causes irreversible changes in the diffraction pattern, and a continuous range of amorphous phases can be made. Similar transformations will probably occur in all solids whose melting point decreases with increasing pressure if they can be cooled sufficiently for a transformation to a crystalline solid to be too slow.

---

SEVERAL solids, such as ice I, melt with a decrease of volume, and so the melting temperature falls as the pressure increases. The melting line usually ends at a triple point, where another solid phase becomes stable, but, as the solid–liquid transition is first-order, it can, in principle, be extrapolated to low temperature and even to zero temperature. It follows that if such a solid is compressed at a temperature that is low enough to prevent transformation to another crystalline phase, it must either "melt", perhaps to an amorphous solid if it is below the glass transition of the liquid, or become a crystal that is greatly superheated into the liquid region. Either case would be new and

# 77 K 和 10 kbar 条件下的"熔融冰" I：制取无定形固体的一种新方法

三岛修等

### 编者按

当水结冰时，分子通过被称为氢键的弱化学键有序地排列在一起。加拿大的研究人员于 1936 年发现冰也具有一种无序的（无定形的）分子结构，即不存在任何规则的晶格。在本文中，加拿大国家研究委员会的三岛修及合作者们描述了一种在高压下融化结晶冰来制备无定形冰的新方法。无定形冰这种新形式对液态水的认知至关重要：在高压且远低于水的正常冰点的情况下，存在不同密度的两种不同类型的（过冷）液态水，无定形冰是其中的"捕获"形式。

---

无定形固体主要是通过将液体不经过结晶而是冷却到玻璃转化点以下来制得，这是一种早在有文字记录的历史之前就已使用的方法 [1]，也可以将蒸汽沉积在冷的平面板上 [2]，以及其他几种方法 [3,4]。在本文中，我们报道一种新办法——用压力使低于液体玻璃转化点的固体"熔化"——并且应用这种方法来制备一种新型的无定形冰。于是，如同 X 射线衍射所测定的那样，通过在 77 K 时将其加压至 10 kbar 外推熔点，冰 I 转化为一种无定形相。在熔点时，流体还远低于它的玻璃转化点。在零压力下以约为 $2.6 \text{ K} \cdot \text{min}^{-1}$ 的速率加热，它会在大约 117 K 时转化为第二种无定形相，同时伴随着 $42 \pm \sim 8 \text{ J} \cdot \text{g}^{-1}$ 的放热，并且在大约为 152 K 时进一步转化为冰 I，伴随着 $92 \pm \sim 15 \text{ J} \cdot \text{g}^{-1}$ 的放热。在一个实例中形成了冰 Ic，而在另一个实例中，则存在着从无定形相中生长出来的冰 Ih 晶体。在低于 117 K 转化温度时，加热导致衍射图案中的不可逆变化，并且可以制得连续范围的无定形相。如果能将它们冷却到足以使向晶态固体的转化变得足够慢的话，类似的转化可能会在所有熔点随压强增加而降低的固体中发生。

---

数种固体，诸如冰 I，在熔化中伴随着体积减小，因此其熔点随着压力的增加而降低。熔融线通常会终结于一个三相点，在那里另一个固相变得稳定，但是，由于固液转变是一级相变，因此从原则上来讲，可以将它外推至低温甚至是零度。由此可知，如果在温度低到足以阻止固体转化为另一晶体相时压缩这种固体，结果一定是：要么它"熔化"，如果温度低于液体的玻璃转化点的话，可能会变成一种无定形固体；要么变成一种晶体，由于严重过热而进入液相区。两种情况都是新的，并且可能使人

could be of great interest. The melting curve of ice Ih extrapolates to ~10 kbar at 77 K (Fig. 1); we have therefore squeezed ice Ih at 77 K and have examined the product that is recovered at zero pressure by determining its density, by thermal analysis, and by X-ray diffraction.

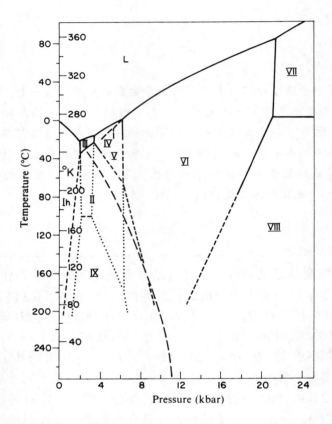

Fig. 1. The phase diagram of ice in the pressure–temperature plane. The melting line of ice I is extrapolated as a dashed line.

Figure 2 plots the compression for four different runs against the nominal pressure, assuming no friction. In each run, a transition started at an estimated real pressure of 10±~1 kbar and appeared complete by ~15 kbar. About two-thirds of the volume change occurred in a pressure range of ~0.7 kbar. The transition goes surprisingly easily for such a low temperature. For comparison, a similar sample of ice IX at the same temperature did not transform below 25 kbar, although it is always metastable relative to ice II and also becomes metastable relative to ice VI at ~9.4 kbar and to ice VIII at ~12.3 kbar. The ease with which ice I transforms at ~10 kbar is, therefore, quite unprecedented. The specific volumes of liquid water, ice and the new phase as a function of pressure are represented in Fig. 3, which may be read in conjunction with Fig. 1. The specific volume at 77 K of ice I and of the new phase, both at 10 kbar, are consistent with the extrapolated specific volumes of ice I on the liquid-I line (labelled *a*), of the liquid on the liquid-I line (labelled *c*) and of the liquid along the 9.8-kbar isobar (labelled *d*) where the dotted lines are extrapolations. The relation of the new phase to

很感兴趣。将冰 Ih 的熔融曲线在 77 K 处外推至大约为 10 kbar（图 1）；我们在 77 K 时挤压冰 Ih，并且在产物回复到零压力时通过测定密度、热分析、X 射线衍射等方法对其进行了检验。

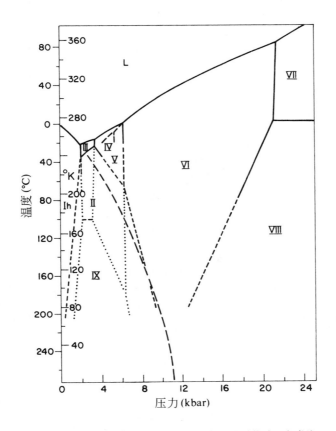

图 1. 压力—温度平面中的冰相图。冰 I 的熔融线外推为一条虚线。

图 2 中绘制出在四轮不同的实验中，假定不存在摩擦力时，压缩量相对于标称压力的变化。在每轮实验中，转化开始于估计为 10±~1 kbar 的真实压力，并且似乎会在约 15 kbar 时完成。约有三分之二的体积变化发生在大约 0.7 kbar 的压力范围内。在如此低的温度条件下，转化进行得令人吃惊地容易。作为对照，在温度相同的条件下，冰 IX 的类似样品在 25 kbar 以下时并不发生转化，尽管它相对于冰 II 来说总是亚稳的，而且在约 9.4 kbar 时相对于冰 VI 变成亚稳的，以及在大约 12.3 kbar 时相对于冰 VIII 亚稳。因此，冰 I 在大约为 10 kbar 的转变出奇地容易。图 3 中显示了液相水、冰和新相的比容作为压力的函数，可以将它与图 1 对照来看。冰 I 与新相在 77 K、10 kbar 时的比容，与液相–I 线（标记为 a）上的冰 I，液相–I 线上的液体（标记为 c）以及沿 9.8 kbar 等压线（标记为 d）上的液体的外推比容值相一致，其

the amorphous ice made by quenching the liquid can be understood by the extrapolation of the liquid along the 1 bar isobar (labelled *b*).

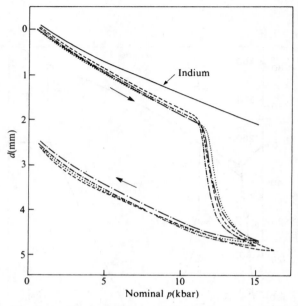

Fig. 2. Compression of ice I as a function of the nominal pressure on the sample for four independent runs at 77 K and on a volume of indium equal to the volume of the indium cup and the ice. About 1.2 cm³ of water in an indium cup was compressed in a steel cylinder by a hydraulic press and the displacement *d* of the piston was measured to 2.5 μm by a dial gauge as a function of the nominal pressure *p*. The pressure of the sample is ~0.9 of the nominal pressure. The measured compression was used with the compression of an equal volume of indium[17] to determine the compression of the ice.

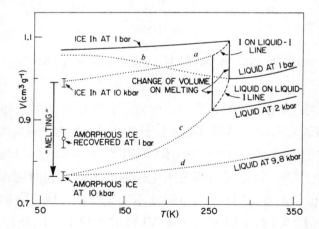

Fig. 3. Graph of the specific volume of ice I at 1 bar, ice I on the liquid-I line (labelled *a*), the liquid at 1 bar (labelled *b*), the liquid along the melting curve from 0 to 2 kbar (labelled *c*), the liquid at 9.8 kbar (labelled *d*), and reasonable extrapolations to 77 K. Measured values are represented by full and dashed lines and extrapolated values by dotted lines. The densities of ice Ih and of the new phase at 77 K and 10 kbar as determined from the compression experiments, and of the new phase (two samples) at 77 K and zero pressure as measured by weighing in liquid and gaseous nitrogen, are also plotted.

中点状线为外推部分。新相与通过将液体骤然降温而制得的无定形冰之间的关系，可以通过将液相沿着 1 bar 的等压线（标记为 $b$）外推来理解。

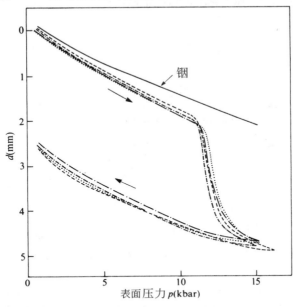

图 2. 冰 I 的压缩量作为标称压力的函数，77 K 时在样品上进行四个独立的实验，同时作用于一块体积与铟杯和冰块相等的铟上。利用水压机将铟杯中的大约 1.2 cm³ 水在一个钢质圆筒中压缩，用度盘式指示表测得活塞的位移 $d$ 为 2.5 µm，它是标称压力 $p$ 的函数。样品压力约为标称压力的 0.9 倍。将所测得压缩量与等体积的铟的压缩量联合使用 [17] 以确定冰的压缩量。

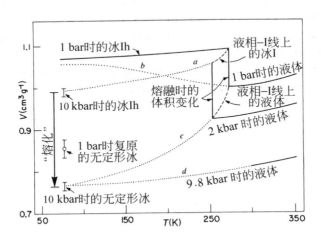

图 3. 1 bar 时的冰 I、液相–I 线（标记为 $a$）上的冰 I、1 bar 时的液体（标记为 $b$）、沿熔融曲线从 0 到 2 kbar 的液体（标记为 $c$）、9.8 kbar 时的液体（标记为 $d$）的比容图，并适当外推到 77 K。测量值用实线和虚线表示，外推值则用点状线。用压缩实验测得的冰 Ih 与新相在 77 K 和 10 kbar 条件下的密度，以及通过在液态和气态氮中称重而测得的新相（两份样品）在 77 K 和零压力条件下的密度，也画在图中。

Figure 4 shows a first-order plot of the heating curve of the recovered phase. There are exothermic events starting at ~117 and ~152 K, at a heating rate of ~2.6 K min⁻¹, with a heat evolution, from two independent experiments, of 42±~8 and 92±~15 J g⁻¹, respectively.

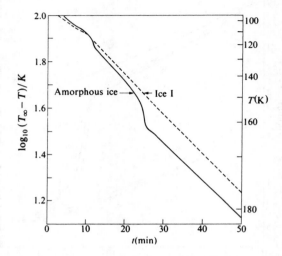

Fig. 4. The first-order plot of a heating curve of the recovered phase. The sample was held in a small silvered glass vacuum flask[5] immersed in a bath of ethanol and carbon dioxide. The heating rate was ~2.6 K min⁻¹.

Two specimens were analysed by X-ray powder diffraction at ~95 K[5], and microphotometer traces of representative patterns of the second are reproduced in Fig. 5. Both specimens as recovered had a halo pattern typical of an amorphous material, having its main peak at 3.0 Å and with rings and spots ascribable to a small amount of untransformed ice Ih. After heating the first specimen, which was a powder, to ~130 and ~170 K and cooling to 95 K, the halo pattern was replaced by a ring pattern typical of ice Ic, and the ice Ih pattern remained. After heating to ~200 K, only the ice Ih pattern remained, and the original Ih crystals had clearly grown.

图4为恢复相加热曲线的一阶图。在约为 2.6 K·min⁻¹ 的加热速率下，存在着开始于约 117 K 和约 152 K 的放热过程，根据两次独立的实验测得其分别伴随 $42\pm\sim8$ J·g⁻¹ 和 $92\pm\sim15$ J·g⁻¹ 的放热。

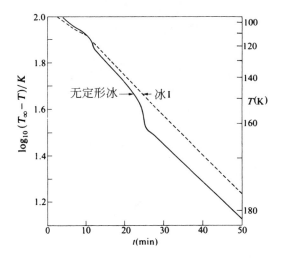

图 4. 恢复相加热曲线的一阶图。样品保存在一个小的镀银玻璃真空瓶[5]中，真空瓶浸入酒精和二氧化碳浴之中。加热速率约为2.6 K·min⁻¹。

利用 X 射线粉末衍射在大约为 95 K 时对两份样品进行分析 [5]，并且将第二份样品典型图案的显微光度计轨迹复制于图 5 中。两份恢复样品都具有无定形物质所特有的晕状图案且其主峰位于 3.0 Å 处，并且有源于少量未转化的冰Ih 的环和点图案。在将第一种粉末样品加热到大约 130 K 和大约 170 K 并冷却到 95 K 时，晕状图案被冰 Ic 特有的环形图案所代替，而冰 Ih 的图案则保留下来。在加热到大约 200 K 后，只有冰 Ih 的图案保留下来，而原始的 Ih 晶体则明显地有所生长。

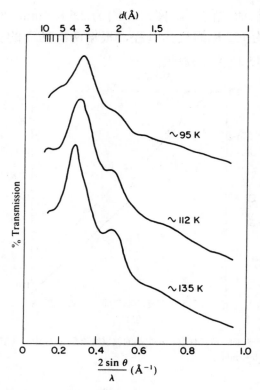

Fig. 5. Representative microphotometer tracings of diffraction patterns of a homogeneous sample of the new phase taken in a flat-plate X-ray camera. The temperature was controlled to ±~5 K by flowing nitrogen gas and was measured by a thermocouple placed near the specimen. Photographs were taken at ~95 K using zirconium-filtered molybdenum radiation[5].

The second specimen was a euhedral fragment ~0.4 mm on edge with a small amount of powder. The principal halo was a broad peak at 3.0 Å; it narrowed and its position, as measured at ~95 K, shifted almost linearly with heating temperature, from 3.0 to 3.65 Å after heating successively to ~105, ~112 and ~135 K for ~10 min and further shifted to 3.67 Å after heating to 155 K. After heating to ~175 K for ~20 min, the halo pattern disappeared and the Ih spots grew considerably, but no Ic pattern was produced. This appears to be the first report of the direct transformation of amorphous ice to ice Ih instead of Ic. The conditions no doubt gave preference to growth of Ih crystals against nucleation of Ic.

The first halo pattern is undoubtedly of a new dense amorphous solid having its principal peak at ~3.0 Å; this is much smaller than that of the first ice-Ih triplet centred at 3.65 Å or the principal peak of amorphous ice made by condensing the vapour[6-9] or rapidly cooling liquid water[10]. The bands are rather broad, showing that the interatomic correlations are relatively weak. When this phase is heated successively to ~105, ~112 and ~135 K, the halo moves to longer spacings, the bands become narrower and a discontinuous change occurs at ~117 K, as shown by the heating curves. The discontinuous change is probably caused by "runaway" heating. The phase so produced resembles the amorphous ice made

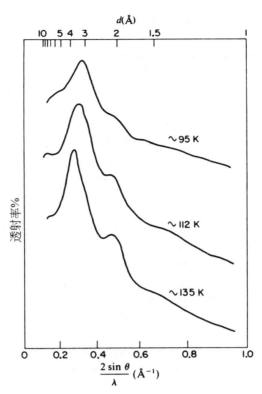

图 5. 用平板 X 射线相机测得的一份均匀新相样品衍射图案的典型显微光度计轨迹。利用流动的氮气控制温度变化约为 ±5 K，并置于样品旁的热电偶来测温度。用锆过滤的钼辐射源在约 95 K 时进行照相 [5]。

第二份样品是一块约 0.4 mm 的自形碎片且边缘带有少量粉末。其主晕是位于 3.0 Å 处的宽峰；随着加热温度变化，峰宽度减小并且其位置（在大约为 95 K 时测得）几乎是线性地变化：在 10 分钟内相继加热到约 105 K、约 112 K 和约 135 K，峰的位置从 3.0 Å 移到 3.65 Å，在加热到 155 K 后进一步移到 3.67 Å；在大约 20 分钟内加热到约 175 K，晕轮图案消失并且 Ih 点有显著的增加，但是没有产生 Ic 图案。这似乎是关于无定形冰直接转化成冰 Ih 而不是 Ic 的首次报道。无疑，这里的条件更有利于 Ih 晶体的生长而不是 Ic 的成核过程。

第一份晕轮图案无疑来自一种新的凝聚态无定形固体，其主峰位于约 3.0 Å 处；这比冰 Ih 集中于 3.65 Å 的第一个三重峰，或者是通过凝聚蒸汽 [6-9] 或快速冷却液相水 [10] 而制得的无定形冰的主峰，都要小得多。谱带较宽，表明原子间关联相当弱。在将这个相连续加热到约 105 K、约 112 K 和约 135 K 时，晕圈移动到较大的间隔，谱带变窄，并且在约 117 K 时发生了一个不连续的变化，如同加热曲线所显示的那样。这个不连续的变化可能是由"逃逸"热导致的。如此产生出的相与通过凝聚蒸汽或

by condensing the vapour or quenching the liquid.

It seems clear that a new amorphous phase of ice of density about 1.31 g cm$^{-3}$ is produced by the transformation of ice Ih at 77 K and 10 kbar, near its extrapolated melting point. Its volume appears to increase reversibly on removing the pressure and its density decreases to 1.17 g cm$^{-3}$, which is about 26% denser than the films made by condensing the vapour in the range 82–110 K[11]. On heating, it transforms irreversibly in stages towards a phase that in some ways resembles amorphous ice made by condensing the vapour or quenching the liquid but is clearly different from it, and a discontinous exothermic change occurs at ~117 K at our heating rate of ~2.6 K min$^{-1}$. A wide range of amorphous phases could probably be made by carefully controlled heating.

Amorphous solids can now be made in several ways, and at least four of them have been used to make amorphous phases of ice: condensing the vapour at low temperature, quenching the liquid, transforming the crystal at high pressure below the glass transition of the liquid, and warming the amorphous phase so produced. Each of them can be used to make phases with a range of properties depending on the conditions, and further studies of them should tell much about how water molecules interact with one another. A possible nomenclature to distinguish the different methods of preparation is amorph-v, amorph-l and amorph-c for the phases made from the vapour, liquid and crystal, respectively, and amorph-c-h for the phases made by heating the phase obtained by transforming the crystal at low temperature.

The transformation crystal-to-amorph-c is obtained surprisingly easily for such a low temperature. This suggests that the crystal becomes unstable and transforms, presumably at its surface, to a phase resembling the supercooled liquid. It is not reversible on the ordinary laboratory time scale and so is not a true melting, and may be viewed as a new kind of transition—an easy transformation of a crystalline solid to a dense amorphous solid.

Similar transformations will probably occur in all solids that have negative volumes of melting when a transformation to a crystalline solid is too slow. Obvious examples are the structure II clathrate hydrates, specifically tetrahydrofuran clathrate hydrate[12], ammonium fluoride I[13], ammonium fluoride monohydrate, indium antimonide[14] and germanium[15], which may transform to an amorphous phase at ~10, ~20, ~20, ~50 and ~170 kbar, respectively, at 77 K. Other obvious candidates for amorphization in this way are graphite, diamond, silicon, germanium, cubic and hexagonal boron nitride and phosphide, and graphite-like boron nitride. A transformation to an amorphous phase, rather than to a supposed metallic crystalline form, may limit the maximum force that can be applied to diamond and other tetrahedral compounds at low temperatures and so limit the pressures attainable in diamond anvil apparatuses. The transformation crystal-to-amorph-c in ice and clathrate hydrates may occur in planets formed by the agglomeration of cold particles of ice I or clathrate hydrate.

将液体快速降温制得的无定形冰相似。

看来很明显的，通过冰 Ih 在 77 K 和 10 kbar 条件——接近于它的外推熔点——下的转化，我们生产出一种密度约为 1.31 g·cm⁻³ 的新的无定形相。它的体积在移去压力后转而增加，而其密度则下降到 1.17 g·cm⁻³，这比通过在 82 K 至 110 K 温度范围内凝聚蒸汽所制得的薄层[11]要稠密 26%。在加热时，它会不可逆地分阶段地转变成一个相，此相在某些程度上类似于通过冷凝蒸汽或快速冷却液体而制得的无定形冰，但很明显又不同于无定形冰，并且，以约 2.6 K·min⁻¹ 的速率加热至大约为 117 K 时会发生一个不连续的放热变化。利用仔细控制的加热，也许能够制得一系列各种各样的无定形相。

现在我们可以用多种方式制备无定形固体，而且其中至少有四种方法已用于制备冰的无定形相：低温下凝聚蒸汽，快速冷却液体，在低于液体的玻璃转化点时高压转化晶体，以及加热该方法所产生的无定形相。每一种方法都能用来制备在不同条件下性质大范围变化的相，而且对于它们的进一步研究应该还可以深入理解水分子的相互作用方式。要区分这些不同的制备方法，可以这样来命名：将利用蒸汽、液体和晶体制得的相分别称为无定形–v，无定形–l 和无定形–c，而用无定形–c–h 来表示通过低温下晶体转化而成的相加热后所得到的相。

从晶体到无定形–c 的转化在如此低温下异常容易地实现了。这意味着晶体变得不稳定，并且转化成——可以假定在其表面上——一个类似于过冷液体的相。在普通的实验室时间标度上它不是可逆的，因此不是真正的熔融过程，而且可以把它看作是一种新型的转化，即一种容易的由晶相固体向稠密的无定形固体的转化。

在所有具有负的熔融体积的固体中，当其向晶态固体转化速度很慢时，都可能会发生类似的转化。明显的实例是 II 型笼状结构水合物，尤其是四氢呋喃的笼状水合物[12]、氟化铵 I[13]、一水合氟化铵、锑化铟[14] 和锗[15]，这几种物质在 77 K 时会分别在约 10 kbar、约 20 kbar、约 20 kbar、约 50 kbar 和约 170 kbar 转化为无定形相。其他明显的能够以这种方式无定形化的候选者是石墨、金刚石、硅、锗、立方和六方的氮化硼与磷化硼，以及类石墨氮化硼。向一种无定形相而不是预期中的金属晶体形式的转化，可能限制了在低温下能够施加于金刚石和其他四面体型化合物的最大力量，并且因此限制了金刚石砧装置中所能达到的压力。这种冰和笼状水合物中从晶体到无定形–c 的转化可以在通过凝聚冷的冰 I 或者笼状水合物粒子而形成的行星上发生。

An obvious way to transform an asymmetrical to a symmetrical hydrogen bond is to squeeze ice I[16]. To compress the O–O distance of 2.75 Å to the ~2.4 Å needed for centrosymmetrical bonds would require only some tens of kilobars. Unfortunately, ice transforms to the amorphous phase at much lower pressures.

National Research Council contribution no. 23539.

(**310**, 393-395; 1984)

**O. Mishima, L. D. Calvert & E. Whalley**

Division of Chemistry, National Research Council, Ottawa, Canada K1A 0R9

Received 20 February; accepted 9 May 1984.

References:

1. Morey, A. W. *The Properties of Glass* 2nd edn, Ch. 1 (Reinhold, New York, 1954).
2. Tammann, G. & Starinkewitsch, J. *Z. Phys. Chem.* **85**, 573-578 (1913).
3. Secrist, D. R. & McKenzie, J. D. in *Modern Aspects of the Vitreous State* Vol. 3, 149-165 (Butterworths, London, 1964).
4. De Carli, P. S. & Jamieson, J. C. *J. Chem. Phys.* **31**, 1675-1676 (1959).
5. Bertie, J. E., Calvert, L. D. & Whalley, E. *J. Chem. Phys.* **38**, 840-846 (1963).
6. Burton, E. F. & Oliver, W. F. *Proc. R. Soc.* **A153**, 166-172 (1938).
7. Dowell, L. G. & Rinfret, A. P. *Nature* **188**, 1144-1148 (1960).
8. Bondot, P. *C. r. hebd. Séanc. Acad. Sci., Paris* **265**, 316-318 (1967).
9. Narten, A. H., Venkatesh, C. G. & Rice, S. A. *J. Chem. Phys.* **64**, 1106-1121 (1976).
10. Mayer, E. & Brügeller, P. *Nature* **298**, 715-718 (1982).
11. Ghormley, J. A. & Hochandel, C. J. *Science* **171**, 62-64 (1971).
12. Gough, R. & Davidson, D. W. *Can. J. Chem.* **49**, 2691-2699 (1971).
13. Kuriakose, A. K. & Whalley, E. *J. Chem. Phys.* **48**, 2025-2031 (1968).
14. Merrill, Leo. *J. Phys. Chem. Ref. Data* **6**, 1205-1252 (1977).
15. Cannon, J. F. *J. Phys. Chem. Ref. Data* **3**, 798-824 (1974).
16. Stillinger, F. H. & Schweitzer, K. S. *J. Phys. Chem.* **87**, 4281-4288 (1983).
17. Bridgman, P. W. *Proc. Am. Acad. Arts Sci.* **76**, 9-24 (1945).

一种明显的将不对称氢键转化为对称氢键的方式就是挤压冰 I[16]。要将 2.75 Å 的 O—O 距离压缩到中心对称键所需要的约 2.4 Å，只需要大约几十 kbar。令人遗憾的是，冰在比这低得多的压力时就转化为无定形相了。

国家研究委员会稿件编号 23539。

（王耀杨 翻译；李芝芬 审稿）

# Appendix: Index by Subject
# 附录：学科分类目录

## Physics
## 物理学

## Chemistry
## 化学

## Biology
## 生物学

# Astronomy
# 天文学

# Geoscience
# 地球科学

# Others
# 其他